5/16/6

THE
PFIZER HANDBOOK
OF
MICROBIAL METABOLITES

THE
PFIZER HANDBOOK
OF
MICROBIAL
METABOLITES

By

MAX W. MILLER, PH.D.

Pfizer Medical Research Laboratories,
Chas. Pfizer & Co., Inc.

The Blakiston Division
McGRAW-HILL BOOK COMPANY, INC.
New York   Toronto   London

Foreword

THE IMPRESSIVE ADVANCES achieved in fermentation techniques have created new and often highly efficient methods for the synthesis of organic compounds. It seems clear that in addition to antibiotics and steroids, an ever-increasing number of structurally less complicated chemicals will be synthesized most economically by fermentation of abundant starting materials of natural or synthetic origin.

The purpose of this handbook is to list the source and physical, chemical and physiological properties of metabolic products isolated from bacteria, molds, fungi and lichens. In addition to this collection of facts and references, it contains chapters outlining the biogenesis of various structural types elaborated mainly by microorganisms. Although some of our present-day views on biogenetic pathways may have to be revised in the future, these chapters should prove to be exceedingly helpful not only to chemists working on the structures of new substances but also to biochemists investigating the mode of action of physiologically active compounds.

There certainly was an urgent need for such a compilation because the original reports are scattered through a wide variety of scientific journals rarely assembled in one place but distributed in chemical, pharmaceutical and medical libraries. It seems highly appropriate that an attempt to cover the literature in this rapidly expanding field should come from the Research Division of Chas. Pfizer & Co., Inc. The group deserves a great deal of credit for pioneering work in industrial fermentation as well as in isolation and structure elucidation of many antibiotics.

G. BÜCHI
Cambridge, Massachusetts

Acknowledgment

A COMPILATION of this sort was suggested by Dr. Ernest M. Weber in 1956, and the first draft was issued as an intra-company report the following year. Later, publication was suggested by Dr. Gilbert M. Shull and urged by a number of university people interested in microbial metabolites.

Most importantly, publication would not have been possible without the consent and support of Dr. Karl J. Brunings and Dr. I. A. Solomons. Other staff members of the Pfizer Medical Research Laboratories have also been very cooperative. Dr. Frank A. Hochstein has been most helpful throughout the preparation for publication, and I wish to thank him especially as well as Dr. Walter D. Celmer for reading the manuscript at an early stage and for their comments on the chapter on macrolide antibiotics.

In addition, Dr. Francis X. Murphy read the entire galley proof and made many constructive suggestions.

Several other authorities have been kind enough to review their specialties. Professor Hans Brockmann of Göttingen contributed information on the actinomycins; Professor Konrad Bloch of Harvard read the sections dealing with lipides; Dr. T. G. Halsall of Oxford reviewed fungal steroids; Dr. Herchel Smith of Manchester, sections concerned with the biosynthesis of various mold metabolites; Professor F. G. Holliman of Capetown, the section on phenazines; Dr. J. D. Bu'Lock of Manchester, the section on acetylenic substances; and Dr. Edward Borowsky of the Institut Medycyny Moskiej, Gdansk, the section on polyene macrolides. Professor George Büchi of Massachusetts Institute of Technology read nearly all of the galley proof and contributed a generous foreword.

We cannot begin to acknowledge all of the assistance received, particularly from the Pfizer library staff and other libraries, from our colleagues on the chemical staff, and from the secretarial staff. Most of the manuscript typing was done by Miss Kathryn Beck, Mrs. Loretta Michaud, Mrs. Terry Lunt, Mrs. Hedy Korst, Mrs. Judith Neff, and Miss Patricia Goepfert. The references were corrected and much indexing was done by Miss Claudette Parent, Miss Grace Olimski, and Miss Patricia French. All of the copy-editing was done by Mrs. Margaret Thompson. Patricia Curtis of Editorial Projects, Inc. was very helpful in coordinating and expediting publication operations.

MAX W. MILLER
Groton, Connecticut

Contents

THE
PFIZER HANDBOOK
OF
MICROBIAL METABOLITES

Introduction

THE CULTURE of bacteria and molds, the collection of higher fungi and lichens and the isolation and characterization of their metabolites is a sophisticated sort of research involving several distinct sciences. As a result the reports of such work are scattered through a variety of chemical, biochemical, microbiological, botanical, medical and pharmaceutical journals as well as general scientific journals and those devoted to antibiotics and fermentation technology. The published reviews of the structures of microbial metabolites have been limited in scope. It is difficult for the novice to gain a total impression of the progress that has been made, and difficult even for the specialist in this area to see the forest entire as well as the trees about him.

Having monitored the literature for several years incidental to our own work, we felt that it would be useful to publish a more general list of chemicals produced by microorganisms. More specifically, what has been attempted is a compilation of data on the structural and simpler physical properties of all of the primary microorganism metabolites which have been reported to be produced by the organisms growing either in the wild state or in culture on artificial sugar-based media. Although many structures are incomplete, generally the compounds in this list have been purified, and at least some physical properties observed. In view of the difficulties mentioned above we do not presume to have achieved absolutely complete coverage, and we should be pleased to receive structures or references to appropriate compounds which have been overlooked. Corrections of errors would be appreciated also. The literature available to us has been watched until the beginning of printing operations in December 1960.

Organization is by general similarity of chemical structures, but not in the strictest sense. For example, all carotenes and carotenoids were grouped together rather than grouping a carotene alcohol with, *e.g.*, a steroid alcohol. Many substances are ambiguous and could have been classified in any of several different chapters. A substance which contains a sugar, a benzene ring, a terpenoid fragment and a heterocycle will most likely be found under the appropriate heterocycle classification. Some arbitrary decisions have been necessary, but indexing by name, by empirical formula and by producing microorganism should serve most purposes. Again quite generally, progression is from the simple to the complex; sugarlike compounds being considered simple because they resemble the substrate, glucose.

In order to make the list more coherent a background has been sketched in, emphasizing occurrence and biosynthetic origin. A considerable literature on the biosynthetic origin of microbial metabolites has accumulated. Familiarity with it is valuable in interpreting experimental results in structure determinations. Several old structures have been revised in the light of this new knowledge.

Many of the biosynthetic and other metabolic schemes worked out in microorganisms are quite general in occurrence and have been found to be operative in mammalian metabolism. Because bacteria and fungi grow rapidly and are easy and inexpensive to handle, they are among the most useful tools in the exploration of metabolic routes. Many of the chemicals in this list were isolated incident to such studies.

Some chemicals of metabolic significance and of a suitable degree of complexity can be produced economically in quantity by fermentation methods and have found industrial uses. An example is citric acid, which now finds an annual market of thousands of tons.

The discovery of the effectiveness of the mold product, penicillin, in treating many bacterial infections in man gave tremendous impetus to the isolation and screening of microorganisms and their metabolites for antibiotics. The isolation and study of microbial metabolites, formerly a scholarly pursuit in a few academic laboratories, suddenly was supported by the resources of a great industry. Experience showed that a genus of filamentous soil organism, the actinomycete (streptomycete), was a particularly prolific source of organisms adaptable to antibiotics production when grown in suitable media.

Research with the actinomycetes resulted in the discovery of agents effective against a broad spectrum of pathogens. The first of these were chloramphenicol, chlortetracycline and oxytetracycline. Since the discovery of oxytetracycline, no antibiotics of broader antibacterial range have been developed.

Prior to the discovery of antibiotics, much work had been done on the structures of lichen substances, and, as mentioned above, a few academic laboratories were interested in mold metabolites. Notable among these was Professor Harold Raistrick's group at the London School of Hygiene and Tropical Medicine. Raistrick, now retired, and his collaborators have published over 100 papers on this topic.

The academic investigators were impelled by no practical motive except perhaps a hope that comparison of the chemical metabolites of various ill-defined groups of fungi would assist in their classification. Some generalizations did become apparent, but on the whole this hope was disappointed. It was found that the same chemical might even be produced by both bacteria and fungi. Some of the old classification schemes based on pigmentation were found to be obsolete.

The structures of the large molecules produced by microorganisms have proved to be more specific and of real value to taxonomy. Since the advent of paper chromatography, the identification of amino acids, sugars and other fragments from cell tissue hydrolysates has been facilitated. From the ensuing proliferation of literature on this subject it is manifest that the compositions of various cell tissues (capsule, wall, protoplast membrane, internal proteins), as well as exotoxins and other high molecular weight exudates, are much more specific. Even strains of species can sometimes be distinguished by the presence or absence of one of these fragments, and these molecules are important in immunology. Work of this sort has become more important since the discovery of evidence that certain antibiotics, *e.g.*, penicillin, interrupt growth and cell division in the bacteria against which they are effective by interfering with normal cell wall synthesis. Although we were unable to pursue this fascinating topic, an appendix of literature titles on the structure of higher molecular weight products of microorganisms and their cell wall structures has been attached.

In comparing the structures of the hundreds of microorganism metabolites which have been characterized thoroughly it is well to remember that the statistical emphasis may be misleading. It is likely that insoluble compounds, lipophilic materials easily extractible from aqueous cultures, organic acids which can be precipitated as insoluble salts and pigments that are easily observed have probably received a disproportionate degree of attention. The same, of course, could be said for antibiotics, which are conspicuous for their biological activity. The most difficultly discoverable metabolites are the relatively inconspicuous, low molecular weight, hydrophilic, perhaps phosphorylated compounds. Eventually many of the precursors of more elaborate metabolites will be found in this category.

Also, the metabolites of certain microorganisms have received disproportionate study. Examples are *Mycobacterium tuberculosis*, the tuberculosis pathogen, and *Claviceps purpurea*, the ergot fungus. By permission of Dr. Esmond R. Long and the Williams and Wilkins Publishing Company a review of the known metabolites of the former organism has been reproduced as an appendix, although many of the compounds included in this review are also to be found in the body of the text and others in the text which were not in the review. Also an appendix dealing with the confusing subject of microbial carotenoids has been attached by permission of the Chemical Publishing Company and of Professor T. W. Goodwin of the University of Liverpool.

Referencing is not exhaustive. It was kept on the lean side intentionally, and we feel that it is more useful that way. On some topics the literature is vast. It would have been virtually impossible to offer complete referencing of, for example, acetic acid, or even of some of the more complex substances such as the gibberellins or β-carotene. Much attention has been given to choice of useful references, although no doubt there have been lapses, and differences of opinion will probably arise. For some of the substances carrying a large literature a review article often is cited. In general an attempt has been made to cite the isolation, final structure determination and synthesis papers insofar as they exist. In the references cited care has been taken to include the complete list of authors as given on the paper. A bibliography of books, general references and reviews is included at the end.

Occasional comments may be found at the bottom of an entry, reflecting the manner in which this material evolved from a card file with a few notes. These comments were allowed to stand without expansion for what they are worth. For the most part the work is uncritical, structures and properties having been transcribed just as given in the literature. Structures and empirical formulas designated as tentative or approximate by the authors have been so designated here.

The indexes were not available prior to printing, and it is hoped that they will point out hitherto unrecognized relationships.

Simple Hydrocarbons, Ketones,
Aldehydes, Esters, etc.

The simple compounds listed here cannot be treated as a class. The biogenetic origins of many of them should become apparent from the introductions to later chapters. Besides the hydrocarbons shown it might be mentioned that lactarius species sporophores contain *cis*-polyisoprene, a rubber-like substance.

W. D. Stewart, W. L. Wachtel, J. J. Shipman and J. A. Yanko, *Science* 122 1271 (1955).

1 **Thiourea,** CH_4N_2S, white crystals, m.p. 180–182°.

$$\overset{S}{\underset{}{\underset{H_2N-C-NH_2}{\parallel}}}$$

Verticillium albo-atrum, Botrytis cinerea
K. Ovcharov, *Compt. rend. acad. sci.*, U.S.S.R. **16** 461 (1937).

2 **Guanidine,** CH_5N_3, alkaline crystals, generally isolated as salts, *e.g.* acetate, m.p. 229°.

$$\overset{NH}{\underset{}{\underset{H_2N-C-NH_2}{\parallel}}}$$

Boletus edulis, Hydnum aspratum Berk.
E. Winterstein, C. Reuter and R. Korolev, *J. Chem. Soc.* **104** 433 (1913).
Seijiro Inagaki, *J. Pharm. Soc. Japan* **54** 824 (1934).

3 **Ethylene,** C_2H_4, colorless gas, b.p. −103°.

$$CH_2=CH_2$$

Penicillium digitatum, Blastomyces dermatitidis, B. brasiliensis, Histoplasma capsulatum
Walter J. Nickerson, *Arch. Biochem.* 17 225 (1948).
Erston V. Miller, J. R. Winston and D. F. Fisher, *J. Agr. Research* 60 269 (1940).
Ray E. Young, Harlan K. Pratt and J. B. Biole, *Plant Physiol.* 26 304 (1951).

4 **Dimethylsulfone,** $C_2H_6O_2S$, colorless prisms, m.p. 107–109°.

$$CH_3SO_2CH_3$$

Cladonia deformis Hoffm.
Torger Bruun and Nils Andreas Sorensen, *Acta Chem. Scand.* 8 703 (1954).

5 **Cellocidin** (Aquamycin), $C_4H_4O_2N_2$, white crystals, m.p. 216–218° (dec.).

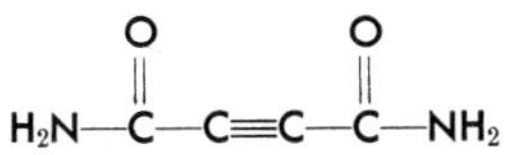

$$\underset{H_2N-C-C\equiv C-C-NH_2}{\overset{O\qquad\quad O}{\qquad}}$$

Streptomyces chibaensis, S. reticuli var. *aquamyceticus*
The yield was 16.5 g. from 420 liters of culture fluid.
Saburo Suzuki, Goto Nakamura, Kazuhiko Okuma and Yoko Tomiyama, *J. Antibiotics* (Japan) 11A 81 (1958).
Hyozo Taniyama, Shoji Takemura, Kimiko Kageyama and Masanao Funaki, *J. Pharm. Soc. Japan* 79 1510 (1959).

6 **Ethyl Acetate,** $C_4H_8O_2$, colorless liquid, b.p. 77°, n_D^{20} 1.3719.

$$CH_3COOC_2H_5$$

Penicillium digitatum
J. H. Birkinshaw and H. Raistrick, *Trans. Roy. Soc.* (London) B220 331 (1931).

7 **2-Methyl-2-butene,** C_5H_{10}, colorless liquid, b.p. 38.4°.

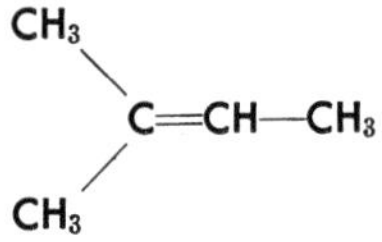

$$\underset{CH_3}{\overset{CH_3}{\diagdown}}C=CH-CH_3$$

Puccinia graminis Pers. var. *tritici* Erikas. and Henn. (uredospores)
F. R. Forsyth, *Can. J. Botany* 33 363 (1955).

8 1-Ethoxy-1,2-ethylenedicarboxamide, $C_6H_{10}O_3N_2$,

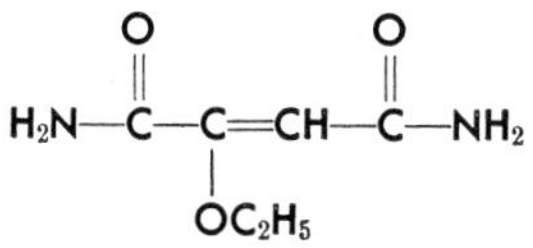

$$H_2N-\overset{\overset{O}{\|}}{C}-\underset{\underset{OC_2H_5}{|}}{C}=CH-\overset{\overset{O}{\|}}{C}-NH_2$$

Streptomyces sp.
Yasuharu Sekizawa, *J. Biochem.* Japan 45 73 (1958).

9 **Isobutyl Acetate,** $C_6H_{12}O_2$, colorless liquid, b.p. 61°, n_D^{15} 1.3936.

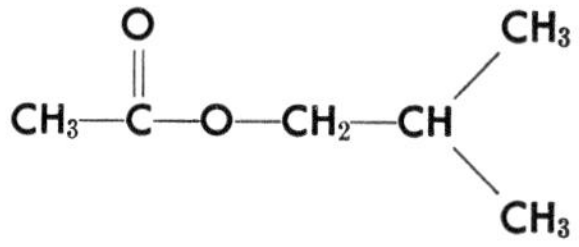

$$CH_3-\overset{\overset{O}{\|}}{C}-O-CH_2-CH\overset{\displaystyle CH_3}{\underset{\displaystyle CH_3}{}}$$

Endoconidiophora coerulescens
J. H. Birkinshaw and E. N. Morgan, *Biochem. J.* 47 55
(1950).

10 **2-Methyl-2-heptene-6-one,** $C_8H_{14}O$, colorless liquid, b.p. 172–174°,
58° (10 mm.), n_D^{20} 1.4445.

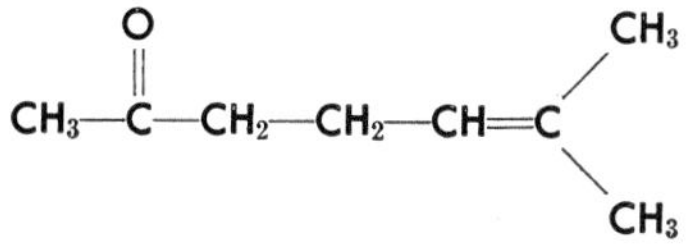

$$CH_3-\overset{\overset{O}{\|}}{C}-CH_2-CH_2-CH=C\overset{\displaystyle CH_3}{\underset{\displaystyle CH_3}{}}$$

Endoconidiophora coerulescens Münch, *E. virescens*
Davidson (artificial medium)
Isobutyl acetate and a mixture of methylheptenols were
isolated from the same culture.
J. H. Birkinshaw and E. N. Morgan, *Biochem. J.* 47 55
(1950).

11 **Octacosane,** $C_{28}H_{58}$, colorless crystals, m.p. 61°.

$$CH_3(CH_2)_{26}CH_3$$

Amanita phalloides
Heinrich Wieland and Gustav Coutelle, *Ann.* 548 270
(1941).

12 **Actinomycin** J_2 (Waksman's Actinomycin B, Dodecyl Ester of
5-Oxostearic Acid), $C_{30}H_{58}O_3$, colorless crystals, m.p.
81.5°.

$$CH_3(CH_2)_{12}CO(CH_2)_3COOC_{12}H_{25}$$

Actinomyces (Streptomyces) flavus
Yoshimasa Hirata and Koji Nakanishi, *Bull. Chem. Soc. Japan* 22 121 (1949).

13 *cis*-**Palmitenone,** $C_{31}H_{60}O$, colorless microcrystals, m.p. 40°.

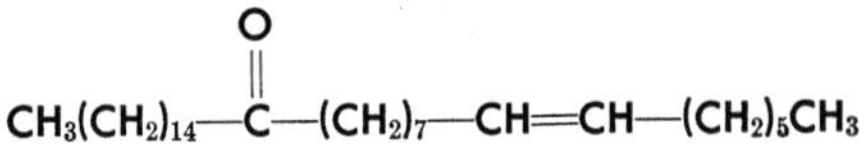

$$CH_3(CH_2)_{14}-\overset{\overset{\displaystyle O}{\|}}{C}-(CH_2)_7-CH{=}CH-(CH_2)_5CH_3$$

Corynebacterium diphtheriae
J. Pudles and E. Lederer, *Biochim. et Biophys. Acta* 11 602 (1953).
Idem., Bull. soc. chim. biol. 36 759 (1954).

14 **Palmitone,** $C_{31}H_{62}O$, colorless leaflets, m.p. 82°.

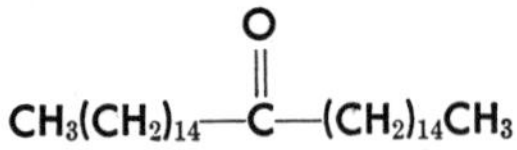

$$CH_3(CH_2)_{14}-\overset{\overset{\displaystyle O}{\|}}{C}-(CH_2)_{14}CH_3$$

Corynebacterium diphtheriae
J. Pudles and E. Lederer, *Bull. soc. chim. biol.* 36 759 (1954).

2

Alcohols, Glycols and Compounds
Related to Sugars

Two of the most important routes of sugar metabolism are the Embden-Meyerhof pathway of anaerobic glycolysis and the oxidative pentose phosphate cycles. Both occur widely in nature, and microorganisms were useful in the discovery of each. Many of the metabolites of this chapter can be pictured as arising from one of these schemes, which are also the main known routes of glucose metabolism in mammals. It should be understood that other paths and fragments of paths of glucose metabolism have been found in various microorganisms.

Yeast was instrumental in the elucidation of the Embden-Meyerhof route[1] and the yeast alcohol fermentation is represented as follows, each step catalyzed by a specific enzyme:

Embden-Meyerhof Route of Anaerobic Glycolysis in Yeast
Enzymes
1. Hexokinase
2. Phosphohexoisomerase
3. Phosphohexokinase
4. Aldolase
5. Triosephosphate isomerase
6. Triosephosphate dehydrogenase (Inhibited by iodoacetate)
7. ATP-Phosphoglyceric transphosphorylase
8. Phosphoglyceromutase
9. Enolase (Inhibited by fluoride)
10. ATP-Phosphopyruvic transphosphorylase
11. Carboxylase
12. Alcohol dehydrogenase

[1] A. J. Kluyver and C. B. Van Niel, "The Microbe's Contribution to Biology," Harvard University Press, Cambridge, Massachusetts, 1956.

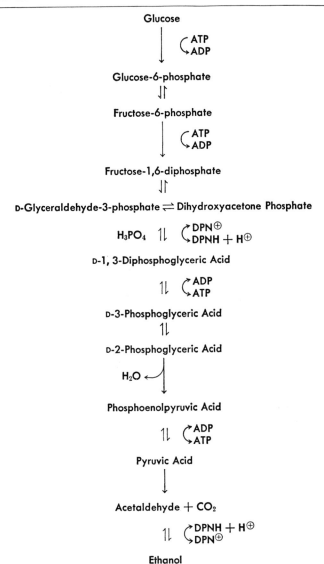

Glucose
ATP
ADP
Glucose-6-phosphate
Fructose-6-phosphate
ATP
ADP
Fructose-1,6-diphosphate
D-Glyceraldehyde-3-phosphate ⇌ Dihydroxyacetone Phosphate
H_3PO_4
DPN⊕
DPNH + H⊕
D-1, 3-Diphosphoglyceric Acid
ADP
ATP
D-3-Phosphoglyceric Acid
D-2-Phosphoglyceric Acid
H_2O
Phosphoenolpyruvic Acid
ADP
ATP
Pyruvic Acid
Acetaldehyde + CO_2
DPNH + H⊕
DPN⊕
Ethanol

Many molds, actinomycetes and bacteria use this system to some degree. Variations occur, and intermediates may feed in from other sources, for example, triose phosphate from the pentose phosphate cycle. Some bacteria are able to produce alcohol by other means.

The pyruvate from anaerobic glycolysis can meet a variety of fates. In some cases it is transformed into acetoin and its oxidation and reduction products, diacetyl and 2,3-butanediol (thiamine pyrophosphate coenzyme). α-Acetolactic acid has been shown to be an intermediate in certain instances:[2]

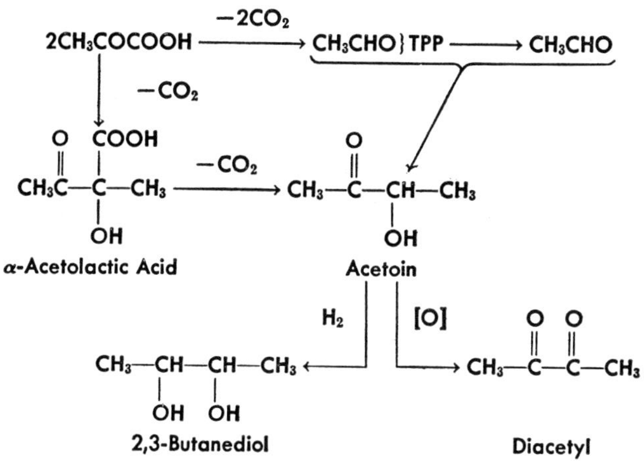

Acetoin has been found in yeast, in other fungi and in bacteria. Large yields of mixtures of these condensation products can be obtained from some bacteria.

Pyruvate is reduced to D-lactic acid in the homofermentative bacteria and lower phycomycetes (and to L-lactic acid in mammalian muscle).

Another reaction of pyruvate is its conversion to acetylcoenzyme A with the participation of lipoic acid; the probable mechanism being:[3]

[2] Elliot Juni, *J. Biol. Chem.* **195** 715 (1952); Yutaka Kobayashi and George Kalnitsky, *ibid.* **211** 473 (1954).

[3] I. A. Gunsalus, Lois S. Barton and H. Gruber, *J. Am. Chem. Soc.* **78** 1763 (1956).

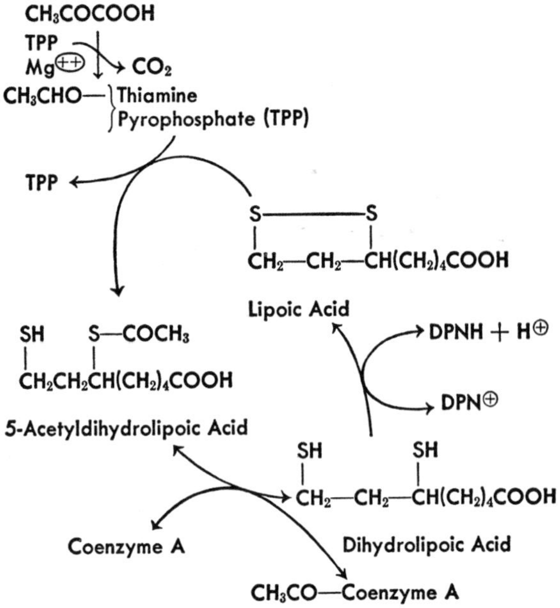

$$CH_3COCOOH$$

$$TPP$$

$$Mg^{\oplus\oplus} \longrightarrow CO_2$$

$$CH_3CHO-\Bigl|\begin{array}{l}\text{Thiamine}\\ \text{Pyrophosphate (TPP)}\end{array}$$

TPP ←

$$\begin{array}{ccc} S & \!\!\!\!-\!\!\!\! & S \\ | & & | \\ CH_2 & \!\!\!-CH_2-\!\!\! & CH(CH_2)_4COOH \end{array}$$

Lipoic Acid

$$\begin{array}{cc} SH & S-COCH_3 \\ | & | \\ CH_2CH_2CH(CH_2)_4COOH \end{array}$$

5-Acetyldihydrolipoic Acid

→ DPNH + H$^{\oplus}$

→ DPN$^{\oplus}$

$$\begin{array}{cc} SH & SH \\ | & | \\ CH_2-CH_2-CH(CH_2)_4COOH \end{array}$$

Coenzyme A   Dihydrolipoic Acid

$$CH_3CO-Coenzyme\ A$$

The nature of the actual catalysis of pyruvate decarboxylation and of aldol condensations by thiamine pyrophosphate coenzyme has been elucidated.[4] It is shown below:

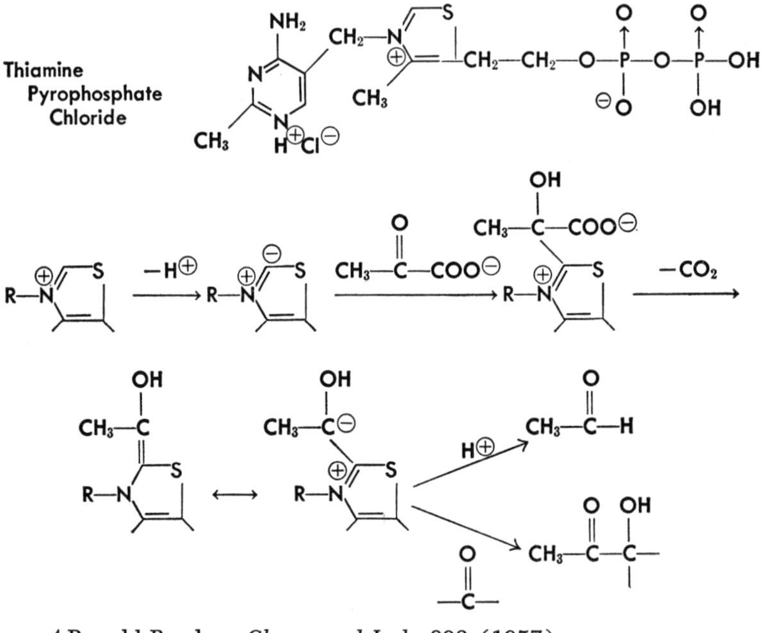

Thiamine Pyrophosphate Chloride

[4] Ronald Breslow, *Chem. and Ind.*, 893 (1957).

Thus, the production of acetaldehyde (and subsequently alcohol) by yeast, the production of acetoin by certain bacteria, etc.

Although the lipoic acid mechanism was first demonstrated in *Streptococcus faecalis*, all bacteria do not require the cofactor for this transformation.

The role of acetylcoenzyme A in cellular synthesis of fatty acids will be seen later. Butanol is probably formed by reduction of acetoacetylcoenzyme A. It is interesting to note that some microorganisms can synthesize a variety of carbohydrates by using acetate as the sole carbon source, in effect reversing the process (*e.g.*[5]). Pyruvate is also converted to succinate by fixation of CO_2.

Various other fates of pyruvate are known. For example, there are bacteria which dismutate 2 moles of pyruvate to 1 mole each of acetic and lactic acids.[6] Also *Bacillus coli* is known to convert pyruvate to a mixture of acetic and formic acids.[7]

The pentose phosphate cycle mentioned earlier probably occurs in many microorganisms. It is outlined below:

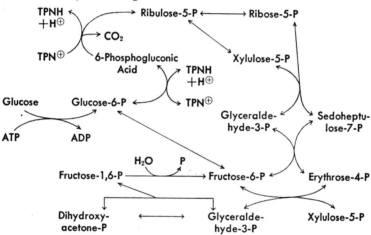

Enzyme-catalyzed reactions of the pentose phosphate pathway*

* This diagram together with the summarizing equations is reprinted with permission from Joseph S. Fruton and Sofia Simmonds, "General Biochemistry," John Wiley and Sons, Inc., New York, N. Y., 1958, p. 531.

[5] V. I. Lyubimov, *Doklady Akad. Nauk* SSSR III No. 4 (1956).

[6] Seymour Karkes, Alice del Campillo, I. C. Gunsalus and Severo Ochoa, *J. Biol. Chem.* 193 721 (1952).

[7] Kenneth V. Thimann, "The Life of Bacteria," Macmillan Co., New York, N. Y. 1955, pp. 441–465.

These reactions in summary are:

6 Hexose phosphate $+ 6O_2 \rightarrow 6$ Pentose phosphate $+ 6CO_2 + 6H_2O$
4 Pentose phosphate $\rightarrow 2$ Hexose phosphate $+ 2$ Tetrose phosphate
2 Pentose phosphate $+ 2$ Tetrose phosphate $\rightarrow$
                                2 Hexose phosphate $+ 2$ Triose phosphate
2 Triose phosphate $+ H_2O \rightarrow$ Hexose phosphate $+$ phosphate

Hexose phosphate $+ 6O_2 \rightarrow 6CO_2 + 5H_2O +$ phosphate

This is, then, a route for the complete degradation of glucose to carbon dioxide and water. The statistical significance and prevalence of this oxidative degradation system among microorganisms remains to be determined.

Ribose can be synthesized by way of the pentose phosphate cycle. In *B. coli* it appears that deoxyribose arises from direct reduction of ribose.[8]

Gluconic acid occurs widely, especially in fungi, and can be formed by enzyme-catalyzed oxidation of the unphosphorylated glucose substrate.[9] In some oxidative bacteria the following scheme occurs:[10]

Glucose $\rightarrow$ Gluconic Acid $\rightarrow$ 6-Phosphogluconic Acid $\rightarrow$
                   2-Keto-3-deoxy-6-phosphogluconic Acid $\rightarrow$ Pyruvic Acid
                                              $+$
                                Glyceraldehyde-3-phosphate

The glyceraldehyde phosphate is easily convertible to another mole of pyruvic acid.

Both glucuronic acid[11] and fucose (6-deoxy-L-galactose)[12] seem to be formed from glucose without cleavage of the carbon skeleton.

Glucosamine is probably most commonly formed by glutamine amination of fructose-6-phosphate,[13] although glucosone

[8] Fillmore K. Bagatell, Elmer M. Wright and Henry Z. Sable, *J. Biol. Chem.* 234 1369 (1959).

[9] Vincent W. Cochrane. "Physiology of Fungi," John Wiley and Sons, Inc., New York, N. Y. 1958, pp. 131–135.

[10] Nathan Entner and Michael Doudoroff, *J. Biol. Chem.* 196 853 (1952); Joseph MacGee and Michael Doudoroff, *ibid.* 210 617 (1954).

[11] Frank Eisenberg, Jr. and Samuel Gurin, *J. Biol. Chem.* 195 317 (1952); Frank Eisenberg, Jr., *ibid.* 212 501 (1955).

[12] J. F. Wilkinson, *Nature* 180 995 (1957); Stanton Segal and Yale J. Topper, *Biochim. et Biophys. Acta* 25 419 (1957).

[13] Luis F. Leloir and Carlos E. Cardini, *Biochim. et Biophys. Acta* 12 15 (1953).

(a logical precursor) has been shown to be formed by some aspergilli.

Mannitol, which is accumulated in quantity by some micro-organisms and occurs widely, is known in some cases to be in a reversible equilibrium with fructose, and it probably serves as a reserve food.[14] This reserve function may be true also of other reduced sugars.

The inositols are not formed by direct hexose cyclization, but their detailed biosynthesis is not known.

Many uncommon sugars have been found as moieties of streptomycete antibiotics. Some of these antibiotics which are predominantly sugar-like in composition are included at the end of this chapter. It might be useful to list the individual sugars here for comparison, including those which occur in streptomycete antibiotics classified in other chapters:

Sugars from Streptomycete Antibiotics
(showing points of attachment and
stereochemistry where known)

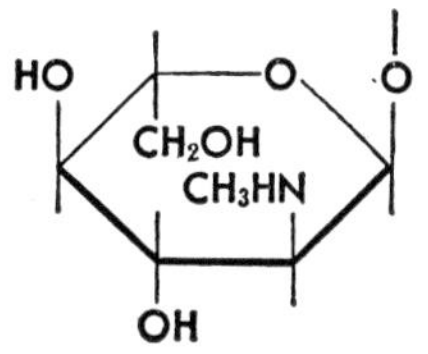

N-Methyl-ʟ-glucosamine
(streptomycins)

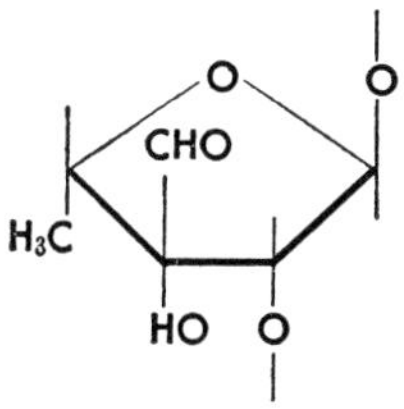

Streptose
(streptomycin)

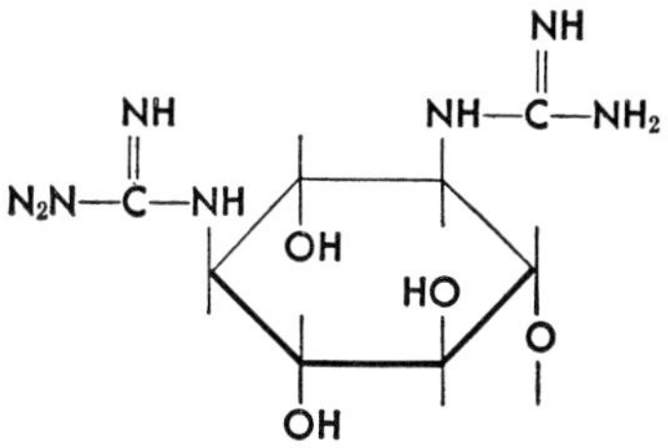

Streptidine
(streptomycin)

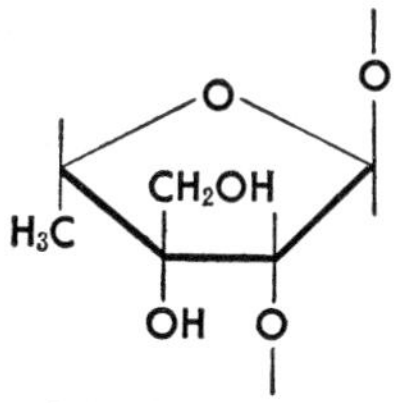

Dihydrostreptose
(dihydrostreptomycin)

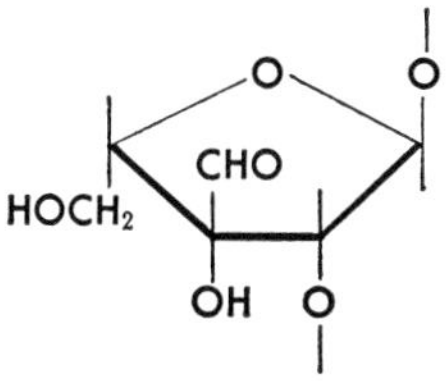

Hydroxystreptose
(hydroxystreptomycin)

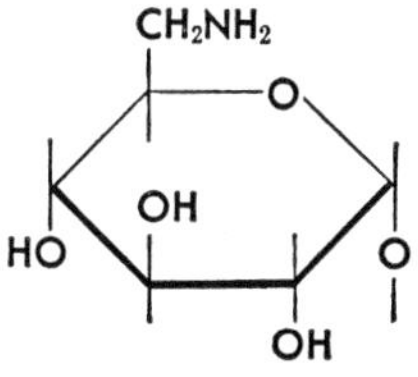

6-Glucosamine
(kanamycin)

[14] Vincent W. Cochrane, "Physiology of Fungi," John Wiley and Sons, Inc., New York, 1958, p. 122.

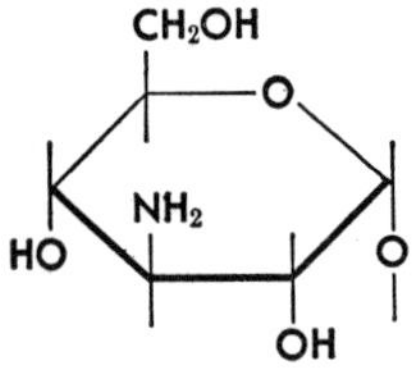
CH₂OH
O
NH₂
HO
O
OH

Kanosamine
(kanamycin)

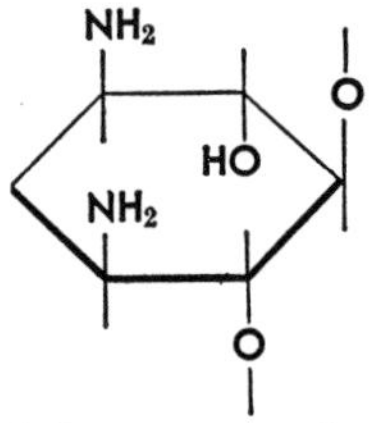
NH₂
O
HO
NH₂
O

2-Deoxystreptamine
(kanamycin, paromomycin)

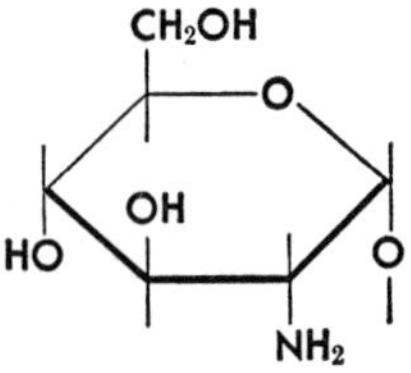
CH₂OH
O
OH
HO
O
NH₂

D-Glucosamine
(paromomycin,
trehalosamine)

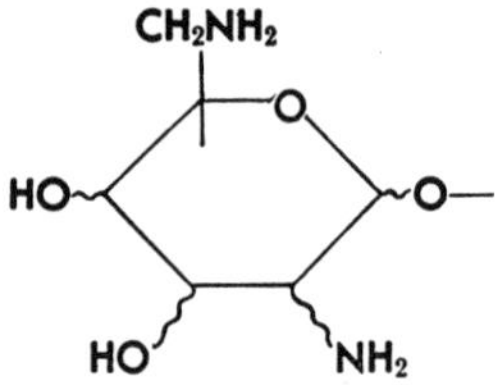
CH₂NH₂
O
HO
O
HO
NH₂

Paromose
(paromomycin)

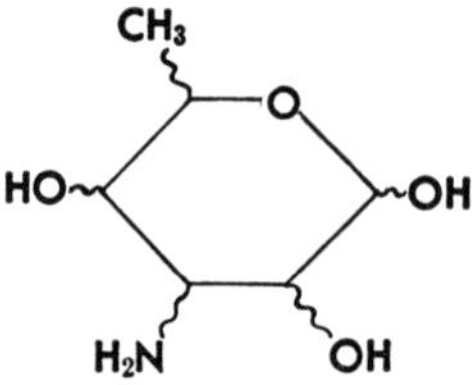
CH₃
O
HO
OH
H₂N
OH

Mycosamine
(nystatin,
amphotericin B,
pimaricin)

(Neosamine C from neomycin is also a 2,6-diaminohexose.)

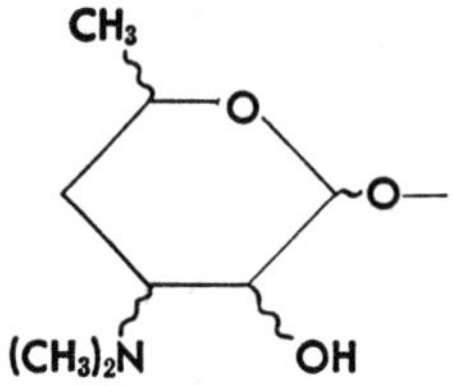
CH₃
O
O
(CH₃)₂N
OH

Desosamine
or
Picrocin

(picromycin, methymycin, neomethymycin, narbomycin, oleandomycin, erythromycins A, B, and C.)

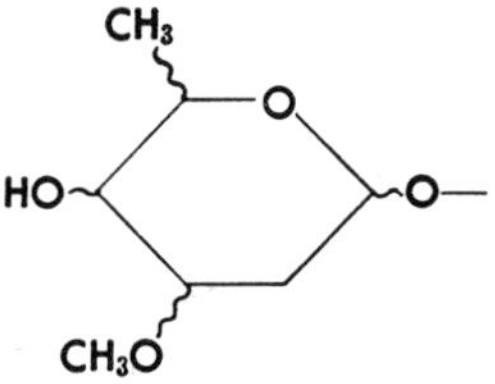
CH₃
O
HO
O
CH₃O

Oleandrose
(oleandomycin)

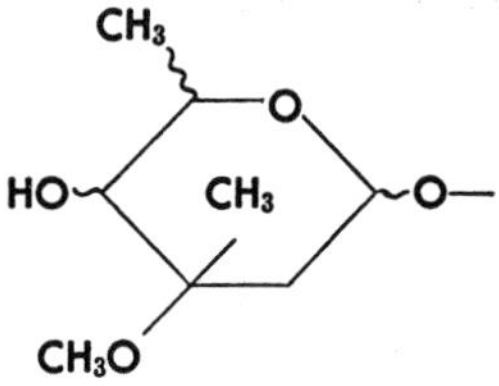
CH₃
O
HO
CH₃
O
CH₃O

Cladinose
(erythromycins A, B)

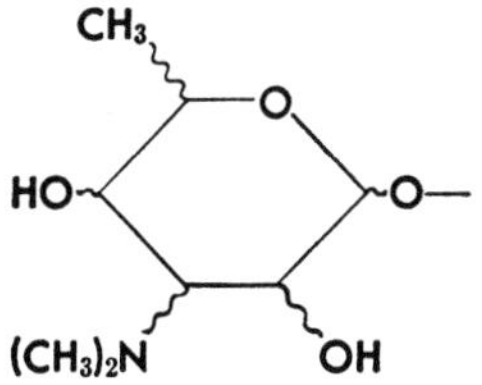

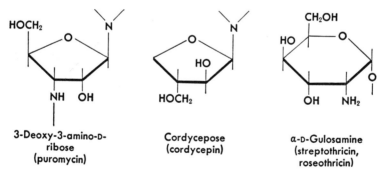

Mycaminose
(carbomycins A, B)

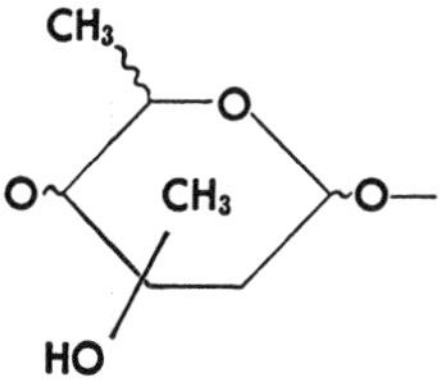

Mycarose
(carbomycins A, B,
spiramycins)

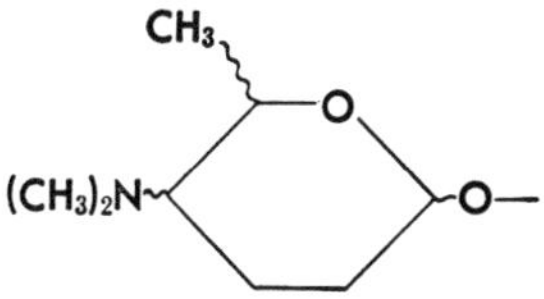

2,3,4,6-Tetradeoxy-4-
dimethylaminohexopy-
ranose (spiramycins)

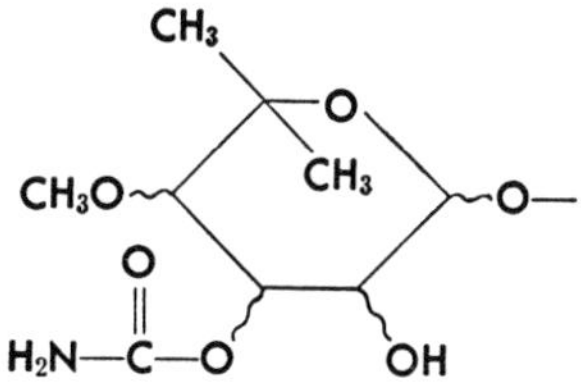

Noviose
(novobiocin)

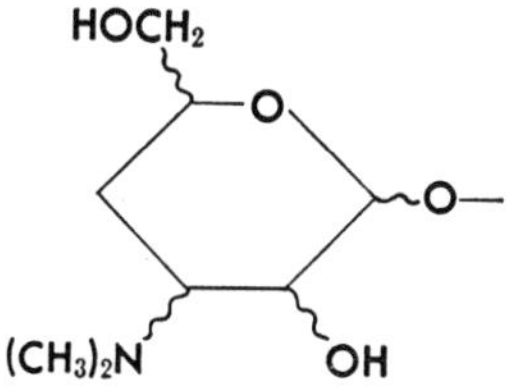

Amosamine
(amicetin)

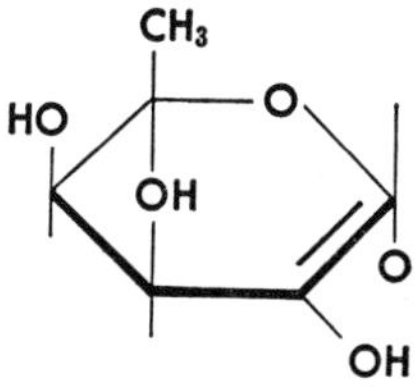

L-2-Ketofucopyranose
(angustmycin A)

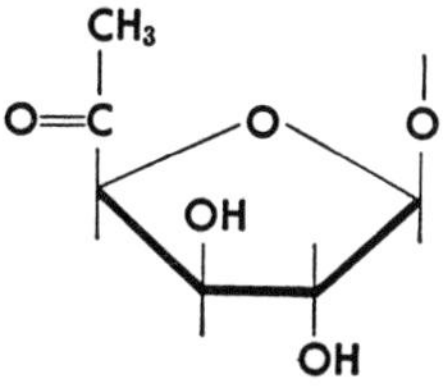

5-Keto-6-deoxy-
arabohexose
(hygromycin A)

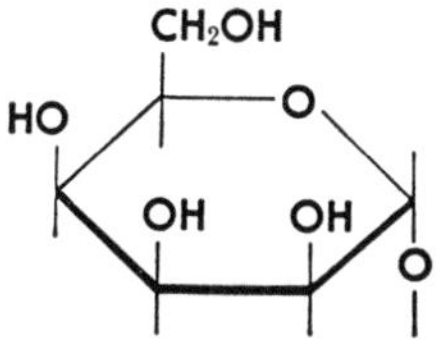

D-Talose
(hygromycin B)

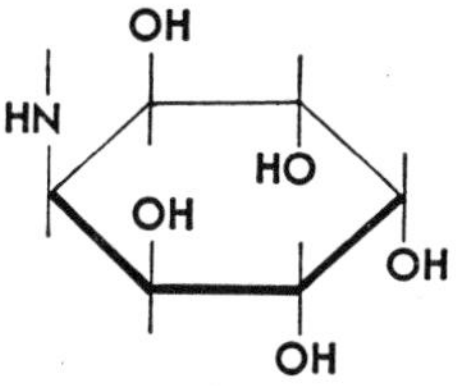

Neoinosamine-2
(hygromycin A)

(Two hydroxyl groups in neoinosamine-2 of hygromycin A are connected in a methylenedioxy bridge. Homomycin contains a similar sugar.)

3-Deoxy-3-amino-D-
ribose
(puromycin)

Cordycepose
(cordycepin)

α-D-Gulosamine
(streptothricin,
roseothricin)

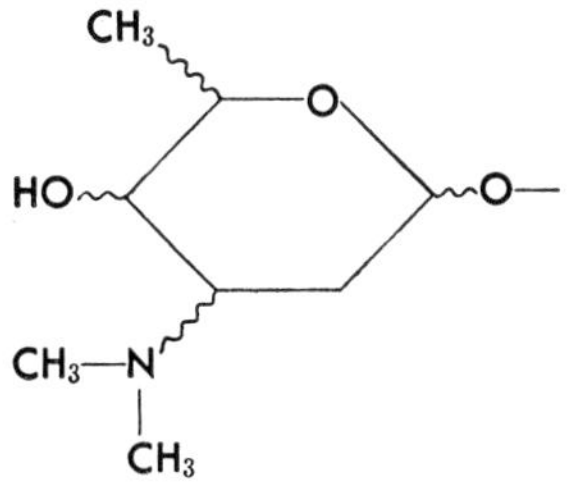

Rhodosamine
(rhodomycin)

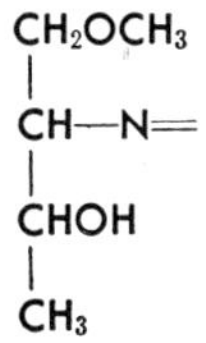

Methyl-2,4-dideoxy-2-aminotetroside
(elaiomycin)

Good reviews of aminosugars have been published.[15,16]

Other unusual sugars have been identified as components of the polysaccharides, mucopolysaccharides, etc., which occur in microbial cell walls and other cell tissues. Information can be obtained on these by way of Appendix A.

No attempt will be made here to discuss thoroughly the polysaccharides. Many references to this subject are listed in Appendix A and in the Bibliography.

As mentioned above many of the large molecules of microorganisms are mucopolysaccharides, etc., which contain sugars other than glucose. Glucose is in fact a relatively rare component of such molecules, but galactose, galacturonic acid, fucose, mannose and other sugars are common. Many hexoses and pentoses can be formed from the parent sugar without chain rupture. The intermediates in these interconversions are known to be sugar nucleotides:[17]

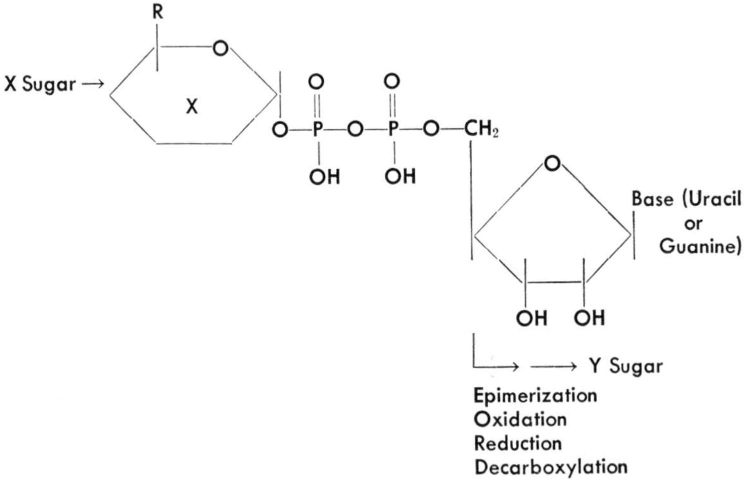

[15] T. Naito, *Jap. J. Pharm. and Chem.* 31 23 (1959).
[16] A. B. Foster and D. Horton, "Advances in Carbohydrate Chem-

Some of these reactions are reversible. Some of the less common aminohexoses are formed also in this way from glucosamine.

Certain fatty alcohols are classified in this chapter because of their functional groups, although biosynthetically they are more compatible with the fatty acids.

15   **Ethanol,** C_2H_6O, colorless liquid, b.p. 78.5°, n_D^{20} 1.3610.

$$CH_3CH_2OH$$

Yeasts, fusaria, mucors, penicillia, aspergilli, etc.
Leland A. Underkofler and Richard J. Hickey, "Industrial Fermentations," Chemical Publishing Co., Inc., New York, 1954 Vol. I pp. 17–196.

16   **Dihydroxyacetone,** $C_3H_6O_3$, colorless microcrystalline powder, m.p. 75–80° (polymorphic).

$$HOCH_2\text{—}\overset{\parallel}{\underset{O}{C}}\text{—}CH_2OH$$

Acetobacter suboxydans (on glycerol)
Aurél Puskás, *Yearbook Inst. Agr. Chem. Technol. Univ. Tech. Sci. Budapest, Hung.* 3 (1952).
Idem., ibid. 8 150 (1954).
A 90% yield of crude and a 70% recovery on recrystallization was reported.

Dihydroxyacetone has been reported also in cultures of *Penicillium brevi-compactum* and *Corynebacterium diphtheriae* (on glucose).
Michizo Asano and Hideo Takahashi, *J. Pharm. Soc. Japan* 68 186 (1948); Paul Godin, *Biochim. et Biophys. Acta* 11 114 (1953).

17   **Glycerol** (Glycerin, 1,2,3-Propanetriol), $C_3H_8O_3$, m.p. 17.8°, b.p. 290° (dec.), n_D^{20} 1.4746.

$$\underset{OH\ \ \ OH\ \ \ OH}{CH_2\text{—}CH\text{—}CH_2}$$

Yeasts, *Bacillus subtilis, Aspergillus wentii, Clasterosporia, Helminthosporia, penicillia,* etc.
Numerous recent patents. The glycerol situation is well summarized in Underkofler and Hickey, "Industrial Fermentations," Chemical Publishing Co., Inc., New York, N. Y., 1954 **Vol. I**; L. A. Underkofler, *Glycerol,* chap. 8, pp. 252–270.

istry," *Aspects of the chemistry of the amino sugars,* Academic Press, New York, N. Y., 1959 Vol. 14 pp. 224–233.
[17] Saul Roseman, *Federation Proc.* 18 984 (1959). (A review)

18 *n*-Butanol, $C_4H_{10}O$, colorless liquid, b.p. 117°, n_D^{20} 1.3993.

$$CH_3CH_2CH_2CH_2OH$$

Clostridium acetobutylicum, Cl. propylbutylicum, Cl. saccharobutylicum

Yields of about 30% mixed solvents, mainly butanol, but containing also acetone, isopropanol and ethanol are common.

Leland A. Underkofler and Richard J. Hickey, "Industrial Fermentations," Chemical Publishing Co., Inc., New York, N. Y., 1954 **Vol. I**; W. N. McCutchan and R. J. Hickey, *The butanol-acetone fermentations*, chap. 11, pp. 347–388.

19 **2,3-Butanediol,** $C_4H_{10}O_2$, colorless liquid, b.p. 180°.

The optical isomer produced depends on the microorganism.

$$CH_3—CH—CH—CH_3$$
$$||$$
$$OHOH$$

Aerobacter aerogenes, Serratia marcescens, Bacillus polymyxa, Bacillus subtilis, Pseudomonas hydrophila, Bacillus mesentericus, yeasts

Acetoin, diacetyl and alcohol are often produced at the same time. Approximately 90% yields of butanediol have been reported.

J. A. Wheat, *Ind. Eng. Chem.* 45 2387 (1953).

Leland A. Underkofler and Richard J. Hickey, "Industrial Fermentations," Chemical Publishing Co., Inc., New York, N. Y., 1954 **Vol. II**; G. A. Ledingham and A. C. Neish, *Fermentative production of 2,3-butanediol,* chap. 2, pp. 27–93.

Heikki Suomalainen and Lauri Jännes, *Nature* 157 336 (1946).

20 **Erythritol,** $C_4H_{10}O_4$.

$$CH_2—CH—CH—CH_2$$
$$||||$$
$$OHOHOHOH$$

Armillaria mellea

J. H. Birkinshaw, C. E. Stickings and P. Tessier, *Biochem. J.* 42 329–332 (1948).

Thirteen % of dry mycelium was the D-threitol isomer, colorless needles, m.p. 88.5°, $[\alpha]_D^{25}$ +4.3° (c 1 in water), −11.1° (in 95% ethanol). Other isomers have been reported, especially *i*-erythritol (*meso*-erythritol). Colorless prisms, m.p. 120° (121.5°) from:

Roccella montagnei (yield 2%) and other *Roccella* species, *Penicillium brevi-compactum, P. cyclopium, Aspergillus terreus,* etc.

Albert E. Oxford and Harold Raistrick, *Biochem. J.* 29 1599 (1935).

Yosio Sakurai, *J. Pharm. Soc. Japan* 61 108 (1941).

21 D-**Lyxuronic Acid** (isolated as the calcium salt) $C_5H_7O_6Ca/2\cdot2H_2O$, $[\alpha]_D^{20}$ $-23°$ $\xrightarrow{\text{30 minutes}}$ $-53°$ (in water).

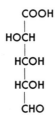

Acetobacter melanogenum

Minoru Ameyama and Keiji Kondo, *Bull. Agr. Chem. Soc.* (Japan) 22 271 (1958).

22 *d*-**Arabitol**, $C_5H_{12}O_5$, colorless spheroid crystals, m.p. 103°, $[\alpha]_D^{20}$ $+7.7°$ (c 9.26 in saturated borax solution).

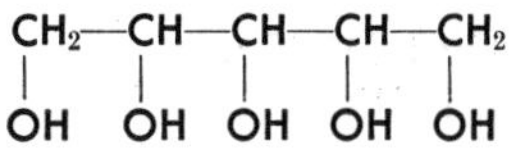

$$CH_2-CH-CH-CH-CH_2$$
$$\quad|\quad\ |\quad\ |\quad\ |\quad\ |$$
$$OH\ \ OH\ OH\ OH\ OH$$

Lobaria pulmonaria Hoffm., *Ramalina geniculata* Tayl., *R. sinensis, R. tayloriana, R. scopulorum* (Retz.) Nyl., *Cladonia impexa* Harm., *Fistulina hepatica, Lecanora gangaleoides, Parmelia latissima* Fée, *Umbilicaria pustulata*

Yasuhiko Asahina and Masaichi Yanagita, *Ber.* **67B** 799 (1934).

T. W. Breaden, J. Keane and T. J. Nolan, *Sci. Proc. Roy. Dublin Soc.* 23 6 (1942).

Yngve Johannes Solberg, *Acta Chem. Scand.* 9 1234 (1955).

23 2,5-Diketogluconic Acid, $C_6H_8O_7$, isolated as Ca salt.   No good
m.p.

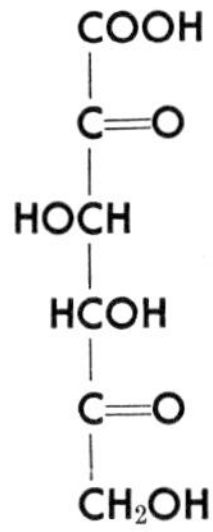

```
COOH
 |
 C=O
 |
HOCH
 |
HCOH
 |
 C=O
 |
CH₂OH
```

Acetobacter melanogenum, Pseudomonas, Phytomonas
spp.
    H. Katznelson, S. W. Tanenbaum and E. L. Tatum, *J. Biol.
Chem.* 204 43 (1953).

24 **Glucosone,** $C_6H_{10}O_6$, levorotatory syrup with reducing properties.

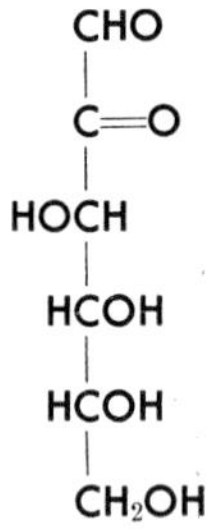

```
CHO
 |
 C=O
 |
HOCH
 |
HCOH
 |
HCOH
 |
CH₂OH
```

Aspergillus parasiticus, A. flavus, some algae
Yields of 13–17% from sucrose have been reported.
    Cecil R. Bond, Edwin C. Knight and Thomas K. Walker,
Biochem. J. 31 1033 (1937).
    Ross C. Bean and W. Z. Hassid, *Science* 124 171 (1956).

25 **2-Ketogluconic Acid,** $C_6H_{10}O_7$, colorless crystals, m.p. 152° (Me
ester, m.p. 172°).

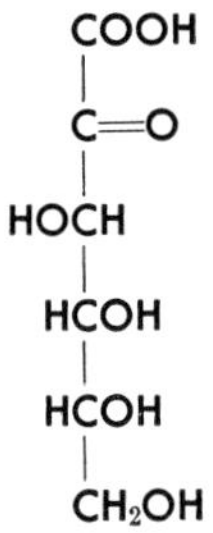

```
COOH
 |
 C=O
 |
HOCH
 |
HCOH
 |
HCOH
 |
CH₂OH
```

Acetobacter melanogenum, Pseudomonas, Phytomonas
spp.

The yields of 2-ketogluconic acid are better than 70%. 2,5-Diketogluconic acid can be made the principal product. This diketo acid is unstable, but can be isolated as a salt.

Leland A. Underkofler and Richard J. Hickey, "Industrial Fermentations," Chemical Publishing Co., Inc., New York, 1954 **Vol. II,** Lewis B. Lockwood, *Ketogenic fermentation processes,* chap. 1, pp. 13–14.

H. Katznelson, S. W. Tanenbaum and E. L. Tatum, *J. Biol. Chem.* **204** 43 (1953).

26 5-Ketogluconic Acid, $C_6H_{10}O_7$, generally isolated as the Ca salt (no sharp m.p.).

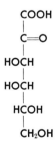

```
        COOH
         |
        HCOH
         |
        HOCH
         |
        HCOH
         |
        C=O
         |
        CH₂OH
```

Acetobacter suboxydans

Yields of about 90% have been reported.

Shiro Teramato, Riichiro Yagi and Ichiro Hori, *J. Fermentation Technol.* (Japan) 24 22 (1946).

Joseph J. Stubbs, Lewis B. Lockwood, Edward T. Roe and George E. Ward, U. S. Patent 2,318,641 (1943).

Leland A. Underkofler and Richard J. Hickey, "Industrial Fermentations," Chemical Publishing Co., Inc., New York, N. Y., 1954 **Vol. II,** Lewis B. Lockwood, *Ketogenic fermentation processes,* chap. 1, pp. 10–12.

27 2-Ketogalactonic Acid, $C_6H_{10}O_7$, colorless crystals, m.p. 170° (K salt, m.p. 139°; Me ester, m.p. 138°).

```
        COOH
         |
        C=O
         |
        HOCH
         |
        HOCH
         |
        HCOH
         |
        CH₂OH
```

Pseudomonas species (on galactose)
Toshinohu Asai, Ko Aida and Yashuiro Ueno, *J. Agr. Chem. Soc. Japan* 25 625 (1951–1952).

28 D-**Glucuronic Acid,** $C_6H_{10}O_7$, colorless needles, m.p. 165°, $[\alpha]_D^{24}$ +11.7° → +36.3° (2 hours, c 1 in water).

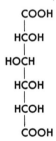

CHO
|
HCOH
|
HOCH
|
HCOH
|
HCOH
|
COOH

Ustulina vulgaricus
H. Wunchendoroff and C. Killian, *Compt. rend.* **187** 572 (1928).
Not isolated—manner of identification not mentioned.
Penicillium sp.
Gizin Itto, *J. Agr. Chem. Soc. Japan* 9 552 (1933).
K. Sivarama Sastry and P. S. Sarma, *Nature* 179 44 (1957).

29 **Saccharic Acid,** $C_6H_{10}O_8$, colorless needles, m.p. 125°, $[\alpha]_D^{19}$ +6.86° → 20.6° (c 1 in water).

COOH
|
HCOH
|
HOCH
|
HCOH
|
HCOH
|
COOH

Aspergillus niger
T. K. Walker, Vira Subramanian and Frederick Challenger, *J. Chem. Soc.*, 3044 (1927).
About 3.6 g. of the potassium salt were obtained from 120 g. of glucose by interrupting the fermentation before the appearance of much citric or oxalic acids. Also fermentation of 20 g. of calcium gluconate gave 3.7 g. of calcium saccharate.

Also reported formed from glucose by two yeasts, *An-thomyces renkaufi* and *Amphierna rubra:*
J. Grüss, *Jahrb. wiss. Botan.* 66 109 (1926).

30 *meso*-**Inositol,** $C_6H_{12}O_6$ (dihydrate), colorless crystals, m.p. 218° (anhydrous) 250–253°.

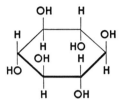

Pseudomonas fluorescens, Serratia marcescens, Proteus vulgaris, Clostridium butylicum, yeasts

Yields of 2700–5000 μg. per gram of dry cell weight are obtained in brewers' yeast.

Inositol Literature Briefs Tech. Bull. Y3–101, Corn Products Refining Co., 1953, 44 pp. (A bibliography with titles and abstracts)

31 **D-Gluconic Acid,** $C_6H_{12}O_7$, colorless syrup, cannot be isolated, but readily forms (principally) the δ-lactone, white crystals, m.p. 153°, $[\alpha]_D$ +63.5° → +6.2° (c 1 in water).

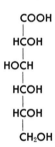

Wide variety of mold species, acetobacter species, etc. Yields 95% with *Aspergillus niger.*

A. J. Mayer, E. J. Umberger and J. J. Stubbs, *Ind. Eng. Chem.* 32 1379 (1940).

Leland A. Underkofler and Richard J. Hickey, "Industrial Fermentations," Chemical Publishing Co., Inc., New York, N. Y., 1954 Vol. I, L. A. Underkofler, *Gluconic acid,* chap. 14, pp. 446–469.

32   D-**Mannonic Acid,** $C_6H_{12}O_7$, forms γ- or δ-lactones, but the free acid cannot be isolated pure.

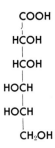

    COOH
     |
    HCOH
     |
    HCOH
     |
    HOCH
     |
    HOCH
     |
    CH₂OH

P. purpurogenum var. *rubrisclerotium* (on D-mannose)
Acetobacters

Galactonic acid, etc., can be produced similarly from the corresponding sugar.

A. Angeletti and C. F. Cerruti, *Ann. chim. applicata* 20 424 (1930).

33   D-**Glucosamine** (Chitosamine) $C_6H_{13}O_5N$, white needles, m.p. 110° (dec.), $[\alpha]_D^{20}$ +47.5° (c 1 in water).

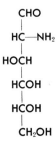

    CHO
     |
    HC—NH₂
     |
    HOCH
     |
    HCOH
     |
    HCOH
     |
    CH₂OH

Many bacteria, fungi and lichens. Present in bound form in mold mycelium. Produced by the action of certain streptomyces species on chitin.

Joseph J. Noval and Walter J. Nickerson, *Bacteriol. Proc.*, 125 (1956).

Leslie Ralph Berger and Donald M. Reynolds, *Biochim. et Biophys. Acta* 29 522 (1958).

34 Mesoinositol Monophosphate, $C_6H_{13}O_9P \cdot 3H_2O$, colorless tablets, m.p. 201° (dec.).

$$
\begin{array}{c}
\text{OH} \quad\quad \text{OH} \\
\text{HO}\diagdown\diagup\diagdown \quad \text{O—PO(OH)}_2 \\
\text{OH} \\
\text{HO} \\
\text{OH}
\end{array}
$$

Mycobacterium tuberculosis var. *hominis*

Michael A. Macheboeuf, Georgette Lévy and Marguerite Faure, *Compt. rend.* 204 1843 (1937). (Occurred as a fatty acid ester)

James Cason and R. J. Anderson, *J. Biol. Chem.* 126 527 (1938). (As a constituent of a polysaccharide)

35 D-Mannitol, $C_6H_{14}O_6$, colorless prisms, m.p. 163° (166°) $[\alpha]_D^{25}$ −0.49°. (C 1 in water. Addition of borax → strong dextrorotation.)

$$
\begin{array}{cccccc}
\text{CH}_2 & \text{CH} & \text{CH} & \text{CH} & \text{CH} & \text{CH}_2 \\
| & | & | & | & | & | \\
\text{OH} & \text{OH} & \text{OH} & \text{OH} & \text{OH} & \text{OH}
\end{array}
$$

Aspergilli, penicillia, other fungi, many lichens, algae and bacteria

For example: Mitizo Asano, Chunoshin Ukita and Tomoyoshi Komai, *Japanese Patent* 130,442 (1949) describe extraction of mannitol and ergosterol from *Penicillium* mycelium. See W. Karrer's compilation (listed in the general reference bibliography) for other references.

36 D-Volemitol, $C_7H_{16}O_7$, silky needles, m.p. 153.5° $[\alpha]_D^{20}$ +17.08° (1.001 g. + 0.7 g. of Borax in 15 ml. of H_2O).

$$
\begin{array}{ccccccc}
\text{CH}_2 & \text{CH} & \text{CH} & \text{CH} & \text{CH} & \text{CH} & \text{CH}_2 \\
| & | & | & | & | & | & | \\
\text{OH} & \text{OH} & \text{OH} & \text{OH} & \text{OH} & \text{OH} & \text{OH}
\end{array}
$$

Dermatocarpon miniatum (L.) Mann.

Yasuhiko Asahina and Motoyasu Kagitani, *Ber.* 67B 804 (1934).

Bengt Lindberg, Alfons Misiorny and Carl Axel Wachtmeister, *Acta Chem. Scand.* 7 591 (1953). (A survey of the occurrence of low molecular weight carbohydrate constituents in lichens)

37 **6-O-Acetylglucose,** $C_8H_{14}O_7$, minute colorless prisms, m.p. 133°, $[\alpha]_D^{20}$ +48° (c 4.0 in water at equilibrium).

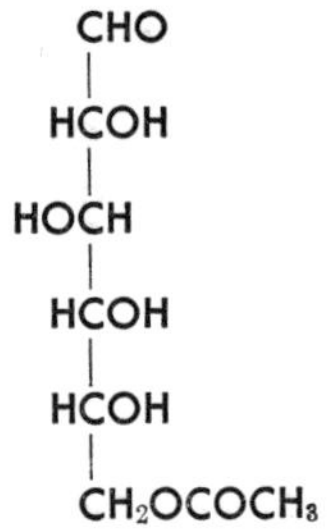

CHO
HCOH
HOCH
HCOH
HCOH
CH₂OCOCH₃

Bacillus megaterium

R. B. Duff, D. M. Webley and V. C. Farmer, *Nature* **179** 103 (1957).

38 **D-Mannopyranosyl-1-*meso*-erythritol,** $C_{10}H_{20}O_9$, colorless crystals, m.p. 160°, $[\alpha]_D$ −36.7°.

CH₂OH
O
O—CH₂—CH—CH—CH₂
OH OH
HO
OH OH OH

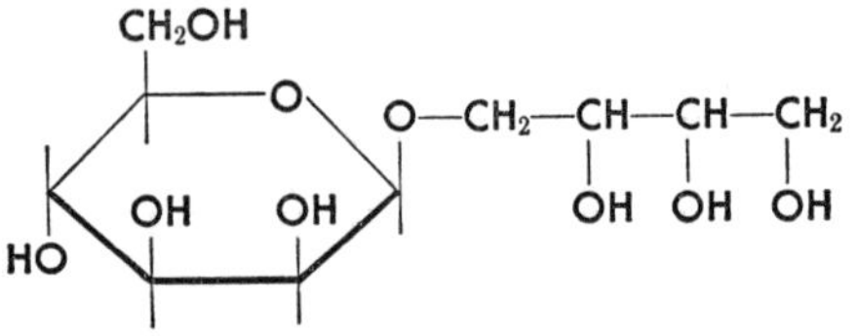

Ustilago sp.

Besides this water-soluble compound the fungus produces 15 g. per liter of an oil, consisting of a mixture of fatty acid esters of D-mannopyranosyl-l-*meso*-erythritol.

B. Boothroyd, J. A. Thorn and R. H. Haskins, *Can. J. Biochem. and Physiol.* 34 10 (1956).

39 **Umbilicin (3-β-D-Galactopyranosido-D-arabitol),** $C_{11}H_{22}O_{10}$, colorless crystals, m.p. 138°, $[\alpha]_D^{20}$ −81° (c 2 in water).

CH₂OH
HOCH
HC—O—CH
HCOH HCOH
CH₂OH HOCH O
HOCH
HC
CH₂OH

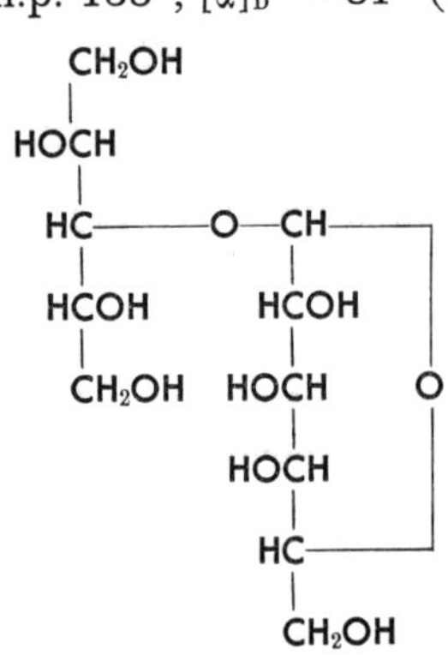

Umbilicaria pustulata
Bengt Lindberg, Carl A. Wachtmeister and Börje Wickberg,
Acta Chem. Scand. **6** 1052 (1952).

40 Trehalosamine, $C_{12}H_{22}O_{10}N$ (Hydrochloride) white microcrystalline powder, $[\alpha]_D^{25}$ +176° (c 2.0 in water).

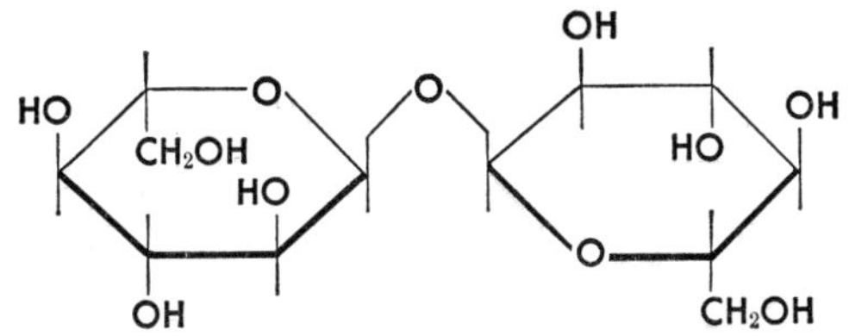

A streptomycete
A yield of about 5 g. per liter was obtained.
Frederico Arcamone and Franco Bizioli, *Gazz. chim. ital.*
87 896 (1957).

41 Leucrose (5-0-α-D-Glucopyranosyl-D-fructopyranose), $C_{12}H_{22}O_{11}$,
colorless hygroscopic bars, m.p. 161–163° (anhydrous),
156–158° (monohydrate), $[\alpha]_D^{25}$ −8.2° → −7.6° (<1 hour,
c 4 in water).

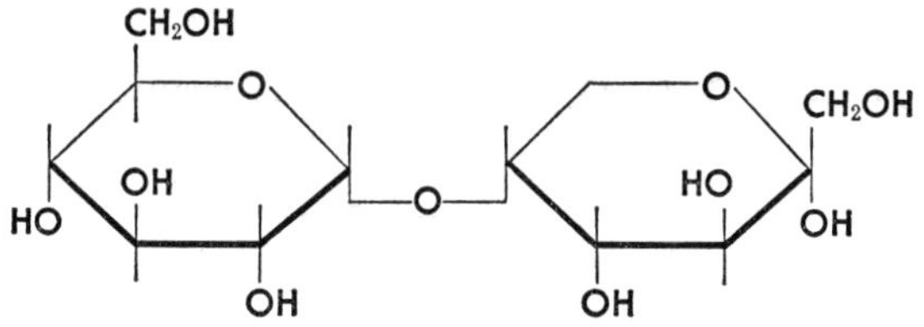

Leuconostoc mesenteroides
Frank H. Stodola, E. S. Sharpe and H. J. Koepsell, *J. Am.
Chem. Soc.* **78** 2514 (1956).

42 Kojibiose (2-0-α-D-Glucopyranosyl-D-glucose), $C_{12}H_{22}O_{11}$, m.p.
(Octaacetate) 166°, $[\alpha]_D$ +150° (c 2.1 in chloroform).
Free sugar: $[\alpha]_D$ +136° (equil., c 0.5 in water).

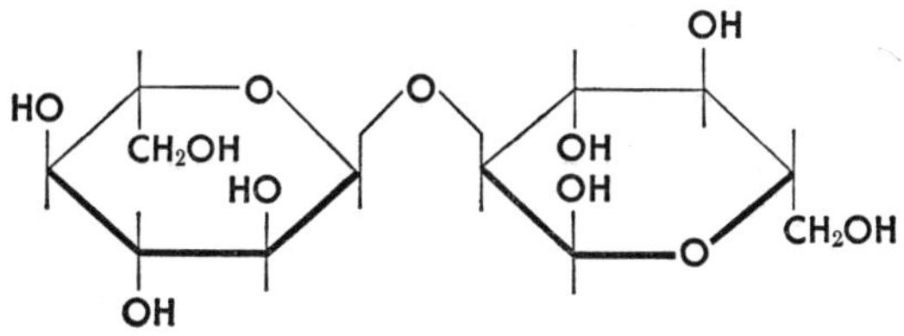

Aspergillus niger
Stanley Peat, W. J. Whelan and Kathleen A. Hinson, *Chem. and Ind.*, 385 (1955).
A. Sato and K. Aso, *Nature* 180 984 (1957).

43 Trehalose (Mycose, α-D-Glucosido-α-D-glucoside), $C_{12}H_{22}O_{11}$, colorless, hygroscopic crystals, m.p. ~210° (dec.) (anhydrous), 97° (hydrate), $[\alpha]_D^{20}$ (hydrate) +178° (in water).

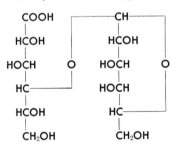

Amanita muscaria, other mushrooms and molds, mycobacteria, yeasts and algae. First isolated from rye ergot (*Claviceps purpurea* (Fr.) Tul.).

Trehalose is present in young mushrooms, but as the plants develop it is replaced by mannitol. It also occurs in seaweeds and higher plants.
E. Bourquelot, *Compt. rend.* 108 568 (1889).
H. Bredereck, *Ber.* 63B 959 (1930). (Structure)
Bengt Lindberg, *Acta Chem. Scand.* 9 917 (1955).

44 Lactobionic Acid, $C_{12}H_{22}O_{12}$, Calcium Salt: granular white powder, $[\alpha]_D^{25}$ +25.1° (c 5.2 in water).

```
COOH            CH
 |               |
HCOH            HCOH
 |               |
HOCH    O       HOCH    O
 |               |
HC              HOCH
 |               |
HCOH            HC
 |               |
CH₂OH           CH₂OH
```

Pseudomonas species, other oxidative bacteria (on lactose)

A 77% yield has been reported. Maltobionic acid was prepared similarly from maltose.
Frank H. Stodola and Lewis B. Lockwood, *J. Biol. Chem.* 171 213 (1947).

Lewis B. Lockwood and Frank H. Stodola, U. S. Patent 2,496,297 (1950).

45 Hygromycin B, $C_{15}H_{28}O_{10}N_2$, amorphous powder, m.p. $\sim$180°. D-Talose has been shown to be one moiety of this antibiotic.

Streptomyces hygroscopicus
Robert L. Mann and W. W. Bromer, *J. Am. Chem. Soc.* **80** 2715 (1958).
Paul F. Wiley and Max V. Sigal, Jr., *ibid.* **80** 1010 (1958).

46 Grifolin, $C_{16}H_{28}O_2$, fine colorless needles, m.p. 40°.

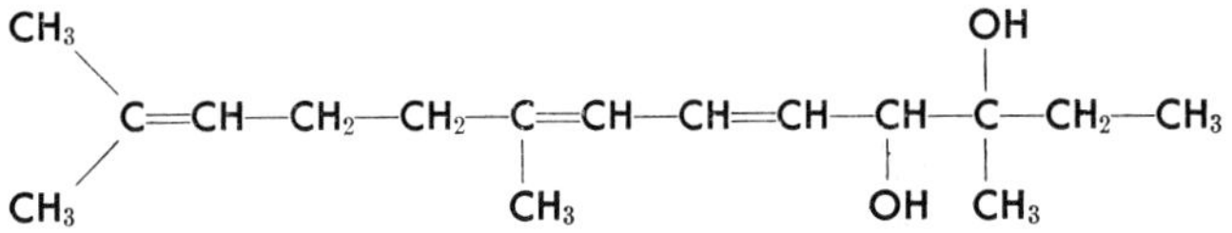

Grifola confluens (=*Polyporus confluens*)
Other components of the extract were mannitol, sterols, a hemin-like substance, a compound $C_8H_{14}O$ (m.p. 145°) and a compound $C_{15}H_{24}O_2$ (m.p. 151°).
Y. Hirata and K. Nakanishi, *J. Biol. Chem.* **184** 135 (1950).

47 Cetyl Alcohol, $C_{16}H_{34}O$, colorless crystals, m.p. 50°, n_D^{79} 1.4283.

$$CH_3(CH_2)_{14}CH_2OH$$

Amanita phalloides
Heinrich Wieland and Gustav Coutelle, *Ann.* **548** 270 (1941).

48 Clavicepsin, $C_{18}H_{34}O_{16}$, colorless crystals, m.p. (anhydr.) 198°, $[\alpha]_D^{20}$ +142°.
A glucoside hydrolyzing to 1 mole of mannitol and 2 moles of glucose. The detailed structure was not determined.

Claviceps purpurea
F. Marino-Zuco and U. Pasquero, *Gazz. chim. ital.* **41** 368 (1912).

49 Stearyl Alcohol, $C_{18}H_{38}O$, colorless leaflets, m.p. 59°.

$$CH_3(CH_2)_{16}CH_2OH$$

Penicillium notatum
A yield of 0.13 g. was obtained from 300 g. of dry mycelium.

A. Angeletti, G. Tappi and G. Biglino, *Ann. chim.* (Rome) 42 502 (1952).

50   *d*-2-Octadecanol, $C_{18}H_{38}O$, colorless needles, m.p. 56°, $[\alpha]_D$ +5.7° (in chloroform).

$$CH_3(CH_2)_{15}CHCH_3$$
$$|$$
$$OH$$

Mycobacterium tuberculosis var. *hominis*, *M. avium*, *M. phlei*

Mary C. Panghorn and R. J. Anderson, *J. Am. Chem. Soc.* 58 10 (1936).

R. E. Reeves and R. J. Anderson, *ibid.* 59 858 (1937).

R. J. Anderson, J. A. Crowder, M. S. Newman and F. H. Stodola, *J. Biol. Chem.* 113 637 (1936).

51   *d*-3-Octadecanol, $C_{18}H_{38}O$, colorless crystals, m.p. 56°.

$$CH_3(CH_2)_{14}CHCH_2CH_3$$
$$|$$
$$OH$$

Corynebacterium diphtheriae

A. A. Kanchukh, *Ukraïn. Biokhim. Zhur.* 26 186 (1954).

52   **Kanamycin,** $C_{18}H_{36}O_{11}N_4$, Sulfate: white prisms which decompose over a wide range above 250°, $[\alpha]_D^{24}$ +146° (c 1 in 0.1 N sulfuric acid).

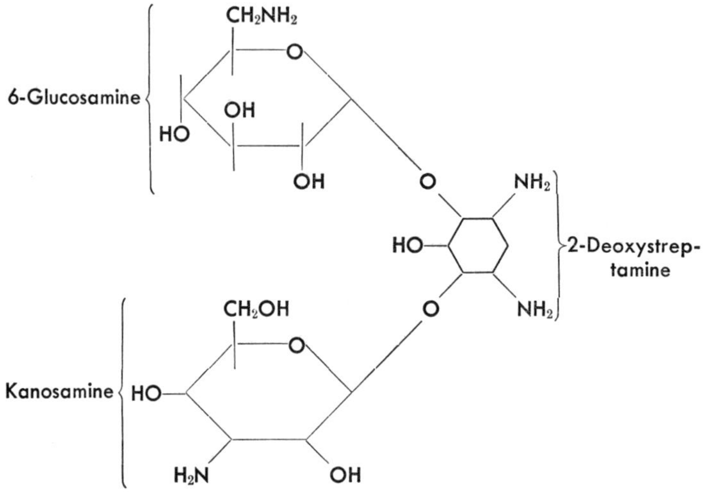

Streptomyces kanamyceticus

Tomio Takeuchi, Tokuro Hikiji, Kazuo Nitta, Seiro Yamazaki, Sadao Abe, Hisaro Takayama and Hamao Umezawa, *J. Antibiotics* (Japan) **10A** 107 (1957).

Hamao Umezawa, Mashiro Ueda, Kenji Maeda, Koki

Yagishita, Shinichi Kondo, Yoshiro Okami, Ryozo Utahara, Yasuke Osato, Kazuo Nitta and Tomio Takeuchi, *ibid.* 10A 181 (1957).

Kenji Maeda, Masahiro Ueda, Koki Yagishita, Shohei Kawaji, Shinichi Kondo, Masao Murase, Tomio Takeuchi, Yoshiro Okami and Hamao Umezawa, *ibid.* 10A 228 (1957).

M. J. Cron, D. L. Johnson, F. M. Palermiti, Y. Perron, H. D. Taylor, D. F. Whitehead and I. R. Hooper, *J. Am. Chem. Soc.* 80 752 (1958).

M. J. Cron, O. B. Fardig, D. L. Johnson, D. F. Whitehead, I. R. Hooper and R. U. Lemieux, *ibid.* 80 4115 (1958).

53 Kanamycin B, colorless crystals, m.p. dec. from 170°, $[\alpha]_D^{24}$ +135° (c 0.63 in water).

Acid hydrolysis yields 2-deoxystreptamine and kanosamine, but no 6-glucosamine as from kanamycin. An unidentified ninhydrin-positive compound was obtained instead. Positive Schiff, Molisch, Elson-Morgan tests.

Streptomyces kanamyceticus

H. Schmitz, O. B. Fardig, F. A. O'Herron, M. A. Rousche and I. R. Hooper, *J. Am. Chem. Soc.* 80 2911 (1958).

54 Streptomycin, $C_{21}H_{39}O_{12}N_7$, m.p. (Reineckate) 164° dec. (Helianthate) 220–226° dec., $[\alpha]_D$ (Hydrochloride) −84° (c 0.5 in water), $[\alpha]_D^{26.6}$ (Trihydrochloride) −86.1° (c 1.0 in water), $[\alpha]_D^{25}$ (Sulfate) −79° (c 1.0 in water). Salts are deliquescent.

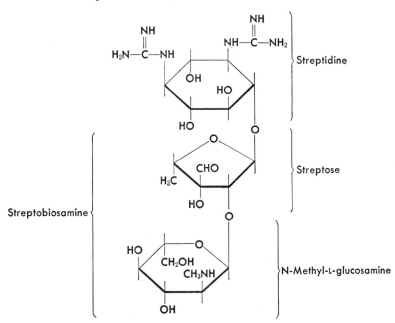

Streptomyces griseus (Krainsky) Waksman et Henrici
S. bikiniensis, S. mashuensis

Albert Schatz, Elizabeth Bugie and Selman A. Waksman.
Proc. Soc. Exptl. Biol. Med. 55 66 (1944). (Isolation)

Selman A. Waksman, "Streptomycin, Its Nature and Applications," Williams and Wilkins Co., Baltimore, Md., 1949. (A review)

Herbert E. Carter, R. K. Clark, Jr., S. R. Dickman, Y. H. Loo, P. S. Skell and W. A. Strong, *J. Biol. Chem.* 160 337 (1945).

Frederick A. Kuehl, Jr., Robert L. Peck, Charles E. Hoffhine, Jr., Robert P. Graber and Karl Folkers, *J. Am. Chem. Soc.* 68 1460 (1946).

Frederick A. Kuehl, Jr., Edwin H. Flynn, Norman G. Brink and Karl Folkers, *ibid.* 68 2096, 2679 (1946). (Structure)

I. R. Hooper, L. H. Klemm, W. J. Polglase and M. L. Wolfrom, *ibid.* 69 1052 (1947).

H. E. Carter, R. K. Clark, Jr., S. R. Dickman, Y. H. Loo, P. S. Skell and W. A. Strong, *Science* 103 540 (1946).

E. P. Abraham and H. W. Florey, "Antibiotics," Oxford University Press, London, 1949 Vol. II chap. 41, pp. 1297–1309.

E. P. Abraham, *ibid.* chap. 42, pp. 1310–1326.

55 Hydroxystreptomycin (Reticulin) $C_{21}H_{39}O_{13}N_7$, Helianthate: red-brown crystals, m.p.: darkening at 200° (dec.), Trihydrochloride: $[\alpha]_D^{28}$ −91° (c 1.0 in water).

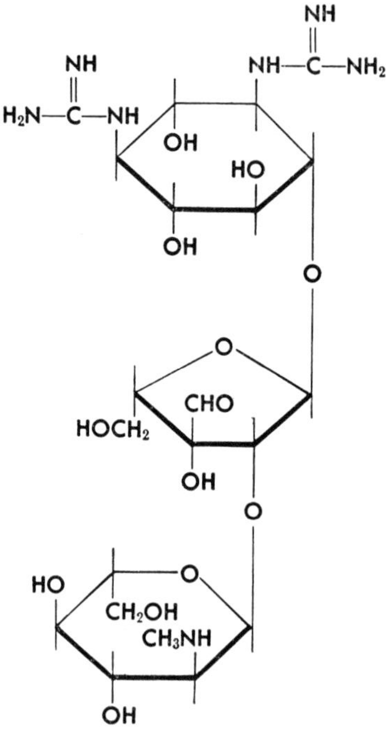

Streptomyces griseocarneus

Seigo Hosaya, Momoe Soeda, Nobuhiko Komatsu and Yoko Sonoda, *Japan. J. Exptl. Med.* 20 327 (1949).

Robert G. Benedict, Frank H. Stodola, Odette L. Shotwell, Anne Marie Borud and Lloyd A. Lindenfelser, *Science* 112 77 (1950).

Frank H. Stodola, Odette L. Shotwell, Anne Marie Borud, Robert G. Benedict and Arthur C. Riley, Jr., *J. Am. Chem. Soc.* 73 2290 (1951). (Structure)

56 Dihydrostreptomycin, $C_{21}H_{41}O_{12}N_7$, non-deliquescent white powder $[\alpha]_D^{25}$ −94.5°. Hydrochloride and sulfate were used.

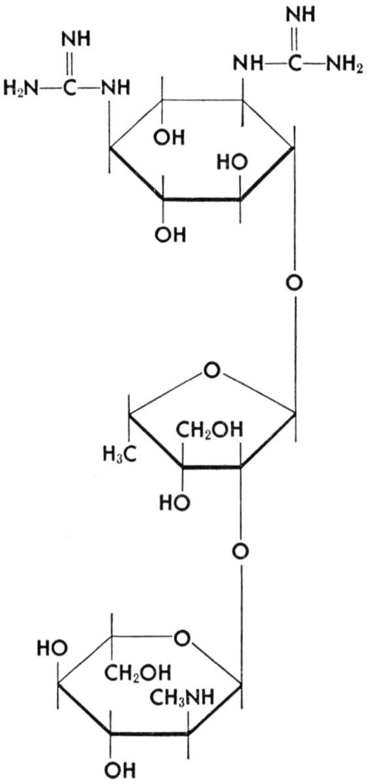

Streptomyces humidus

Sueo Tatsuoka, Tsunaharu Kusaka, Akira Miyake, Michitaka Inoue, Hiromu Hitomi, Yutaka Shiraishi, Hidesuke Iwasaki and Masahiko Imanishi, *Pharm. Bull.* 5 343 (1957). (Primary fermentation product)

57 Hygromycin A, $C_{23}H_{29}O_{12}N$, amorphous (some crystalline derivatives have been prepared). $[\alpha]_D^{25}$ $-126°$ (c 1 in water). Partial structure:

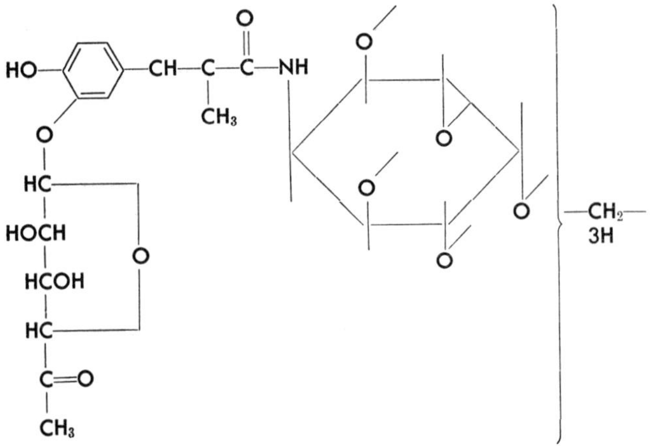

Streptomyces hygroscopicus (Jensen) Waksman and Henrici

R. L. Mann, R. M. Gale and F. R. Van Abeele, *Antibiotics and Chemotherapy* 3 1279 (1953). (Isolation)

Robert L. Mann and D. O. Wolf, *J. Am. Chem. Soc.* 79 120 (1957). (Structure)

58 Homomycin, white powder, m.p. 105–109° (dec. >160°).

Homomycin has been shown to be the same as hygromycin except that the homomycin amino sugar moiety is:

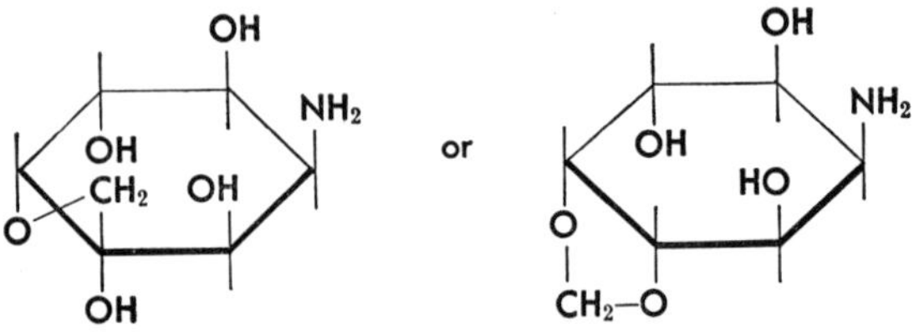

Streptomyces noboritoensis n. sp.

Yusuke Sumiki, Gotaku Nakamura, Makoto Kawasaki, Satoru Yamashita, Kentaro Anzai, Kiyoshi Isono, Yoshiko Serizawa, Yoko Tomiyama and Saburo Suzuki, *J. Antibiotics* (Japan) 8A 170 (1955). (Isolation)

Mitsuo Namiki, Kiyoshi Isono, Kentaro Anzai and Saburo Suzuki, *ibid.* 10A 36 (1957). (Structure)

59 Paromomycin, $C_{23}H_{45}O_{14}N_5$, white amorphous solid, $[\alpha]_D^{25}$ $+64°$ (c 1.0 in water), Hydrochloride $[\alpha]_D^{25}$ $+56.5°$ (c 1.0 in water).

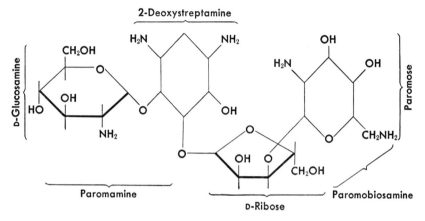

Streptomyces rimosus forma paromomycinus
Paromomycin seems to be identical with catenulin.
Theodore H. Haskell, James C. French and Quentin R. Bartz, J. Am. Chem. Soc. 81 3480 (1959).
Ibid. Belgian Patent 547,976.

60 Neomycins. (Fradiomycins, Streptothricins, Neomins, Mycifradin, Nivemycins, Myacins)

Neomycin A is identical with neamine, a moiety of neomycins B and C. Neomycins B and C are identical except for the diaminohexose components.

Neomycin B (Streptothricin B II), $C_{23}H_{46}O_{12}N_6$, amorphous hygroscopic white powder, no definite m.p., $[\alpha]_D^{25}$ $+83°$ (in 0.2 N H_2SO_4).

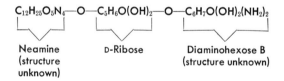

Neomycin C (Streptothricin B I), $C_{23}H_{46}O_{12}N_6$, amorphous, hygroscopic white powder, no definite m.p., $[\alpha]_D^{25}$ $+121°$ (in 0.2 N H_2SO_4).

Also contains neamine. The disaccharide portion (neobiosamine C) has been characterized, however, as:

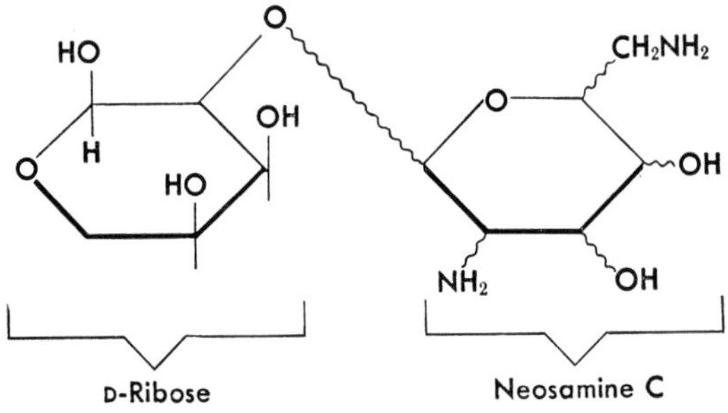

D-Ribose   Neosamine C

Streptomyces fradiae, other *Streptomyces* spp.

Selman A. Waksman and Hubert A. Lechevalier, *Science* **109** 305 (1949). (Isolation)

Byron E. Leach, William H. DeVries, Harrison A. Nelson, William G. Jackson and John S. Evans, *J. Am. Chem. Soc.* **73** 2797 (1951). (Isolation)

Jared H. Ford, Malcolm E. Bergy, A. A. Brooks, Edward R. Garrett, Joseph Alberti, John R. Dyer and H. E. Carter, *ibid.* **77** 5311 (1955).

Kenneth L. Rinehart, Jr., Peter W. K. Woo, Alexander D. Argoudelis and Astrea M. Giesbrecht, *ibid.* **79** 4567 (1957).

Kenneth L. Rinehart, Jr., Peter W. K. Woo and Alexander D. Argoudelis, *ibid.* **79** 4568 (1957).

Idem., ibid. **80** 6461 (1958).

Kenneth L. Rinehart, Jr., and Peter W. K. Woo, *ibid.* **80** 6463 (1958). (Structure)

61 **Catenulin** (Sulfate) $[\alpha]_D^{25}$ +51.9° (c 1 in water).

A substance resembling paromomycin. Acid hydrolysis yields neamine.*

Streptomyces catenulensis

J. W. Davisson, I. A. Solomons and T. M. Lees, *Antibiotics and Chemotherapy* **2** 460 (1952).

62 **Dextromycin,** Helianthate: m.p. 227°, Hydrochloride: $[\alpha]_D^{25}$ +61° (c 1 acetone).

Similar to neomycin B.*

Streptomyces sp. resembling *S. fradiae*

Koichi Ogata and Koichi Nakazawa, *J. Antibiotics* (Japan) **3** 440 (1950).

* Probably identical with paromomycin. (Private communication from Drs. W. Celmer and C. Shaffner)

Toyonari Araki, Akira Miyake, Yoshitamo Aramaki, Hiroshi Kojima, Hajime Yokotani, Koichi Ogata and Koichi Nakazawa, *Ann. Repts. Takeda Research Lab.* 13 1 (1954).
* Identical with neomycin B.   See addendum.

63 **Framycetin** (Actilin, Soframycin, Antibiotic E.F. 185), Hydrochloride: white powder, $[\alpha]_D$ +57° (c 1.0 in water), m.p. (picrate) 189° (dec.).

Framycetin resembles neomycin and streptomycin in some respects, but is distinct.   Hydrolysis yields neamine, a pentose, and a diaminohexose.   Framycetin forms peptide derivatives such as a reineckate and a picrate.   The molecular weight is about 1400–1500.   No guanidine tests were observed, and all the nitrogen is present as primary amine groups.

Streptomyces sp. resembling *S. lavendulae*

Louis Jacques Decaris, *Ann. pharm. franç.* 11 44 (1953).

Maurice Marie Janot, Henry Pénau, Digna van Stolk, Guy Hagemann and Lucien Pénasse, *Bull. Soc. chim. France,* 1458 (1954).

A. Lutz and M. A. Witz, *Compt. rend. soc. biol.* 149 1467 (1955).

A. Saito and C. P. Schaffner, *Congr. intern. biochim.,* Résumés communs., *3ᵉ Congr.,* Brussels, 1955, p. 98.

64 **Hydroxymycin,** probable empirical formula $C_{25}H_{47}O_{15}N_5$, white powder, $[\alpha]_D^{20}$ 63° $\pm$ 2° (c. 1.0 in water) (Sulfate) white powder, $[\alpha]_D^{20}$ +51° (c 1.0 in water).

A basic antibiotic similar to streptomycin and neomycin.   Contains 6.2% total nitrogen and 6.0% amino nitrogen.   It is water soluble and insoluble in most organic solvents with a molecular weight of about 610.   Hydrolysis yields a fragment called pseudoneamine and others which show pentose and 2-aminohexose reactions.

An antifungal substance was produced in the same culture.

Streptomyces paucisporogenes

M. M. Janot, H. Pénau, G. Hagemann, H. Velu, J. Teillon and G. Bouet, *Ann. pharm. franç.* 12 440 (1954).

G. Hagemann, G. Nominé and L. Pénasse, *Ann. pharm. franç.* 16 585 (1958).

H. Pénau, G. Hagemann and H. Velu, *Bull. soc. chim. biol.* 41 761 (1959).

J. Bartos, *Ann. pharm. franç.* 16 596 (1958).

65 **Mannosidostreptomycin** (Streptomycin B), $C_{27}H_{49}O_{17}N_7$, color-less crystals, m.p. (Anhydrous Reineckate) 178° dec. (Trihydrochloride) 190–200° dec., $[\alpha]_D^{25}$ (Trihydrochloride) −47° (c 1.35 in water).

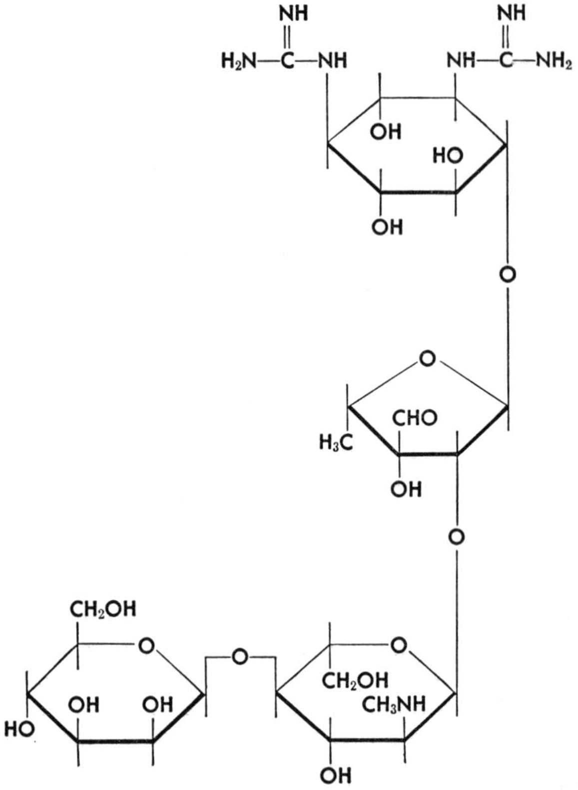

Occurs together with streptomycin in some cultures. *Streptomyces griseus*

Josef Fried and Homer E. Stavely, *J. Am. Chem. Soc.* **74** 5461 (1952). (Structure)

66 **Phthiocerol,** $C_{36}H_{74}O_3$, colorless plates, m.p. 71.5–73°, $[\alpha]_D$ −4.50° (c 11.48 in chloroform).

It is claimed (in the most recent reference below) that phthiocerol, as ordinarily isolated, is a mixture of the following two substances:

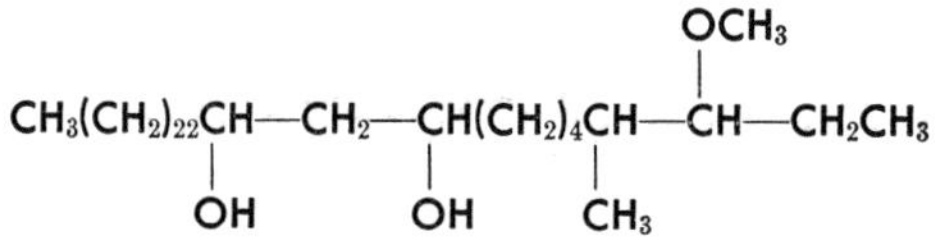

$$CH_3(CH_2)_{22}CH{-}CH_2{-}CH(CH_2)_4CH{-}\overset{\displaystyle OCH_3}{\overset{|}{CH}}{-}CH_2CH_3$$
$$\underset{\displaystyle OH}{|}\qquad\underset{\displaystyle OH}{|}\quad\underset{\displaystyle CH_3}{|}$$

and

$$CH_3(CH_2)_{20}CH{-}CH_2{-}CH(CH_2)_4{-}CH{-}\overset{\displaystyle OCH_3}{\overset{|}{CH}}{-}CH_2CH_3$$
$$\underset{\displaystyle OH}{|}\qquad\underset{\displaystyle OH}{|}\quad\underset{\displaystyle CH_3}{|}$$

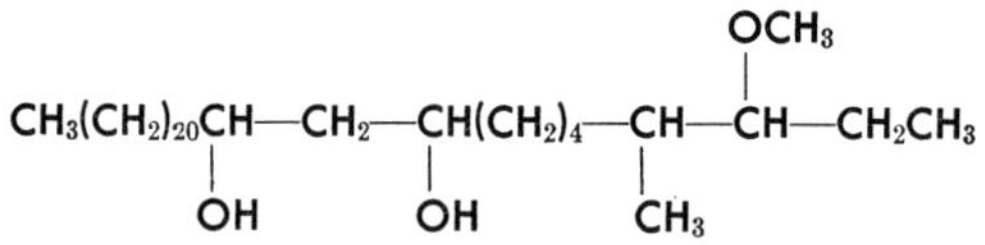

Mycobacterium tuberculosis (human, bovine and avian)

In the wax of the mycobacteria phthiocerol is present mainly as the dimycoceranate.

J. A. Hall, J. W. Lewis and N. Polgar, *J. Chem. Soc.,* 3971 (1955).

Hans Noll, *J. Biol. Chem.* 224 149 (1957).

H. Demarteau-Ginsburg, E. Lederer, R. Ryhage, S. Ställberg-Stenhagen and E. Stenhagen, *Nature* 183 1117 (1959).

3

Aliphatic Acids and Glycolipides

The metabolic origins of some of the acids in this section can be deduced from the foregoing chapter. Among these are pyruvic, glyceric, acetic, formic, propionic and lactic acids.

Many of the other simpler acids are recognizable as members of the citric acid cycle and ancillary routes. The citric acid cycle (tricarboxylic acid cycle or Krebs cycle) is outlined below:

The Citric Acid Cycle

Enzymes:
1. Condensing enzyme
2. Aconitase
3. Isocitric dehydrogenase
4. Oxalosuccinic decarboxylase
5. Succinic dehydrogenase
6. Fumarase
7. Malic dehydrogenase

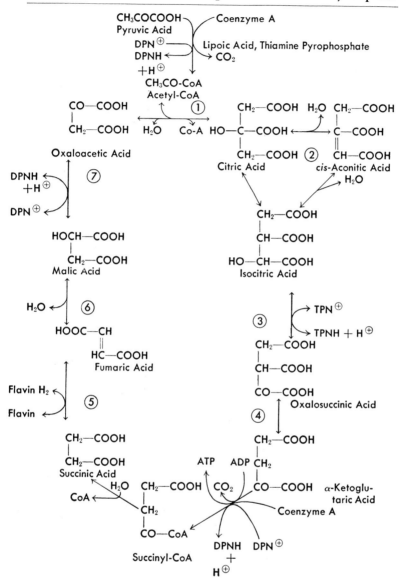

The net effect of the cycle is to oxidize pyruvic acid to carbon dioxide and water:

$$CH_3COCOOH + 5O \rightarrow 3CO_2 + 2H_2O$$

Enzymes of the citric acid cycle occur widely among microorganisms, and it is likely that the cycle and variants of it are equally ubiquitous. Its primary physiological function in microorganisms (if a primary function can be singled out) is less clear, two possibilities being: (a) an energy source and (b) a source of amino acid skeletons. Interruption of the cycle or imbalances under certain conditions lead to accumulation of certain acids. Thus high yields of citric, isocitric, α-ketoglutaric, fumaric and malic acids can be obtained in controlled fungal fermentations.

It was mentioned in the preceding chapter that certain microorganisms are capable of growing on a medium containing acetate as the sole carbon source, synthesizing all their carbohydrate requirements from it. In some of these microorganisms, at least, this ability may be due to possession of a pair of enzymes (malate synthetase and isocitritase) which permit operation of a cycle ancillary to the citric acid cycle or replacement of the steps from isocitric acid to malic acid and commonly called the glyoxylic acid cycle:

The Glyoxylic Acid Cycle

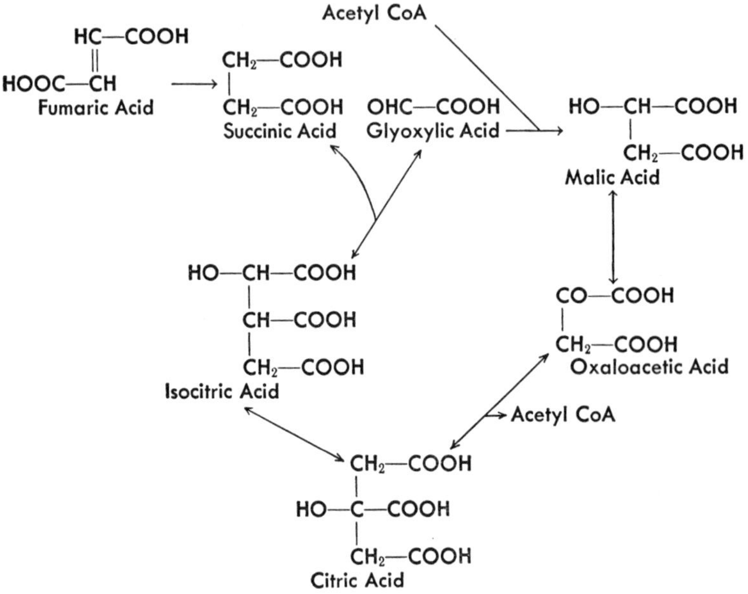

The origin of certain other acids can be deduced; for example, itaconic acid by decarboxlration of aconitic, oxalic acid by oxidation of glyoxylic and epoxysuccinic by oxidation of fumaric.

$$
\begin{array}{ccc}
\text{CH—COOH} & & \text{CH}_2 \\
\| & \xrightarrow{\ -\text{CO}_2\ } & \| \\
\text{C—COOH} & & \text{C—COOH} \\
| & & | \\
\text{CH}_2\text{—COOH} & & \text{CH}_2\text{—COOH} \\
\text{Aconitic Acid} & & \text{Itaconic Acid}
\end{array}
$$

$$
\begin{array}{ccc}
& [\text{O}] & \\
\text{OHC—COOH} & \longrightarrow & \text{HOOC—COOH} \\
\text{Glyoxylic Acid} & & \text{Oxalic Acid}
\end{array}
$$

Fumaric Acid   trans-Epoxysuccinic Acid

Certain higher fungi and some molds produce acids such as caperatic, agaricic, rangiformic, mineoluteic, roccellic, and spiculisporic, which appear to be essentially aldol condensation products of various keto acids of the citric acid cycle with long chain fatty acids.

$$
\begin{array}{cc}
\text{CH}_3(\text{CH}_2)_{13}\text{—CH—COOH} & \text{CH}_3(\text{CH}_2)_{15}\text{—CH—COOH} \\
| & | \\
\text{HO—C—COOH} & \text{HO—C—COOH} \\
| & | \\
\text{CH}_2\text{—COOH} & \text{CH}_2\text{—COOH} \\
\text{Caperatic Acid} & \text{Agaricic Acid} \\
\text{(one carboxyl group a} & \\
\text{methyl ester)} &
\end{array}
$$

$$
\begin{array}{cc}
\text{CH}_3(\text{CH}_2)_{13}\text{—CH—COOH} & \text{CH}_3(\text{CH}_2)_9\text{—CH——C}{=}\text{O} \\
| & | \\
\text{CH—COOH} & \text{HOOC—C—OH} \\
| & | \\
\text{CH}_2\text{—COOH} & \text{CH——O} \\
& | \\
& \text{COOH} \\
\text{Rangiformic Acid} & \text{Minioluteic Acid} \\
\text{(one carboxyl group a} & \\
\text{methyl ester)} &
\end{array}
$$

```
CH3(CH2)11—CH—COOH          CH3(CH2)9—CH—COOH
           |                          |
           CH—COOH              O——C—COOH
           |                   /       |
           CH3             O=C         |
                              \        |
                               CH2—CH2
```

Roccellic Acid   Spiculisporic Acid

Lipide production by microorganisms varies widely, some yeasts and molds producing up to 50% of their dry weight. Yeasts were used for commercial submerged culture production of fat during World War II in Germany.

It has been estimated that 80–90% of all fatty acids in plants and higher animals occur as esters—triglycerides and phospholipides. In microorganisms a high percentage of the lipides seem to be bound in some way, perhaps as lipoproteins, liposaccharides, sterol esters, etc., and a preliminary acid hydrolysis is required before complete extraction.

The fatty acid contents of the fats produced by a few molds and yeasts have been studied in detail, and several of these are reproduced in the following table.

TABLE I

Component Fatty Acids of Fats Produced by Microorganisms

	Aspergillus nidulans[1]	Penicillium soppii.[2]	Penicillium lilacinum[3]	Penicillium spinulosum[4]	Yeast Strain No. 72[5]	Rhodotorula sp.[6]	Torulopsis sp.[7]
Free acidity (% oleic)..........	0.8	0.6	0.2	5.8	33	18	51.2
Component Acids							
Myristic........	0.7	0.3	0.1	—	0.1	1.1	0.3
Palmitic........	20.9	22.0	32.3	18.0	25.6	29.8	7.9
Stearic.........	15.9	7.6	9.4	11.9	5.9	8.8	3.8
Arachidic, Behenic, Lignoceric........	1.4	0.9	1.4	1.4	5.1	1.4	0.2
Hexadecenoic...	1.2	3.3	3.4	3.8	1.3	1.8	7.6
Oleic..........	40.3	45.2	38.6	43.3	54.5	40.1	21.5
Linoleic.........	17.0	20.0	13.4	21.1	5.7	11.2	49.7
Linolenic........	0.2	0.3	—	0.3	0.7	4.8	4.4
Unsaturated C_{20}..	2.4	0.4	1.4	0.2	1.1	1.0	—

Generally microorganism lipides have a higher free fatty acid content than those of animals. Bacterial fats seem to have received less quantitative study. cis-Vaccenic and lactobacillic acids have been shown to be major constituents of the lipides of lactobacilli,[8] streptococci[9] and *Agrobacterium tumefaciens*.[10] An analysis of the fatty acids of two strains of *Mycobacterium tuberculosis* has been published:[11]

TABLE II

Higher Fatty Acid Content (%) in the Phosphatides and Fats of Mycobacterium tuberculosis H_{37} Rv and BCG

	Phosphatide		Fat	
	H_{37}Rv	BCG	H_{37}Rv	BCG
Mycolic Acid......................	20.0	20.4	——	——
I. Unknown Acid...................	3.0	3.0	0.7	3.1
II. " "	13.8	8.6	1.1	2.1
III. " "	——	——	2.7	1.5
III. Phthioic Acid..................	5.7	12.3	20.0	5.5
III. Unknown Acid..................	3.7	14.0	——	——
IV. " "	——	——	8.0	——
Arachidonic Acid...................	——	——	——	2.3
Stearic Acid.......................	13.0	13.0	24.5	22.1
Oleic and Palmitic Acids............	28.0	19.2	34.0	48.2
Linoleic Acid......................	12.8	10.4	10.0	15.2

The waxes and fats in which the acid-fast mycobacteria and corynebacteria abound have been investigated extensively, and a variety of oxidized, methylated and branched chain fatty acids and alcohols isolated and characterized. In the oxidized and

[1] J. Singh, T. K. Walker and M. L. Meara, *Biochem. J.* 61 85 (1955).

[2] J. Singh, Sudha E. Philip and T. K. Walker, *J. Sci. Food and Agr.* 8 697 (1957).

[3] J. Singh, Sudha Shah and T. K. Walker, *Biochem. J.* 62 222 (1956).

[4] I. Shimi, Ph.D. Thesis, Univ. of Manchester, 1955.

[5] T. P. Hilditch and R. K. Shrivastava, *Biochim. et Biophys. Acta* 2 80 (1948).

[6] John Holmberg, *Svensk Kem. Tidskr.* 60 14 (1948).

[7] R. Reichert, *Helv. Chim. Acta* 28 484 (1945).

[8] Klaus Hofmann and Sylvan M. Sax, *J. Biol. Chem.* 205 55 (1953).

[9] Klaus Hofmann and Fred Tausig, *ibid.* 213 415 (1955).

[10] *Idem., ibid.* 213 425 (1955).

[11] Josef Pokorný, *Naturwissenschaften* 10 241 (1958).

methylated acids the oxygen and methyl groups usually appear in positions consistent with the acetate theory of fatty acid biogenesis. These bacteria seem to be able also (in effect) to couple two long chain fatty acids to form ketones and branched chain acids.

Bacterial lipopolysaccharides are irritating pyrogens, relatively toxic to higher animals. The polysaccharide component is the carrier of serological effects, while the lipide moiety has an affinity for the surface of erythrocytes and produces the toxic and pyrogenic effect.[12] The high molecular weight wax called cord factor from mycobacteria is quite toxic (quantitatively comparable to diphtheria toxin) and is believed by some to be the principal factor responsible for the virulence of tuberculosis pathogens. Some of the simpler liposaccharides are shown in this section. References to those of higher molecular weight are included in an appendix.

Phosphatides are widely distributed in nature, though generally in small quantities. They are difficult to handle intact, and few have been well characterized. The metabolism, theories of function and biosynthesis of phospholipides have been reviewed.[13]

For many years chemists speculated on the reason for the predominance of compounds with an even number of carbon atoms among natural fatty acids. The mystery was intensified by such animal feeding experiments as those of Knoop and Dakin,[14] which showed that in mammalian metabolism stepwise degradation of fatty acids and similar substances occurred two carbon atoms at a time.

Microorganisms have been instrumental in the discovery of the significance of acetate in the catabolism and in the biosynthesis of fatty acids. The enzymatic methods, particularly those of anaerobic microorganisms, may differ in detail from those of higher animals. This work has been well reviewed.[15]

Great advances were made in the discovery of coenzyme A,[16]

[12] O. Westphal, O. Lüderitz, E. Eichenberger and E. Neter, *Deut. Z. Verdauungs-u. Stoffwechselkrankh.* 15 170 (1955).

[13] E. P. Kennedy, *Ann. Rev. Biochem.* 26 130 (1957).

[14] H. D. Dakin, "Oxidations and Reductions in the Animal Body," Longmans, Green and Co., London, 1922.

[15] H. A. Barker, "Bacterial Fermentations," John Wiley and Sons, Inc., New York, N. Y., 1956, p. 30.

[16] Fritz A. Lipmann, "Les Prix Nobel," Stockholm, 1954.

the isolation of acetyl coenzyme A (from yeast), the demonstration that the acetyl group was attached to its sulfur atom in a thioester linkage and that acetyl coenzyme A was an active acetylating agent.[17] The enzymic steps in what must be a very general scheme of fatty acid catabolism now can be written as follows:[18]

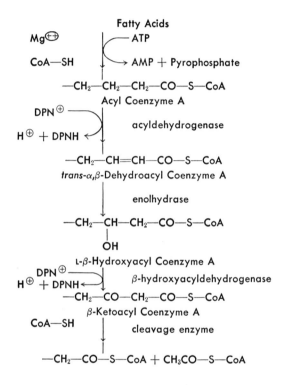

At first this process was thought to be reversible or cyclic. It has since been shown that a separate set of enzymes controls fatty acid biosynthesis. The required enzymes and cofactors for the synthetic process have been isolated, and in outline the

[17] Feodor Lynen, Ernestine Reichert and Luistraud Rueff, *Ann.* **574** 1 (1951).

[18] Feodor Lynen, *Ann. Rev. Biochem.* 24 653 (1955).

process is at present believed to be represented by the scheme:[19]

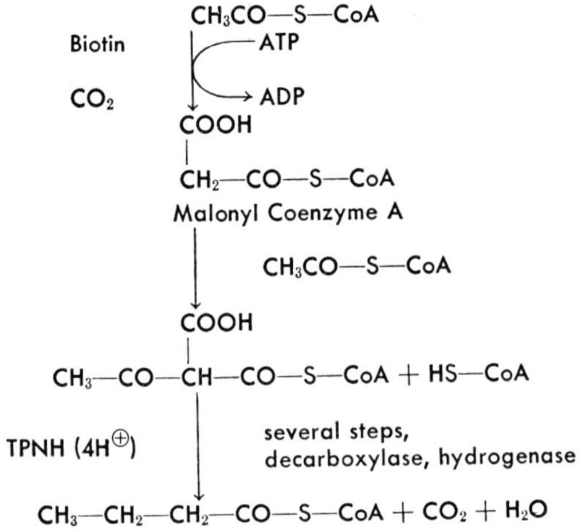

$$CH_3CO—S—CoA$$

Biotin

CO_2 → ADP (ATP)

$$COOH$$
$$|$$
$$CH_2—CO—S—CoA$$
Malonyl Coenzyme A

$$CH_3CO—S—CoA$$

$$COOH$$
$$|$$
$$CH_3—CO—CH—CO—S—CoA + HS—CoA$$

TPNH ($4H^{\oplus}$)   several steps,
decarboxylase, hydrogenase

$$CH_3—CH_2—CH_2—CO—S—CoA + CO_2 + H_2O$$

The butyryl coenzyme A can then react with another molecule of malonyl coenzyme A and the process repeats. There is a statistical distribution peak at 14–18 carbon atom length chains.

Certain bacteria can couple chains of considerable length as, for example, in corynomycolic acid produced by corynebacteria:

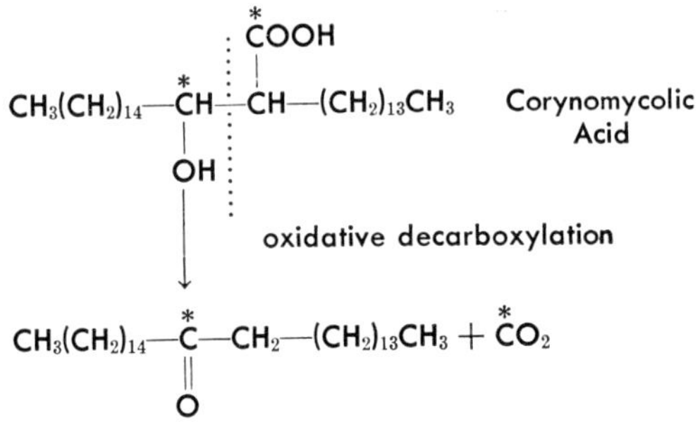

$$\overset{*}{C}OOH$$
$$|$$
$$CH_3(CH_2)_{14}—\overset{*}{C}H—CH—(CH_2)_{13}CH_3 \quad \text{Corynomycolic Acid}$$
$$|$$
$$OH$$

oxidative decarboxylation

$$CH_3(CH_2)_{14}—\overset{*}{C}—CH_2—(CH_2)_{13}CH_3 + \overset{*}{C}O_2$$
$$\|$$
$$O$$

This compound is formed by the coupling of two palmitic acid molecules as shown by a labeling experiment.[20] C^{14}-1-Labeled

[19] Salih J. Wakil, Edward B. Titchener and David M. Gibson, *Biochim. et Biophys. Acta* 29 225 (1958); Salih J. Wakil, *J. Am. Chem. Soc.* 80 6465 (1958); David M. Gibson, Edward B. Titchener and Salih J. Wakil, *Biochim. et Biophys. Acta* 30 376 (1958).

[20] Mireille Gastambide-Odier, E. Lederer, *Nature* 184 1563 (1959).

palmitic acid was incorporated into mycolic acid, and the product degraded to show that the carboxyl group and the oxidized C-atom β-to it in the corynomycolic acid were labeled. A similar biosynthetic path was suggested for the higher molecular weight mycolic acids produced by mycobacteria. Thus, condensation of 2 moles of n-C_{26} and 2 moles of n-C_{18} acids would yield the C_{88} mycolic acids of cord factor. A C_{26} acid is known to be produced by mycobacteria, and a C_{52} acid, corynine, by corynebacteria.

The biotin requirement for enzymatic carboxylations is becoming generally recognized. It was in connection with his studies in lipide metabolism that Lynen isolated and synthesized a reaction product of biotin and carbon dioxide in which CO_2 had reacted at one of the nitrogen atoms to give an allophanic acid type of intermediate, the side-chain carboxyl group perhaps

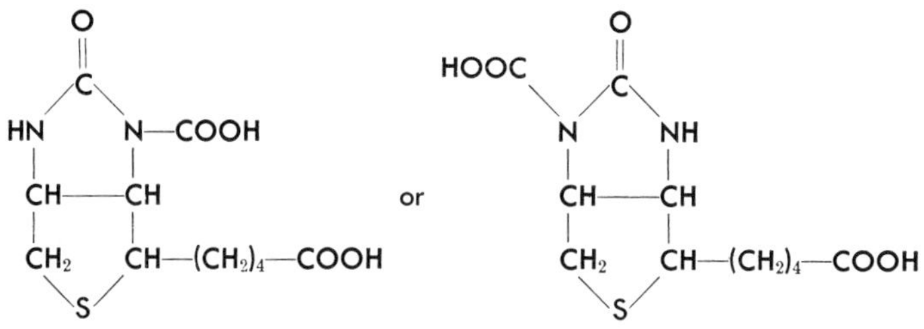

being bound to the protein apoenzyme by an amide bond.

An intermediate may be adenosine diphosphoryl biotin (from ATP):

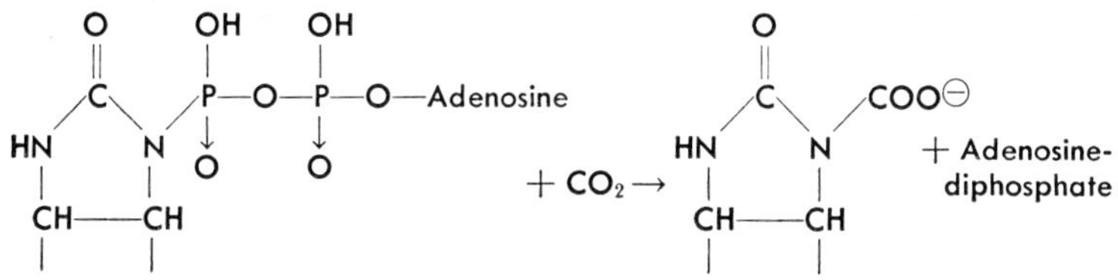

Other suggestions concerning the detailed function of this carboxylase cofactor were made.[21]

The lecithins are formed by initial ATP phosphorylation of one glycerol hydroxyl group followed by esterification of the re-

[21] F. Lynen, J. Knappe, E. Lorch, G. Jütting and E. Ringelmann, *Angew. Chem.* **71** 481 (1959).

maining two hydroxyls by fatty acids as their coenzyme A esters. The phosphate group is then displaced by a choline phosphate group contributed by a coenzyme, cytidine diphosphocholine:

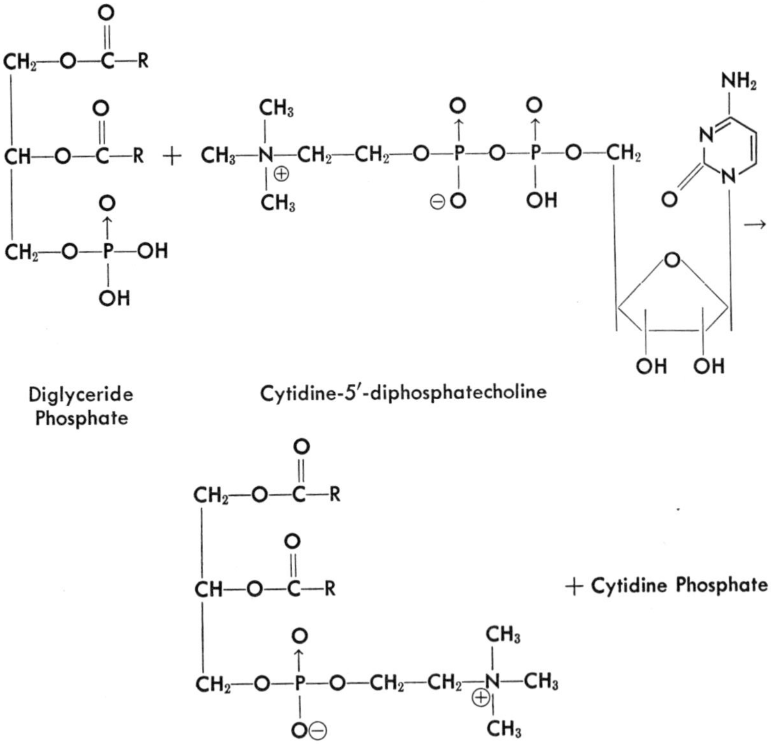

Diglyceride
Phosphate

Cytidine-5'-diphosphatecholine

+ Cytidine Phosphate

The mechanism for cephalin formation is probably similar.

67 Formic Acid, CH_2O_2, colorless liquid, b.p. 100.5°, n_D^{20} 1.3714.

HCOOH

Pseudomonas formicans n. sp., etc.
See the reference below for earlier work.
Irving P. Crawford, *J. Bacteriol.* 68 734 (1954).

68 Oxalic Acid, $C_2H_2O_4$ (Dihydrate), colorless tablets, m.p. 101°.

HOOC—COOH

Aspergillus niger, Penicillium oxalicum, Citromyces spp., many other fungus species and most lichens.
It occurs as the calcium salt in most lichens and higher fungi, but occasionally also as the free acid.

Jackson W. Foster, "Chemical Activities of Fungi," Academic Press Inc., New York, N. Y., 1949, chap. 10, pp. 326–350.

G. Walter, "Organic Acid Production by some Wood-Rotting Basidiomycetes," Univ. Microfilms Pub. 10,417, 1955, 99 pp.

69 Acetic Acid, $C_2H_4O_2$, colorless liquid, b.p. 118°, n_D^{20} 1.3718.

$$CH_3COOH$$

Saccharomyces cerevisiae, other yeasts.   Present in small quantities in many microorganisms.

Leland A. Underkofler and Richard J. Hickey, "Industrial Fermentations," Chemical Publishing Co., Inc., New York, N. Y., 1954, Vol. I, Ruse H. Vaughn, *Acetic acid-vinegar,* chap. 17, pp. 498–535.

70 Pyruvic Acid, $C_3H_4O_3$, colorless liquid, b.p. 165° (dec.), n_D^{20} 1.4138.

$$CH_3COCOOH$$

Pseudomonas saccharophila, etc.

Approximately 2 moles of pyruvic acid were produced per mole of glucose.

Nathan Entner and Michael Doudoroff, *J. Biol. Chem.* **196** 853 (1952).

71 Malonic Acid, $C_3H_4O_4$, colorless plates, m.p. 135°.

$$HOOC—CH_2—COOH$$

Penicillium funiculosum, P. islandicum Sopp, other fungi

D-Mannitol was isolated from the same culture.

Takeo Yamamoto, *J. Pharm. Soc. Japan* **75** 761 (1955).

72 Tartronic Acid, $C_3H_4O_5$, colorless crystals, m.p. 163° (dec.).

$$HOOC—\overset{\displaystyle |}{\underset{\displaystyle OH}{CH}}—COOH$$

Acetobacter acetosum, Gluconoacetobacter liquefaciens

The first organism also produced 2-keto-D-gluconic acid and 5-keto-D-gluconic acid.   The second organism also produced acetaldehyde, formic acid, acetic acid, 5-ketogluconic acid, glycolic acids, other reducing acids, rubiginol, rubiginic acid and 3,5-dihydroxy-1,4-pyrone.

D. Kulka, A. N. Hall and T. K. Walker, *Nature* **167** 905 (1951).

Ko Aida, Toshio Kojima and Toshinobu Asai, *J. Gen. and Appl. Microbiol.* 1 18 (1955).

73 *β*-**Nitropropionic Acid**, $C_3H_5O_4N$, colorless crystals, m.p. 65°.

$$O_2N—CH_2CH_2COOH$$

Aspergillus flavus, A. oryzae
Milton T. Bush, Oscar Touster and Jean Early Brockman, *J. Biol. Chem.* 188 685 (1951).
Seiji Nakamura and Chuji Shimoda, *J. Agr. Chem. Soc. Japan* 28 909 (1954).
H. Raistrick and A. Stössl, *Biochem. J.* 68 647 (1958).
See addendum for reference on biosynthesis.

74 **Propionic Acid**, $C_3H_6O_2$, colorless liquid with sharp odor, b.p. 140.5°.

$$CH_3CH_2COOH$$

Amanita muscaria L., Propionibacteria, Clostridium propionicum
Julius Zellner, *Monatsh.* 26 727 (1905).
Kenneth V. Thimann, "The Life of Bacteria," The Macmillan Company, New York, 1955, pp. 429–440.

75 L(+)-**Lactic Acid** (*d*-Lactic Acid, Sarcolactic Acid), $C_3H_6O_3$, colorless crystals, m.p. 52.8°, $[\alpha]_D^{15}$ +3.33° (c 5.022 in water), hygroscopic, polymerizes.

$$CH_3CHCOOH$$
$$|$$
$$OH$$

Lactobacilli, Rhizopus species, etc.
Yields of 90% or better have been reported.
Leland A. Underkofler and Richard J. Hickey, "Industrial Fermentations," Chemical Publishing Co., Inc., New York, N. Y., 1954 **Vol. I**, Ruse H. Vaughn, *Acetic acid-vinegar*, chap. 17, pp. 498–535; H. H. Shopmeyer, *Lactic acid*, chap. 12, pp. 391–419.

76 L(−)-**Glyceric Acid**, $C_3H_6O_4$, unstable, usually isolated as a salt. Ca salt (dihydrate), m.p. 138°, $[\alpha]_D^{20}$ +13.3° (c 4.5 in water).

$$COOH$$
$$|$$
$$HCOH$$
$$|$$
$$CH_2OH$$

We have observed (by paper chromatographic comparison with an authentic sample on several solvent systems) the production of this acid by a wide variety of fungi. It is always accompanied by gluconic acid.

77   **2-Phosphoglyceric Acid,** $C_3H_7O_7P$.

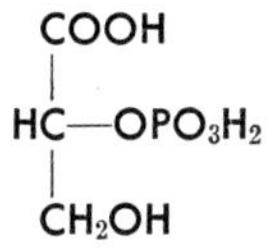

$$\begin{array}{c} \text{COOH} \\ | \\ \text{HC—OPO}_3\text{H}_2 \\ | \\ \text{CH}_2\text{OH} \end{array}$$

Yeast
O. Meyerhof and W. Kiessling, *Biochem. Z.* 276 239 (1935).

78   **Fumaric Acid,** $C_4H_4O_4$, colorless crystals, m.p. 290° (subl.) (dec.).

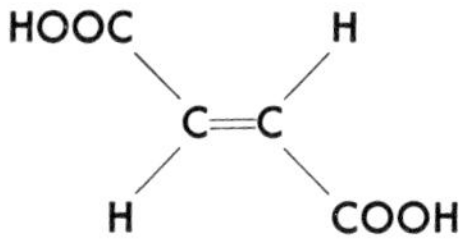

Rhizopus species, also *Mucor, Cunninghamella* and *Circinella* species, *Aspergillus* and *Penicillium* species, *Boletus* spp., *Fusaria*, etc.
Yields are about 59%.
Leland A. Underkofler and Richard J. Hickey, "Industrial Fermentations," Chemical Publishing Co., Inc., New York, N. Y., 1954 **Vol. I,** Ruse H. Vaughn, *Acetic acid-vinegar,* chap. 17, pp. 498–535; Jackson W. Foster, *Fumaric acid,* chap. 15, pp. 470–487.

79   *l-trans-*Ethylene Oxide α,β-Dicarboxylic Acid (Epoxysuccinic Acid), $C_4H_4O_5$, colorless crystals, m.p. 185° (dec.) $[\alpha]_D^{24}$ −117° (c 1 in water).

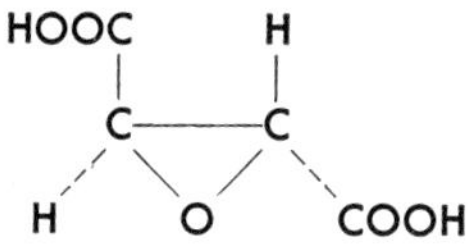

Aspergillus fumigatus, Monilia formosa, Penicillium viniferum
Yields greater than 20 g. per liter have been obtained.
Andrew J. Moyer, U. S. Patent 2,674,561 (1950).

80 **Succinic Acid,** $C_4H_6O_4$, colorless prisms, m.p. 185–187°.

$$HOOC—CH_2—CH_2—COOH$$

Mucor stolonifer, Aspergillus terreus, Ustilina vulgaris, Penicillium aurantio-virens, Fusarium oxysporum, lichens, etc.

Occurrence is wide, but yields are generally rather low.
Ve. S. Butkevich and M. V. Fedorov, *Biochem. Z.* **219** 103 (1930).

Jackson W. Foster, "Chemical Activities of Fungi," Academic Press Inc., New York, N. Y., 1949, p. 373.

81 *l*-**Malic Acid,** $C_4H_6O_5$, colorless crystals, m.p. 99°, $[\alpha]_D^{30}$ −1.43° (c 21.65 in water).

$$HOOC—CH—CH_2—COOH$$
$$|$$
$$OH$$

White aspergilli, clasterosporium spp., many other fungi.

Yields are high in some cases.
Reinhold Schreyer, *Biochem. Z.* **240** 295 (1931).
John L. Yuill, *Chem. Ind.* **55** 155 (1936).

82 L(+)-**Tartaric Acid,** $C_4H_6O_6$, colorless powder or crystals, m.p. 168–170° (dec.), $[\alpha]_D^{20}$ +11.98° (c 20 in water).

Gibberella saubinetii, Acetobacter suboxydans
Citric and acetic acids were produced also.
Lyle E. Hessler and Ross A. Gortner, *J. Biol. Chem.* **119** 193 (1937).
Jonas Kamlet, U. S. Patent 2,314,831 (1943).

83 **Itaconic Acid,** $C_5H_6O_4$, colorless crystals, m.p. 162–164°.

$$CH_2{=}C—COOH$$
$$|$$
$$CH_2—COOH$$

Aspergillus terreus, Ustilago zeae, Helicobasidium monpa, other fungi

Jasper H. Kane, Alexander C. Finlay and Philip F. Amann, U. S. Patent 2,385,283 (1945).

Leland A. Underkofler and Richard J. Hickey, "Industrial Fermentations," Chemical Publishing Co., Inc., New York, N. Y., 1954 **Vol. I,** Lewis B. Lockwood, *Itaconic acid,* chap. 16, pp. 488–498.

Yields are high in the case of *A. terreus. Ustilago zeae* is reported to produce 15 g. per liter as well as some dianthrone and glycolipides.

R. H. Haskins, J. A. Thorn and B. Boothroyd, *Can. J. Microbiol.* 1 749 (1955).

84 *trans*-**Glutaconic Acid,** $C_5H_6O_4$, colorless needles, m.p. 138°.

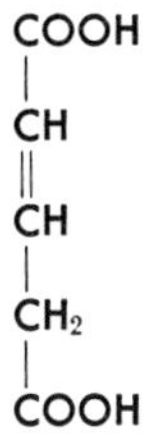

$$
\begin{array}{c}
\text{COOH} \\
| \\
\text{CH} \\
|| \\
\text{CH} \\
| \\
\text{CH}_2 \\
| \\
\text{COOH}
\end{array}
$$

Aspergillus niger (on *l*-xylose)
Shinichiro Baba and Kinichiro Sakaguchi, *Bull. Agr. Chem. Soc.* (Japan) 18 93 (1942).

85 α-**Ketoglutaric Acid,** $C_5H_6O_5$, colorless crystals, m.p. 115–116°.

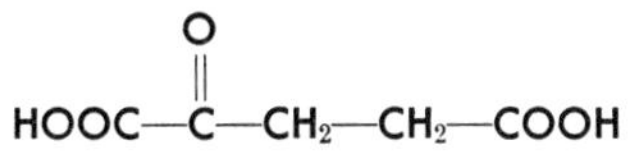

$$
\underset{\text{HOOC}}{}\overset{\overset{\text{O}}{||}}{\text{C}}\text{—CH}_2\text{—CH}_2\text{—COOH}
$$

Pseudomonas fluorescens
Harold J. Koepsell, Frank H. Stodola and Eugene S. Sharpe, U. S. Patent 2,724,680 (1955).

Leland A. Underkofler and Richard J. Hickey, "Industrial Fermentations," Chemical Publishing Co., Inc., New York, N. Y., 1954 **Vol. II,** Lewis B. Lockwood, *Ketogenic fermentation processes,* chap. 1, pp. 18–19.

86 **Dimethylpyruvic Acid,** $C_5H_8O_3$, leaflets, m.p. ~24°, b.p. 76–78°.

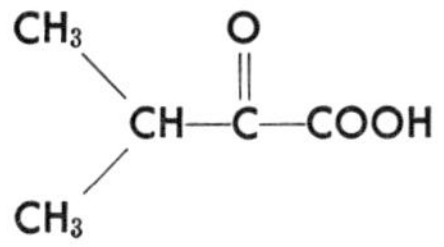

$$
\begin{array}{c}
\text{CH}_3 \\
\diagdown \\
\quad\quad \text{CH—C—COOH} \\
\diagup \quad\; || \\
\text{CH}_3 \quad\quad\; \text{O}
\end{array}
$$

Aspergillus spp., *Piricularia oryzae* (biotin-deficient medium)
K. Ramachandran and V. Radha, *Current Sci.* (India) 24 50 (1955).
Hirohiko Katsuki, *J. Am. Chem. Soc.* 77 4686 (1955).

87   Other Keto-Acids:
Many of the transitory α-keto-acids present in cultures of microorganisms can be isolated by means of interceptors such as 2,4-dinitrophenylhydrazine. One recent paper reported the following acids identified principally in lactic and propionic bacteria cultures:

Glyoxylic Acid	p-Hydroxyphenylpyruvic Acid
Pyruvic Acid	
α-Ketoisovaleric Acid	Hydroxypyruvic Acid
α-Ketoisocaproic Acid	Oxalacetic Acid
α-Ketocaproic Acid	α-Ketoglutaric Acid

Matti Kreula and Artturi I. Virtanen, *Acta. Chem. Scand.* 11 1431 (1957).

88   Glutaric Acid, $C_5H_8O_4$, colorless needles, m.p. 97°.

$$
\begin{array}{c}
COOH \\
| \\
CH_2 \\
| \\
CH_2 \\
| \\
CH_2 \\
| \\
COOH
\end{array}
$$

Aspergillus niger (on *l*-xylose)
Shinichiro Baba and Kinichiro Sakaguchi, *Bull. Agr. Chem. Soc.* (Japan) 18 93 (1942).

89   Itatartaric Acid, $C_5H_8O_6$, occurs as a gummy equilibrium mixture of lactone and free acid. Characterized as the methyl ester derivative.

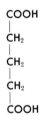

Aspergillus terreus mutant
Frank H. Stodola, M. Friedkin, Andrew J. Moyer and Robert D. Coghill, *J. Biol. Chem.* 161 739 (1945).

90 α-**Methylbutyric Acid,** $C_5H_{10}O_2$, colorless crystals, m.p. 176°, $[\alpha]_D^{21}$ +17.6°.

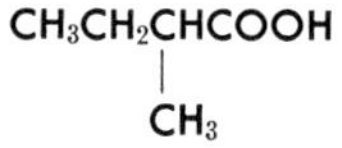

$$CH_3CH_2CHCOOH$$
$$|$$
$$CH_3$$

Penicillium notatum
Donald J. Cram and Max Tishler, *J. Am. Chem. Soc.* **70** 4238 (1948).

91 α,β-**Dihydroxyisovaleric Acid,** $C_5H_{10}O_4$, colorless syrup, $[\alpha]_D^{23}$ −12.4° (c 2 in dilute HCl, pH 1) and +10° (c 2 in water, pH 5.5–6.5). Forms crystalline quinine salt.

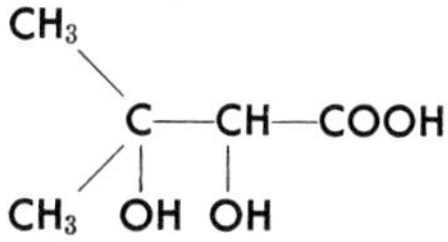

$$CH_3$$
$$\backslash$$
$$C—CH—COOH$$
$$/\;|\;\;\;|$$
$$CH_3\;\;OH\;\;OH$$

A valine precursor isolated from a *Neurospora crassa* mutant
John R. Sjölander, Karl Folkers, Edward A. Adelberg and E. L. Tatum, *J. Am. Chem. Soc.* **76** 1085 (1954).

92 *cis*-**Aconitic Acid,** $C_6H_6O_6$, colorless crystals, m.p. 125°.

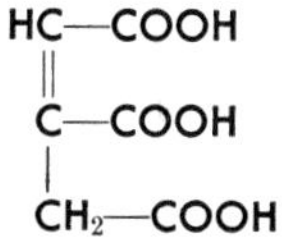

$$HC—COOH$$
$$||$$
$$C—COOH$$
$$|$$
$$CH_2—COOH$$

Aspergillus niger
This acid presumably is present to some extent in all organisms with the citric acid cycle.
Kinichiro Sakaguchi and Shinichiro Baba, *Bull. Agr. Chem. Soc.* (Japan) **18** 95 (1942). (Not isolated)

93 *allo*-**Isocitric Acid (Lactone),** $C_6H_6O_6$, m.p. 140–141° $[\alpha]_D^{190}$ +42.3° (c 4.83 in water).

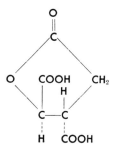

Penicillium purpurogenum Stoll *var. rubrisclerotium* Thom.

Yields greater than 20% of the glucose substrate supplied have been reported. Probably the isomer normal to the mammalian citric acid cycle also occurs in some microorganisms, but it has not been reported to accumulate.

Teruhiko Beppu, Shigeo Abe and Kinichiro Sakaguchi, *Bull. Agr. Chem. Soc.* (Japan) 21 263 (1957).

94 *trans*-β-**Methylglutaconic Acid**, $C_6H_8O_4$, colorless crystals, m.p. 131–134°.

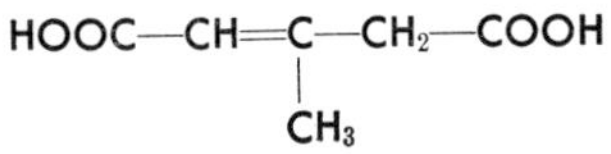

$$HOOC-CH=C-CH_2-COOH$$
$$\underset{\displaystyle CH_3}{|}$$

Ustilago sphaerogena

This substance is a component of ferrichrome A pigment,* in which its monohydroxamate is complexed with iron.

Thomas Emery and J. B. Neilands. (In press)
* See addendum.

95 **Citric Acid**, $C_6H_8O_7$ (occurs as monohydrate), colorless crystals or white powder, m.p. (monohydrate) ~100°, (anhydrous) 153°.

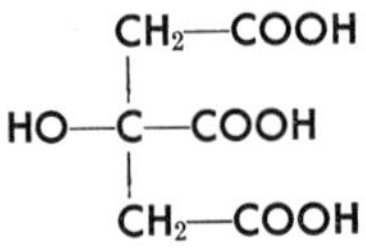

$$CH_2-COOH$$
$$|$$
$$HO-C-COOH$$
$$|$$
$$CH_2-COOH$$

Wide variety of fungi, *e.g., Aspergillus niger.*
Yields are high.

Leland A. Underkofler and Richard J. Hickey, "Industrial Fermentations," Chemical Publishing Co., Inc., New York, N. Y., 1954 **Vol. I**; Marvin J. Johnson, *The citric acid fermentation,* chap. 13, pp. 420–445.

96 **Mevalonic Acid Lactone** (Hiochic Acid, β-Hydroxy-β-methyl-δ-valerolactone), $C_6H_{10}O_3$, colorless, hygroscopic crystals, m.p. 27°, b.p. 90° (0.3 mm.). (Synthetic racemate.)

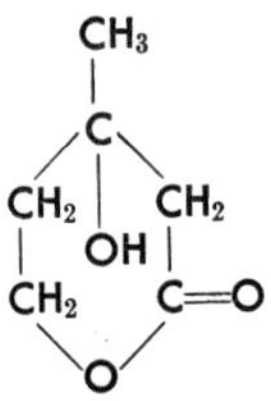

Yeasts (Isolated from Distillers' Dried Solubles).

Donald E. Wolf, Carl H. Hoffman, Paul E. Aldrich, Helen R. Skeggs, Lemuel D. Wright and Karl Folkers, *J. Am. Chem. Soc.* **78** 4499 (1956).

Helen R. Skeggs, Lemuel D. Wright, Emlen L. Cresson, Gloria D. E. MacRae, Carl H. Hoffman, Donald E. Wolf and Karl Folkers, *J. Bact.* **72** 519 (1956).

Carl H. Hoffman, Arthur F. Wagner, Andrew N. Wilson, Edward Walton, Clifford H. Shunk, Donald E. Wolf, Frederick W. Holly and Karl Folkers, *J. Am. Chem. Soc.* **79** 2316 (1957).

Clifford H. Shunk, Bruce O. Linn, Jesse W. Huff, James L. Gilfillan, Helen R. Skeggs and Karl Folkers, *ibid.* **79** 3294 (1957).

97 α,β-**Dihydroxy-β-methylvaleric Acid,** $C_6H_{12}O_4$, colorless syrup, $[\alpha]_D^{23}$ +3° (c 2.3 in water containing 1 equiv. of $Ca(OH)_2$) and −16.7° (c 2.3 in dilute HCl, pH 1). Forms crystalline quinine salt.

$$CH_3CH_2-\underset{\underset{OH}{|}}{\overset{\overset{CH_3}{|}}{C}}-\underset{\underset{OH}{|}}{CH}-COOH$$

A precursor of isoleucine isolated from a *Neurospora crassa* mutant.

John R. Sjölander, Karl Folkers, Edward A. Adelberg and E. L. Tatum, *J. Am. Chem. Soc.* **76** 1085 (1954).

98   **2-Phospho-4-hydroxy-4-carboxyadipic Acid,** $C_7H_{11}O_{11}P$.

$$
\begin{array}{l}
OPO_3H_2 \\
| \\
HC-COOH \\
| \\
CH_2 \\
| \\
HO-C-COOH \\
| \\
CH_2-COOH
\end{array}
$$

Escherichia coli

W. W. Umbreit, *J. Bacteriol.* **66** 74 (1953).

99   **Lipoic Acid** (6,8-Thioctic Acid), $C_8H_{14}O_2S_2$, pale yellow crystals, m.p. 47°, $[\alpha]_D^{23}$ +10.4°.

$$
\begin{array}{l}
CH_2-CH_2-CH-(CH_2)_4-COOH \\
| \qquad\qquad\quad | \\
S\text{------------}S
\end{array}
$$

Yeast, *E. coli* mutant

Lester J. Reed, Quentin F. Soper, Geo. H. F. Schnakenberg, Stanley F. Kern, Harold Boaz and I. C. Gunsalus, *J. Am. Chem. Soc.* 74 2383 (1952); Lester J. Reed, I. C. Gunsalus, G. H. F. Schnakenberg, Quentin F. Soper, Harold E. Boaz, Stanley F. Kern and Thomas V. Parke, *ibid.* 75 1267 (1953). (Isolation)

Edward Walton, Arthur F. Wagner, Louis H. Peterson, Frederick W. Holly and Karl Folkers, *ibid.* 76 4748 (1954); Edward Walton, Arthur F. Wagner, Frank W. Bachelor, Louis H. Peterson, Frederick W. Holly and Karl Folkers, *ibid.* 77 5144 (1955). (Synthesis)

100 **2-Decene-1,10-dioic Acid,** $C_{10}H_{16}O_4$, colorless crystals, m.p. 172°.

$$HOOC—CH=CH—(CH_2)_6—COOH$$

Penicillium notatum
Donald J. Cram and Max Tishler, *J. Am. Chem. Soc.* 70 4238 (1948). (Isolation)

101 **10-Undecynoic Acid,** $C_{11}H_{18}O_2$, colorless crystals, m.p. 39°.

$$HC≡C—(CH_2)_8—COOH$$

Rhodotorula glutinis var. *lusitanica*
Undecenoic acid was isolated from the same culture. Nagueira Prista, *Anais. fac. farm. Porto* 14 19 (1954).

102 **10-Undecenoic Acid** (10-Undecylenic Acid), $C_{11}H_{20}O_2$, colorless crystals, m.p. 24°, n_D^{24} 1.4464.

$$CH_2=CH(CH_2)_8COOH$$

Rhodotorula glutinis var. *lusitanica*
Nogueira Prista, *Anais. fac. farm. Porto* 14 19 (1954).

103 **Myristic Acid,** $C_{14}H_{28}O_2$, colorless soft leaflets, m.p. 54°.

$$CH_3(CH_2)_{12}COOH$$

Widely distributed, especially as its triglyceride.

104 **D-β-Hydroxymyristic Acid,** $C_{14}H_{28}O_3$, colorless crystals, m.p. 73°, $[\alpha]_D^{25}$ −16° (c 2.0 in chloroform).

$$CH_3(CH_2)_{10}CHCH_2COOH$$
$$|$$
$$OH$$

Escherichia coli
Obtained together with lauric, myristic and palmitic acids from an acid hydrolysate of the phospholipide fraction.

Miyoshi Ikawa, J. B. Koepfli, S. G. Mudd and Carl Niemann, *J. Am. Chem. Soc.* 75 1035 (1953).

105   **Mineoluteic Acid,** $C_{16}H_{26}O_7$, colorless needles, m.p. 171°, $[\alpha]_{5461}^{16}$ +108.1° (c 1.07 in acetone)

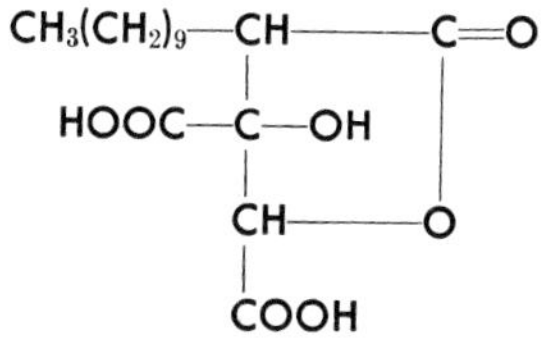

$$CH_3(CH_2)_9—CH\text{————}C=O$$
$$HOOC—C—OH$$
$$CH\text{————}O$$
$$COOH$$

Penicillium minioluteum Dierckx
Spiculisporic acid is produced in the same culture.
John H. Birkinshaw and Harold Raistrick, *Biochem. J.* 28 828 (1934).

106   **Palmitoleic Acid** (Physetolic Acid, 9-Hexadecenoic Acid), $C_{16}H_{30}O_2$, colorless crystals, m.p. 30–33°.

$$CH_3(CH_2)_5CH=CH(CH_2)_7COOH$$

Yeast, *Corynebacterium diphtheriae*, *Streptococcus* spp., *Penicillium lilacinum* occurs widely.
E. Chargaff, *Z. physiol. Chem.* 218 223 (1933).
Klaus Hofmann and Fred Tausig, *J. Biol. Chem.* 213 415 (1955).
J. Singh, Sudha Shah and T. K. Walker, *Biochem. J.* 62 222 (1956).

107   **Pyolipic Acid,** $C_{16}H_{30}O_7$, colorless, viscous oil.

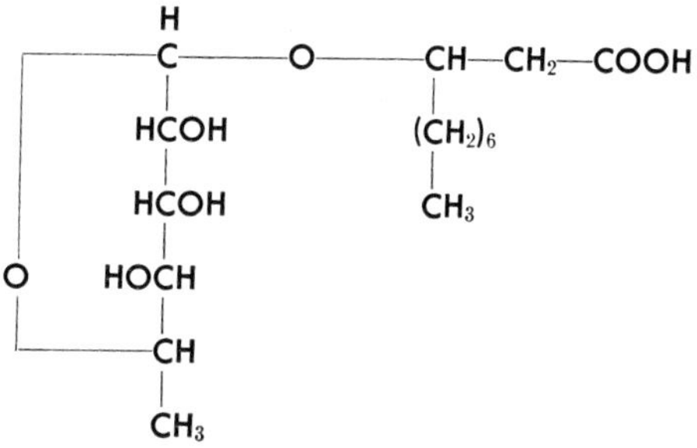

$$H$$
$$C\text{————}O\text{————}CH—CH_2—COOH$$
$$HCOH \qquad (CH_2)_6$$
$$HCOH \qquad CH_3$$
$$O \quad HOCH$$
$$CH$$
$$CH_3$$

Pseudomonas pyocyanea
The yield was 1-2 g. per liter.
Sune Bergström, Hugo Theorell and Hans Davide, *Arch. Biochem.* 10 165 (1946).

108 **Palmitic Acid,** $C_{16}H_{32}O_2$, soft white crystals, m.p. 62.5°.

$$CH_3(CH_2)_{14}COOH$$

Widely distributed, especially as esters.

109 **Spiculisporic Acid,** $C_{17}H_{28}O_6$, colorless crystals, m.p. 145°, $[\alpha]_{5461}$ −14.76° (in alcohol).

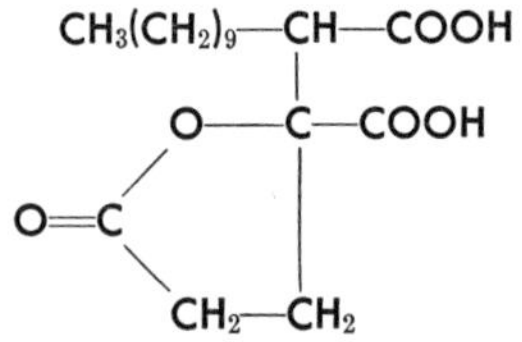

Penicillium spiculisporum Lehman, *P. crateriforme* Gilman and Abbott and *P. minioluteum* Dierckx

P. W. Clutterbuck, H. Raistrick and M. L. Pintoul, *Trans. Roy. Soc.* (London) B220 301 (1931). (Isolation and structure)

Albert E. Oxford and Harold Raistrick, *Biochem. J.* 28 1321 (1934). (Isolations)

110 **Roccellic Acid,** $C_{17}H_{32}O_4$, colorless crystals, m.p. 131°, $[\alpha]_D^{26}$ +16.80°.

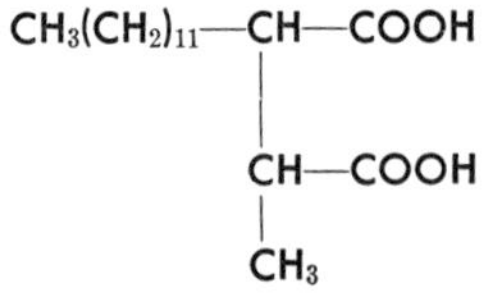

Roccella tinctoria (L.), *R. montagnei* Bel., etc., also *Lecanora* species

Yields 1–4%. Erythrin and *i*-erythritol also were present.

G. Kennedy, J. Breen, J. Keane and T. J. Nolan, *Sci. Proc. Roy. Dublin Soc.* 21 557 (1937).

111 *cis*-**Vaccenic Acid,** $C_{18}H_{34}O_2$, soft white platelets, m.p. 43°.

$$CH_3(CH_2)_5CH{=}CH(CH_2)_9COOH$$

Lactobacillus arabinosus, L. casei, Agrobacterium tumefaciens, Streptococcus spp.

Klaus Hofmann, Robert A. Lucas and Sylvan M. Sax, *J. Biol. Chem.* 195 473 (1952).

Klaus Hofmann and Fred Tausig, *ibid.* 213 425 (1955).

112 **Lactarinic Acid** (5-Ketostearic Acid), $C_{18}H_{34}O_3$, colorless plates, m.p. 87°.

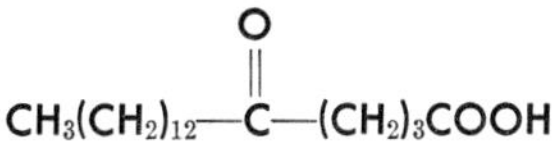

$$CH_3(CH_2)_{12}-\overset{\overset{\displaystyle O}{\|}}{C}-(CH_2)_3COOH$$

Lactarius rufus Scopol.
A. K. Schneider and M. A. Spielman, *J. Biol. Chem.* 142 345 (1942).

113 **Stearic Acid,** $C_{18}H_{36}O_2$, colorless leaflets m.p. 69°.

$$CH_3(CH_2)_{16}COOH$$

Widely distributed.

114 **Lactobacillic Acid** (Phytomonic Acid), $C_{19}H_{36}O_2$, colorless crystals, m.p. 33.6–35°.

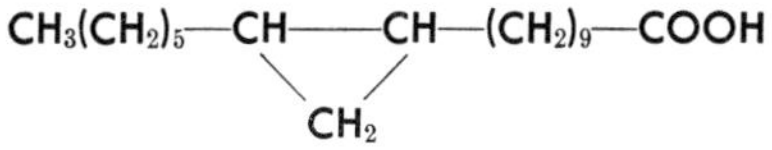

$$CH_3(CH_2)_5-CH\underline{\qquad}CH-(CH_2)_9-COOH$$
$$\diagdown\qquad\diagup$$
$$CH_2$$

Lactobacillus arabinosus, L. casei, Agrobacterium (Phytomonas) tumefaciens
Klaus Hofmann, Otto Jucker, William R. Miller, Alfred C. Young, Jr. and Fred Tausig, *J. Am. Chem. Soc.* 76 1799 (1954).
Klaus Hofmann, Gino J. Marco and George A. Jeffrey, *ibid.* 80 5717 (1958). (Structure)

115 **Tuberculostearic Acid** (*l*-10-Methyloctadecanoic Acid), $C_{19}H_{38}O_2$, colorless oil, m.p. 12.8–13.4°, n_D^{25} 1.4514, $[\alpha]_D^{26}$ −0.045°.

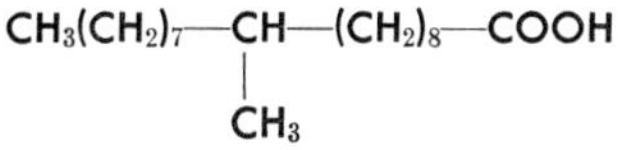

$$CH_3(CH_2)_7-CH-(CH_2)_8-COOH$$
$$|$$
$$CH_3$$

Mycobacterium tuberculosis var. *hominis*
Franklin S. Prout, James Cason and A. W. Ingersoll, *J. Am. Chem. Soc.* 70 298 (1948). (Synthesis)

116 **Alternaric Acid,** $C_{21}H_{30}O_8$, colorless crystals, m.p. 138°.

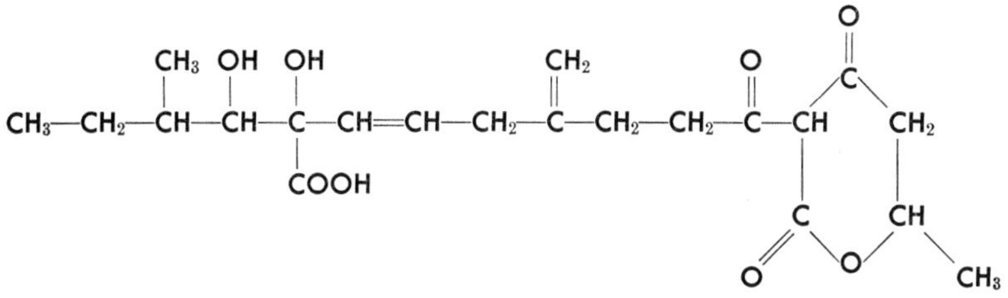

Alternaria solani Ell. and Mart., Jones and Grout

John Frederick Grove, *J. Chem. Soc.*, 4059 (1952). (Isolation)

J. R. Bartels-Keith and John Frederick Grove, *Proc. Chem. Soc.*, 398 (1959). (Structure)

117 **Rangiformic Acid,** $C_{21}H_{38}O_6$, colorless needles, m.p. 106°, $[\alpha]_D^{24}$ +16.2°.

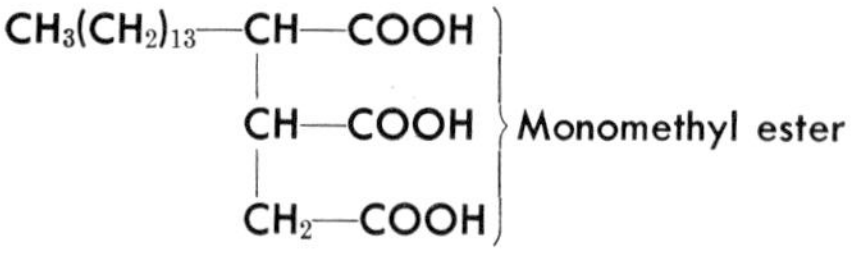

$$CH_3(CH_2)_{13}-CH-COOH$$
$$CH-COOH \quad \text{Monomethyl ester}$$
$$CH_2-COOH$$

Cladonia rangiformis Hoffm., *C. mitis* Sandst.
Masaru Aoki, *J. Pharm. Soc. Japan* **66A** 52 (1946).

118 **Caperatic Acid,** $C_{21}H_{38}O_7$, colorless leaflets, m.p. 132°, $[\alpha]_D^{10}$ −3.85°.

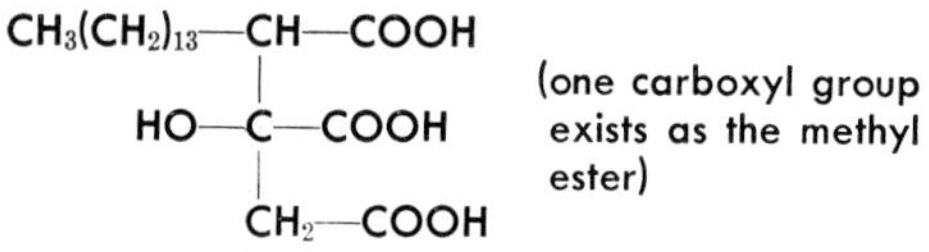

$$CH_3(CH_2)_{13}-CH-COOH$$
$$HO-C-COOH \quad \text{(one carboxyl group}$$
$$\text{exists as the methyl}$$
$$CH_2-COOH \quad \text{ester)}$$

Parmelia caperata (L.), *Nephromopsis stracheyi, f. ectocarpisma* Hue.
Protocetraric acid also was present.
Michizo Asano, Yukio Kameda and Osamu Tamemasa, *J. Pharm. Soc. Japan* **64** 203 (1944).

119 **Ungulinic Acid,** $C_{22}H_{38}O_6$, colorless microcrystalline needles, m.p. 78–80°.

Tentative structure of hydrate (ordinarily a γ-lactone):

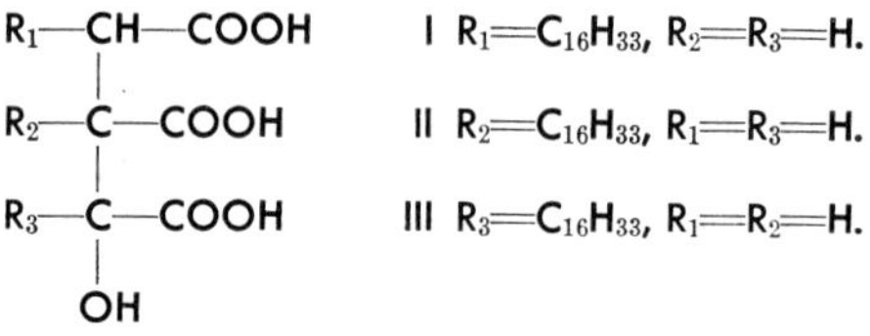

$$R_1-CH-COOH \qquad I \;\; R_1{=}C_{16}H_{33}, R_2{=}R_3{=}H.$$
$$R_2-C-COOH \qquad II \;\; R_2{=}C_{16}H_{33}, R_1{=}R_3{=}H.$$
$$R_3-C-COOH \qquad III \;\; R_3{=}C_{16}H_{33}, R_1{=}R_2{=}H.$$
$$OH$$

Polyporus betulinus
J. H. Birkinshaw, E. N. Morgan and W. P. K. Findlay, *Biochem. J.* **50** 509 (1952).
Sidonie Marcus, *ibid.* **50** 516 (1952).

120   **Agaricic Acid** (Agaricin, Laricic Acid, Agaric Acid) $C_{22}H_{40}O_7$, colorless microcrystalline powder, m.p. 142° (dec.), $[\alpha]_D^{19}$ −9° (in dilute NaOH solution).

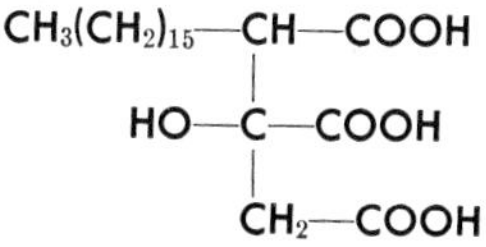

$$CH_3(CH_2)_{15}-CH-COOH$$
$$HO-C-COOH$$
$$CH_2-COOH$$

Polyporus officinalis (=*Fomes officinalis, Fomes laricis*) A yield of 18% of the weight of the fruiting body has been reported.

H. Thomas and J. Vogelsang, *Ann.* 357 145 (1907).

121   **Ventosic Acid**, $C_{22}H_{44}O_6$, white amorphous powder, m.p. 183°. A tetrahydroxybehenic acid.

Haematomma ventosum, other lichens
Thamnolic acid was isolated from the same source.
Yngve Johannes Solberg, *Acta Chem. Scand.* 11 1477 (1957).

122   **Tetracosanoic Acid** (Lignoceric Acid), $C_{24}H_{48}O_2$, colorless plates, m.p. 87.5°.

$$CH_3(CH_2)_{22}COOH$$

Mycobacterium tuberculosis, Phycomyces blakesleeanus, Penicillium chrysogenum

Robert L. Peck and R. J. Anderson, *J. Biol. Chem.* 140 89 (1941).
Karl Bernhard and Hans Albrecht, *Helv. Chim. Acta* 31 977 (1948).
Yoshiro Abe, *Proc. Fac. Eng. Keiogijuku Univ.* 2 15 (1949). (*Chem. Abstr.* 47 4949i)

123   **Pentacosanoic Acid**, $C_{25}H_{50}O_2$, colorless crystals, m.p. 84°.

$$CH_3(CH_2)_{23}COOH$$

Mycobacterium tuberculosis var. *hominis*
A. Aebi, J. Asselineau and E. Lederer, *Bull. soc. chim. biol.* 35 661 (1953).

124   **Hexacosanoic Acid** (Phthioic Acid, Cerotic Acid, Cerinic Acid), $C_{26}H_{52}O_2$, colorless crystals, m.p. 88°.

$$CH_3 (CH_2)_{24}COOH$$

Mycobacterium tuberculosis, Phycomyces blakesleeanus

Obtained together with palmitic, tuberculostearic and mycoceranic acids.

R. J. Anderson, *J. Biol. Chem.* 83 505–519 (1929).

Karl Bernhard and Hans Albrecht, *Helv. Chim. Acta* 31 977 (1948).

Jean Asselineau, *Compt. rend.* 237 1804 (1953).

125 **Mycolipenic Acid** ((+)-2,4L,6L-Trimethyltetracos-2-enoic Acid), $C_{27}H_{52}O_2$, low melting solid $[\alpha]_D^{20}$ +7.9° (c 25.2 in ether), n_D^{36} 1.4600.

$$CH_3(CH_2)_{17}-\underset{\underset{CH_3}{|}}{CH}-CH_2-\underset{\underset{CH_3}{|}}{CH}-CH=\underset{\underset{CH_3}{|}}{C}-COOH$$

Mycobacterium tuberculosis var. *hominis*

J. D. Chanley and N. Polgar, *J. Chem. Soc.*, 1003 (1954). (Isolation)

D. J. Millin and N. Polgar, *Proc. Chem. Soc.*, 122 (1957). (Synthesis)

126 **C_{27}-Phthienoic Acid** (*trans*-2,4-Dimethyl-13-*n*-amyl-2-eicosenoic Acid), $C_{27}H_{52}O_2$, soft white crystals, m.p. 26° and 39° (polymorphic), $[\alpha]_D^{25}$ +17.8° ±0.2°, n_D^{25} 1.4666.

Tentative structure:

$$\begin{array}{c} CH_3(CH_2)_6 \\ \qquad\qquad\qquad\setminus \\ \qquad\qquad CH-(CH_2)_8-\underset{\underset{CH_3}{|}}{CH}-CH=\underset{\underset{CH_3}{|}}{C}-COOH \\ \qquad\qquad/ \\ CH_3(CH_2)_4 \end{array}$$

The author emphasizes the difference of this compound from mycolipenic acid.

Mycobacterium tuberculosis var. *hominis*

James Cason, Hans-Ruedi Urscheler and C. Freeman Allen, *J. Org. Chem.* 22 1284 (1957). (Structure) and earlier papers in this series.

127 **Ustilagic Acids.**

The corn smut fungus produces a group of related glycolipides. As originally isolated, the properties of the partially purified mixture were given as: $C_{37}H_{62-66}O_{17}$, color-less, needle-like crystals, m.p. 144–147°, $[\alpha]_D^{23}$ +7° (c 1.0

in pyridine). Two of the component structures have been characterized as shown:

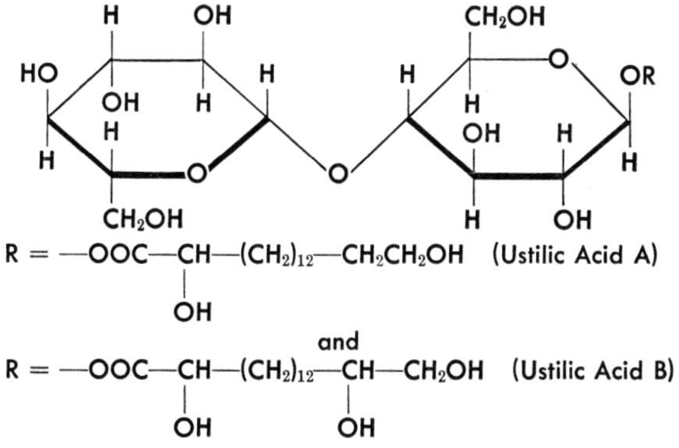

R = —OOC—CH—(CH₂)₁₂—CH₂CH₂OH   (Ustilic Acid A)
$\qquad\qquad$ |
$\qquad\qquad$ OH

and

R = —OOC—CH—(CH₂)₁₂—CH—CH₂OH   (Ustilic Acid B)
$\qquad\qquad$ | $\qquad\qquad\quad$ |
$\qquad\qquad$ OH $\qquad\qquad\quad$ OH

Ustilago zeae, other *Ustilaginales* spp.

Yields of 12–33% of the glucose supplied were reported.

R. H. Haskins and J. A. Thorn, *Can. J. Botany* **29** 585 (1951).

R. U. Lemieux, J. A. Thorn, Carol Brice and R. H. Haskins, *Can. J. Chem.* **29** 409 (1951). (Isolation)

R. U. Lemieux, *ibid.* **29** 415 (1951).

R. U. Lemieux, J. A. Thorn and H. F. Bauer, *ibid.* **31** 1054 (1953).

128   **Bongkrekic Acid,** $C_{29}H_{40}O_7$, unstable, resinous, $[\alpha]_D^{22}$ +165° (c 2.0 in $NaHCO_3$).

The stabler hydrogenated compound, $C_{29}H_{54}O_7$, was given the following partial structure.

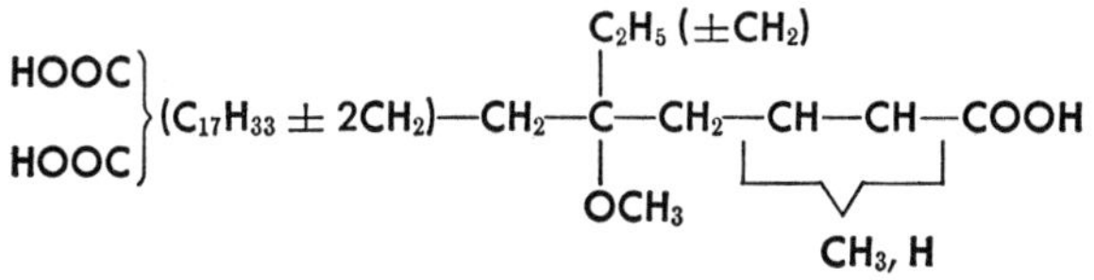

Pseudomonas cocovenenans (on a special copra-containing medium)

Bongkrekic acid is a toxin and has antibiotic properties.

D. H. Nugteren and W. Berends, *Rec. trav. chim.* **76** 13 (1957).

129 **Mycoceranic Acid** (Mycocerosic Acid), $C_{31}H_{62}O_2$, white solid, m.p. 30°, $[\alpha]_D^{21}$ −6.9° (c 16.8 in ether).

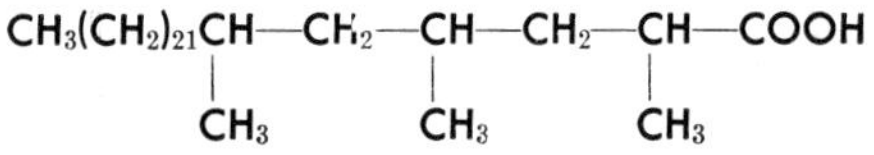

$$CH_3(CH_2)_{21}CH—CH_2—CH—CH_2—CH—COOH$$
$$\qquad\qquad CH_3 \qquad\quad CH_3 \qquad\; CH_3$$

Mycobacterium tuberculosis
Occurs esterified with phthiocerol.
J. D. Chanley and N. Polgar, *J. Chem. Soc.*, 1003, 1011 (1954).

130 **Glycolipide from** *Pseudomonas aeruginosa*, $C_{32}H_{60}O_{14}$ (Monohydrate), colorless rectangular platelets, m.p. 86°, $[\alpha]_D$ −84° (c 3.0 in chloroform).
Probable structure:

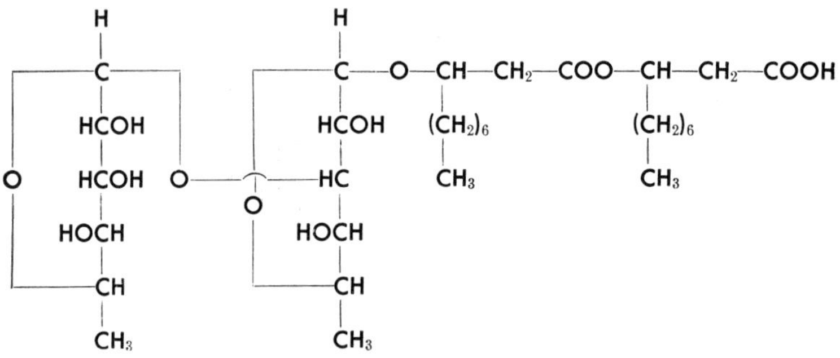

Pseudomonas aeruginosa (three different strains)
F. G. Jarvis and M. J. Johnson, *J. Am. Chem. Soc.* 71 4124 (1949). (Isolation)

131 **Corynomycolenic Acid,** $C_{32}H_{62}O_3$, colorless oil, n_D^{19} 1.4758. Methyl ester: $[\alpha]_{5461}^{20}$ +9.0 ±0.3°.

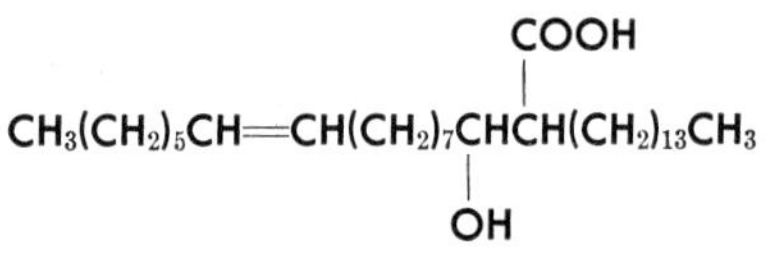

$$\overset{\displaystyle COOH}{\underset{\displaystyle OH}{CH_3(CH_2)_5CH=CH(CH_2)_7CHCH(CH_2)_{13}CH_3}}$$

Corynebacterium diphtheriae
J. Pudles and E. Lederer, *Biochim. et Biophys. Acta* 11 163 (1953).

132   **Corynomycolic Acid,** $C_{32}H_{64}O_3$, colorless crystals, m.p. $70°$, $[\alpha]_D$ $7.5°$.

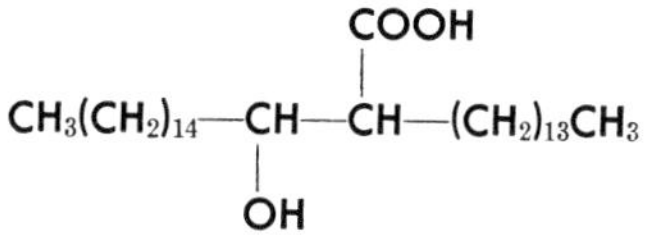

$$CH_3(CH_2)_{14}-\underset{\underset{OH}{|}}{CH}-\underset{\underset{COOH}{|}}{CH}-(CH_2)_{13}CH_3$$

Corynebacterium diphtheriae, C. ovis

E. Lederer, J. Pudles, S. Barbezat and J. J. Trillat, *Bull. soc. chim. France* 93 (1952).

Anne Diara and Julia Pudles, *Bull. soc. chim. biol.* 41 481 (1959).

133 **Fungal Cerebrins**

      A. $C_{42}H_{85}O_5N$

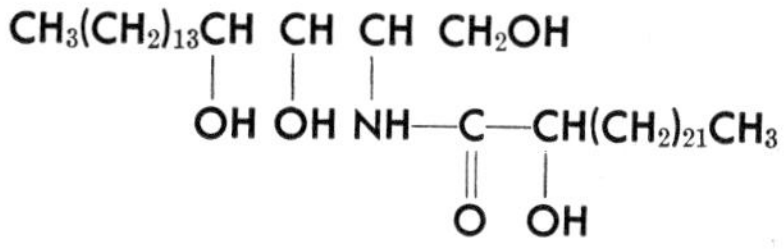

$$CH_3(CH_2)_{13}\underset{\underset{OH}{|}}{CH}\ \underset{\underset{OH}{|}}{CH}\ \underset{\underset{NH-\underset{\underset{O}{||}}{C}-CH(CH_2)_{21}CH_3}{|}}{CH}\ CH_2OH$$

      B. $C_{42}H_{85}O_6N$

$$CH_3(CH_2)_{13}\underset{\underset{OH}{|}}{CH}\ \underset{\underset{OH}{|}}{CH}\ \underset{\underset{NH-\underset{\underset{O}{||}}{C}-\underset{\underset{OH}{|}}{CH}-\underset{\underset{OH}{|}}{CH}-(CH_2)_{20}CH_3}{|}}{CH}\ CH_2OH$$

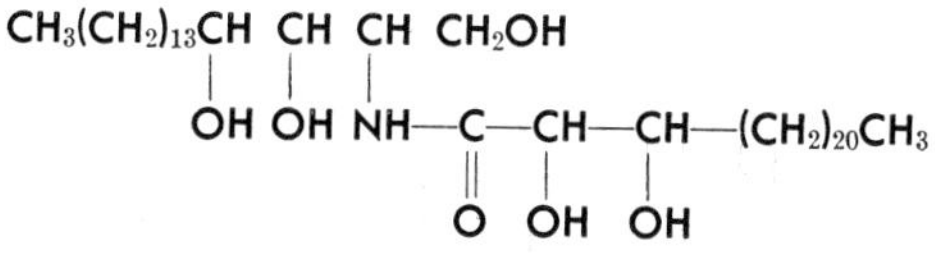

Penicillium spp., yeasts

Takeshi Oda, *J. Pharm. Soc. Japan* 72 136 (1952). (Isolation); *idem., ibid.* 72 142 (1952). (Structure)

A. H. Cook, "The Chemistry and Biology of Yeasts," A. A. Eddy, *Aspects of the chemical composition of yeast,* Academic Press, Inc., New York, N. Y., 1958, p. 203.

134 **Yeast Cerebrin,** $C_{44}H_{89}O_5N$, colorless crystals, m.p. $87-89°$, $[\alpha]_D$ $+31°$.

Tentative structure:

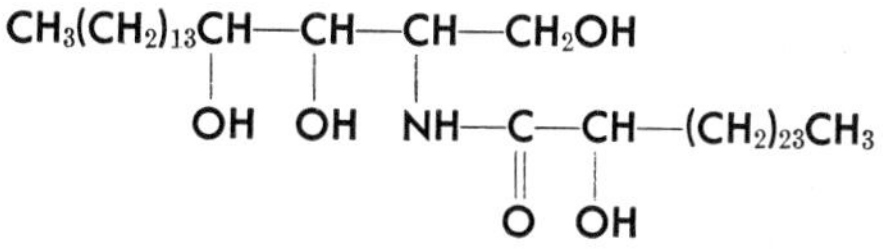

$$CH_3(CH_2)_{13}\underset{\underset{OH}{|}}{CH}-\underset{\underset{OH}{|}}{CH}-\underset{\underset{NH-\underset{\underset{O}{||}}{C}-\underset{\underset{OH}{|}}{CH}-(CH_2)_{23}CH_3}{|}}{CH}-CH_2OH$$

Yeasts

Fritz Reindel, A. Weichmann, S. Picard, Karl Luber and Paul Turula, *Ann.* 544 116 (1940).

A. H. Cook, "The Chemistry and Biology of Yeasts," A. A. Eddy, *Aspects of the chemical composition of yeast,* Academic Press, Inc., New York, N. Y., 1958, p. 203.

135 Lecithins and Cephalins

The lecithins and cephalins are widely occurring phospholipides. They are generally oily or partially crystalline materials with mixed fatty acids. Lecithin and Cephalin Structures (R = various fatty acids).

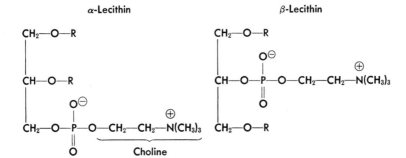

α-Lecithin   β-Lecithin

The cephalins are similar except that the choline residue is replaced by ethanolamine.

Yeast, *Aspergillus sydowi,* etc.

F. M. Strong and W. H. Peterson, *J. Am. Chem. Soc.* 56 952 (1934).

D. W. Woolley, F. M. Strong, W. H. Peterson and E. A. Prill, *ibid.* 57 2589 (1935).

L. F. Salisbury and R. J. Anderson, *J. Biol. Chem.* 112 541 (1936).

136 Dipalmitoleyl-α-lecithin, $C_{40}H_{76}O_8NP$, semi-solid material, $[\alpha]_D$ +6.6°.

$$CH_2-O-CO-(CH_2)_7-CH=CH-(CH_2)_5-CH_3$$
$$CH-O-CO-(CH_2)_7-CH=CH-(CH_2)_5-CH_3$$
$$CH_2-O-P(=O)-O-CH_2-CH_2-N(CH_3)_3^{\oplus}$$
$$O^{\ominus}$$

Yeast

Donald J. Hanahan and Michael E. Jayko, *J. Am. Chem. Soc.* 74 5070 (1952). (Isolation)

137   **Corynine** (Corynodic Acid), $C_{52}H_{104}O_4$, colorless crystals, m.p. 70°.

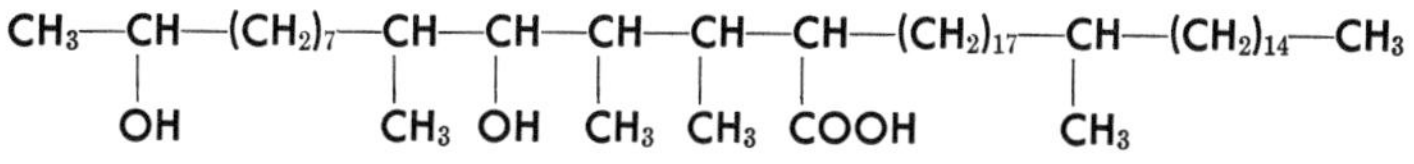

$$CH_3-CH-(CH_2)_7-CH-CH-CH-CH-CH-(CH_2)_{17}-CH-(CH_2)_{14}-CH_3$$

with substituents: OH ; CH_3 OH CH_3 CH_3 $COOH$; CH_3

Corynebacterium diphtheriae
Obtained from the saponification of the phospholipide fraction.

Hideo Takahashi, *J. Pharm. Soc. Japan* 68 292 (1948).

138   **A Mycolic Acid,** $C_{84}H_{174}O_4$ ($\pm 5CH_2$), colorless microcrystals, m.p. 56–58°, $[\alpha]_D$ +2° (c 2.446 in chloroform).

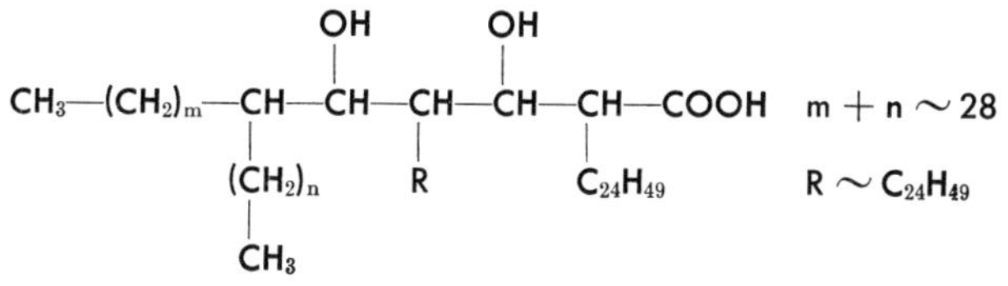

$$CH_3-(CH_2)_m-CH-CH-CH-CH-CH-COOH \quad m+n \sim 28$$

with substituents: $CH-$ has OH ; next CH has $(CH_2)_n$ below with CH_3; CH has R; CH has $C_{24}H_{49}$; $R \sim C_{24}H_{49}$

Mycobacterium tuberculosis human Canetti strain
This acid was isolated by chromatography from a saponification of the chloroform soluble wax.

Jean Asselineau, *Bull. soc. chim. France* 135 (1960).

139   **Cord Factor,** $C_{186}H_{366}O_{17}$ ± 10 CH_2, nearly colorless wax, m.p. 43–45°, $[\alpha]_J$ +40 $\pm 5°$ (c 1.37 in chloroform).

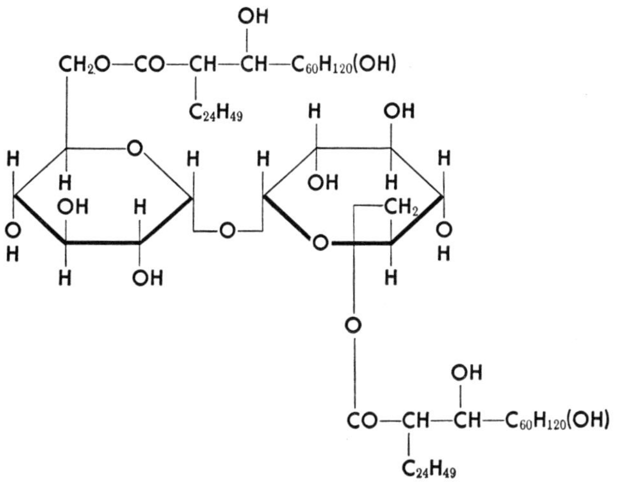

$$CH_2O-CO-CH-CH-C_{60}H_{120}(OH)$$

with OH above second CH, and $C_{24}H_{49}$ below first CH

(disaccharide ring structure with substituents H, OH, O)

$$CO-CH-CH-C_{60}H_{120}(OH)$$

with OH above second CH, and $C_{24}H_{49}$ below first CH

Mycobacterium tuberculosis (six different virulent human and bovine strains as well as the BCG strain).

Hydrolysis yields 1 mole of trehalose and 2 moles of mycolic acid.

H. Noll, H. Bloch, J. Asselineau and E. Lederer, *Biochim. et Biophys. Acta* **20** 299 (1956).

4

Tetronic Acids and Other Lactones
and Lactams

This chapter includes derivatives of tetronic acid as well as some related lactones. Ascorbic acid is included in this section because it is structurally similar to the tetronic acids, although it might equally well have been placed with the sugar acids.

The tetronic acids appear to be condensation products of two simple molecules. Ehrensvärd and his collaborators have obtained experimental confirmation of this in two cases.[1] By labeled acetate studies on carlosic and carolic acids, they have shown the B portions of the molecules as indicated below to be

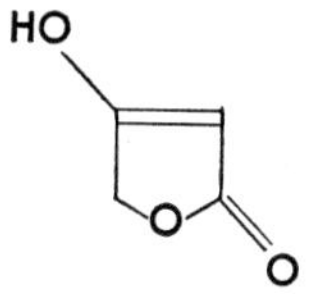

Tetronic Acid 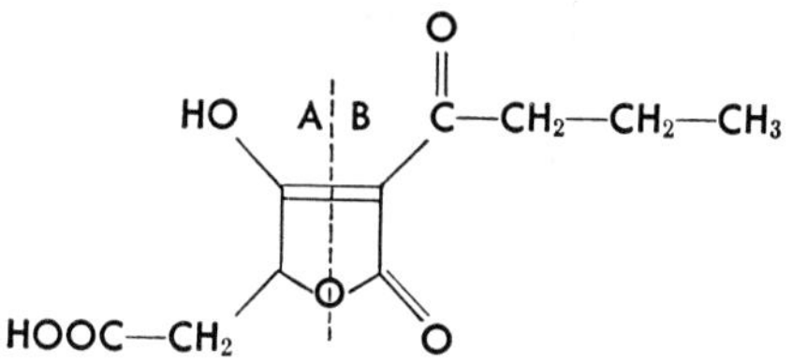   Carlosic Acid

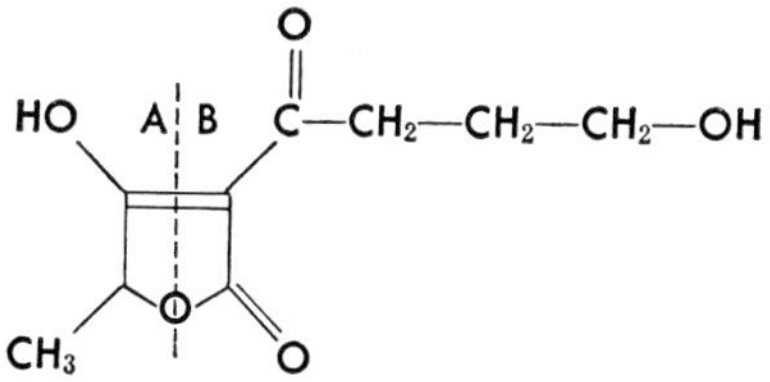

Carolic Acid

[1] Gösta Ehrensvärd, "Chemical Society Symposia," Special Publication No. 12, The Chemical Society, London, 1958, p. 14.

composed of three acetate units, while the A part is probably derived from another source related to carbohydrate biosynthesis. It would seem as if in the case of carlosic acid the A portion were derived from oxaloacetic acid, and in carolic acid from lactic or pyruvic acids.

Inspecting other structures it appears (formally at least) that in zymonic acid, isolated by Stodola from many yeasts, the A portion could be from tartronate.

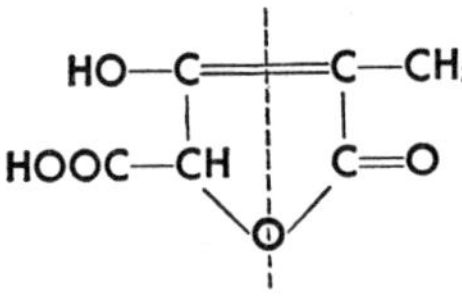

Zymonic Acid

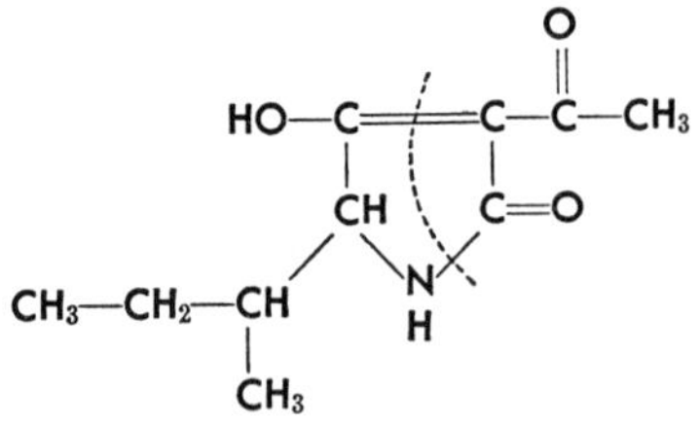

Tenuazonic Acid

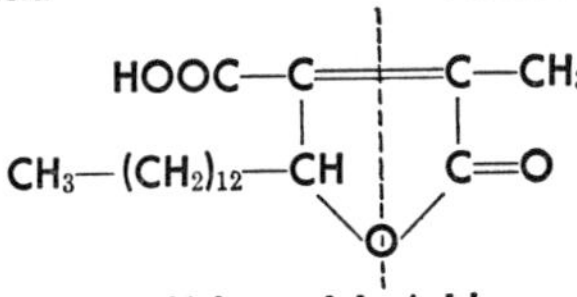

Lichesterinic Acid

There are other possibilities in this case, however. Tenuazonic acid, a lactam similar to the tetronic acids, must surely be derived from isoleucine and acetoacetate.* Lichesterinic acid apparently is the result of a condensation between pyruvate and 3-oxypalmitate. Nephromopsic acid, which sometimes is found with lichesterinic acid, may be a reduction product.

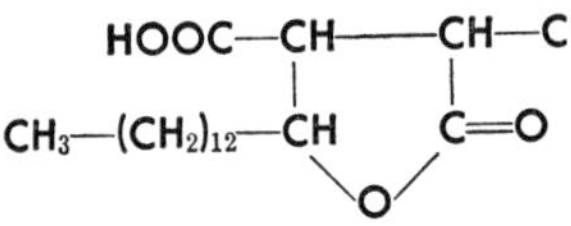

Nephromopsic Acid

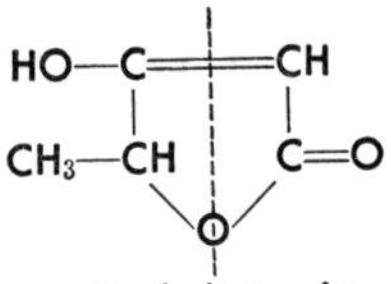

γ-Methyltetronic Acid

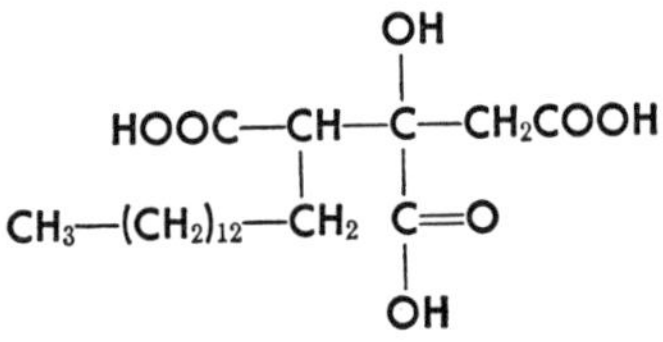

Caperatic Acid

It is interesting to note the co-occurrence of nephromopsic acid and caperatic acid, the former being (apparently) a condensa-

* See addendum.

tion product of a C_{15} fatty acid and pyruvate while the latter seems to be the condensation product of a C_{16} fatty acid with oxaloacetate. Many other such apparent biosynthetic origins can be detected.

The biosynthesis of penicillic acid has been studied.[2] At first glance this would appear to be derived from acetate and dimethylpyruvate, β-methylglutaconate or a similar unit. It was found that 2-C^{14}-mevalonic acid lactone was not incorporated into the penicillic acid molecule when added to the growth medium of *Penicillium cyclopium* Westling. However, $CH_3C^{14}OOH$ was incorporated with equal labeling at the sites shown:

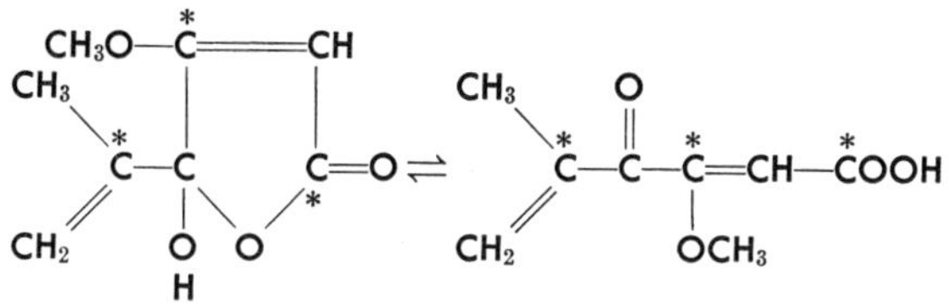

Penicillic Acid

With a relationship to the terpene biosynthetic route ruled out and a similarity to the valine biogenetic pathway also unlikely, the authors suggested a precursor of the orsellinic acid type, perhaps the 4-methyl ether:†

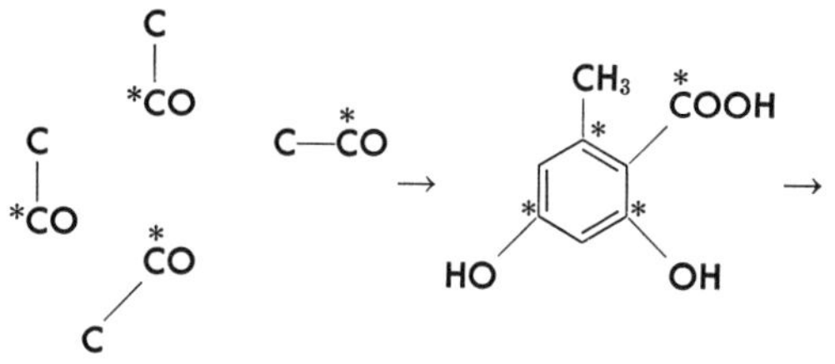

Orsellinic Acid

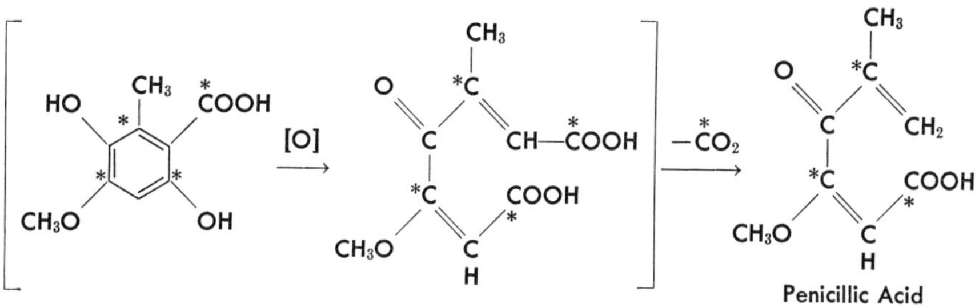

Penicillic Acid

[2] A. J. Birch, G. E. Blance and Herchel Smith, *J. Chem. Soc.*, 4582 (1958).

† See addendum.

A somewhat similar aromatic ring cleavage has been proposed[3] in the biosynthesis of patulin.

It is likely that the biosynthetic origins of the two recently reported streptomycete antibiotics, acetomycin and 3-carboxy-2,4-pentadienal lactol (PA-147) are mutually related.

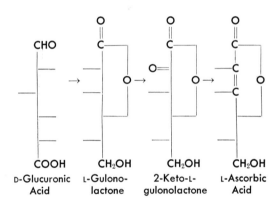

3-Carboxy-2,4-pentadienal Lactol

The biosynthesis of ascorbic acid in *Aspergillus niger* is known to involve the following stages:[4]

D-Glucuronic Acid	L-Gulono-lactone	2-Keto-L-gulonolactone	L-Ascorbic Acid

The glucuronic acid probably quite generally can arise from glucose by a hexose interconversion of the type discussed earlier in the section on sugars. In muscle tissue it may also come from myoinositol.

[3] J. D. Bu'Lock and A. J. Ryan, *Proc. Chem. Soc.*, 222 (1958).
[4] K. Sivarama Sastry and P. S. Sarma, *Nature* 179 44 (1957).

140 γ-Methyltetronic Acid, $C_5H_6O_3$, colorless crystals, m.p. 115°, $[\alpha]_{5461}$ −21° (c 0.526 in water).

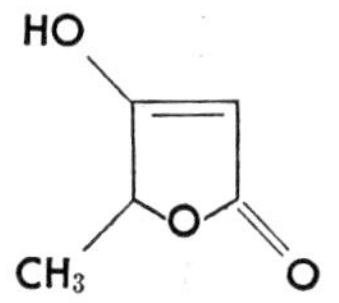

Penicillium charlesii G. Smith, *P. fellutanum*
The yield of this and the following tetronic acids from *P. charlesii* totaled 14% of the glucose consumed.
Percival Walter Clutterbuck, Harold Raistrick and Fritz Reutter, *Biochem. J.* **29** 1300 (1935).
V. C. Vora, *J. Sci. Ind. Research* (India) **13B** 504 (1954).

141 3-Carboxy-2,4-pentadienal Lactol (PA-147), $C_6H_6O_3$, viscous oil which polymerizes on standing at room temperature, $[\alpha]_D$ 0 ±2° (c 2 in $CHCl_3$).

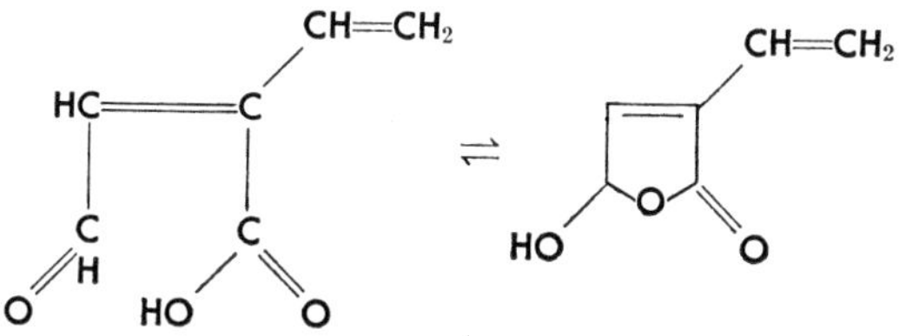

Streptomyces sp.
Hans Els, B. A. Sobin and W. D. Celmer, *J. Am. Chem. Soc.* **80** 878 (1958).

142 **Zymonic Acid**, $C_6H_6O_5$, isolated as the stable methyl ester, b.p. 118–123° (1 mm.), n_D^{28} 1.4640.

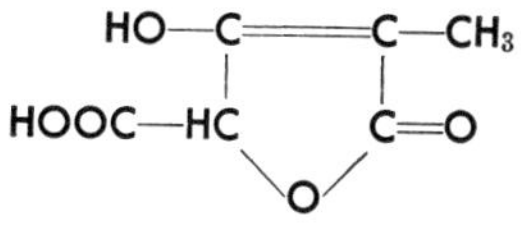

Trichosporon capitatum, Hansenula subpelliculosa, Kloeckera brevis, Sporobolomyces salmonicolor, Cryptococcus laurentii, Debaryomyces hansenii, Nematospora coryli, Torula mellis

Frank H. Stodola, Odette L. Shotwell and Lewis B. Lockwood, *J. Am. Chem. Soc.* 74 5415 (1952).

Frank H. Stodola, "Chemical Transformations of Microorganisms," Squibb Lectures on Chemistry of Microbial Products, John Wiley and Sons, New York, N. Y., 1958, pp. 97–102.

143 **Ascorbic Acid** (Vitamin C), $C_6H_8O_6$, colorless crystals, m.p. 190–192°, $[\alpha]_D^{23}$ +48° (c 1 in methanol).

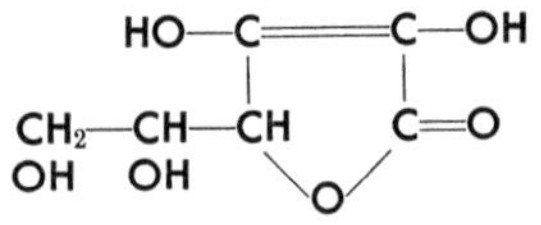

Serratia marcescens (on xylose), *Aspergillus niger* (Up to 140 mg. per liter yields have been reported from *A. niger*.)

M. Geiger-Huber and H. Galli, *Helv. Chim. Acta* 28 248 (1945).

Adelheid Galli, *Ber. schweiz. botan. Ges.* 56 113 (1946).

J. M. Van Lanen and F. W. Tanner, Jr., *Vitamins and Hormones* 6 163 (1948).

144 **Penicillic Acid,** $C_8H_{10}O_4$, colorless crystals, m.p. 87° (anhydrous), 64° (hydrate).

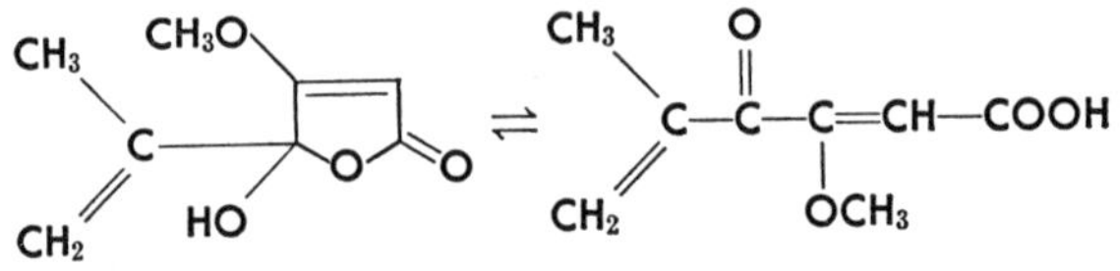

Penicillium cyclopium Westling, *P. puberulum* Bainier, *P. thomii, P. baarnense, Aspergillus ochraceus*

John H. Birkinshaw, Albert E. Oxford and Harold Raistrick, *Biochem. J.* 30 394 (1936). (Structure)

O. F. Black and C. L. Alsberg, *U. S. Dept. Agr., Bur. Plant Ind. Bull.* No. 199 (1910); Carl L. Alsberg and Otis F. Black, *Bur. Plant Ind. Bull.* No. 270 (1913). (Isolation)

R. A. Raphael, *J. Chem. Soc.*, 805 (1947). (Synthesis of dihydropenicillic acid)

E. O. Karow, H. B. Woodruff and J. W. Foster, *Arch. Biochem.* 5 279 (1944). (Isolations)

145   **Dehydrocarolic Acid,** $C_9H_8O_4$, colorless fine platelets, polymerizes above 80°.

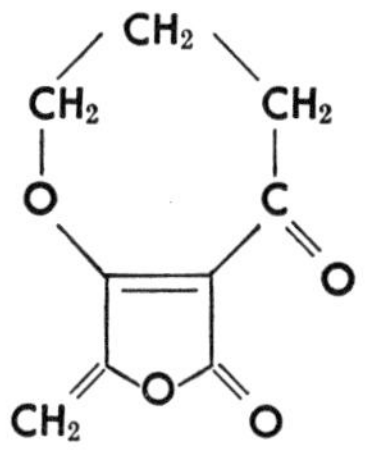

Penicillium cinerascens Biourge
Carlosic acid, spinulosin and gliotoxin also were produced.
A. Bracken and H. Raistrick, *Biochem. J.* 41 569 (1947).

146   **Carolic Acid,** $C_9H_{10}O_4$, colorless needles, m.p. 132° $[\alpha]_{5461}$ +84° (c 0.50 in water).

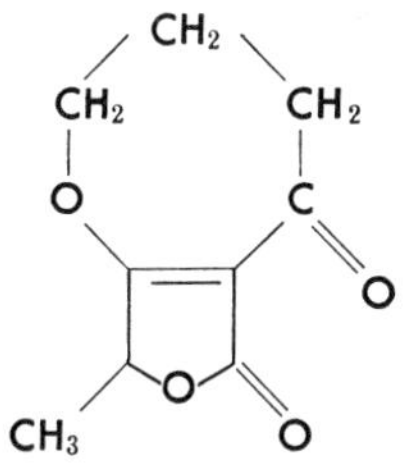

P. charlesii G. Smith
Percival W. Clutterbuck, Walter N. Haworth, Harold Raistrick, Geo. Smith and Maurice Stacey, *Biochem. J.* 28 94 (1934).

147   **Carolinic Acid,** $C_9H_{10}O_6$, colorless prisms, m.p. 123° (dec.), $[\alpha]_{5461}$ +60° (c 0.34 in water).

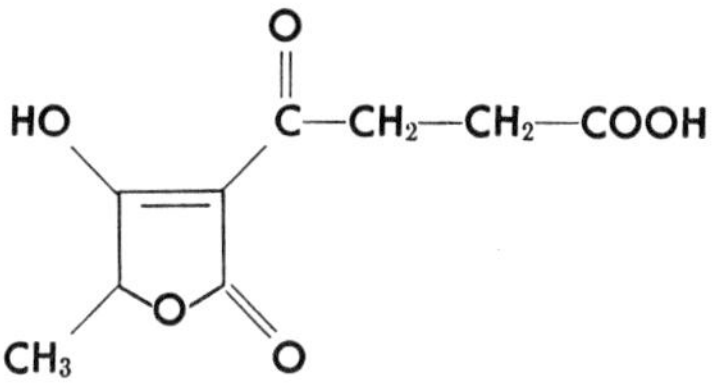

Penicillium charlesii G. Smith

L. J. Haynes, J. R. Plimmer, and (in part) A. H. Stanners, *J. Chem. Soc.*, 4661 (1956). (Synthesis)

Percival W. Clutterbuck, Walter N. Haworth, Harold Raistrick, Geo. Smith and Maurice Stacey, *Biochem. J.* 28 94 (1934).

148 **Carlic Acid,** $C_{10}H_{10}O_6$, colorless needles, m.p. 176° (dec.) $[\alpha]_{5461}$ $-160°$ (c 0.28 in water).

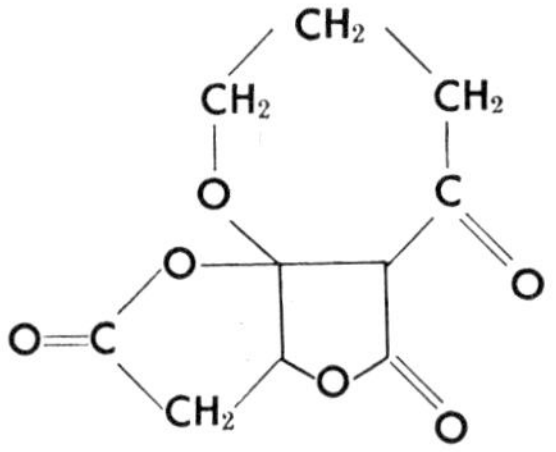

P. charlesii G. Smith

Percival W. Clutterbuck, Walter N. Haworth, Harold Raistrick, Geo. Smith and Maurice Stacey, *Biochem. J.* 28 94 (1934). (Isolation)

149 **Carlosic Acid,** $C_{10}H_{12}O_6$, colorless needles, m.p. 181°, $[\alpha]_{5461}$ $-160°$ (c 0.21 in water).

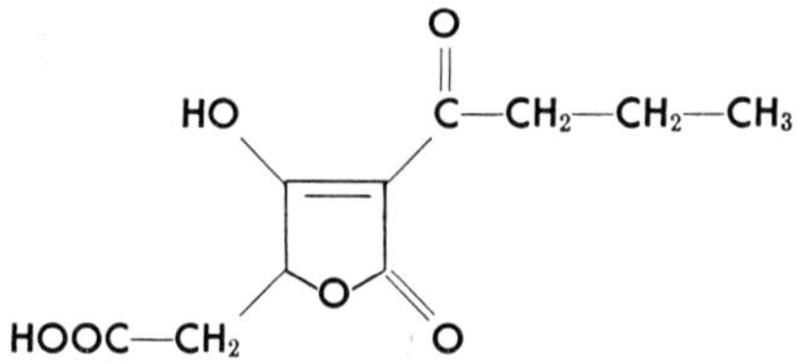

P. charlesii G. Smith

Percival W. Clutterbuck, Walter N. Haworth, Harold Raistrick, Geo. Smith and Maurice Stacey, *Biochem. J.* 28 94 (1934). (Isolation)

150 **Acetomycin,** $C_{10}H_{14}O_5$, colorless rods, m.p. 115° (subl. 70°), $[\alpha]_D$ $-167°$ (in ethanol).

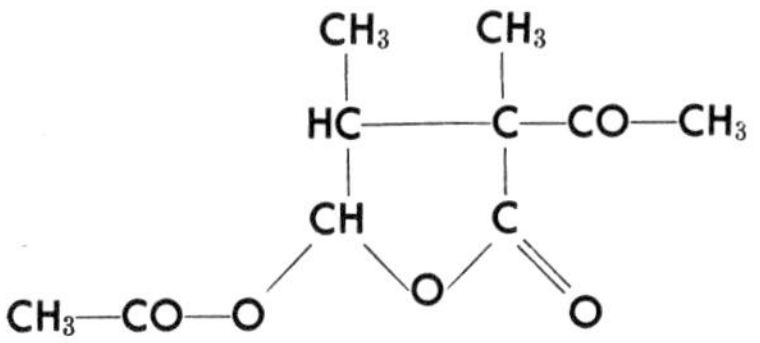

Streptomyces ramulosus n. sp.

The yield was about 1 g. per liter.

L. Ettlinger, E. Gäumann, R. Hütter, W. Keller-Schierlein, F. Kradolfer, L. Neipp, V. Prelog and H. Zähner, *Helv. Chim. Acta* **41** 216 (1958). (Isolation)

151 **Tenuazonic Acid,** $C_{10}H_{15}O_3N$, straw-colored gum, b.p. 117° (0.035 mm.), $[\alpha]_{5461}^{20}$ −136 ±5° (c 0.2 in chloroform).

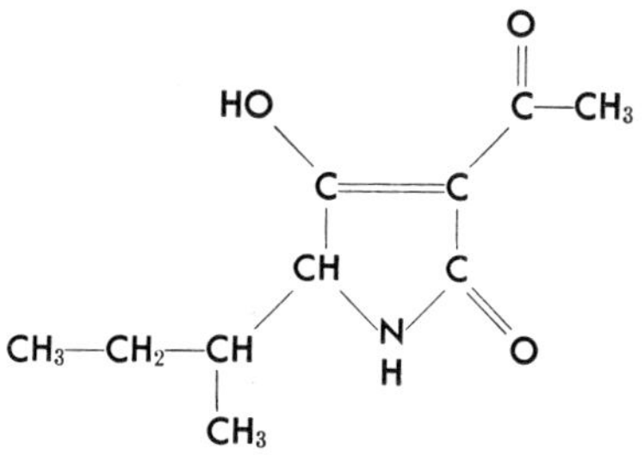

Alternaria tenuis Auct.

Tenuazonic acid is one of several compounds isolated from culture filtrates of this fungus. The other substances (structures still unknown) were: Altenuic acids I, II and III, altenusin, dehydroaltenusin and altertenuol. Alternariol and its methyl ether were isolated from the mycelium.

T. Rosett, R. H. Sankhala, C. E. Stickings, M. E. U. Taylor and R. Thomas, *Biochem. J.* **67** 390 (1957). (Isolation)

C. E. Stickings, *ibid.* **72** 332 (1959). (Structure)

152 **Terrestric Acid,** $C_{11}H_{14}O_4$, colorless crystals, m.p. 89°, $[\alpha]_{5461}^{20}$ +61.1° (c 0.53 in water).

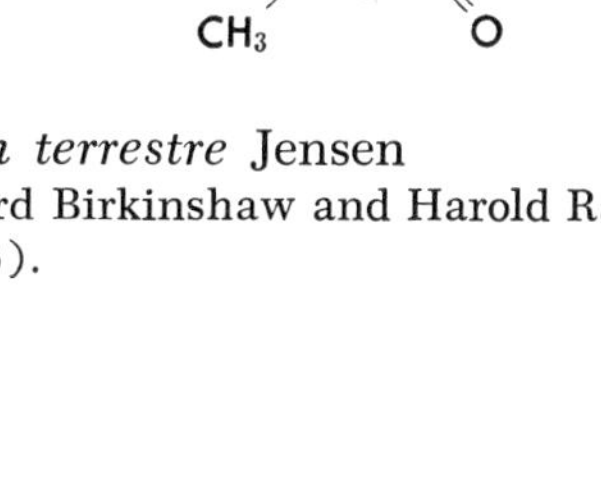

Penicillium terrestre Jensen

John Howard Birkinshaw and Harold Raistrick, *Biochem. J.* **30** 2194 (1936).

153 **Viridicatic Acid** (Ethylcarlosic Acid), $C_{12}H_{16}O_6$, colorless platelets, m.p. 174.5°, $[\alpha]_{5461}{}^{20}$ −105° (c 1.0 in ethanol).

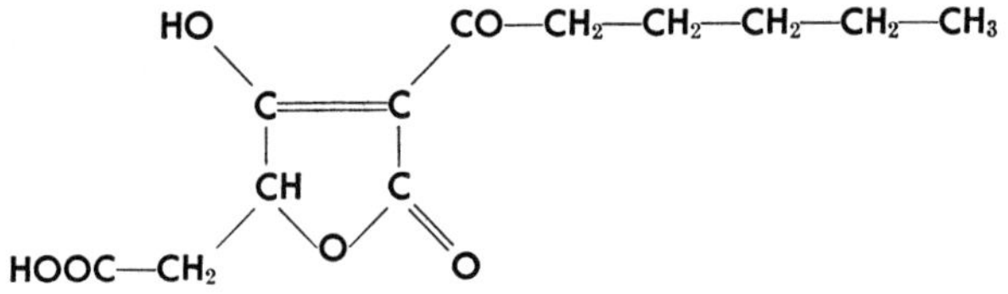

HO   CO—CH₂—CH₂—CH₂—CH₂—CH₃

C═══C

CH   C

HOOC—CH₂   O   O

Penicillium viridicatum Westling
J. H. Birkinshaw and M. S. Samant, *Biochem. J.* 74 369 (1960).

154 **Nephrosterinic Acid,** $C_{17}H_{28}O_4$, colorless leaflets, m.p. 96°, $[\alpha]_D{}^{10}$ +10.81°.

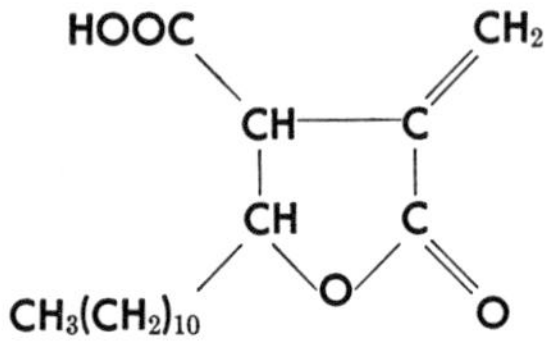

HOOC   CH₂

CH———C

CH   C

CH₃(CH₂)₁₀   O   O

Nephromopsis endocrocea Asahina (=*Cetraria endocrocea* (Asahina) Sato)
Nephrosteranic acid, endocrocin and caperin were also present.
Yasuhiko Asahina, Masaiti Yanagita and Y. Sakurai, *Ber.* **70B** 227 (1937).

155 **Nephrosteranic Acid,** $C_{17}H_{30}O_4$, colorless plates, m.p. 95°.

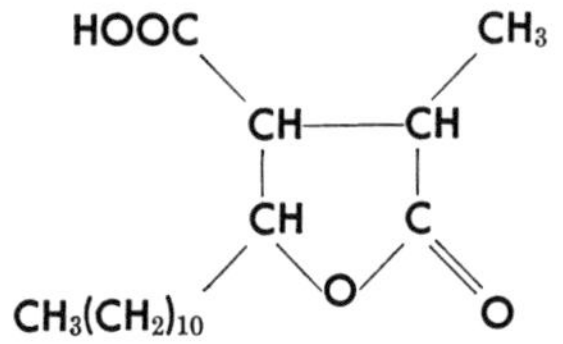

HOOC   CH₃

CH———CH

CH   C

CH₃(CH₂)₁₀   O   O

Nephromopsis endocrocea Asahina
Yasuhiko Asahina, Masaiti Yanagita and Y. Sakurai, *Ber.* **70B** 227 (1937).

156 *l*-**Lichesterinic Acid,** $C_{19}H_{32}O_4$, colorless needles, m.p. 124°, $[\alpha]_D{}^{25}$ −32.66°.

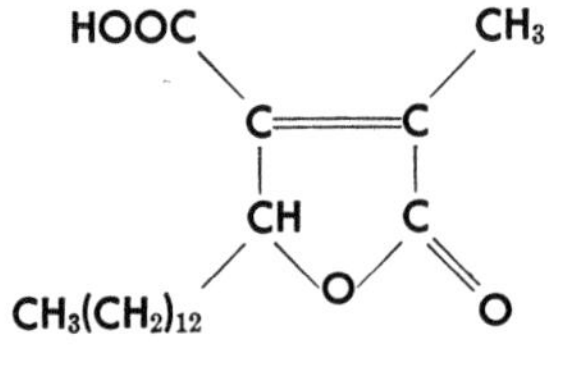

HOOC   CH₃

C═══C

CH   C

CH₃(CH₂)₁₂   O   O

Cetraria islandica f. *tenuifolia, Nephromopsis stracheyi* f. *ectocarpisma* Hue.

Yasuhiko Asahina and Masaiti Yasue, *Ber.* **70B** 1053 (1937).
Yukio Kameda, *J. Pharm. Soc. Japan* **61** 266 (1941). (German abstract)

157 *d*-**Protolichesterinic Acid,** $C_{19}H_{32}O_4$, colorless leaflets, m.p. 107.5°, $[\alpha]_D^{19.5}$ +12.1°.

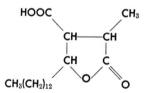

Cetraria islandica Ach., *Parmelia sinodensis* Asahina, *Cladonia papillaria* (Ehrh.) Hoffm.

Yasuhiko Asahina, *J. Japan. Botan.* **18** 489 (1942).

The *l*-isomer, m.p. 107.5°, $[\alpha]_D^{19.5}$ −12.7°, has been isolated from *Cetraria crispa* Nyl. (=*C. tenuifolia* Howe).

Y. Asahina and M. Asano, *J. Pharm. Soc. Japan* No. 539, 1 (1927).

Eugene E. van Tamelen and Shirley Rosenberg Bach, *J. Am. Chem. Soc.* **80** 3079 (1958). (Synthesis)

158 *l-allo*-**Protolichesterinic Acid,** $C_{19}H_{32}O_4$, colorless plates, m.p. 107°, $[\alpha]_D^{18}$ −102°.

Cetraria islandica Ach. var. *orientalis* Asahina

Yasuhiko Asahina and Masaiti Yasue, *Ber.* **70B** 1053 (1937).

159 Nephromopsic Acid, $C_{19}H_{34}O_4$, colorless leaflets, m.p. 137°.

HOOC   CH₃
  \   /
   CH────CH
   | |
   CH   C
  / \   / \\
CH₃(CH₂)₁₂ O   O

Nephromopsis stracheyi f. *ectocarpisma* Hue.

Occurs with usnic acid, *l*-lichesterinic acid, *l*-protolichesterinic acid and caperatic acid.

Michizo Asano and Tiaki Azumi, *Ber.* **68B** 995 (1935).

5

Carotenes and Carotenoids

Carotene pigments are widely distributed throughout nature, and many microorganism pigments are carotenoid. Their isolation and characterization are often complicated by the co-occurrence of closely related compounds, and in some cases by poor stability. Many identifications have been made on the basis of ultraviolet absorption spectra alone.

For these reasons, and because of duplications in nomenclature, the literature dealing with microorganism carotenoids is confused. The situation has been reviewed by T. W. Goodwin,[1] and to augment the entries in this section some pertinent tables and references from this book have been incorporated as an appendix.

Carotenoids occur in both photosynthetic and non-photosynthetic microorganisms, and their functions are not established clearly. In fungi they may stimulate photokinetic responses such as phototropic bending. In sarcina and staphylococcus species there may be some protection of the cell from ultraviolet light. In photosynthetic genera it has been suggested that carotenoids may serve as blue-light energy absorbers, as oxygen carriers and in the prevention of chlorophyll-catalyzed photooxidations.

The work that has been done on carotene biogenesis in microorganisms has been well summarized.[2,3] It has been found[4,5]

[1] T. W. Goodwin, "Comparative Biochemistry of Carotenoids," Chemical Publishing Co., Inc., New York, N. Y., 1954.

[2] G. E. W. Wolstenholme and Maeve O'Connor, "CIBA Foundation Symposium on the Biosynthesis of Terpenes and Sterols," E. C. Grob, *The biosynthesis of carotenoids by microorganisms*, Little, Brown and Co., Boston, Mass., 1959, pp. 267–278.

[3] T. W. Goodwin, *ibid.*, pp. 279–294.

that *Mucor hiemalis* uses acetate for the production of β-carotene. The product derived from C^{14}-labeled acetate has been partially degraded, and the following partial distribution pattern demonstrated:

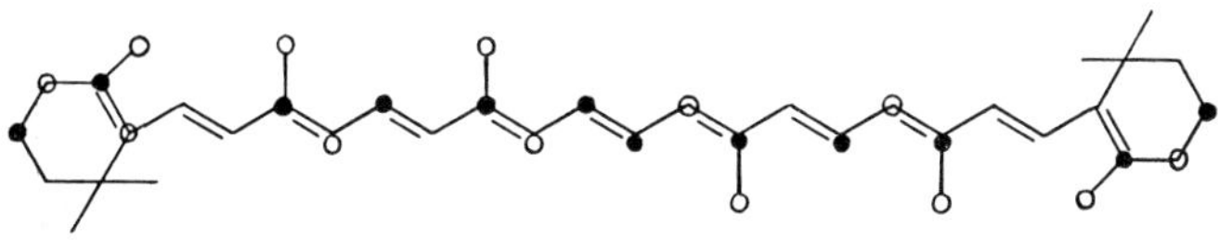

β-carotene
o Carbon atom from the methyl group of acetate
• Carbon atom from the carboxyl group of acetate

Mevalonic acid is an effective carotene precursor in at least certain microorganisms.[6, 7] In this connection it is noteworthy that in *Phycomyces blakesleeanus* and in *Mucor hiemalis* the production of sterols and carotenoids always runs proportionally.[8] The scheme shown below has been proposed for the mode of condensation.[2]

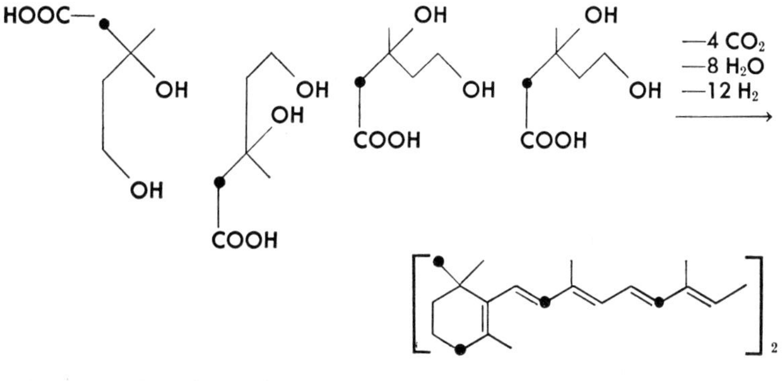

Leucine has been known for many years to have ketogenic and carotenogenic properties to a greater extent than other amino acids. The discovery of mevalonic acid facilitated an

---

[4] E. C. Grob and R. Bütler, *Helv. Chim. Acta* 39 1975 (1956).
[5] E. C. Grob, *Chimia* 10 73 (1956).
[6] G. D. Braithwaite and T. W. Goodwin, *Biochem. J.* 66 31p (1957).
[7] E. C. Grob, *Chimia* 11 338 (1957).
[8] E. C. Grob, M. Bein and W. H. Schopfer, *Bull. soc. chim. biol.* 33 1236 (1951).

explanation of this effect, and this interesting work has been reviewed.[9, 10]

Some of the relationships thought to exist are:

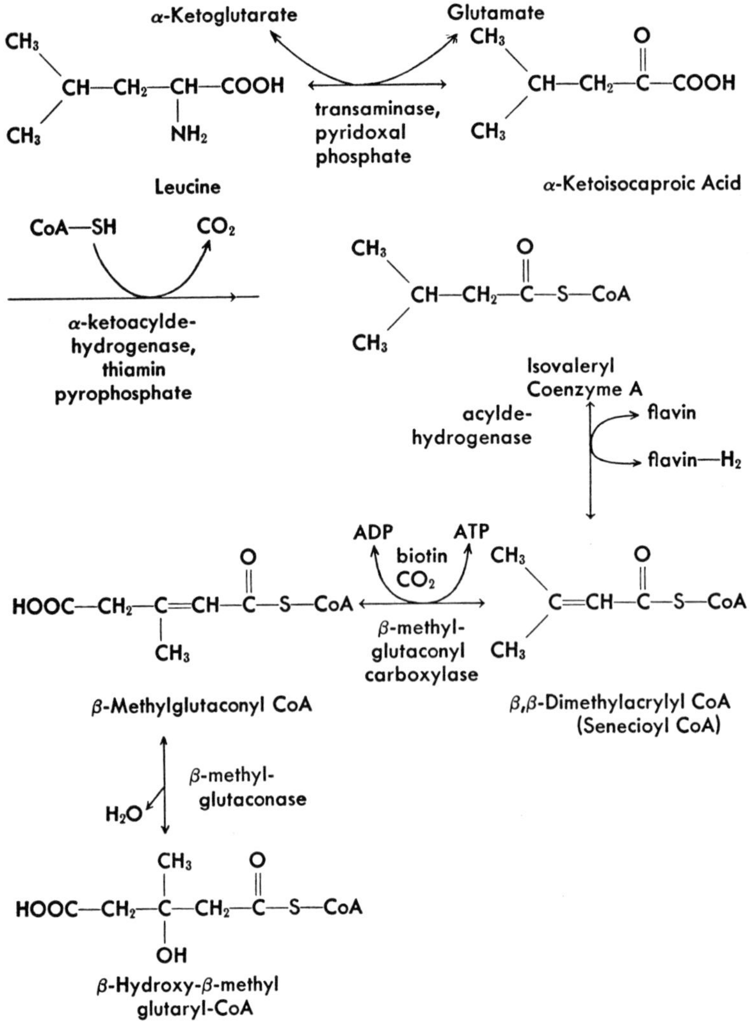
α-Ketoglutarate
Glutamate
CH3
CH—CH2—CH—COOH
CH3
NH2
transaminase,
pyridoxal
phosphate
CH3
O
CH—CH2—C—COOH
CH3
Leucine
α-Ketoisocaproic Acid
CoA—SH
CO2
α-ketoacylde-
hydrogenase,
thiamin
pyrophosphate
CH3
O
CH—CH2—C—S—CoA
CH3
Isovaleryl
Coenzyme A
acylde-
hydrogenase
flavin
flavin—H2
ADP
ATP
biotin
CO2
O
HOOC—CH2—C=CH—C—S—CoA
CH3
β-methyl-
glutaconyl
carboxylase
CH3
O
C=CH—C—S—CoA
CH3
β-Methylglutaconyl CoA
β,β-Dimethylacrylyl CoA
(Senecioyl CoA)
β-methyl-
glutaconase
H2O
CH3
O
HOOC—CH2—C—CH2—C—S—CoA
OH
β-Hydroxy-β-methyl
glutaryl-CoA

[9] G. E. W. Wolstenholme and Maeve O'Connor, "CIBA Foundation Symposium on the Biosynthesis of Terpenes and Sterols," M. J. Coon, F. P. Kupiecki, E. E. Dekker, M. J. Schlesinger and Alice del Campillo, *The enzymic synthesis of branched-chain acids,* Little, Brown and Co., Boston, Mass., 1959, pp. 62–74.

[10] *Idem., ibid.,* Harry Rudney, *The biosynthesis of β-hydroxy-β-methylglutaryl coenzyme A and its conversion to mevalonic acid,* pp. 75–94.

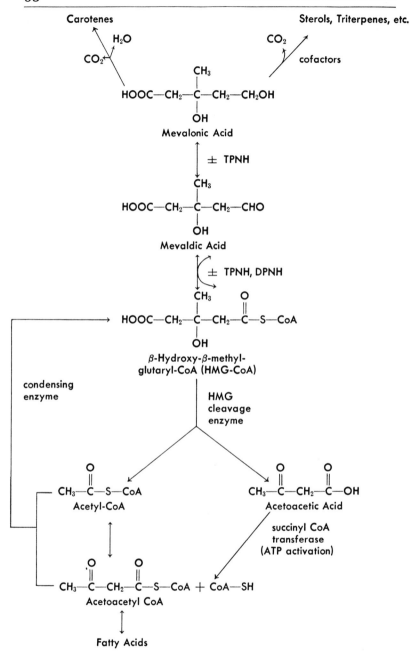

The precursors of the carotenes are colorless, more reduced compounds. These substances then are dehydrogenated in a stepwise fashion, a process which requires light and oxygen.

Oxygen-containing carotenoids appear at an early stage in the biosynthetic scheme. Based on the order of appearance in cultures of *Neurospora crassa*, Grob has proposed* the following partial pathway of carotenoid formation:

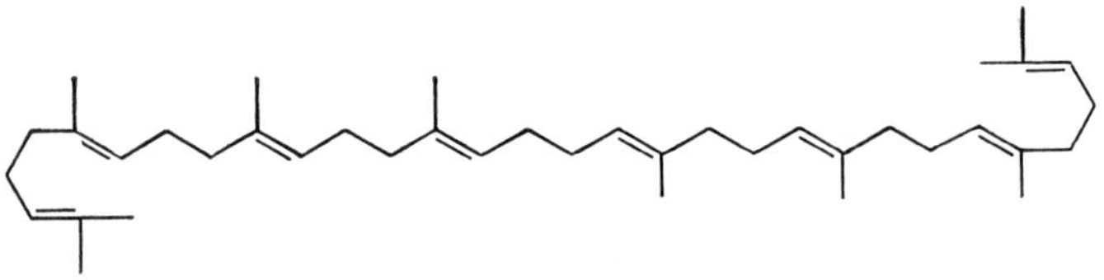

Lycopersene

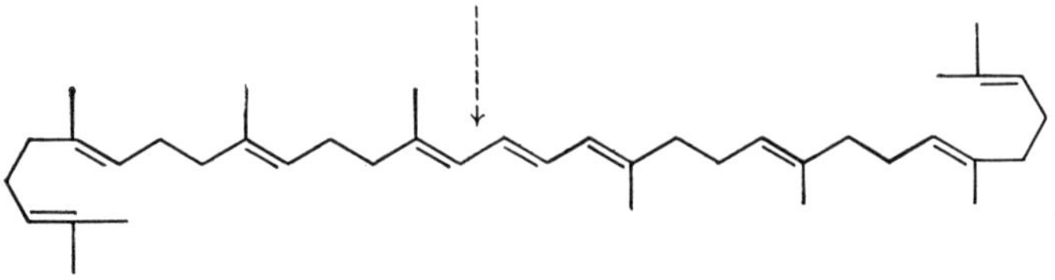

Phytoene

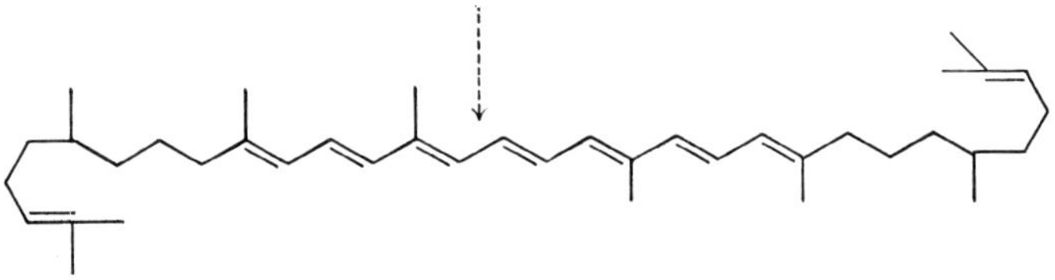

Neurosporene

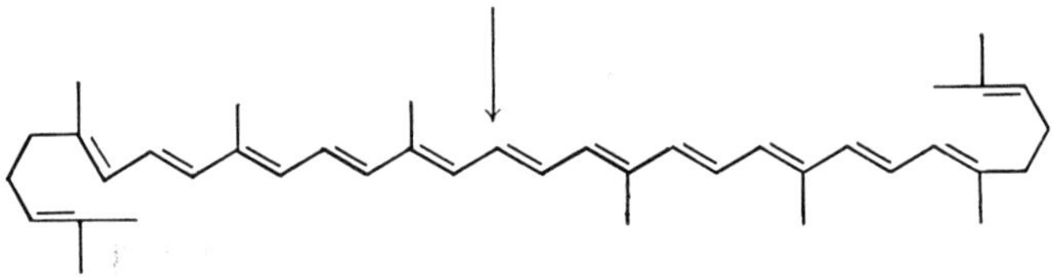

Lycopene

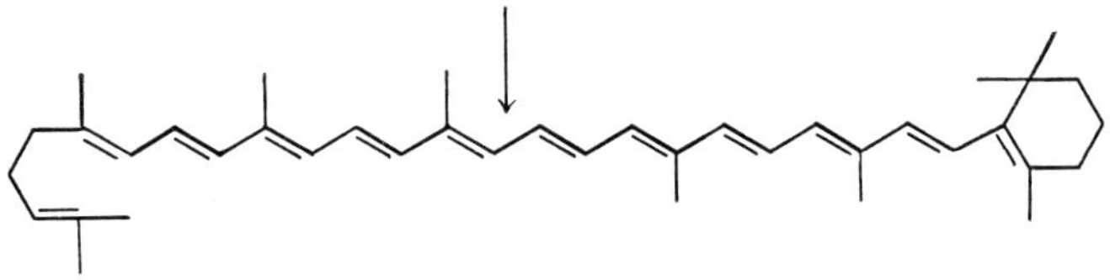

γ-Carotene

Lycopersene has not been isolated from a natural source, but this colorless polyene has been synthesized and seems to be a logical early member of this sequence.

* See addendum.

160 **Azafrin** (Escobedin), $C_{27}H_{38}O_4$, orange crystals, m.p. 213°, $[\alpha]_{6438}{}^{20}$ −75° (c 0.28 in alcohol), U.V. 428, 458 mμ in chloroform.

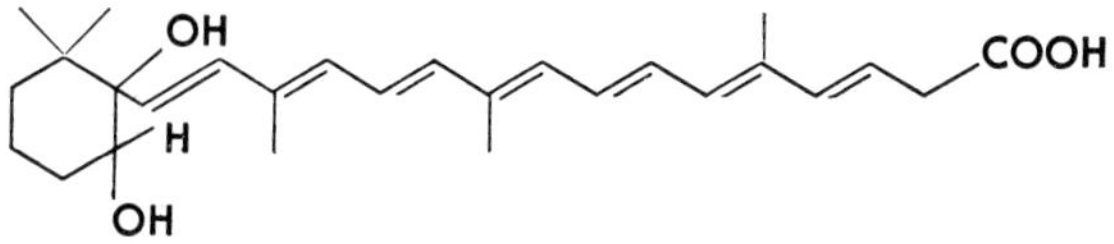

Mycobacterium phlei
Mary A. Ingraham and Harry Steenbock, *Biochem. J.* **29** 2553 (1935).
Richard Kuhn, Alfred Winterstein and Hubert Roth, *Ber.* **64A** 333 (1931).

161 **Torularhodin** (May = Lusomycin), $C_{37}H_{48}O_2$, red needles, m.p. 202° (vac.) (dec.), U.V. 554, 515, (483) mμ in chloroform.

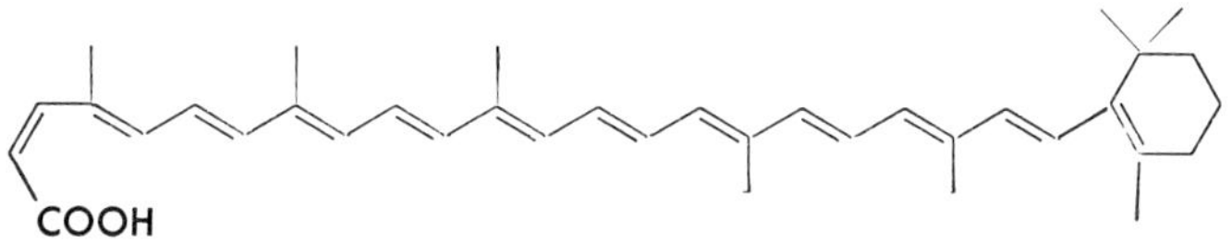

Rhodotorula rubra, R. sanniei
The yield from *R. sanniei* was 2900 γ per gram of dry cells. Also obtained were torulene (143 γ per gram) and β-carotene (10 γ per gram) and traces of γ-carotene and lycopene.
Edgar Lederer, *Bull. soc. chim. biol.* **20** 611 (1938).
Claude Fromageot and Joué Léon Tchang, *Arch. Mikrobiol.* **9** 424 (1938).
L. Nogueira Prista, *Congr. Luso-Espan. farm.* **2** 274 (1952). (Chem. Abstr. **48** 13807a)
R. Entschel and P. Karrer, *Helv. Chim. Acta* **42** 466 (1959).

162 **Astacin** (3,4,3′,4′-Tetraoxo-β-carotene), $C_{40}H_{48}O_4$, violet, metalloid needles, m.p. 240–243°, U.V. 500 mμ in carbon disulfide.

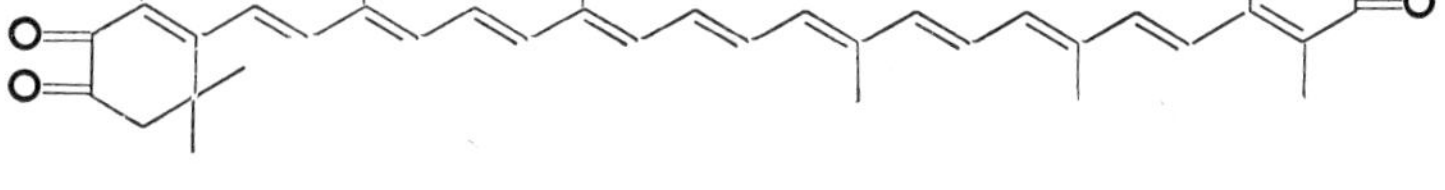

Mycobacterium laticola

H. F. Haas and L. D. Bushnell, *J. Bacteriol.* 48 219 (1944). (Isolation)

R. Kuhn, E. Lederer and A. Deutsch, *Hoppe-Seylers Z.* 220 229 (1933).

R. Kuhn and E. Lederer, *Ber.* 66 448 (1933).

163 **Canthaxanthin** (4,4'-Dioxo-β-carotene) $C_{40}H_{52}O_2$, red crystals, m.p. 218°, U.V. 480 mμ in benzene.

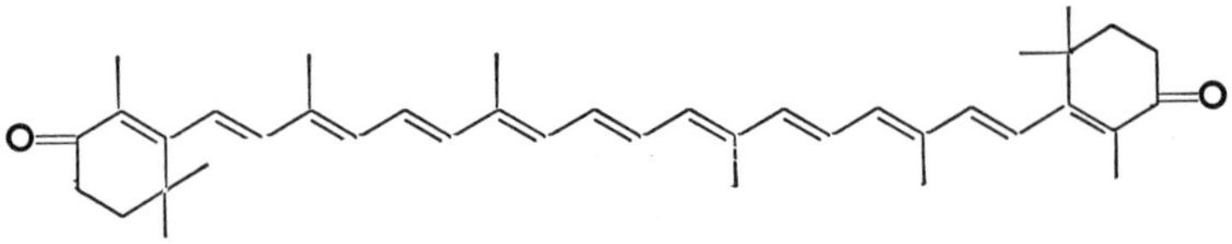

Cantharellus cinnabarinus, Corynebacterium michiganense

Francis Haxo, *Botan. Gaz.* 112 228 (1950). (Isolation)

S. Saperstein and M. P. Starr, *Biochem. J.* 57 273 (1954).

F. J. Petracek and L. Zechmeister, *Arch. Biochem. and Biophys.* 61 137 (1956). (Structure)

C. K. Warren and B. C. L. Weedon, *J. Chem. Soc.*, 3986 (1958). (Synthesis)

164 α-**Carotene**, $C_{40}H_{56}$, deep purple prisms, m.p. 187.5° (vac.), $[\alpha]_D^{18}$ +385° (c 0.08 in benzene), U.V. 446, 473 mμ in light petroleum ether.

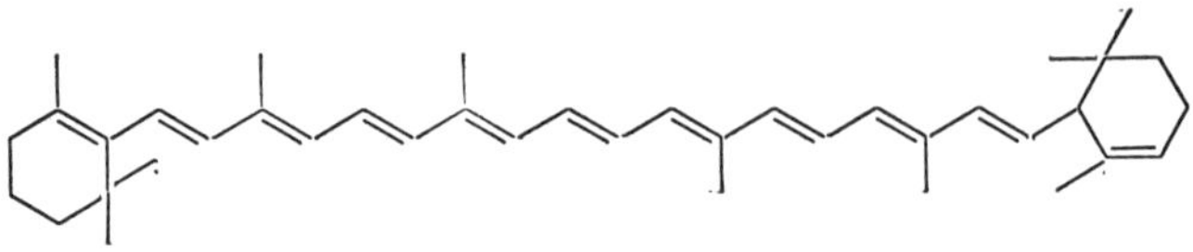

Dacromyces stillatus, Neurospora crassa (mutants), *Mycobacterium phlei, Phycomyces blakesleeanus, Rhodotorula rubra, Gymnosporangium juniperi-virginianae, Puccinia coronifera, Aleuria aurantia, Cantharellus cibarius, Coleosporium senecionis, Penicillium sclerotiorum*

Edgar Lederer, *Bull. soc. chim. biol.* 20 611 (1938).

Harry Willstaedt, *Svensk. Kem. Tidskr.* 49 318 (1937).

B. L. Smits and W. J. Peterson, *Science* 96 210 (1942).

J. Bonner, A. Sandoval, W. Tang and L. Zechmeister, *Arch. Biochem.* 10 113 (1946).

T. W. Goodwin, *Biochem. J.* 53 538 (1953).

165 β-Carotene, $C_{40}H_{56}$ dark violet prisms from benzene-methanol, red leaflets from petroleum ether, m.p. 183° (vac.), U.V. 425, 450, 476 mμ in light petroleum ether.

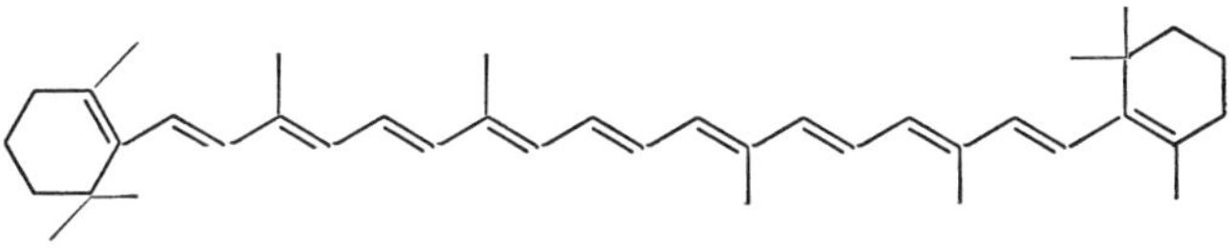

Phycomyces blakesleeanus, Neurospora crassa, Rhodotorula rubra, R. sanniei, R. glutinis, Sporobolomyces roseus, S. salmonicolor, Cantharellus cibarius, C. cinnabarinus, Allomyces javanicus, Coleosporium senecionis, Mitrula paludosa, Penicillium sclerotiorum, Fremella mesenterica, Puccinia coronifera, Pilobolus bleinii, Gymnosporangium juniperi-virginianae, Dacromyces stillatus, Aleuria aurantia, Cryptococcus laurentii, C. luteolus, Monilia sitophila, Corynebacterium michiganense (mutants), Mycobacterium phlei, Sarcina aurantiaca

For references see:

T. W. Goodwin, *Ann. Rev. Biochem.* 24 497 (1955).

Idem., "Carotenoids," Chemical Publishing Co., Inc., New York, N. Y. 1954, p. 108 etc.

166 γ-Carotene, $C_{40}H_{56}$, fine deep red crystals with a blue luster from benzene-methanol, m.p. 177.5°, U.V. 493, 462, 437 mμ in petroleum ether.

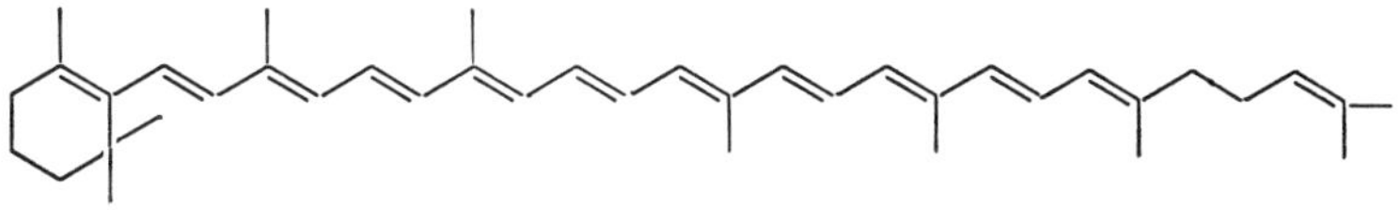

Allomyces arbuscula, A. javanicus, A. macrocygna, A. moniliformis, Puccinia coronifera, Phycomyces blakesleeanus, Neurospora crassa, Cantharellus cibarius, Coleosporum senecionis, Dacromyces stillatus, Gymnosporangium juniperi-virginianae, Cryptococcus laurentii, C. luteolus, Mycobacterium phlei, Chlorobium spp. Penicillium sclerotiorum

For references see:

T. W. Goodwin, *Ann. Rev. Biochem.* 24 497 (1955).

Idem., "Carotenoids," Chemical Publishing Co., Inc., New York, N. Y. 1954, p. 108 etc.

J. Bonner, A. Sandoval, W. Tang and L. Zechmeister, *Arch. Biochem.* 10 113 (1946).

167 **δ-Carotene,** $C_{40}H_{56}$, fine orange to red needles, m.p. 140.5°, U.V. 488, 456, 430, 280 mμ in isooctane.

Proposed structure:

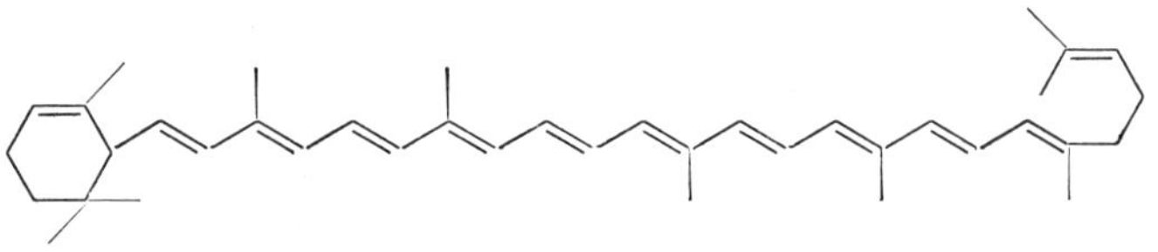

Cantharellus cibarius, Neurospora crassa (mutants), *Staphylococcus aureus*

Harry Willstaedt, *Svensk Kem. Tidskr.* 49 318 (1937).

Ben Sobin and Grant L. Stahly, *J. Bacteriol.* 44 265 (1942).

J. W. Porter and M. M. Murphy, *Arch. Biochem. and Biophys.* 32 21 (1951). (Isolation)

Francis Haxo, *Biol. Bull.* 103 268 (1952).

168 **Lycopene** (Solanorubin, Rhodopurpurene) $C_{40}H_{56}$, brownish red to carmine crystals, m.p. 174°, U.V. 446, 474, 506 mμ in petroleum ether.

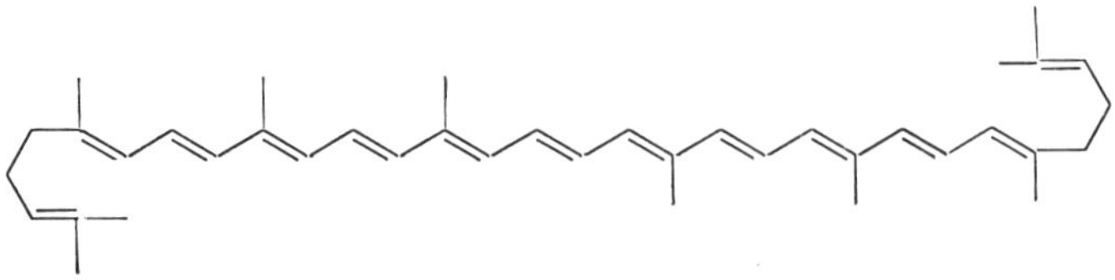

Phycomyces blakesleeanus, certain *Cantharellus* spp., *Neurospora crassa, Micrococcus tetragenus* (pink type), *Anthurus aserioformis, Allomyces javanicus, Rhodotorula glutinis, R. rubra, R. sanniei, Corynebacterium michiganense, C. diphtheriae, Mycobacterium phlei, Staphylococcus aureus, Coleosporium senecionis, Sarcina aurantiaca*

Harry Willstaedt, *Svensk. Kem. Tidskr.* 49 318 (1937).

Francis Haxo, *Arch. Biochem.* 20 400 (1949).

P. Karrer, C. H. Eugster and E. Tobler, *Helv. Chim. Acta* 33 1349 (1950). (Synthesis)

T. W. Goodwin, *Ann. Rev. Biochem.* 24 497 (1955).

Synnove Liaaen Jensen, Germaine Cohen-Bazire, T. O. M. Nakayama and R. Y. Stanier, *Biochim. et Biophys. Acta* 29 477 (1958).

169 **Rhodopin,** $C_{40}H_{56}O$, violet-red needles, m.p. 168° (171°), U.V. 440, 470, 501 mμ in light petroleum.

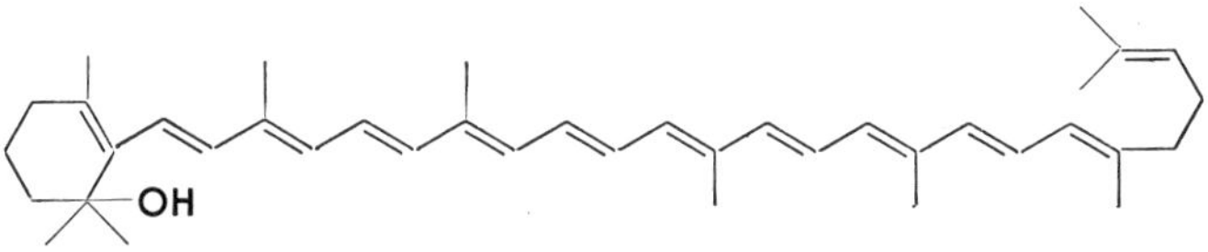

Polystigma rubrum
Edgar Lederer, *Bull. soc. chim. biol.* **20** 611 (1938).
Synnöve Liaaen Jensen, *Acta Chem. Scand.* **13** 842 (1959). (Structure)
Paul Karrer and Ulrich Solmssen, *Helv. Chim. Acta* **18** 25, 1306 (1935); **21** 454 (1938).

170 **Rubixanthin** (3-Hydroxy-γ-carotene), $C_{40}H_{56}O$, coppery red needles, m.p. 160°, U.V. 432, 462, 494 mμ in hexane.

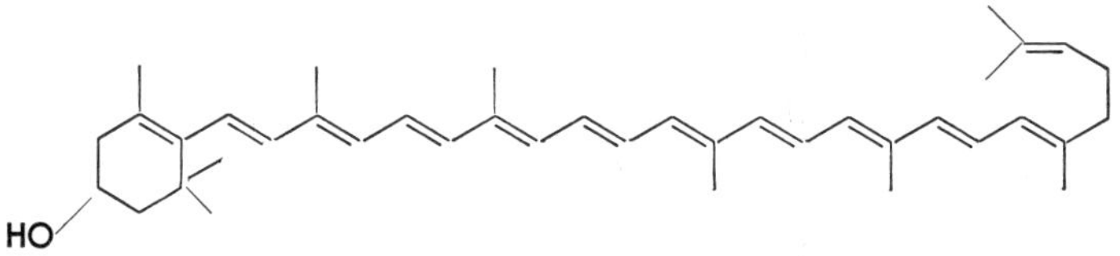

Staphylococcus aureus, Coleosporium senecionis, Micrococcus tetragenus
E. Lederer, *Bull. soc. chim. biol.* **20** 611 (1938).
Ben Sobin and Grant L. Stahly, *J. Bacteriol.* **44** 265 (1942).
H. A. Reimann and C. M. Eklund, *J. Bact.* **42** 605 (1941).
Richard Kuhn and Christoph Grundmann, *Ber.* **67** 339 (1934).

171 **Cryptoxanthin** (Cryptoxanthol, 3- or 4-Oxy-β-carotene, $C_{40}H_{56}O$) deep red prisms, m.p. 169° (vac.), optically inactive, U.V. 425s, 450, 480 mμ in hexane.

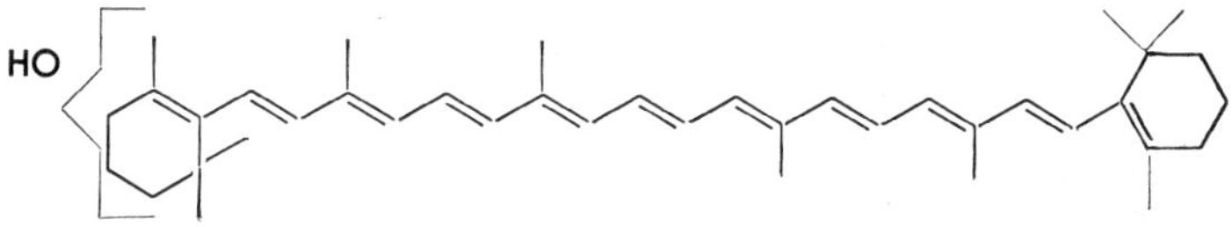

Mycobacterium phlei, Dacromyces stillatus, Vibrio adaptatus, Pseudomonas xanthochrus, P. aestumarina, Rocella montagnei

Richard Kuhn and Christoph Grundmann, *Ber.* **66** 174 (1933).

Mary A. Ingraham and Harry Steenbock, *Biochem. J.* **29** 2553 (1935).

F. P. Zscheile, J. W. White, B. W. Beadle and J. R. Roach, *Plant Physiol.* **17** 331 (1942).

T. R. Seshadry and S. S. Subramanian, *Proc. Indian Acad. Sci.* **30A** (1949).

172 **Lycophyll** (3,3'-Dihydroxylycopene), $C_{40}H_{56}O_2$, purple crystals, m.p. 179°, U.V. 444, 473, 504 mμ in petroleum ether.

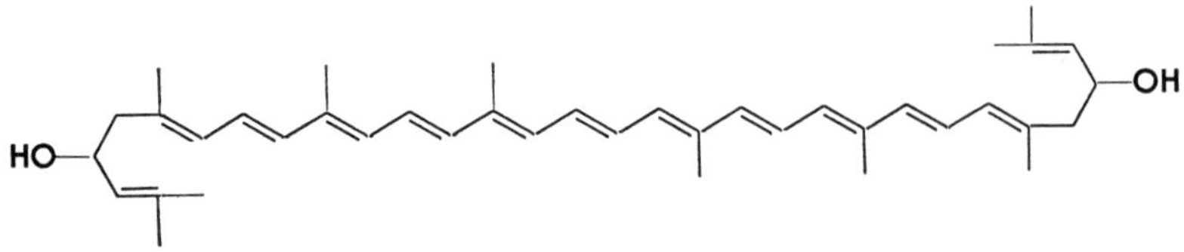

Rhodospirillum rubrum, Chromatium spp.

M. S. Barber, L. M. Jackson and B. C. L. Weedon, *Proc. Chem. Soc.,* 96 (1959). (Structure)

L. Zechmeister and L. V. Cholnoky, *Ber.* **69B** 422 (1936).

173 **Zeaxanthin** (Zeaxanthol), $C_{40}H_{56}O_2$, yellow crystals, m.p. 207° (215°), optically inactive, U.V. 451, 476 mμ in petroleum ether.

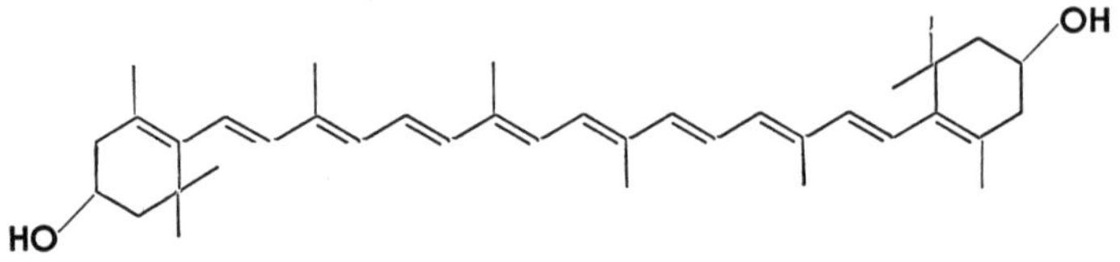

Mycobacterium phlei, Dacromyces stillatus, Staphylococcus aureus, Pseudomonas xanthochrus, P. aestumarina, Vibrio adaptatus

Erwin Chargaff and Joseph Dieryck, *Naturwissenschaften* **20** 872 (1932).

Mary A. Ingraham and Harry Steenbock, *Biochem. J.* **29** 2553 (1935).

Walter Steuer, *Zentr. Bakteriol. Parasitenk.* **167** 210 (1956).

T. W. Goodwin, *Biochem. J.* **53** 538 (1953).

174 Lutein (Xanthophyll, Luteol), $C_{40}H_{56}O_2$, yellow prisms, m.p. 190°, $[\alpha]_{cd}^{18}$ +165° (c 0.7 in benzene), U.V. 420, 446.5, 476 mμ in petroleum ether.

Mycobacterium phlei, Staphylococcus aureus, Sarcina lutea, Micrococcus lysodeikticus
Erwin Chargaff, *Compt. rend.* 197 946 (1933).
Mary A. Ingraham and Harry Steenbock, *Biochem. J.* 29 2553 (1935).
Tatsuo Ohta, *J. Pharm. Soc. Japan* 71 1319 (1951). (Isolation)
A. R. Gilby and A. V. Few, *Nature* 182 55 (1958).

175 Neurosporene (6,7,6',7'-Tetrahydrolycopene), $C_{40}H_{60}$, yellow-orange or yellow-brown crystals, m.p. 124°, U.V. 414, 438.5, 469 mμ in petroleum ether.

Neurospora crassa, Rhodotorula rubra, etc.
Neurosporene and hydroxylated neurosporenes are probable intermediates in the biogenesis of other carotenoids occurring in microorganisms.
J. Bonner, A. Sandoval, W. Tang and L. Zechmeister, *Arch. Biochem.* 10 113 (1946).
Francis Haxo, *ibid.* 20 400 (1949).
L. Zechmeister and B. Kenneth Koe, *J. Am. Chem. Soc.* 76 2923 (1954).
Synnöve Liaaen Jensen, Germaine Cohen-Bazire, T. O. M. Nakayama and R. Y. Stanier, *Biochim. et Biophys. Acta* 29 477 (1958).

176 η-Carotene, $C_{40}H_{64}$, probably has not been entirely purified, U.V. 376 (380), 396 (404), 418 (424), 450.

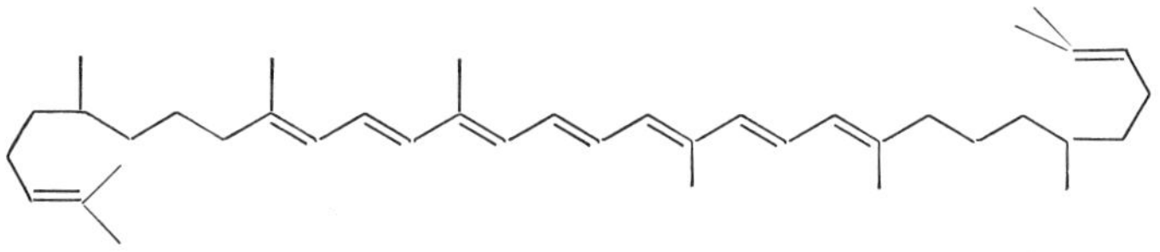

Phycomyces blakesleeanus, Neurospora crassa (mutants), Dacromyces stillatus
H. A. Nash and F. P. Zscheile, Arch. Biochem. 7 305 (1945).
T. W. Goodwin, "Carotenoids," Chemical Publishing Co., Inc., New York, N. Y. 1954, p. 108, etc.
G. MacKinney, C. O. Chichester and Patricia S. Wong, Arch. Biochem. and Biophys. 53 480 (1954).

177 **Phytoene** (7,8,11,12,12′,11′,8′,7′-Octahydrolycopene), $C_{40}H_{64}$, colorless, viscous oil with a strong fluorescence in ultraviolet light, U.V. 275s, 283, 295s in isooctane.

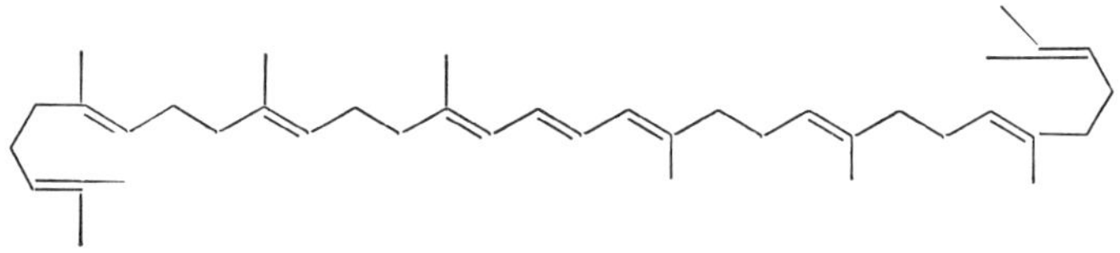

Mycobacterium phlei, Rhodopseudomonas spheroides (mutant), Rhodospirillum rubrum
J. W. Porter and F. P. Zscheile, Arch. Biochem. and Biophys. 10 537 (1946).
W. J. Rabourn and F. W. Quackenbush, Arch. Biochem. and Biophys. 61 111 (1956). (Structure)
T. W. Goodwin, and Malini Jamikorn, Biochem. J. 62 269 (1956).

178 **Phytofluene** (5,6,7,8,9,10,10′,9′,8′,7′,6′,5′-Dodecahydrolycopene), $C_{40}H_{68}$, colorless, viscous oil with a strong fluorescence in ultraviolet light, U.V. 332, 347, 367 mμ in petroleum ether.

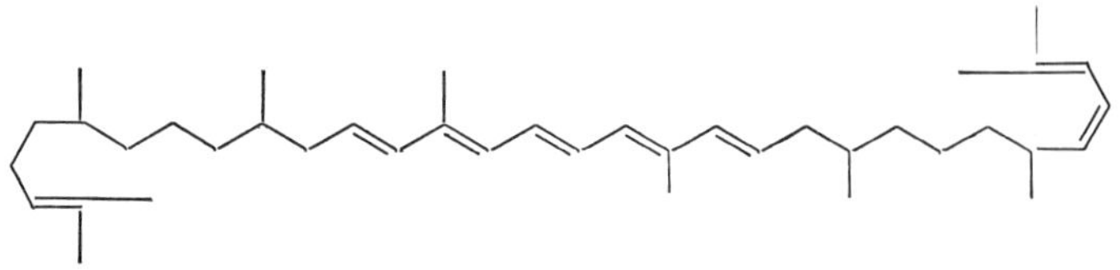

Neurospora crassa, N. sitophila, Mycobacterium phlei, Phycomyces blakesleeanus, etc.

Phytofluene probably occurs widely among microorganisms. It is a probable precursor of many of the carotene pigments.

L. Zechmeister and F. Haxo, *Arch. Biochem.* 11 539 (1946). (Isolation from neurospora)

L. Zechmeister, *Experientia* 10 1 (1954). (Structure)

179 **P-481,$C_{41}H_{58}O$,** U.V. 455, 482, 514 mμ in petroleum ether. Tentative structure:

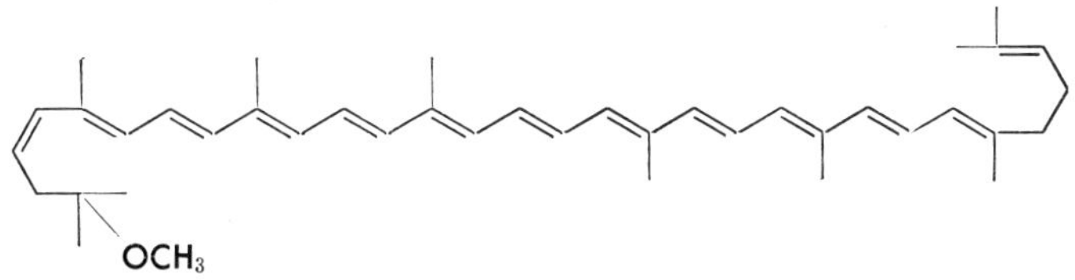

Rhodospirillum rubrum, Chromatium spp.

M. S. Barber, L. M. Jackson and B. C. L. Weedon, *Proc. Chem. Soc.,* 96 (1959). (Structure)

Synnöve Liaaen Jensen, *Acta Chem. Scand.* 12 1698 (1958).

180 **Hydroxy-P-481** (May = Rhodovibrin), $C_{41}H_{58}O_2$, U.V. 455, 482, 515 mμ in petroleum ether. Tentative structure:

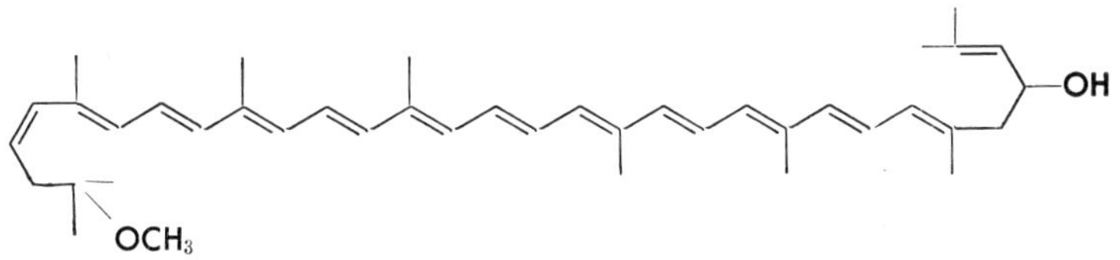

Rhodospirillum rubrum, Chromatium spp.

M. S. Barber, L. M. Jackson and B. C. L. Weedon, *Proc. Chem. Soc.,* 96 (1959).

Synnöve Liaaen Jensen, *Acta Chem. Scand.* 12 1698 (1958).

181 **Hydroxyspirilloxanthin** (May = Bacteriopurpurin, Bacterioerythrin) $C_{41}H_{58}O_2$, U.V. 489, 523 mμ in petroleum ether. Tentative structure:

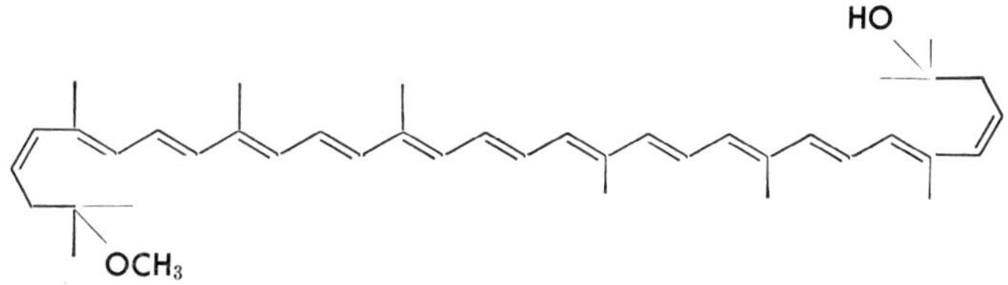

Rhodospirillum rubrum, Chromatium spp.

M. S. Barber, L. M. Jackson and B. C. L. Weedon, *Proc. Chem. Soc.*, 96 (1959).

182 Pigment R (Spheroidenone), $C_{41}H_{58}O_2$, red crystals, m.p. 155.5–158°, U.V. 460 (455), 482 (487), 513 (516.5) mμ in light petroleum.

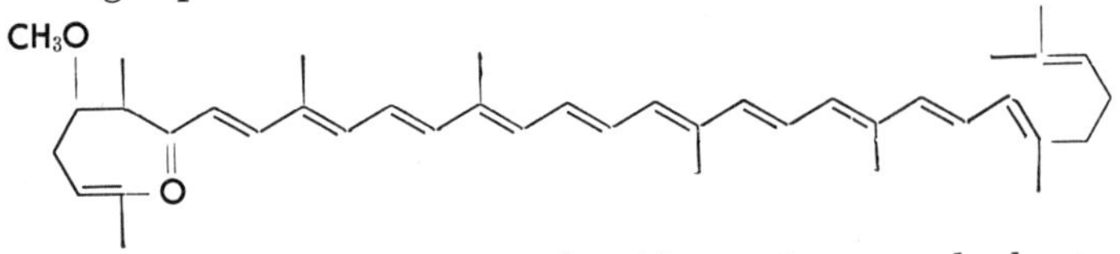

CH₃O

O

Rhodopseudomonas spheroides, other purple bacteria
C. B. Van Niel, *Antonie Van Leeuwenhoek J. Microbiol. Serol. Jubilee Vol. Albert J. Kluyver* 12 156 (1947). (Isolation)
T. W. Goodwin, D. G. Land and M. E. Sissins, *Biochem. J.* 64 486 (1956). (Structure)

183 Pigment Y, $C_{41}H_{60}O$, yellow unstable crystals, m.p. 116–135° (dec.). Stable in solution. U.V. 426.5, 452 (454), 484 (486) mμ in petroleum ether.

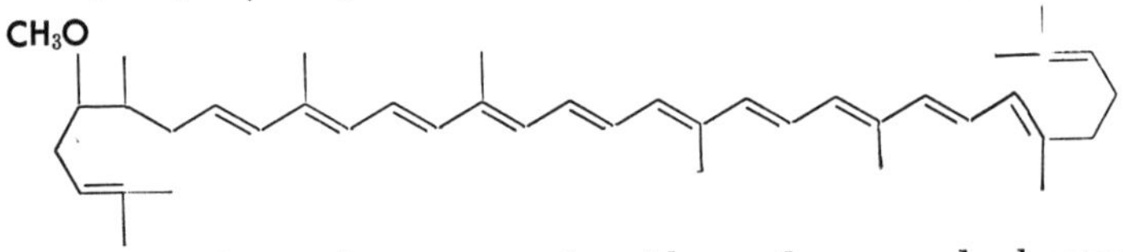

CH₃O

Rhodopseudomonas spheroides, other purple bacteria
A hydroxylated pigment Y was produced in the same fermentation, but could not be crystallized.
C. B. Van Niel, *Antonie Van Leeuwenhoek J. Microbiol. Serol. Jubilee Vol. Albert J. Kluyver* 12 156 (1947). (Isolation)
T. W. Goodwin, D. G. Land and M. E. Sissins, *Biochem. J.* 64 486 (1956). (Structure)
Synnöve Liaaen Jensen, *Acta Chem. Scand.* 12 1698 (1958).

184 Spirilloxanthin (Rhodoviolascin), $C_{42}H_{60}O_2$, violet spindle-form crystals, m.p. 218°, U.V. 464, 491, 524 mμ in petroleum ether.

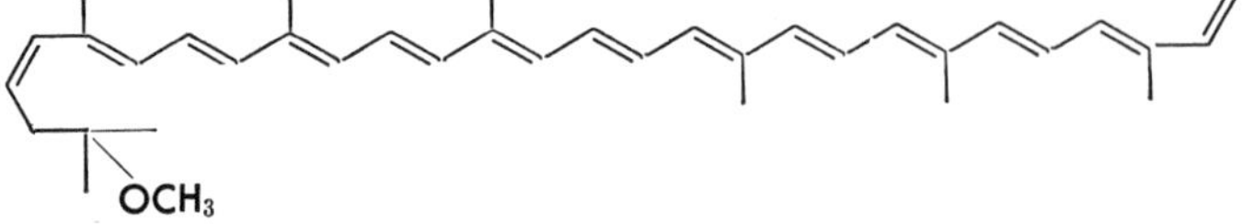

CH₃O

OCH₃

Rhodospirillum rubrum, other purple bacteria, *Neurospora crassa* (mutants), *Chromatium* spp.

P. Karrer and U. Solmssen, *Helv. Chim. Acta* **18** 1306 (1935).

C. B. Van Niel and James H. C. Smith, *Arch. Mikrobiol.* **6** 219 (1935). (Isolation)

A. Polgar, C. B. Van Niel and L. Zechmeister, *Arch. Biochem.* **5** 243 (1944).

Synnöve Liaaen Jensen, Germaine Cohen-Bazire, T. O. M. Nakayama and R. Y. Stanier, *Biochim. et Biophys. Acta* **29** 477 (1958). (Synthesis)

M. S. Barber, L. M. Jackson and B. C. L. Weedon, *Proc. Chem. Soc.*, 96 (1959).

185 Torulene, $C_{42}H_{60}O_2$, dark red crystals, m.p. 185°, U.V. 460, 486, 519 mμ in petroleum ether.

Tentative structure:

Rhodotorula rubra

Occurs together with β-carotene, torularhodin and an unstable, uncharacterized carotene.

Edgar Lederer, *Bull. soc. chim. biol.* **20** 611 (1938).

J. Bonner, A. Sandoval, W. Tang and L. Zechmeister, *Arch. Biochem.* **10** 113 (1946).

186 Sarcinaxanthin, yellow crystals, m.p. 149°, U.V. 415, 440, 469 mμ in petroleum ether.

About 3.4 mg. of this mono-hydroxy xanthophyll were obtained from 385 g. of dried *Sarcina lutea* cells. It is also produced by *Flavobacterium marinotypicum* and by *Staphylococcus citreus.*

A closely related hydrocarbon, sarcinene, occurs in all these species as well as in *Flavobacterium sulfureum.*

Yoshiharu Takeda and Tatuo Ota, *Z. physiol. Chem.* **268** 1 (1941). (Isolation)

Doris P. Courington and T. W. Goodwin, *J. Bacteriol.* **70** 568 (1955).

Tatsuo Ohta, Toshio Miyazaki and Teruo Minomiya, *Chem. Pharm. Bull.* **7** 254 (1959).

187 **Neurosporaxanthin,** dark grayish purple leaflets, m.p. 192° (vac.), U.V. 472 mμ in hexane (486 mμ in benzene).

An uncharacterized carotenoid which gives yellow solutions and a red color adsorbed on sucrose.

Neurospora crassa

Marko Zalokar, *Arch. Biochem. and Biophys.* **70** 568 (1957). (Isolation)

188 **Leprotene** (Leprotin), coppery red needles, m.p. 197°, U.V. 429, 452, 479 mμ in petroleum ether.

The principal carotene of *Mycobacterium phlei* and other mycobacteria. It contains no ionone rings and does not function as a provitamin A.

Yoshiharu Takeda and Tatsuo Ohta, *J. Biochem.* Japan **36** 535 (1944). (Isolation)

Tatsuo Ohta, *J. Pharm. Soc. Japan* **71** 462 (1951).

189 **Mycoxanthin,** U.V. 385, 406, 430 mμ in petroleum ether.

A new yellow carotenoid with a relatively short chromophore.

Mycobacterium phlei, M. marianum, M. battaglini

Aldo Gaudiano, *Atti. accad. nazl. Lincei, Rend., Classe sci. fis., mat. e nat.* **21** 308 (1956). (*Chem. Abstr.* **51** 8876 f) (Isolation)

6

Polyenes and Polyynes,

Excluding Polyene Macrolides

The polyenes of this section somewhat resemble crocetin, bixin and the carotenes in their long systems of conjugated double bonds with the resultant color and other physical properties, but they lack the isoprenoid structure.

The acetylenic compounds often occur in low yields and in complex mixtures. While generally colorless, they are conspicuous by their strong and characteristic ultraviolet absorption spectra. Many of them are unstable.

From the examples reported to date it seems that basidiomycetes are the principal producers of such metabolites among microorganisms, although such substances occur widely in higher plants. That lower fungi are capable of forming polyenes is demonstrated, however, by the side-chains of metabolites classified elsewhere, for example fumagillin, sorbicillin and auroglaucin:

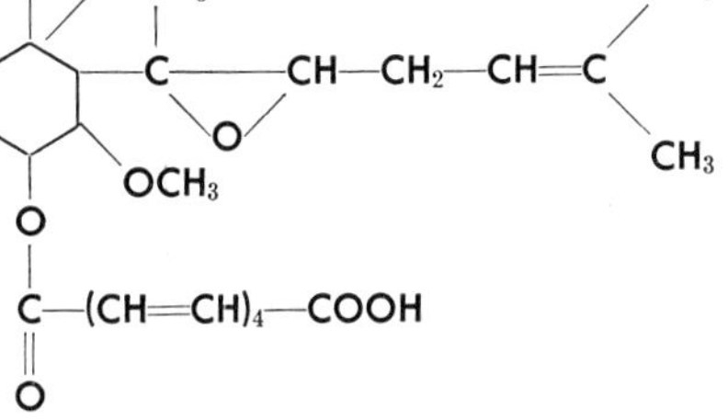

Fumagillin

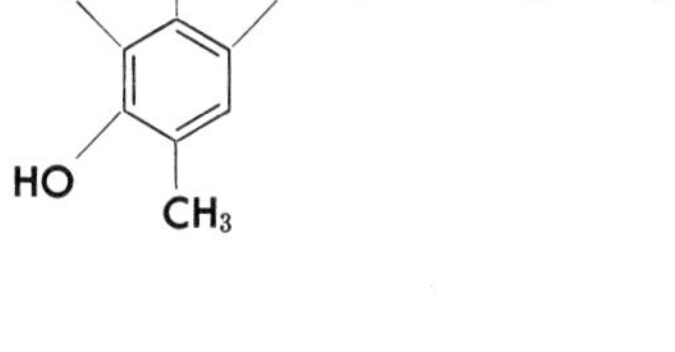

Sorbicillin

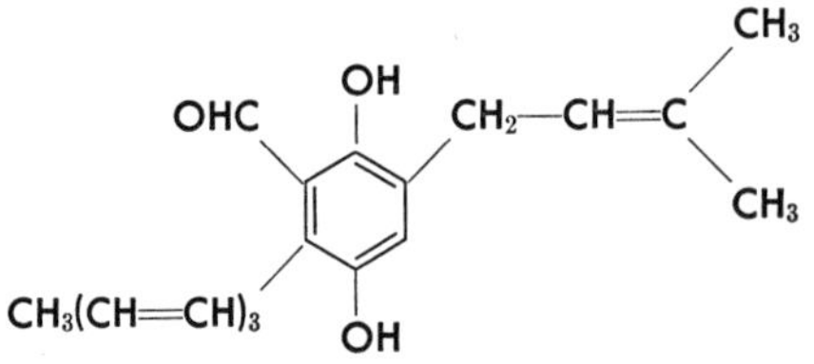

Auroglaucin

It is likely that both polyenes and polyynes are acetate-derived. It has been demonstrated[1] that nemotinic acid with 11 carbon atoms is formed from 6 moles of an acetic acid derivative, with head to tail linkage and elimination of the terminal methyl group.

$$HC\equiv C-C\equiv C-CH=C=CH-CH-CH_2-CH_2-COOH$$
$$\underset{\displaystyle OH}{|}$$

Nemotinic Acid

$$CH_3-C\equiv C-C\equiv C-CH=C=CH-CH-CH_2-CH_2-COOH$$
$$\underset{\displaystyle OH}{|}$$

Odyssic Acid

Odyssic acid was presumed to be formed similarly, but with terminal methyl group retention.

In the examples available the acetylenic acids with an odd number of carbon atoms terminate in an acetylenic bond. This seems to indicate elimination of the terminal methyl group by oxidation and decarboxylation. It is interesting to note that the reverse process has been demonstrated in the conversion of propynoic acid to acetylenedicarboxylic acid by a soil isolate.[2]

$$CO_2 + HC\equiv C-COOH \rightarrow HOOC-C\equiv C-COOH$$

The xyloside of nemotinic acid also has been isolated.[3] When isolated from a culture grown on glucose with $1\text{-}C^{14}$-labeled acetic acid added to the medium, labeling is found in the polyacetylenes but not in the xylose moiety. When isolated from

[1] J. D. Bu'Lock and H. Gregory, *Biochem. J.* 72 322 (1959).
[2] Akira Hanaoka, Tokuya Harada and Takeo Takizawa, *J. Agr. Chem. Soc. Japan* 26 151 (1952).
[3] J. D. Bu'Lock and H. Gregory, *Experientia* 15 420 (1959).

$$HC\equiv C-C\equiv C-CH=C-CH-CH-CH_2-CH_2-COOH$$

a culture grown on ethanol with 1-C^{14}-labeled acetic acid added to the medium, labeling was found in the xylose as well as in the acetylenic acid. It was assumed that in the latter case, where the molecule was synthesized entirely from C_2 units, the xylose was produced by way of intermediates closely related to glucose. Glucose itself acted as the xylose precursor, then, in the first experiment. A closer analysis of the labeling pattern of the xylose moiety led to the suggestion that the pentose was formed from glucose by way of glucuronic acid followed by decarboxylation.

Many of the acetylenic acids have antibiotic properties.

A review of polyacetylenes was published recently.[4]

About a dozen more compounds of this type are listed in the addendum.

190   **Agrocybin,** $C_8H_5O_2N$, unstable compound white crystals, darkening in air, m.p. 130–140° (dec. explosively), U.V. 216, 224, 269, 286, 304, 325 mμ in 95% ethanol.

$$HOCH_2-C\equiv C-C\equiv C-C\equiv C-CONH_2$$

Agrocybe dura

Marjorie Anchel, *J. Am. Chem. Soc.* 74 1588 (1952).

J. D. Bu'Lock, E. R. H. Jones, G. H. Mansfield, J. W. Thompson and M. C. Whiting, *Chem. and Ind.,* 990 (1954). (Structure)

P. J. Ashworth, E. R. H. Jones, G. H. Mansfield, K. Schlögl, J. M. Thompson, M. C. Whiting, *J. Chem. Soc.,* 950 (1958). (Synthesis)

191   **Diatretyne 1,** $C_8H_5O_3N$, unstable crystals, m.p. 198° (dec. explosively), U.V. 223, 260, 275, 290, 309 mμ in 95% ethanol.

$$HOOC-CH=CH-C\equiv C-C\equiv C-CONH_2$$

and

---

[4] E. R. H. Jones, *Proc. Chem. Soc.,* 199–211 (1960).

192 **Diatretyne 2** (Nudic Acid B), $C_8H_3O_2N$, short colorless needles, m.p. 179° (dec.), U.V. 228, 238, 268, 283, 299, 322 mμ in 95% ethanol.

$$HOOC—CH{=}CH—C{\equiv}C—C{\equiv}C—C{\equiv}N$$

Clitocybe diatreta
Marjorie Anchel, *J. Am. Chem. Soc.* 74 1588 (1952).
Idem., ibid. 75 4621 (1953).
Idem. Science 121 607 (1955). (Structure)
P. J. Ashworth, E. R. H. Jones, G. H. Mansfield, K. Schlögl, J. M. Thompson and M. C. Whiting, *J. Chem. Soc.,* 950 (1958). (Synthesis)

193 *trans*-**Non-2-ene-4,6,8-triyn-1-al,** C_9H_4O, colorless needles, which rapidly decompose in light at room temperature. U.V. 210.5 (220), 228, 240, 257, 271, 287, 306, 327 mμ in ethanol.

$$HC{\equiv}C—C{\equiv}C—C{\equiv}C—CH{=}CH—CHO$$

Coprinus quadrifidus
Six related compounds occurred in the same culture.
E. R. H. Jones and J. S. Stephenson, *J. Chem. Soc.,* 2197 (1959).

194 *trans*-**Non-2-ene-4,6,8-triyn-1-ol,** C_9H_6O, colorless crystals, decomposing at ordinary conditions, U.V. 233, 243, 255, 283, 300, 320 mμ in hexane.

$$HC{\equiv}C—C{\equiv}C—C{\equiv}C—CH{=}CH—CH_2OH$$

Coprinus quadrifidus
E. R. H. Jones and J. S. Stephenson, *J. Chem. Soc.,* 2197 (1959).

195 **(2d,3d)-Nona-4,6,8-triyn-1,2,3-triol,** $C_9H_8O_3$, colorless crystals (dec.) $\sim$40°, $[\alpha]_D$ +6° (c 0.82 in ethanol), U.V. 208, 254, 269.5, 286.5, 305 mμ in ethanol.

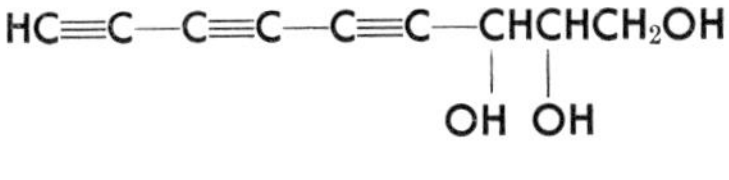

$$HC{\equiv}C—C{\equiv}C—C{\equiv}C—\underset{\underset{\displaystyle OH}{|}}{C}H\underset{\underset{\displaystyle OH}{|}}{C}HCH_2OH$$

Coprinus quadrifidus
E. R. H. Jones and J. S. Stephenson, *J. Chem. Soc.,* 2197 (1959).

196 **Biformin,** highly unstable crystals.

    Probably a straight-chain, nine carbon atom glycol, containing two acetylenic and two ethylenic bonds in conjugation.

Polyporus biformis

A similar substance, biforminic acid, occurred in the same culture.

William J. Robbins, Frederick Kavanagh and Annette Hervey, *Proc. Nat. Acad. Sci.* **33** 176 (1947).

Marjorie Anchel and Marvin P. Cohen, *J. Biol. Chem.* **208** 319 (1954).

197 *trans*-**Dec-2-ene-4,6,8-triyn-1-al,** $C_{10}H_6O$, pale yellow needles, m.p. 108°, U.V. (225) (234.5), 245.5, 258 (272), 288, 306, 326, 350, mμ in hexane.

$$CH_3-C{\equiv}C-C{\equiv}C-C{\equiv}C-CH{=}CH-CHO$$

Pleurotus ulmarius

J. N. Gardner, E. R. H. Jones, P. R. Leeming and J. S. Stephenson, *J. Chem. Soc.,* 691 (1960).

198 **Diatretyne-3** (*trans*-10-Hydroxydec-2-ene-4,6,8-triynoic Acid), $C_{10}H_6O_3$, nearly colorless rods from ethyl acetate, rapidly becoming coated with blue-green polymer, U.V. 253, 280, 297, 316, 339 mμ.

$$HOCH_2-C{\equiv}C-C{\equiv}C-C{\equiv}C-CH{=}CH-COOH$$

Clitocybe diatreta

The author noted the similarity to the antibiotic principle of the royal jelly of bees:

trans

$$HOCH_2CH_2CH_2CH_2CH_2CH_2CH_2-CH{=}CH-COOH$$

Helen Flon and Marjorie Anchel, *Arch. Biochem. and Biophys.* **78** 111 (1958).

Marjorie Anchel, *Arch. Biochem. and Biophys.* **85** 569 (1959).

199 **Deca-*trans*-2,*trans*-8-diene-4,6-diyne-1,10-dioic** Acid, $C_{10}H_6O_4$, amorphous powder, m.p. (dec.) ~200°, U.V. 216 (258), 267, 296, 315, 338 mμ in ethanol.

$$HOOC-CH{=}CH-C{\equiv}C-C{\equiv}C-CH{=}CH-COOH$$

Polyporus anthracophilus

J. D. Bu'Lock, E. R. H. Jones and W. B. Turner, *J. Chem. Soc.*, 1607 (1957).

200 **Marasin** [(-)-Nona-3,4-diene-6,8-diyne-1-ol], $C_{10}H_8O$, unstable oily substance, polymerized spontaneously, $[\alpha]_D^{25}$ about $-325°$ (c 0.2).

$$HC \equiv C - C \equiv C - CH = C = CH - CH_2 - CH_2 - OH$$

Marasmius ramealis
Gerd Benz, *Arkiv for Kemi* 14 305 (1959).

201 *trans*-Dec-2-ene-4,6,8-triyn-1,10-diol, $C_{10}H_8O_2$, colorless needles, (dec.) 138°, U.V. 205, 212, 231, 243.5, 259, 279, 290.5, 309.5, 330.5 mμ in ethanol.

$$HOCH_2 - C \equiv C - C \equiv C - C \equiv C - CH = CH - CH_2OH$$

Coprinus quadrifidus
E. R. H. Jones and J. S. Stephenson, *J. Chem. Soc.*, 2197 (1959).

202 *trans,trans*-Matricaria Acid, $C_{10}H_8O_2$, colorless plates, m.p. 175° (dec.), U.V. 245, 256, 310, 329 mμ in ethanol.

$$CH_3 - CH = CH - C \equiv C - C \equiv C - CH = CH - COOH$$

Polyporus anthracophilus
J. D. Bu'Lock, E. R. H. Jones and W. B. Turner, *J. Chem. Soc.*, 1607 (1957).

203 *trans,trans*-Matricarianol, $C_{10}H_{10}O$, colorless needles, m.p. 105.5°, U.V. 217.5, 231.5, 237, 247, 261, 276, 293, 312 mμ in ethanol.

$$CH_3 - CH = CH - C \equiv C - C \equiv C - CH = CH - CH_2OH$$

Polyporus anthracophilus
J. D. Bu'Lock, E. R. H. Jones and W. B. Turner, *J. Chem. Soc.*, 1607 (1957).

204 **Deca-*cis*-2-*trans*-8-diene-4,6-diyn-1-ol,** $C_{10}H_{10}O$, m.p. <20°, U.V. 213.5, 230, 237.5, 246.5, 261.5, 276.5, 293.5, 312.5 mμ.

$$CH_3 - CH = CH - C \equiv C - C \equiv C - CH = CH - CH_2OH$$

Polyporus guttalatus
J. N. Gardner, E. R. H. Jones, P. R. Leeming and J. S. Stephenson, *J. Chem. Soc.*, 691 (1960).

205 10-Hydroxydec-*trans*-2-ene-4,6-diynoic Acid, $C_{10}H_{10}O_3$, colorless plates, m.p. 154.5°, U.V. 215, 222 (243) (225), 270, 285, 303 mμ in ethanol.

$$HOCH_2-CH_2-CH_2-C{\equiv}C-C{\equiv}C-CH{=}CH-COOH$$

Polyporus anthracophilus
J. D. Bu'Lock, E. R. H. Jones and W. B. Turner, J. *Chem. Soc.*, 1607 (1957).

206 Dimethyl Octa-*trans*-2,*trans*-6-dien-4-yne-1,8-dioate, $C_{10}H_{10}O_4$, colorless plates, m.p. 117–119.5°, U.V. (205), 214 (240) (278), 292, 307 mμ in ethanol.

$$CH_3OOC-CH{=}CH-C{\equiv}C-CH{=}CH-COOCH_3$$

Polyporus anthracophilus
J. D. Bu'Lock, E. R. H. Jones and W. B. Turner, J. *Chem. Soc.*, 1607 (1957).

207 Undec-3,5,6-triene-8,10-diynoic Acid, $C_{11}H_8O_2$.

$$HC{\equiv}C-C{\equiv}C-CH{=}C{=}CH-CH{=}CH-CH_2-COOH$$

Drosophila semivestita
Marjorie Anchel, *Science* 126 1229 (1957).

208 Nemotin, $C_{11}H_8O_2$, unstable except in solutions, $[\alpha]_D^{17}$ +380° (c 0.3 in ether), U.V. 207, 236, 248, 262, 276 mμ in water.

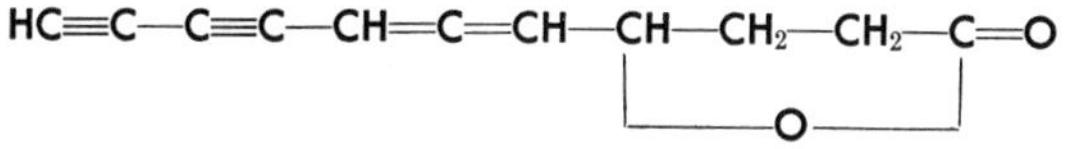

$$HC{\equiv}C-C{\equiv}C-CH{=}C{=}CH-CH-CH_2-CH_2-C{=}O$$
(with ring: CH—...—C=O closed through —O—)

and

209 Nemotinic Acid, $C_{11}H_{10}O_3$, unstable except in solutions, $[\alpha]_D^{17}$ +320° (c 0.2 in ether), U.V. 208, 237, 249, 263, 277 mμ in water.

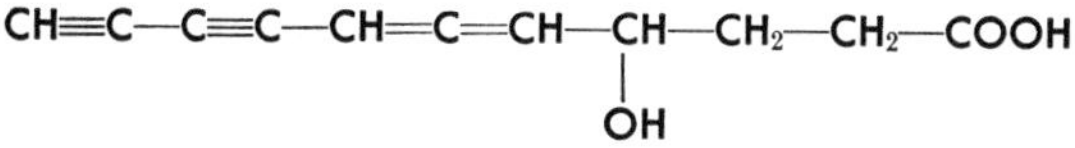

$$CH{\equiv}C-C{\equiv}C-CH{=}C{=}CH-CH-CH_2-CH_2-COOH$$
$$\overset{|}{\underset{OH}{}}$$

Poria corticola, *P. tenuis* and another unidentified basidiomycete
Yields of mixed acetylenes from one of the fungi were:

TABLE I

Compound	Concentration in the medium (mg. per liter)	Per cent of total
Nemotinic Acid.........	110	67.5
Nemotin...............	14	8.5
Odyssic Acid..........	34	21
Odyssin...............	5	3

J. D. Bu'Lock, E. R. H. Jones and P. R. Leeming, *J. Chem. Soc.*, 4270 (1955). (Structure)

210 **Methyl** *trans*-**10-Hydroxydec-2-ene-4,6,8-triyn-1-oate,** $C_{11}H_8O_3$, needles (dec. ~115°), U.V. 245, 256.5, 283, 301, 320.5, 343.5 mμ in carbon tetrachloride.

$$HOCH_2—C{\equiv}C—C{\equiv}C—C{\equiv}C—CH{=}CH—COOCH_3$$

Pleurotus ulmarius, Merulius lachrymans
J. N. Gardner, E. R. H. Jones, P. R. Leeming and J. S. Stephenson, *J. Chem. Soc.*, 691 (1960).

211 *trans,trans*-**Matricaria Ester,** $C_{11}H_{10}O_2$, colorless needles, m.p. 62°, U.V. (234), 246, 258 (296), 314, 333 mμ in ethanol.

$$CH_3—CH{=}CH—C{\equiv}C—C{\equiv}C—CH{=}CH—COOCH_3$$

Polyporus anthracophilus
J. D. Bu'Lock, E. R. H. Jones and W. B. Turner, *J. Chem. Soc.*, 1607 (1957).

212 **Methyl 10-Hydroxydec-***trans***-2-ene-4,6-diynoate,** $C_{11}H_{12}O_3$, nearly colorless oil, U.V. 215, 223 (243), 258, 273, 287, 305 mμ in ethanol.

$$HOCH_2—CH_2—CH_2—C{\equiv}C—C{\equiv}C—CH{=}CH—COOCH_3$$

Polyporus anthracophilus, Merulius lachrymans
J. D. Bu'Lock, E. R. H. Jones and W. B. Turner, *J. Chem. Soc.*, 1607 (1957).

213 **Odyssin,** $C_{12}H_{10}O_2$, unstable except in solutions, $[\alpha]_D^{20}$ +360° (c 0.2 in ethanol), U.V. 210, 237.5, 250, 264, 280 mμ.

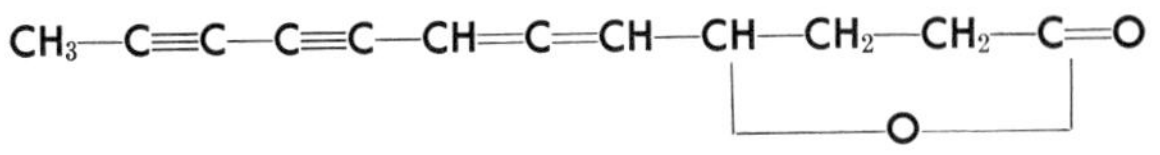

$$CH_3—C{\equiv}C—C{\equiv}C—CH{=}C{=}CH—CH—CH_2—CH_2—C{=}O$$

and

214 Odyssic Acid, $C_{12}H_{12}O_3$, unstable except in solutions, $[\alpha]_D^{20}$ $+300°$ (c 0.25 in ethanol), U.V. 211, 238, 250.5, 265, 280.5 mμ.

$$CH_3-C\equiv C-C\equiv C-CH=C=CH-CH-CH_2-CH_2-COOH$$
$$|$$
$$OH$$

Poria corticola, P. tenuis
J. D. Bu'Lock, E. R. H. Jones and W. B. Turner, *J. Chem. Soc.*, 1607 (1957).

215 Dimethyl Deca-2,4,6-triyne-1,10-dioate, $C_{12}H_{10}O_4$, colorless needles, m.p. 45°, U.V. 209, 217, 226, 257, 272, 288, 307, 329 mμ in carbon tetrachloride.

$$CH_3OOC-C\equiv C-C\equiv C-C\equiv C-CH_2-CH_2-COOCH_3$$

Merulius lachrymans
J. N. Gardner, E. R. H. Jones, P. R. Leeming and J. S. Stephenson, *J. Chem. Soc.*, 691 (1960).

216 Dimethyl Deca-*trans*-2,*trans*-8-diene-4,6-diyne-1,10-dioate, $C_{12}H_{10}O_4$, colorless plates, m.p. 104.5–107.5°, U.V. 216, 269, 298, 317, 339 mμ in ethanol.

$$CH_3OOC-CH=CH-C\equiv C-C\equiv C-CH=CH-COOCH_3$$

Polyporus anthracophilus
J. D. Bu'Lock, E. R. H. Jones and W. B. Turner, *J. Chem. Soc.*, 1607 (1957).

217 Dimethyl Dec-*trans*-2-ene-4,6-diyne-1,10-dioate, $C_{12}H_{12}O_4$, colorless crystals, m.p. 56.5–58°, U.V. 214.5, 223 (243) (255), 270, 285, 303 mμ in ethanol.

$$CH_3OOC-CH_2-CH_2-C\equiv C-C\equiv C-CH=CH-COOCH_3$$

Polyporus anthracophilus
J. D. Bu'Lock, E. R. H. Jones and W. B. Turner, *J. Chem. Soc.*, 1607 (1957).

218 Mycomycin, $C_{13}H_{10}O_2$, colorless needles, m.p. 75° (dec. explosively), $[\alpha]_D^{25}$ $-130°$ (c 0.4 in ethanol), U.V. 256, 267, 281 mμ in diethyl ether.

$$HC\equiv C-C\equiv C-CH=C=CH-CH=CH-CH=CH-CH_2-COOH$$

Nocardia acidophilus
Walter D. Celmer and I. A. Solomons, *J. Am. Chem. Soc.* 74 1870, 3838 (1952). (Structure)
Edwin A. Johnson and Kenneth L. Burdon, *J. Bacteriol.* 54 281 (1947).

219 **Corticrocin,** $C_{14}H_{14}O_4$, orange-red, amorphous powder or yellow needles and prisms, m.p. subl. 270°, m. 317° (sealed tube), U.V. 374, 393, 416 mμ in ethanol.

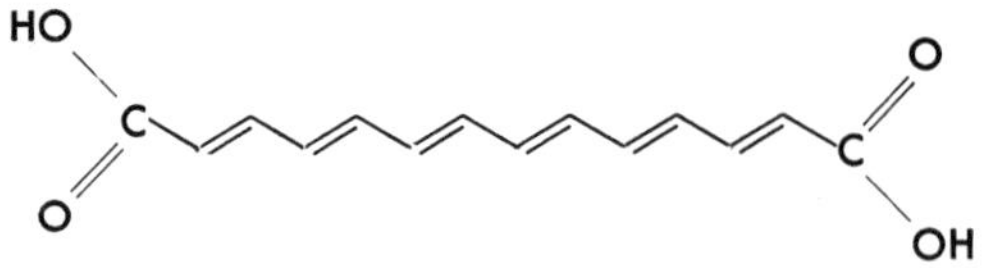

Corticeum croceum Bres. (= *Corticium sulfureum* (Fr.) Fr.)

Yields of about 4% of the mycorrhizal weight have been reported.

Holger Erdtman, *Acta Chem. Scand.* 2 209 (1948). (Isolation and Structure)

B. L. Shaw and M. C. Whiting, *J. Chem. Soc.*, 3217 (1954). (Synthesis)

B. C. L. Weedon, *ibid.* 4168 (1954). (Synthesis)

220 **Nemotinic Acid Xyloside,** $C_{18}H_{18}O_7$, $[\alpha]_D^{25}$ +237° (c 0.1 ethanol).

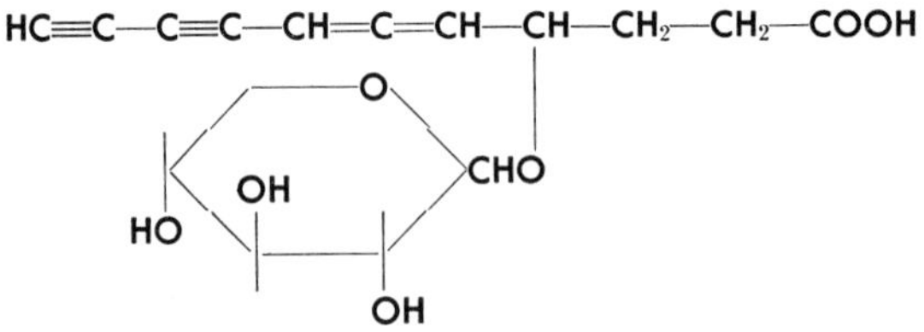

Basidiomycete B-841

J. D. Bu'Lock and H. Gregory, *Experientia* 15 420 (1959).

221 **Deca-*trans*-2-*trans*-8-diene-4,6-diynyl Deca-*trans*-2,*trans*-8-diene-4,6-diynoate,** $C_{20}H_{16}O_2$, colorless crystals, m.p. 124–126°, U.V. 213 (233), 238.5, 246, 259, 277.5, 295, 314, 335 mμ in ethanol.

CH_3—CH=CH—C≡C—C≡C—CH=CH—COO—CH_2—CH=CH—C≡C—C≡C—
CH=CH—CH_3

Polyporus anthracophilus

J. D. Bu'Lock, E. R. H. Jones and W. B. Turner, *J. Chem. Soc.*, 1607 (1957).

222   **Methyl 10-(Deca-*trans*-2,*trans*-8-diene-4,6-diyn-1-oyloxy)-dec-*trans*-2-ene-4,6-diynoate,** $C_{21}H_{18}O_4$, colorless plates, m.p. 91–93°, U.V. 223, 246.5, 259, 287, 305, 334 mμ in ethanol.

$$CH_3-CH=CH-C\equiv C-C\equiv C-CH=CH-COO-CH_2-CH_2-CH_2-C\equiv C-C\equiv C$$
$$-CH=CH-COOCH_3$$

Polyporus anthracophilus
J. D. Bu'Lock, E. R. H. Jones and W. B. Turner, *J. Chem. Soc.*, 1607 (1957).

223   **Cortisalin,** $C_{21}H_{20}O_3$, violet-red needles, m.p. dec. >290°, U.V. (318), 345 (420), 443 (462) mμ in pyridine.

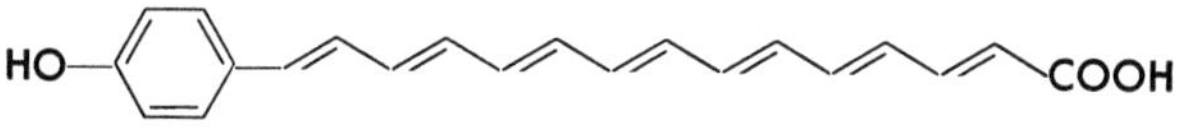

Corticium salicinum Fries
A yield of 2.6 g. of crude material was obtained from 222 g. of fungal fruiting body.
Jarl Gripenberg, *Acta Chem. Scand.* 6 580 (1952).
D. Marshall and M. C. Whiting, *J. Chem. Soc.*, 537 (1957). (Synthesis)

224   **Limocrocin,** $C_{26}H_{26}O_6N_2$, a yellow actinomycete pigment. Dark red crystals from AcOH m.p. 316° (dec.). Dimethyl ester of perhydro-deriv., fine, colorless needles, m.p. 146–147°. Partial structure:

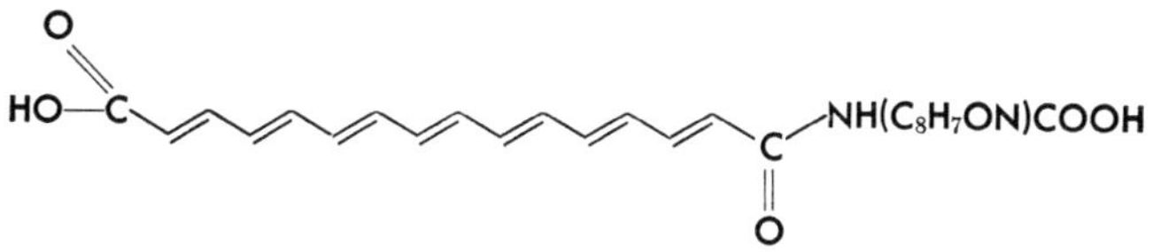

A demethylcrocetin derivative with the C_8H_7ON probably a heterobicyclic residue. Eq. wt. 225 (232).
Streptomyces limosus (Glycine-glycerol substrate)
Hans Brockmann and Hans-Ulrich May, *Chem. Ber.* 88 419 (1955).
Hans Brockmann and Gerhard Grothe, *Chem. Ber.* 86 1110 (1953).

7

Macrocyclic Lactones (Macrolides)

The macrolide (macrocyclic lactone) antibiotics are an interesting new class of compounds elaborated by members of the order actinomycetales and particularly by the genus streptomyces. The lactone moieties of these molecules resemble the partially oxidized and alkylated aliphatic acids characteristic of the related mycobacterium genus. A partial listing according to Bergey's Manual of the members of the order actinomycetales is shown below to clarify these relationships.

Order... Actinomycetales*

Families...	Actino-mycetaceae	Strepto-mycetaceae	Myco-bacteriaceae	Actino-planaceae

Genera...	Nocardia Actinomyces*	Streptomyces* Micromonospora Thermoactino-myces	Mycobacterium Mycococcus	Actinoplanes Streptosporan-gium

A resemblance to the steroid glycosides, for example strophanthin and oleandrin shown below, also has been noted.[1]

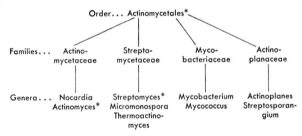

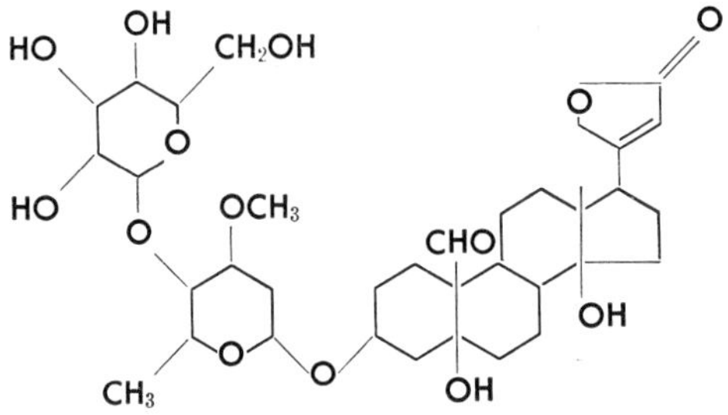

Strophanthin

---

* In the vernacular usage streptomycete-streptomyces and actinomycete may indicate either order or genus, perhaps more commonly the order.

[1] R. B. Woodward, *Festschr. Arthur Stoll.*, 524 (1957).

Oleandrin

In this regard it is striking that the sugar L-oleandrose occurs in both oleandrin and in the macrolide oleandomycin.

The macrolide antibiotics are most effective against gram-positive bacteria. In the introduction to the section on steroids and terpenoids, it was mentioned that no true steroids have ever been detected conclusively in bacteria. It was noted also that certain investigators exploring the utilization of mevalonic acid by gram-positive bacteria (especially lactobacilli) found that partially oxidized aliphatic substances with more than 15 carbon atoms were produced.[2] While these products were not thoroughly characterized, the properties as described were reminiscent of the lactone portions of the macrolides. It also has been mentioned elsewhere that the general chemical structure and metabolism of the actinomycetales seem to be more closely related to that of the bacteria than to that of the fungi, which they resemble superficially. From these premises, it is tempting to speculate that the macrolide antibiotics may interfere in some way with a primitive kind of hormonal or steroid metabolism in gram-positive bacteria. In this connection it should be noted, however, that the sugar portions of most of the known macrolide antibiotics are essential to their antibacterial activity. Tylosin and lankamycin may be exceptions.

Several of the many macrocyclic lactones which have been isolated from streptomycete cultures have been well characterized structurally. Complete structures have been reported for picromycin, methymycin, neomethymycin, erythromycin, erythromycin B, erythromycin C, carbomycin (Magnamycin), carbomycin B, oleandomycin and pimaricin. A considerable amount of information has been reported concerning the structures of narbomycin, the foromacidins (spiramycins) and the pentaenes lagosin and filipin.*

The few cases available for comparison fall into a general pattern. This involves the lactone of a long chain aliphatic

[2] E. Kodicek, Abstracts of the Gordon Conference on Vitamins and Metabolism, 1958.

* See addendum.

acid, quite evidently acetate-derived, in conjugation with one or more sugar-like moieties. These sugars are uncommon ones, and one of them is usually an amino-sugar, desosamine being particularly prevalent so far. Several of the incompletely characterized macrolides, especially those of the polyene type, have been reported to contain no nitrogen, however. Among these are lagosin, fungichromin, A-246, miamycin and filipin. One macrolide, celesticetin,* contains sulfur. Lankamycin also contains no nitrogen.

Of all the macrolides the biosynthesis of erythromycin has been investigated most thoroughly. One of the questions to be answered was whether the erythronolide moiety is derived from acetate or from propionate. A labeling and degradation study with C^{14}-containing precursors has shown that propionate or its biological equivalent is the true precursor.[3] Propionate-C-1 was incorporated only into the "methylene" carbon atoms, while propionate C-2 was incorporated largely into the tertiary carbon atoms and not at all into the carbon-bound methyl groups. Additional evidence against the acetate hypothesis was the fact that C^{14}-labeled formate or C^{14}-methyl methionine did not label the terminal three carbon atom subunit of erythronolide.

A previous study[4] had shown that C^{14}-1-labeled propionate caused labeling of erythronolide, but not of the sugars desosamine and cladinose. The reverse was true when the labeled precursor was C^{14}-methyl methionine.[5]

Other evidence which has been published suggests or is consistent with derivation of erythronolide from propionate.[6]

A notice has been published that a labeling study on the biogenesis of erythromycin is in progress with the use of propionic acid-1-C^{14}-H^3.[7]

It remains to be seen whether or not some of the less highly

[3] John W. Corcoran, Toshi Kaneda and John C. Butte, *J. Biol. Chem.* 235 pc29 (1960).

[4] Z. Vanek, J. Majer, A. Babický, J. Liebster, K. Vereš and L. Doležilová, Abstr. IVth Intern. Congr. Biochem., Vienna, 1958; *cf. Angew. Chem.* 71 40 (1959).

[5] Z. Vanek, J. Majer, J. Liebster, K. Vereš and L. Doležilová, Symposium on Antibiotics, Prague, 1959.

[6] V. Musilek and V. Ševcik, *Naturwissenschaften* 45 86 215 (1958); *idem.,* Symposium on Antibiotics, Prague, 1959.

[7] H. Grisebach, H. Achenbach and U. C. Grisebach, *Naturwissenschaften* 47 206 (1960).

* See entry 923 for non-macrolide structure.

branched lactones are derived in whole or in part from acetate.

It is obvious that in each case many modifications of the macrolide moiety have occurred from the simplest intermediate ring which could be envisaged. These include complete or partial reduction of carbonyl groups, dehydration of the corresponding secondary alcohols, epoxidation or reduction of carbon-carbon double bonds, oxidation of tertiary carbon atoms, cleavage of epoxides to glycols, etc. Yet, despite the confusing detail, the fundamental pattern of oxidation and reduction remains apparent, just as it does in many of the metabolites of the mycobacteria and corynebacteria.

It will be interesting to see how much of the information concerning the biogenesis of the macrolides can be transposed to metabolites of the mycobacteria and corynebacteria and vice versa.

In the cases of picromycin, methymycin, erythromycin, narbomycin and oleandomycin it is possible to follow the course of alternate oxidation throughout the lactone rings with remarkable regularity, the hypothetical intermediate being, apparently, a single continuous chain, unbranched except for the methyl groups. In the cases of carbomycin and pimaricin, anomalies occur. These could be explained by a junction of shorter chains, perhaps as shown below, in a manner similar to the formation of corynomycolic acid by the coupling of 2 moles of palmitic acid:

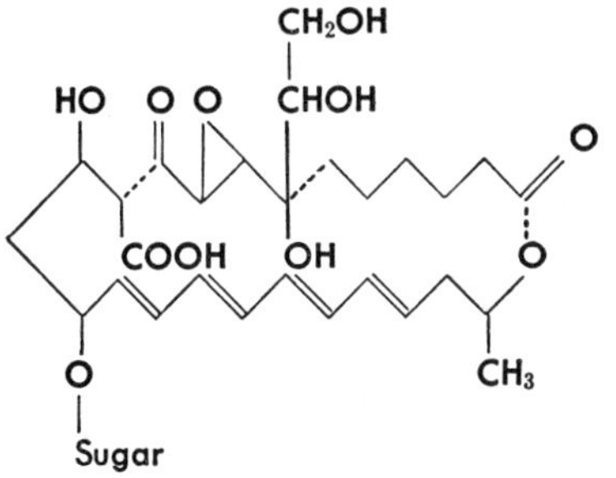

Pimaricin 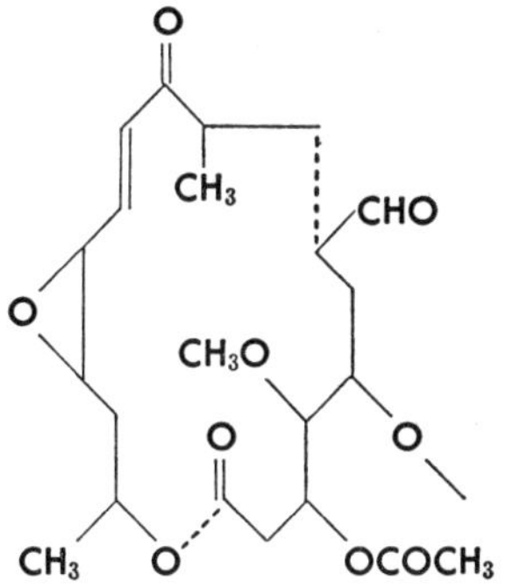   Lactone Portion of Carbomycin

Another suggestion has been made in the case of carbomycin,[1] namely that a protocarbomycin may occur which later rearranges by a glycol-aldehyde shift:

Proposed Precursor of the   Proposed Glycol-aldehyde
Lactone Portion of Carbomycin   Rearrangement at 7,8-Positions

Such a precursor is the more plausible because it would have an 18-membered carbon atom chain and a C-19 carbon skeleton, the same as that of the known tuberculostearic acid, even including the stereochemistry of the branching methyl group.

Streptomyces species produce many antifungal antibiotics which have in common chains of conjugated olefinic bonds. By means of the ultraviolet absorption spectra it is possible to classify them according to the length of the conjugated chain. Generally these substances are rather intractable with low solubilities and indefinite melting points.

A structure has been proposed for pimaricin, a tetraene. Whether or not this structure proves to be entirely correct, there is evidence from several sources that at least certain of these substances are macrocyclic lactones.

So many of these compounds have been reported lately that any listing is likely to be incomplete. The following table must include most of them, however, grouped by number of conjugated olefinic bonds.

TABLE I

Tetraene	Hexaene	Pentaene	Heptaene
Nystatin (Fungicidin)	Fradicin	Eurocidin	Amphotericin B
Rimocidin	Flavacid	Fungichromatin	Candidin
Pimaricin	Mediocidin	Fungichromin	Candicidin
Amphotericin A	Endomycin B (Helixin B)	Filipin	Candimycin
Protocidin		PA-153	Ayfactin
Chromin		Pentamycin	Ascosin
Antimycoin			Trichomycin
Sistomycosin			PA-150
Endomycin A (Helixin A)			Antibiotic 1968
Etruscomycin			
PA-166			
Tennecetin			
Flavofungin			

Various other substances, *e.g.* the etamycin, valinomycin and actinomycin types of antibiotics, could be classed as macrolides since they all contain large rings in which lactone groups participate.

a. POLYENE MACROLIDES

225 **Flavofungin,** $C_{30}H_{48}O_9$ Dihydrate.

A polyene macrolide containing 7 acetylatable hydroxyl groups, 5 hydrogenatable carbon-carbon double bonds of which at least 4 are conjugated, contains no alicyclic ring, has at least 2 and probably 3 C—CH$_3$. Ozonolysis indicates a CH$_3$(C$_6$H$_{11}$) group. The most important structural elements are:

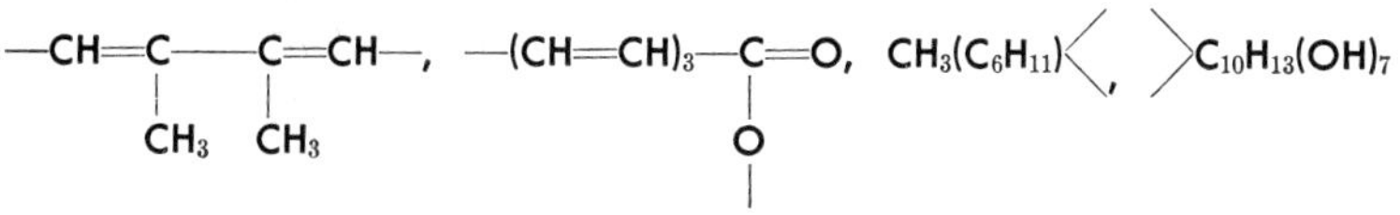

Shown to be distinct from pimaricin, nystatin, amphotericin-B, fungichromin, lagosin, filipin and fumagillin.

A streptomycete

R. Bognar, *Angew. Chem.* **72** 139 (1960).

226 **Pimaricin** (Myprozine), $C_{34}H_{49}O_{14}N$, colorless crystals, m.p. 200° (dec.), U.V. 279, 290, 303, 318 mμ in methanol. Proposed structure:

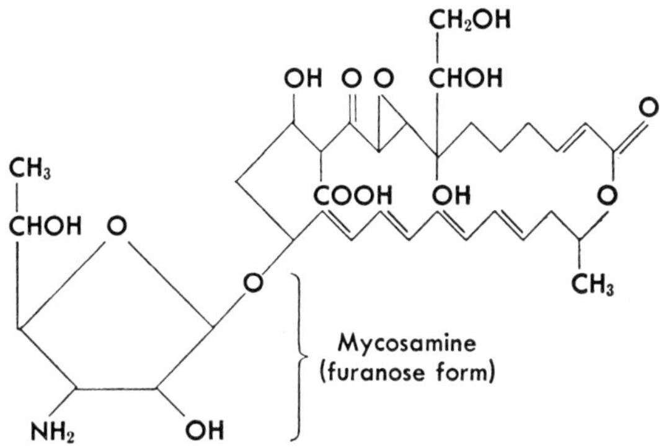

Streptomyces natalensis n. sp.

A. P. Struyk, I. Hoette, G. Drost, J. M. Waisvisz, T. Van Eek and J. C. Hoogerheide, "Antibiotics Annual 1957–1958," Medical Encyclopedia, Inc., New York, p. 878.

James B. Patrick, Richard P. Williams and John S. Webb, *J. Am. Chem. Soc.* **80** 6689 (1958). (Structure)

227 **PA-166**, $C_{35}H_{53}O_{14}N$ (proposed), colorless powder, m.p. gradual
dec. up to 260°, $[\alpha]_D^{25}$ +275° (c 0.2 in pyridine).
An amphoteric tetraene. U.V. maxima: 291, 304, 319
in aqueous methanol. Positive ninhydrin, 2,4-DNPH and
Fehling's tests. Three C-methyl groups.
Streptomyces n. sp.
B. K. Koe, F. W. Tanner, Jr., K. V. Rao, B. A. Sobin and
W. D. Celmer, "Antibiotics Annual 1957–1958," Medical En-
cyclopedia, Inc., New York, p. 897.

228 **Etruscomycin**, $C_{36}H_{57}O_{14}N$, white crystals, $[\alpha]_D^{20}$ +296° (c 1 in
pyridine).
A tetraene antibiotic. I.R. peaks at: 2.91, 3.38, 5.83,
6.30, 9.44, 9.55, 11.85μ. U.V. peaks at: 290, 300, 316 mμ.
Streptomyces lucensis n. sp.
F. Arcamone, C. Bertazzoli, G. Canevazzi, A. DiMarco, M.
Ghione and A. Grein, *Giorn. Microbiol.* 4 119 (1957).

229 **Lagosin** (Antibiotic A-246), $C_{41}H_{66-70}O_{14}$, m.p. ~235° (dec.),
$[\alpha]_D^{20}$ −160° (c 0.2 in methanol).
An antifungal pentaene macrolide antibiotic with the
following partial structure:*

Streptomyces sp.
M. L. Dhar, V. Thaller and M. C. Whiting, *Proc. Chem. Soc.*,
148 (1958).
M. L. Dhar, V. Thaller, M. C. Whiting, Ragnar Ryhage,
Stina Stälberg-Stenhagen and Einar Stenhagen, *ibid.*, 154
(1959). (Structure)
S. Ball, Christine J. Bessell and Aileen Mortimer, *J. Gen.
Microbiol.* 17 96 (1957). (Isolation)

230 **Nystatin** (Fungicidin, Mycostatin) $C_{46}H_{77}O_{19}N$ (tentative), yellow powder, m.p. dec. above 160°, but no definite m.p.,
$[\alpha]_D^{25}$ +10° (in glacial acetic acid).
An amphoteric tetraene. U.V. maxima at: 280, 291,
304, 318 mμ. Contains a mycosamine moiety:

* See addendum.

Streptomyces noursei

Elizabeth L. Hazen and Rachel Brown, *Proc. Soc. Expl. Biol. Med.* **76** 93 (1951).

James D. Dutcher, Gerald Boyack and Sidney Fox, "Antibiotics Annual 1953–1954," Medical Encyclopedia, Inc., New York, p. 191.

David R. Walter, James D. Dutcher and O. Wintersteiner, *J. Am. Chem. Soc.* **79** 5076 (1957). (Structure)

231 Rimocidin (Sulfate heptahydrate), large fragile plates, m.p. ~151° (dec.), $[\alpha]_D^{25}$ (sulfate) +75° (c 1 in methanol).

An amphoteric tetraene. U.V. maxima at: 279, 291, 304, 318 mμ. Analysis (hydrated sulfate): C 57.65, H 7.82, N 1.81, S 2.03.

Streptomyces rimosus

J. W. Davisson, F. W. Tanner, Jr., A. C. Finlay and I. A. Solomons, *Antibiotics and Chemotherapy* **1** 289 (1951).

232 Protocidin, m.p. dec. from 120°.

A polyene antifungal agent. U.V. maxima 277, 290, 303 and 318 mμ. Reduces KMnO$_4$. Green Fehling. Negative biuret, Sakaguchi, Molisch, ninhydrin, anthrone, FeCl$_3$.

Streptomyces sp.

The yield was about 100 mg. per liter.

Jean Marie Sakimoto, *J. Antibiotics* (Japan) **10A** 128 (1957).

233 Amphotericin-A, m.p. gradual dec. above 153°, $[\alpha]_D^{23.5}$ +32° (in acid dimethylformamide).

An amphoteric tetraene. U.V. maxima: 291, 305, 320 mμ. Analysis: C 60.32, H 8.39, N 1.72.

Streptomyces sp.

J. Vandeputte, J. L. Wachtel and E. T. Stiller, "Antibiotics Annual 1955–1956," Medical Encyclopedia, Inc., New York, p. 587.

234 Sistomycosin, buff or light yellow microcrystals, m.p. ~230° (browning from 130°).

A neutral tetraene. U.V. maxima: 218, 292.5, 306, 320.5 mμ in aqueous solution. Positive Benedict and Molisch tests.

Streptomyces viridosporus n. sp.

J. Ehrlich, M. Knudsen and Q. Bartz, Canadian Patent 514,894 (1955).

235 Endomycin A (Helixin A), yellow-brown powder.

An acidic tetraene. U.V. maxima at 292, 301, 319 mμ.

Streptomyces hygroscopicus (*S. endus*)

A yield of 11.7 g. of mixed endomycins from about 15 liters of broth has been reported.

L. C. Vining and W. A. Taber, *Can. J. Chem.* 35 1461 (1957).

David Gottlieb, P. K. Bhattacharyya, H. E. Carter and H. W. Anderson, *Phytopathology* 41 393 (1951). (Isolation)

Curt Leben, G. J. Stessel and G. W. Keitt, *Mycologia* 44 159 (1952).

R. R. Smeby, Curt Leben, G. W. Keitt and F. M. Strong, *Phytopathology* 42 506 (1952).

236 Tennecetin, yellow amorphous powder.

A tetraene antibiotic. U.V. absorption peaks at 288, 300–302, and 315–318 mμ.

Streptomyces chattanoogensis

James Burns and D. Frank Holtman, *Antibiotics and Chemotherapy* 9 398 (1959).

237 Antimycoin, organic acid, U.V. maxima: 291, 304–305, 318 mμ in ethanol. Similar to fungicidin. (A tetraene)

Streptomyces aureus Waksman and Curtis

Carl P. Schaffner, Irwin D. Steinman, Robert S. Safferman and Hubert Lechevalier, "Antibiotics Annual 1957–1958," Medical Encyclopedia, Inc., New York, pp. 5869–5873.

Frederick Raubitscheck, Robert F. Acker and Selman A. Waksman *Antibiotics and Chemotherapy* 2 179 (1952).

238 Filipin, $C_{32}H_{54}O_{10}$, fine yellow needles, m.p. 195–205° (dec.) (s. 147°), $[\alpha]_D^{22}$ −148.3° (c 0.89 in methanol).

A neutral pentaene. U.V. maxima at 322, 338, 355 mμ. Contains 7–8 acetylatable non-vicinal hydroxyl groups and 3–4 C—CH_3 groups.

Possible partial structure: *

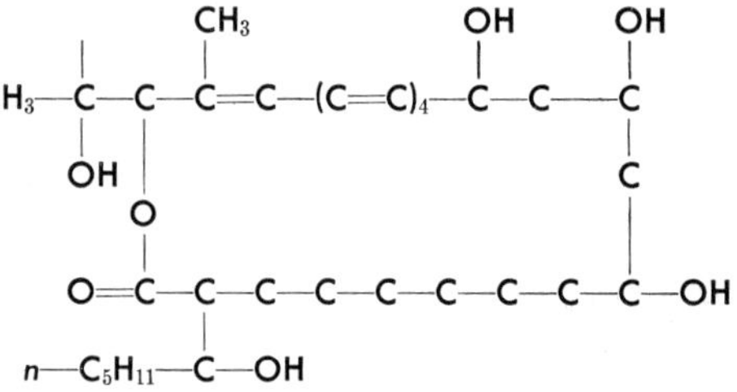

Streptomyces filipinensis n. sp.

Geo. B. Whitfield, Thomas D. Brock, Alfred Ammann, David Gottlieb and Herbert E. Carter, *J. Am. Chem. Soc.* 77 4799 (1955). (Isolation)

Alfred Ammann, David Gottlieb, Thomas D. Brock, Her-

* See addendum.

bert E. Carter and George B. Whitfield, *Phytopathology* 45 559 (1955).

Belig Berkoz and Carl Djerassi, *Proc. Chem. Soc.*, 316 (1959). (Structure)

239   Fungichromin, $C_{35}H_{60}O_{13}$, pale yellow crystals, m.p. 205–210°. A pentaene. U.V. maxima: 322.5, 338.5, 356.5 mμ. The following moiety has been obtained by alkaline hydrolysis followed by periodate oxidation:

$$OHC-C=CH(CH=CH)_4-CHO$$
$$|$$
$$CH_3$$

Streptomyces cellulosae

A similar substance, fungichromatin, occurred in the same culture.

Alfred A. Tytell, Frank J. McCarthy, W. P. Fisher, William A. Balhofer and Jesse Charney, "Antibiotics Annual 1954–1955," Medical Encyclopedia, Inc., New York, p. 716.

Arthur C. Cope and Herbert E. Johnson, *J. Am. Chem. Soc.* 80 1504 (1958).

240   PA-153, $C_{37}H_{61}O_{14}N$ (proposed), colorless powder, m.p. gradual dec. up to 260° (triethylamine salt dec. 126–129°), $[\alpha]_D^{25}$ +398° (c 0.2 in pyridine).

An amphoteric pentaene. U.V. maxima: 303, 317, 332, 349 in aqueous methanol. Positive ninhydrin, 2,4-DNPH and Fehlings tests. Three C-methyl groups.

Streptomyces n. sp.

B. K. Koe, F. W. Tanner, Jr., K. V. Rao, B. A. Sobin and W. D. Celmer, "Antibiotics Annual 1957–1958," Medical Encyclopedia, Inc., New York, p. 897.

241   Pentamycin, pale yellow needles, m.p. 237° (dec.).

An antifungal pentaene antibiotic resembling filipin in some properties. U.V. maxima at: 322, 338, 356 mμ. Contains only C, H, O.

About 60 g. of fairly pure material were obtained from 100 liters of culture (mycelium).

Streptomyces penticus

Sumio Umezawa and Yoshiaki Tanaka, *J. Antibiotics* (Japan) 11A 26 (1958).

242   Eurocidin.

A pentaene. U.V. maxima: 318, 333, 351 mμ.

Streptomyces alboreticuli n. sp.

Yashiro Okami, Ryazo Utahara, Shashiro Nakamura and Hamao Umezawa, *J. Antibiotics* (Japan) 7A 98 (1954).

Ryozo Utahara, Yashiro Okami, Shashiro Nakamura and Hamao Umezawa, *ibid.* 7A 120 (1954).

243 **Fradicin,** $C_{30}H_{34}O_4N_4$, pale greenish yellow crystals, m.p. darkens without melting 180–300°, $[\alpha]_D^{25}$ +65° (c 1 dioxane). Weakly basic hexaene. U.V. maxima: 290–295. Two methoxyls.

Streptomyces fradiae

E. Augustus Swart, Antonio H. Romano and Selman A. Waksman, *Proc. Soc. Exptl. Biol. Med.* 73 376 (1950).

Richard J. Hickey and Phil Harter Hidy, *Science* 113 361 (1951).

244 **Flavacid,** pale yellow microcrystalline powder, m.p. 102–105° (dec.).

A weakly acidic hexaene. U.V. maxima: 340, 360, 380 mμ. A tetraene with peaks at 293, 306 and 324 is also present.

A streptomycete resembling *S. flavus*

Isao Takahashi, *J. Antibiotics* (Japan) 6A 117 (1953).

L. C. Vining and W. A. Taber, *Can. J. Chem.* 35 1461 (1957).

245 **Mediocidin,** yellow amorphous powder.

A hexaene. U.V. maxima: 340, 357, 378 mμ. A tetraene, probably identical with that in the flavacid complex, is also present. U.V. maxima: 293, 306, 324.

Streptomyces mediocidicus, n. sp.

Ryazo Utahara, Yoshiro Okami, Shashiro Nakamura and Hamao Umezawa, *J. Antibiotics* (Japan) 7A 120 (1954).

L. C. Vining and W. A. Taber, *Can. J. Chem.* 35 1461 (1957).

246 **Endomycin B** (Helixin B), yellow-brown powder.

An acidic hexaene. For U.V. spectrum see first reference below.

Streptomyces hygroscopicus (*S. endus*)

L. C. Vining and W. A. Taber, *Can. J. Chem.* 35 1461 (1957).

David Gottlieb, P. K. Bhattacharyya, H. E. Carter and H. W. Anderson, *Phytopathology* 41 393 (1951). (Isolation)

Curt Leben, G. J. Stessel and G. W. Keitt, *Mycologia* 44 159 (1952).

R. R. Smeby, Curt Leben, G. W. Keitt and F. M. Strong, *Phytopathology* 42 506 (1952).

247 Helixins.

A complex of three or four compounds. Helixin B is identical with endomycin B.

Streptomyces sp.

Curt Leben, G. J. Stessel and G. W. Keitt, *Mycologia* 44 159 (1952).

248 Amphotericin-B, $C_{46}H_{73}O_{20}N$ (tentative) deep yellow prisms or needles from dimethylformamide, m.p: gradual dec. above 170°, $[\alpha]_D$ +333° (in acid dimethylformamide).

An amphoteric heptaene, U.V. maxima at: 364, 383, 408 mμ. Contains a mycosamine moiety:

Streptomyces nodosus

J. Vandeputte, J. L. Wachtel and E. T. Stiller, "Antibiotics Annual 1955–1956," Medical Encyclopedia, Inc., New York, p. 587. (Isolation)

David R. Walters, James D. Dutcher and O. Wintersteiner, *J. Am. Chem. Soc.* 79 5076 (1957). (Structure)

249 Zaomycin, m.p. 242–246° (dec.).

An amphoteric antibiotic said to resemble amphotericin. Positive ninhydrin, Millon, biuret, $FeCl_3$ tests. Negative Fehling and Liebermann reactions.

Streptomycin zaomyceticus

Yorio Hinuma, *J. Antibiotics* (Japan) 7A 134 (1954).

250 PA-150, $C_{54}H_{82}O_{18}N_2$ (proposed), yellow powder, m.p. gradual dec. up to 260°, $[\alpha]_D^{25}$ +294° (c 0.2 in pyridine).

An amphoteric heptaene. U.V. maxima: 340, 358, 377, 397 mμ in aqueous methanol. Positive 2,4-DNPH and Fehlings tests. Four C-methyl groups.

Streptomyces n. sp.

B. K. Koe, F. W. Tanner, Jr., K. V. Rao, B. A. Sobin and W. D. Celmer, "Antibiotics Annual 1957–1958," Medical Encyclopedia, Inc., New York, p. 897.

251 Trichomycin, yellow powder, m.p. 155° (dec.).

A heptaene. U.V. maxima: 286, 346, 364, 384, 405 mμ. May be a mixture of two heptaenes.

Streptomyces hachijoensis n. sp.

Seigo Hosoya, Nobuhiko Komatsu, Momoe Soeda and Yoko Sonoda, *Japan J. Exptl. Med.* 22 505 (1952).

Seigo Hosoya, Nobuhiko Komatsu, Momoe Soeda, Tatsuro Yuwaguchi and Yoko Sonoda, *J. Antibiotics* (Japan) 5 564 (1952).

252 Candidin, yellow powder.

Acidic heptaene. U.V. maxima: (Na salt) 234, 282, 345, 360, 383, 405 mμ in aqueous solution. The free acid lacks the 345 peak. Contains nitrogen and gives positive ketone tests.

Streptomyces viridoflavus

Willard A. Taber, Leo C. Vining and Selman A. Waksman, *Antibiotics and Chemotherapy* 4 455 (1954).

Leo C. Vining, Willard A. Taber and Francis J. Gregory, "Antibiotics Annual 1954–1955," Medical Encyclopedia, Inc., New York, p. 980.

Candicidins.

Heptaenes. U.V. maxima:

253 Candicidin A: 360, 380, 403 mμ.

254 Candicidin B: 362, 381, 404 mμ.

255 Candicidin C: 358, 379, 402 mμ.

Streptomyces griseus, other *Streptomyces* spp.

Hubert A. Lechevalier, R. F. Acker, C. T. Corke, C. M. Haenseler and S. A. Waksman, *Mycologia* 45 155 (1953).

256 Ascosin, yellow-orange powder.

A weakly acidic heptaene. U.V. maxima: 234, 288, 340, 357, 376, 398 mμ in methanol.

Streptomyces canescus

Richard J. Hickey, Cyril J. Corum, Phil H. Hidy, I. Ray Cohen, Urs F. B. Nager and Eleonore Kropp, *Antibiotics and Chemotherapy* 2 472 (1952).

Isadore R. Cohen, U. S. Patent 2,723,216, (1955).

b. OTHER MACROLIDES

257 Nitrosporin, $C_{20}H_{26}O_6N_2$, colorless crystals, m.p. 130–140° (dec.). Crystals brown on exposure to air.

A basic substance, apparently a macrolide.

Streptomyces nitrosporeus

Hamao Umezawa and Tomio Takeuchi, *J. Antibiotics* (Japan) 5 270 (1952).

258 Celesticetin I, amphoteric, crystalline and dextrorotatory, $C_{24}H_{36-40}O_9N_2S$ (suggested empirical formula), Oxalate and Salicylate water soluble.   Oxalate m.p. 149–154°; Salicylate m.p. 139° (tabular monoclinic crystals).
Erythromycin-like.   (See entry 923, however)
Positive tests—$FeCl_3$, Molisch, Ekkert
White ppt.—Br_2 water, Millon's Reagent, $HgCl_2$
Negative tests—$AgNO_3$, PbAc, Benedict, ninhydrin, iodoform, nitroprusside (becomes + after standing several days in 6 N hydrochloric acid)
No immediate reaction with Br_2—CCl_4.
Streptomyces caelestis
Herman Hoeksema, Glen F. Crum, William H. DeVries, *Antibiotics Annual* 2 837–841 (1954–1955). (Isolation and purification)

259 Amaromycin, $C_{25}H_{39}O_7N$ (proposed), colorless prisms, m.p. 164.5°, $[\alpha]_D^{25}$ +6.19° (c 1 in ethanol).
Basic substance, analysis: C 63.66, H 8.73, N 3.0. Negative $FeCl_3$, biuret, ninhydrin, Sakaguchi, Schiff. Positive Tollens, Fehlings.   Precipitated by Reinecke's salt. Probably a macrolide.
Streptomyces flavochromogenes
Toju Hata, Yashimoto Sano, Hideo Tatsuta, Ryazo Sugawara, Akihiro Matsumae and Kokichi Kanamori, *J. Antibiotics* (Japan) 8A 9 (1955).

260 PA-133 A, $C_{25}H_{43}O_6N$, colorless amorphous solid, $[\alpha]_D^{25}$ +39.6° (c 0.5 in methanol).
A macrolide antibiotic.
Streptomyces sp.
K. Murai, B. A. Sobin, W. D. Celmer and F. W. Tanner, *Antibiotics and Chemotherapy* 9 485 (1959).

261 Methymycin, $C_{25}H_{43}O_7N$, colorless prisms, needles, m.p. 195–197° (203°), $[\alpha]_D^{25}$ +61° (in methanol).

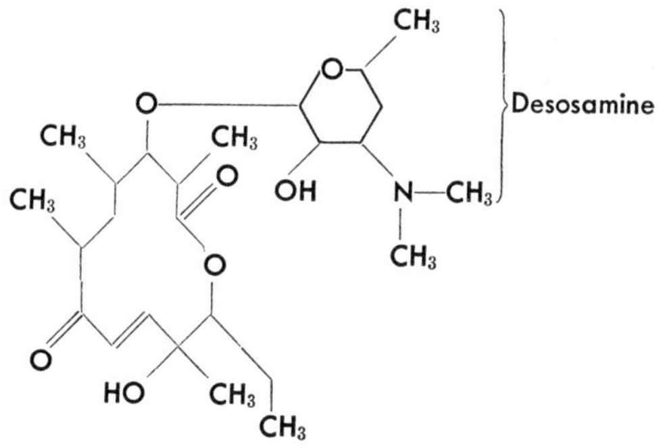

A streptomycete

Carl Djerassi and John A. Zderic, *J. Am. Chem. Soc.* **78** 2907 (1956). (Structure)

Milton N. Donin, Joseph Pagano, James D. Dutcher and Clara M. McKee, "Antibiotics Annual 1953–1954," Medical Encyclopedia, Inc., New York, p. 179. (Isolation)

262 Neomethymycin, $C_{25}H_{43}O_7N$, colorless crystals, m.p. 156°, $[\alpha]_D^{25}$ +93° (in chloroform).

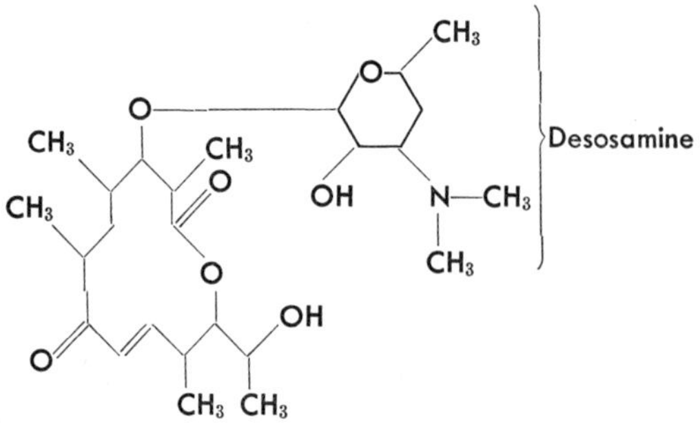

Same streptomycete which produces Methymycin

Carl Djerassi and O. Halpern, *J. Am. Chem. Soc.* **79** 2022 (1957). (Structure)

J. Vandeputte, unpublished. (Isolation)

263 Picromycin, $C_{25}H_{43}O_7N$, colorless crystals, m.p. 169.5°, $[\alpha]_D^{20}$ −33.5° (c 2.07 in chloroform).

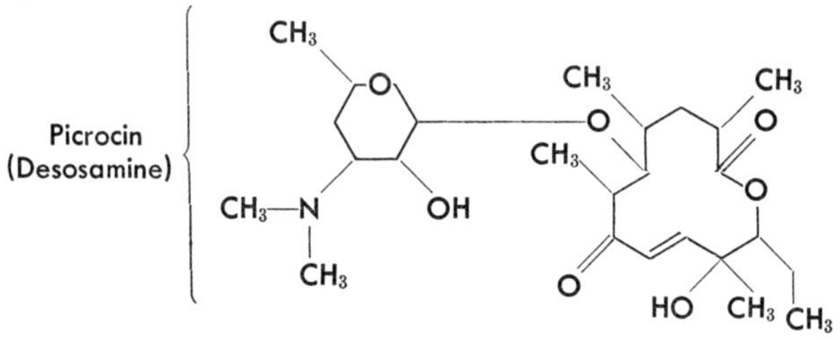

Streptomyces felleus n. sp.

Hans Brockmann and Rudolf Oster, *Chem. Ber.* **90** 605 (1957). (Partial structure)

R. Anliker and K. Gubler, *Helv. Chim. Acta* **40** 119 (1957). (Structure)

Hans Brockmann and Willfried Henkel, *Chem. Ber.* **84** 284 (1951). (Isolation)

Ibid., Naturwissenschaften **37** 138 (1950). (Isolation)

264 **PA-133-B,** $C_{25}H_{45}O_{10}N$, colorless crystals, m.p. 99.8–101°, $[\alpha]_D^{25}$ +22.5° (c 0.5 in methanol).
A macrolide antibiotic.
Streptomyces sp.
K. Murai, B. A. Sobin, W. D. Celmer and F. W. Tanner, *Antibiotics and Chemotherapy* 9 485 (1959).

265 **Griseomycin** (Lomycin) (Hydrochloride) $C_{25}H_{46}O_8NCl$, white powder, m.p. 76–80° (dec.), $[\alpha]_D^{25}$ +32° (c 1 in chloroform).
Precipitated by Reinecke salt, bromine water, picric acid. Thought to be a macrolide.
Streptomyces griseolus
P. J. Van Dijck, H. P. Van de Voorde and P. DeSomer, *Antibiotics and Chemotherapy* 3 1243 (1953).
Ibid. Belgian Patent 522,647 (1954).

266 **Proactinomycin A,** $C_{27}H_{47}O_8N$ (proposed), colorless crystals, m.p. 168°.

267 **Proactinomycin B,** $C_{28}H_{49}O_8N$ (proposed), colorless crystals, m.p. 83–87°.

268 **Proactinomycin C,** $C_{24}H_{41}O_6N$ (proposed), amorphous.
Basic substances, precipitated by Reineckes salt, picric or flavianic acids, etc. Probably macrolides.
Nocardia gardneri
A. D. Gardner and E. Chain, *Brit. J. Exptl. Path.* 23 123 (1942).
R. Q. Marston, *ibid.* 30 398 (1949). (Isolation)

Antimycins (Antipiriculins)*

269 **Antimycin A$_1$,** $C_{28}H_{40}O_9N_2$, colorless crystals, m.p. 149–150°, $[\alpha]_D^{26}$ +76 (c 1 in chloroform).

270 **Antimycin A$_{2a}$,** $C_{26}H_{36}O_9N_2$, colorless crystals, m.p. 143–149°.

271 **Antimycin A$_{2b}$** (may be isomeric with A$_{2a}$), colorless crystals, m.p. 168°.

272 **Antimycin A$_3$** (Blastmycin), $C_{26}H_{36}O_9N_2$, colorless crystals, m.p. 170.5–171.5°, $[\alpha]_D^{26}$ +64.3° (c 1 in chloroform).

* The antimycins might also be classified as depsipeptides (peptolides).

273 Antimycin A_4, oily.

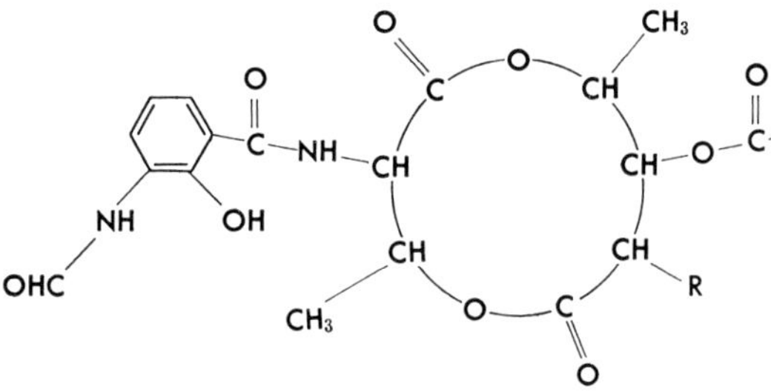

$R = n\text{---}C_6H_{13}$ in A_1.
$R = n\text{---}C_4H_9$ in A_3.

At least seven streptomyces species produce antimycins, including S. *kitazawaensis* Harada et Tanaka nov. sp. and S. *blastmyceticus*. The former organism also produces carzinocidin. Blastmycin is identical with antimycin A_3. Virosin is probably a mixture of antimycin components. Certain antimycin-producing cultures also contain actinomycin B.

Wen-chik Liu and F. M. Strong, *J. Am. Chem. Soc.* 81 4387 (1959).

Wen-chik Liu, E. E. Van Tamelen and F. M. Strong, *ibid.* 82 1652 (1960). (Degradations, etc.)

F. M. Strong, J. P. Dickie, M. E. Loomans, E. E. Van Tamelen and R. S. Dewey, *ibid.* 82 1513 (1960). (Structure)

Bryant R. Dunshee, Curt Leben, G. W. Keitt and F. M. Strong, *ibid.* 71 2436 (1949). (Isolation)

Yoshio Sakagami, Setsuo Takeuchi, Hiroshi Yonehara, Heiichi Sakai and Matso Takashima, *J. Antibiotics* (Japan) 9A 1 (1956).

Kiyoshi Nakayama, Fukusaburo Okamoto and Yujiro Harada, *ibid.* 9A 63 (1956).

Yujiro Harada, Keizo Uzu and Masaru Asai, *ibid.* 11A 32 (1958).

Hiroshi Yonehara and Setsuo Takeuchi, *ibid.* 11A 122 (1958). (Proposed structure)

Kiyoshi Watanabe, Tsutomo Tanaka, Keiko Fukuhara, Norisama Miyairi, Hiroshi Yonehara and Hamao Umezawa, *ibid.* 10A 39 (1957).

F. M. Strong, "Topics in Microbial Chemistry" (Squibb Lectures on the Chemistry of Microbial Products), John Wiley and Sons, Inc., New York, 1956, pp. 1–44. (A review to that date)

274   Narbomycin, $C_{28}H_{49}O_7N$, colorless crystals, m.p. 113.5–115°, $[\alpha]_D$ +68.5° (c 1.35 in chloroform).

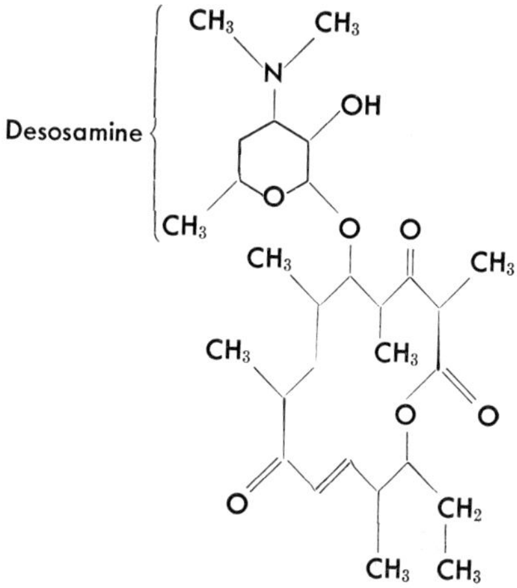

Streptomyces narboensis n. sp.

R. Corbaz, L. Ettlinger, E. Gäumann, W. Keller-Schierlein, F. Kradolfer, E. Kyburz, L. Neipp, V. Prelog, P. Reusser, and H. Zähner, *Helv. Chim. Acta* **38** 935 (1955).

R. Anliker, D. D. Dvornik, K. Gubler, H. Heusser and V. Prelog, *ibid.* **39** 1785 (1956).

V. Prelog, A. M. Gold, G. Talbot and A. Zamojski. (To be published)

275 Leucomycin, $C_{33-38}H_{54-66}O_{11-13}N$, colorless crystals, m.p. 124–125.5°, $[\alpha]_D{}^{20}$ −67.1° (c 1 in ethanol).

Leucomycin appears to be a macrolide antibiotic.*

Streptomyces kitasatoensis n. sp.

Toju Hata, Yoshimoto Sano, Natsuo Ohki, Yasuhiku Yoko-yama, Akihiro Matsumae and Shinya Ito, *J. Antibiotics* (Japan) **6A** 87 (1953).

Yoshimoto Sano, Tadashi Hoshi and Toju Hata, *ibid.* **7A** 88 (1954).

Yoshimoto Sano, *ibid.* **7A** 93 (1954).

* See addendum.

276 Oleandomycin (PA-105), $C_{35}H_{61}O_{12}N$, colorless prisms, m.p. 110° (dec.), $[\alpha]_D^{25}$ −65° (c 1 in methanol).

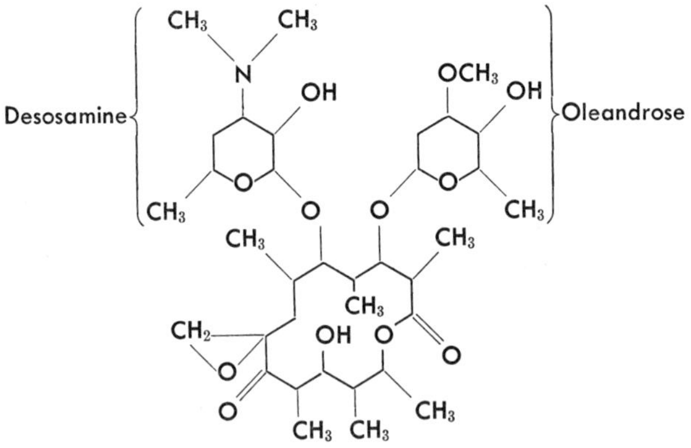

Streptomyces antibioticus

B. A. Sobin, A. R. English and W. D. Celmer, "Antibiotics Annual 1954–1955," Medical Encyclopedia, Inc., New York, p. 827.

W. D. Celmer, H. Els and K. Murai, "Antibiotics Annual 1957–1958," Medical Encyclopedia, Inc., New York, p. 476.

Hans Els, Walter D. Celmer and Kotaro Murai, *J. Am. Chem. Soc.* 80 3777 (1958).

W. D. Celmer, "Antibiotics Annual 1958–1959," Medical Encyclopedia, Inc., New York, p. 277. (Biochemical correlations)

F. A. Hochstein, H. Els, W. D. Celmer, B. L. Shapiro and R. B. Woodward, *J. Am. Chem. Soc.* 82 3225 (1960). (Structure)

277 Erythromycin C, $C_{36}H_{65}O_{13}N$, white needles, m.p. 121–125°.

Erythromycin C differs from erythromycin only in the neutral sugar moiety, so that the following partial structure can be written:

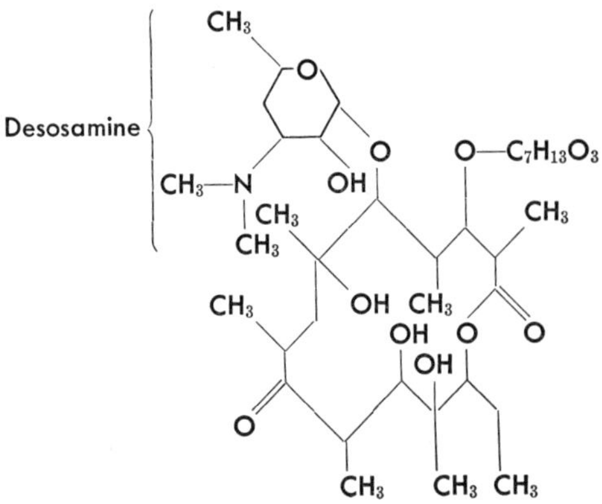

Streptomyces erythreus

Paul F. Wiley, Richard Gale, C. W. Pettinga and Koert Gerzon, *J. Am. Chem. Soc.* **79** 6074 (1957). (Structure and isolation)

278 Erythromycin B, $C_{37}H_{67}O_{12}N$, colorless crystals, m.p. 198°, $[\alpha]_D^{25}$ −78° (c 2 in ethanol).

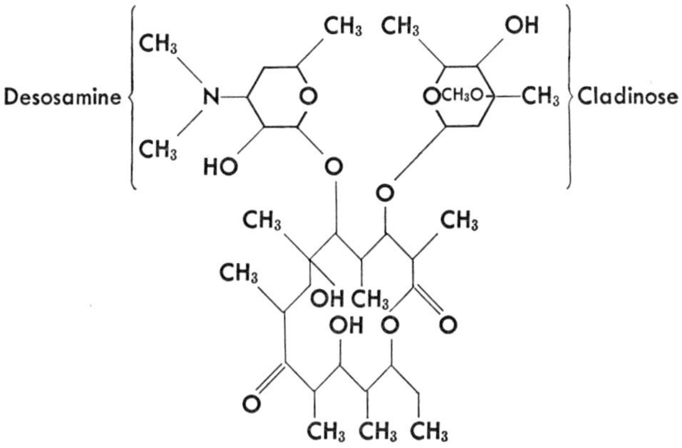

Streptomyces erythreus

Paul F. Wiley, Max V. Sigal, Jr., Allidene Weaver, Rosemarie Monahan and Koert Gerzon, *J. Am. Chem. Soc.* **79** 6070 (1957). (Structure)

C. W. Pettinga, W. M. Stark and F. R. Van Abeele, *ibid.* **76** 569 (1954). (Isolation)

279 Erythromycin (Ilotycin, Erythrocin), $C_{37}H_{67}O_{13}N$, white needles, m.p. 136–140°, $[\alpha]_D^{25}$ −78° (c 1.99 in alcohol).

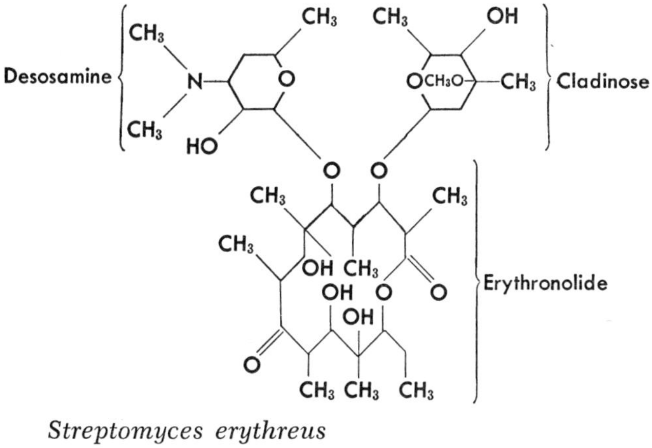

Streptomyces erythreus

R. K. Clark, Jr. *Antibiotics and Chemotherapy* **3** 663 (1953). (Isolation)

Paul F. Wiley, Koert Gerzon, Edwin H. Flynn, Max V. Sigal, Jr., Allidene Weaver, U. Carol Quarck, Robert R. Chau-

vette and Rosemarie Monahan, *J. Am. Chem. Soc.* 79 6062
(1957). (Structure)

280 **PA-108**, $C_{38}H_{63}O_{14}N$, colorless solid, m.p. 121–123°, $[\alpha]_D^{25}$ −36.8°
(c 1 in chloroform).
A macrolide antibiotic.
Streptomyces sp.
K. Murai, B. A. Sobin, W. D. Celmer and F. W. Tanner,
Antibiotics and Chemotherapy, 9 485 (1959).

281 **PA-148**, $C_{38}H_{65}O_{15}N$, colorless amorphous solid, m.p. 115–118°,
$[\alpha]_D^{25}$ −69.3° (c 0.5 in methanol).
A macrolide antibiotic.
Streptomyces sp.
K. Murai, B. A. Sobin, W. D. Celmer and F. W. Tanner,
Antibiotics and Chemotherapy, 9 485 (1959).

282 **Carbomycin B**, $C_{42}H_{67}O_{15}N$, colorless plates, m.p. 141–144°
(dec.), Hydrochloride 164–166° (dec.), $[\alpha]_D^{25}$ −35° (c 2.0
in chloroform).

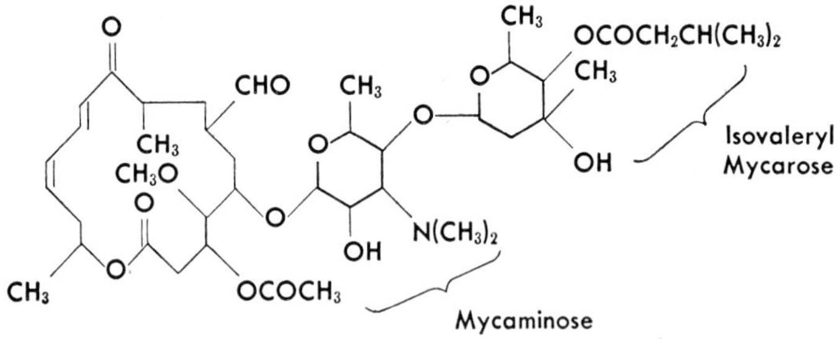

Streptomyces halstedii
F. A. Hochstein and Kotaro Murai, *J. Am. Chem. Soc.* 76
5080 (1954). (Isolation)
R. B. Woodward, *Angew. Chem.* 69 50 (1957). (Structure)

283 **Carbomycin** (Magnamycin), $C_{42}H_{67}O_{16}N$, colorless laths, m.p.
212–214° (dec.), $[\alpha]_D^{25}$ −58.6° (c 1 in chloroform).

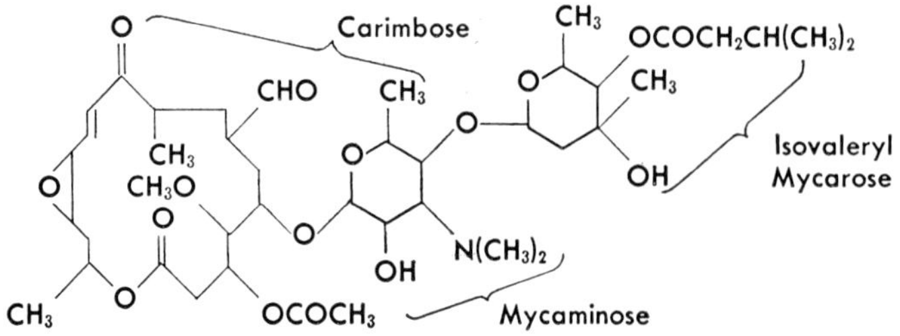

Streptomyces halstedii, S. alboreticuli

R. B. Woodward, *Angew. Chem.* 69 50 (1957). (Structure)
Richard L. Wagner, F. A. Hochstein, Kotaro Murai, N. Messina and Peter B. Regna, *J. Am. Chem. Soc.* 75 4684 (1953). (Isolation)

284 Tertiomycin A, $C_{42}H_{49}O_{16}N$, white needles, m.p. 215–217° (s. 208°) (dec.), $[\alpha]_D^{17}$ −49° (c 1 in chloroform) $[\alpha]_D^{16}$ −47° (c 1.0 in ethanol).
A macrolide antibiotic. Carbomycin produced also by *S. alboreticuli.*
Streptomyces eurocidicus, S. alboreticuli
Teisuke Osato, Masahiro Ueda, Setsuko Fukuyama, Koki Yagishita, Yoshiro Okami and Hamao Umezawa, *J. Antibiotics* (Japan) 8A 105 (1955).

285 Tertiomycin B, $C_{43}H_{71}O_{17}N$ (proposed), white needles, m.p. 97°, $[\alpha]_D^{22}$ −56° (c 1 in ethanol).
A macrolide antibiotic.
Streptomyces eurocidicus
The same organism produces eurocidin, tertiomycin A and azomycin.
Teisuke Osato, Koki Yagishita and Hamao Umezawa, *J. Antibiotics* (Japan) 8A 161 (1955).
Akira Miyoke, Hidesuke Iwasaki and Torao Tawewaka, *J. Antibiotics* (Japan) 12A 59 (1959).

286 Foromacidin A (Spiramycin I): $C_{45}H_{78}O_{15}N_2$, colorless powder, m.p. 134–138°, $[\alpha]_D$ −81° (c 0.34 in methanol).

287 Foromacidin B (Spiramycin II): $C_{47}H_{80}O_{16}N_2$, colorless powder, m.p. 130–132°, $[\alpha]_D$ −83° (c 0.82 in ethanol).

288 Foromacidin C (Spiramycin III): $C_{48}H_{82}O_{16}N_2$, colorless powder, m.p. 124–128°, $[\alpha]_D$ −79° (c 1.19 in ethanol).

289 Foromacidin D: Equiv. Wt. 452, colorless powder, m.p. 135–140°, $[\alpha]_D$ −75° (c 0.81 in ethanol).
Two streptomycetes
R. Corbaz, L. Ettlinger, E. Gäumann, W. Keller-Schierlein, F. Kradolfer, E. Kyburz, L. Neipp, V. Prelog, A. Wettstein and H. Zähner, *Helv. Chim. Acta* 39 304 (1956).
The foromacidins (or spiramycins) are apparently macrolide antibiotics. On degradation they yield three sugars typical of this class.

$$\text{Spiramycins} \begin{cases} \text{I} & C_{45}H_{78}O_{15}N_2 \\ \text{II} & C_{47}H_{80}O_{16}N_2 \\ \text{III} & C_{48}H_{82}O_{16}N_2 \end{cases}$$

$$\downarrow$$

$$\text{Neospiramycins} \begin{cases} \text{I} & C_{38}H_{66}O_{12}N_2 \\ \text{II} & C_{40}H_{68}O_{13}N_2 \\ \text{III} & C_{41}H_{70}O_{13}N_2 \end{cases} +$$

Mycarose
$C_7H_{14}O_4$

$$\downarrow$$

$$\text{Forocidins} \begin{cases} \text{A} & C_{30}H_{51}O_{11}N \\ \text{B} & C_{32}H_{53}O_{12}N \\ \text{C} & C_{33}H_{55}O_{12}N \end{cases} +$$

$C_8H_{17}O_2N$

Raymond Paul and Serge Tchelitcheff, *Bull. soc. chim. France* 442, 734 (1957).

Idem., ibid., 150 (1960).

290 **Tylosin,** $C_{45}H_{79}O_{17}N$, colorless crystals, m.p. 128–132°, $[\alpha]_D^{25}$ −46° (c 2 in methanol).

A macrolide antibiotic, containing the sugars mycarose and mycaminose. Also has an α, β, γ, δ-unsaturated carbonyl system.

Streptomyces fradiae

R. L. Hamill, M. E. Haney, Martha C. Stamper and Paul Wiley, Abstr. Atlantic City Meeting, Am. Chem. Soc., September, 1959. (To be published)

J. M. McGuire, W. S. Boniece, W. A. Daily, C. E. Higgens, M. M. Hoehn, W. M. Stark, W. B. Sutton, J. Westhead and R. N. Wolfe. (To be published)

291 **Angolamycin,** $C_{49-50}H_{87-91}O_{18}N$, colorless crystals, m.p. 165–168°, $[\alpha]_D^{21}$ −64° (c 1.3 in chloroform).

A macrolide antibiotic apparently similar to carbomycin, but with characteristic sugars.

Streptomyces eurythermus

R. Corbaz, L. Ettlinger, E. Gäumann, W. Keller-Schierlein, L. Neipp, V. Prelog, P. Reusser and H. Zähner, *Helv. Chim. Acta* 38 1202 (1955).

292 **Miamycin,** colorless crystals, m.p. 221° (dec.), $[\alpha]_D^{25}$ −18° (c 1.0 in 0.02 N hydrochloric acid).

A macrolide antibiotic.   Analysis: C 61.4, 61.5, H 8.7, 8.6.   Mol. wt. ~609.

Streptomyces ambofaciens

H. Schmitz, M. Misiek, B. Heinemann, J. Lein and I. R. Hooper, *Antibiotics and Chemotherapy* **7** 37 (1957).

8

Alicyclic Compounds Other Than
Terpenoids and Steroids

This section contains non-terpenoid, non-steroid alicyclics of diverse biosynthetic origin. Many of these, especially the streptomycete products, were antibiotic isolates.

Included here are some of the intermediates in the biosynthetic route from carbohydrates to aromatic amino acids and to certain other aromatic compounds. Part of this sequence, worked out largely by Tatum, Davis, Sprinson and collaborators,[1, 2, 3] is reproduced below in brief outline only since it has been widely reviewed and publicized. (P indicates phosphorylation):

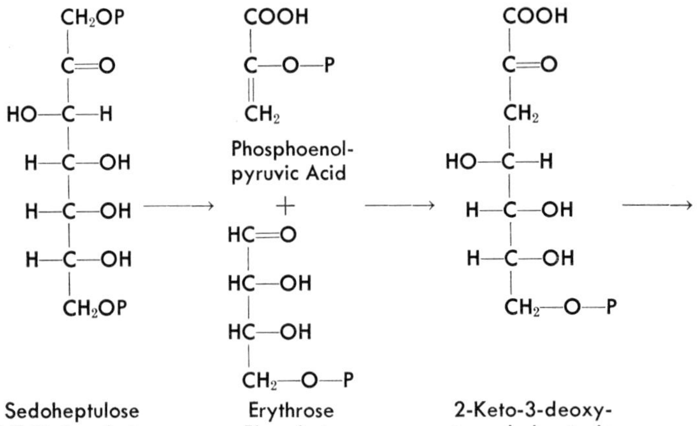

| Sedoheptulose 1,7-Diphosphate | Erythrose Phosphate | 2-Keto-3-deoxy-D-araboheptonic Acid |

[1] Bernard D. Davis, *Intermediates in amino acid biosynthesis*, *Advances in Enzymology* 16 247–312 (1955). (A review)

[2] Alton Meister, "Biochemistry of the Amino Acids," Academic Press, Inc., New York, 1957, pp. 346–349.

[3] P. R. Srinivasan, Masayuki Katagiri and David B. Sprinson, *J. Biol. Chem.* 234 713 (1959); P. R. Srinivasan and David B. Sprinson, *ibid.* 234 716 (1959).

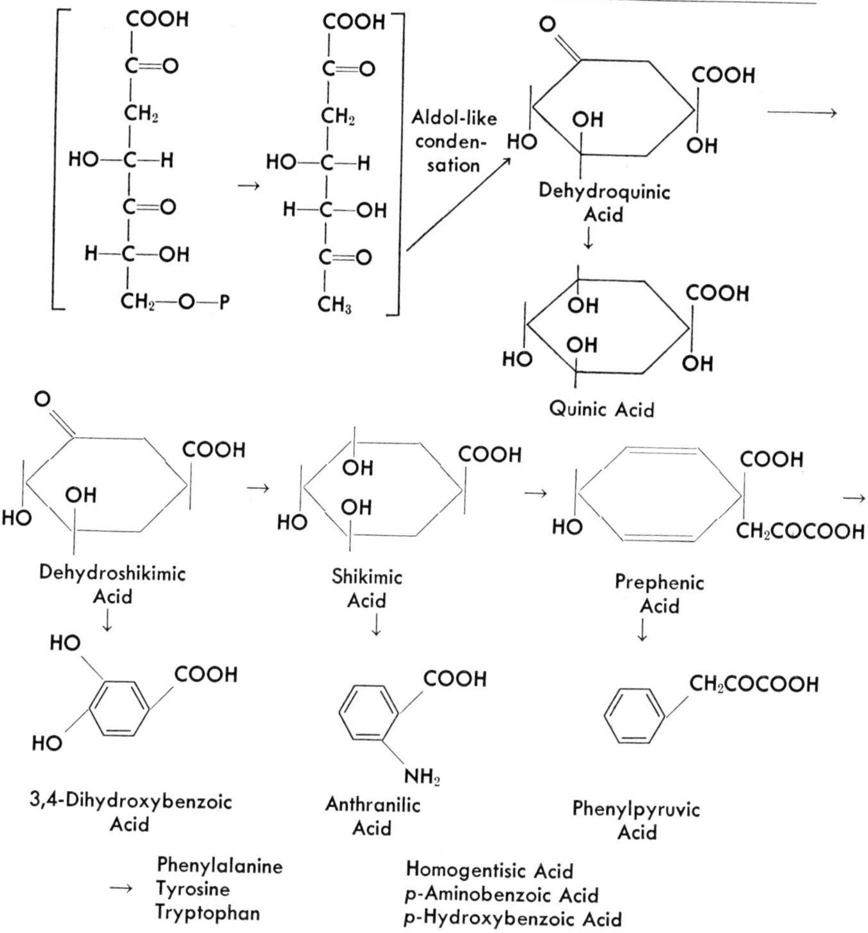

Dehydroquinic Acid

Quinic Acid

Dehydroshikimic Acid

Shikimic Acid

Prephenic Acid

3,4-Dihydroxybenzoic Acid

Anthranilic Acid

Phenylpyruvic Acid

→ Phenylalanine Tyrosine Tryptophan

Homogentisic Acid
p-Aminobenzoic Acid
p-Hydroxybenzoic Acid

Microorganisms were the principal tools in this work, especially the mold *Neurospora crassa* and the bacteria *Escherichia coli* and *Aerobacter aerogenes* mutated so that the biosynthesis of aromatic amino acids was blocked at various points. These mutants accumulated intermediates in the sequence prior to the blocks, and these substances could then be isolated. Also when such mutants (auxotrophs) were supplied with the critical substance whose biosynthesis was blocked, the microorganisms were capable of completing the sequence to the aromatic acids.

This route from carbohydrates to certain types of aromatic substances has been established as quite general in metabolism.

Biosynthesis of the chlorinated cyclopentane, caldariomycin, has been studied.[4] β-Ketoadipic acid and δ-chlorolevulinic acid were found to be intermediates.   The sequence shown here, then, probably represents at least part of the biogenetic scheme for this metabolite.

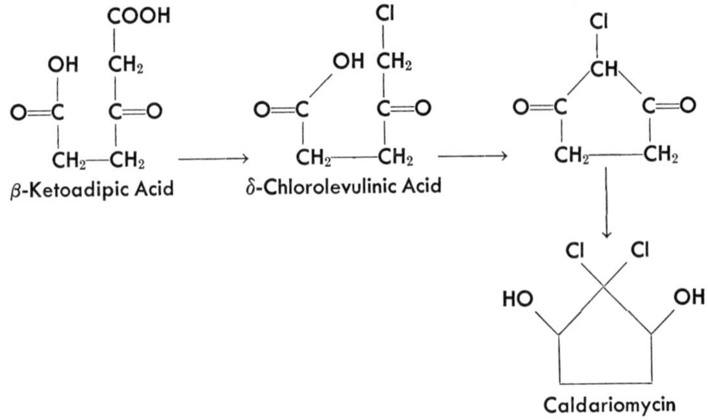

β-Ketoadipic Acid δ-Chlorolevulinic Acid

Caldariomycin

Palitantin appears to be an interesting example of an un-aromatized acetate derivative.   Its origin is revealed by the 14-carbon atoms, the uneven-numbered side-chains and the pattern of oxidation and unsaturation.

The cycloheximides also seem to be acetate derivatives, although apparently no study of their biosynthesis has been published.

Without having made a detailed analysis of the experimental work it would seem that the proposed structures for the glauconic acids are unique if not improbable.

293   **Caldariomycin,** $C_5H_8O_2Cl_2$, colorless needles, m.p. 121°, $[\alpha]_{5461}^{20}$ +59.2° (c 0.338 in water).

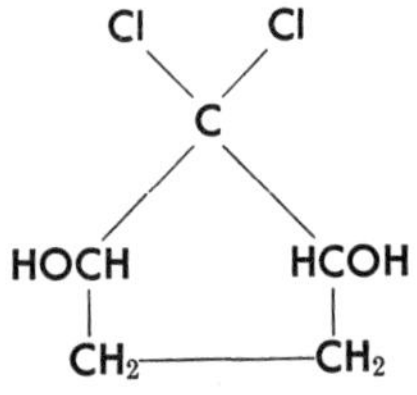

Caldariomyces fumago

[4] Paul D. Shaw, Jonathon R. Beckwith and Lowell P. Hager, *J. Biol. Chem.* 234 2560 (1959).

Percival W. Clutterbuck, Sudhir L. Mukhopadhyay, Albert E. Oxford and Harold Raistrick, *Biochem. J.* 34 664 (1940).

294   Sarkomycin, $C_7H_8O_3$, oil (dihydro-derivative), m.p. 99° with sublimation, $[\alpha]_D^{25}$ +66.7° (in water).

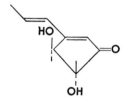

Streptomyces erythrochromogenes
A yield of about 5 g. from 2 liters of broth has been reported.

Hamao Umezawa, Tadashi Yamamato, Tomio Takeushi, Teisuke Osato, Yashiro Okami, Seizaburo Yamaoka, Tomoharu Okuda, Kazuo Nitta, Koki Yagishita, Ryazo Utahara and Sumio Umezawa, *Antibiotics and Chemotherapy* 4 514 (1954). (Isolation)

I. R. Hooper, L. C. Cheney, M. J. Cron, O. B. Fardig, D. A. Johnson, D. L. Johnson, F. M. Palermiti, H. Schmitz and W. B. Wheatley, *ibid.* 5 585 (1955). (Structure)

M. M. Shemyakin, L. A. Shchukina, E. I. Vinogradova, M. N. Kolosov, R. G. Vdovina, M. G. Karapetyan, V. Ya. Rodionov, G. A. Ravdel, Yu. B. Shvetsov, E. M. Bamdas, E. S. Chaman, K. M. Ermolaev and E. P. Semkin, *Zhur. Obschchei Khim.* 27 742 (1957). (Synthesis of dihydrosarkomycin)

295   Terrein, $C_8H_{10}O_3$, m.p. 127°, $[\alpha]_{5461}^{20}$ +185° (c 1 in water).

Aspergillus terreus Thom, *Penicillium raistrickii*
Harold Raistrick and Geo. Smith, *Biochem. J.* 29 606 (1935). (Isolation)
D. H. R. Barton and E. Miller, *J. Chem. Soc.,* 1028 (1955). (Structure)

296 5-Dehydroshikimic Acid, $C_7H_8O_5$, colorless prisms, m.p. 150–152°, $[\alpha]_D^{28}$ −57° (in ethanol).

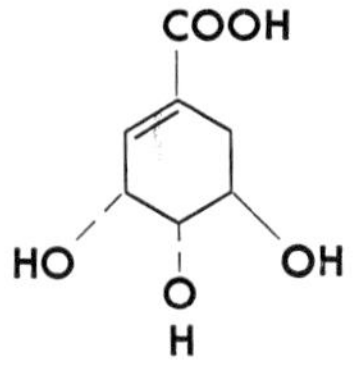

Escherichia coli mutants
Ivan I. Salamon and Bernard D. Davis, *J. Am. Chem. Soc.*
75 5567 (1953).

297 Shikimic Acid, $C_7H_{10}O_5$, colorless crystals, m.p. 184°, $[\alpha]_D^{20}$ −246° (in water).

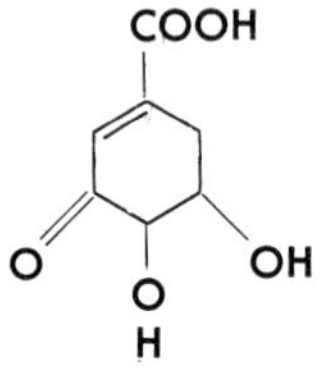

Escherichia coli
Yields of about 0.5 g. per liter have been reported.
P. R. Srinivasan, Harold T. Shigeura, Milton Sprescher, David B. Sprinson and Bernard D. Davis, *J. Biol. Chem.* 220 477 (1956).

298 5-Dehydroquinic Acid, $C_7H_{10}O_6$, colorless crystals, m.p. 140–142°.

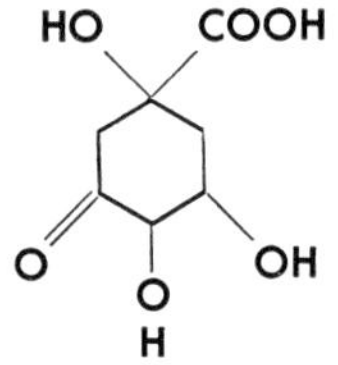

Escherichia coli
Ulrich Weiss, Bernard D. Davis and Elizabeth S. Mingioli, *J. Am. Chem. Soc.* 75 5572 (1953).

299 Dihydroshikimic Acid, $C_7H_{12}O_5$, colorless prisms, m.p. 135°, $[\alpha]_D^{25}$ −63° (c 10 in water).

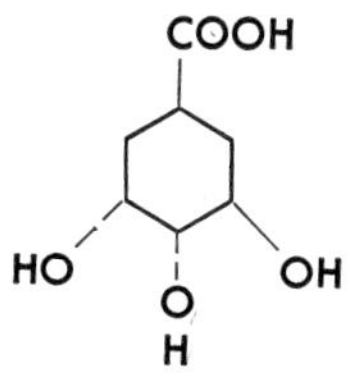

COOH

HO   OH

O
H

Lactobacillus pastorianus var. *quinicus*
A 96% yield was reported.
   J. G. Carr, A. Pollard, G. C. Whiting and A. H. Williams, *Biochem. J.* 66 283 (1957).

300 Cordycepic Acid, $C_7H_{12}O_6$, colorless needles, m.p. 168°, $[\alpha]_D^{26}$ +6.8° (in water).

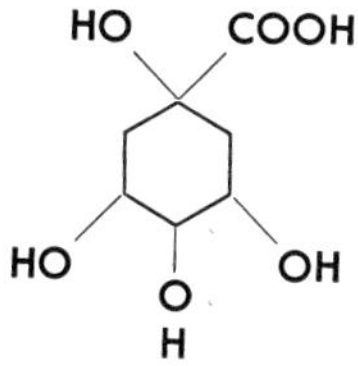

HO   COOH

HO   OH

O
H

Cordyceps sinensis (Berkeley) Saccardo
The yield was 7% of the weight of the dried and defatted mycelium.
   R. Chatterjee, K. S. Srinivasan and P. C. Maiti, *J. Am. Pharm. Assoc.* 46 114 (1957).

301 Prephenic Acid, $C_{10}H_{10}O_6$, unstable in aqueous solution, isolated as the barium salt.

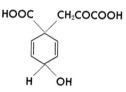

HOOC   CH₂COCOOH

H   OH

Mutants of *Escherichia coli* and *Neurospora crassa*
   Ulrich Weiss, Charles Gilvarg, Elizabeth S. Mingioli and Bernard D. Davis, *Science* 119 774 (1954).

302 **Frequentin,** $C_{14}H_{20}O_4$, colorless needles, m.p. 128°, $[\alpha]_D^{26}$ +68° (0.5 in chloroform).

Probably similar to palitantin in structure.

Penicillium frequentans Westling, *P. cyclopium*

P. J. Curtis, H. G. Hemming and W. K. Smith, *Nature* 167 557 (1951).

303 **Palitantin,** $C_{14}H_{22}O_4$, colorless needles, m.p. 163°, $[\alpha]_{5461}^{23}$ +4.4° (c 0.8 in chloroform).

Penicillium palitans Westling, *P. frequentans, P. cyclopium*

John Howard Birkinshaw and Harold Raistrick, *Biochem. J.* 30 801 (1936).

P. J. Curtis, H. G. Hemming and W. K. Smith, *Nature* 167 557 (1951).

A. Bracken, Anna Pocker and H. Raistrick, *Biochem. J.* 57 587 (1954).

K. Bawden, B. Lythgoe and D. J. S. Marsden, *J. Chem. Soc.,* 1162 (1959). (Structure)

304 **B-73,** $C_{15}H_{16}O_2N_2$, colorless plates, m.p. 275°, $[\alpha]_D^{25}$ +3.43° (c 0.4 in dimethylformamide).

Negative ferric chloride test, non-fluorescent under U.V. light, soluble in aqueous sodium hydroxide.

Streptomyces albulus

Non-antibiotic compound isolated from a broth containing cycloheximide, 4-acetoxycycloheximide, C-73, and fungicidin.

K. Rao, Abstracts, 134th Meeting of the American Chemical Society, Chicago, September 1958.

305 **C-73,** $C_{15}H_{17}O_4N$, pale yellow needles, m.p. 199°, $[\alpha]_D^{25}$ +5.06° (c 0.4 in dimethylformamide).

Green ferric chloride test, bright yellow fluorescence in U.V. light, soluble in sodium hydroxide solution.

Streptomyces albulus

This antibiotically inert compound was isolated from a culture containing cycloheximide and stereoisomers, 4-acetoxycycloheximide, fungicidin, E-73 and B-73.

K. Rao, Abstracts, 134th Meeting of the American Chemical Society, Chicago, September 1958.

306   **Actiphenol,** $C_{15}H_{17}O_4N$, colorless crystals, m.p. 199°.

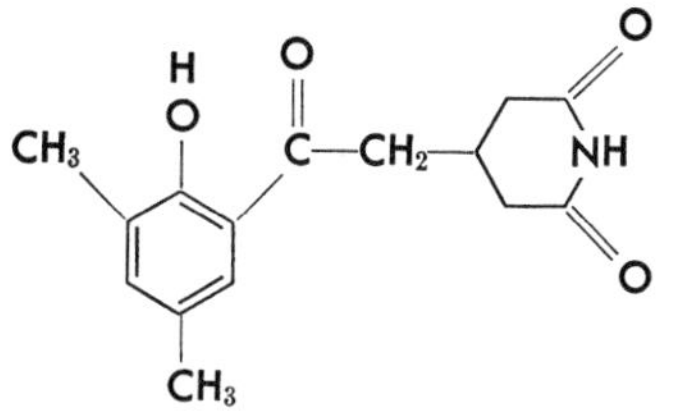

An actidione-producing streptomycete (ETH 7796).
R. J. Highet and V. Prelog, *Helv. Chim. Acta* **42** 1523 (1959).

307   **Inactone,** $C_{15}H_{21}O_4N$, colorless needles, m.p. 116°, $[\alpha]_D^{26}$ −55° (c 2 in water).

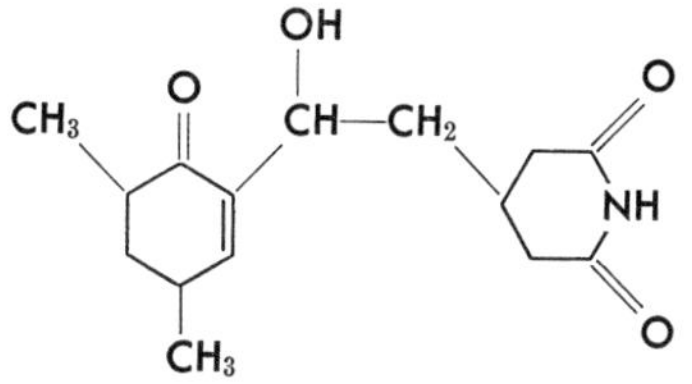

Streptomyces griseus
Raymond Paul and Serge Tchelitcheff, *Bull. soc. chim. France* 1316 (1955).

308   **Cycloheximide** (Actidione, Naramycin A), $C_{15}H_{23}O_4N$, colorless crystals, m.p. 119.5–121°, $[\alpha]_D^{29}$ −3.4° (c 9.47 in ethanol).

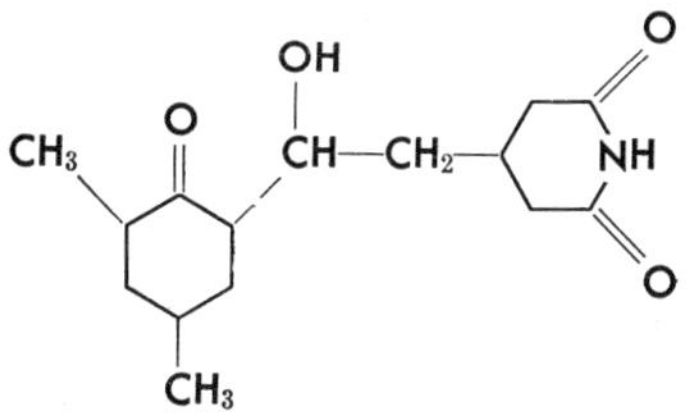

Streptomyces griseus, S. noursei
Byron E. Leach, Jared H. Ford and Alma J. Whiffen, *J. Am. Chem. Soc.* **69** 474 (1947).
Jared H. Ford and Byron E. Leach, *ibid.* **70** 1223 (1948).

Edmund C. Kornfeld, Reuben G. Jones and Thomas V. Parke, *ibid.* **71** 150 (1949). (Structure)
Tomoharu Okuda, *Chem. Pharm. Bull.* (Japan) **7** 659 (1959). (Stereochemistry)

309 Cycloheximide Diasterioisomer, $C_{15}H_{23}O_4N$, colorless rectangular plates, m.p. 100–105°, $[\alpha]_D^{25}$ +12°.

The crystal form differed from that of cycloheximide, and a mixture with authentic cycloheximide melted at 85–95°.

Streptomyces albulus
Cycloheximide, 4-acetoxycycloheximide, two antibiotically inert compounds B-73 and C-73 and fungicidin were isolated from the same culture.

K. Rao, Abstracts, 134th Meeting of the American Chemical Society, Chicago, September 1958.

310 Naramycin B, $C_{15}H_{23}O_4N$, colorless plates, m.p. 109°, $[\alpha]_D^{12.5}$ +50.2° (c 2.0 in methanol).

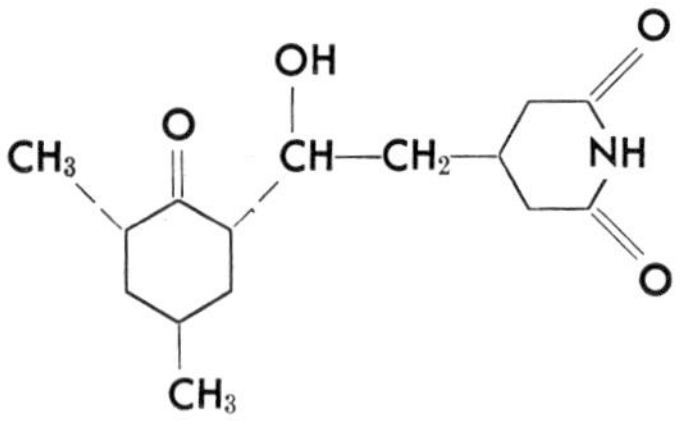

Streptomyces sp.
A stereoisomer of cycloheximide.
Tomoharu Okuda, Makato Suzuki, Yoshiyuki Egawa and Kokichi Ashino, *Chem. Pharm. Bull.* (Japan) **6** 328 (1958). (Isolation)
Tomoharu Okuda, *ibid.* **7** 659 (1959). (Stereochemistry)

311 Streptovitacin A, $C_{15}H_{23}O_5N$, colorless crystals, m.p. 156–159°.

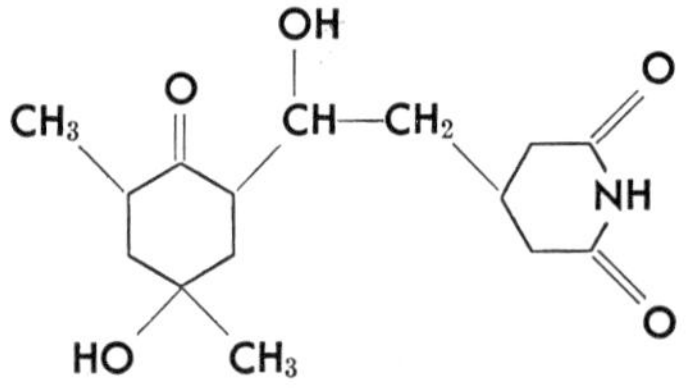

Streptomyces griseus
T. E. Eble, M. E. Bergy, C. M. Large, R. R. Herr and W. G. Jackson, "Antibiotics Annual 1958–1959," Medical Encyclopedia, Inc., New York, p. 555. (Isolation)

Ross R. Herr, *J. Am. Chem. Soc.* **81** 2595 (1959). (Structure)

312 Streptovitacin B, $C_{15}H_{23}O_5N$, colorless crystals, m.p. 124–128°.

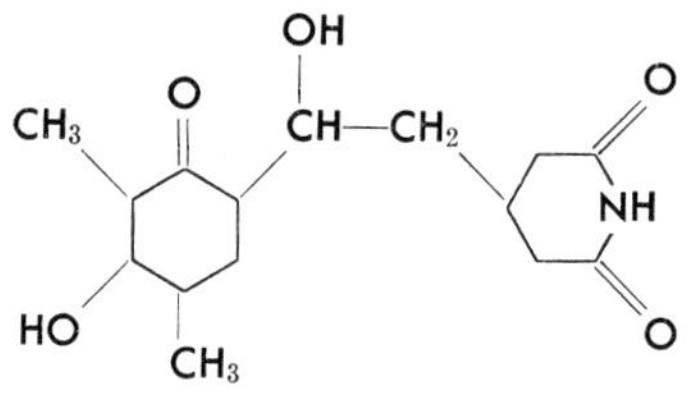

Streptomyces griseus
  T. E. Eble, M. E. Bergy, C. M. Large, R. R. Herr and W. G. Jackson, "Antibiotics Annual 1958–1959," Medical Encyclopedia, Inc., New York, p. 555. (Isolation)
  Ross R. Herr, *J. Am. Chem. Soc.* **81** 2595 (1959). (Structure)

313 Streptovitacin C_2, $C_{15}H_{23}O_5N$, colorless crystals, m.p. 91–96°.

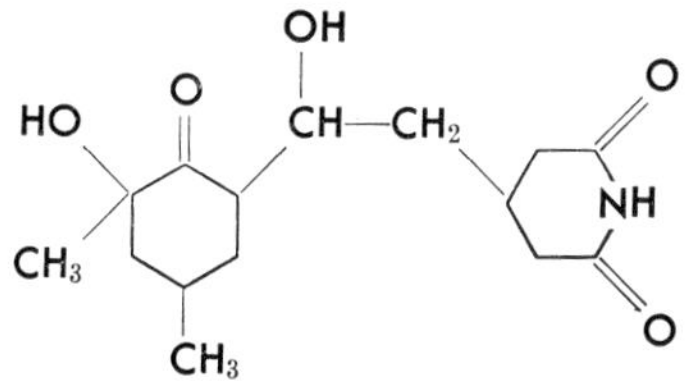

Streptomyces griseus
  Ross R. Herr, *J. Am. Chem. Soc.* **81** 2595 (1959). (Structure)

314 Streptovitacin D, $C_{15}H_{23}O_5N$, colorless crystals, m.p. 67–69°.
  A ring-hydroxylated cycloheximide of unknown structure.
  Streptomyces griseus
  Ross R. Herr, *J. Am. Chem. Soc.* **81** 2595 (1959).

315 Streptimidone, $C_{16}H_{23}O_4N$, colorless crystals, m.p. 72°.

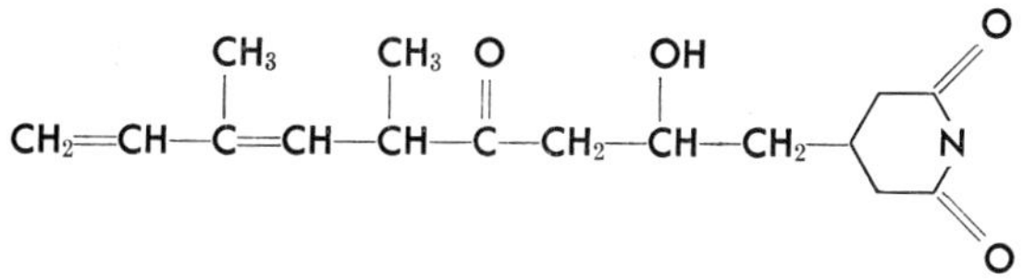

  A streptomycete

Roger P. Frohardt, Henry W. Dion, Zbigniew L. Jukabow-
ski, Albert Ryder, James C. French and Quentin R. Bartz,
J. Am. Chem. Soc. 81 5500 (1959).
E. E. Van Tamelen and V. Haarstad, *J. Am. Chem. Soc.* 82
2974 (1960). (Revised structure)

316 **3-[2-(3,5-Dimethyl-5-acetoxy-2-oxocyclohexyl)-2-hydroxyethyl] glu-
tarimide (4-Acetoxycycloheximide, E-73),** $C_{17}H_{25}O_6N$, colorless crystals, m.p. 140°, $[\alpha]_D^{25}$ −8.8° (c 1.0 in methanol.)

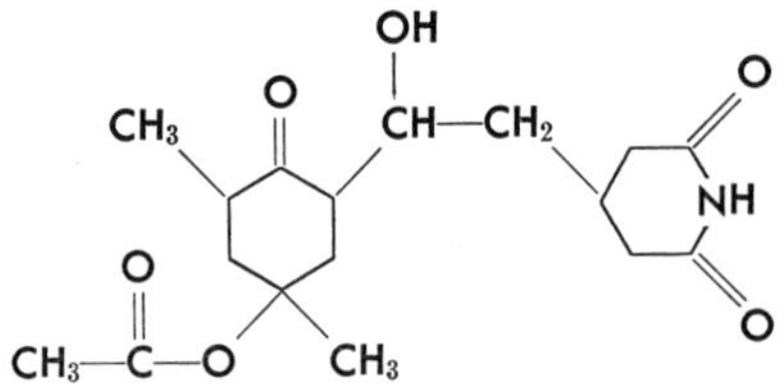

Streptomyces albulus
Two diastereoisomers of cycloheximide were isolated
from the same broth. Fungicidin and two unknown compounds also were isolated.
Koppaka V. Rao and Walter P. Cullen, *J. Am. Chem. Soc.*
82 1127 (1960). (Isolation)
Koppaka V. Rao, *ibid.* 82 1129 (1960). (Structure)

317 **Glauconic Acids.**
Glauconic Acid I, $C_{18}H_{20}O_7$, colorless crystals, m.p.
202°, optically inactive.
Proposed structure:

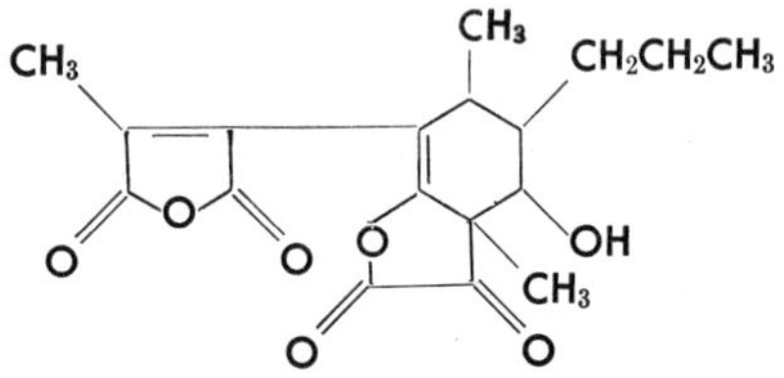

and
Glauconic Acid II, $C_{18}H_{20}O_6$, colorless crystals, m.p.
186°, optically inactive.
Proposed structure:

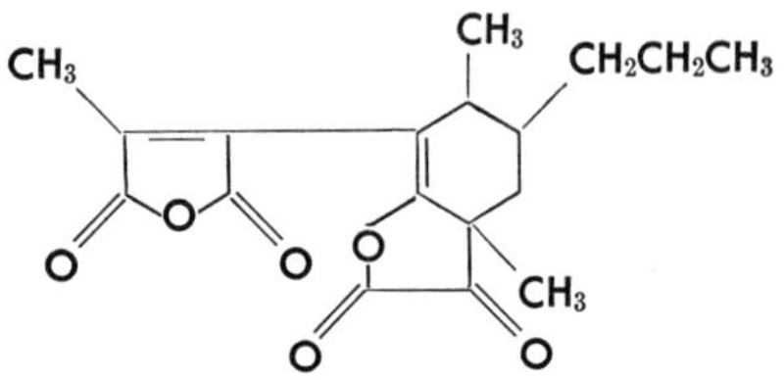

Penicillium glaucum, P. purpurogenum
Nadine Wijkman, *Ann.* 485 61 (1931). (Isolation)
Kurt Kraft, *ibid.* 530 20 (1937). (Structure)
Matao Takashima, Akira Kitajima and Kenichi Otsuka, *Nippon Nôgei-kagaku Kaishi* 29 25 (1955). (Isolation from *P. purpurogenum*) (*Chem. Abstr.* 52 20379d)

318 **Fumagillin** (Amebacilin, Fumidil) $C_{26}H_{34}O_7$, colorless or pale yellow crystals, m.p. 189–194° (dec.), $[\alpha]_D^{25}$ −26.6° (c 0.25 in methanol).

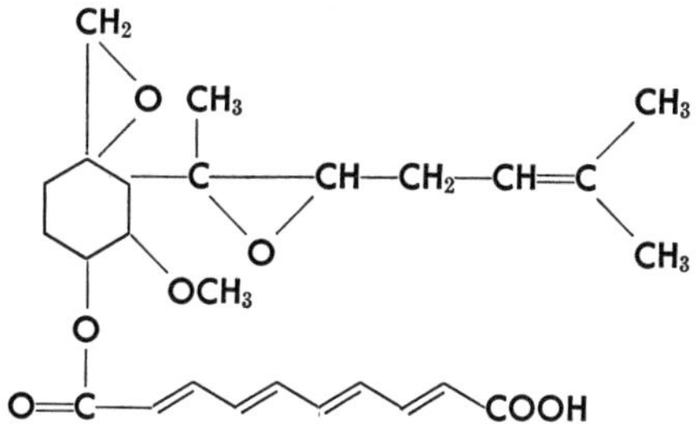

Aspergillus fumigatus Fres.
J. Landquist, *J. Chem. Soc.*, 4237 (1956).
J. McNally and D. Tarbell, *J. Am. Chem. Soc.* 80 3676 (1958).
D. Chapman and D. Tarbell, *ibid.* 80 3679 (1958).
A. Cross and D. Tarbell, *ibid.* 80 3682 (1958).
R. Carman, D. D. Chapman, N. J. McCorkindale, D. S. Tarbell, F. H. L. Varino, R. L. West and D. L. Wilson, *J. Am. Chem. Soc.* 81 3151 (1959).
D. S. Tarbell, R. M. Carman, D. D. Chapman, K. R. Huffman and N. J. McCorkindale, *J. Am. Chem. Soc.* 82 1005 (1960). (Structure)
T. E. Eble and F. R. Hanson, *Antibiotics and Chemotherapy* 1 54 (1951). (Isolation)

9

Terpenoids and Steroids

Ergosterol is the principal fungal sterol. It was named for its occurrence in ergot, and it has been isolated from a wide variety of other fungi as well as from lichens. It has been reported to be the only sterol in certain molds,[1] but it is often accompanied by related compounds. It has been identified also in algae. Some yeasts produce several per cent of their dry cell weight in ergosterol. Yeasts which produce large quantities of fat do not necessarily produce a higher proportion of ergosterol.

There have been few reports of the isolation or detection of sterols in bacteria, and there is doubt as to whether bacteria produce sterols. A critical historical review of this question has been published.[2] Mevalonic acid is an acetate-replacing factor in lactobacilli, and a labeling study[3] with paper chromatography and spectral work on the labeled non-saponifiable lipides showed the presence of non-steroid, hydroxylated and unsaturated compounds with more than 15 carbon atoms. It may be that simpler substances of this sort replace sterols in bacteria. An artificial requirement for vitamin D_2 can be induced in some bacteria. The resulting inhibition of growth can be reversed by vitamins D_2, D_3 or suprasterol, but not by 7-dehydroergosterol nor by cholesterol.[3]

Yeasts and higher fungi produce squalene and C_{27} to C_{31} compounds, some of which have been shown to be precursors of cholesterol in mammalian metabolism. Some higher fungi and many lichens produce triterpenes or close derivatives.

Since the availability of isotopes, which permit the tracing of small quantities of material, much of the biosynthetic route to

[1] Joseph V. Fiore, *Arch. Biochem.* 16 161 (1948).

[2] Audrey Fiertel and Harold P. Klein, *J. Bacteriol.* 78 738 (1959).

[3] E. Kodicek, Abstracts of the Gordon Conference on Vitamins and Metabolism, 1958.

the principal mammalian sterol, cholesterol, has been worked out. Good reviews of this work are available.[4] Many of the proved intermediates in this route have been isolated from fungi, and evidently the biogenesis of ergosterol and the triterpenes is quite similar to that of cholesterol up to the later stages.[5]

The conversion of acetate to mevalonate follows the course:[6, 6a]

$$CH_3CO—S—CoA + CH_3COCH_2CO—S—CoA \rightarrow$$
Acetyl CoA   Acetoacetyl CoA

$$\underset{\substack{| \\ OH}}{CoA—S—COCH_2—\overset{\substack{CH_3 \\ |}}{C}—CH_2—COOH} \rightarrow \left[\underset{\substack{| \\ OH}}{OHC—CH_2—\overset{\substack{CH_3 \\ |}}{C}—CH_2—COOH} \right]$$

3-Methyl-3-oxyglutaryl CoA   Mevaldic Acid
(Hydroxymethylglutaryl CoA,
HMG-CoA)

$$\underset{\substack{| \\ OH}}{HOCH_2—CH_2—\overset{\substack{CH_3 \\ |}}{C}—CH_2—COOH}$$

Mevalonic Acid

In the light of the newer knowledge concerning the role of malonyl CoA in fatty acid biosynthesis there may eventually be some minor modifications in this scheme. It should be mentioned that mevalonic acid has been shown to be an irreversible intermediate in the biosynthesis of terpenoids.[7, 8, 9]

Isopentenyl pyrophosphate, a further intermediate in the bio-

[4] Louis F. Fieser and Mary Fieser, "Steroids," Reinhold Publishing Corp., New York, 1959, pp. 403–420.

[5] Pierre Crabbé, *Record of Chemical Progress* 20 189 (1959).

[6] J. W. Cornforth, R. H. Cornforth, A. Pelter, M. G. Horning and G. Popják, *Tetrahedron* 5 311 (1959).

[6a] G. E. W. Wolstenholme and Maeve O'Conner (Eds.), "CIBA Foundation Symposium on the Biosynthesis of Terpenes and Sterols," Harry Rudney, *The biosynthesis of β-hydroxy-β-methylglutaryl coezyme A and its conversion to mevalonic acid*, Little, Brown and Co., Boston, 1959, pp. 75–94.

[7] A. J. Birch, R. J. English, R. A. Massy-Westropp and Herchel Smith, *Proc. Chem. Soc.*, 233 (1957).

[8] *Idem., J. Chem. Soc.*, 369 (1958).

[9] J. Fishman, E. R. H. Jones, G. Lowe and M. C. Whiting, *Proc. Chem. Soc.*, 127 (1959).

synthetic process, apparently arises from phosphorylated meva-lonic acid by a concerted decarboxylation with elimination of the C-3-hydroxyl group, since it has been shown that no proto-nation of the carbon chain occurs during decarboxylation.[10]

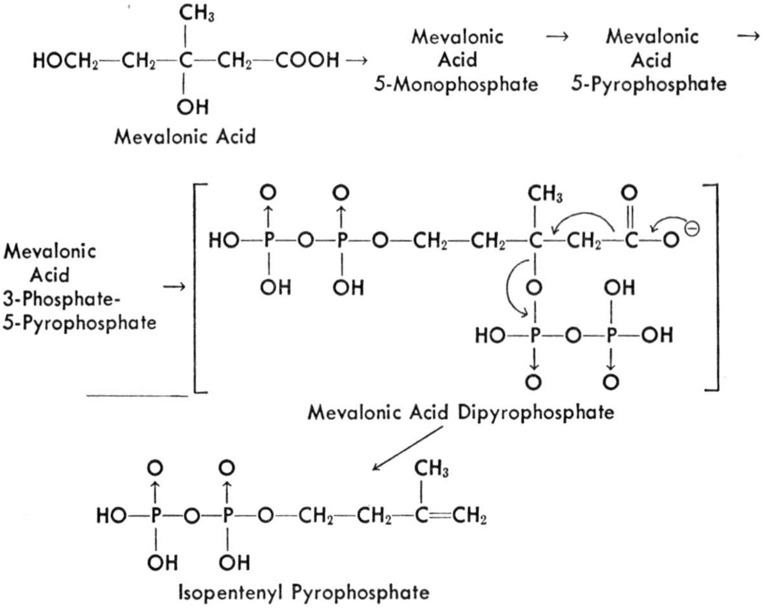

Mevalonic Acid

Mevalonic   →   Mevalonic   →
Acid   Acid
5-Monophosphate 5-Pyrophosphate

Mevalonic
Acid
3-Phosphate-
5-Pyrophosphate   →

Mevalonic Acid Dipyrophosphate

Isopentenyl Pyrophosphate

Since both γ,γ-dimethylallyl pyrophosphate[11] and farnesyl pyrophosphate[12] have been isolated, it is possible to envisage a continuation:

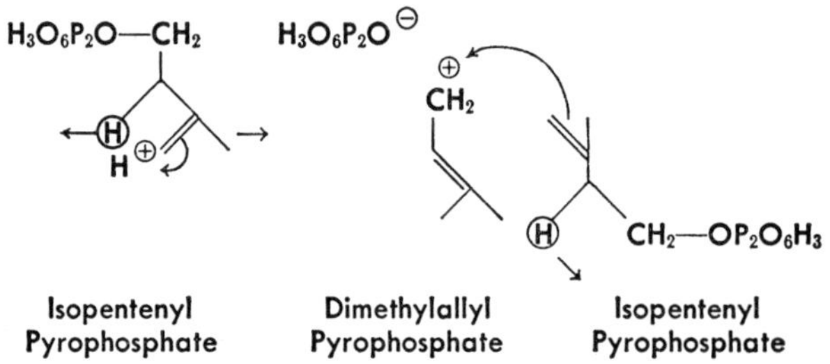

Isopentenyl   Dimethylallyl   Isopentenyl
Pyrophosphate   Pyrophosphate   Pyrophosphate

[10] A. de Waard, A. H. Phillips and Konrad Bloch, *J. Am. Chem. Soc.* **81** 2913 (1959).

[11] B. W. Agranoff, H. Eggerer, U. Henning and F. Lynen, *J. Am. Chem. Soc.* **81** 1254 (1959).

[12] F. Lynen, H. Eggerer, U. Henning and Ingrid Kessel, *Angew. Chem.* **70** 738 (1958).

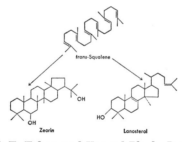

Farnesyl Pyrophosphate

Two moles of farnesyl pyrophosphate then unite head-to-head in what, deuterium experiments indicate,[13, 14] is probably a reductive process to form squalene.* All *trans*-squalene is formed, and this is the only isomer which can cyclize to triterpenes and steroids.[15]

The significance of the stereoisomer has been considered, and a generalized scheme devised for the various modes of cyclization of squalene, supported by the current theories of conformational analysis and ionic cyclization.[16, 17, 18]

Squalene can cyclize with no skeletal rearrangement to form compounds such as the lichen substance, zeorin. It also can rearrange to the lanostane skeleton found so frequently among the steroids of the higher fungi. Lanosterol itself, a known intermediate in the biosynthetic route to cholesterol, has been found in yeast, as has squalene.

[13] H. Rilling, T. T. Tchen and Konrad Bloch, *Proc. Nat. Acad. Sci.* **44** 163 (1958).

[14] H. C. Rilling and Konrad Bloch, *J. Biol. Chem.* **234** 1424 (1959).

* See addendum for a recent modification of this scheme.

[15] Robert G. Langdon and Konrad Bloch, *ibid.* **200** 135 (1953).

[16] L. Ruzicka, A. Eschenmoser and H. Heusser, *Experientia* **9** 362 (1953).

[17] A. Eschenmoser, L. Ruzicka, O. Jeger and D. Arigoni, *Helv. Chim. Acta* **38** 1890 (1955).

[18] Alexander Todd, "Perspectives in Organic Chemistry," L. Ruzicka, *Bedeutung der theoretischen organischen Chemie für die Chemie der Terpenverbindungen,* Interscience Publishers, Inc., New York, 1956, pp. 265–315; L. Ruzicka, *Proc. Chem. Soc.,* 341–360 (1959); Faraday Lecture, *History of the isoprene rule.*

It is likely that the cyclization of squalene to form such structures occurs by a concerted mechanism which proceeds from ring to ring until complete and that this all occurs on one enzyme surface. Thus, isolation of intermediates between squalene and an initial cyclization product such as the one shown is improbable. The cyclization is oxygen-initiated, explaining the frequent occurrence of the 3-hydroxyl groups in natural steroids.

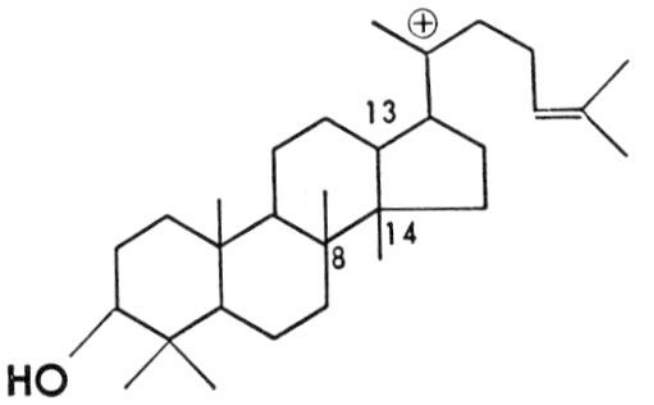

Proposed initial cyclization
product of the Squalene → Lanosterol
route

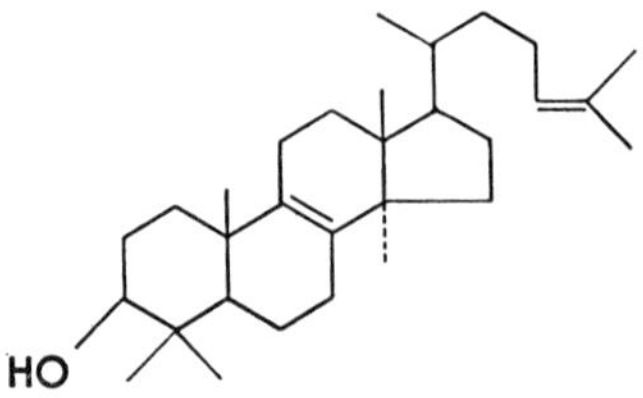

Lanosterol

Transformation of the proposed tetracyclic precursor to lanosterol involves two 1,2-methyl group migrations (14 → 13 and 8 → 14) as shown by tracer experiments.[6, 19]

Eburicoic acid has the lanostane skeleton, but with a methylene group attached to carbon atom 24 of the side-chain. Similarly, ergosterol has a methyl group in this position. Labeling

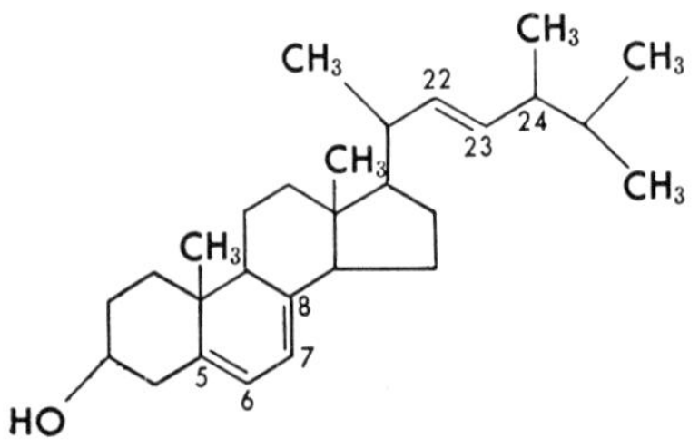

Ergosterol

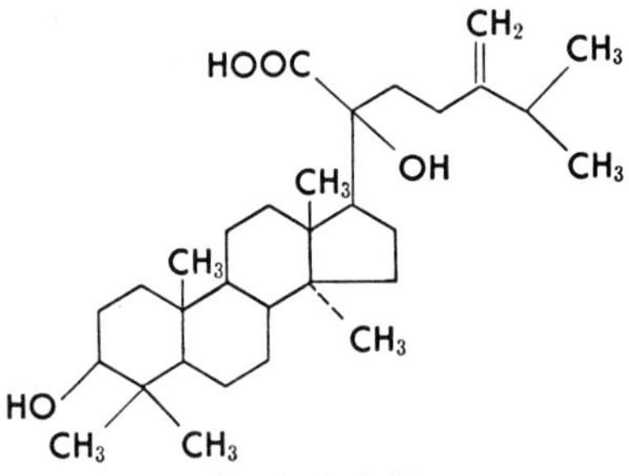

Eburicoic Acid

[19] R. K. Maudgal, T. T. Tchen and Konrad Bloch, *J. Am. Chem. Soc.* 80 2589 (1958).

experiments[20, 21, 22, 23] have shown that this "extra" carbon atom is not derived from acetate, but is furnished by formate and, more efficiently, by methionine.

Progressing along the biosynthetic route from squalene to ergosterol (and cholesterol), it is obvious that lanosterol must lose the two methyl groups at C-4 and one at C-14. These are probably removed oxidatively, and eventually some of the intermediates may be isolated. Zymosterol has been considered as an intermediate in the biosynthesis of cholesterol; but while it occurs together with ergosterol in yeasts, it has been found[20] that squalene, but not zymosterol, is converted to ergosterol by yeast homogenates.

The biogenesis of the interesting diterpenoids gibberellic acid, rosenonolactone and trichothecin has been studied. In the case of gibberellic acid[24] studies with $CH_3C^{14}OOH$ and with C-2-la-

beled mevalonate gave the labeling pattern shown. A precursor was inferred, and the following deductions made: (a) The methyl carbon atom attached to ring A is derived specifically from position 2 of mevalonic acid lactone. (b) The carboxyl carbon atom is derived specifically from position 9 of the precursor. (c) The phyllocladene ring system of gibberellic acid is formed by migration of C-6 to C-18.

Rosenonolactone, rosololactone and trichothecin are all produced by the fungus *Trichothecium roseum*.

[20] George J. Alexander, Allen M. Gold and Erwin Schwenk, *ibid.* **79** 2967 (1957).

[21] William G. Dauben and John H. Richards, *ibid.* **78** 5329 (1956).

[22] William G. Dauben, Yoshio Ban and John H. Richards, *ibid.* **79** 968 (1957).

[23] William G. Dauben, Gerhard J. Fonken and George A. Boswell, *ibid.* **79** 1000 (1957).

[24] A. J. Birch, R. W. Rickards and Herchel Smith, *Proc. Chem. Soc.*, 192 (1958).

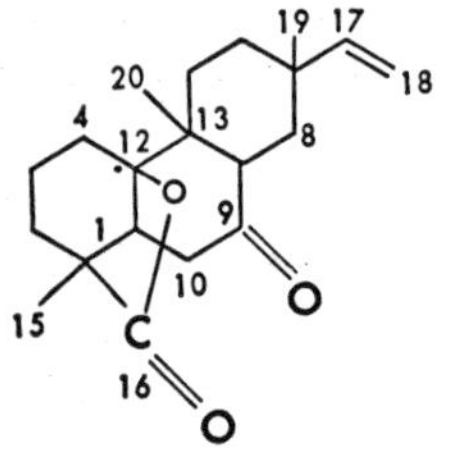

Rosenonolactone 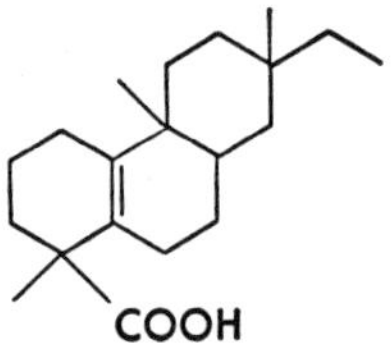   Rosololactone 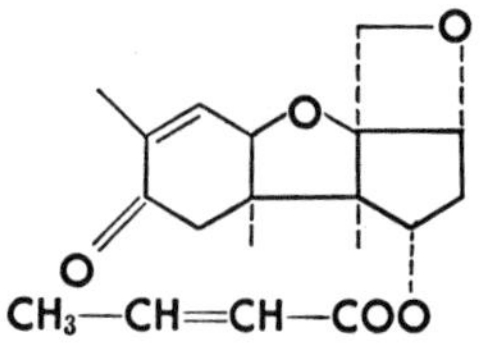   Trichothecin

The carbon skeleton of rosenonolactone[9] is apparently derived from the same kind of precursor as gibberellic acid, but in a simpler way. All that is required is the migration of a methyl group from C-12 to C-13 in the same manner as in the biosynthesis of steroids.

The carbon skeleton of trichothecin[10] can be derived from a sesquiterpenoid intermediate by way of two 1,2-methyl group shifts:

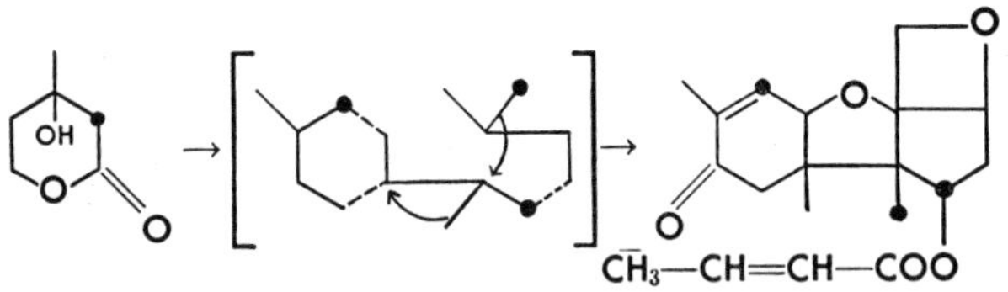

2-C^{14}-Me-   Proposed sesquiter-   Trichothecin
valonate   penoid intermediate

When labeled acetate was used in this study, 95% of the activity appeared in the crotonic acid moiety. These results, considered together, are another confirmation of the irreversibility of the acetate-mevalonate process.

A symposium has been published thoroughly reviewing current research on the biosynthesis of terpenes and sterols.[25]

319 **Lactaroviolin,** $C_{15}H_{14}O$, red-violet crystals, m.p. 53°.

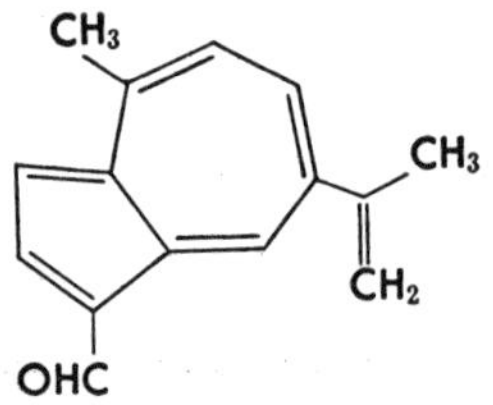

[25] G. E. W. Wolstenholme and Maeve O'Conner (Eds.), "CIBA Foundation Symposium on the Biosynthesis of Terpenes and Sterols," Little, Brown and Co., Boston, 1959.

Lactarius deliciosus L.

Harry Willstaedt and B. Zetterberg, *Svensk Kem. Tidskr.* **58** 306 (1946).

Pl. A. Plattner, E. Heilbronner, R. W. Schmid, R. Sandrin and A. Fürst, *Chem. and Ind.*, 1202 (1954). (Structure)

E. Heilbronner and R. W. Schmid, *Helv. Chim. Acta* **37** 2018 (1954).

320 **Lactarazulene,** $C_{15}H_{16}$, blue liquid, b.p. 155–160° (2.5–3 mm.).

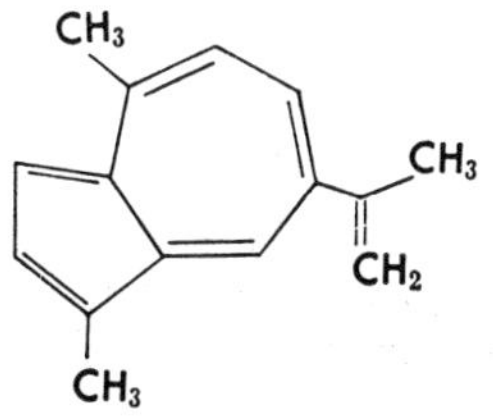

Lactarius deliciosus L.

321 Occurs together with lactaroviolin (q.v.) and a green crystalline compound, **Verdazulene,** $C_{15}H_{16}$, m.p. 90°.

Frantisek Sorm, Vera Benesova and Vlastimil Herout, *Chem. Listy* **47** 1856 (1953). (Structure)

Gibberellins and Gibberellenic Acid

Although gibberellic acid is the gibberellin produced in highest yield by *Gibberella fujikuroi,* three minor gibberellins are produced also, and the crude mixture is commonly isolated. The minor gibberellins are called A_1, A_2 and A_4, gibberellic acid being A_3. (It also has been called gibberellin X.) Their structures are similar to those of gibberellic acid.

Gibberellin A_1 has been found in plants as well as in fungi. All of the four gibberellins show plant hormone activity. A fifth, inactive, compound called gibberellenic acid has been isolated recently. It may be an artifact.

A structure for gibberellic acid was advanced in 1956 by an English group. Structure work has continued in Japan, where the gibberellins were originally isolated, and recently structures for all the gibberellins have been published which differ somewhat from the one first advanced in England. Even more recently a third set of structures, complete with stereochemistry, has been proposed by the English school. It is these structures which are shown here.

322 **Gibberellenic Acid,** $C_{19}H_{22}O_6$, colorless crystals, m.p. 185° (dec.). Strong U.V. absorption at 253 mμ ($\epsilon = 19{,}200$).

OH
HO
HOOC CH$_3$
COOH CH$_2$

Fusarium moniliforme
Koert Gerzon, Harold L. Bird, Jr. and Don O. Woolf, Jr., *Experientia* 13 487 (1957).

323 **Gibberellic Acid** (Gibberellin A$_3$, Gibberellin X), $C_{19}H_{22}O_6$, colorless crystals, m.p. 235° (dec.), $[\alpha]_D^{20}$ +92°.
Proposed complete stereochemical structure:

O H
CO H
H
---OH
HO
CH$_3$ COOH
CH$_2$

P. J. Curtis and B. E. Cross, *Chem. and Ind.*, 1066 (1954). (Isolation)
B. E. Cross, John Frederick Grove, J. MacMillan and T. P. C. Mulholland, *Chem. and Ind.*, 954 (1956). (Structure)
Brian E. Cross, *J. Chem. Soc.*, 4670 (1954).
Nobutaka Takahashi, Yasuo Seta, Hiroshi Kitamura and Yusuke Sumiki, *Bull. Agr. Chem. Soc.* (Japan) 23 405 (1959).
Hiroshi Kitamura, Yasuo Seta, Nobutaka Takahashi, Akira Kawarada and Yusuke Sumiki, *ibid.* 23 408 (1959).
Yasuo Seta, Nobutaka Takahashi, Akira Kawarada, Hiroshi Kitamura and Yusuke Sumiki, *ibid.* 23 412 (1959).
Nobutaka Takahashi, Yasuo Seta, Hiroshi Kitamura, Akira Kawarada and Yusuke Sumiki, *ibid.* 23 493 (1959).
Yasuo Seta, Nobutaka Takahashi, Hiroshi Kitamura, Makoto Takai, Sahuro Tamura and Yusuke Sumiki, *ibid.* 23 499 (1959).
Nobutaka Takahashi, Yasuo Seta, Hiroshi Kitamura and Yusuke Sumiki, *ibid.* 23 509 (1959).
B. E. Cross, J. F. Grove, P. McCloskey and T. P. C. Mulholland, *Chem. and Ind.*, 1345 (1959); B. E. Cross, John Frederick Grove, J. MacMillan, J. S. Moffatt, T. P. C. Mulholland and J. C. Seaton, *Proc. Chem. Soc.*, 302 (1959).

324 Gibberellin A_4, $C_{19}H_{24}O_5$, colorless crystals, m.p. 222° (dec.), $[\alpha]_D^{20}$ −20.8° (c 0.34 in methanol).

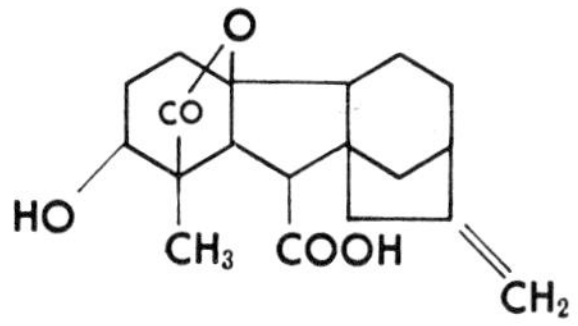

Gibberella fujikuroi (Saw.) Wollenweber

Nobutaka Takahashi, Yasuo Seta, Hiroshi Kitamura and Yusuke Sumiki, *Bull. Agr. Chem. Soc.* (Japan) **21** 396 (1957). (Isolation of Gibberellin A₄)

See other references under Gibberellin A₁ for structure work.

325 Gibberellin A_1, $C_{19}H_{24}O_6$, colorless crystals, m.p. 255–258° (dec.), $[\alpha]_D^{25}$ +36°.

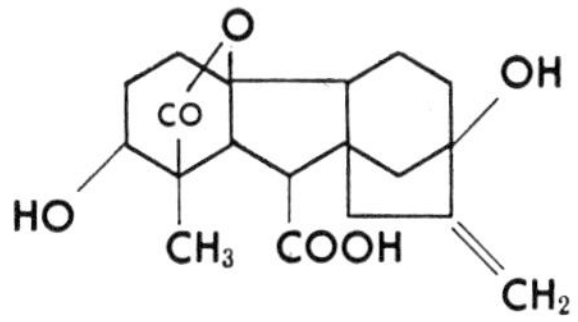

Gibberella fujikuroi (Saw.) Wollenweber

Nobutaka Takahashi, Hiroshi Kitamura, Akira Kawarada, Yasuo Seta, Makato Takai, Suburo Tamura and Yusuke Sumiki, *Bull. Agr. Chem. Soc.* (Japan) 19 267 (1955). (Isolation of gibberellins and their properties)

Nobutaka Takahashi, Yasuo Seta, Hiroshi Kitamura and Yusuke Sumiki, *ibid.* 23 405 (1959).

Hiroshi Kitamura, Yasuo Seta, Nobutaka Takahashi, Akira Kawarada and Yusuke Sumiki, *ibid.* 23 408 (1959). (Structures of the gibberellins)

Nobutaka Takahashi, Yasuo Seta, Hiroshi Kitamura, Akira Kawarada and Yusuke Sumiki, *ibid.* 23 493 (1959). (Structures of the gibberellins).

Yasuo Seta, Nobutaka Takahashi, Hiroshi Kitamura, Makato Tokai, Saburo Tamura and Yusuke Sumiki, *ibid.* 23 499 (1959). (Structures of the gibberellins)

Nobutaka Takahashi, Yasuo Seta, Hiroshi Kitamura and Yusuke Sumiki, *ibid.* 23 509 (1959). (Structures of the gibberellins)

B. E. Cross, John Frederick Grove, J. MacMillan, J. S. Moffatt, T. P. C. Mulholland and J. C. Seaton, *Proc. Chem. Soc.*, 302 (1959). (Above structure)

326 **Gibberellin A$_2$,** C$_{19}$H$_{26}$O$_6$, colorless crystals, m.p. 235–237° (dec.), [α]$_D$ +11.7°.

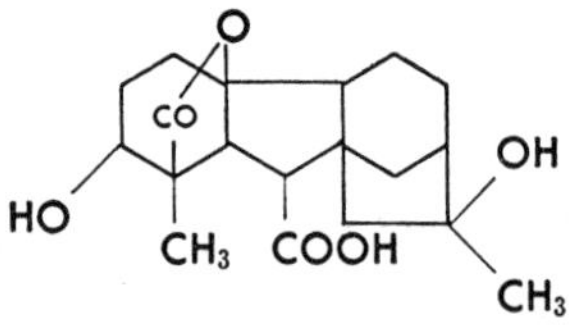

Gibberella fujikuroi (Saw.) Wollenweber
See references under **Gibberellin A$_1$.**

327 **Trichothecin,** C$_{19}$H$_{24}$O$_5$, colorless needles, m.p. 118°, [α]$_D^{18}$ +44° (c 1.0 in chloroform).

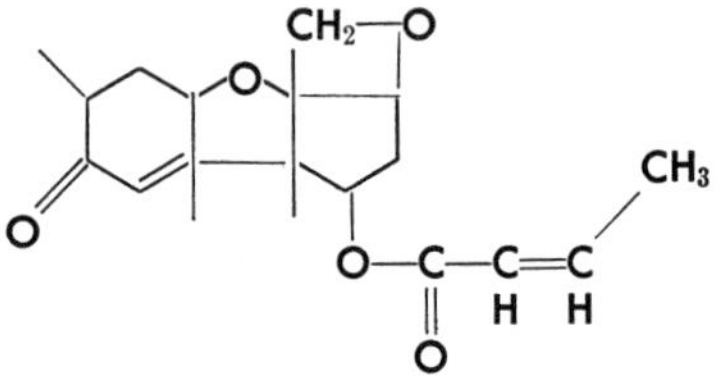

Trichothecium roseum (Link)
G. G. Freeman and R. I. Morrison, *Nature* 162 30 (1948).
G. G. Freeman, J. E. Gill and W. S. Waring, *J. Chem. Soc.*, 1105 (1959). (Structure)
J. Fishman, E. R. H. Jones, G. Lowe and M. C. Whiting, *Proc. Chem. Soc.*, 127 (1959). (Structure)

328 **Rosenonolactone,** C$_{20}$H$_{28}$O$_3$, white prisms, m.p. 208°, [α]$_D^{18}$ −116° (c 2.0 in chloroform).

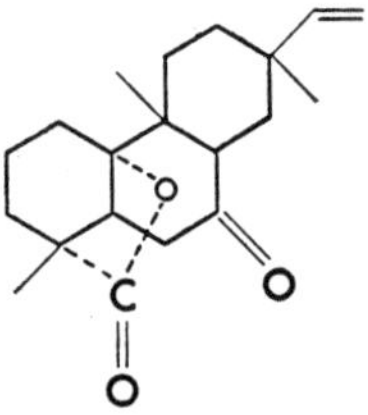

Trichothecium roseum (Link)
About 6 g. of dry mycelium were obtained from a liter of culture solution, and from this about 0.2 g. of rosenonolactone was extracted.

Alexander Robertson, W. R. Smithies and Eric Tittensor, *J. Chem. Soc.*, 879 (1949). (Isolation)

Adelaide Harris, Alexander Robertson and W. B. Whalley, *ibid.*, 1799 (1958). (Structure)

329 9-Deoxorosenonolactone, $C_{20}H_{30}O_2$, colorless crystals, m.p. 115°, $[\alpha]_D$ +57° (in chloroform).

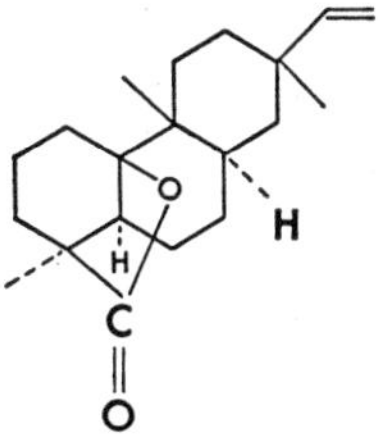

Trichothecium roseum (Link)
W. B. Whalley, B. Green, D. Arigoni, J. J. Britt and Carl Djerassi, *J. Am. Chem. Soc.* 81 5520 (1959).

330 Rosololactone, $C_{20}H_{30}O_3$, white crystals, m.p. 186°, $[\alpha]_D^{18}$ +6.3° (c 2.3 in chloroform).

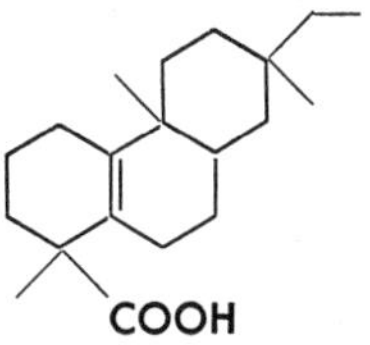

Trichothecium roseum (Link)
Rosololactone is a minor product of this fermentation. It occurs in the mycelium together with rosenonolactone and mannitol.
Alexander Robertson, W. R. Smithies and Eric Tittensor, *J. Chem. Soc.*, 879 (1949). (Isolation)
Adelaide Harris, Alexander Robertson and W. B. Whalley, *ibid.*, 1807 (1958). (Structure)

331 Zymosterol, $C_{27}H_{44}O$, colorless crystals, m.p. 110°, $[\alpha]_D$ +49°.

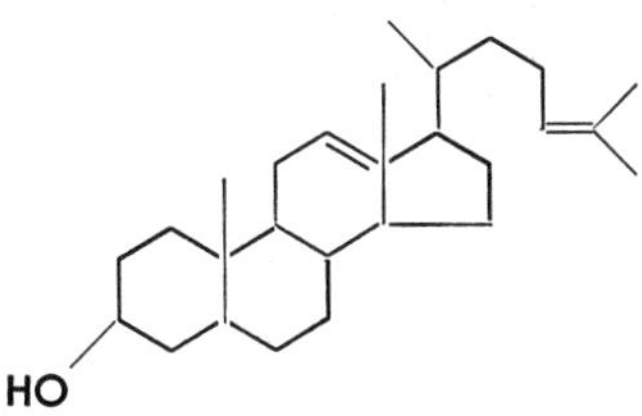

Zymosterol is second to ergosterol in abundance in yeast fat.

Ida Smedley-MacLean, *Biochem. J.* 22 22 (1928). (Isolation)

332 **Hyposterol,** tentatively $C_{27}H_{42}O$ or $C_{27}H_{44}O$, colorless unstable crystals, m.p. 100–102°, $[\alpha]_D^{20}$ +12.5° (in chloroform).
Structure unknown. May be a C_{28} sterol.
Yeasts
Heinrich Wieland and G. A. C. Gaugh, *Ann.* 482 36 (1930).

333 **Anasterol,** $C_{27}H_{44}O$, colorless crystals, m.p. 157–159°, $[\alpha]_D^{25}$ −8.1° (in chloroform).
Structure unknown. May be a C_{28} sterol.
Yeasts
Heinrich Wieland and G. A. C. Gaugh, *Ann.* 482 36 (1930).

334 **14-Dehydroergosterol,** $C_{28}H_{42}O$, colorless needles, m.p. 198–201°, $[\alpha]_D$ −396° (in carbon tetrachloride).

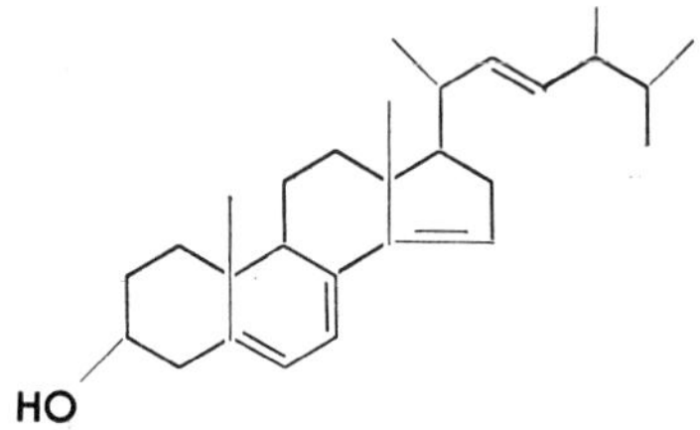

Aspergillus niger
Ergosterol was isolated from the same culture.
D. H. R. Barton and T. Bruun, *J. Chem. Soc.,* 2728 (1951).

335 **24(28)-Dehydroergosterol** **(5,7,22,24(28)-Ergostatetraen-3-β-ol),** $C_{28}H_{42}O$, colorless crystals (Monohydrate), m.p. 118–120°, $[\alpha]_D^{25}$ −78° (1% in chloroform).
Probable structure:

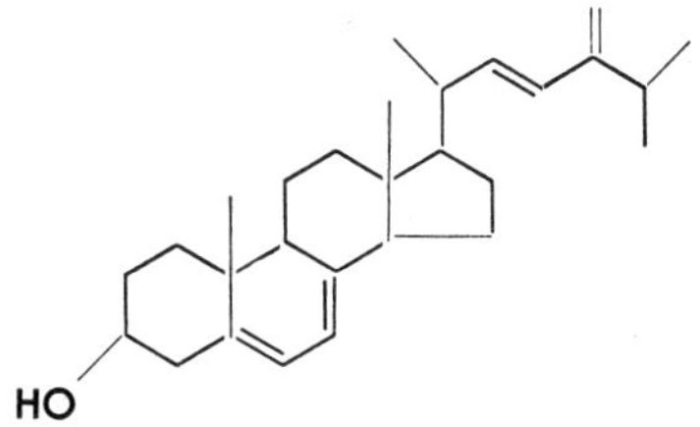

Yeasts
Under appropriate growth conditions, yields of this sterol equal those of ergosterol.

O. N. Breivek, J. L. Owades and R. F. Light, *J. Org. Chem.*
19 1734 (1954).

336 Ergosterol, $C_{28}H_{44}O$, colorless crystals, m.p. 165°, $[\alpha]_D^{25}$ —130°
(in chloroform).

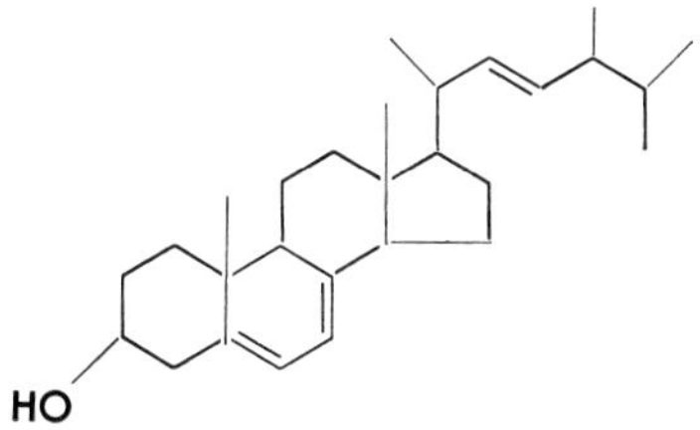

HO

Ergosterol is the most abundant sterol of yeasts and
molds. It occurs widely and was isolated first from ergot
(*Claviceps purpurea*). It also occurs in lichens and has
been detected in *Euglena* spp. There is much literature,
one recent example being:
Akira Saito, *J. Fermentation Technol.* (Japan) 31 140
(1953).
Yields as high as 2–2.7% of dry cell weight have been
reported, by using *Saccharomyces carlsbergensis*. Ergosterol is reported to be the only sterol occurring in several
species of Fusaria. It occurs as the palmitate in *Penicillium* spp. and in *Aspergillus fumigatus*.
Albert E. Oxford and Harold Raistrick, *Biochem. J.* 27 1176
(1933).
P. Wieland and V. Prelog, *Helv. Chim. Acta* 30 1028 (1947).
Joseph V. Fiore, *Arch. Biochem.* 16 161 (1948).

337 Pyrocalciferol, $C_{28}H_{44}O$, colorless needles, m.p. 93–95°, $[\alpha]_D^{20}$
+502° (in alcohol).

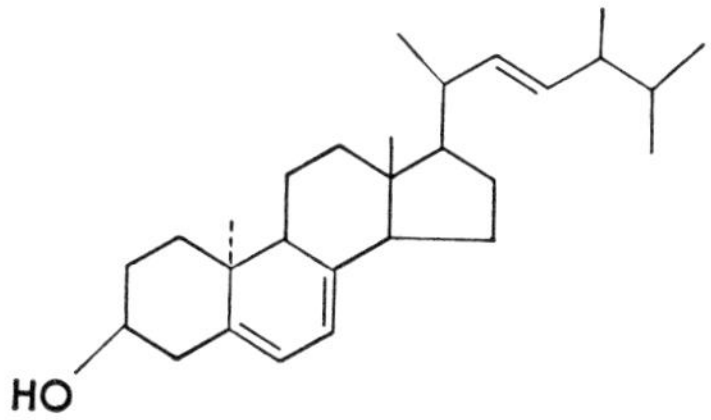

HO

Penicillium notatum
A yield of 12 mg. was obtained from 450 g. of dry
mycelium.

A. Angeletti, G. Tappi and G. Biglino, *Ann. Chim.* (Rome)
42 502 (1952).
J. Castells, E. R. H. Jones, G. D. Meakins and R. W. J. Williams, *J. Chem. Soc.*, 1159 (1959). (Structure)

338 Ergosta-7,22-dien-3-one, $C_{28}H_{44}O$, m.p. 184–187°, $[\alpha]_D$ +6° (in chloroform).

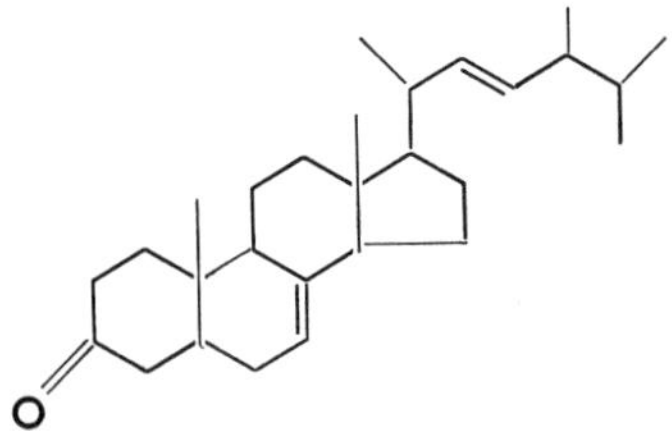

Fomes fomentarius
H. R. Arthur, T. G. Halsall and R. D. Smith, *J. Chem. Soc.*, 2603 (1958).

339 Ergosterol Peroxide, $C_{28}H_{44}O_3$, colorless crystals, m.p. 178°, $[\alpha]_D$ −36°.

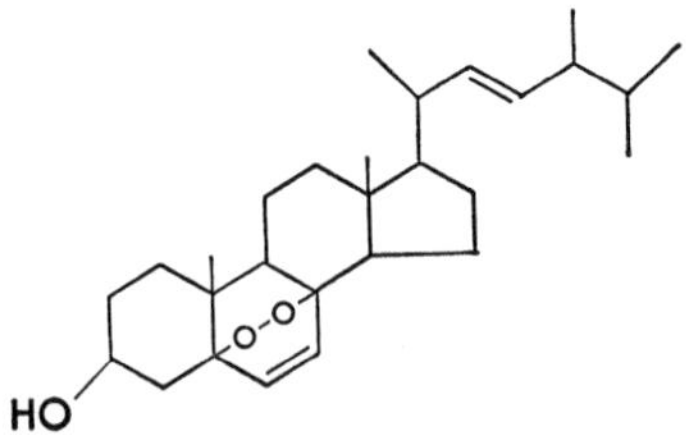

Aspergillus fumigatus (mycelium)
P. Wieland and V. Prelog, *Helv. Chim. Acta* 30 1028 (1947).

340 Episterol ($\Delta^{7,24(28)}$-Ergostadien-3β-ol), $C_{28}H_{46}O$, colorless crystals, m.p. 150°, $[\alpha]_D$ −5° (in chloroform).

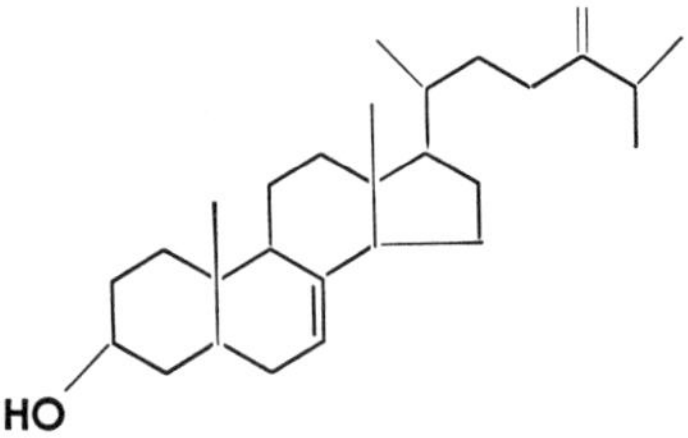

Yeasts

Heinrich Wieland, Fridolf Rath and Horst Hesse, *Ann.* 548 34 (1941).

341 **5,6-Dihydroergosterol** ($\Delta^{7,22}$-Ergostadien-3β-ol), $C_{28}H_{46}O$, colorless crystals, m.p. 176°, $[\alpha]_D^{20\ \pm5}$ −19° (in chloroform).

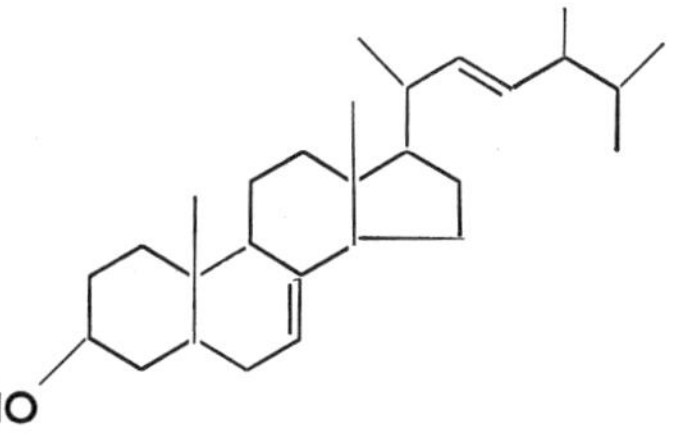

Yeasts, *Claviceps purpurea*
Heinrich Wieland and Willi Benend, *Ann.* 554 1 (1943).
D. H. R. Barton and J. D. Cox, *J. Chem. Soc.*, 1354 (1948).

342 **Fecosterol** ($\Delta^{8,24(28)'}$-Ergostadien-3β-ol), $C_{28}H_{46}O$, colorless crystals, m.p. 161–163°, $[\alpha]_D^{25}$ +42° (in chloroform).

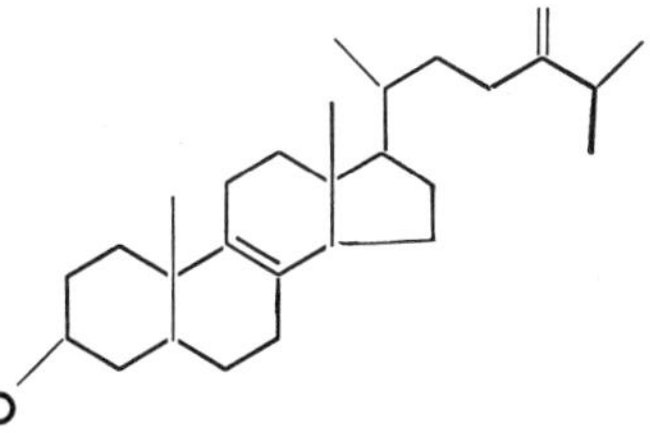

Yeasts
Heinrich Wieland, Fridolf Rath and Horst Hesse, *Ann.* 548 34 (1941).
D. H. R. Barton and J. D. Cox, *J. Chem. Soc.*, 214 (1949).

343 **Ascosterol** ($\Delta^{8,23(?)}$-Ergostadien-3β-ol), $C_{28}H_{46}O$, colorless crystals, m.p. 146°, $[\alpha]_D^{23}$ +45° (in chloroform).

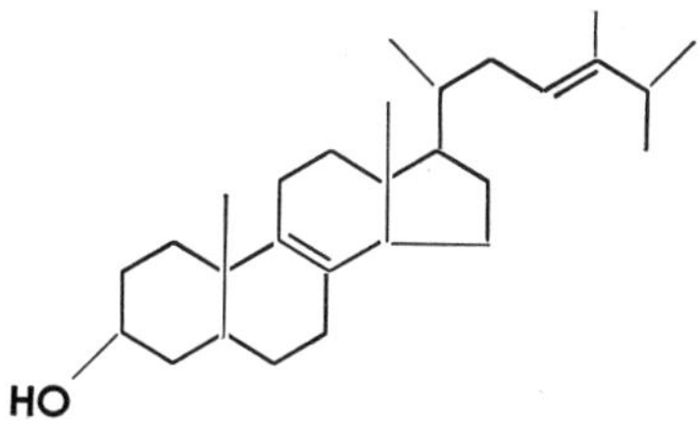

Yeasts

Heinrich Wieland, Fridolf Rath and Horst Hesse, *Ann.* 548 34 (1951).

344 Cerevisterol ($\Delta^{7,22}$-Ergostadiene-$3\beta,5\alpha,6\beta$-triol), $C_{28}H_{46}O_3$, colorless crystals, m.p. 256–259°, $[\alpha]_D$ −83° (c 0.89 in pyridine).

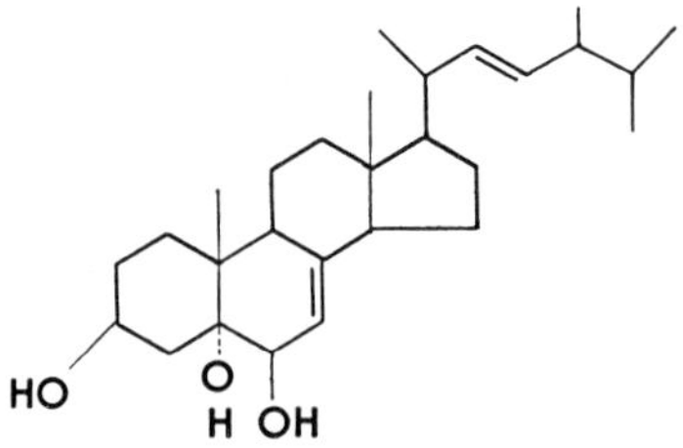

HO   O
    H OH

Yeasts, *Claviceps purpurea* (ergot), *Amanita phalloides*
About 10 g. were obtained from 4500 kg. of dried yeast.
Some 20 g. were obtained from 17 kg. of dry *Amanita phalloides*.

Heinrich Wieland and Gustav Coutelle, *Ann.* 548 275 (1941). (Isolation)

G. H. Alt and D. H. R. Barton, *J. Chem. Soc.,* 1356 (1954). (Structure)

345 Fungisterol (Δ^7-Ergosten-3β-ol), $C_{28}H_{48}O$, colorless crystals, m.p. 149°, $[\alpha]_D^{23}$ −0.2° (in chloroform).

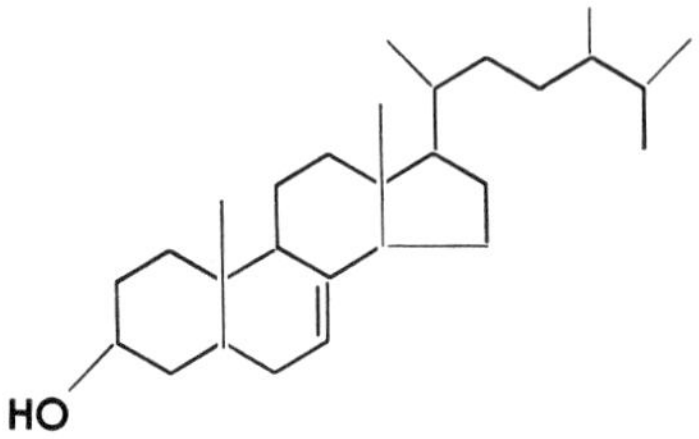

HO

Fungisterol accompanies ergosterol in ergot, occurs in *Amanita phalloides*, *Penicillium chrysogenum*, *Rhizopus saponicus*, *Calocera viscosa*, *Polyporus confluens* Fr., P. *sulfureus* (Bull.) Fr., *Hydnum imbricatum* L., *Geaster fimbriatus* Fr.

Heinrich Wieland and Gustav Coutelle, *Ann.* 548 270 (1941). (Structure)

Akira Saito, *J. Fermentation Technol.* (Japan) 29 310 (1951).

346   **21-Hydroxylanosta-7,9(11)-24-triene-3-one,** $C_{30}H_{46}O_2$,   colorless needles, m.p. 119–121°, $[\alpha]_D$ +56° (c 0.97 in chloroform).

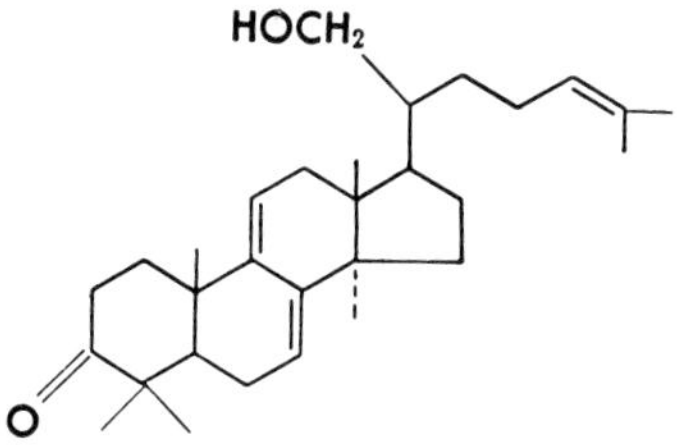

Polyporus pinicola Fr.

The derivative reduced and acetylated in the 3-position was isolated from the same specimen as were fungisterol and ergosta-7,22-diene-3-one.

T. G. Halsall and G. C. Sayer, *J. Chem. Soc.*, 2031 (1959).

347   **Pinicolic Acid A,** $C_{30}H_{46}O_3$, colorless needles, m.p. 197–202°, $[\alpha]_D$ +68° (c 0.83 in chloroform).

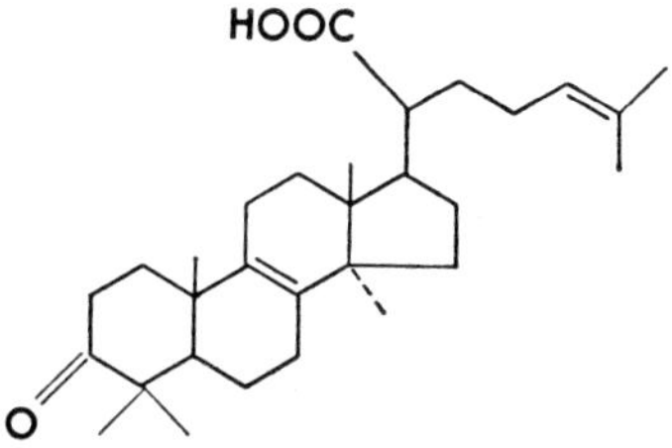

Polyporus pinicola Fr.

Joyce M. Guider, T. G. Halsall and E. R. H. Jones, *J. Chem. Soc.*, 4471 (1954).

348   **Lanosta-7,9(11)-24-triene-3β,21-diol,** $C_{30}H_{48}O_2$, colorless needles, m.p. 194–197°, $[\alpha]_D$ +72° (c 1.06 in chloroform).

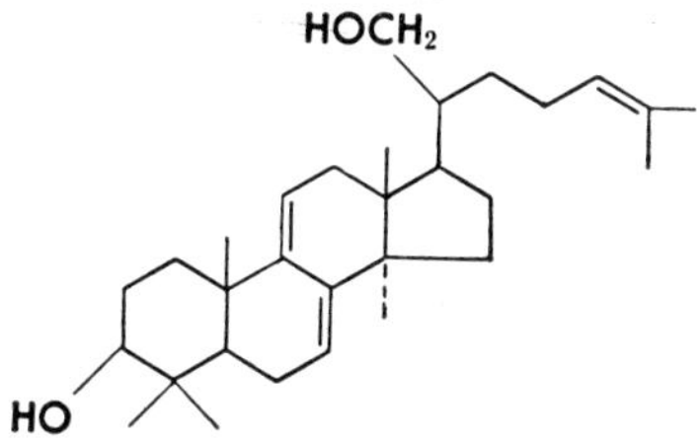

Polyporus pinicola Fr.

The corresponding 3-ketone was isolated from the same specimen as well as a mixture of fungisterol and ergosta-7,22-diene-3-one.

T. G. Halsall and G. C. Sayer, *J. Chem. Soc.*, 2031 (1959).

349 **3β-Hydroxylanosta-8,24-diene-21-oic Acid** (Trametenolic Acid B), $C_{30}H_{48}O_3$, colorless needles, m.p. 253–258°, $[\alpha]_D$ +43° (c 0.94 in pyridine).

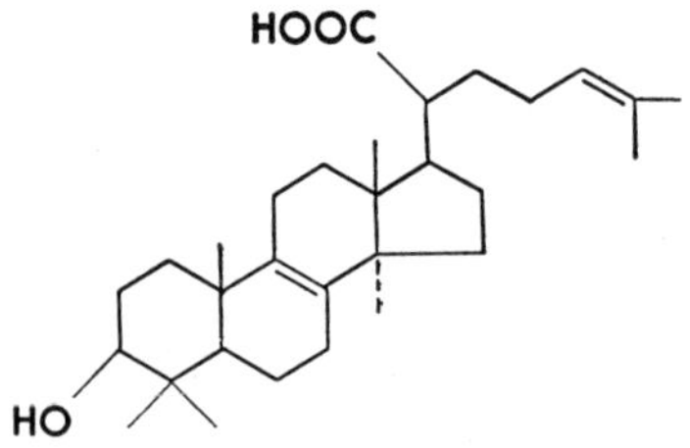

Trametes odorata (Wulf.) Fr.

Three other acids were isolated as their methyl esters from the same specimen: Ester A; m.p. 159–165°, $[\alpha]_D$ +49°. Ester B, m.p. 152°, $[\alpha]_D$ +66° and Ester C, m.p. 197–199°.

T. G. Halsall, R. Hodges and G. C. Sayer, *J. Chem. Soc.*, 2036 (1959).

T. G. Halsall and E. R. H. Jones, *Fortschr. Chem. org. Naturst.* 12 95 (1955). (A review)

350 **3α-Oxylanosta-8,24-diene-21-oic Acid**, $C_{30}H_{48}O_3$, isolated as the methyl ester-acetate.

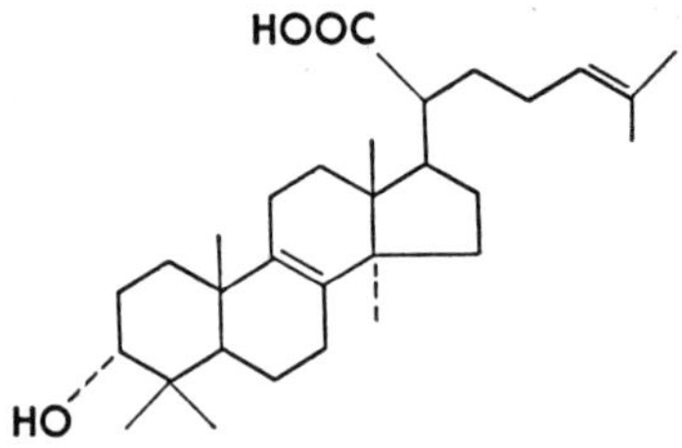

Polyporus pinicola Fr.

J. J. Beereboom, H. Fazakerley and T. G. Halsall, *J. Chem. Soc.*, 3437 (1957).

351 Squalene, $C_{30}H_{50}$, pale yellow oil with blue fluorescence, b.p. 203° (0.15 mm.), n_D^{20} 1.4965. Often isolated as the hydrogen chloride addition product.

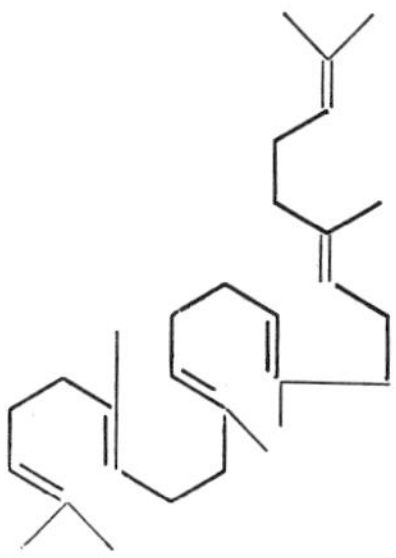

Yeasts, *Claviceps purpurea* (ergot), *Amanita phalloides*
Squalene may constitute as much as 16% of brewers' yeast lipide.

A. H. Cook, "The Chemistry and Biology of Yeasts," A. A. Eddy, *Aspects of the chemical composition of yeast,* Academic Press, New York, 1958, pp. 207–208.

K. Täufel, H. Thaler and H. Schreyegg, *Fettchem. Umschau* 43 26 (1936).

About 3 g. were obtained from 17 kg. of *Amanita phalloides.*

Heinrich Wieland and Gustav Coutelle, *Ann.* 548 275 (1941).

Nearly 25% of the unsaponifiable fraction of the fat of *Torula utilis* were found to be squalene.

R. Reichert, *Helv. Chim. Acta* 28 484 (1945).

352 Lanosterol (Kryptosterol, $\Delta^{8,24}$-Lanostadien-3-ol), $C_{30}H_{50}O$, colorless crystals, m.p. 138°, $[\alpha]_D$ +62° (in chloroform).

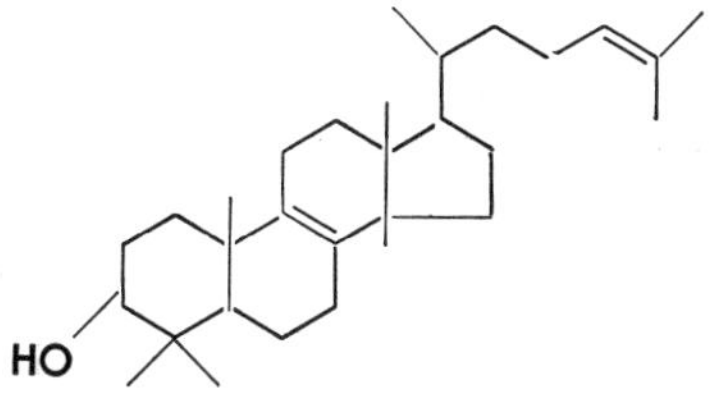

HO

Yeasts
Heinrich Wieland, Heinrich Pasedach and Albert Ballauf, *Ann.* 529 68 (1937).

L. Ruzicka, R. Denss and O. Jeger, *Helv. Chim. Acta* 29 204 (1946).
W. Voser, M. V. Mijovic, H. Heusser, O. Jeger and L. Ruzicka, *ibid.* 35 2414 (1952).

353 Physarosterol, $C_{30}H_{52}O_3$, colorless crystals, m.p. 137–139°, $[\alpha]_D^{28}$ −55.3° (c 0.5 in chloroform).

Probably a C_{30}, unsaturated, trihydroxy sterol with one hydroxyl group in the 3β-position.

Physarum polycephalum

This organism also produces a yellow pigment.

C. F. Emanuel, *Nature* 182 1234 (1958).

354 Polyporenic Acid C, $C_{31}H_{46}O_4$, colorless crystals, m.p. 273–276°, $[\alpha]_D$ +8° (in pyridine).

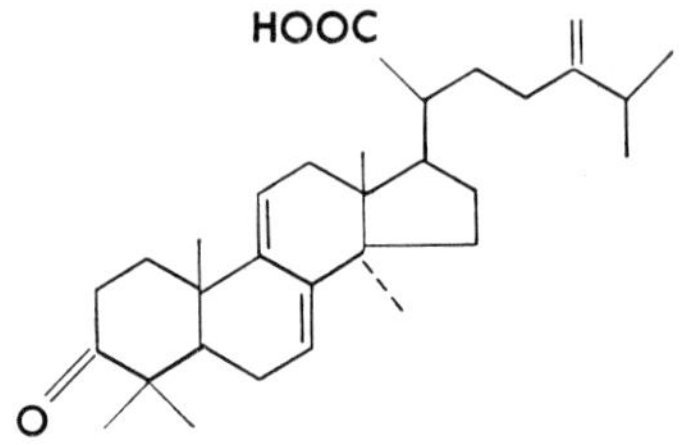

Polyporus betulinus, P. benzoinus, P. pinicola

A. Bowers, T. G. Halsall and G. C. Sayer, *J. Chem. Soc.,* 3070 (1954).

355 Agaricolic Acid, $C_{31}H_{48}O_3$ (probably), colorless crystals, m.p. 226°, $[\alpha]_D^{20}$ +34.4° (in pyridine).

Probably a monohydroxy triterpene acid. It occurs together with ergosterol and eburicoic acid, agaricic acid and other metabolites.

Polyporus officinalis

J. Valentin and S. Knülter, *Pharm. Zentralhalle* 96 478 (1957).

356 Dehydrotumulosic Acid, $C_{31}H_{48}O_4$.

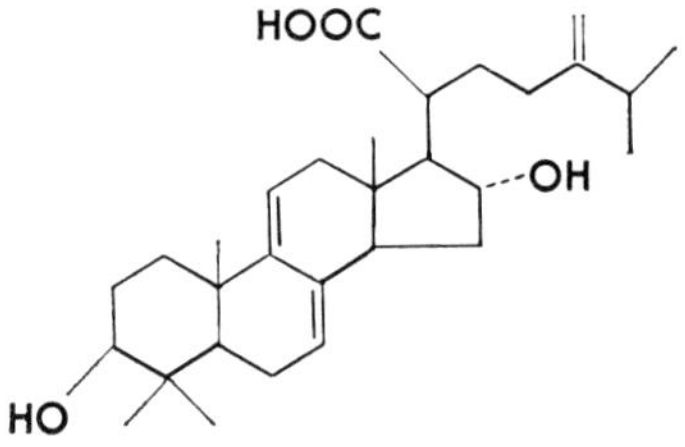

Polyporus tumulosus Cooke, *P. australiensis* Wakefield, *P. betulinus, Poria cocos*

This acid has never been separated completely from its mixture with tumulosic aicd, but the structure has been deduced from physical measurements.

L. A. Cort, R. M. Gascoigne, J. S. E. Holker, B. J. Ralph, Alexander Robertson and J. J. H. Simes, *J. Chem. Soc.*, 3713 (1954).

357 Eburicoic Acid, $C_{31}H_{50}O_3$, colorless crystals, m.p. 292–293°, $[\alpha]_D^{17}$ +50° (c 1.2 in chloroform).

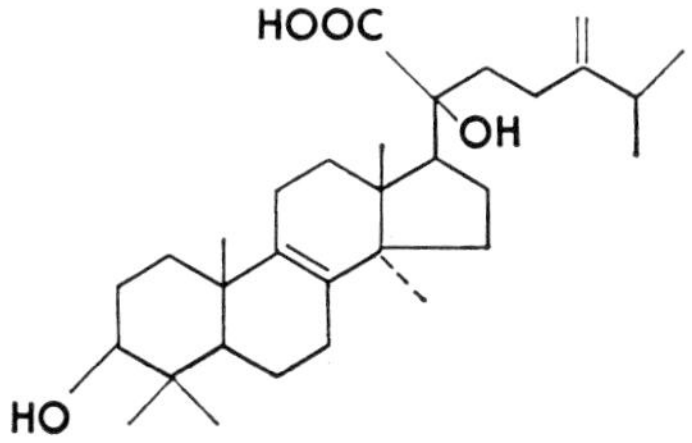

Polyporus officinalis Fr., *P. anthracophilus*, Cooke, *P. eucalyptorum* Fr., *P. sulfureus* (Bull.) Fr., *P. hispidus* (Bull.) Fr., *Poria cocos* (Schw.) Wolf, *Lentinus dacty-loides* Cleland.

The yield is 50% of the dry mycelial weight in some cases. The 3β-acetate also occurs naturally in at least some of these basidiomycetes.

J. S. E. Holker, A. D. G. Powell, Alexander Robertson, J. J. H. Simes, R. S. Wright and (in part) R. M. Gascoigne, *J. Chem. Soc.*, 2422 (1953). (Structure)

358 Tumulosic Acid, $C_{31}H_{50}O_4$, colorless fine needles, m.p. 306° (dec.), $[\alpha]_D$ +8.1° (c 3.30 in pyridine).

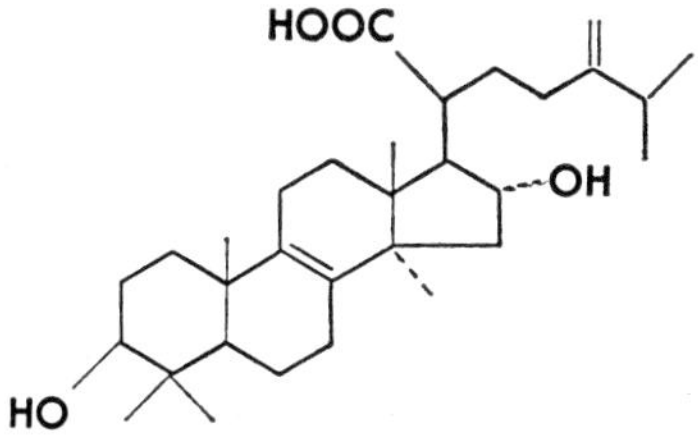

Polyporus tumulosus Cooke, *P. australiensis* Wakefield, *P. betulinus* Fr., *Poria cocos* Wolf, *Poria cocos* (Schw.) Wolf (syn. *Pachyma hoelen* Rumph.)

L. A. Cort, R. M. Gascoigne, J. S. E. Holker, B. J. Ralph, Alexander Robertson and J. J. H. Simes, *J. Chem. Soc.,* 3713 (1954).

359 Polyporenic Acid A (Ungulinic Acid), $C_{31}H_{50}O_4$, colorless needles, m.p. 199–200° (dec.), $[\alpha]_D{}^{20}$ +64° (c 1.28 in pyridine).

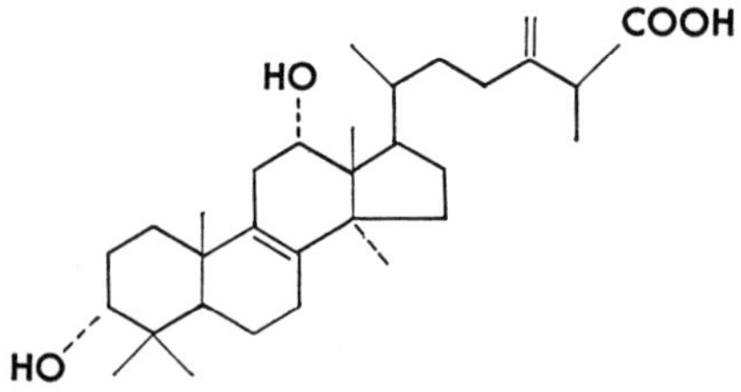

Polyporus betulinus Fr.
T. G. Halsall and R. Hodge, *J. Chem. Soc.,* 2385 (1954). (Structure)

360 O-Acetyleburicoic Acid, $C_{33}H_{52}O_4$, colorless needles, m.p. 256–259°, $[\alpha]_D{}^{25}$ +33.4° (in pyridine).

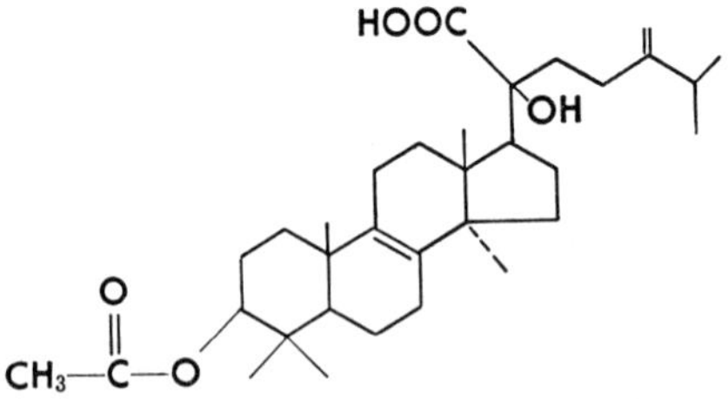

Polyporus anthracophilus
R. M. Gascoigne, J. S. E. Holker, B. J. Ralph and Alexander Robertson, *J. Chem. Soc.,* 2346 (1951).
F. N. Lakey and P. H. A. Strasser, *ibid.,* 873 (1951). (Structure)

361 Ursolic Acid (probable structure), $C_{30}H_{48}O_3$, colorless crystals, m.p. 291–292°, $[\alpha]_D{}^{27}$ +72° (in 1:1 chloroform-methanol).

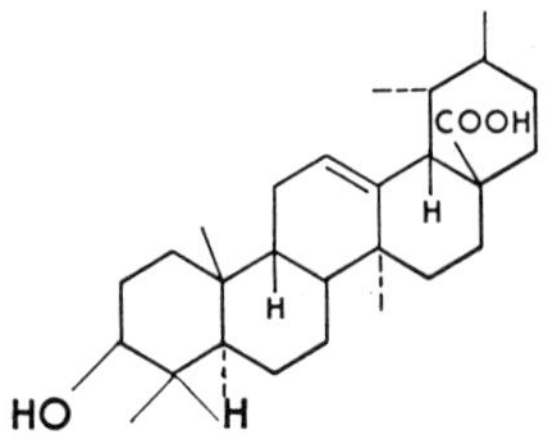

Cladonia sylvatica L. Harm., *Cl. impexa* Harm.

This acid also occurs in animals and plants. Since pentacyclic triterpenes are not characteristic of molds, they may be produced by the algal partner of the symbiont lichen.

T. W. Breaden, J. Keane and T. J. Nolan, *Sci. Proc. Roy. Dublin Soc.* 23 197 (1944).

A. Zürcher, O. Jerger and L. Ruzicka, *Helv. Chim. Acta* 37 2145 (1954).

362 **Taraxerene,** $C_{30}H_{50}$, colorless crystals, m.p. 237°, $[\alpha]_D$ +1° (c 0.81 in chloroform).

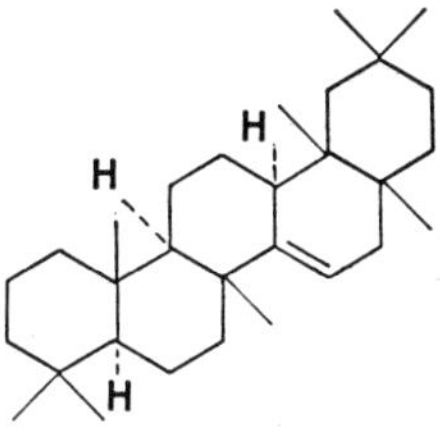

Cladonia deformis Hoffm.

About 15 mg. of pure hydrocarbon were obtained from 2.9 kg. of dry lichen.

Torger Bruun, *Acta Chem. Scand.* 8 71 (1954).

363 **Friedelin,** $C_{30}H_{50}O$, colorless crystals, m.p. 267–269° (dec.) (vac.), $[\alpha]_D$ −21° (c 2.34 in chloroform).

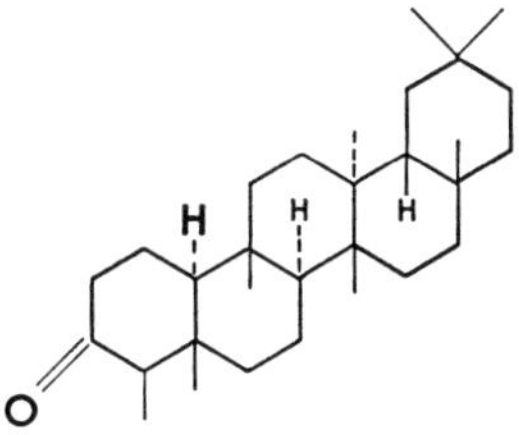

Cetraria nivalis (L.) Ach., *C. islandica* (L.) Ach., *C. cucullata* (Bell.) Ach., *C. crispa* (Ach.) Nyl., *C. delisei* (Bory) Th. Fr. (syn. *hiascens* Fr.), *Cladonia alpestris* (L.) Rabh., *Alectoria ochroleuca* (Ehrh.) Nyl. and *Stereocaulon paschale* (L.) Fr.

Torger Bruun, *Acta Chem. Scand.* 8 71 (1954).

364 epi-Friedelinol, $C_{30}H_{52}O$, colorless crystals, m.p. 280° (vac.), $[\alpha]_D$ +23° (c 0.52 in chloroform).

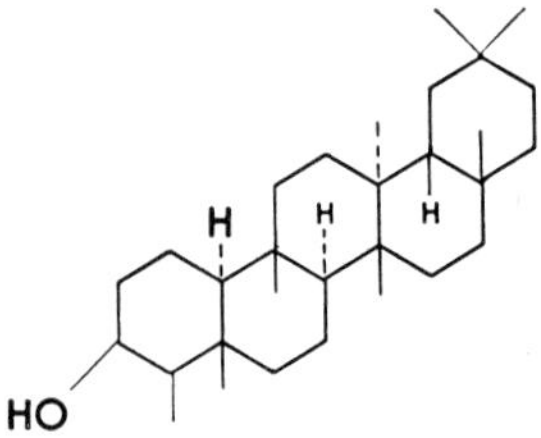

Cetraria nivalis (L.) Ach.
Torger Bruun, *Acta Chem. Scand.* 8 71 (1954).

365 **Zeorin,** $C_{30}H_{52}O_2$, colorless crystals, m.p. 223–227°, $[\alpha]_D$ +54° (c 0.50 in chloroform).

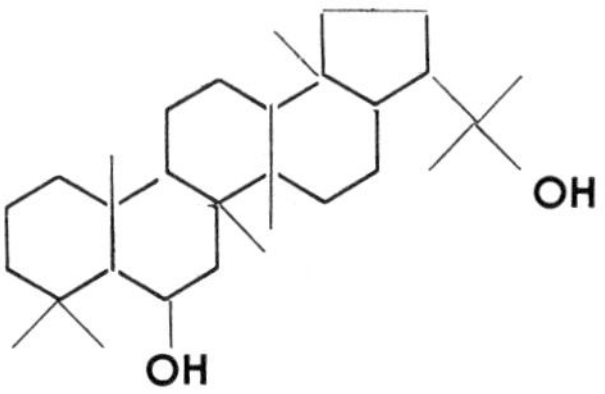

Lecanora sordida, L. thiodes, L. epanora, L. sulfurea, Physcia caesia, Ph. endococcina, Anaptychia speciosa, A. hypoleuca, Parmelia leucotyliza, Dimelaena oreina, Haematomma coccineum, H. leiphaemum, H. prophyrium, Placodium saxicolum, Peltigera malacea, P. horizontalis, P. propagulifera, Nephroma arcticum, N. antarcticum, N. laevigatum, N. parile, Cladonia deformis, Coccifera pleurota, C. bellidiflora, Urceolaria cretacea, Lepraria latebrarum

"Elsevier's Encyclopedia of Organic Chemistry," 14 Suppl., Elsevier Publishing Co., London, 1952, p. 1197S. (Occurrence)

D. H. R. Barton and T. Bruun, *J. Chem. Soc.*, 1683 (1952).

D. H. R. Barton, P. de Mayo and J. C. Orr, *ibid.*, 2239 (1958).

366 **Leucotylin,** $C_{30}H_{52}O_3$, colorless prisms, m.p. 333°, $[\alpha]_D^{24}$ +49.43°. A triterpenoid compound accompanying zeorin.
Parmelia leucotyliza Nyl.
Yasuhiko Asahina and Hirosi Akagi, *Ber.* **71B** 980 (1938).

367 **Helvolic Acid** (Fumigacin, May = Mycocidin), $C_{32}H_{42}O_8$, colorless fine needles, m.p. 211° (dec.), $[\alpha]_D^{25}$ −124° (in chloroform).

Tentative partial structure:

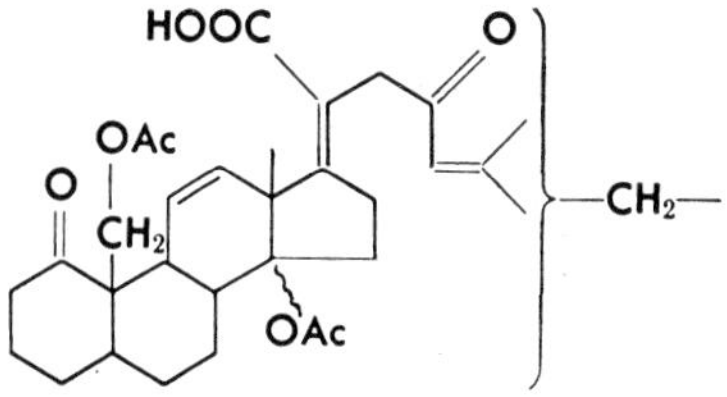

Aspergillus fumigatus mut. *helvola* Yuill

Donald J. Cram and Norman L. Allinger, *J. Am. Chem. Soc.* 78 5275 (1956). (Structure)

E. Chain, H. W. Florey, M. A. Jennings and T. I. Williams, *Brit. J. Exp. Pathol.* 24 108 (1943). (Isolation)

CIBA Lectures in Microbial Chemistry, E. P. Abraham, "Biochemistry of Some Peptide and Steroid Antibiotics," *The cephalosporins,* John Wiley and Sons, New York, 1957, pp. 30–63. (A review)

Cephalosporins P

These non-peptide compounds accompany cephalosporins N and C in *Cephalosporium salmosynnematum* fermentations.

TABLE I

	Compound	Crystal form	Melting point	$[\alpha]_D$	Molecular formula
368	**Cephalosporin P_1**	colorless needles	147°	+28° (c 2.7 in chloroform)	$C_{32}H_{48}O_8$
369	**Cephalosporin P_2**		151°		
370	**Cephalosporin P_3**	white, amorphous solid			
371	**Cephalosporin P_4**	Fawn-colored crystals	220–230°		

Cephalosporin P_1 resembles helvolic acid (from *Aspergillus fumigatus*). A complete (steroid) structure has been determined by T. G. Halsall and associates, but has not been published yet.

H. S. Burton and E. P. Abraham, *Biochem. J.* **50** 168 (1951). (Isolation)

H. S. Burton, E. P. Abraham and H. M. E. Cardwell, *ibid.* **62** 171 (1956).

CIBA Lectures in Microbial Biochemistry, E. P. Abraham, "Biochemistry of Some Peptide and Steroid Antibiotics," *The cephalosporins,* John Wiley and Sons, New York, 1957, pp. 30–63. (A review)

368 Cephalosporin P_1, $C_{32}H_{48}O_8$, colorless crystals, m.p. 147°, $[\alpha]_D^{20}$ +28° (2.7 in chloroform).

Cephalosporium spp.

A number of similar substances, called cephalosporins P_2, P_3, P_4 and P_5 were isolated from the same fermentation, but were not obtained in high enough yields to permit much structure work.

H. S. Burton and E. P. Abraham, *Biochem. J.* **50** 168 (1951). (Isolation)

H. S. Burton, E. P. Abraham and H. M. E. Cardwell, *Biochem. J.* **62** 171 (1956).

CIBA Lectures in Microbial Chemistry, E. P. Abraham, "Biochemistry of Some Peptide and Steroid Antibiotics," *The cephalosporins,* John Wiley and Sons, New York, 1957, pp. 30–63. (A review)

10

Tropolone Acids

The detailed biosynthetic origin of the tropolone acids remains obscure. Various suggestions have been made. One of these[1,2] proposed enlargement of the aromatic ring of 3,5-dihydroxyphthalic acid, a known mold metabolite:

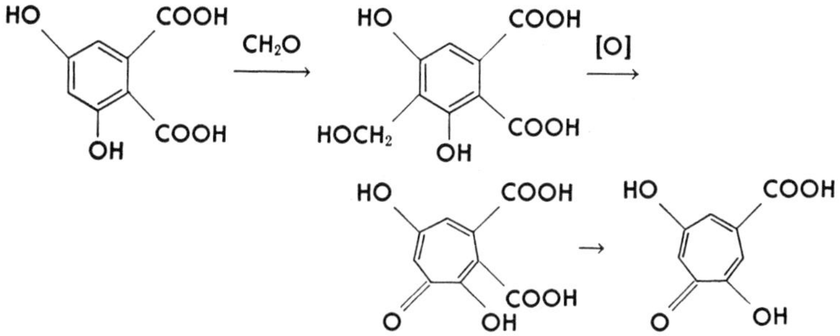

Another[3] proposed enlargement of an alicyclic ring in a C_6—C_3 type of intermediate from the shikimic acid route:

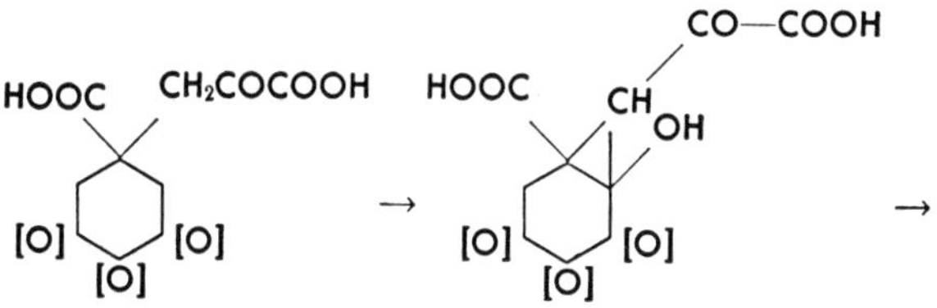

[1] T. R. Seshadri, *J. Sci. Ind. Research* (India) 14B 248 (1955).
[2] R. Robinson, "The Structural Relations of Natural Products," Oxford Univ. Press, London, 1955.
[3] A. J. Birch, *Fortschr. Chem. org. Naturstaffe* 14 186 (1957)

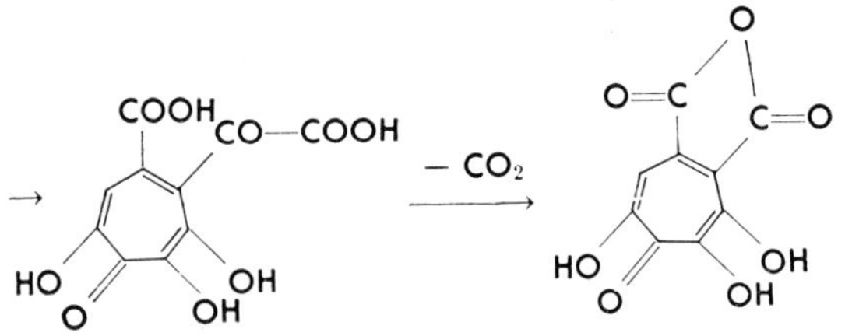

Labeling studies[4, 5, 6] show that acetate and formate are the primary precursors rather than glucose. Tanenbaum, Bassett and Kaplan found that stipitatic acid isolated from a *Penicillium stipitatum* culture grown on 1-C^{14}-glucose had an activity about five times as great as phenylalanine or tyrosine (shikimic acid route) isolated from the same culture. Richards and Ferretti grew *Penicillium aurantio-virens* on media containing (a) 1-C^{14}-acetate, (b) 2-C^{14}-acetate and (c) 1-C^{14}-glucose. Puberulic acid and puberulonic acid were isolated, separated and degraded. Their results, in agreement with Bentley's where the same precursors were used, indicate the incorporation of formate and acetate as follows:

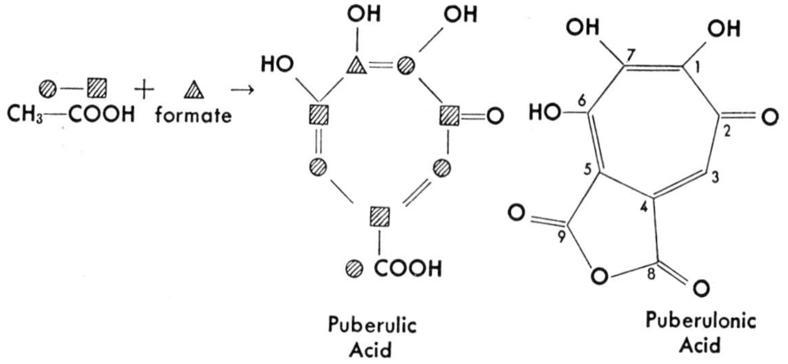

Puberulic Acid

Puberulonic Acid

That is, C_1, C_3, C_5 and C_8 of the tropolones (as numbered in the puberulonic acid structure shown) are derived from the methyl carbon atom of acetate, while C_2, C_4 and C_6 are from the acetate carboxyl group carbon atom. The C_7 carbon atom of the tropolones was shown by Bentley[5] to be derived from formate.

The origin of the C_9 carbon atoms present in puberulonic and

[4] John H. Richards and Louis D. Ferretti, *Biochem. and Biophys. Res. Comms.* 2 107 (1960).

[5] Ronald Bentley, *Biochim. et Biophys. Acta* 29 666 (1958).

[6] S. W. Tanenbaum, E. W. Bassett and M. Kaplan, *Arch. Biochem. and Biophys.* 81 169 (1959).

stipitatonic acids remains undetermined. It, too, may arise from formate. A study has been made[7] of the enzymatic decarboxylation of stipitatonic and puberulonic acids. A biochemical relationship was concluded by way of this enzyme, and the suggestion made that the intermediate tropolone precursors must be at least C_9 compounds, and that direct closure of an acyclic to a seven-membered ring structure must occur.

The results of Richards and Ferretti seem to leave it an open question as to whether the tropolone ring is formed by direct cyclization of a long-chain acyclic compound or by expansion of a six-membered ring, and the exact nature of the intermediate precursors of this interesting series of mold metabolites remains a mystery.

372 **Stipitatic Acid,** $C_8H_6O_5$, pale yellow plates, m.p. 282° (dec.).

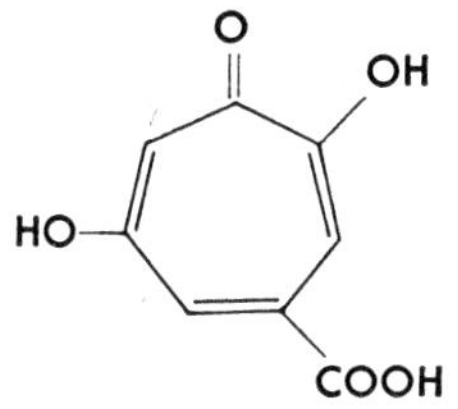

Penicillium stipitatum Thom
J. R. Bartels-Keith, A. W. Johnson and W. I. Taylor, *J. Chem. Soc.,* 2352 (1951). (Synthesis)
Peter L. Pauson, *Chem. Revs.* 55 9 (1955). (A review of tropolones)

373 **Puberulic Acid,** $C_8H_6O_6$, nearly colorless plates, m.p. 318°.

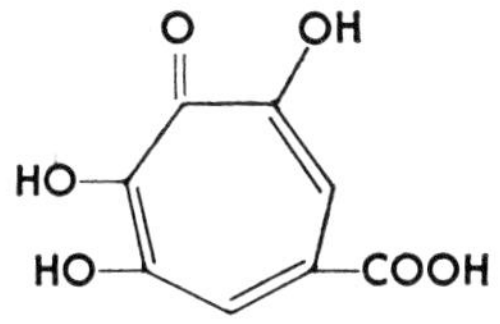

Penicillium puberulum Bainier, *P. aurantio-virens* Biourge, *P. cyclopium-viridicatum* and *P. johannioli* Zaleski
R. E. Corbett, C. H. Hassall, A. W. Johnson and A. R. Todd, *J. Chem. Soc.,* 1 (1950).

[7] Ronald Bentley and Clara P. Thiessen, *Nature* 184 552 (1959).

374 Stipitatonic Acid, $C_9H_4O_6$, yellow crystals, m.p. 237° (dec.).

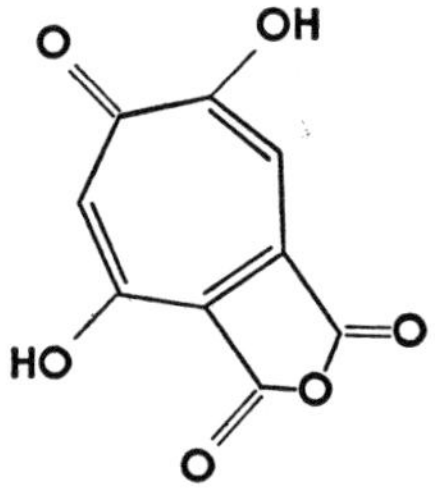

Penicillium stipitatum Thom
W. Segal, *Chem. and Ind.*, 1040 (1957). (Isolation)
Kozo Doi and Yoshio Kitahara, *Bull. Chem. Soc. Japan* 31
788 (1958). (Structure)
W. Segal, *Chem. and Ind.*, 1726 (1958). (Corrected structure)

375 Puberulonic Acid, $C_9H_4O_7$, fine yellow needles, m.p. 298° (dec.).

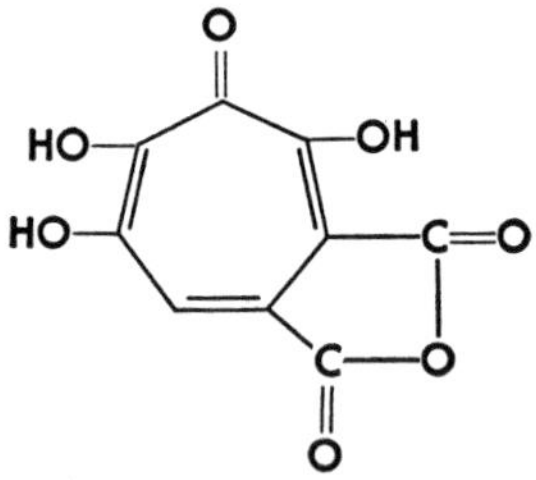

Penicillium johannioli Zaleski, *P. cyclopium-viridicatum, P. puberulum* Bainier and *P. aurantio-virens* Biourge
See preceding reference.
Gunhild Aulin-Erdtman, *Chem. and Ind.*, 29 (1951).
Idem., Acta Chem. Scand. 5 301 (1951). (Structure)

376 Compound T, $C_{10}H_8O_4$ or $C_{10}H_{10}O_4$, colorless crystals, m.p. 150°.
This compound shows the typical tropolone spectrum,
and it is apparently a new tropolone acid.
Penicillium stipitatum
S. W. Tanenbaum, E. W. Bassett and M. Kaplan, *Arch.
Biochem. and Biophys.* 81 169 (1959).

11

Phenolic Substances

a. PHENOLS AND PHENOL ETHERS (GENERAL)

Phenolic substances are commonly encountered as microorganism metabolites. Besides the compounds listed in this chapter phenolic moieties are present in other structures such as the xanthones, alternariol, blastmycin, hygromycin, fulvic acid, citromycetin, atrovenetin, the tetracyclines, mycobactin, anthraquinones and naphthoquinones. Benzoquinones are undoubtedly oxidation products of phenolic precursors.

Practically all of the phenolic materials in this section are mold metabolites. Perhaps that is because more isolation work has been done with fungi than with bacteria. It is evident that similar compounds are produced by bacteria, since 6-methylsalicylic acid, a typical penicillium metabolite, also occurs as a moiety of mycobactin from *Mycobacterium phlei.* Also, 2,3-dihydroxybenzoic acid occurs as a moiety of a metabolite from *Bacillus subtilis,* and 2,6-dihydroxybenzoic acid as a part of pyoluteorin from *Pseudomonas aeruginosa.* It is interesting that these bacterial phenolic acids are conjugates of nitrogen-containing substances.

The phenolic acid production of certain cultures has been studied in depth. *Penicillium brevi-compactum,* for example, has been found to produce the following:

3,5-Dihydroxyphthalic Acid $C_8H_6O_6$

1-Carboxy-2,5-dioxyphenyl Acetyl Carbinol $C_{10}H_{10}O_6$

2,4-Dioxy-6-pyruvylbenzoic Acid $C_{10}H_8O_6$

Mycophenolic Acid $C_{17}H_{20}O_6$

Another investigation[1] in fact found a total of 11 different phenolic substances in a culture of this organism. In addition to the above were found a compound $C_{10}H_{10}O_7$, two derivatives of mycophenolic acid, two "intermediates between $C_{10}H_{10}O_7$ and $C_8H_6O_6$" and two reduction products of $C_{10}H_{10}O_5$.

The mold *Penicillium griseofulvum* produces:

6-Methylsalicylic Acid $C_8H_8O_3$
Orsellinic Acid $C_8H_8O_4$
Griseofulvin $C_{17}H_{17}O_6Cl$
Dechlorogriseofulvin $C_{17}H_{18}O_6$
Bromogriseofulvin $C_{17}H_{17}O_6Br$
Gentisic Acid $C_7H_6O_4$
Fulvic Acid $C_{14}H_{12}O_8$
Mycelianamide $C_{22}H_{28}O_5N_2$

Another study[2] found three more unidentified phenolic substances in this culture.

A *Penicillium patulum* culture has been found[3] to produce:

Patulin $C_7H_6O_4$
Gentisaldehyde $C_7H_6O_3$
Gentisic Acid $C_7H_6O_4$
Gentisyl Alcohol $C_7H_8O_3$
6-Methylsalicylic Acid $C_8H_8O_4$
6-Formylsalicylic Acid $C_8H_6O_4$
3-Hydroxyphthalic Acid $C_8H_6O_5$
Pyrogallol $C_6H_6O_3$
p-Hydroxybenzoic Acid $C_7H_6O_3$
Anthranilic Acid $C_7H_7O_2N$

Also an "aliphatic precursor of patulin" and a depside-like compound were detected but not entirely characterized.

Many such families of metabolites can be assembled by reference to the microorganism index. Studies such as those above facilitate the development of biosynthetic routes. For example, Bassett and Tanenbaum suggest the following interrelationships among the *Penicillium patulum* phenolic metabolites:

[1] Paul Godin, *Antonie van Leeuwenhoek J. Microbiol. Serol.* 21 215 (1955).

[2] Paul Simonart and Renaat de Lathouwer, *Zentr. Bakteriol., Parasitenk.*, Abt. II 110 339 (1957).

[3] E. Bassett and S. Tanenbaum, *Experientia* 14 38 (1958).

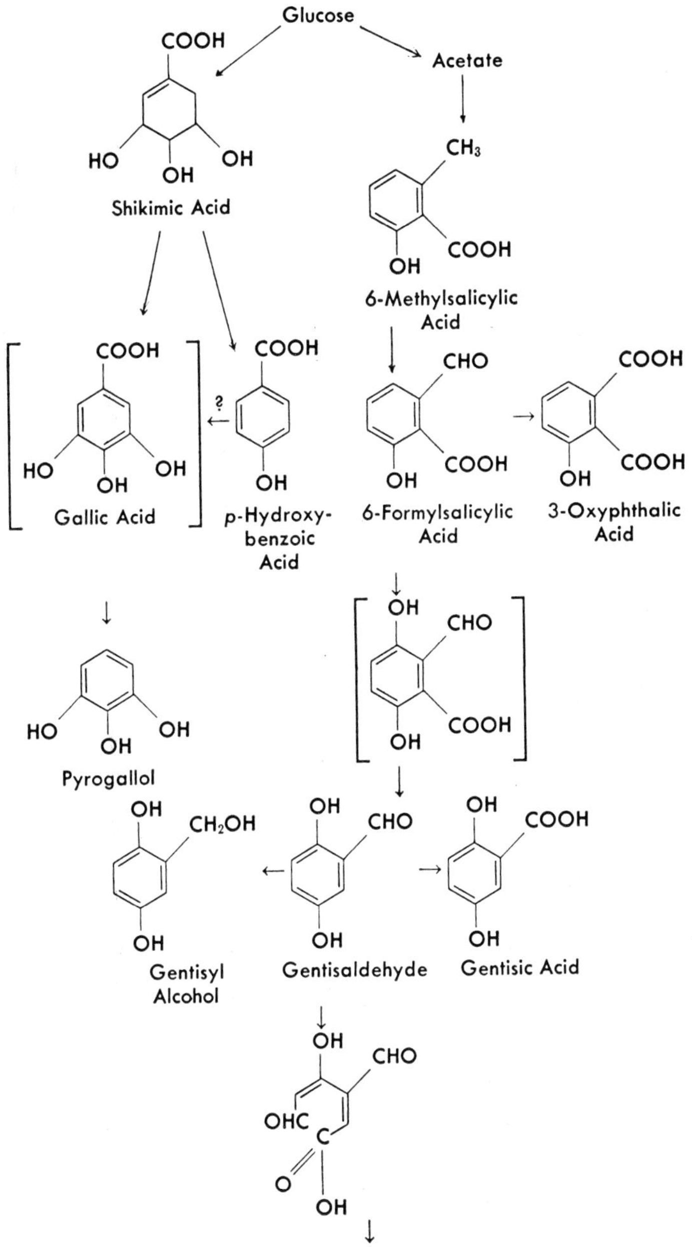

Glucose

Acetate

COOH

HO OH OH

Shikimic Acid

CH₃

OH COOH

6-Methylsalicylic Acid

COOH

HO OH OH

Gallic Acid

COOH

?

OH

p-Hydroxy-benzoic Acid

CHO

OH COOH

6-Formylsalicylic Acid

COOH

OH COOH

3-Oxyphthalic Acid

HO OH OH

Pyrogallol

OH CHO

OH COOH

OH CH₂OH

OH

Gentisyl Alcohol

OH CHO

OH

Gentisaldehyde

OH COOH

OH

Gentisic Acid

OH CHO

OHC C

O OH

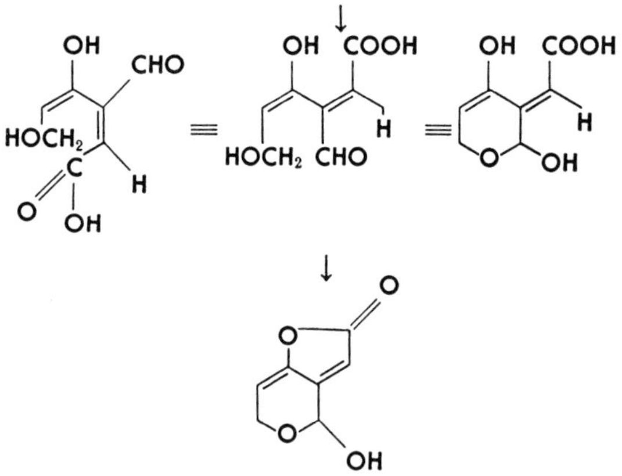

Patulin

Thus, the acetate and shikimic acid routes to aromatic compounds seem to be operating in a single microorganism.

It was a kind of statistical consideration of the structures of natural products which led to the revival of the acetate hypothesis of biogenesis as applied to substances other than fatty acids.

Phenolic compounds were particularly instrumental since the frequent occurrence of *meta*-hydroxyl groups (resorcinol and phloroglucinol types) was easy to recognize and challenging to explain. The case first was stated clearly by Collie many years ago.[4] Lately Birch and others have developed a firm experimental basis for the theory by isotopic labeling and chemical degradation studies.

Some phenolic compounds which have been shown in this way to be acetate-derived are:

6-Methylsalicylic Acid[5]

Griseofulvin[6]

Mycophenolic Acid[7]

Emodin[8]

[4] John Norman Collie, *Proc. Chem. Soc.* 23 230 (1907); *idem.*, *J. Chem. Soc.* 91 1806 (1907).

[5] A. J. Birch, R. A. Massy-Westropp and C. J. Moye, *Australian J. Chem.* 8 539 (1955).

[6] A. J. Birch, R. A. Massy-Westropp, R. W. Rickards and Herchel Smith, *J. Chem. Soc.*, 360 (1958).

[7] A. J. Birch, R. J. English, R. A. Massy-Westropp, M. Slaytor and Herchel Smith, *ibid.*, 365 (1958); A. J. Birch, R. J. English, R. A. Massy-Westropp and Herchel Smith, *ibid.*, 369 (1958).

[8] Sten Gatenbeck, *Acta Chem. Scand.* 12 1211 (1958).

Auroglaucin[9]
Helminthosporin[10]

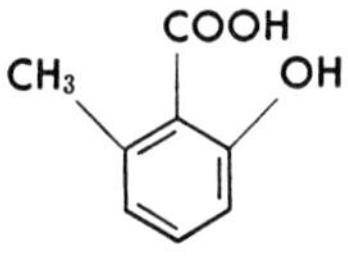

6-Methylsalicylic
Acid

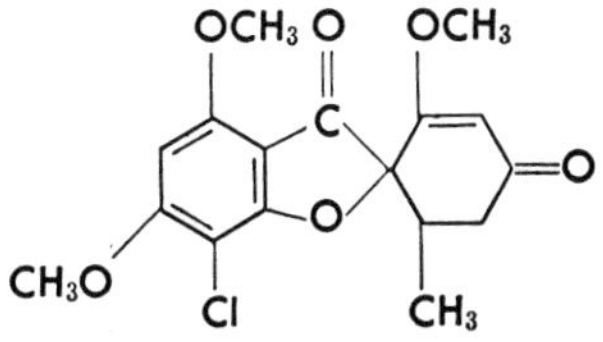

Griseofulvin

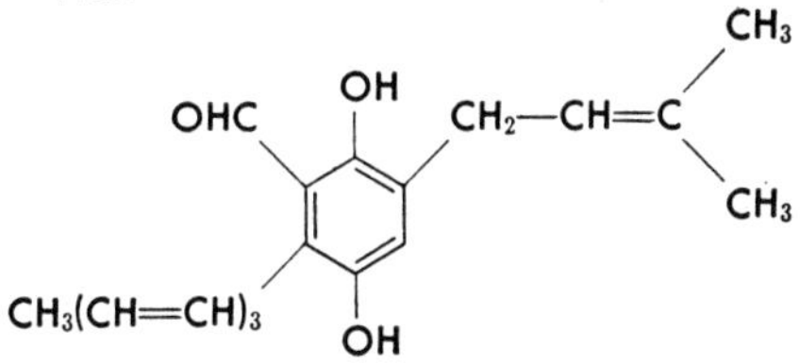

Auroglaucin

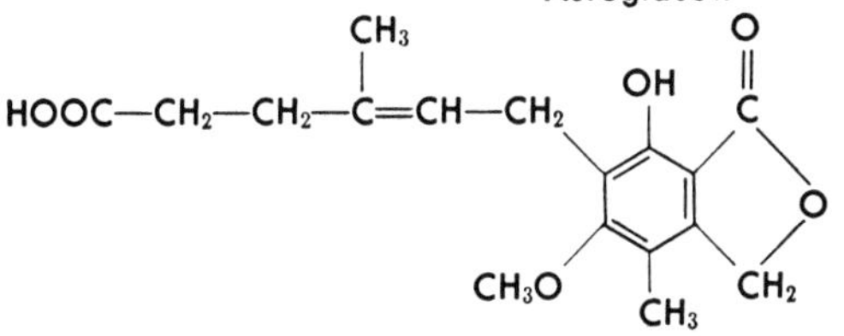

Mycophenolic Acid

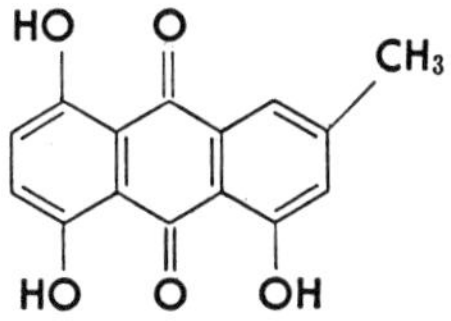

Helminthosporin

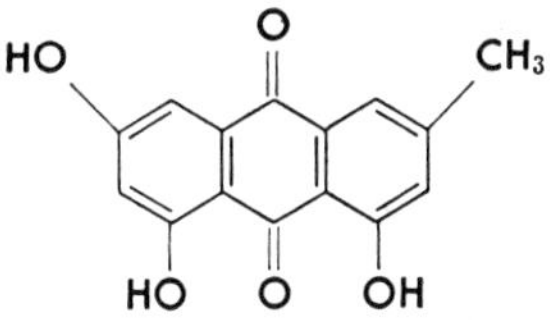

Emodin

Interesting details have been discovered. For example,[7] the methyl group attached to the aromatic ring in mycophenolic acid is furnished by methionine, probably at a relatively early stage in the synthetic sequence. The methoxyl methyl group also is furnished by methionine. The aromatic nucleus is acetate-derived, while mevalonic acid was shown to be a specific

[9] A. J. Birch, J. Schofield and Herchel Smith, *Chem. and Ind.*, 1321 (1958).

[10] A. J. Birch, A. J. Ryan and Herchel Smith, *J. Chem. Soc.*, 4773 (1958).

and irreversible intermediate for the terpenoid side-chain. There was no incorporation of mevalonic acid into the aromatic nucleus. Mevalonic acid also was incorporated exclusively into the isopentene side-chain of auroglaucin.

Both bacteria and fungi are able to hydroxylate aromatic rings, and the acetate pattern of alternate oxidation often is confused by further oxidations of this sort.

Other details remain to be determined. The predominance of metabolites indicating derivation from an even number of acetate units has led to speculation concerning a four-carbon intermediate such as acetoacetate. Even larger intermediates have been proposed, such as orsellinic acids as precursors of anthraquinones.[11] So far this possibility has not been ruled out in each case[8] by rigorous experimental evidence although there is an intuitive tendency to favor the simplest and most flexible unit and to apply the accumulated body of knowledge about intermediary metabolism. The co-occurrence in a natural source of the anthraquinone and related phenanthrenequinone mentioned in the introduction to the section on quinones is presumptive evidence against orsellinic acid intermediates, since the two quinone molecules appear to be formed merely by a different mode of folding or arrangement on an enzyme surface of the same intermediate polyketomethylene chain. On the other hand the isolation of such orsellinic acids from isolated fungus members of lichens incapable of completing the anthraquinone synthesis is interesting.

The structural relationships (some obvious, others more obscure) among the mold products fulvic acid, citromycetin, fusarubin, purpurogenone, etc.[12, 13] argue in favor of a flexible intermediate in the sense of a single polyketomethylene chain that could be folded and modified in various ways to give related metabolites. Comparison of the structures of the lactone moieties of the macrolide antibiotics with those of the tetracyclines (both classes of compounds produced by streptomycetes) also seems to point to intermediates of this type. While this is a good working hypothesis, such intermediates have not been isolated and in fact could not long exist in the free state. Perhaps eventually a better knowledge of enzymes will let us know

[11] K. Aghoramurthy and T. R. Seshadri, *J. Sci. Ind. Research* (India) 13A 114 (1954).

[12] F. M. Dean, R. A. Eade, R. A. Moubasher and A. Robertson, *Nature* 179 366 (1957).

[13] W. B. Whalley, *Chem. and Ind.*, 131 (1958).

in more detail how such acetate-derived mold metabolites are formed, and why the chain lengths seldom exceed 14 to 18 carbon atoms.

The recent discovery and characterization of asterric acid, a mold metabolite in which two phenolic units are joined by an ether linkage, have inspired the suggestion that the final phases of its biogenetic scheme may involve a geodin-like intermediate and sulochrin as follows:

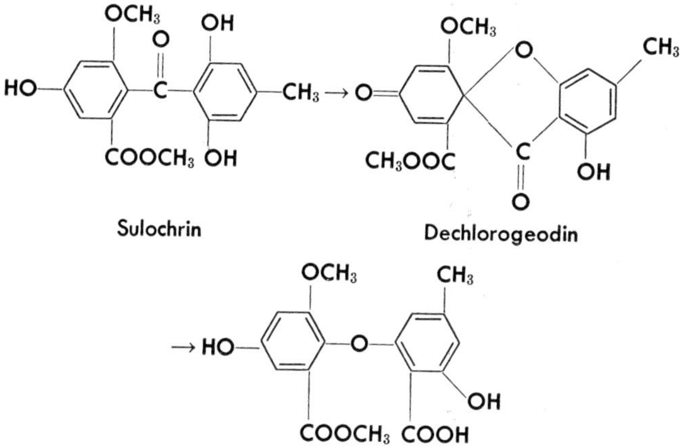

Sulochrin   Dechlorogeodin

Asterric Acid

The authors believe that the known occurrence of sulochrin and geodin as mold metabolites supports this argument.[14]

The transformation of sulochrin to dechlorogeodin, incidentally, is an example of intramolecular phenol coupling, a phenomenon discussed at greater length under Part *b* of this section.

377 Pyrogallol, $C_6H_6O_3$, colorless crystals which turn brown in air, m.p. 133°.

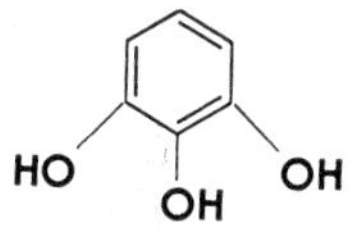

Penicillium patulum
    E. W. Bassett and S. W. Tanenbaum, *Biochim. et Biophys. Acta* 28 247 (1958).

[14] R. F. Curtis, C. H. Hassall and D. W. Jones, *Chem. and Ind.*, 1283 (1959).

378 *p*-Methoxytetrachlorophenol (Drosophilin A), $C_7H_4O_2Cl_4$, yellow crystals, m.p. 118°.

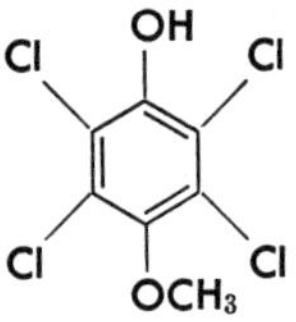

$$OH$$

Drosophila subatrata (Batsch ex Fr.) Quel.
The yield was 100 mg. from 31 liters of culture solution.

Frederick Kavanagh, Annette Hervey and William J. Robbins, *Proc. Natl. Acad. Sci. U. S.* 38 555 (1952).

379 *p*-Hydroxybenzoic Acid, $C_7H_6O_3$, colorless crystals, m.p. 213°.

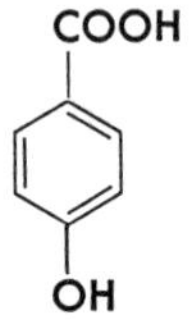

$$COOH$$

Penicillium patulum
E. W. Bassett and S. W. Tanenbaum, *Biochim. et Biophys. Acta* 28 247 (1958).

380 Protocatechuic Acid, $C_7H_6O_4$, white or tan crystalline powder which darkens in air, m.p. ~200° (dec.). Monohydrate from water.

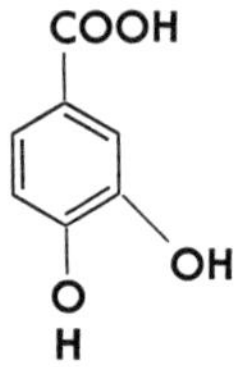

$$COOH$$

Phycomyces blakesleeanus (sugar substrate)
H. B. Schröter, *Angew. Chem.* 68 158 (1956).

381 Gentisic Acid, $C_7H_6O_4$, colorless crystals, m.p. 199°.

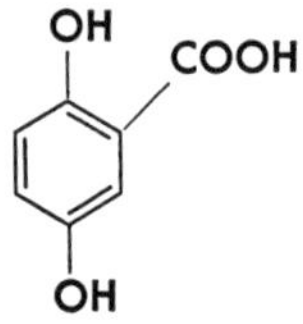

$$OH \quad COOH$$

Penicillium griseofulvum Dierckx, *P. jenseni, P. divergens*

Harold Raistrick and Paul Simonart, *Biochem. J.* **27** 628 (1933).

J. Barta and R. Mecir, *Experientia* **4** 277 (1948).

A. Brack, *Helv. Chim. Acta* **30** 1 (1947). (Isolation)

382   Gallic Acid, $C_7H_6O_5$, colorless or pale tan crystals (Monohydrate from water), m.p. 225–250° (dec.).

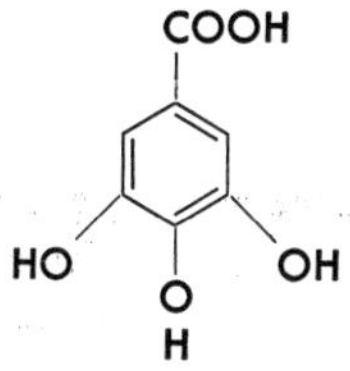

Phycomyces blakesleeanus (sugar substrate)

Protocatechuic acid and another unidentified phenol also were shown to be present by paper chromatography.

H. B. Schröter, *Angew. Chem.* **68** 158 (1956).

383   Gentisyl Alcohol, $C_7H_8O_3$, colorless crystals, m.p. 100°.

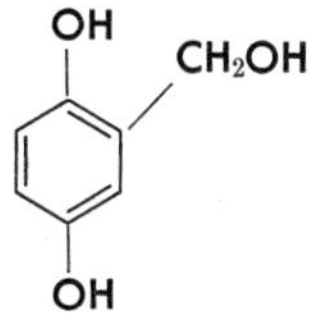

Penicillium patulum Bainier, *P. divergens* Bainier and Sartory

A. Brack, *Helv. Chim. Acta* **30** 1 (1947). (Isolation)

B. G. Engel and W. Brzeski, *ibid.* **30** 1472 (1947).

J. Barta and R. Mecir, *Experientia* **4** 277 (1948).

384   2,5-Dihydroxyphenylglyoxylic Acid, $C_8H_6O_5$, yellow needles, m.p. 141°.

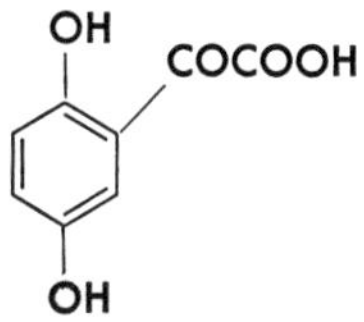

Polyporus tumulosus Cooke (artificial medium)

Oxalic acid, homoprotocatechuic acid and 2,4,5-trihydroxyphenylglyoxylic acid are produced in the same culture.

Otto Neubauer and L. Flatow, *Hoppe-Seyler's Zeitschrift für physiol. Chem.* **52** 375 (1907).

G. F. J. Moir and B. F. Ralph, *Chem. and Ind.*, 1143 (1954).

385 **3-Hydroxyphthalic Acid,** $C_8H_6O_5$, colorless crystals m.p.: anhydride formation near 150°, melting 166°. Sublimes.

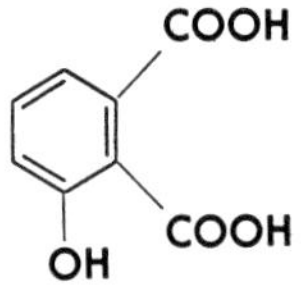

Penicillium islandicum, P. patulum
A yield of only 1–2 mg. per liter was obtained.

Sten Gatenbeck, *Acta Chem. Scand.* 11 555 (1957).

E. W. Bassett and S. W. Tanenbaum, *Experientia* 14 38 (1958).

386 **3,5-Dihydroxyphthalic Acid,** $C_8H_6O_6$, colorless prisms, m.p. 188° (resolidifying at 206°).

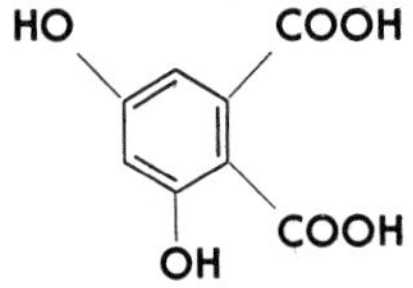

Penicillium brevi-compactum Dierckx

Albert E. Oxford and Harold Raistrick, *Biochem. J.* 26 1902 (1932). (Isolation)

John Howard Birkinshaw and Arthur Bracken, *J. Chem. Soc.*, 368 (1942). (Synthesis)

387 **2,4,5-Trihydroxyphenylglyoxylic Acid,** $C_8H_6O_6$, bright red prisms, m.p. 193°.

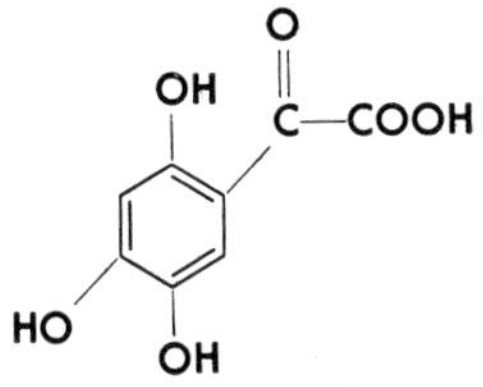

Polyporus tumulosus (artificial medium)
Homoprotocatechuic acid and oxalic acid were present in the same culture.

B. J. Ralph and Alexander Robertson, *J. Chem. Soc.*, 3380 (1950).

388 2,6-Dihydroxyacetophenone, $C_8H_8O_3$, yellow needles, m.p. 154–158°.

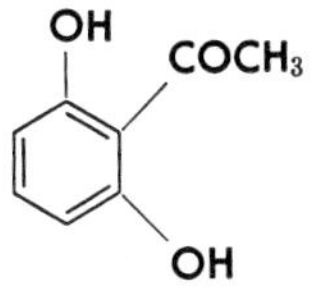

Daldinia concentrica
D. C. Allport and J. D. Bu'Lock, *J. Chem. Soc.*, 654 (1960).

389 6-Methylsalicylic Acid (2,6-Cresotic Acid, 3-Hydroxy-5-toluic Acid, 6-Hydroxy-2-methylbenzoic Acid), $C_8H_8O_3$, colorless needles, m.p. 170°.

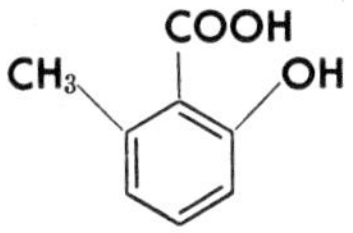

Penicillium griseofulvum Dierckx, *P. flexuosum, P. patulum* Bainier, *P. urticae*
Winston Kennay Anslow and Harold Raistrick, *Biochem. J.* 25 39 (1931).
E. W. Bassett and S. W. Tanenbaum, *Experientia* 14 38 (1958).

390 *p*-Hydroxyphenylacetic Acid, $C_8H_8O_3$, colorless crystals, m.p. 148° (subl.).

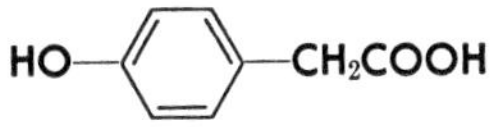

Hypochnus sasakii Shirai (*Corticium sasakii, Pellicularia sasakii*)
Ysu Shik Chen, *Bull. Agr. Chem. Soc.* (Japan) 22 136 (1958).

391 Homoprotocatechuic Acid, $C_8H_8O_4$, colorless plates, m.p. 128.5°.

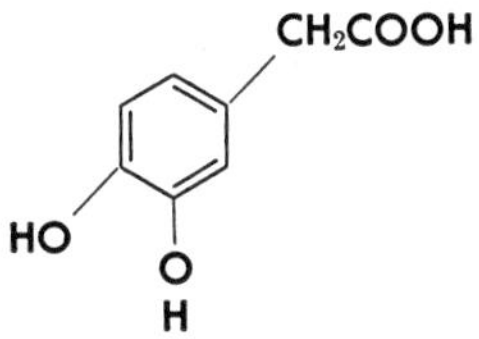

Polyporus tumulosus (artificial medium)
B. J. Ralph and Alexander Robertson, *J. Chem. Soc.,* 3380 (1950).

392 **Orsellinic Acid,** $C_8H_8O_4$, colorless crystals, m.p. (Monohydrate) 176°.

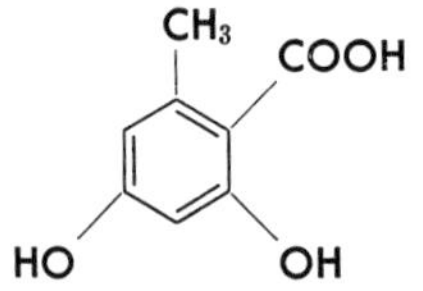

Penicillium griseofulvum, Chaetomium cochlioides
L. Reio, *J. Chromatography* 1 338 (1958).
Klaus Mosbach, *Zeitschr. Naturforsch.* 14b 69 (1959).

393 **Compound D,** $C_9H_8O_5$, cream-colored prisms, m.p. 259° (dec.).
A meta diphenol with a carboxyl group para to a hydroxyl and an aldehyde group ortho to a hydroxyl.
Paecilomyces victoriae V. Szilvinyi
Ustic acid, dehydroustic acid and 4,6-dihydroxy-3-methoxyphthalic acid were isolated from the same culture.
V. C. Vora, *J. Sci. Ind. Research* (India) **13B** 842 (1954).

394 **Flavipin,** $C_9H_8O_5$, pale yellow light-sensitive rods, m.p. 233° (dec.).

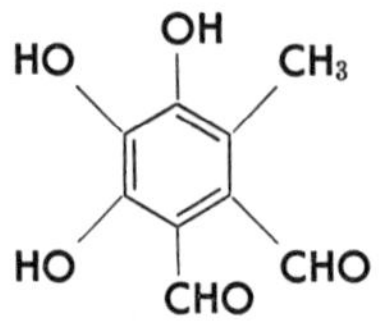

Aspergillus flavipes (Bainier and Sartory) Thom and Church, *A. terreus* Thom
P. Rudman, "Metabolic Products of *A. flavipes, A. terreus* and Certain Other Molds," Doctoral Thesis, Univ. of London, London, 1955.
H. Raistrick and P. Rudman, *Biochem. J.* 63 395 (1956).

395 **4,6-Dihydroxy-3-methoxyphthalic Acid,** $C_9H_8O_7$, colorless prisms, m.p. 193°.

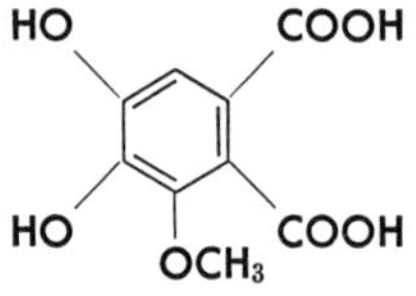

Paecilomyces victoriae V. Szilvinyi
Ustic acid, dehydroustic acid and another incompletely characterized phenolic acid were isolated from the same culture.
V. C. Vora, *J. Sci. Ind. Research* (India) 13B 842 (1954).

396   **2,3-Dihydroxybenzoylglycine,** $C_9H_9O_5N$, colorless needles, m.p. 210°.

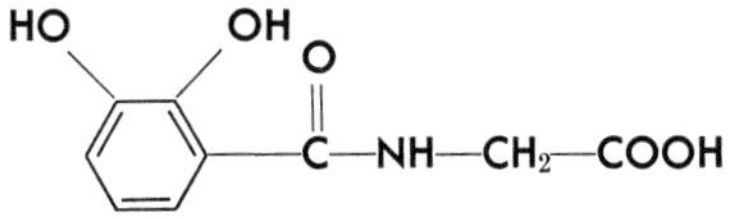

Bacillus subtilis (iron-deficient medium)
Coproporphyrin and succinic acid were also produced.
Takeru Ito and J. B. Neilands, *J. Am. Chem. Soc.* 80 4645 (1958).

397   **8-Hydroxy-3-methylisocoumarin,** $C_{10}H_8O_3$, colorless needles, m.p. 99°.

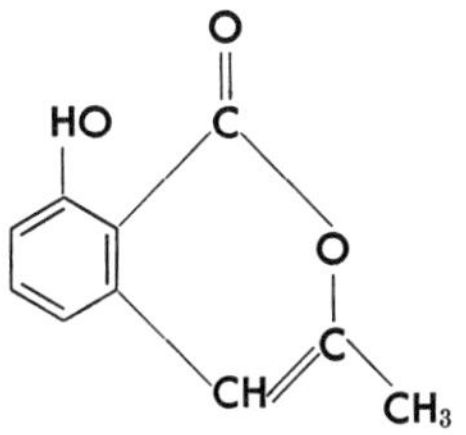

Marasmius ramealis
Gerd Benz, *Arkiv för Kemi* 14 511 (1959).

398   **2,4-Dioxy-6-pyruvylbenzoic Acid,** $C_{10}H_8O_6$, fine colorless crystals, m.p. 125–135°.

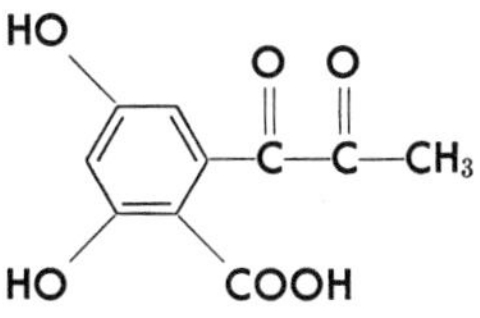

Penicillium brevi-compactum (syn. *P. stoloniferum* Thom*)
Percival W. Clutterbuck, Albert E. Oxford, Harold Raistrick and Geo. Smith, *Biochem. J.* 26 1441 (1932). (Isolation)
Albert E. Oxford and Harold Raistrick, *ibid.* 27 634 (1933).

399 Mellein (Ochracin), $C_{10}H_{10}O_3$, colorless prisms, m.p. 58°, $[\alpha]_D$
     $-124.86°$ ($[\alpha]_D^{12}$ $-108.15°$ in chloroform).

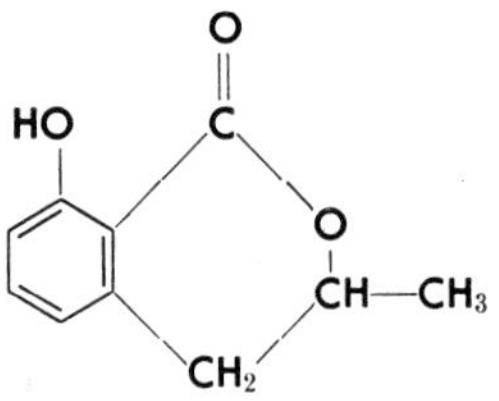

Aspergillus melleus Yugawa, *A. ochraceus*
Eijiro Nishikawa, *J. Agr. Chem. Soc. Japan* **9** 772 (1933).
(Isolation) (*Chem. Abstr.* **28** 2751)
Teijiro Yabuta and Yusuke Sumiki, *ibid.* **9** 1264 (1933).
(Isolation) (*Chem. Abstr.* **28** 2350)
John Blair and G. T. Newbold, *J. Chem. Soc.*, 2871 (1955).
(Structure)
It is interesting to note that a similar compound:

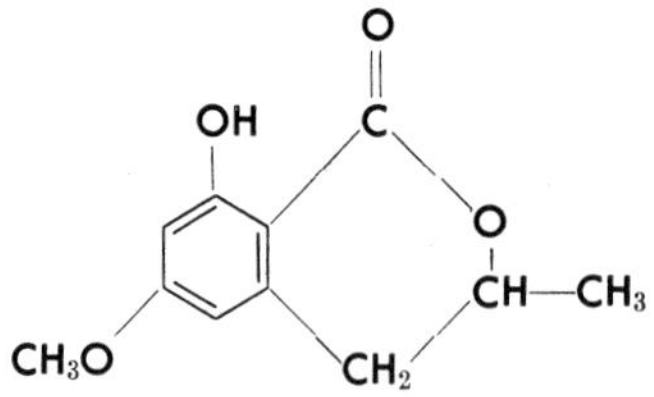

has been isolated from carrots which had developed a
bitter taste during cold storage.
Ernest Sondheimer, *J. Am. Chem. Soc.* **79** 5036 (1957).
(Isolation)

400 3,5-Dimethyl-6-oxyphthalide, $C_{10}H_{10}O_3$, colorless needles, m.p.
     156–158°.

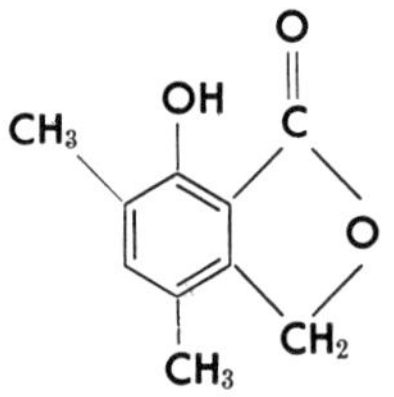

Penicillium gladioli

H. Raistrick and D. J. Ross, *Biochem. J.* 50 635 (1952).

401 **Quadrilineatin,** $C_{10}H_{10}O_4$, colorless needles, m.p. 172° (dec.).

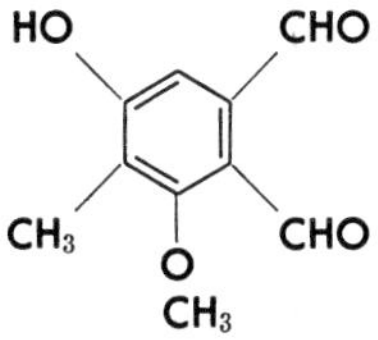

Aspergillus quadrilineatus Thom and Raper

J. H. Birkinshaw, P. Chaplen and R. Lahoz-Oliver, *Biochem. J.* **67** 155 (1957).

402 **1-Carboxy-2,5-dioxybenzyl Methyl Ketone,** $C_{10}H_{10}O_5$, large diamond-shaped crystals, m.p. 152–156° (dec.), remelting at 220–230°.

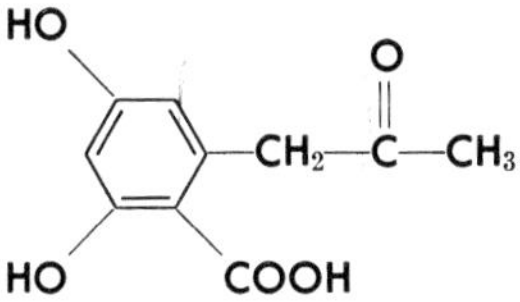

Penicillium brevi-compactum (syn. *P. stoloniferum* Thom)

Percival W. Clutterbuck, Albert E. Oxford, Harold Raistrick and Geo. Smith, *Biochem. J.* 26 1441 (1932).

Albert E. Oxford and Harold Raistrick, *ibid.* 27 634 (1933).

403 **1-Carboxy-2,5-dioxyphenyl Acetyl Carbinol,** $C_{10}H_{10}O_6$, colorless rhombs, m.p. 202–204° (dec.).

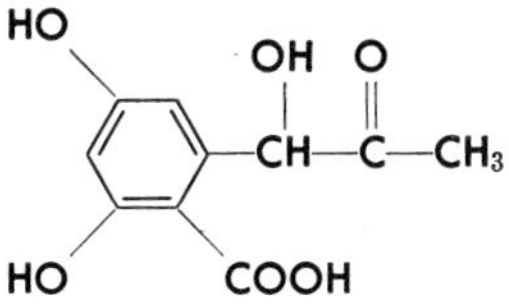

Penicillium brevi-compactum (syn. *P. stoloniferum* Thom)

Percival W. Clutterbuck, Albert E. Oxford, Harold Raistrick and Geo. Smith, *Biochem. J.* 26 1441 (1932).

404 2,6-Dihydroxybutyrophenone, $C_{10}H_{12}O_3$, yellow needles, m.p. 116.5–118°.

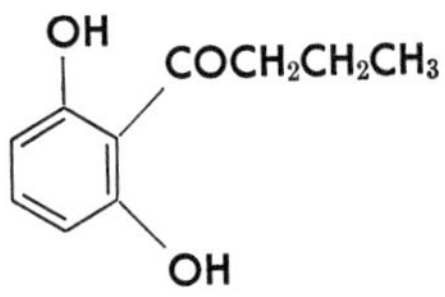

Daldinia concentrica
D. C. Allport and J. D. Bu'Lock, *J. Chem. Soc.*, 654 (1960).

405 Clavatol, $C_{10}H_{12}O_3$, colorless plates, m.p. 183°.

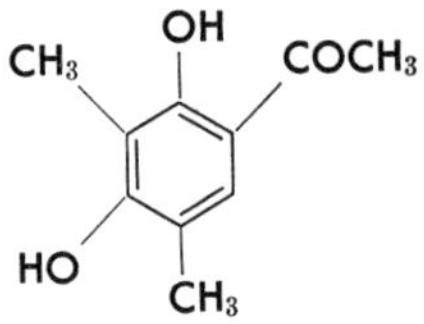

Aspergillus clavatus
Occurs as a minor product with patulin in this culture.
F. Bergel, A. C. Morrison, A. R. Moss and H. Rinderknecht, *J. Chem. Soc.*, 415 (1944). (Isolation)
C. H. Hassall and A. R. Todd, *ibid.*, 611 (1947). (Structure)

406 Sparassol, $C_{10}H_{12}O_4$, colorless microcrystals, m.p. 67°.

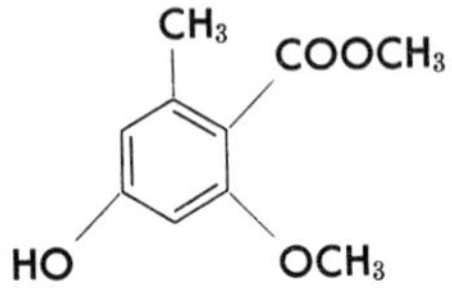

Sparassis ramosa, Evernia prunastri
John Stenhouse, *Ann.* **68** 55 (1848).
Emil Fischer and Kurt Hoesch, *ibid.* **391** 347 (1912). (Structure)
Richard Falck, *Ber.* **56B** 2555 (1923).
E. Wedekind and K. Fleischer, *ibid.* **56B** 2556 (1923). (Structure)
Ernst Späth and Karl Jeschki, *ibid.* **57A** 471 (1924).

407 N-Acetyltyramine, $C_{10}H_{13}O_2N$, colorless crystals, m.p. 135° (s. 128°).

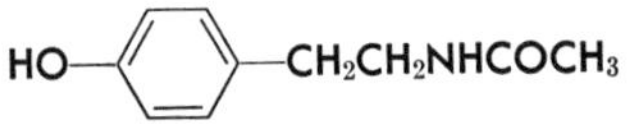

Streptomyces griseus (Krainski) Waksman et Henrici, *Mycobacterium tuberculosis*

J. Comin and W. Keller-Schierlein, *Helv. Chim. Acta* 42 1730 (1959).

Yutaka Shirai, *Kekkaku* (Tuberculosis) 30 628 (1955). (*Chem. Abstr.* 50 5839g)

408 Gladiolic Acid, $C_{11}H_{10}O_5$, colorless needles, m.p. 158–160°.

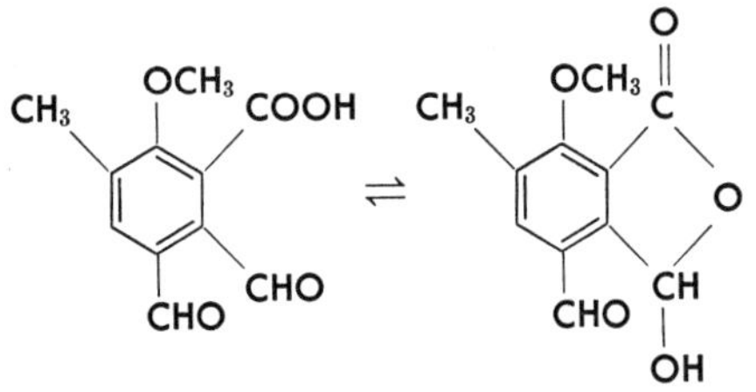

Penicillium gladioli McCull. and Thom
Yield 300 mg. per liter.

Besides dihydrogladiolic acid and 3,5-dimethyl-6-oxyphthalide, a third "contaminant," $C_{11}H_{10}O_4$ (a lactone), was present in the culture.

John Frederick Grove, *Biochem. J.* 50 648 (1952). (Structure)

P. W. Brian, P. J. Curtis and H. G. Hemming, *J. Gen. Microbiol.* 2 341 (1948). (Isolation)

409 Cyclopaldic Acid, $C_{11}H_{10}O_6$, colorless needles, m.p. 224° (subl.).

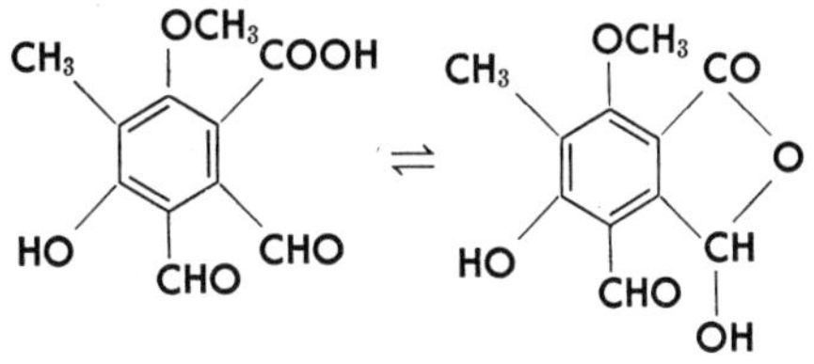

Penicillium cyclopium Westling

J. H. Birkinshaw, H. Raistrick, D. J. Ross and C. E. Stickings, *Biochem. J.* 50 610 (1952).

410 Dihydrogladiolic Acid, $C_{11}H_{12}O_5$, colorless crystals, m.p. 135° (dec.).

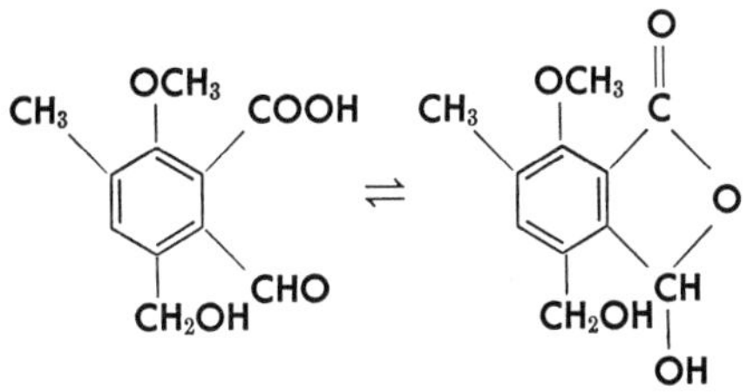

Penicillium gladioli

H. Raistrick and D. J. Ross, *Biochem. J.* 50 635 (1952).

411 Cyclopolic Acid, $C_{11}H_{12}O_6$, colorless plates, m.p. 147° (dec.).

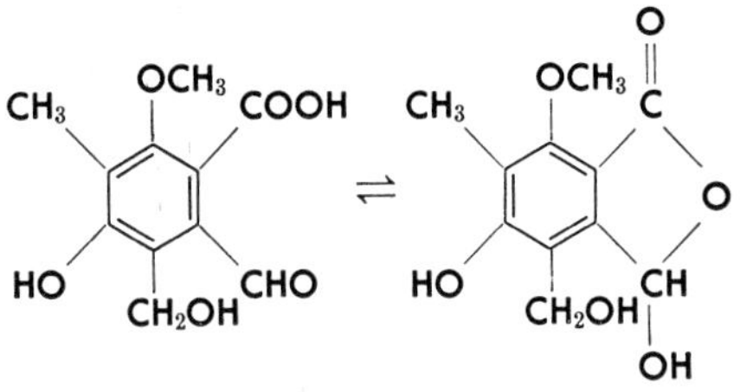

Penicillium cyclopium
J. H. Birkinshaw, H. Raistrick, D. J. Ross and C. E. Stickings, *Biochem. J.* 50 610 (1952).

412 Ustic Acid, $C_{11}H_{12}O_7$, colorless crystals, m.p. 169° (dec.).

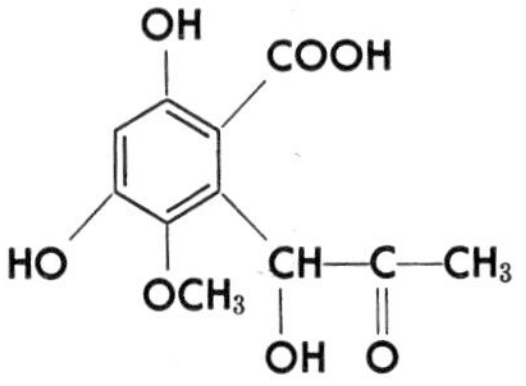

Aspergillus ustus, Paecilomyces victoriae, Ustilago zeae
H. Raistrick and C. E. Stickings, *Biochem. J.* 48 53 (1951).
Yield about 0.5 g. per liter.
V. C. Vora, *J. Sci. Ind. Research* (India) 13B 842 (1954).
Occurred together with dehydroustic acid, 4,5-dihydroxy-3-methoxyphthalic acid and a fourth compound, $C_9H_8O_5$, m.p. 259°; an *m*-dihydroxyphenol with a carbonyl group and a carboxyl group.

413 Radicinin,* $C_{12}H_{10}O_5$, optically active crystals.
Proposed Structure:

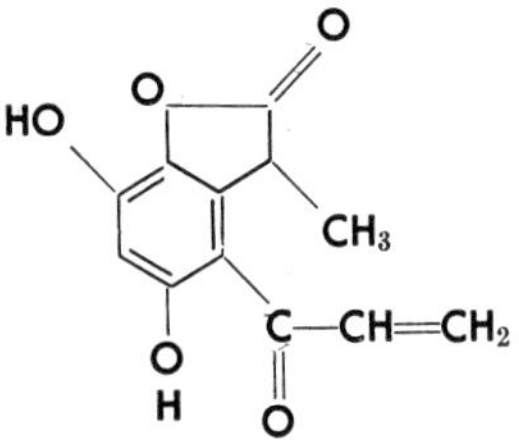

Stemphylium radicinum
D. D. Clarke and F. F. Nord, *Arch. Biochem. and Biophys.*
59 269–284 (1955).
* See also entry **871.**

414   **Alternariol,** $C_{14}H_{10}O_5$, colorless needles, m.p. 350° (dec.)
and

415   **Alternariol Methyl Ether,** $C_{15}H_{12}O_5$, colorless needles, m.p. 267°
(dec.).

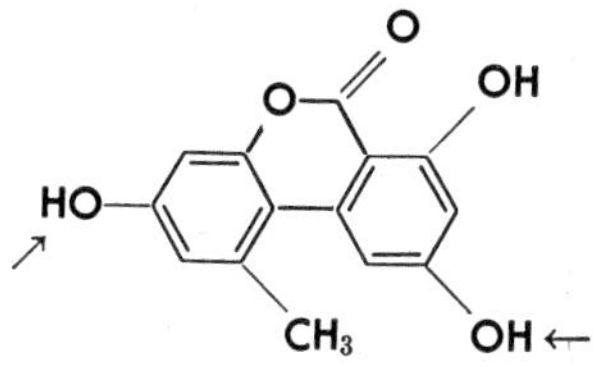

The methyl ether is at one of the positions indicated.
Alternaria tenuis
The yield was about ½ g. per liter.
H. Raistrick, C. E. Stickings and R. Thomas, *Biochem. J.*
55 421 (1953).

416   **Altertenuol,** $C_{14}H_{10}O_6$, buff-colored rods, m.p. 284° (dec. and
subl.).
Forms a triacetate and a trimethyl derivative. Probably related to alternariol.
Alternaria tenuis
T. Rosett, R. H. Sankhala, C. E. Stickings, M. E. U. Taylor
and R. Thomas, *Biochem. J.* 67 390 (1957).

417   **Sorbicillin,** $C_{14}H_{16}O_3$, orange plates, m.p. 113° (remelting at
129°).

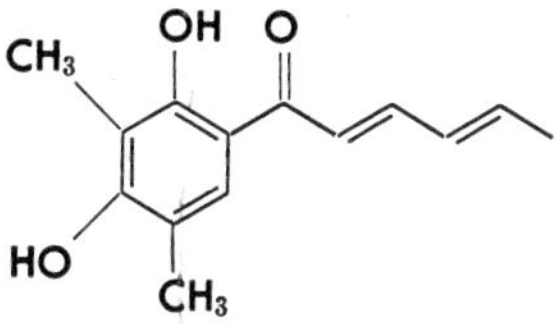

Penicillium notatum Westling
Donald J. Cram and Max Tishler, *J. Am. Chem. Soc.* 70
4238 (1948). (Isolation from Clinical Sodium Penicillin)
Donald J. Cram, *ibid.* 70 4240 (1948). (Structure)
Besides sorbicillin several other compounds were iso-
lated from careful investigation of a sample of early clini-
cal sodium penicillin. In view of the source it is hard to
say which of these may be considered true metabolites.
The other compounds were:
Tiglic Acid, $C_5H_8O_2$, m.p. 63°
d-α-Methylbutyric Acid, $C_5H_{10}O_2$ b.p. 175°, $[\alpha]_D^{20}$ +15.2°
Furoic Acid, m.p. 129°

β-Indoleacetic Acid, m.p. 167°
Phenylacetic Acid, m.p. 76°
2-Decenedioic Acid, $C_{10}H_{16}O_4$, m.p. 172°
Pigment I (β-Penetrin), m.p. 207°.

β-Penetrin is identical with an alkaline hydrolysis product of penetrinic acid, a metabolite of *P. notatum* reported earlier

Pigment II, $C_{10}H_{11}O_6N$, orange prisms, m.p. 105°, N.E. indicates a dicarboxylic acid. Optically inactive. Negative $FeCl_3$ test. Decolorizes permanganate. Decolorized by sodium hydrosulfite and apparently reduced to a hydroquinone, m.p. 129°.

Frank H. Stodola, Jacques L. Wachtel, Andrew J. Moyer and Robert D. Coghill, *J. Biol. Chem.* 159 67 (1945).

418 **Dehydroaltenusin,** $C_{15}H_{12}O_6$, yellow needles, m.p. 189° (dec.).
An acidic compound probably related to altenusin.
Alternaria tenuis
T. Rosett, R. H. Sankhala, C. E. Stickings, M. E. U. Taylor and R. Thomas, *Biochem. J.* 67 390 (1957).

419 **Altenusin,** $C_{15}H_{14}O_6$, colorless prisms, m.p. 202° (dec.).
An acidic compound which forms a tetramethyl derivative. Probably related to alternariol.
Alternaria tenuis
T. Rosett, R. H. Sankhala, C. E. Stickings, M. E. U. Taylor and R. Thomas, *Biochem. J.* 67 390 (1957).

420 **Altenuic Acid I,** $C_{15}H_{14}O_8$, colorless needles, m.p. 183°, second m.p. 224–230° (dec.).
A dibasic acid probably related to alternariol.
Alternaria tenuis
T. Rosett, R. H. Sankhala, C. E. Stickings, M. E. U. Taylor and R. Thomas, *Biochem. J.* 67 390 (1957).

421 **Altenuic Acid II,** $C_{15}H_{14}O_8$, colorless plates, m.p. 245° (dec.).
A dibasic acid probably related to alternariol.
Alternaria tenuis
T. Rosett, R. H. Sankhala, C. E. Stickings, M. E. U. Taylor and R. Thomas, *Biochem. J.* 67 390 (1957).

422 **Altenuic Acid III,** $C_{15}H_{14}O_8$, colorless prisms, m.p. 198–202°, second m.p. 225° (dec.).
A dibasic acid probably related to alternariol.
Alternaria tenuis
T. Rosett, R. H. Sankhala, C. E. Stickings, M. E. U. Taylor and R. Thomas, *Biochem. J.* 67 390 (1957).

423 **Penitrinic Acid,** $C_{15}H_{17}O_5N$, pale yellow bars, m.p. 217–223° (dec.), $[\alpha]_D^{23}$ −549° (in dimethylformamide).

Similar in structure to sorbicillin. The two pigments occur together.

Penicillium notatum Westling

Frank H. Stodola, Jacques L. Wachtel, Andrew J. Moyer and Robert D. Coghill, *J. Biol. Chem.* 159 67 (1945).

Kei Arima, Kazuo Kamagata and Hideo Nakamura, *J. Agr. Chem. Soc. Japan* 27 389 (1953). (Structure work)

424 *d,l*-**Erdin,** $C_{16}H_{10}O_7Cl_2$, yellow crystals, m.p. 210–212°.

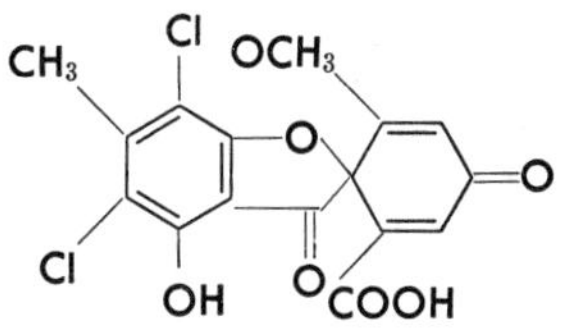

CH₃   Cl   OCH₃   O   Cl   OH   COOH   O

Aspergillus terreus Thom

Erdin occurs naturally as the racemate although the closely related geodin, which is present in the same culture, is the *d*-isomer.

Harold Raistrick and George Smith, *Biochem. J.* 30 1315 (1936). (Isolation)

D. H. R. Barton and A. I. Scott, *J. Chem. Soc.,* 1767 (1958). (Structure)

425 **Curvularin,** $C_{16}H_{20}O_5$, colorless crystals, m.p. 206°, $[\alpha]_D^{18}$ −36.3° (c 3.8 in ethanol).

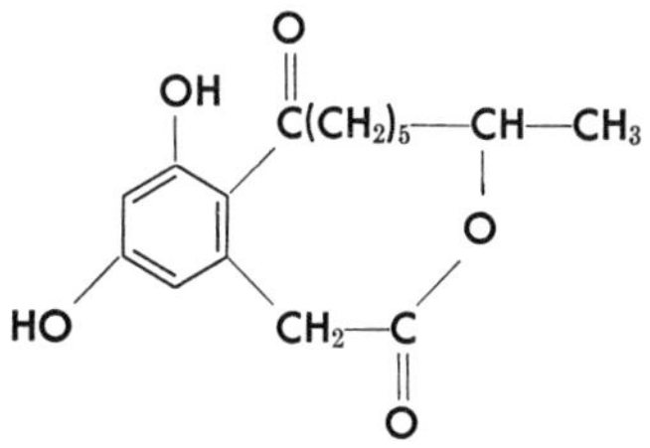

OH   O   C(CH₂)₅—CH—CH₃   O   HO   CH₂—C   O

Curvularia sp.

The yield was 0.40 to 0.48 g. per liter of culture broth. A second compound $C_{16}H_{18}O_5$, m.p. 224.5°, $[\alpha]_D^{18}$ −83°, (also phenolic) was isolated from the same culture.

C. Calam (Imperial Chemical Industries), unpublished. (Isolation)

O. C. Musgrave, *J. Chem. Soc.,* 4301 (1956). (Isolation)

Idem., ibid., 1104 (1957).

A. J. Birch, O. C. Musgrave, R. W. Rickards and Herchel Smith, *ibid.,* 3146 (1959). (Structure)

426 *d*-**Geodin,** $C_{17}H_{12}O_7Cl_2$, yellow crystals, m.p. 228–231°, $[\alpha]_D$ +140° (c 0.80 in chloroform).

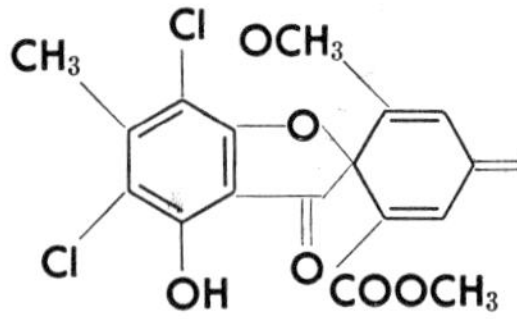

Aspergillus terreus Thom
Harold Raistrick and George Smith, *Biochem. J.* 30 1315 (1936). (Isolation)
D. H. R. Barton and A. I. Scott, *J. Chem. Soc.,* 1767 (1958). (Structure)

427 **Geodoxin,** $C_{17}H_{12}O_8Cl_2$, yellow needles, m.p. 216° (dec.).

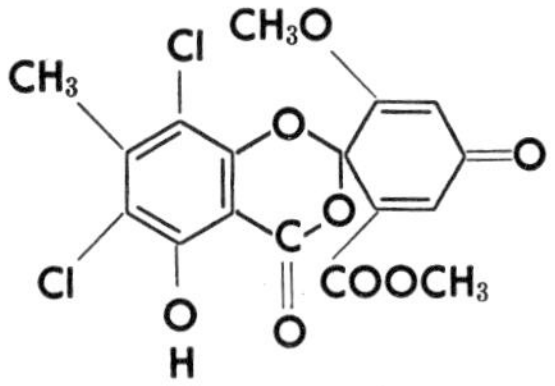

Aspergillus terreus Thom
C. H. Hassall and T. C. McMorris, *J. Chem. Soc.,* 2831 (1959).

428 **Sulochrin,** $C_{17}H_{16}O_7$, colorless crystals, m.p. 262°.

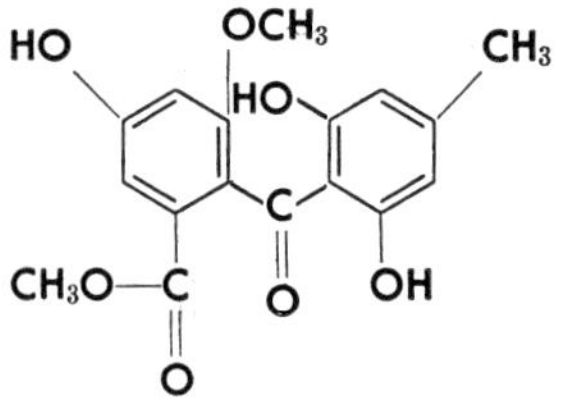

Oospora sulfurea-ochracea
Hidejiro Nichikawa, *Bull. Agr. Chem. Soc.* (Japan) 12 47 (1936).
Idem., J. Agr. Chem. Soc. Japan 13 1 (1937).

Idem., Bull. Agr. Chem. Soc. (Japan) 16 97 (1940).

429   **Geodin-like Antibiotic,** yellow crystals, m.p. 229° (subl. 175° at 3 mm.), $[\alpha]_D^{20}$ +175° (in chloroform).

The chlorine-containing part of the molecule is the same as that of geodin as shown by hydrolysis fragments. Other chemical and physical properties are similar to those of geodin.

Aspergillus flavipes

Paul Delmotte, Julia Delmotte-Plaquée and René Bastin, *J. Pharm. Belg.* 11 200 (1956).

430   **Griseofulvin** (Fulvicin, Grisovin) $C_{17}H_{17}O_6Cl$, colorless crystals, m.p. 220°, $[\alpha]_D^{21}$ +337° (c 1.0 in acetone).

Penicillium griseofulvum Dierckx, *P. patulum, P. albidum* Sopp., *P. raciborskii* Zal., *P. melinii* Thom, *P. urticae* Bain., *P. raistrickii, P. janczewski* Zal. (*P. nigricans* Thom and Bainier), *Carpenteles brefeldianum* Dodge (Shear)

Albert Edward Oxford, Harold Raistrick and Paul Simonart, *Biochem. J.* 33 240 (1939). (Isolation)

J. C. McGowan, *Trans. Brit. Mycol. Soc.* 29 188 (1946).

P. J. Curtis and J. F. Grove, *Nature* 160 574 (1947).

P. W. Brian, P. J. Curtis and H. G. Heming, *Brit. Mycol. Soc. Trans.* 32 30 (1949).

John Frederick Grove, Doreen Ismay, J. MacMillan, T. P. C. Mulholland, M. A. Thorold Rogers, *Chem. and Ind.*, 219 (1951). (Structure)

Idem., J. Chem. Soc., 3958 (1952).

John Frederick Grove, J. MacMillan, T. P. C. Mulholland and M. A. Thorold Rogers, *ibid.*, 3949, 3977 (1952). (Structure)

John Frederick Grove, J. MacMillan, T. P. C. Mulholland and (Mrs.) J. Zealley, *ibid.*, 3967 (1952).

T. P. C. Mulholland, *ibid.*, 3987, 3994 (1952).

A. J. Birch, R. A. Massy-Westropp, R. W. Rickards and Herchel Smith, *Proc. Chem. Soc.*, 98 (1957). (Biosynthesis)

431 Bromogriseofulvin, $C_{17}H_{17}O_6Br$, colorless crystals, m.p. 204°.

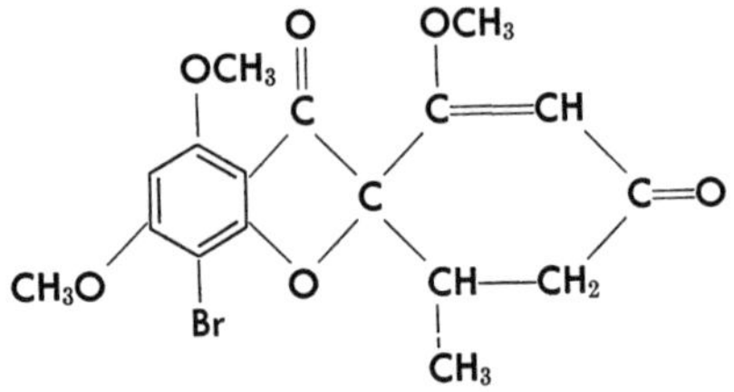

OCH₃ O OCH₃ C=CH C C=O CH₃O Br O CH—CH₂ CH₃

On the proper medium bromogriseofulvin generally can be produced by the same molds which produce griseofulvin.

J. MacMillan, *J. Chem. Soc.*, 2585 (1954). (Isolation)

432 Dechlorogriseofulvin, $C_{17}H_{18}O_6$, colorless needles, m.p. 179–181°, $[\alpha]_D^{19}$ +390° (c 1 in acetone).

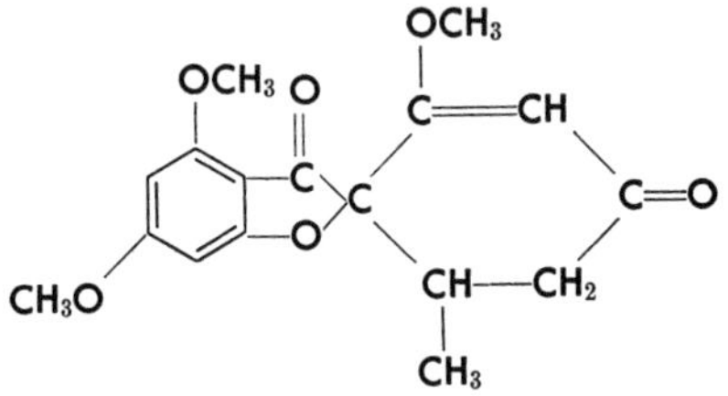

OCH₃ OCH₃ O C=CH C C C=O CH₃O O CH—CH₂ CH₃

Penicillium griseofulvum Dierckx, *P. janczewski* Zal.
J. MacMillan, *Chem. and Ind.*, 719 (1951).
Idem., J. Chem. Soc., 1697 (1953).
D. H. R. Barton and T. Bruun, *J. Chem. Soc.*, 603 (1953).

433 Mycophenolic Acid, $C_{17}H_{20}O_6$, colorless needles, m.p. 141°.

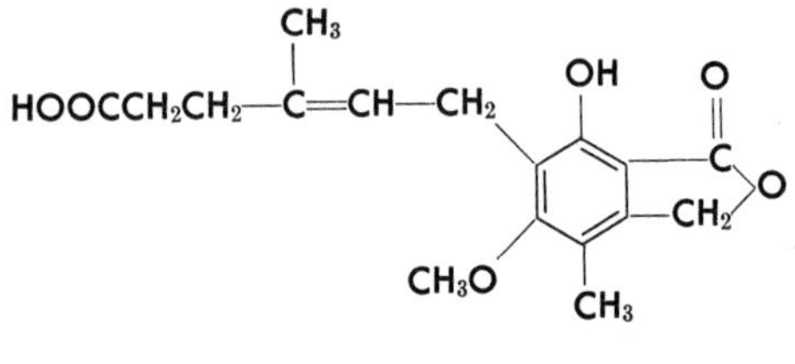

CH₃
HOOCCH₂CH₂—C=CH—CH₂ OH O C O CH₂ CH₃O CH₃

Penicillium brevi-compactum Dierckx
C. L. Alsberg and O. F. Black, *Bull. U. S. Bur. Pl. Ind.*, No. 270 (1913). (Isolation)
Percival Walter Clutterbuck, Albert Edward Oxford, Harold Raistrick and George Smith, *Biochem. J.* 26 1441 (1932).

J. H. Birkinshaw, A. Bracken, E. N. Morgan and H. Raistrick, *ibid.* 43 216 (1948).
J. H. Birkinshaw, H. Raistrick and D. J. Ross, *Biochem. J.*
50 630 (1952). (Structure)

434 Xanthocillin-X, $C_{18}H_{12}O_2N_2$, yellow crystals, m.p. ~200° (dec.).

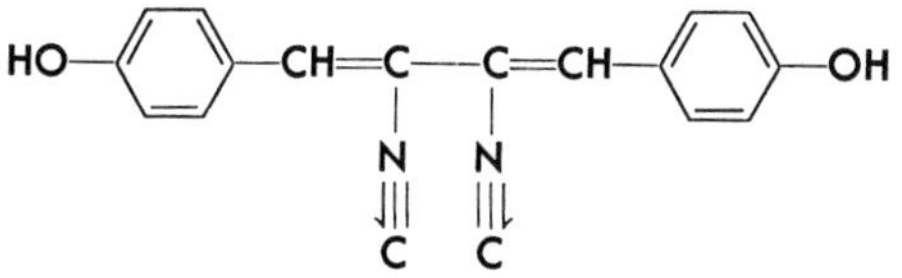

Penicillium notatum Westling
Xanthocillin constitutes about 70% of a mixture containing a second constituent, xanthocillin-Y.

W. Rothe, *Deutsche Med. Wochenschr.* 79 1080 (1954).
(Isolation)
I. Hagedorn and H. Tönjes, *Pharmazie* 11 409 (1956).
(Structure)
Ilse Hagedorn, Ulrich Eholzer and Arthur Luttringhaus,
Chem. Ber. 93 1584 (1960). (Experimental work)

435 Auroglaucin, $C_{19}H_{22}O_3$, orange-red crystals, m.p. 153°.

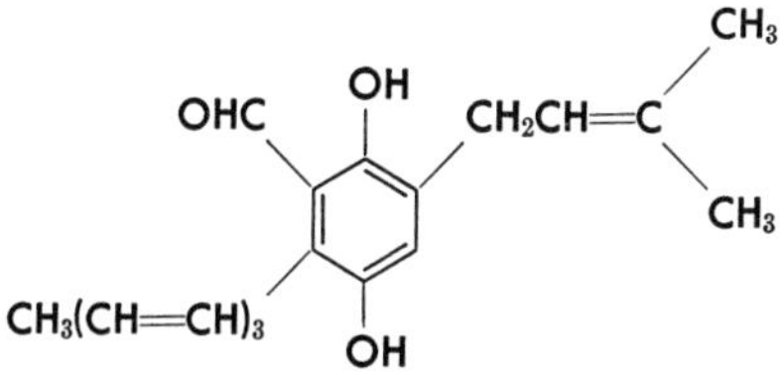

Aspergillus glaucus, A. mangini, other aspergilli

H. Raistrick, Robert Robinson and A. R. Todd, *J. Chem. Soc.,*
80 (1937).
Adolfo Quilico, Cesare Cardani and Luigi Panizzi, *Atti
accad. nazl. Lincei Rend., Classe sci. fis., Mat. e nat. sci.* 14 358
(1953). (Structure)

436 Flavoglaucin, $C_{19}H_{28}O_3$, pale yellow crystals, m.p. 103°.

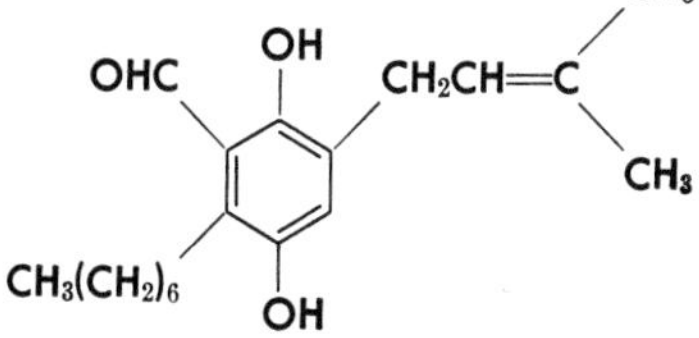

Aspergillus glaucus, other aspergilli

H. Raistrick, Robert Robinson and A. R. Todd, *J. Chem. Soc.,* 80 (1937).

Adolfo Quilico, C. Cardani and G. Stagno d'Alcontres, *Gazz. chim. ital.* 83 754 (1953). (Structure)

437 **Picrolichenic Acid,** $C_{25}H_{30}O_7$, colorless crystals, m.p. 178° (dec.). Proposed structure:

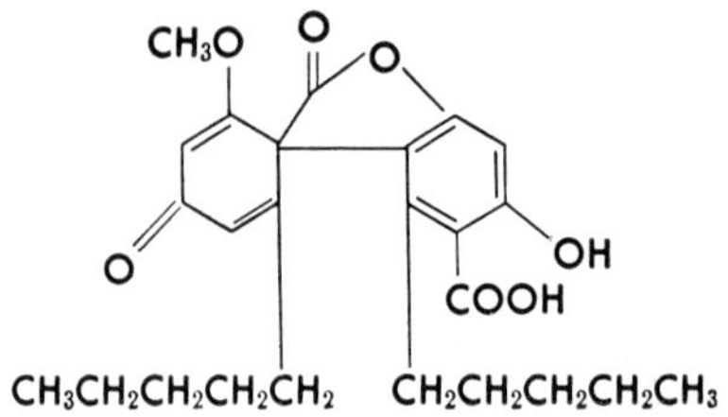

CH3O
O
O
O
OH
COOH
CH3CH2CH2CH2CH2
CH2CH2CH2CH2CH3

Pertusaria amara (Ach.) Nyl., *Variola amara* (Ach.) The yield was 5–10% of the dry weight of the lichen.

H. Erdtman and C. A. Wachtmeister, *Chem. and Ind.,* 1042 (1957).

Carl Axel Wachtmeister, *Acta Chem. Scand.* 12 147 (1958). (Structure)

438 **α-Tocopherol** (Vitamin E), $C_{29}H_{50}O_2$, viscous oil, b.p. 200–220° (0.1 mm.), n_D^{25} 1.5045, U.V. max. 294 mμ.

HO
CH3
(CH2)3—CH—(CH2)3—CH—(CH2)3—CH—CH3
CH3
CH3
CH3
O
CH3
CH3
CH3

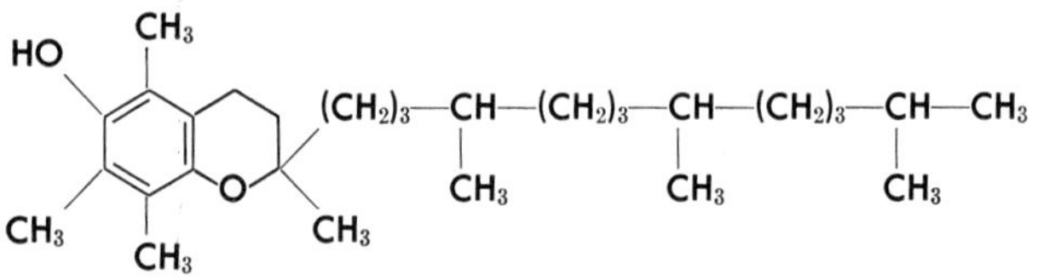

Identified in about a dozen varieties of chlorophyll-containing bacteria by paper chromatographic comparisons. (Not isolated.)

J. Green, S. A. Price and L. Gare, *Nature* 184 1339 (1959).

439 **Chartreusin** (Antibiotic X-465A), $C_{32}H_{32}O_{14}$, greenish yellow crystals, m.p. 184–186°, $[\alpha]_D^{25}$ +132° ±6° (c 0.2 in pyridine).

Proposed Structure:

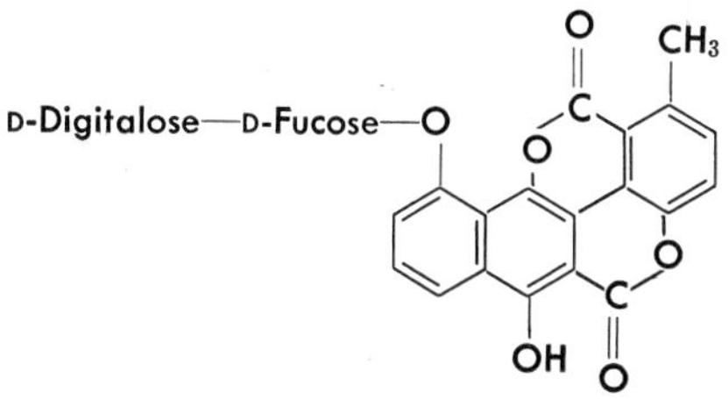

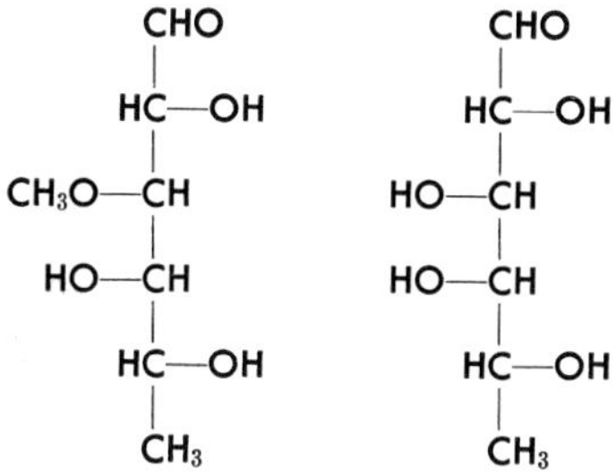

D-Digitalose—D-Fucose—O

CHO
|
HC—OH
|
CH₃O—CH
|
HO—CH
|
HC—OH
|
CH₃

D-Digitalose

CHO
|
HC—OH
|
HO—CH
|
HO—CH
|
HC—OH
|
CH₃

D-Fucose

Streptomyces chartreusis and probably other *Streptomyces* spp.

Byron E. Leach, Kenneth M. Calhoun, LeRoy E. Johnson, Charlotte M. Teeters and William G. Jackson, *J. Am. Chem. Soc.* **75** 4011 (1953). (Isolation)

K. M. Calhoun and L. E. Johnson, *Antibiotics and Chemotherapy* **6** 294 (1956).

Julius Berger, L. H. Sternbach, R. G. Pollock, E. R. LaSala, S. Kaiser and M. W. Goldberg, *J. Am. Chem. Soc.* **80** 1636 (1958).

L. H. Sternbach, S. Kaiser and M. W. Goldberg, *ibid.* **80** 1639 (1958).

E. Simonitsch, W. Eisenhuth, O. A. Stamm and H. Schmid, *Helv. Chim. Acta* **43** 58 (1960). (Structure)

440 Chartreusin-like Antibiotic, $C_{32}H_{34}O_{14}$, m.p. 186°.

A weakly acidic glucoside.

Streptomyces sp.

F. Arcamone, F. Bizioli and T. Scotti, *Antibiotics and Chemotherapy* **6** 283 (1956).

b. DEPSIDES AND DEPSIDONES

Lichens are symbiotic partnerships of fungi and algae. While this slow-growing combination is visible without the aid of lenses, the extractable metabolites so resemble those of micro-organisms that they are included in this listing for comparison.

Lichens and the fruiting bodies of the higher fungi were long used in folk medicine in the damp northern lands where they are prominent members of the flora. It was only natural, then, that the tool of organic chemistry was applied at an early date in these locations to elucidate the structures of their metabolites. Thus, historically, a large body of knowledge on such structures existed long before systematic work was begun on the fungi and streptomycetes, which have been so much more rewarding to modern medicine.

Depsides, *e.g.* microphyllic acid and olivetoric acid, frequently contain aliphatic side-chains attached to their phenolic rings. The fact that these invariably consisted of an uneven number of carbon atoms was soon recognized and used as a rule in structure determinations. It was considered a curious phenomenon until it became apparent that such molecules are particularly obvious examples of derivation from acetate.

Certain lichen metabolites, for example some of the anthraquinone pigments, have been found also in fungi. Moreover, some of the fungal partners have been isolated from lichens and grown alone in pure culture. In a few such cases the same metabolites have been isolated which are produced by the partnership itself. Examples are the anthraquinones physcion (parietin) and rhodocladonic acid, the dibenzofurans usnic and didymic acids, as well as pulvic anhydride (stictaurin) and the nidulins.[1, 2, 3]

In contrast there is evidence that depsides and depsidones cannot be produced by the isolated fungus partner, but are the unique products of a collaborative effort.[4] In the work just cited it was found that the fungal components of various cla-

---

[1] E. Thomas, *Beitr. z. Kryptogamenflora der Schweiz* 9 1 (1939).

[2] Hempstead Castle and Flora Kubsch, *Arch. Biochem.* 23 158 (1949).

[3] F. M. Dean, A. D. T. Erni and Alexander Robertson, *J. Chem. Soc.,* 3545 (1956).

[4] Dieter Hess, *Z. Naturforsch.* 14b 345 (1959).

donia, parmelia and placodium species, grown alone in pure culture, produced no depsides nor depsidones. Orsellinic and

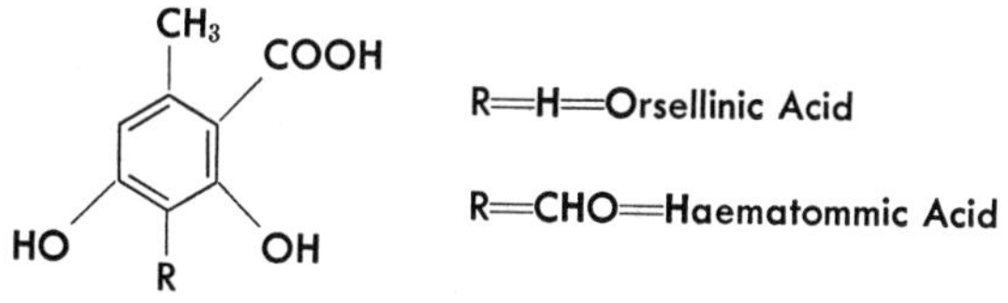

R=H=Orsellinic Acid

R=CHO=Haematommic Acid

haematommic acids, simpler moieties which could not be shown to be present as such in the parent lichens, were isolated. This could indicate that these phenols are precursors, and that the algae are necessary to effect coupling as well as final, characteristic modifications. It is interesting that orsellinic acid (q.v.) has been isolated recently from other fungus cultures. Phenolic acids of this sort are obviously acetate-derived.

Depsidones probably are formed by phenol coupling of the depsides. Phenol coupling (phenol dehydrogenation) is undoubtedly a widespread phenomenon among natural products. It involves the removal of one electron from the phenol with formation of a phenol-free radical. Such radicals are relatively stable due to the resonance possibilities. In complex natural products such phenol radicals can form new bonds by intramolecular attack. Thus the formation of a depsidone (in this case protocetraric acid) from a depside might be represented as follows:

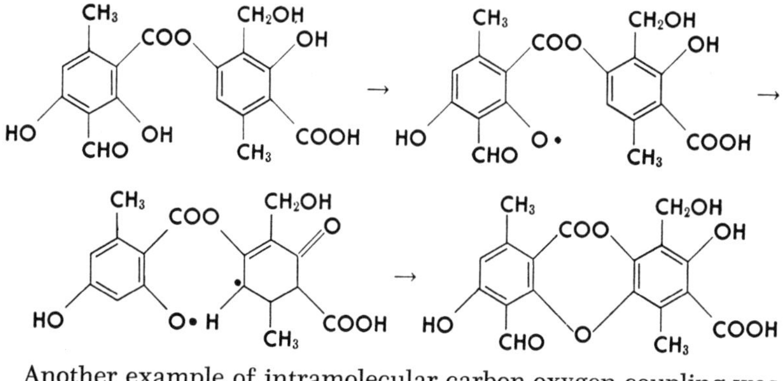

Another example of intramolecular carbon-oxygen coupling was noted earlier in this chapter in the formation of the geodin, griseofulvin type of skeleton.

Carbon-carbon bonds can be formed similarly (by coupling

of the ortho and para resonance isomers of the phenol-free radical). Biphenyl, binaphthyl and *bis*-anthraquinone skeletons might be formed in this way.

A combination of the two types of bond formation (*i.e.* first an intermolecular carbon-carbon coupling followed by an intramolecular oxygen-carbon coupling) probably occurs in the biosynthesis of compounds such as the dibenzofurans, etc.

More thorough considerations of phenol coupling as a biosynthetic process have been published.[5, 6]

In vitro couplings of phenolic compounds have been accomplished in the laboratory, by using simple electron acceptors such as molecular oxygen or ferric chloride, and natural products have been prepared in this way. Yields under such conditions are generally low, and the orienting influence of the enzyme surface seems to be required for real efficiency.

Referencing of this section is lean because of the very thorough existing work.[7] In general the final structure determination or synthesis is mentioned.

441 **Diploicin,** $C_{16}H_{10}O_5Cl_4$, colorless crystals, m.p. 232°.

Buellia canescens (Dicks.) DeNot.

Thomas J. Nolan, Joseph Algara, Eugene P. McCann, Wm. A. Manahan and Niall Nolan, *Sci. Proc. Roy. Dublin Soc.* 24 319 (1948).

442 **Variolaric Acid** (Ochrolechaic Acid, Parellic Acid), $C_{16}H_{10}O_7$, colorless crystals, m.p. 296°.

[5] D. H. R. Barton and T. Cohen, *Festschrift Arthur Stoll*, 117 (1957).

[6] Holger Erdtman and Carl Axel Wachmeister, *ibid.*, 144 (1957).

[7] Yasuhiko Asahina and Shoji Shibata, "Chemistry of Lichen Substances," Japan Society for the Promotion of Science, Tokyo, 1954. (In English)

Lecanora parella Ach.
The yield was about 1%. Mannitol also was present.
D. Murphy, J. Keane and T. J. Nolan, *Sci. Proc. Roy. Dublin Soc.* **23** 71 (1943).

443 Lecanoric Acid (Glabratic Acid), $C_{16}H_{14}O_7$, colorless needles, m.p. 175°.

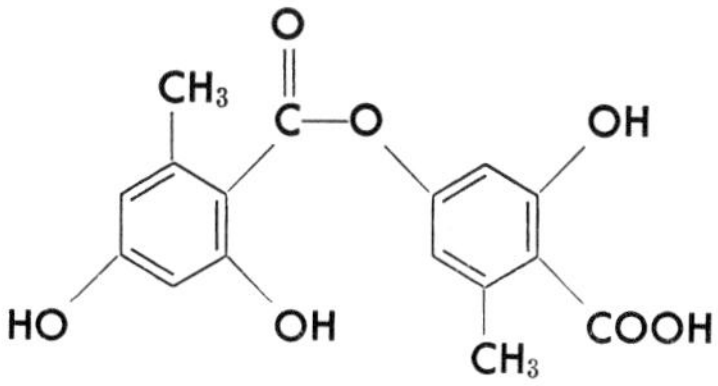

Parmelia tinctorum Despr., *P. borreri* Turm., *P. scortea* Ach. and *P. latissima* Fee.
Emil Fischer and Hermann O. L. Fischer, *Ber.* **46** 1138 (1913). (Synthesis)

444 Diploschistesic Acid, $C_{16}H_{14}O_8$, colorless leaflets, m.p. 174°.

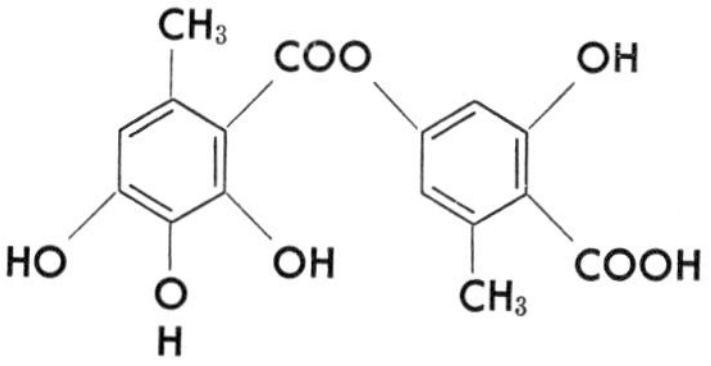

Diploschistes scruposus (*L.*) and *D. bryophilus* (Ehrh.)
Lecanoric acid was isolated from the same source.
Yasuhiko Asahina and Masaichi Yasue, *Ber.* **69B** 2327 (1936). (Synthesis)

445 Vicanicin, $C_{17}H_{14}O_5Cl_2$, colorless needles, m.p. 248–250°.

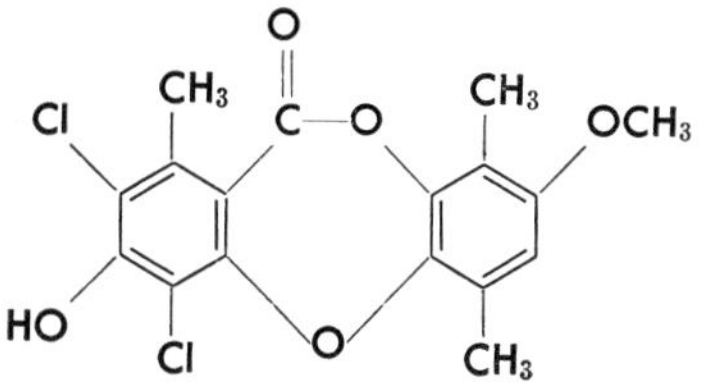

Teloschistes flavicans
A yield of about 1% of the dry lichen weight was obtained.

S. Neelakantan, T. R. Seshadri and S. S. Subramanian, *Tetrahedron Letters* No. 9, pp. 1–4 (1959).

446 Evernic Acid, $C_{17}H_{16}O_7$, colorless prisms, m.p. 169°.

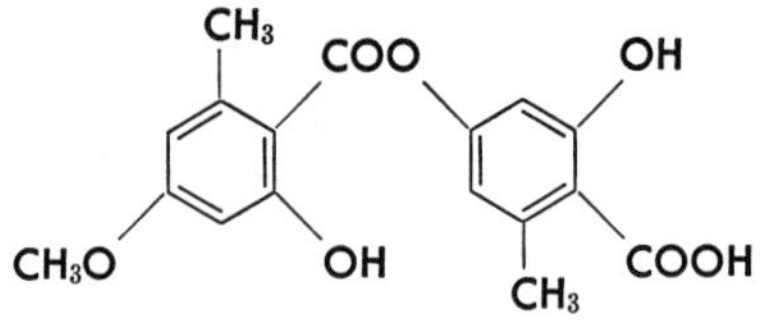

Evernia prunastri L., *Ramalina pollinaria* Wests., *Usnea jesoensis* Asahina

Fukuziro Fuzikawa and Kumao Ishiguro, *J. Pharm. Soc. Japan* 56 837 (in German, 149) (1936). (Synthesis)

447 Norstictic Acid, $C_{18}H_{12}O_9$, nearly colorless needles, m.p. 283° (dec.).

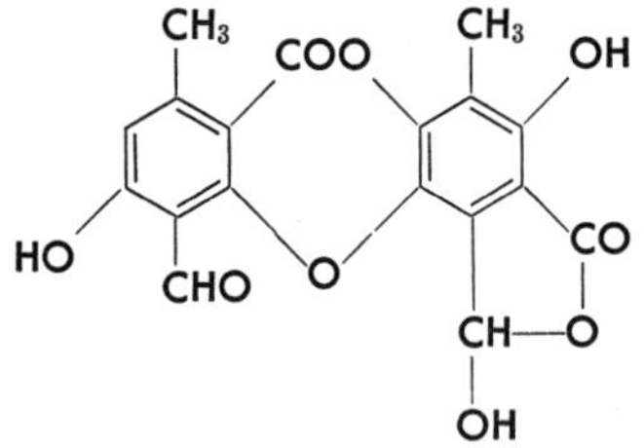

Lobaria pulmonaria Hoffm., *Parmelia acetabulum* Duby., *Usnea japonica,* Wain., etc.

Yasuhiko Asahina and Masaichi Yanagita, *Ber.* **67B** 799 (1934).

448 Salazinic Acid (Saxatilic Acid), $C_{18}H_{12}O_{10}$, colorless needles, m.p. 260° (dec. from 240°).

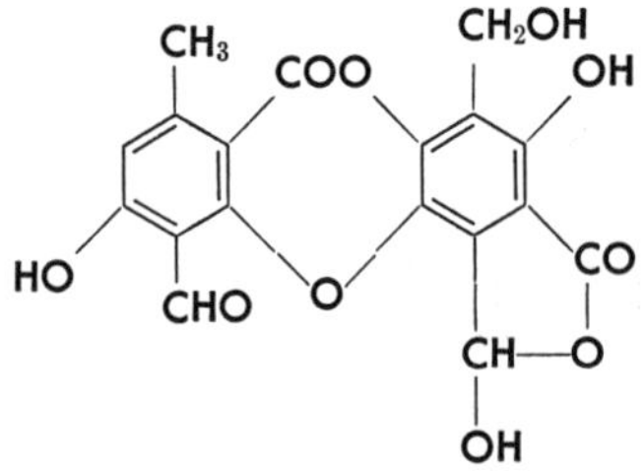

Parmelia cetrata Ach., *P. conspersa* Ach., *P. marmariza*
Nyl., *P. saxatilis* Ach., *P. abyssinica* Kremp.
Yasuhiko Asahina and Juntaro Asano, *Ber.* **66B** 689, 893,
1215 (1933).

449 **Gangaleoidin,** $C_{18}H_{14}O_7Cl_2$, colorless needles, m.p. 213°.

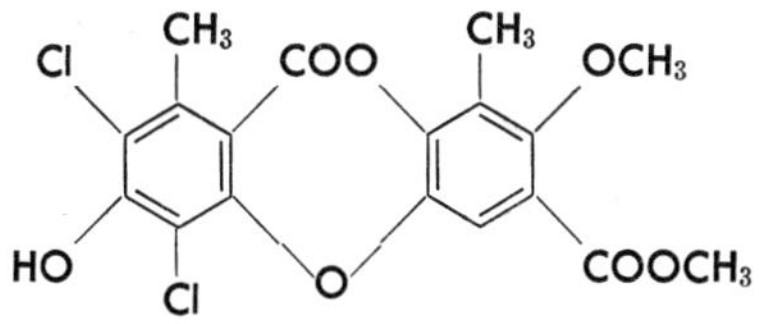

Lecanora gangaleoides Nyl.
V. E. Davidson, J. Keane and T. J. Nolan, *Sci. Proc. Roy.
Dublin Soc.* 23 143 (1943). (Structure)

450 **Psoromic Acid** (Sulcatic Acid, Parellic Acid), $C_{18}H_{14}O_8$, colorless
needles, m.p. 265°.

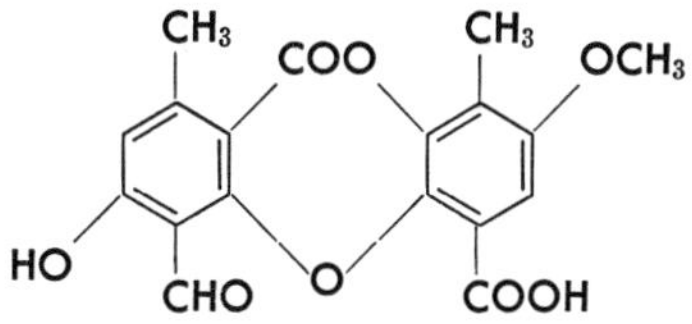

Psoroma crassum Körber, *Alectoria zopfii* Asahina, etc.
Syozi Shibata, *J. Pharm. Soc. Japan* **59** 323 (in German,
111) (1939). (Synthesis)

451 **Protocetraric Acid** (Capraric Acid, Ramalinic Acid), $C_{18}H_{14}O_9$,
colorless fine needles, m.p. 250° (dec. from 220°).

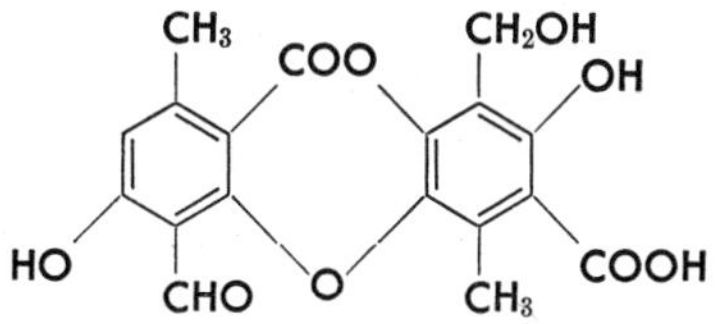

Parmelia caperata, Ramalina farinacea, etc.
Yasuhiko Asahina and Yaichiru Tanase, *Ber.* **66B** 700
(1933).
Yasuhiko Asahina and Juntaro Asano, *ibid.* **66B** 893, 1215
(1933).

452 **Barbatolic Acid,** $C_{18}H_{14}O_{10}$, colorless crystals, m.p. 206° (dec.) (s. 190°).

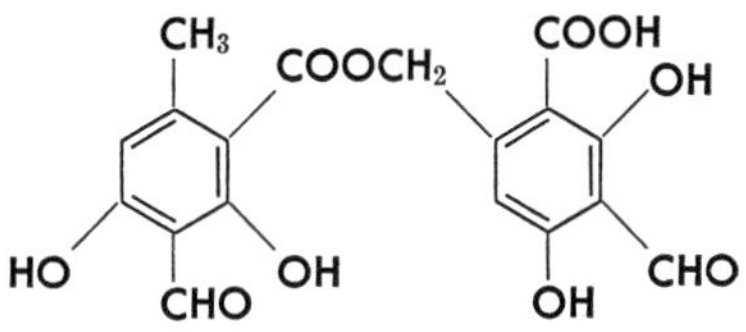

CH₃ COOCH₂ COOH OH

HO CHO OH OH CHO

Usnea barbata, Alectoria implexa (Hoffm.) Nyl. f. *fuscidula* Arn.

Eero E. Suominen, *Suomen Kemistileht;* **12B** 26 (1939).

453 **Pannarin,** $C_{18}H_{15}O_6Cl$, colorless prisms, m.p. 216°.

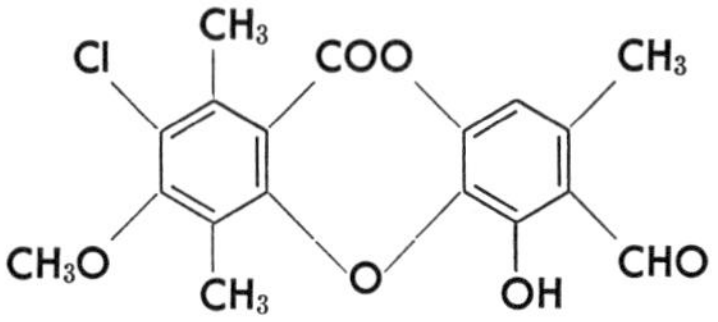

Cl CH₃ COO CH₃

CH₃O CH₃ O OH CHO

Pannaria lanuginosa Korb., *P. fulvescens* Nyl., *P. lurida* Nyl.

Itiro Yosioka, *J. Pharm. Soc. Japan* **61** 332 (1941).

454 **Obtusatic Acid** (Ramalic Acid), $C_{18}H_{18}O_7$, colorless needles, m.p. 208° (dec.).

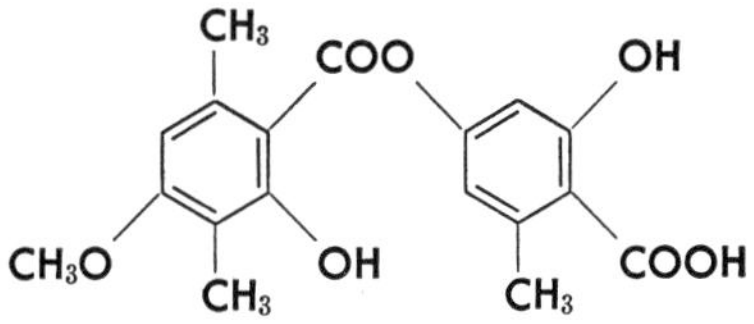

CH₃ COO OH

CH₃O CH₃ OH CH₃ COOH

Ramalina pollineria Ach. other *Ramalina* species
Evernic acid, usnic acid and sometimes sekikaic acid were isolated from the same sources.

Fukuziro Fuzikawa, *J. Pharm. Soc. Japan* **56** 237 (in German, 25) (1936). (Synthesis)

455 Stictic Acid (Stictaic Acid, Pseudopsoromic Acid, Scopularic Acid), $C_{19}H_{14}O_9$, colorless microcrystals, m.p. 268° (dec.).

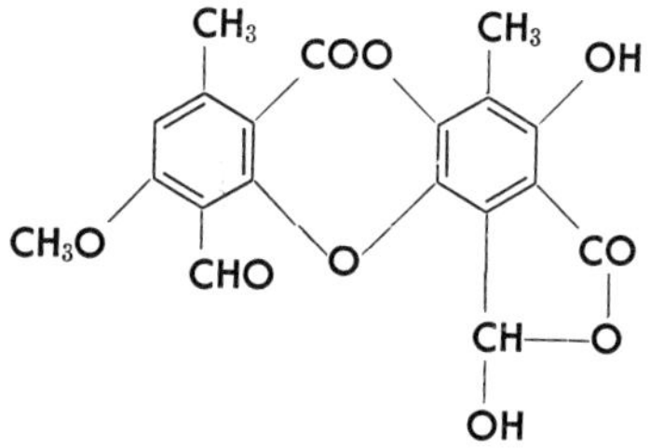

Lobaria pulmonaria Hoffm., *L. oregana* Müll. Arg., *Stereocaulon nabewariense* Zahlb., etc.

Yasuhiko Asahina and Masaiti Yanagita, *Ber.* **67B** 1965 (1934).

456 Nornidulin (Ustin), $C_{19}H_{15}O_5Cl_3$, hexagonal plates or prisms, m.p. 185°.

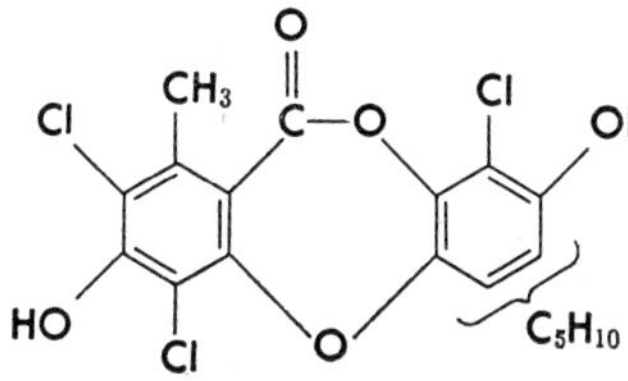

Aspergillus nidulans, NRRL No. 2006

A little succinic acid was isolated from the same culture.

F. M. Dean, John C. Roberts and Alexander Robertson, *J. Chem. Soc.*, 1432 (1954).

457 Dechloronornidulin (Ustin II), $C_{19}H_{16}O_5Cl_2$, needles, m.p. 212–214°.

Partial structure:

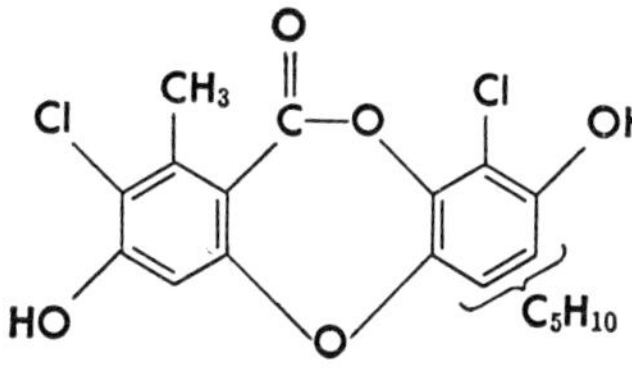

Aspergillus nidulans NRRL No. 2006
F. M. Dean, A. D. T. Erni and Alexander Robertson, *J. Chem. Soc.*, 3545 (1956).

458 **Thamnolic Acid,** $C_{19}H_{16}O_{11}$, pale yellow crystals, m.p. 223° (dec.).

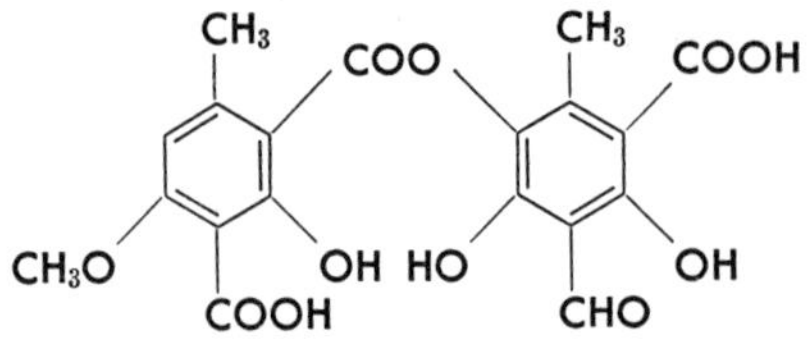

Thamnolia vermicularis (Sw.) Schaer., *Cladonia polydactyla* Flk., *Cl. digitata,* other *Cladonia, Parmeliopsis* and *Pertusaria* spp.
Yasuhiko Asahina and Michio Hiraiwa, *Ber.* **69B** 330 (1936).
Idem., ibid. **72** 1402 (1939).

459 **Chloroatranorin,** $C_{19}H_{17}O_8Cl$, colorless crystals, m.p. 208°.

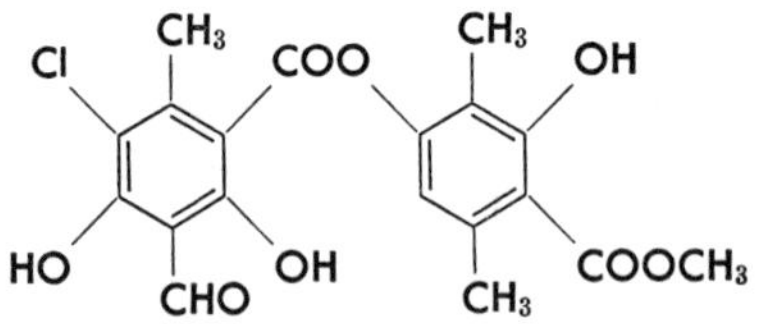

Parmelia furfuracea Ach., *P. physodes* Ach., *Evernia prunastri,* etc., wide occurrence
Georg Koller and Karl Pöpl, *Monatsh.* **64** 106 (1934).
Idem., ibid. **64** 126 (1934).

460 **Atranorin** (Atranoric Acid, Usnarin, Parmelin), $C_{19}H_{18}O_8$, colorless prisms, m.p. 196°.

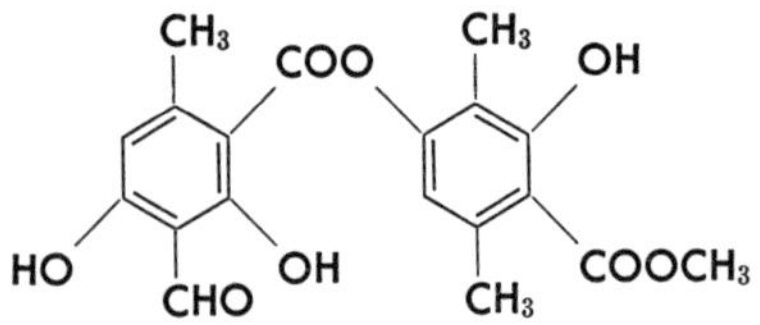

Atranorin occurs in about 90 different lichens.
d-Usnic acid also often is present.

Alexander St. Pfau, *Helv. Chim. Acta* **9** 650 (1926).

461 Baeomycesic Acid, $C_{19}H_{18}O_8$, colorless crystals, m.p. 233°.

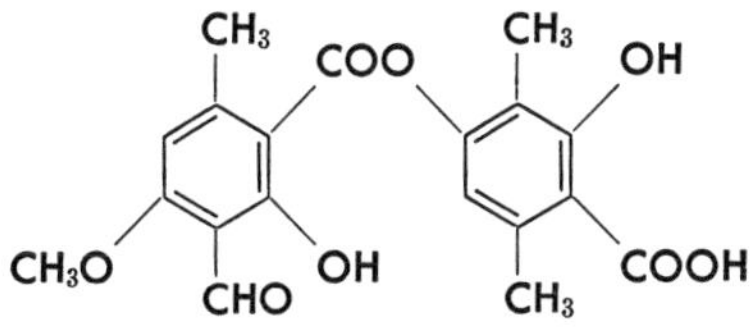

CH₃ — COO — CH₃ — OH / CH₃O — CHO — OH — CH₃ — COOH

Baeomyces roseus Pers., *B. fungoides* Ach., *Thamnolia subvermicularis* Asahina
Squamatic acid also was present in some cases.
Georg Koller and Walter Maass, *Monatsh.* **66** 57 (1935).

462 Squamatic Acid (Sphaerophoric Acid), $C_{19}H_{18}O_9$, colorless crystals, m.p. 228° (dec.).

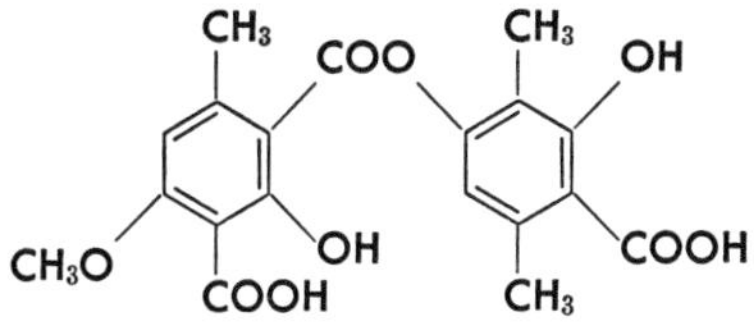

CH₃ — COO — CH₃ — OH / CH₃O — COOH — OH — CH₃ — COOH

Cladonia bellidiflora var. *coccocephala* Ach., *Cl. squamosa* Hoffm., *Cl. uncialis* (L.) Web., *Thamnolia subvermicularis* Asahina
A little *l*-usnic acid was present also.
Yasuhiko Asahina and Yoshio Sakurai, *Ber.* **70B** 64 (1937).
(Synthesis)

463 Hypothamnolic Acid, $C_{19}H_{18}O_{10}$, colorless needles, m.p. 217.5°.

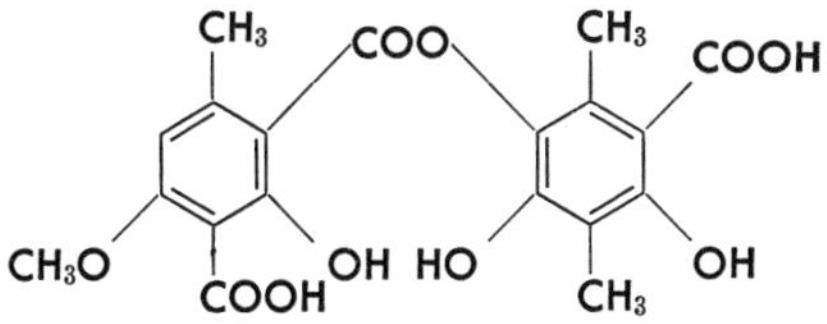

CH₃ — COO — CH₃ — COOH / CH₃O — COOH — OH HO — CH₃ — OH

Cladonia pseudostellata Asahina
The yield was about 0.1%. Usnic acid was present also.
Yasuhiko Asahina, Masaru Aoki and Fukuziro Fuzikawa, *Ber.* **74B** 824 (1941).

464 **Barbatic Acid** (Rhizoic Acid, Coccellic Acid), $C_{19}H_{20}O_7$, colorless prisms, m.p. 187° (dec.).

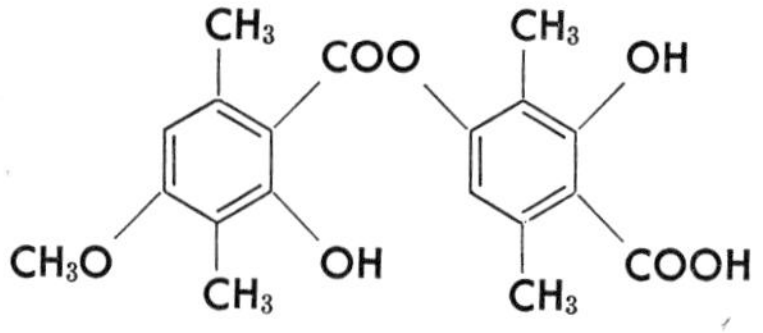

Cladonia floerkeana Sommerf., *Cl. bacillaris* Nyl., *Cl. macilenta* (Hoff.) Flk., *Cl. coccifera* (L.), *Cl. amaurocraea* (Fl.) Schaer., *Rhizocarpon geographicum* (L.), *Usnea longissima* Ach.

Usnic acid also was present.

Fukuziro Fuzikawa, *J. Pharm. Soc. Japan* 56 237 (in German, 25) (1936). (Synthesis)

465 **Physodalic Acid** (Monoacetylprotocetraric Acid), $C_{20}H_{16}O_{10}$, colorless plates, m.p. 260° (dec. from 230°).

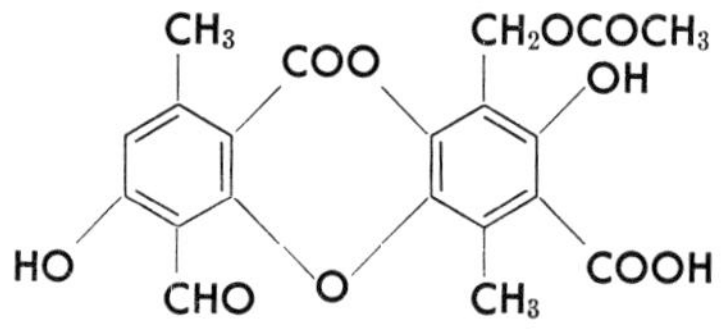

Parmelia physodes Ach., *P. hypotrypella* Asahina
Wilhelm Zopf, *Ann.* 295 287 (1897).
Idem., ibid. 300 350 (1898).

466 **Nidulin,** $C_{20}H_{17}O_5Cl_3$, colorless crystals, m.p. 180°.

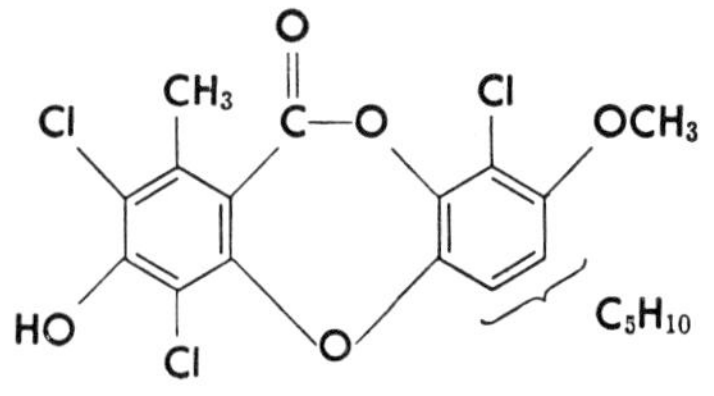

Aspergillus nidulans NRRL, No. 2006

The yield was about 6 g. from 126 g. of dry mycelium; a little mannitol also was found.

F. M. Dean, John C. Roberts and Alexander Robertson, *J. Chem. Soc.,* 1432 (1954).

467 **Diffractaic Acid** (Dirhizonic Acid), $C_{20}H_{22}O_7$, colorless needles, m.p. 189°.

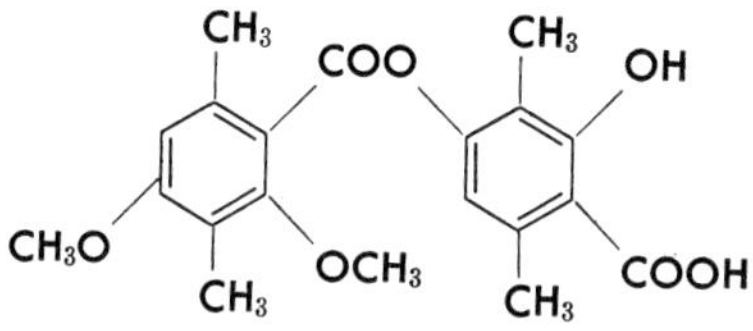

Usnea diffracta Wain., *Usnea longissima* Ach., *Alectoria ochroleuca* Mass.

The yield was 3.6%.

Yasuhiko Asahina and Fukuziro Fuzikawa, *Ber.* **65B** 583 (1932). (Synthesis)

468 **Erythrin,** $C_{20}H_{22}O_{11}$, colorless needles, m.p. 148°, $[\alpha]_D^{29}$ +10.63°.

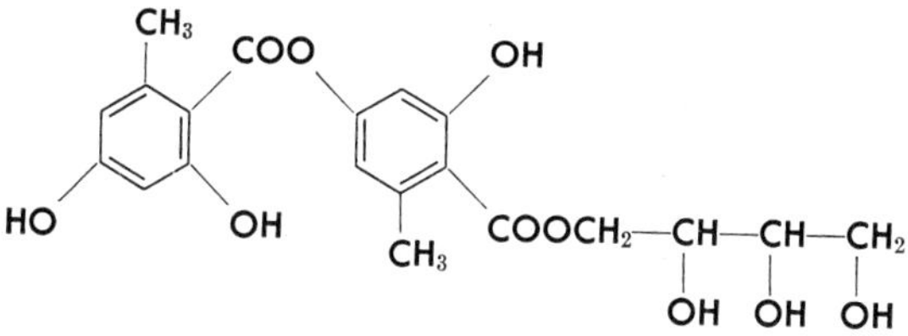

Roccella montagnei Bel. and *R. fuciformis* DC

This is an erythritol ester of lecanoric acid. The yield was about 5% of the weight of the lichen. Free erythritol and rocellic acid were isolated from the same source.

Yosio Sakurai, *J. Pharm. Soc. Japan* **61** 108 (in German, 45) (1941).

469 **Divaricatic Acid,** $C_{21}H_{24}O_7$, colorless needles, m.p. 137°.

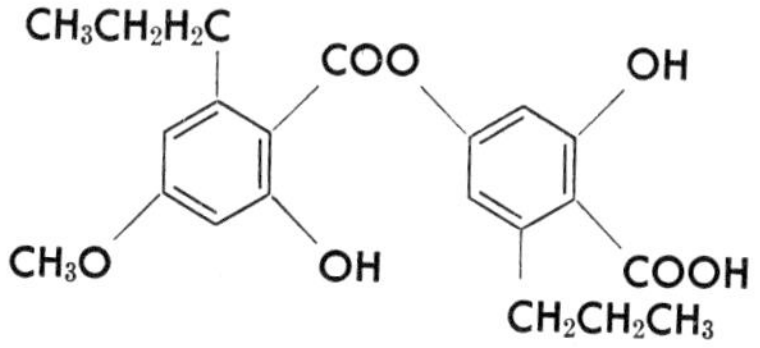

Evernia divaricata L., *E. mesomorpha* f. *esorediosa* Müll., Arg.

The yield from *E. mesomorpha* was recorded as 2.5% of the lichen weight. Usnic acid was isolated from the same source.

Yasuhiko Asahina and Michio Hiraiwa, *Ber.* **70B** 1826 (1937). (Synthesis)

470 Fumarprotocetraric Acid, $C_{22}H_{16}O_{12}$, colorless needles, m.p. 250–260° (dec. from 230°).

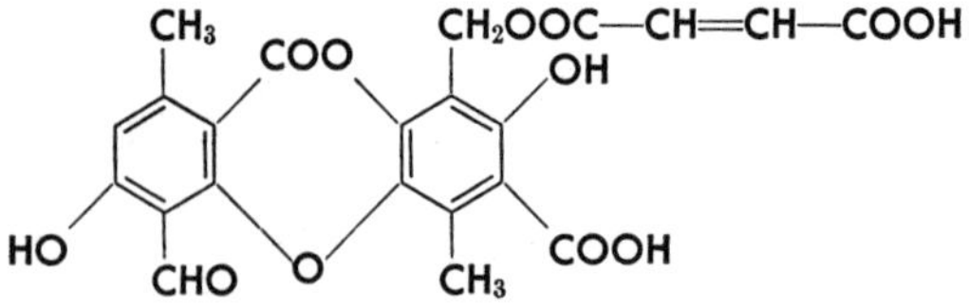

Cetraria islandica Ach., *Cladonia rangiferina* (L.) Web., *Cl. sylvatica* (L.) Hoffm.

Yasuhiko Asahina and Yaichiro Tanase, *Ber.* **67B** 766 (1934).

471 Sekikaic Acid, $C_{22}H_{26}O_8$, colorless needles, m.p. 147° (dec.).

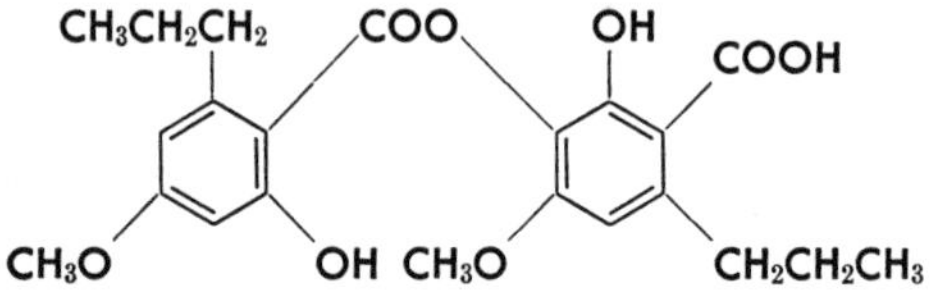

Ramalina geniculata Hook et Tayl., *R. calicaris* Rohl, and *R. intermediella* Wain.

The yield was about 1%. A little *d*-usnic acid also was present as well as ramalinolic acid.

Yasuhiko Asahina and Masaichi Yasue, *Ber.* **68B** 132 (1935). (Synthesis)

472 Sphaerophorin, $C_{23}H_{28}O_7$, colorless crystals, m.p. 137°.

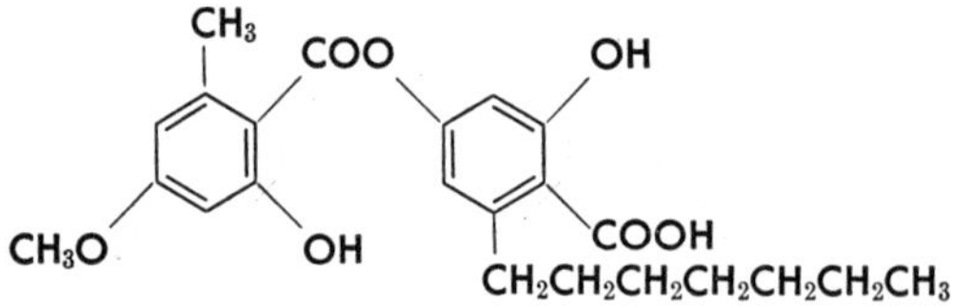

Sphaerophorus fragilis Pers., *S. coralloides* Pers., *S. melanocarpus*

Akira Hasimoto, *J. Pharm. Soc. Japan* 58 776 (in German, 221) (1938). (Synthesis)

473 **Imbricaric Acid,** $C_{23}H_{28}O_7$, colorless needles, m.p. 125°.

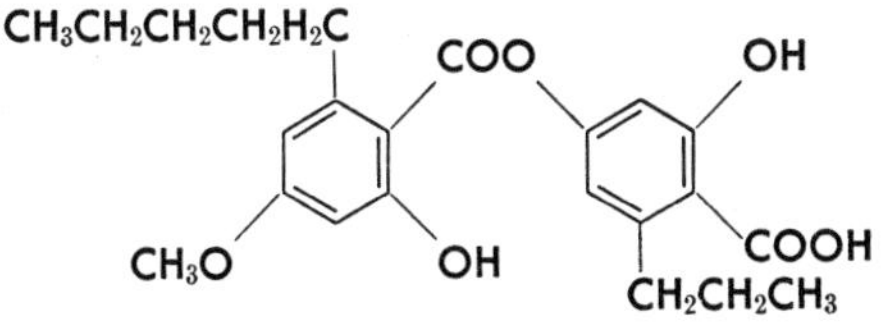

$CH_3CH_2CH_2CH_2H_2C$ COO   OH

CH_3O OH   COOH $CH_2CH_2CH_3$

Parmelia perlata Ach., *Cladonia impexa* Harm., *Cl. evansi* f. Abb., *Cl. pseudoevansi* Asahina

Yasuhiko Asahina and Itiro Yoshioka, *Ber.* **70B** 1823 (1937). (Synthesis)

474 **Ramalinolic Acid,** $C_{23}H_{28}O_7$, colorless crystals, m.p. 163°.

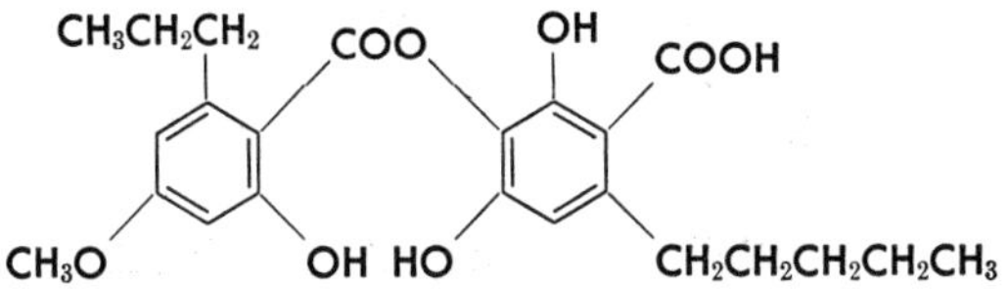

$CH_3CH_2CH_2$ COO   OH   COOH

CH_3O OH   HO $CH_2CH_2CH_2CH_2CH_3$

Ramalina intermediella Wain., *R. calicaris* Rohl, *R. geniculata* Hook et Tayl. and *R. usneoides* Mont.

Yasuhiko Asahina and Tunaharu Kusaka, *Ber.* **69B** 1896 (1936). (Synthesis)

475 **Gyrophoric Acid,** $C_{24}H_{20}O_{10}$, colorless needles, m.p. 220°.

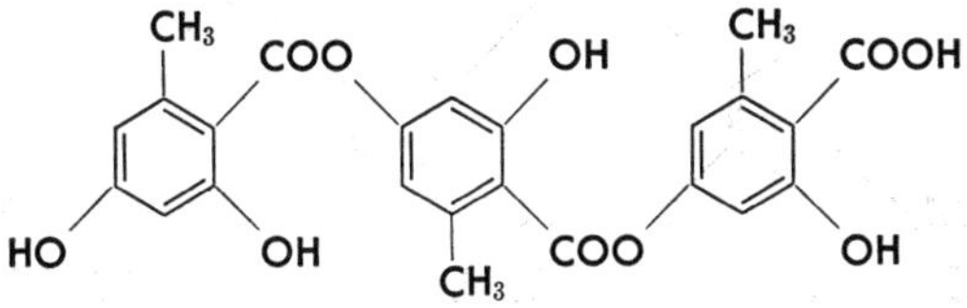

CH_3 COO   OH CH_3 COOH

HO   OH CH_3 COO   OH

Gyrophora esculenta Miyoshi, *G. proboscidea* L., *Umbilicaria pustulata* L. Hoffm. *Ochrolechia pallescens*, *Lobaria pulmonaria* var. *meridionalis* (Wain.) Zahlbr.

Yasuhiko Asahina and Itiro Yasioka, *Ber.* **70B** 200 (1937). (Synthesis)

476 **Hiascic Acid,** $C_{24}H_{20}O_{11}$, colorless crystals, m.p. 190.5° (dec.).

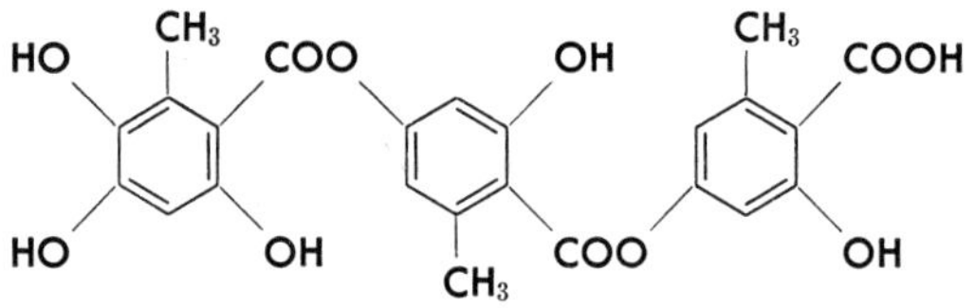

Cetraria hiascens Th. Fr.
Gyrophoric acid also was present.
Yasuhiko Asahina and Tunaharu Kusaka, *Bull. Chem. Soc. Japan* **17** 152 (in German) (1942).

477 **Anziaic Acid,** $C_{24}H_{30}O_7$, colorless, fine needles, m.p. 124° (dec.).

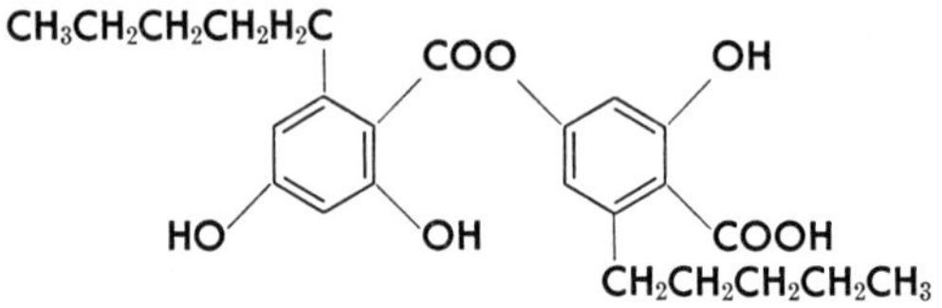

Anzia opuntiella Müll. Arg., *A. gracilis, A. leucobatoides* f. *hypomelaena* and *Cetraria sanguinea*
Yasuhiko Asahina and Michio Hiraiwa, *Ber.* **70B** 1826 (1937). (Synthesis)

478 **Homosekikaic Acid** (Nemoxynic Acid), $C_{24}H_{30}O_8$, colorless prisms, m.p. 137.5°.

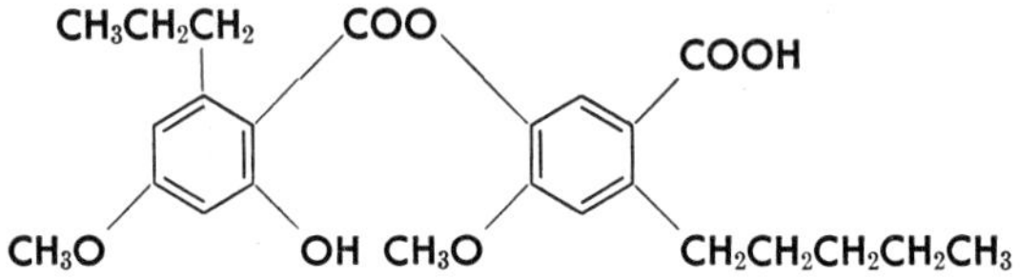

Cladonia pityrea Flk. f. *phyllophora* Mudd, *Cladonia nemoxyna* (Ach.) Nyl.
The yield was about 0.1%. A little fumarprotocetraric acid also was present.
Yasuhiko Asahina and Tsunakaru Kusaka, *Ber.* **70B** 1815 (1937). (Synthesis)

479 **Umbilicaric Acid,** $C_{25}H_{22}O_{10}$, colorless crystals, m.p. 203° (dec.). Synthetic sample m.p. 189°.

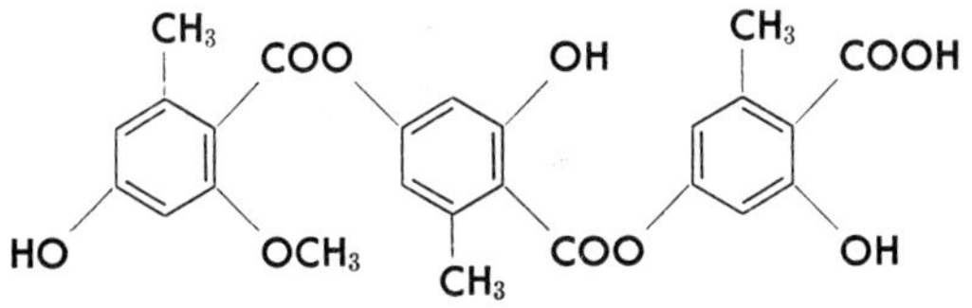

Gyrophora polyphylla (L.), *G. deusta* (L.) and *G. vellea* (L.)

Yasuhiko Asahina and Itiro Yosioka, *Ber.* **70B** 200 (1937). (Synthesis)

480 **Lobaric Acid** (Stereocaulic Acid, Usnetic Acid), $C_{25}H_{28}O_8$, colorless needles, m.p. 192°.

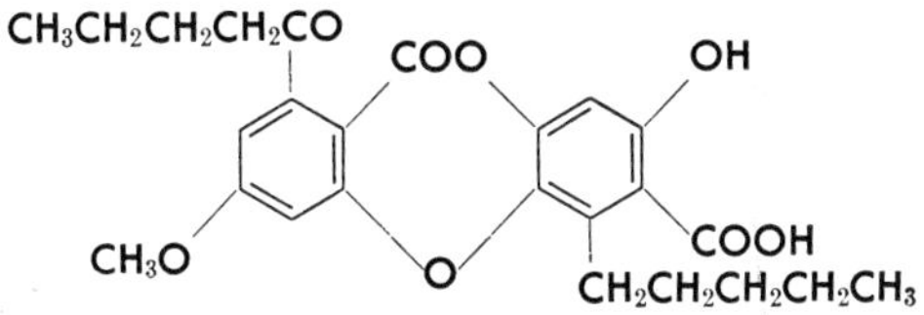

Stereocaulon paschale Ach., *S. exutum* Nyl., etc. (wide occurrence)

Yasuhiko Asahina and Masaiti Yasue, *Ber.* **69B** 643 (1936).

481 **Glomelliferic Acid,** $C_{25}H_{30}O_8$, colorless prisms, m.p. 143°.

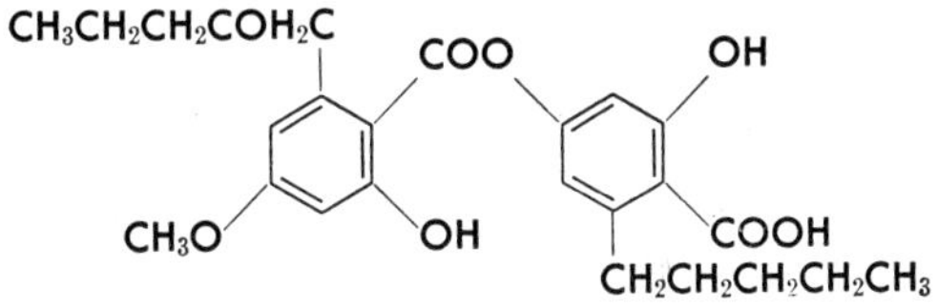

Parmelia glomellifera Nyl.

W. Zopf, *Ann.* 297 303 (1897), 313 341 (1900).

Yasuhiko Asahina and Hisasi Nogami, *Ber.* **70B** 1498 (1937).

K. Minami, *J. Pharm. Soc. Japan* 64 315 (1944).

482 **Perlatolic Acid,** $C_{25}H_{32}O_7$, colorless needles, m.p. 108°.

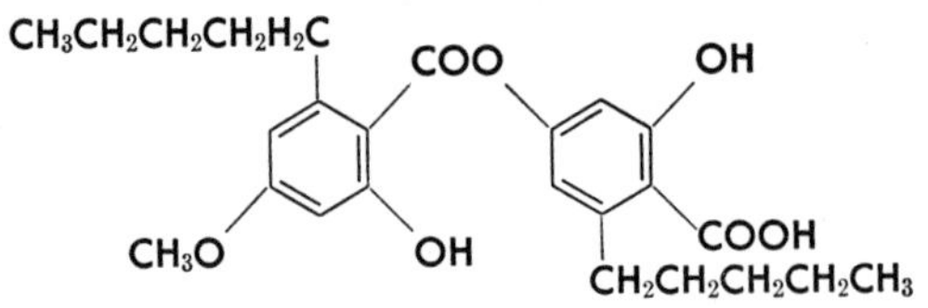
CH₃CH₂CH₂CH₂H₂C
COO
OH
CH₃O
OH
COOH
CH₂CH₂CH₂CH₂CH₃

Parmelia perlata Ach., *Cladonia impexa* Harm., *Cl. evansi* f. Abb., *Cl. pseudoevansi* Asahina

Yasuhiko Asahina and Itiro Yoshioka, *Ber.* **70B** 1823 (1937). (Synthesis)

483 **Boninic Acid,** $C_{25}H_{32}O_8$, colorless plates, m.p. 134.5°.

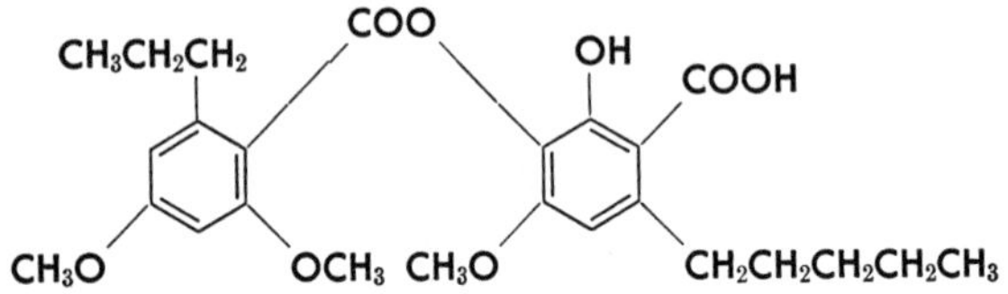
COO
CH₃CH₂CH₂
OH
COOH
CH₃O
OCH₃
CH₃O
CH₂CH₂CH₂CH₂CH₃

Ramalina boninensis Asahina

The yield was about 0.5%, and a little *d*-usnic acid was present.

Yasuhiko Asahina and Tsunaharu Kusaka, *Ber.* **70B** 1815 (1937). (Synthesis)

484 **Tenuiorin,** $C_{26}H_{24}O_{10}$, colorless crystals, m.p. 238° (dec.) s. 180°.

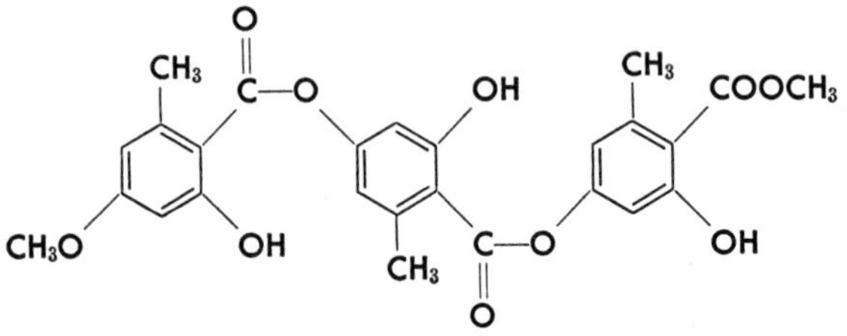
O
CH₃
C—O
OH
CH₃
COOCH₃
CH₃O
OH
CH₃
C—O
O
OH

Lobaria pulmonaria Hoffm. f. *tenuior* Hue.

Mannitol also was present.

Yasuhiko Asahina and Masaiti Yanagita, *Ber.* **66B** 1910 (1933).

485 **Physodic Acid** (Farinacic Acid), $C_{26}H_{30}O_8$, colorless prisms, m.p. 205° (dec.).

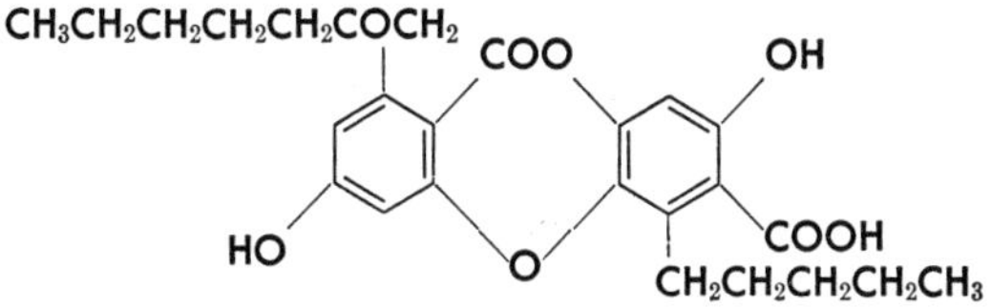

$CH_3CH_2CH_2CH_2CH_2COCH_2$ COO OH

HO O COOH $CH_2CH_2CH_2CH_2CH_3$

Parmelia physodes Ach., *P. furfuracea* Ach.
A yield of 5% was reported.
Yasuhiko Asahina and Hirasi Nogami, *Ber.* **67B** 805 (1934).
Idem., ibid. **68B** 77, 1500 (1935).

486 **Olivetoric Acid,** $C_{26}H_{32}O_8$, colorless crystals, m.p. 151°.

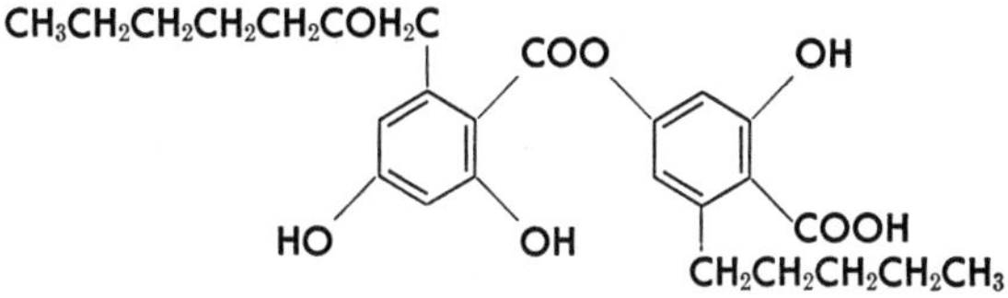

$CH_3CH_2CH_2CH_2CH_2COH_2C$ COO OH

HO OH COOH $CH_2CH_2CH_2CH_2CH_3$

Parmelia olivetorum Nyl., *Cornicularia pseudosatoana* Asahina and *C. divergens* Ach.
Yasuhiko Asahina and Fukuziro Fuzikawa, *Ber.* **67B** 163 (1934).

487 **Alectoronic Acid,** $C_{28}H_{32}O_9$, colorless prisms, m.p. 193°.

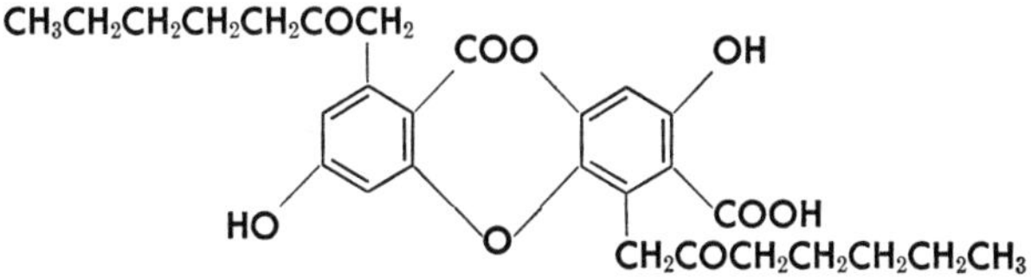

$CH_3CH_2CH_2CH_2CH_2COCH_2$ COO OH

HO O COOH $CH_2COCH_2CH_2CH_2CH_2CH_3$

Alectoria japonica Tuck., *A. sarmentosa* Ach., *Cetraria pseudocomplicata* Asahina, *Nephromopsis cilialis* Hue.
Yasuhiko Asahina, Yoshinari Kanaoka and Fukuziro Fuzikawa, *Ber.* **66B** 649 (1933).

488 α-Collatolic Acid (Lecanorolic Acid, Lecanoral), $C_{29}H_{34}O_9$ color-less needles, m.p. 124°.

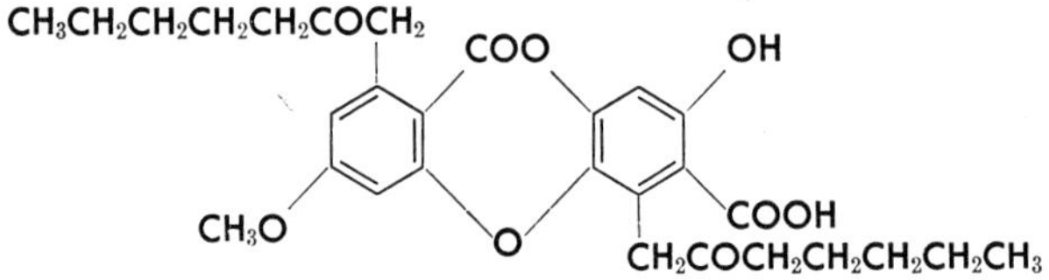

CH$_3$CH$_2$CH$_2$CH$_2$CH$_2$COCH$_2$ COO OH

CH$_3$O O COOH
CH$_2$COCH$_2$CH$_2$CH$_2$CH$_2$CH$_3$

Cetraria collata Müll. Arg., *Lecanora atra* (Hudson) Ach., *L. grumosa* (Pers.) Röhl.

Yasuhiko Asahina, Yoshinari Kanaoka and Fukuziro Fuzikawa, *Ber.* **66B** 649 (1933).

489 Microphyllic Acid, $C_{29}H_{36}O_9$, colorless needles, m.p. 116°.

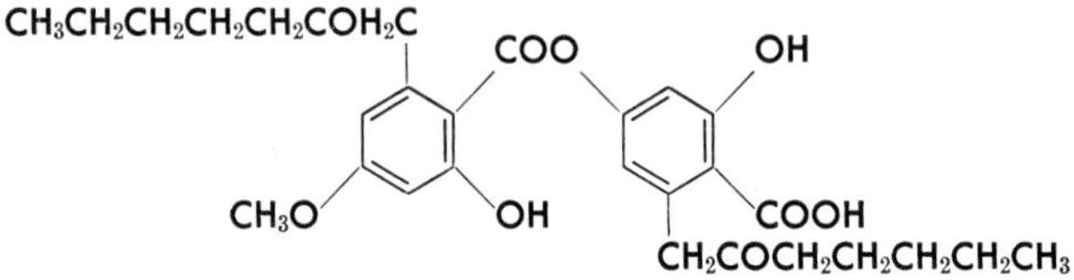

CH$_3$CH$_2$CH$_2$CH$_2$CH$_2$COH$_2$C COO OH

CH$_3$O OH COOH
CH$_2$COCH$_2$CH$_2$CH$_2$CH$_2$CH$_3$

Cetraria japonica Zahlbr.

Some chloroatranorin was isolated from the same extract. The yield of microphyllic acid was about 4% of the lichen weight.

Yasuhiko Asahina and Fukuziro Fuzikawa, *Ber.* **68B** 2022 (1935).

12

Quinones and Related Compounds

Quinones occur widely in nature, and this topic has been reviewed.[1, 2, 3] Even allowing for their conspicuousness due to color, solubility characteristics and (often) quantity, it seems that they are broadly distributed among plants, and fungi are no exceptions.

Anthraquinones, in particular, have been isolated frequently from fungus cultures. Some 80 anthraquinones and related substances of known structure were listed by W. Karrer[3] as having been reported from plant sources in general. About half of this number have been isolated and characterized from fungi and lichens. Since no anthraquinones have been reported from algae, it may be that those present in lichens are formed primarily by the fungus component. There is some evidence, however, that in lichens both partners are required for the biosynthesis of depsides and depsidones.[4]

In fungi anthraquinones occur mainly in the mycelium, often as mixtures of closely related materials. It is likely, for this reason, that some of the quinones reported in the early literature were impure.

The frequent identification of anthraquinone pigments in molds has caused some speculation on their function. Arguments in favor of a biological function have been summarized

[1] S. Shibata, *Kagaku* (*Science*) **26** 391–396 (1956).

[2] R. H. Thomson, "Naturally Occurring Quinones," Academic Press, New York, 1957, 302 pp.

[3] W. Karrer, "Konstitution und Vorkommen der Organischen Pflanzenstoffe," Birkhauser Verlag, Basel, 1958.

[4] Dieter Hess, *Zeitschr. Naturforsch.* 14b 345 (1959).

as follows:[5] (1) Some pigment complexes are produced in large quantities, up to 30 percent of the total dry weight of the mycelium. (2) In many cases, the maximal pigment content is reached while usable carbohydrate is still present. If harvesting is delayed, pigment disappears as autolysis sets in. (3) The same pigment often is present in different genera or families, suggesting solution of a metabolic problem in the same way. (4) Reduction products such as anthranols, anthrones and quinhydrones sometimes are present together with the parent quinone, perhaps indicating a hydrogen or electron transport function. (5) Several mold pigments are antibiotic toward other fungi and bacteria.

On the other hand, it has been pointed out[6] that, in fungi, induced mutations leading to full blocking of the production of acetate-derived aromatic compounds such as anthraquinones do not seem to affect the vitality of the organism. The antifunctionalists believe that anthraquinones and perhaps some other mold metabolites are merely waste or storage products due to an overflow of acetate metabolism. If some of these products happen to inhibit competitors, they facilitate species survival.

A similar concept of the significance of such mold metabolites has been mentioned by Dalgliesh.[7] He proposed that enzyme systems unable to deal with substrate because it is in large excess, or for some other reason, might convert it to anthraquinones and other substances, which are eliminated, then, in a kind of "detoxication" disposal mechanism.

An enzyme chemist, F. F. Nord, has suggested[8] that many of the metabolites produced in yields exceeding functional requirements, or for which there is no function, accumulate because some of the enzyme systems involved in the oxidative sequences become saturated with respect to their substrates. They are thus, in his opinion, probably products of anaerobic

[5] G. Smith, Congr. intern. botan. Paris, Rapps. et communs., 8 Sec. 83–89 (1954).

[6] Gösta Ehrensvärd, "Developments in Aromatic Chemistry," Special Publication No. 12, English Chemical Society, London, 1958, p. 29.

[7] C. E. Dalgliesh, ibid., p. 14.

[8] F. F. Nord and D. D. Clarke, Arch. Biochem. and Biophys. 59 285 (1955).

metabolism, and arise in a manner analogous to the accumulation of citric acid, which is induced under the same conditions.[9]

There is no convincing experimental evidence that anthraquinones are important in electron transport.

It has been suggested[10] that anthraquinones are acetate-derived, and there is some experimental confirmation.[11, 12, *]

This proof was obtained by growing the mold in the presence of C[14]-labeled acetate, isolating the metabolite, which incorporated the label to some degree, then degrading the molecule by ingenious chemical methods to determine the sites of labeling.

Although an acetate origin is indicated, the detailed natures of the intermediates in the biosynthetic mechanism are still unknown. Intermediates such as orsellinic acid,[13] dihydroxyphthalic acid,[14] and 6-methylsalicylic acid[15] (all known mold metabolites) have been proposed, e.g.:

3,5-Dihydroxy-   6-Methylsali-   Endocrocin
  phthalic Acid   cylic Acid

Birch prefers to think in terms of an intermediate formally resembling a polyketomethylene chain, which can be modified in various ways on an enzyme surface to yield related metabolites. This concept is supported by the occasional discovery of related metabolites in the same culture or plant. For example, the co-occurring anthraquinone and phenanthrenequinone

[9] H. A. Krebs, *Biochem. J.* 31 2095 (1937).

[10] A. J. Birch and F. W. Donovan, *Austral. J. Chem.* 6 360 (1953).

[11] Sten Gatenbeck, *Acta Chem. Scand.* 12 1211 (1958).

[12] A. J. Birch, A. J. Ryan and Herchel Smith, *J. Chem. Soc.*, 4473 (1958).

* Also see addendum for later work.

[13] K. Aghoramurthy and T. R. Seshadri, *J. Sci. Ind. Res.* (India) 13A 114 (1959).

[14] E. L. Tatum, *Ann. Rev. Biochem.* 13 667 (1944).

[15] Harold Raistrick, *Acta Chem. Fenn.* 10A 237 (1950).

shown below could be envisaged as derivatives of a common precursor chain, which is laid down upon the enzyme surface in different patterns before cyclization.[16]

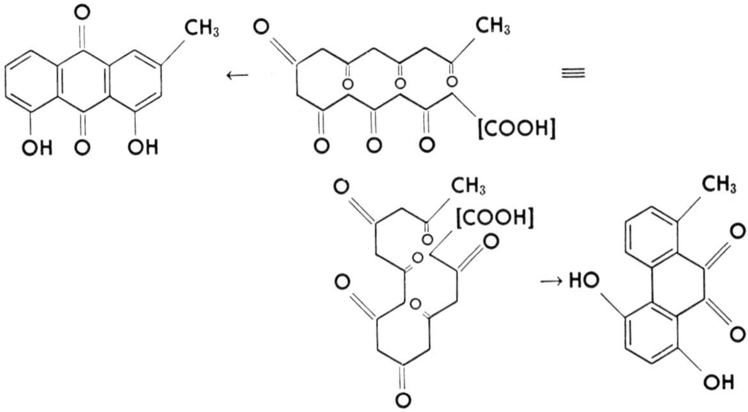

It is likely that the dianthraquinones are formed by oxidative phenolic radical coupling, *e.g.:* *

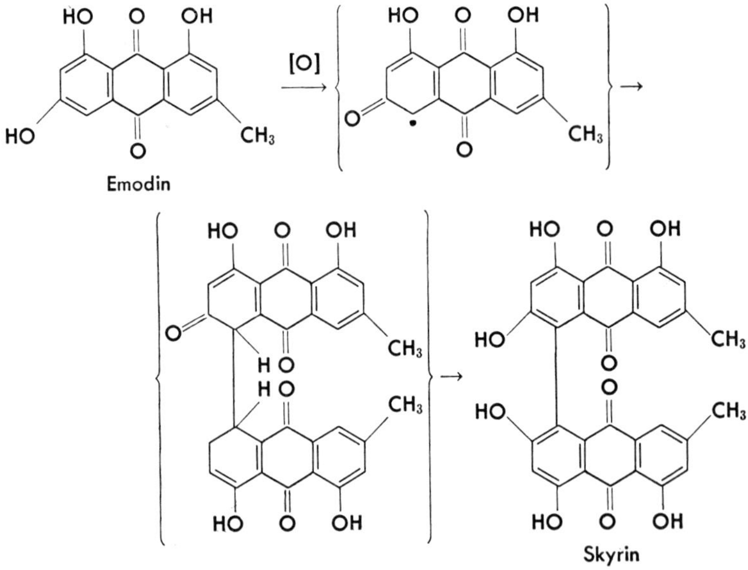

Emodin

Skyrin

[16] A. J. Birch, private communication.
* See addendum for evidence to the contrary.

Other metabolites, such as actinorhodin and the perylene-quinones may be formed similarly.

Structures such as mollisin and javanicin seem to indicate an acetate derivation for naphthoquinones.

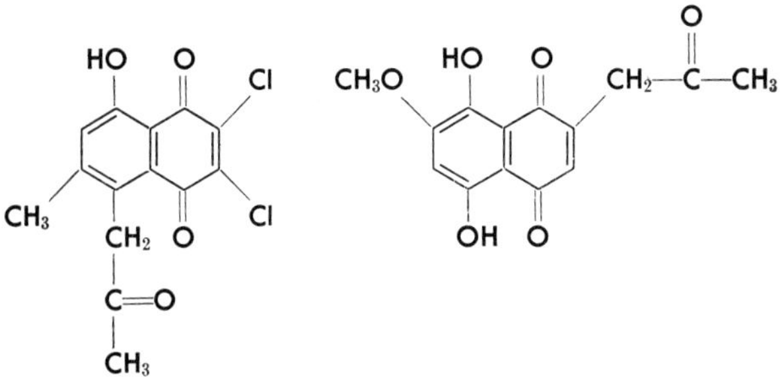

Mollisin   Javanicin

The suggestion has been made[17] that the terphenylquinones might be formed by autocondensation of a phenylpyruvic acid type of molecule in the following sense:

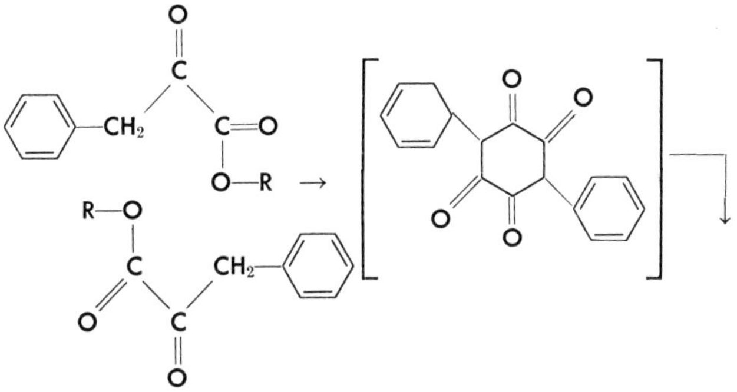

Phenylpyruvate

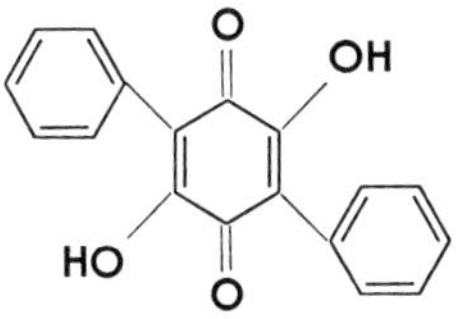

Polyporic Acid

Similarly p-hydroxyphenylpyruvate would form atromentin. Polyporic acid might be transformed by oxidation to pulvinic

[17] G. Read and L. Vining, *Chem. and Ind.*, 1546 (1959).

acid, and by further hydroxylations to leucomelone or other terphenylquinones.

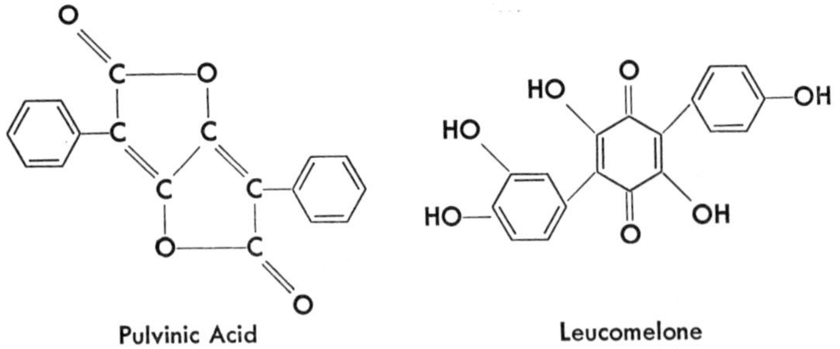

Pulvinic Acid   Leucomelone

If this suggestion can be confirmed experimentally, it will relate this type of benzoquinone metabolite to the shikimic acid route of biogenesis.

The biosynthesis of a benzoquinone, aurantiogliocladin, has been studied, by using C^{14}-labeled formate and acetate.[18] The results demonstrated formation from 4 moles of acetate with decarboxylation, C-methylation, post-oxidation in the aromatic

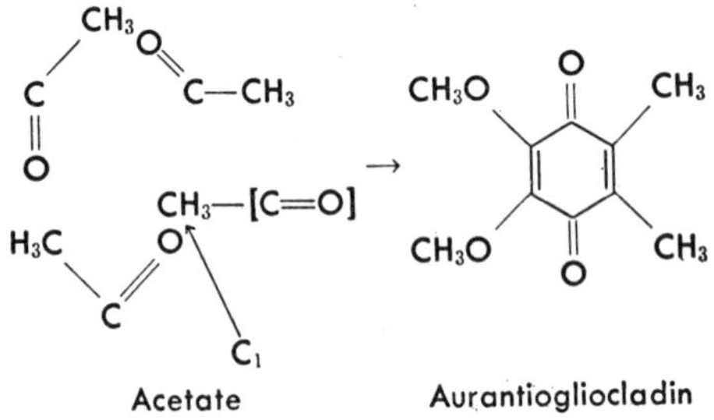

Acetate   Aurantiogliocladin

ring and O-methylation of the phenolic hydroxyl groups.

6-Methylsalicylic acid appears to be an intermediate.[19]

Aurantiogliocladin, isolated from a gliocladium specimen, resembles the coenzymes Q. These substances occur in the cell mitochondria of a wide variety of organisms. They are benzoquinones substituted similarly to aurantiogliocladin, but with

[18] A. J. Birch, R. I. Fryer and Herchel Smith, *Proc. Chem. Soc.*, 343 (1958).

[19] Private communication from Herchel Smith.

additional polyisoprenoid side-chains. There is a marked re-

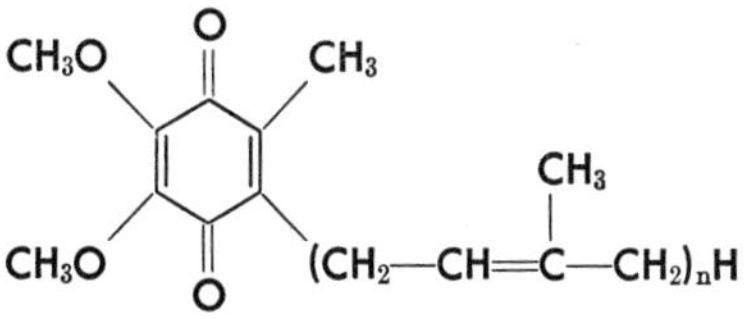

Coenzyme Q_n 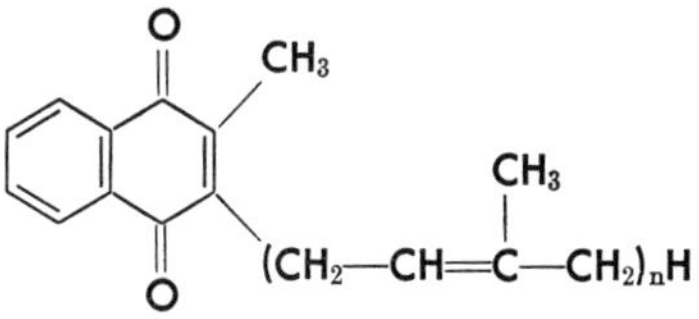   Vitamin K_n

semblance to the previously discovered vitamins K.   The following substances have been isolated, purified, and the structures
determined:

TABLE I

Origin	Numbers of side-chain isoprene units (n)	Number of carbon atoms	Melting point (°C)	Designation	References
Saccharomyces cere-					
visiae	6	39	16°	Coenzyme Q_6	20
Torula utilis	7	44	30.5°	Coenzyme Q_7	20, 21
Azotobacter vine-					
landii	8	49	37°	Coenzyme Q_8	20, 21
Torula utilis	9	54	45.2°	Coenzyme Q_9	20, 21
Beef heart	10	59	48°	Coenzyme Q_{10}	21, 22

A survey was made, by using methods sometimes short of isolation and purification (paper chromatographic comparisons,
spectra, etc.) of the occurrence of coenzyme Q and of vitamin K
in a wide variety of biological types.[23]   Many bacteria contain
coenzyme Q.   The mycobacteria and streptomycetes seem to
contain vitamin K instead.   *Escherichia coli* and chromatium
species contain both.   Obligate anaerobes such as the clostridia

[20] R. L. Lester, F. L. Crane and Y. Hatefi, *J. Am. Chem. Soc.* **80**
4751 (1958).
[21] R. L. Lester and F. L. Crane, *Biochim. et Biophys. Acta* 32 492
(1959).
[22] F. L. Crane, Y. Hatefi, R. L. Lester and Carl Widmer, *Biochim.
et Biophys. Acta* 25 220 (1957); *idem., ibid.* 32 73 (1959).
[23] R. L. Lester and F. L. Crane, *J. Biol. Chem.* 234 2169 (1959).

contain neither, and facultative anaerobes such as *Saccharomyces cerevisiae* and *E. coli* contain neither when grown anaerobically. A chart of microbial occurrence was published:

TABLE II

Organism	Coenzyme Q	Vitamin K
Saccharomyces cerevisiae (anaerobic)	—	—
Saccharomyces cerevisiae (aerobic)	Q_6	
Saccharomyces cavalieri	Q_6	
Saccharomyces fragilis	Q_6	
Neurospora crassa	Q_{10}	
Mucor corymbifer	Q_9	
Streptomyces griseus		+
Mycobacterium smegmatis		+
Mycobacterium tuberculosis		+
Bacillus mesentericus		+
Escherichia coli	Q_8	
Chromatium spp.	Q_7	
Rhodospirillum rubrum	Q_9	
Pseudomonas fluorescens	Q_9	
Hydrogenomonas sp.	Q_8	

Basidiomycetes contain neither coenzyme Q nor vitamin K, but produce another quinone which seems to have the same function in this family. It has been extracted and purified to some extent and called basidioquinone.

A comparison of all the animal, plant and microorganism sources indicated that, in general, lower organisms contain lower homologues of coenzyme Q.

Evidence has been obtained for the coenzyme function of the Q (and K) quinones: (1) Extraction from mitochondria destroys enzymatic activity, which is restored by restoration of the coenzymes. (2) Inhibitors of electron transport, such as the antibiotic, antimycin A, affect the oxidation state of the quinones in a predictable manner. (3) The rate of oxidation or reduction in mitochondria is what might be anticipated for participation in electron transport. The pattern of occurrence in aerobic and anaerobic microorganisms also is suggestive.

The general structure of the electron transport system in cell mitochondria in the light of the new discoveries has been reviewed.[24]

Apparently coenzyme Q is formed by a combination of the

[24] D. E. Green and R. L. Lester, *Federation Proc.* **18** 987–1000 (1959).

simple acetate and terpenoid biosynthetic routes.   Mevalonic acid was incorporated into the molecule by rats (especially vitamin A-deficient rats) and by rat liver, while 2,3-dimethoxy-5-methyl-1,4-benzoquinone and D,L-tocopherol were not.[25]   This contrasts with evidence that 2-methyl-1,4-naphthoquinone is used as a precursor of vitamin K by rats.[26]   Evidently, no experimental work has been published on biosynthesis in microorganisms.

a. BENZOQUINONES

490   **Tetrahydroxybenzoquinone,** $C_6H_4O_6$, bluish black plates, no melting point.

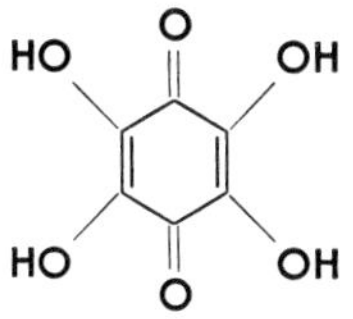

Pseudomonas beijerinckii Hof grown on salted beans. The substrate is *meso*-inositol, which probably is a normal constituent of beans.

T. Hof, *Rec. Trav. Botan. Néerland.* 32 92 (1935).   (Isolation)

A. J. Kluyver, T. Hof and A. G. J. Boezaardt, *Enzymologia* 7 257 (1939).   (Structure)

Paul W. Preisler and Louis Berger, *J. Am. Chem. Soc.* 64 67 (1942).

491   **Gentisylquinone,** $C_7H_6O_3$, yellow needles, m.p. 76°.

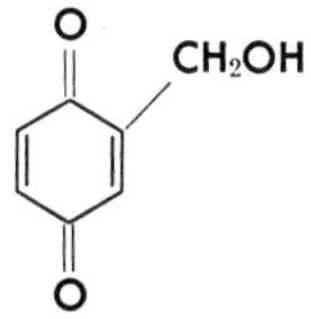

Penicillium patulum Bainier probably produces a little of this quinone under certain conditions, although it may be an artifact, since larger quantities of the corresponding hydroquinone are produced.   It has been isolated as a deep violet colored complex, m.p. 86–89°, with the hydroquinone.

[25] U. Gloor and O. Wiss, *Arch. Biochem. and Biophys.* 83 216 (1959).

[26] C. Martius and H. O. Esser, *Biochem. Z.* 331 1 (1958).

B. G. Engel and W. Brzeski, *Helv. Chim. Acta* **30** 1472 (1947).

492 Terreic Acid, $C_7H_6O_4$, pale yellow, large, glistening plates, m.p. 127–127.5°, $[\alpha]_D^{22}$ −28.6° (c 1 in 50% methanol-benzene). Sublimes.

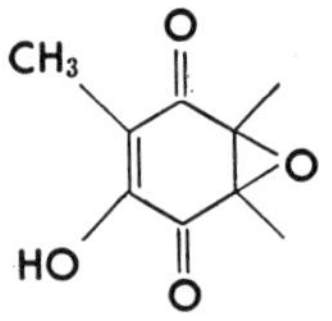

Aspergillus terreus grown in a glucose and corn-steep liquor-cottonseed meal medium.

H. M. Florey, E. Chain, N. G. Heatley, M. A. Jennings, A. G. Sanders, E. P. Abraham and M. E. Florey, "Antibiotics," Oxford University Press, London, 1949 Vol. I p. 388.

Murray A. Kaplan, Irving R. Harper and Bernard Heinemann, *Antibiotics and Chemotherapy* **4** 746 (1954). Yield 138 g. from 200 liters.

J. Sheehan, W. Lawson and R. Gaul, *J. Am. Chem. Soc.* **80** 5536–5538 (1958). (Structure)

493 4-Methoxytoluquinone (Coprinin), $C_8H_8O_3$, yellow spangles, m.p. 175°.

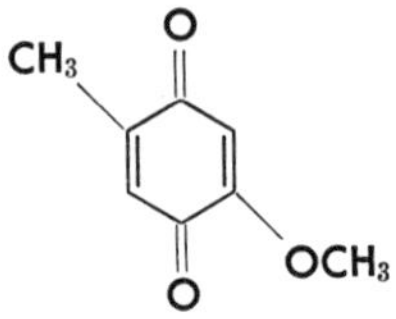

Coprinus similis B. and Br., *Lentinus degener* Kalchbr. grown on a Czapek-Dox medium, containing glucose and corn-steep solids.

Marjorie Anchel, Annette Hervey, Frederick Kavanagh, Jerome Polatnick and William J. Robbins, *Proc. Nat. Acad. Sci. U. S.* **34** 498 (1948). (Isolation)

R. B. Woodward, Franz Sondheimer, David Taub, Karl Heusler and W. M. McLamore, *J. Am. Chem. Soc.* **74** 4234 (1952). (Synthesis)

494 2,5-Dimethoxybenzoquinone, $C_8H_8O_4$, yellow prisms, m.p. 250° (dec.).

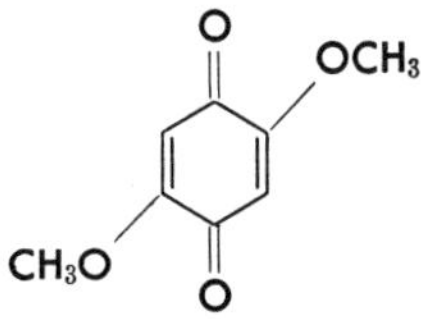

Polyporus fumosus (Pers.) Fries grown on an artificial medium including glucose and corn-steep liquor.
Yield: 0.1 g. from 2 liters of culture broth.
J. D. Bu'Lock, J. Chem. Soc., 575 (1955). (Isolation)
E. Knoevenagel and C. Bückel, Ber. 34 3993 (1901). (Synthesis)

495 Fumigatin, $C_8H_8O_4$, maroon needles, m.p. 116°.

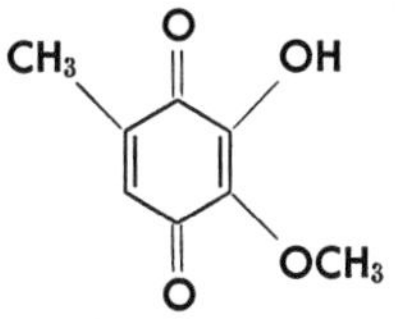

496 Fumigatin Hydroquinone is produced as well, the ratio of the two compounds varying with the age of the culture.

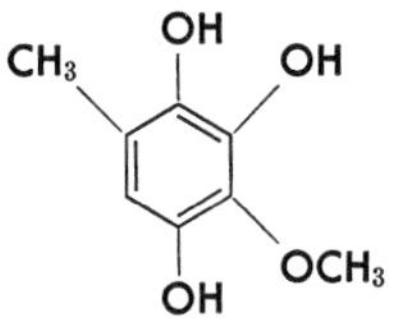

Aspergillus fumigatus Fres. grown on a Raulin-Thom medium.
Winston Kennay Anslow and Harold Raistrick, Biochem. J. 32 687 (1938). (Isolation)
W. K. Anslow, J. N. Ashley and H. Raistrick, J. Chem. Soc., 439 (1938). (Synthesis)

497 Spinulosin, $C_8H_8O_5$, purple-black plates, m.p. 203°.

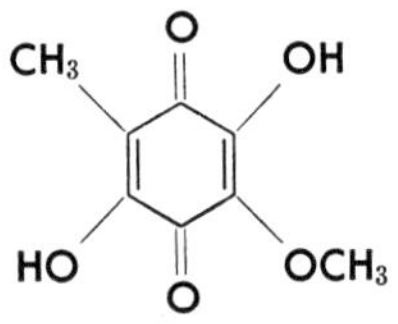

First isolated from three strains of *Penicillium spinulosum* Thom grown on a modified Czapek-Dox-glucose medium. Later isolated from two out of seven strains of *Aspergillus fumigatus* examined. *Spinulosin* as well as an orange pigment, m.p. 184–185°, with antibiotic properties resembling those of fumigatin, also has been isolated from an unidentified *Penicillium* (perhaps *Penicillium spinulosum*). *Penicillium cinerascens* Biourge is another producer.

J. H. Birkinshaw and H. Raistrick, *Trans. Roy. Soc.* (London) **B220** 245 (1931).

Winston K. Anslow and Harold Raistrick, *Biochem. J.* 32 687, 2288 (1938). (Isolation)

A. Bracken and H. Raistrick, *ibid.* 41 569 (1947).

Keichiro Hoshishima, *Tohuku J. Exptl. Med.* 52 273 (1950).

Winston K. Anslow and Harold Raistrick, *Biochem. J.* 32 803 (1938). (Synthesis)

498 Aurantiogliocladin, $C_{10}H_{12}O_4$, orange plates, m.p. 62.5°.

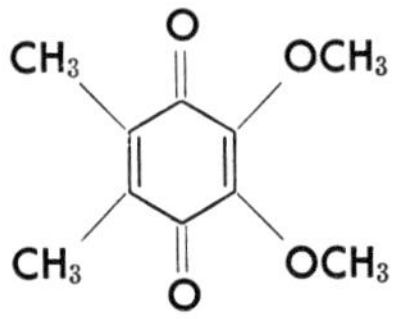

The corresponding quinhydrone, a dark red compound called rubrogliocladin, occurs together with aurantiogliocladin.

A *Gliocladium* specimen, probably *G. roseum* Bainier produces these substances as well as:

499 Gliorosein, $C_{10}H_{14}O_4$, colorless crystals, m.p. 48°.

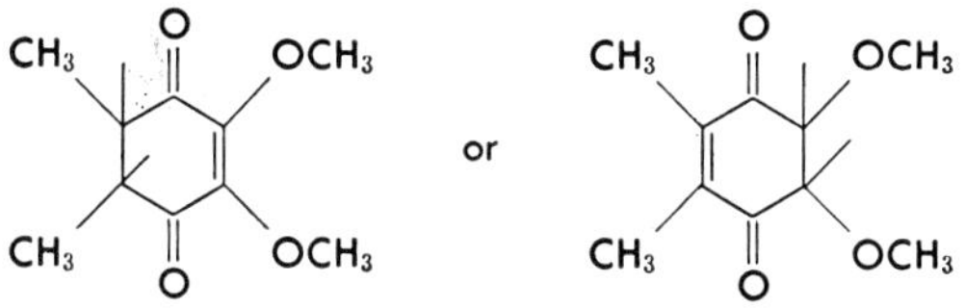

P. W. Brian, P. J. Curtis, S. R. Howland, E. G. Jeffreys and
H. Raudnitz, *Experientia* 7 266 (1951). (Isolation)
E. B. Vischer, *J. Chem. Soc.*, 815 (1953). (Structure)
Wilson Baker, J. F. W. McOmie and D. Miles, *ibid.*, 820
(1953). (Synthesis)

500 Phoenicin, $C_{14}H_{10}O_6$, yellow-brown tablets, m.p. 231°.

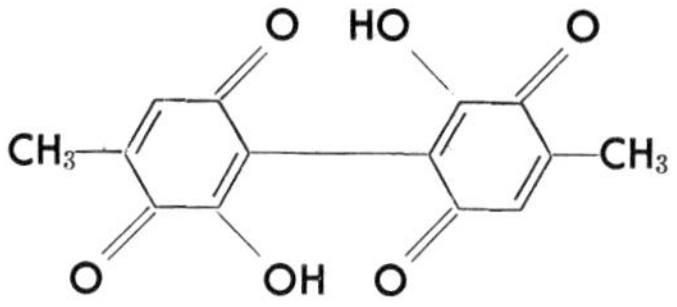

Penicillium phoeniceum van Beyma, *P. rubrum* O. Stoll.
Theodore Posternak, Hans W. Ruelius and Jacques Tcher-
niak, *Helv. Chim. Acta* 26 2031 (1943). (Synthesis)

501 Oosporein (Chaetomidin), $C_{14}H_{10}O_8$, bronze plates, m.p. 260–
275°.

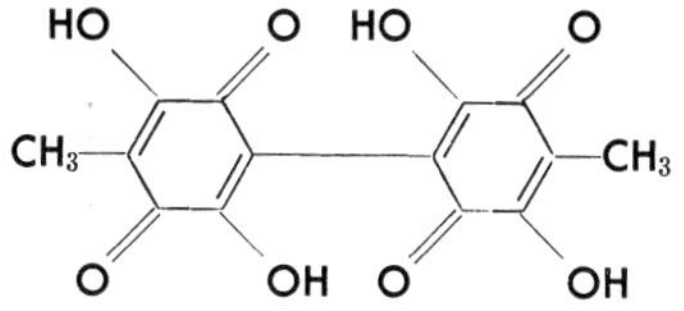

Oospora colorans van Beyma, *Chaetomium aureum*
Chivers, *Verticillium psalliotae, Acremonium* sp.
F. Kögl and G. C. Van Wessem, *Rec. trav. chim.* 63 5
(1944). (Isolation)
F. M. Dean, A. M. Osman and Alexander Robertson,
J. Chem. Soc., 11 (1955).
G. Lloyd, Alexander Robertson, G. B. Sankey and W. B.
Whalley, *ibid.*, 2163 (1955).

502 Isooösporein,* $C_{14}H_{10}O_8$, purple crystals, no m.p., subl. 220–250°, dec. 250°.

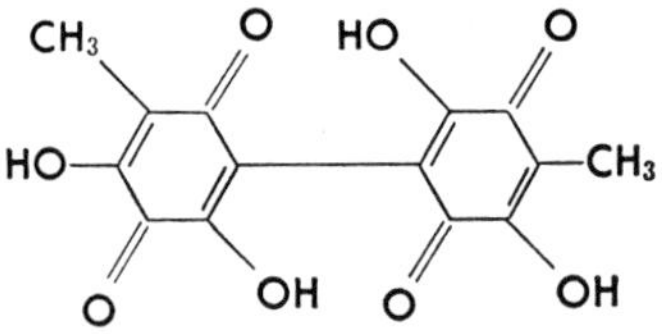

Unclassified citric acid-forming fungus.
Maximal yield 2.5 g. per liter.
Nobuyo Shigematsu, *J. Inst. Polytech.*, Osaka City Univ. Ser. C **5** 100 (1956).

503 **Volucrisporin,** $C_{18}H_{12}O_4$, red plates, m.p. >300°.

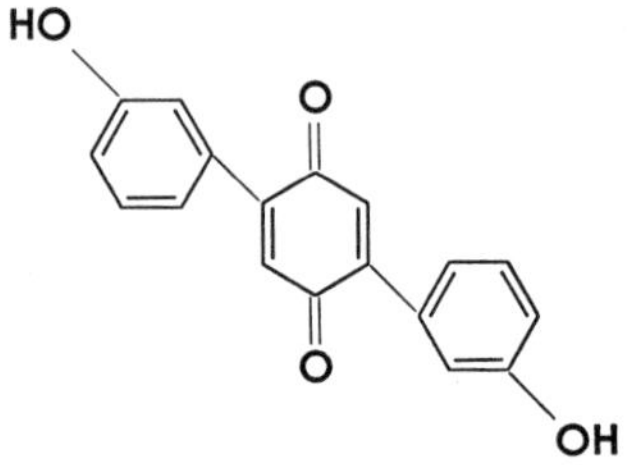

Volucrispora aurantiaca
Occasionally small quantities of the leuco derivative (hydroquinone) occur with the pigment.
P. V. Divekar, G. Read and L. C. Vining, *Chem. and Ind.*, 731 (1959).

504 **Polyporic Acid,** $C_{18}H_{12}O_4$, bronze leaflets, m.p. 305–307° (dec.).

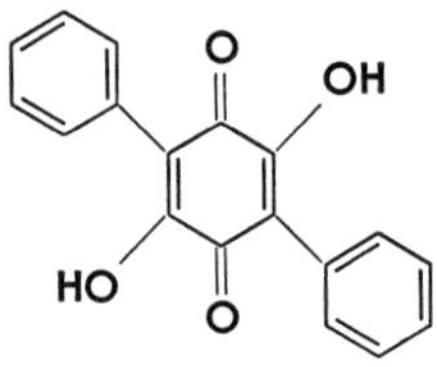

Polyporus nidulans Fries, *P. rutilans* (Pers.) Fries, *Peniophora filamentosa* (B. and C.) Burt, *Sticta coronata* Muell., *S. colensoi* Bab.
Fritz Kögl, *Ann.* **465** 243 (1928).
J. Murray, *J. Chem. Soc.*, 1345 (1952).

* See addendum.

The air-dried fruiting body of *P. rutilans* contains 23%. It is not produced by the fungal mycelium in artificial culture.

Robert L. Frank, George R. Clark and James N. Coker, *J. Am. Chem. Soc.* 72 1824 (1950).

Polyporic acid is probably identical with the lichen pigment, orygmaeic acid, first described by Zopf.

Wilhelm Zopf, *Ann.* 317 124 (1901).

505 Atromentin, $C_{18}H_{12}O_6$, bronze leaflets, no m.p.

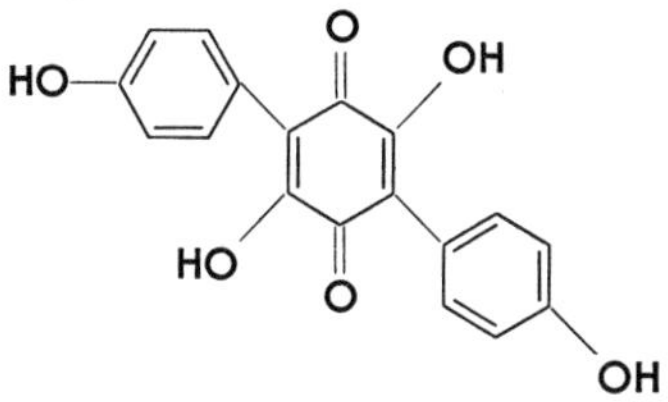

Paxillus atromentosus (Batsch.) Fr.

This basidiomycete often grows on old tree trunks and produces the pigment first in a leuco-form, which air-oxidizes to the colored form on the outer portions of the fruiting body and during isolation. The yield was about 2% of the weight of the air-dried fruiting body.

Fritz Kögl, *Ann.* 465 243 (1928).

506 Leucomelone, $C_{18}H_{12}O_7$, brown leaflets, m.p. 320° (dec.).

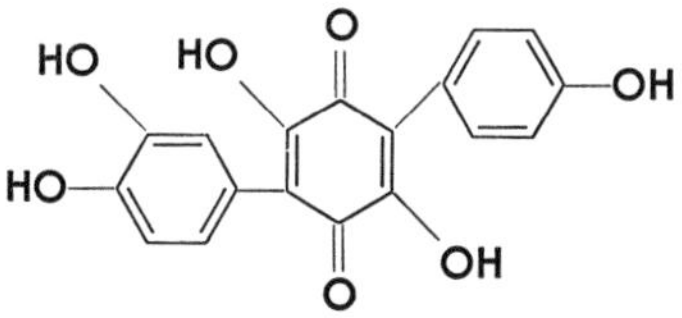

Polyporus leucomelas Pers. ex Fr.

Yield 3 g. per kilogram of fruiting body.

Masuo Akagi, *J. Pharm. Soc. Japan* 62 129 (1942). Synthesis)

507 Thelephoric Acid, $C_{20}H_{12}O_9$, lustrous, nearly black prisms, no m.p.

Partial structure:

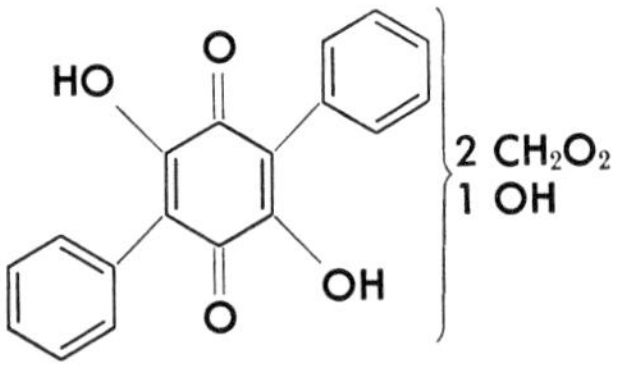

Thelephora palmata, other *Thelephora* spp., *Lobaria retigera* Trev., *L. pulmonaria* (L.) Hoffm., *Hydnum* spp., *Cantharellus multiplex* Underw., *Polystictus versicolor* (L.) Fr.

Fritz Kögl, Hanni Erxleben and Ludwig Jänecke, *Ann.* 482 105 (1930).

K. Aghoramurthy, K. G. Sarma and T. R. Seshadri, *Tetrahedron Letters* No. 8 20 (1959). (Revised structure)

508 **Muscarufin,** $C_{25}H_{16}O_9 \cdot H_2O$, orange-red needles, m.p. 275.5°.

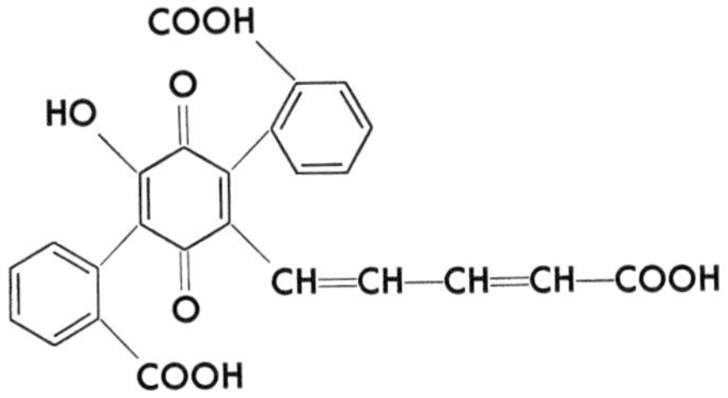

Amanita muscaria (Linn.) Fries

This pigment causes the red color of the caps of this common poisonous toadstool (fly agaric), yet 500 kg. of the fungus yielded only 850 mg. of pure material.

Fritz Kögl and Hanni Erxleben *Ann.* 479 11 (1930).

509 **Auriantiacin** (Atromentin-3,6-dibenzoate), $C_{32}H_{20}O_8$, dark red needles, m.p. 285–295°.

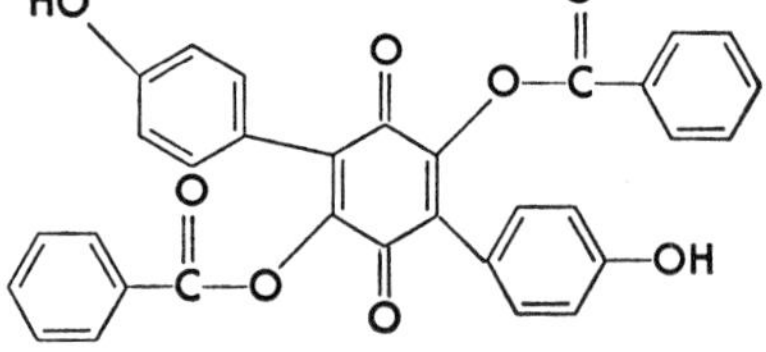

Hydnum aurantiacum Batsch.

Jarl Gripenberg, *Acta Chem. Scand.* 10 1111 (1956).

510 Protoleucomelone, $C_{32}H_{28}O_{14}$, colorless crystals, m.p. 203–205°. Probable structure:

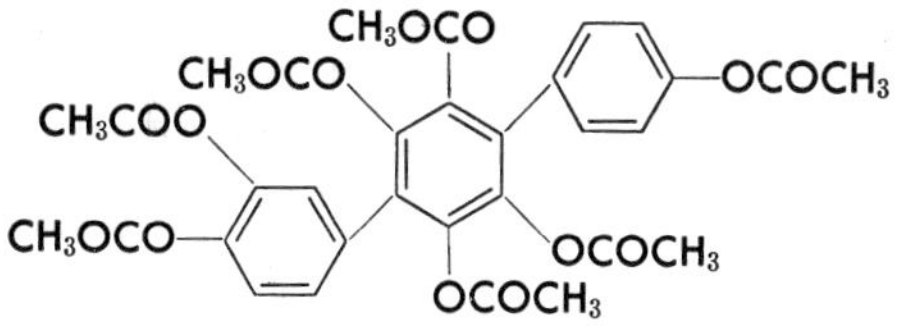

Polyporus leucomelas Pers. ex Fr.
Yield 3–4 g. per kilogram of mushrooms.
Masuo Akagi, *J. Pharm. Soc. Japan* 62 129 (1942).

511 Metabolite of *Hydnum aurantiarum*, $C_{46}H_{30}O_{10}$, colorless needles. m.p. 305–307°.

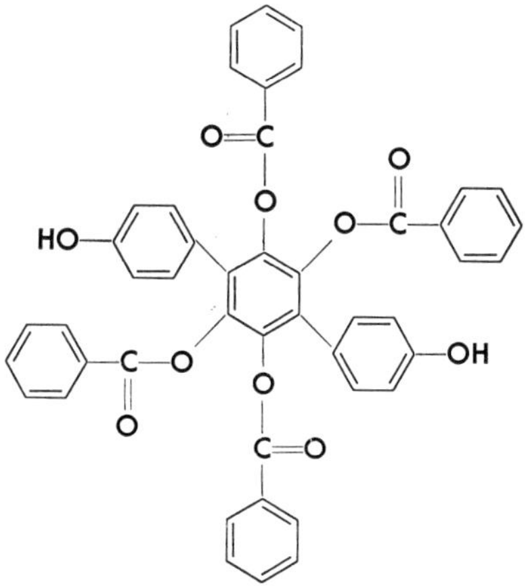

Hydnum aurantiacum Batsch.
Aurantiacin and thelephoric acid are produced by the same organism.
Jarl Gripenberg, *Acta Chem. Scand.* 12 1411 (1958).

Coenzymes Q (Mitoquinone, Ubiquinone, Q_{275}, SA).
These compounds occur widely in the cell mitochondria of microorganisms and higher animals, where they play a part in the electron transport system. Variations in side-chain length occur as in the case of vitamin K. Compounds in which n = 6, 7, 8 and 9 have been isolated from microbial sources. The quinone moiety resembles aurantioglioclandin.

General structure:

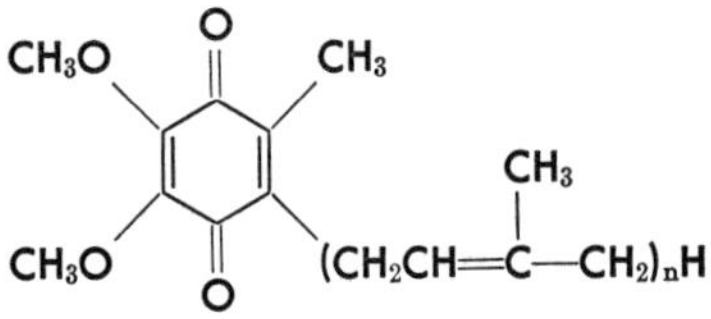

512 Coenzyme Q$_6$, C$_{39}$H$_{58}$O$_4$, m.p. 16°.
Saccharomyces cerevisiae

513 Coenzyme Q$_7$, C$_{44}$H$_{66}$O$_4$, orange crystals, m.p. 30.5°.
Torula utilis

514 Coenzyme Q$_8$, C$_{49}$H$_{74}$O$_4$, orange crystals, m.p. 37°.
Azotobacter vinelandii

515 Coenzyme Q$_9$, C$_{54}$H$_{82}$O$_4$, orange crystals, m.p. 45.2°.
Torula utilis
R. L. Lester, F. L. Crane and Y. Hatefi, *J. Am. Chem. Soc.*
80 4751 (1958). (Isolation)
F. W. Heaton, J. S. Lowe and R. A. Morton, *J. Chem. Soc.*,
4094 (1956).

b. NAPHTHOQUINONES

516 Flaviolin, C$_{10}$H$_6$O$_5$, garnet red rhombs containing solvent of
crystallization, m.p.: dec. near 250°.

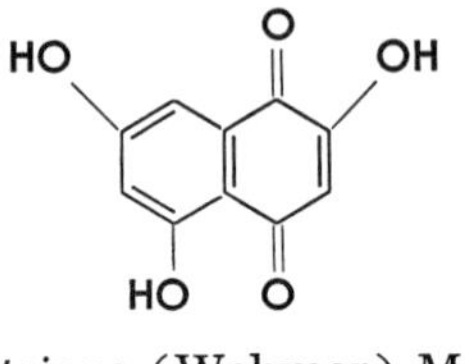

Aspergillus citricus (Wehmer) Mosseray
J. E. Davies, F. E. King and John C. Roberts, *Chem. and
Ind.*, 1110 (1954). (Structure)

517 6-Methyl-1,4-naphthoquinone, C$_{11}$H$_8$O$_2$, golden yellow needles,
m.p. 90–91°.

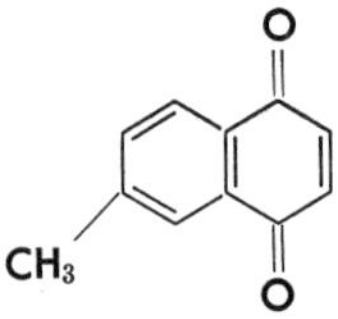

Marasmius gramineum Lib.

Gerd Bendz, *Acta Chem. Scand.* 2 192 (1948).
Idem., ibid. 5 489 (1951).

518 Phthiocol, $C_{11}H_8O_3$, yellow prisms, m.p. 173–174°.

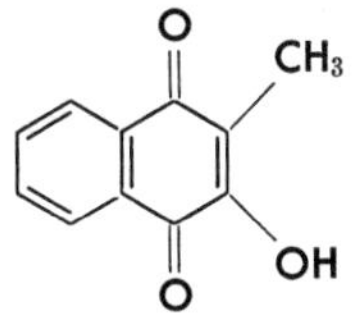

Mycobacterium tuberculosis var. *hominis, Corynebacterium diphtheriae*
R. J. Anderson and M. S. Newman, *J. Biol. Chem.* 103 197 (1933).
Rudolph J. Anderson, R. L. Peck and M. M. Creighton, *ibid.* 136 211 (1940).
Michizo Asano and Hideo Takahashi, *J. Pharm. Soc. Japan* 65 17 (1945).
M. Terni, *Boll. soc. ital. biol. sper.* 25 60 (1949).
There is evidence that phthiocol is an artifact, and that the precursor is a compound related to vitamin K_2, but of higher molecular weight.
J. Francis, J. Madinaveitia, H. M. Macturk and G. A. Snow, *Nature* 163 365 (1949).

519 Mollisin, $C_{14}H_{10}O_4Cl_2$, orange-yellow needles, m.p. 202° (dec.).

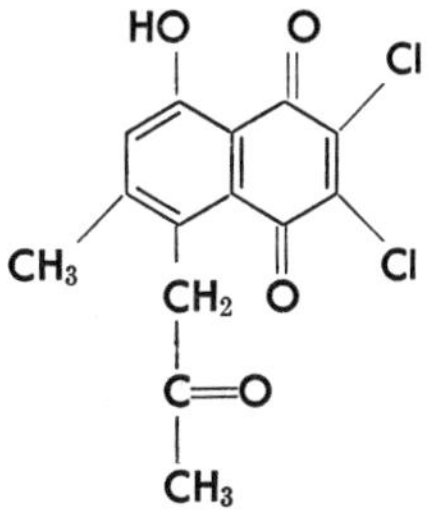

Mollisia caesia, Sacc. sensu Sydow, *M. gallens* Karst.
G. J. M. van der Kerk and J. C. Overum, *Rec. trav. chim.* 76 425 (1957).

520 Javanicin, $C_{15}H_{14}O_6$, red laths, m.p. 208°.

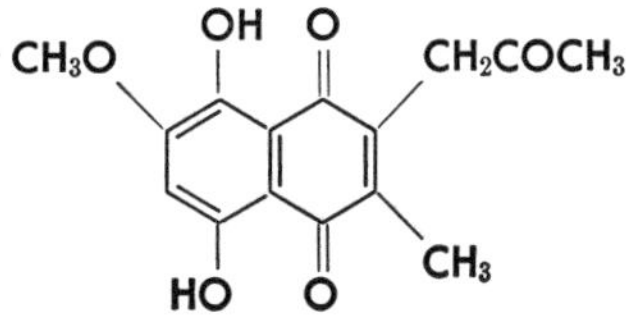

Fusarium javanicum Koorders

Yield about 20 mg. per liter (purified pigment). Occurs together with fusarubin.

H. R. V. Arnstein and A. H. Cook, *J. Chem. Soc.*, 1021 (1947). (Isolation)

521 **Fusarubin** (Oxyjavanicin), $C_{15}H_{14}O_7$, red prisms, m.p. 218° (preheated block).

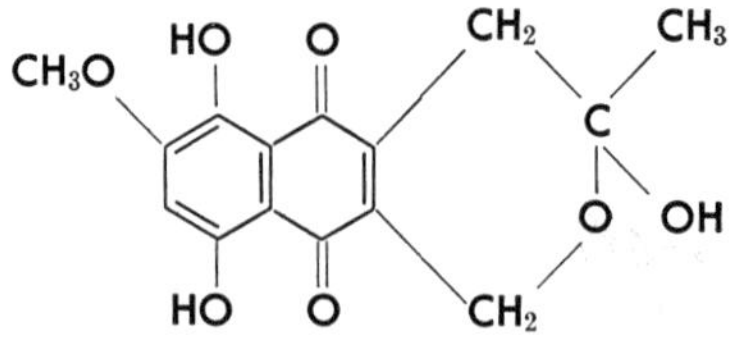

CH₃O · HO · O · CH₂ · CH₃ · C · O · OH · HO · O · CH₂

Fusarium solani (Mart.) App. and Wr.

Yield about 50 mg. per liter (mixed with javanicin).

H. R. V. Arnstein and A. H. Cook, *J. Chem. Soc.*, 1021 (1947).

Hans W. Ruelius and Adeline Gauhe, *Ann.* 569 38 (1950).

After ether extraction of the acidified broth, a water-soluble derivative of fusarubin remains behind. This has been identified as a sulfate ester occurring at one of the hydroquinone hydroxyl groups and was called fusarubinogen. Fusarubinogen actually is present in the broth in a reduced form, which is probably a derivative of β-hydro-naphthazarin.

Hans W. Ruelius and Adeline Gauhe, *Ann.* 570 121 (1951).

522 **Bostrycoidin,** $C_{18}H_{14}O_7$ (proposed), red or brown lath clusters, m.p. 243°.

A substituted naphthoquinone similar to javanicin.

Fusarium bostrycoides Wr. and Rkg.

Mary Alice Hamilton, Marjorie S. Knorr and Florian A. Cajori, *Antibiotics and Chemotherapy* 3 853 (1953).

F. A. Cajori, Theodore T. Otani and Mary Alice Hamilton, *J. Biol. Chem.* 208 107 (1954). (Isolation)

523 **4,9-Dihydroxyperylene-3,10-quinone,** $C_{20}H_{10}O_4$, dark red needles, dec. near 350°.

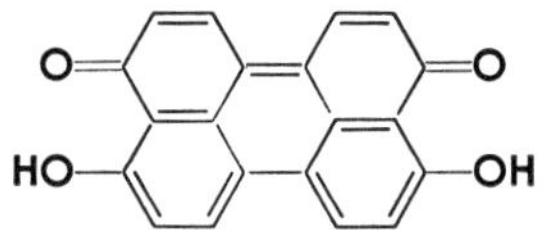

O= · =O · HO— · —OH

Daldinia concentrica (Bolt) Ces. and de Not.

J. M. Anderson and J. Murray, *Chem. and Ind.*, 376 (1956). (Isolation)

524   It has since been reported that this perylenequinone is probably an artifact of 4,5,4′5′-tetrahydroxy-1,1′-dinaphthyl.

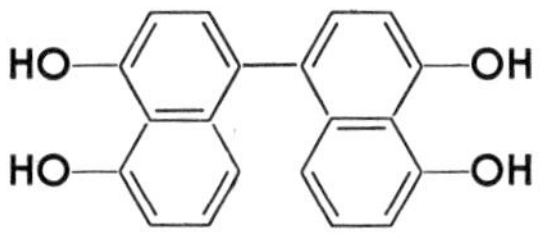

This polyphenol was obtained from the same organism. It was found to oxidize in part to a dark, melanin-like polymer, and in part to the perylenequinone. The structure was proved by synthesis.

J. D. Bu'Lock and D. C. Allport, *Proc. Chem. Soc.*, 264 (1957).

D. C. Allport and J. D. Bu'Lock, *J. Chem. Soc.*, 654 (1960).

525 **Mycochrysone,** $C_{20}H_{14}O_7$, orange-red crystals, m.p.: slow dec. above 180°.

No N, —OCH_3, C—CH_3 nor halogen. Three active hydrogens.

Partial structure:

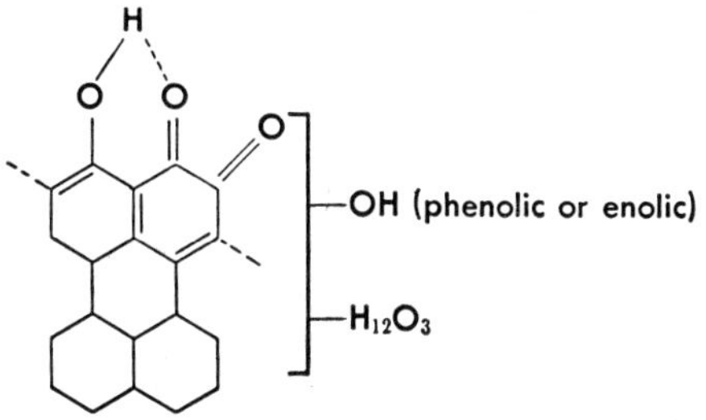

An inoperculate discomycetous fungus.

G. Read, P. Shu, L. C. Vining and R. H. Haskins, *Can. J. Chem.* **37** 731 (1959).

526 **Actinorhodin,** $C_{32}H_{26-30}O_{14}$, bright red needles, dec. 270°.

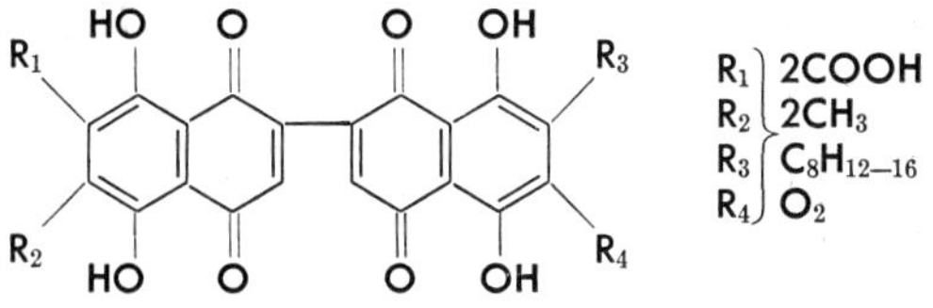

R_1 2COOH
R_2 2CH$_3$
R_3 C_8H_{12-16}
R_4 O_2

Streptomyces coelicolor (Müller) Waksman and Henrici

The yield was about 15% of the mycelial weight.

Hans Brockmann and Ernst Hieronymus, *Chem. Ber.* **88** 1379 (1955).

This compound has been shown to be an artifact, and by careful isolation under acidic conditions the precursor, protoactinorhodin, with the nucleus below, can be isolated.

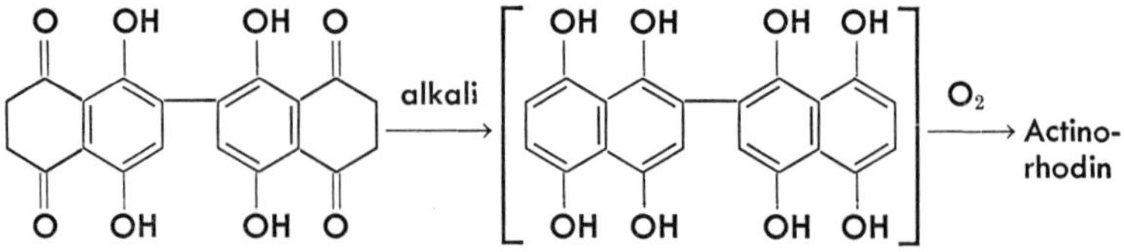

527　Protoactinorhodin was isolated as pale red prisms, dec. near 330°, probably $C_{32}H_{32}O_{14}$.

Hans Brockmann and Volkmar Loeschcke, *Chem. Ber.* **88** 778 (1955).

528　**Xylindein,** $C_{34}H_{26}O_{11}$, deep brown high-melting, pleochroic leaflets.

The structure is obscure, but an extended quinone system of the type

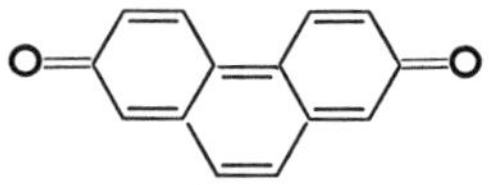

was postulated.

Chlorosplenium aeruginosum (Oeder ex Fries) De Not

Fritz Kögl and G. von Taeuffenbach, *Ann.* 445 170 (1925).

Fritz Kögl and Hanni Erxleben, *ibid.* 484 65 (1930).

529　**Rhodomycetin,** gradual darkening at 300°.

Dark red powder, red in acid solution and blue in alkaline. U.V. 235, 540, 580 mμ.

Reddish violet in H_2SO_4, positive $FeCl_3$, H_2O_2 and $Na_2S_2O_4 \cdot 2H_2O$ reduction.

Resembles actinorhodin.

Streptomyces griseus

Gerald Shockman and Selman A. Waksman, *Antibiotics and Chemotherapy* 1 68 (1951).

530　**Naphthoquinone from *Mycobacterium phlei*,** yellow oil, U.V. 243, 249, 261, 270, 328 mμ in isooctane.

Appears to have about 30 carbon atoms and is probably a vitamin K_1. Mol. wt. about 620.

Mycobacterium phlei
Ten mg. were obtained from 450 g. of wet cells.
A. F. Brodie, B. R. Davis and L. G. Fieser, *J. Am. Chem. Soc.* **80** 6454 (1958).

Vitamins K₂:

Vitamin K_2 was first isolated from putrefied fish meal in 1939 by Doisy and collaborators. Tishler and Sampson later found that it was produced by pure cultures of *Bacillus brevis*. Isler and collaborators corrected the structure originally proposed to A. below. They also isolated a lower isoprenolog, B., from putrefied fish meal. Both structures were proved by synthesis. The later group also determined the structure of (and synthesized) a higher isoprenolog C. isolated earlier in England.

531   A., $C_{46}H_{64}O_2$, light yellow plates, m.p. 54°.

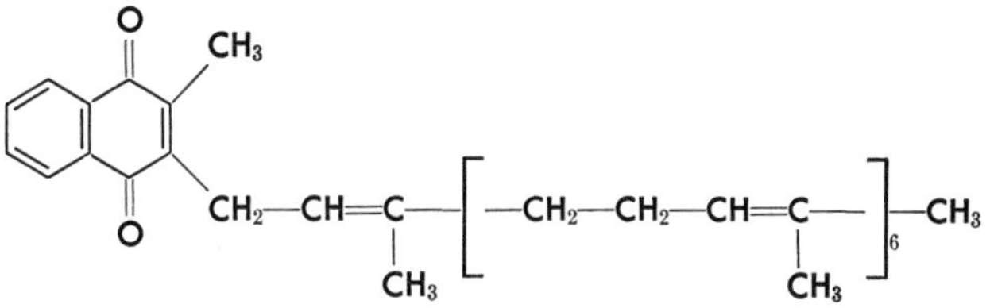

Bacillus brevis
R. W. McKee, S. B. Binkley, Sidney A. Thayer, D. W. Maccorquodale and Edward A. Doisy, *J. Biol. Chem.* **131** 327 (1939).
M. Tishler and W. Sampson, *Proc. Soc. Exp. Biol.* **68** 136 (1948).

532   B., $C_{41}H_{56}O_2$, light yellow plates, m.p. 50°.

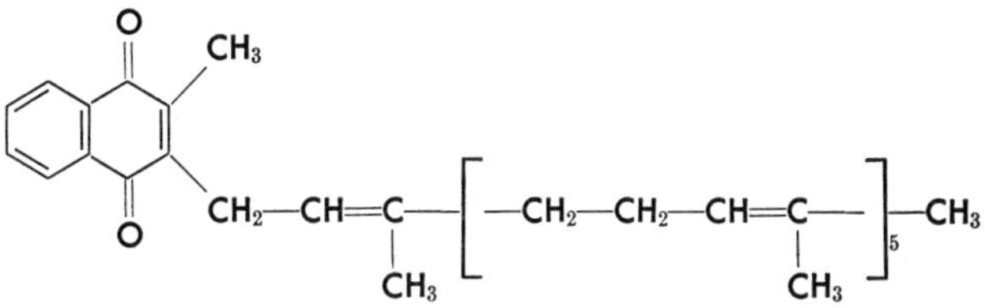

O. Isler, R. Rüegg, L. Chopard-dit-Jean, A. Winterstein and O. Wiss, *Helv. Chim. Acta* **41** 786 (1958).

533 C. $C_{56}H_{80}O_2$, yellow crystals, m.p. 58–59°.

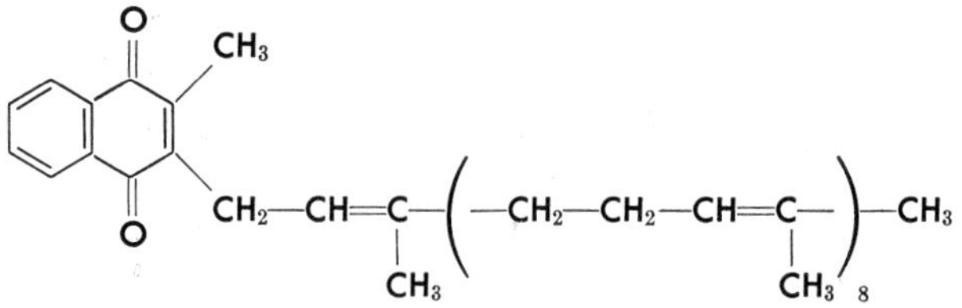

Mycobacterium tuberculosis (Brevannes)
This substance constituted about 0.5% of the dry cell weight.

J. Francis, J. Madinaveitia, H. M. Macturk and G. A. Snow, *Nature* 163 365 (1949). (Isolation)
H. Noll, R. Rüegg, U. Gloor, G. Ryser and O. Isler, *Helv. Chim. Acta* 43 433 (1960). (Structure and synthesis)

C. ANTHRAQUINONES

534 Anthraquinone pigment from *Gibberella fujikuroi*, probably $C_{14}H_{10}O_7$, red crystals, m.p. 325° (sealed tube).
Partial and tentative structure:

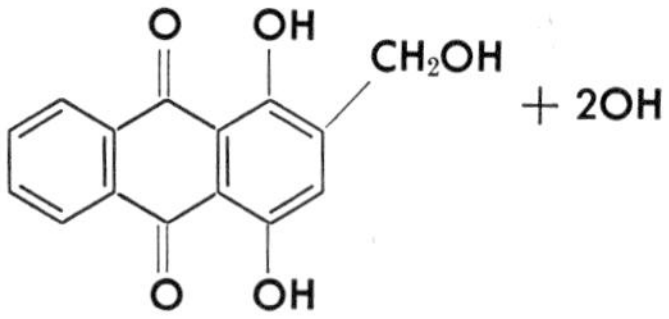

The structure may resemble that of cynodontin.
Gibberella fujikuroi (Saw.) Wollenweber
Yukihiko Nakamura, Tokuji Shimomura and Joji Ono, *J. Agr. Chem. Soc. Japan* 31 669 (1957). (Isolation)

535 **Clavorubin,** $C_{14}H_{12}O_9$, red crystals.
Has one C—CH_3 group. U.V. absorption resembles a 1,5,8-trihydroxyanthraquinone. The leuco-acetate (like that of chrysergonic acid) has a diphenyl-like absorption.
Claviceps purpurea
B. Franck and T. Reschke, *Angew. Chem.* 71 407 (1959).

536 **Emodic Acid,** $C_{15}H_8O_7$, orange needles, m.p. 363–365°.

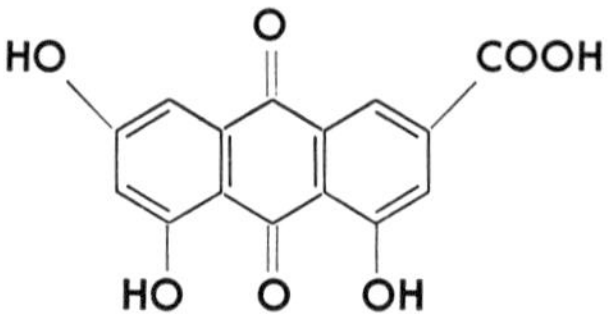

Penicillium cyclopium Westling
Winston K. Anslow, John Breen and Harold Raistrick, *Biochem. J.* **34** 159 (1940).

537 Boletol, $C_{15}H_8O_7$, red needles, m.p. 275–280° (dec.).

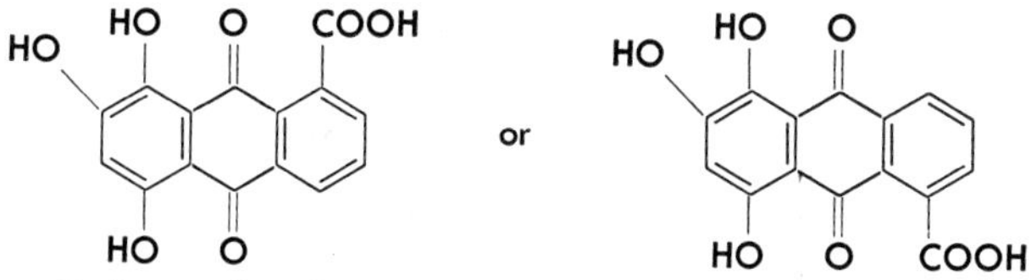

or

Boletus luridus Schaeff. ex Fries, *B. badius* Fr., *B. chrysenteron* Bull., *B. satanas* Lenz, *B. subtomentosus* Linn.

The higher yielding species gave about 1 g. of pure material from 20 kg. of fruiting body.

Fritz Kögl and W. B. Deijs, *Ann.* **515** 10, 23 (1935). (Synthesis)

538 Pachybasin, $C_{15}H_{10}O_3$, yellow needles, m.p. 78°.

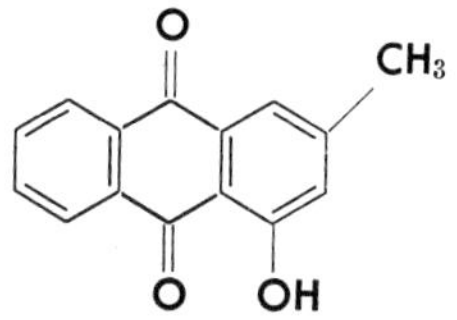

Pachybasium candidum (Sacc.) Peyronel
Pachybasin, like most of the other anthraquinone pigments, occurs as one constituent of a mixture of pigments. Chrysophanol was identified as one of the other constituents of this mixture.

Shoji Shibata and Michio Takido, *Pharm. Bull.* (Tokyo) **3** 156 (1955).

539 Chrysophanol (Chrysophanic Acid), $C_{15}H_{10}O_4$, dark yellow leaflets, m.p. 196°.

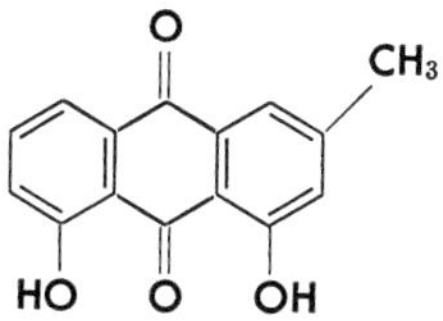

Penicillium islandicum Sopp, *Pachybasium candidum* (Sacc.) Peyronel, *Chaetomium affine* Corda

The 9-anthrone corresponding to chrysophanol has been isolated from higher plants.

B. H. Howard and H. Raistrick, *Biochem. J.* 46 49 (1950).
Shoji Shibata, *Kagaku (Science)* 26 391 (1956).

540 Islandicin, $C_{15}H_{10}O_5$, dark red plates, m.p. 218°.

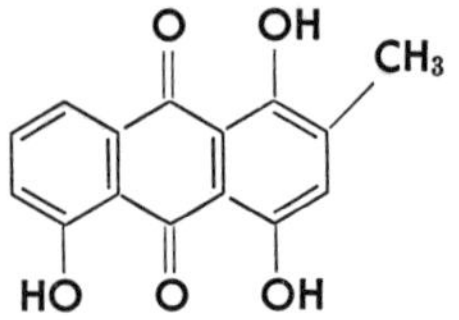

Penicillium islandicum Sopp.

This mold produces a complex mixture of pigments constituting up to 20% of the mycelial weight.

B. H. Howard and H. Raistrick, *Biochem. J.* 44 227 (1949).

Islandicin seems to be identical with funiculosin, a trihydroxyanthraquinone pigment of the same melting point and empirical formula isolated from *Penicillium funiculosum* Thom, a species closely related to *P. islandicum*.

Hisanao Igarasi, *J. Agr. Chem. Soc. Japan* 15 225 (1939).

541 Helminthosporin, $C_{15}H_{10}O_5$, dark maroon needles, m.p. 227°.

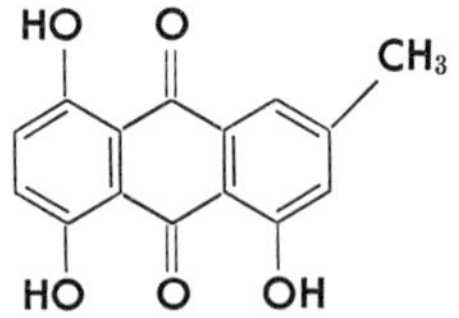

Helminthosporium gramineum Rabenhorst, *H. cynodontis* Marignoni, *H. catenarium, H. triticivulgaris* Nisikado

About 30% of the dry mycelium of *H. gramineum* consisted of anthraquinone pigments, mainly helminthosporin and catenarin.

Harold Raistrick, Robert Robinson and Alexander R. Todd, *J. Chem. Soc.,* 488 (1933).

542 Emodin (Frangula-Emodin), $C_{15}H_{10}O_5$, orange needles, m.p. 255°.

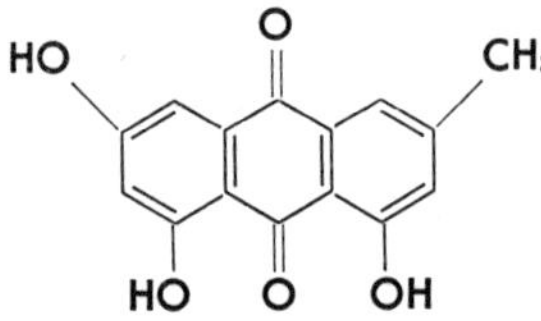

Cortinarius sanguineus (Wulf.) Fries, *Chaetomium affine* Corda.

A yield of about 3% of the dry mycelial weight has been mentioned.

Fritz Kögl and J. J. Postowcky, *Ann.* 444 1 (1925).

R. A. Jacobson and Roger Adams, *J. Am. Chem. Soc.* 46 1312 (1934). (Synthesis)

543 Versicolorin, $C_{15}H_{10}O_6$, yellow-orange needles, m.p. 282°.

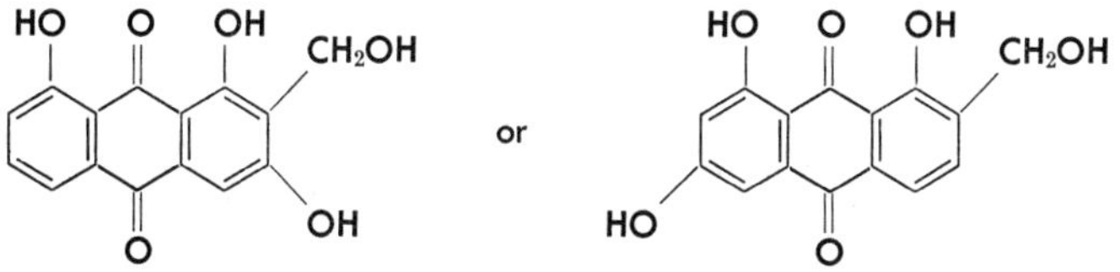

or

Aspergillus versicolor (Vuillemin) Tiraboschi

The same organism produces an uncharacterized xanthone pigment.

Yuishi Hatsuda and Shimpei Kuyama, *J. Agr. Chem. Soc. Japan* 29 11 (1955).

544 Cynodontin, $C_{15}H_{10}O_6$, bronze plates, m.p. 260°.

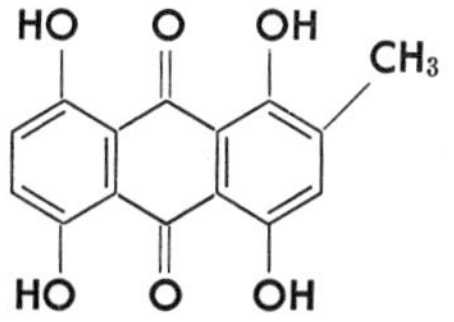

Helminthosporium cynodontis Marignoni, *H. euclaenae* Zimmermann, *H. avenae* Ito and Kurib, *H. victoriae*

Winston Kennay Anslow and Harold Raistrick, *Biochem. J.* 34 1546 (1940). (Synthesis)

545 ω-Hydroxyemodin (Citreorosein), $C_{15}H_{10}O_6$, orange needles, m.p. 288°.

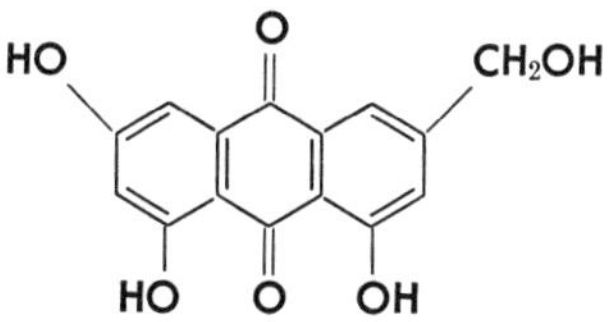

Penicillium cyclopium Westling, *P. citreo-roseum* Dierckx.

Winston K. Anslow, John Breen and Harold Raistrick, *Biochem. J.* 34 159 (1940).

Theodore Posternak, *Compt. rend. soc. phys. his. nat. Genève* 56 28 (1939).

546 **Catenarin,** $C_{15}H_{10}O_6$, red plates, m.p. 246°.

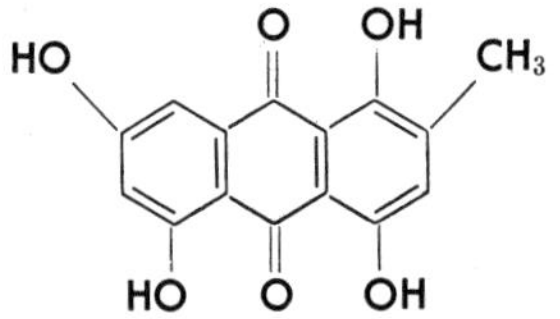

Helminthosporium catenarium Drechsler, *H. gramineum* Rabenhorst, *H. velutinum* Link, *H. triticivulgaris* Nisikado, *Penicillium islandicum* Sopp, *Aspergillus amstelodami* (Mangin) Thom and Church

More than 15% of the mycelial weight of *H. catenarium* was catenarin.

Winston Kennay Anslow and Harold Raistrick, *Biochem. J.* 35 1006 (1941). (Synthesis)

547 **Asperthecin,** $C_{15}H_{10}O_8$, chestnut brown needles, no m.p.

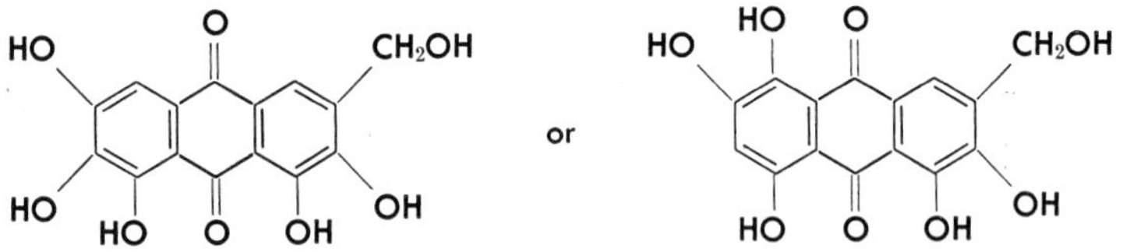

or

Aspergillus quadrilineatus Thom and Raper and other species of the *Aspergillus nidulans* group

S. Neelakantan, Anna Pocker and H. Raistrick, *Biochem. J.* 66 234 (1957).

A closely related pigment has been observed, which may have been a tautomeric or reduced form of asperthecin. It could not be isolated because of its ready conversion to asperthecin.

B. H. Howard and H. Raistrick, *Biochem. J.* 59 475 (1955).

548 **Fallacinal,** $C_{16}H_{10}O_6$, orange-yellow needles, m.p. 251°.

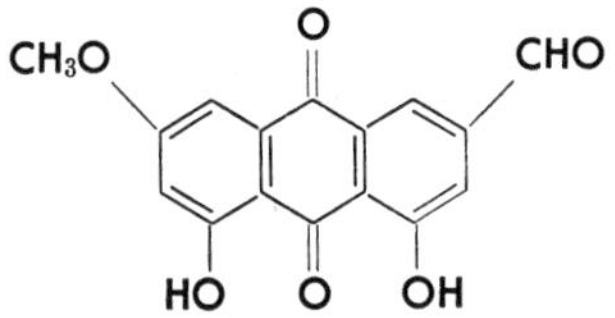

Xanthoria fallax (Hepp.) Arn.
Takao Murakami, *Pharm. Bull.* (Tokyo) 4 298 (1956).

549 **Tritisporin** (ω-Hydroxycatenarin), $C_{15}H_{10}O_7$, brown needles, m.p. 260–262°.

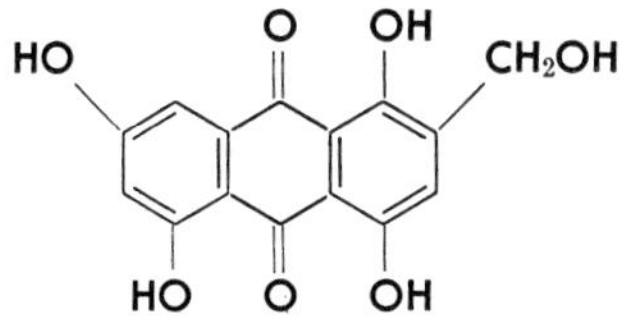

Helminthosporium triticivulgaris Nisikado
S. Neelakantan, Anna Pocker and H. Raistrick, *Biochem. J.* 64 464 (1956).

550 **Flavoskyrin,** $C_{15}H_{12}O_5$, yellow crystals, m.p. 208° (dec.), $[\alpha]_D$ −295° (in dioxane).

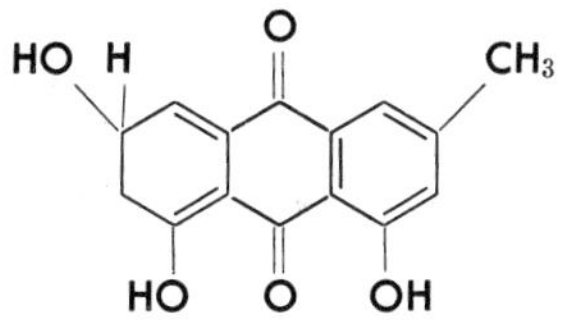

Penicillium islandicum Sopp.
Shoji Shibata, Takao Murakami and Michio Takito, *Pharm. Bull.* (Tokyo) 4 303 (1956). (Structure)

551 **Compound A** (1,4,7,8-Tetrahydroxy-2-methylanthraquinone), $C_{15}H_{12}O_7$.

An optically inactive compound (no melting point given). Treatment with conc. H_2SO_4 yields an anthraquinone, $C_{15}H_{10}O_5$, red crystals, m.p. 255°, with the following structure:

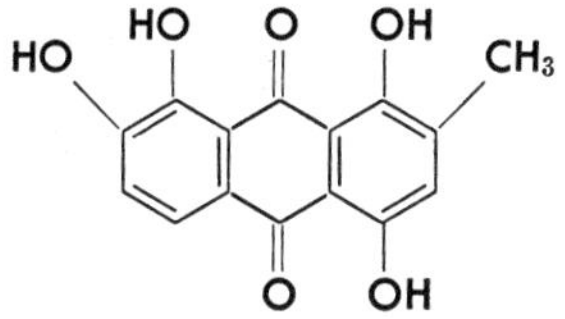

Penicillium islandicum
Sten Gatenbeck, *Acta Chem. Scand.* 12 1985 (1958).
Idem., *ibid.* 13 705 (1959).

552 Endocrocin, $C_{16}H_{10}O_7$, copper-red leaflets, m.p. 318° (dec.).

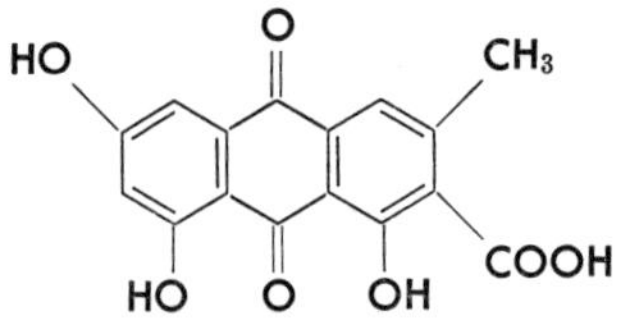

Nephromopsis endocrocea Asahina
Yasuhiko Asahina and Fukuziro Fuzikawa, *Ber.* **68B** 1558 (1935).
Aspergillus amstelodami (Mangin) Thom and Church.
Shoji Shibata and Shinsaku Natori, *Pharm. Bull.* (Tokyo) 1 160 (1953).

553 Clavoxanthin, $C_{16}H_{10}O_7$, yellow needles, m.p. 340° (dec.).
Apparently similar to endocrocin.
Claviceps purpurea
B. Franck and T. Reschke, *Angew. Chem.* 71 407 (1959).

554 Parietinic Acid, $C_{16}H_{10}O_7$, yellow needles, m.p. ~300° (sublimes).

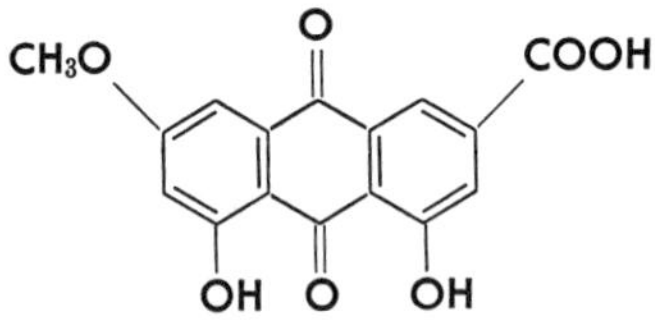

Xanthoria parietina (L.) Th. Fr.
Walter Escherich, *Biochem. Z.* 330 73 (1958).

555 Physcion (Parietin), $C_{16}H_{12}O_5$, orange-yellow leaflets, m.p. 207°.

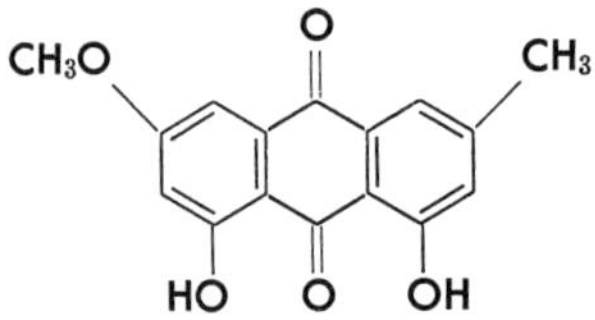

Aspergillus glaucus spp., *A. chevalieri*, *A. ruber* (Mangin) Raper and Thom, *Penicillium herquei* Bainier and Sartory, *Xanthoria parietina* (L.) Beltram, *X. fallax*, *Teloschistes flavicans* (Sw.) Norm., *T. exilis* Wainio, *Placodium* spp., *Caloplaca elegans* (Link)

F. Rochleder and W. Heldt, *Ann.* 48 1 (1843).

Harold Raistrick, *Enzymologia* 4 76 (1937).

H. Raistrick, Robert Robinson and A. R. Todd, *J. Chem. Soc.*, 80 (1937).

Julius Nicholson Ashley, Harold Raistrick and Taliesin Richards, *Biochem. J.* 33 1291 (1939).

T. R. Seshadri and S. Sankara Subramanian, *Proc. Indian Acad. Sci.* 30A 67 (1949).

Walter B. Mors, *Bol. Inst. Quim. Agric.* No. 23 7 (1951).

S. Neelakantan and T. R. Seshadri, *J. Sci. Ind. Research* (India) 11B 126 (1952).

Shoji Shibata and Shinsaku Natori, *Pharm. Bull.* (Tokyo) 1 160 (1953).

Mitizo Asano and Yosio Arata, *J. Pharm. Soc. Japan* 60 521 (1940).

J. A. Galarraga, K. G. Mill and H. Raistrick, *Biochem. J.* 61 456 (1955).

Jiro Kitamura, Uzuhiko Kurimoto and Matatsugu Zoko-yama, *J. Pharm. Soc. Japan* 76 972 (1956).

556 **Macrosporin,** $C_{16}H_{12}O_5$, orange-yellow rhombic crystals, m.p. 300° (dec.).

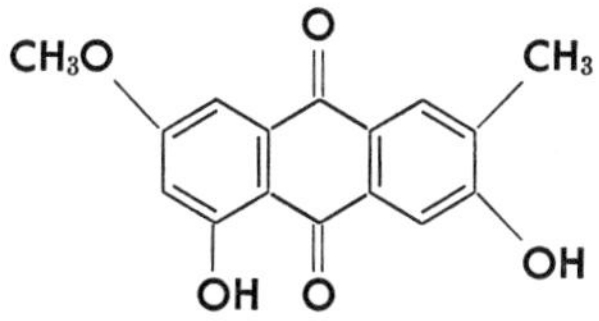

Macrosporium porri Elliott

R. Suemitsu, Y. Matsui and M. Hiura, *Bull. Agr. Chem. Soc.* (Japan) 21 1–4, 337 (1957). (Isolation)

R. Suemitsu, M. Nakajima and M. Hiura, *ibid.* 23 547 (1959).

557 **Teloschistin** (Fallacinol), $C_{16}H_{12}O_6$, orange plates, m.p. 245–247°.

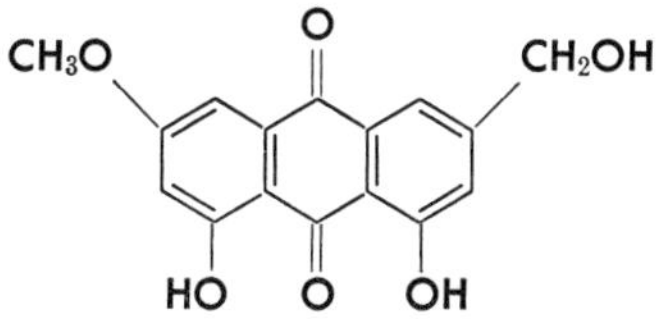

Teloschistes flavicans (Sw.) Norm., *Xanthoria fallax* (Hepp.) Arn.

T. R. Seshadri and S. Sankara Subramanian, *Proc. Indian Acad. Sci.* 30A 67 (1949).

558 Roseopurpurin (Carviolin), $C_{16}H_{12}O_6$, yellow needles, m.p. 286°.

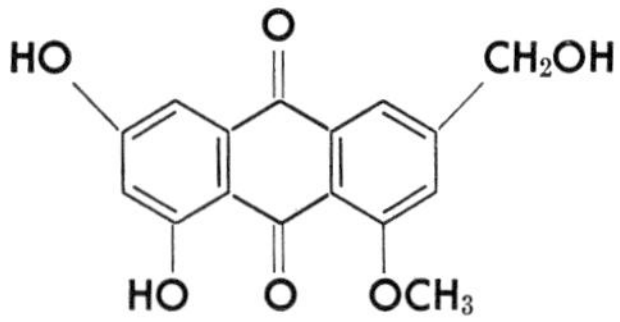

Penicillium roseopurpureum Dierckx

559 A second pigment, **carviolacin**, $C_{20}H_{16}O_7$, light brown needles, m.p. 243° (dec.), was isolated from this mold. It is apparently closely related in structure.

Theodore Posternak, *Helv. Chim. Acta* 23 1046 (1940).
H. G. Hind, *Biochem. J.* 34 67, 577 (1940).

560 Erythroglaucin (Catenarin 6-Methyl Ether), $C_{16}H_{12}O_6$, deep red plates or needles, m.p. 205°.

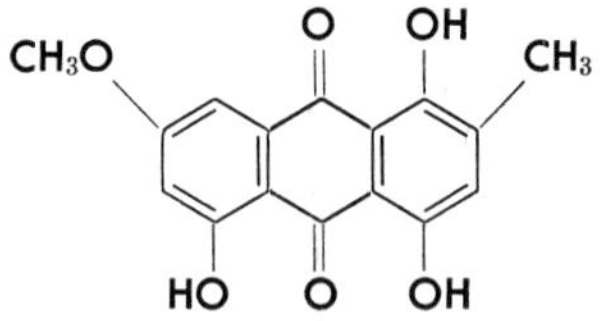

Aspergillus glaucus (ten spp.)
The former rubroglaucin was shown to be a mixture of physcion and erythroglaucin.

Julius Nicholson Ashley, Harold Raistrick and Taliesin Richards, *Biochem. J.* 33 1291 (1939).

561 Neophromin, $C_{16}H_{12}O_6$, ocher colored needles, m.p. 198° (dec.). A quinone-like pigment.
Neophromium lusitanicum
O. Hesse, *J. prakt. Chem.* 57 409 (1898).

562 Dermocybin, $C_{16}H_{12}O_7$, red needles, m.p. 228°.
This is an incompletely characterized anthraquinone pigment. It has five nuclear hydroxyl groups, one of them methylated. It is produced along with emodin by

Cortinarius sanguineus (Wulf.) Fries and constitutes 0.2–0.4% of the mycelial weight.

Cortinarius cinnabarinus Fries produces a pigment which is the same or similar.

Fritz Kögl and J. J. Postowsky, *Ann.* 444 1 (1925).

563, 564 Physcion Anthranols, $C_{16}H_{14}O_4$, m.p.'s 260° and 181°.

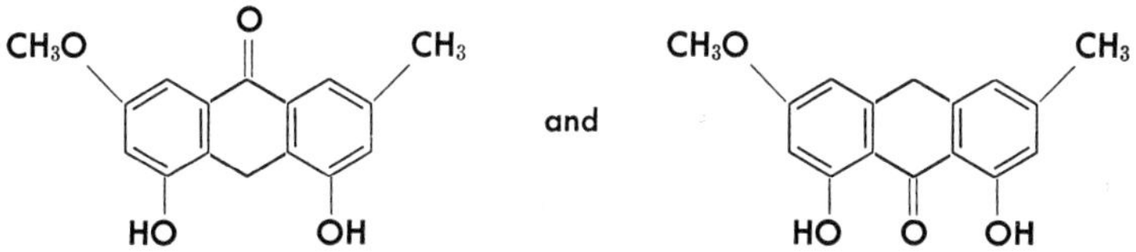

Aspergillus glaucus (five types)
Julius Nicholson Ashley, Harold Raistrick and Taliesin Richards, *Biochem. J.* 33 1291 (1939).

565 Rhodocladonic Acid, $C_{17}H_{12}O_9$, red needles, m.p. >360°.

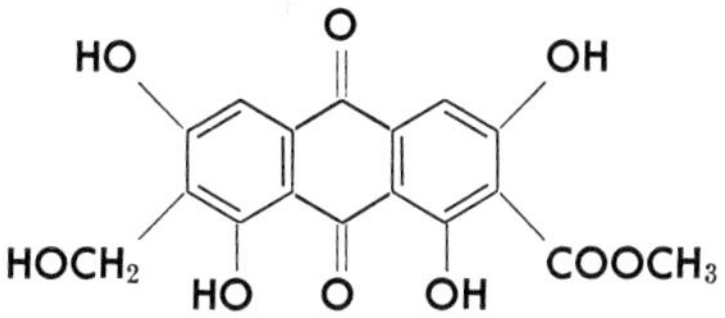

Thirteen *Cladonia* species
Shoji Shibata, Michio Takido and Osamu Tanaka, *J. Am. Chem. Soc.* 72 2789 (1950).

566 Nalgiolaxin, $C_{18}H_{15}O_6Cl$, yellow plates or needles, m.p. 248°, $[\alpha]_{5790}^{22}$ +40.3° (in chloroform).

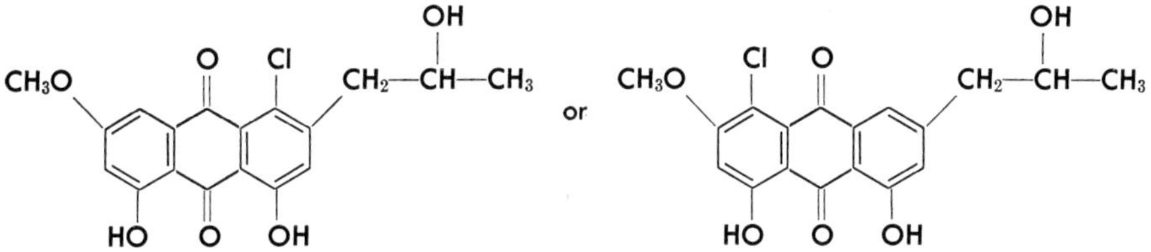

Penicillium nalgiovensis Laxa
H. Raistrick and J. Ziffer, *Biochem. J.* 49 563 (1951).

567 Nalgiovensin, $C_{18}H_{15}O_6$, orange needles or plates, m.p. 199–200°, $[\alpha]_{5790}^{20}$ +39.7° (in chloroform).

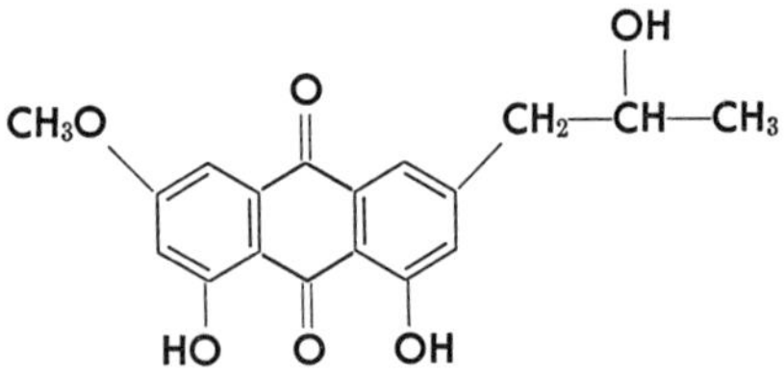

Penicillium nalgiovensis Laxa
H. Raistrick and J. Ziffer, *Biochem. J.* **49** 563 (1951). (Isolation)
A. J. Birch and R. A. Massy-Westropp, *J. Chem. Soc.*, 2215 (1957). (Structure)

568 Thermophillin, $C_{18}H_{18}O_9$, golden plates, m.p. subl. 245° (dec. 260° sealed tube).
Quinonoid properties.
Lenzites thermophila
H. S. Burton, *Nature* **166** 570 (1950).

569 Phomazarin,* $C_{19}H_{17}O_8N$, orange needles, m.p., 197° (dec.).

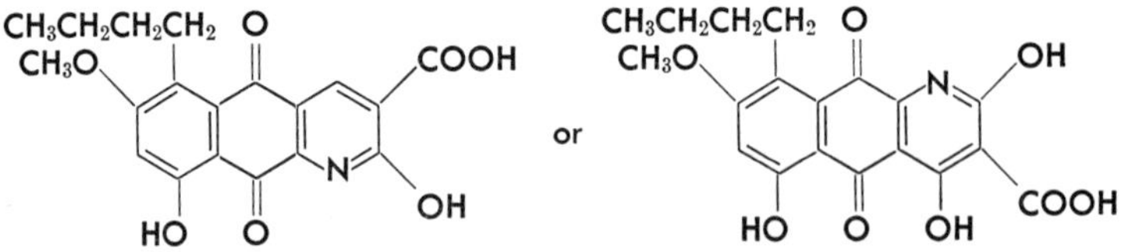

or

Phoma terrestris Hansen
F. Kögl and J. Sparenburg, *Rec. trav. chim.* **59** 1180 (1940).
F. Kögl and F. S. Quackenbush, *ibid.* **63** 251 (1944).
F. Kögl, G. C. van Wessem and O. I. Elsbach, *ibid.* **64** 23 (1945). (Synthesis)

570 Atrovenetin, $C_{19}H_{18}O_6$, brownish yellow prisms, m.p. 295° (dec.), $[\alpha]_{5461}^{21}$ +154° (c 0.486 in dioxan).

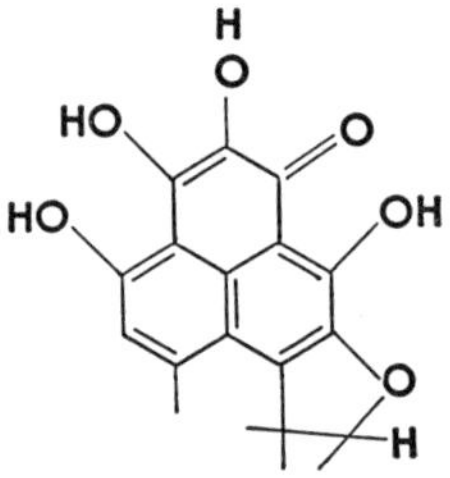

Penicillium atrovenetum G. Smith
* See addendum.

K. G. Neill and H. Raistrick, *Chem. and Ind.*, 551
(1956). (Isolation)
  Idem., Biochem. J. 65 166 (1957). (Isolation)
  D. H. R. Barton, P. de Mayo, G. A. Morrison and H. Raistrick, *Tetrahedron* 6 48 (1959). (Structure)

571 Norherqueinone, $C_{19}H_{18}O_7$, dark red needles, m.p. 279° (dec.),
      $[\alpha]_D^{23}$ +1080° ±60° (c 0.048 in pyridine).
      Structure: Unmethylated herqueinone
      See herqueinone for organism, structure and references.

572 Herquein, $C_{19}H_{20}O_8$ (proposed), yellow-brown crystals, m.p.
      129° (dec.).
      Water-soluble. Fluoresces in alkali.
      Penicillium herquei
      H. Stowar Burton, *Brit. J. Exptl. Path.* 30 151 (1949).

573 Herqueinone, $C_{20}H_{20}O_7$, red needles, m.p. 226° (dec.) (sublimes), $[\alpha]_D^{22}$ +440° ±40° (c 0.063 in ethanol).
      Partial structure:

Penicillium herquei Bainier and Sartory
A crude pigment yield of 17% of the weight of the dry
mycelium was obtained. The major constituents were
norherqueinone and its methyl ether, herqueinone. Minor constituents were physcion and *meso*-erythritol.
The plant pigment, haemocorin, also contains the peri-
naphthenone nucleus.
Frank H. Stodola, Kenneth B. Raper and Dorothy I. Fennell, *Nature* 167 773 (1951). (Isolation)
J. A. Galarraga, K. G. Neill and H. Raistrick, *Biochem. J.* 61 456 (1955).
D. H. R. Barton, P. de Mayo, G. A. Morrison, W. H. Schaeppi and H. Raistrick, *Chem. and Ind.*, 552 (1956). (Structure)
Robert E. Harman, James Cason, Frank H. Stodola and A. Lester Adkins, *J. Org. Chem.* 20 1260 (1955).

574 Solorinic Acid, $C_{21}H_{20}O_7$, red-brown plates, m.p. 203.5°.

Solorina crocea (L.) Ach.

G. Koller and H. Russ, *Monatsh.* **70** 54 (1937).

575 Resistomycin, $C_{22}H_{16}O_6$, yellow needles, m.p. 315° (dec.) (sublimes from 215°).

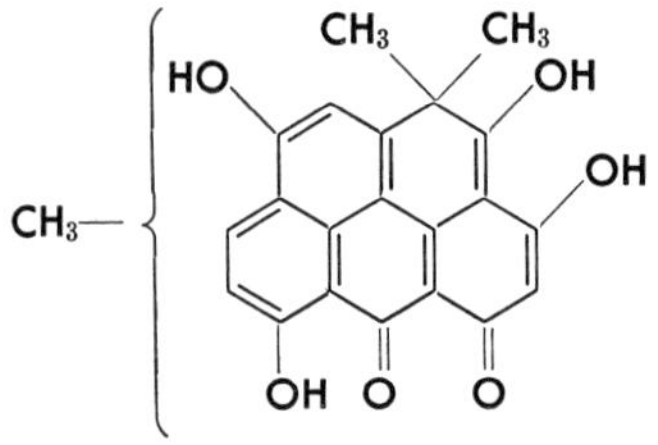

Streptomyces resistomycificus

Hans Brockmann and Günter Schmidt-Kastner, *Chem. Ber.* **87** 1460 (1954). (Isolation)

H. Brockmann, E. Meyer and K. Schrempp, Dissertations, University of Göttingen, 1954, 1958. (Partial structure by courtesy of Prof. Brockmann)

576 Granatacin, $C_{22}H_{20}O_{10}$, pomegranate-red crystals, m.p. 204–206° (dec.).

A tricyclic tetrahydroxyquinonedicarboxylic acid with antibiotic properties.

Streptomyces olivaceus (Waksman) Waksman and Henrici

R. Corbaz, L. Ettlinger, E. Gäumann, J. Kalvoda, W. Keller-Schierlein, F. Kradolfer, B. K. Manukian, L. Neipp, V. Prelog, P. Reusser and H. Zähner, *Helv. Chim. Acta* **40** 1262 (1957).

577 Luteomycin (Antibiotic 289), $C_{26}H_{33}O_{12}N$ (proposed), (Hydrochloride) orange-yellow crystals, m.p. 199° (dec.).

Color changes to purple in alkali. Positive quinone-Na_2CO_3, $FeCl_3$. Negative ninhydrin, biuret, Molisch, Fehling, Sakaguchi. Can be precipitated as reineckate, helianthate or picrate.

Streptomyces flaveolus, S. tanashiensis related to *S. antibioticus*

Toju Hata, Tomojiro Higuchi, Yoshimoto Sano and Katuko Sawashi, *Kitasato Arch. Exptl. Med.* **22** 229 (1949).

Hamao Umezawa, Tomio Takeuchi, Kazuo Nitta, Kenji

Maeda, Tadashi Yamamoto and Seizaburo Yamaoka, *J. Antibiotics* (Japan) 6A 45 (1953).

Teisuke Osato, Koki Yagishita, Ryozo Utahara, Masahiro Ueda, Kenji Maeda and Hamao Umezawa, *ibid.* 6A 52 (1953).

Berislav Govorčin, *Tehnički Pregled* 8 43 (1956).

578 Luteoleersin, $C_{26}H_{38}O_7$, yellow crystals, m.p. 135°, $[\alpha]_{5461}^{18}$ 214° (c 0.456 in ethanol).

Believed to be a substituted quinone, containing two active hydrogens. It was accompanied by a reduction product:

579 Alboleersin, $C_{26}H_{40}O_7$, colorless crystals, m.p. 215°, $[\alpha]_{5461}^{18}$ 274° (c 0.430 in ethanol).

Contains three active hydrogens.

Helminthosporium leersii Atkinson

Julius N. Ashley and Harold Raistrick, *Biochem. J.* 32 449 (1938).

580 Skyrin (Endothianin), $C_{30}H_{18}O_{10}$, dark orange rods, m.p. >380°.

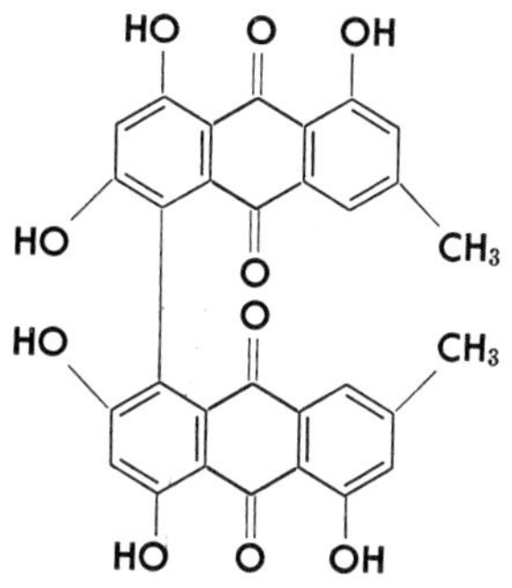

Penicillium islandicum Sopp, *P. wortmanni* Klocker, *P. tardum* Thom, *P. rugulosum* Thom, *Endothia parasitica* (Murr.) Anderson and Anderson, *E. fluens* Shear and Stevens

All of these fungi produce a mixture of skyrin with rugulosin.

F. Kögl and F. S. Quackenbush, *Rec. trav. chim.* 63 251 (1944).

Shoji Shibata, Osamu Tanaka, Goro Chihara and Horoshi Mitsuhashi, *Pharm. Bull.* (Tokyo) 1 302 (1953).

Shoji Shibata, Takao Murakami, Osamu Tanaka, Goro Chihara, Isao Kitagawa, Masashi Sumimoto and Chikara Kaneko, *ibid.* 3 160 (1955). (Structure)

Shoji Shibata, Takao Murakami, Osamu Tanaka, Goro Chihara and Masashi Sumimoto, *ibid.* 3 274 (1955).

J. Breen, J. C. Dacre, H. Raistrick and G. Smith, *Biochem. J.* 60 618 (1955).

Shoji Shibata, Michio Takido and Terumi Nakajima, *Pharm. Bull.* (Tokyo) 3 286 (1955).

Yuzuru Yamamoto, Takeo Yamamoto, Skoichi Kanatomo and Kiyoshi Tanimichi, *J. Pharm. Soc. Japan* 76 192 (1956).

Yazuru Yamamoto, Akira Hamaguchi, Isao Yamamoto and Sumie Imai, *ibid.* 76 1428 (1956).

581 Pigment B: $C_{30}H_{18}O_{11}$.

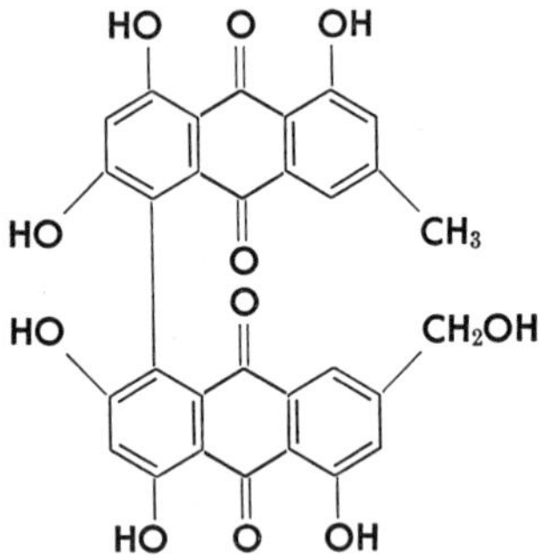

582 Pigment C: $C_{30}H_{18}O_{12}$.

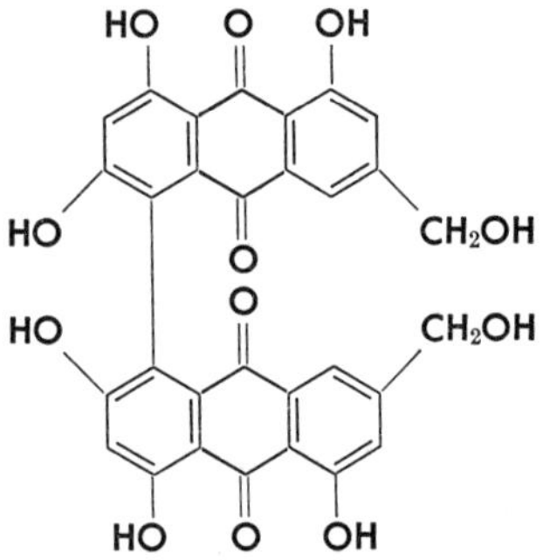

These are oxidized skyrins.

Penicillium islandicum N.R.R.L. 1175
Shoji Shibata, Michio Takido and Terumi Nakajima,
Pharm. Bull. (Tokyo) 3 286 (1955).

583 Iridoskyrin, $C_{30}H_{18}O_{18}$, irridescent red rods or plates, m.p. 358°.

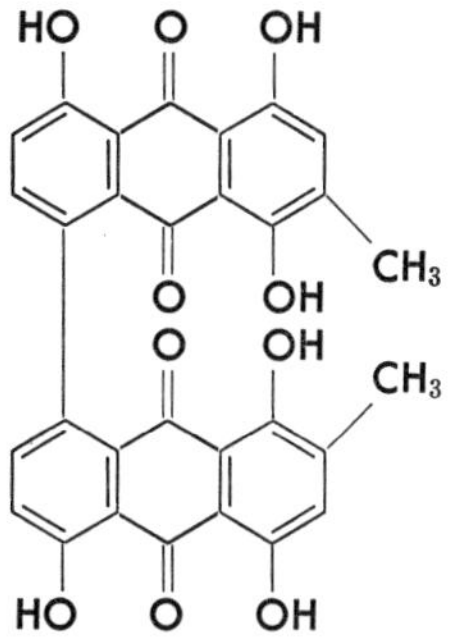

Penicillium islandicum Sopp.
B. H. Howard and H. Raistrick, *Biochem. J.* 57 212 (1954).

584 Aurofusarin, $C_{30}H_{20}O_{12}$, m.p. >360°.
This incompletely characterized pigment produced by
Fusarium culmorum W. G. Smith may be a dianthraqui-
none.
Julius N. Ashley, Betty C. Hobbs and Harold Raistrick,
Biochem. J. 31 385 (1937).

585 Penicilliopsin, $C_{30}H_{22}O_8$, orange crystals, m.p. 330° (dec.).

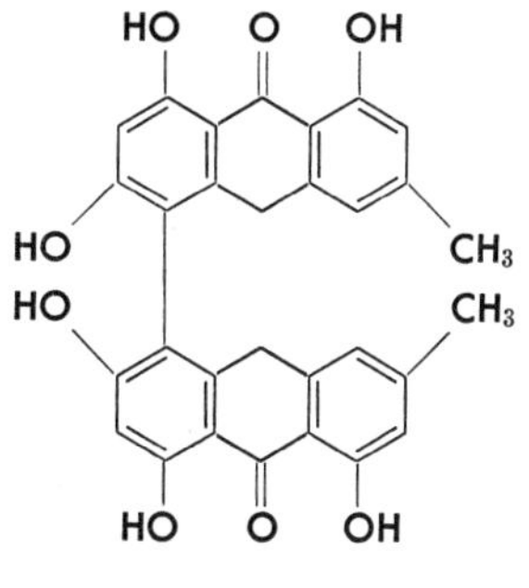

Penicilliopsis clavariaeformis Solms-Laubach
H. Brockmann and H. Eggers, *Angew. Chem.* 67 706 (1955).

586 Rugulosin (Radicalisin), $C_{30}H_{22}O_{10}$, yellow prisms, m.p. 293° (dec.), $[\alpha]_{5461}^{18}$ +605° (dioxane).

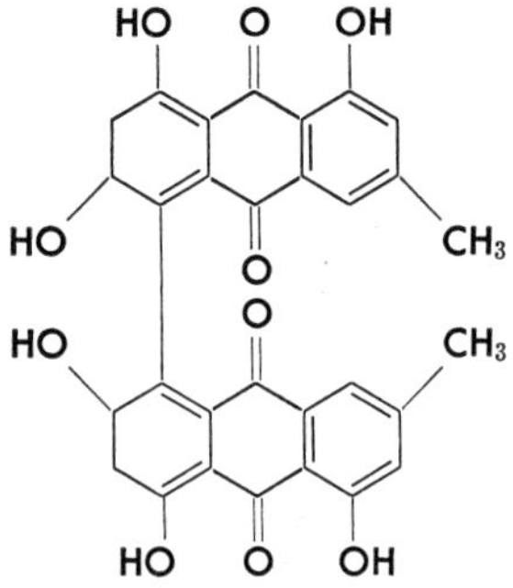

Penicillium rugulosum Thom, *P. tardum* Thom, *P. wortmanni* Klöcker, *Endothia parasitica* (Murr.) Anderson and Anderson, *E. fluens* Shear and Stevens.

About 20% of the dry weight of *P. rugulosum* mycelium is rugulosin.

J. Breen, J. C. Dacre, H. Raistrick and G. S. Smith, *Biochem. J.* **60** 618 (1955).

Shoji Shibata, Osamu Tanaka, Goro Chihara and Horoshi Mitsuhashi, *Pharm. Bull.* (Tokyo) **1** 302 (1953).

Shoji Shibata, Takao Murakami, Osamu Tanaka, Goro Chihara, Isao Kitagawa, Masashi Sumimoto and Chikara Kaneko, *ibid.* **3** 160 (1955). (Structure)

Shoji Shibata, Takao Murakami, Osamu Tanaka, Goro Chihara and Masashi Sumimoto, *ibid.* **3** 274 (1955).

Yazuru Yamamoto, Akira Hamaguchi, Isao Yamamoto and Sumie Imai, *J. Pharm. Soc. Japan* **76** 1428 (1956).

Shoji Shibata and Isao Kitagawa, *Pharm. Bull.* (Tokyo) **4** 309 (1956). (Structure)

587 Rubroskyrin, $C_{30}H_{22}O_{12}$, dark red plates, m.p. 289° (dec.).

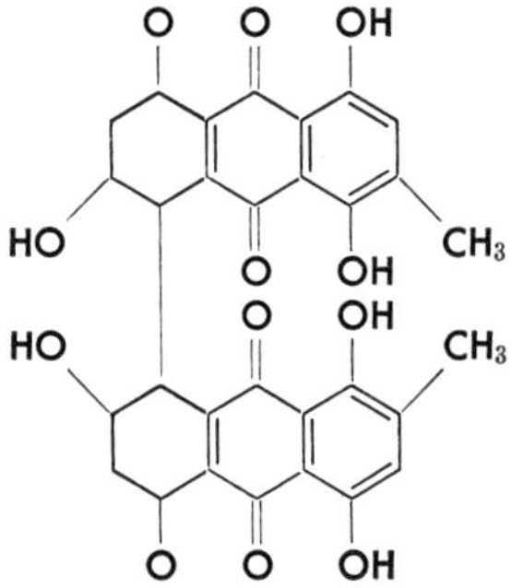

Penicillium islandicum Sopp.

This pigment is produced in a mixture including islandicin, iridoskyrin, erythroskyrin, catenarin, luteoskyrin and skyrin. The weight of the pigment mixture is about 10% of the weight of the dry mycelium.

Shoji Shibata and Isao Kitagawa, *Pharm. Bull.* (Tokyo) 4 309 (1956).

588 Luteoskyrin, $C_{30}H_{22}O_{12}$, yellow needles, m.p. 273° (dec.), $[\alpha]_D^{25}$ −880° (in acetone).

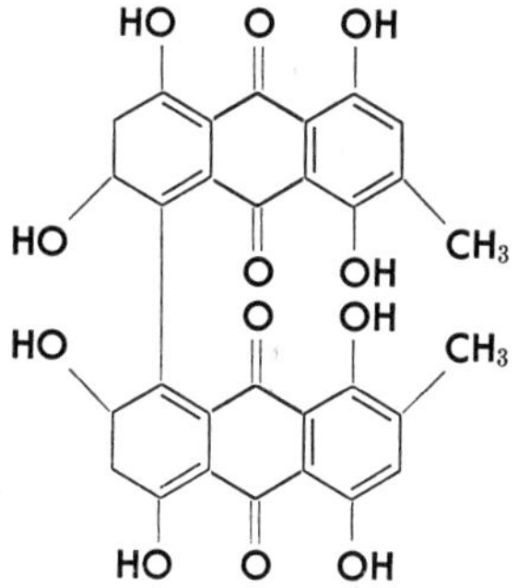

Penicillium islandicum Sopp.

Shoji Shibata and Isao Kitagawa, *Pharm. Bull.* (Tokyo) 4 309 (1956). (Structure)

589 Cercosporin, $C_{30}H_{28}O_{10}$, red crystals, m.p. 241°, $[\alpha]_{7000}^{20}$ +470° (c 0.5 in chloroform).

This pigment contains two methoxyl groups, two quinoid carbonyls, two phenolic hydroxyls and two alcoholic hydroxyls. The yield was 79 mg. per gram of dry mycelium.

Shimpei Kuyama and Teiichi Tamura, *J. Am. Chem. Soc.* 79 5725, 5726 (1957).

590, 591 Chaetochrysin and Chaetoflavin, $C_{31}H_{26}O_{11}$, yellow crystals, no
592   melting point, and **Chaetoalbin,** $C_{30}H_{28-30}O_{11}$, white crystals, no melting point.

These uncharacterized compounds were isolated from mycelial extracts along with chrysophanol. They seem to be modified dianthraquinones. They yield some chrysophanol on alkaline oxidation, contain one methoxyl group and have high optical rotations.

Chaetomium affine Corda

Vincent Arkley, F. M. Dean, Peter Jones, Alexander Robertson and John Tetaz, *Croat. Chem. Acta* 29 141 (1957).

593 **Rifomycin B,** $C_{39}H_{51}O_{14}N$, m.p. 160–164° (dec.).
A dibasic acid (pKs 2.8, 6.7). Probably a quinone
(U.V. peaks at 400–460, also at 223, 234).
Streptomyces mediterranean
P. Sensi, A. Greco and R. Ballotta, 7th Annual Symposium
on Antibiotics, Washington, 1959.

594 **Vinacetin,** yellow platelets, m.p. 157°.
Apparently quinoid. Positive $FeCl_3$, violet color in
alkali, positive Molisch, Liebermann, Fehling. Negative
ninhydrin, Millon, Sakaguchi.
Streptomyces sp.
Kyuzo Omachi, *J. Antibiotics* (Japan) **6A** 73 (1953).

595 **Rhodophyscin,** red leaflets, m.p. 260° (dec.).
A quinone-like substance.
Physica endococcina
Wilhelm Zopf, *Ann.* **340** 276 (1905).

13

Tetracycline, Analogues and Related Substances

The tetracycline antibiotics display features indicative of an acetate origin. The oxygenation pattern is generally consistent as are the points of occurrence of methyl groups and halogen atoms. There is also at least a superficial resemblance to proved acetate derivatives such as the anthraquinones. So far the experimental evidence published concerning the biosynthetic origin of the tetracyclines has been limited, and some interesting obscurities remain.

The general concept of an acetate-derived precursor in the sense of a polyketomethylene chain is, in the case of oxytetracycline as follows:

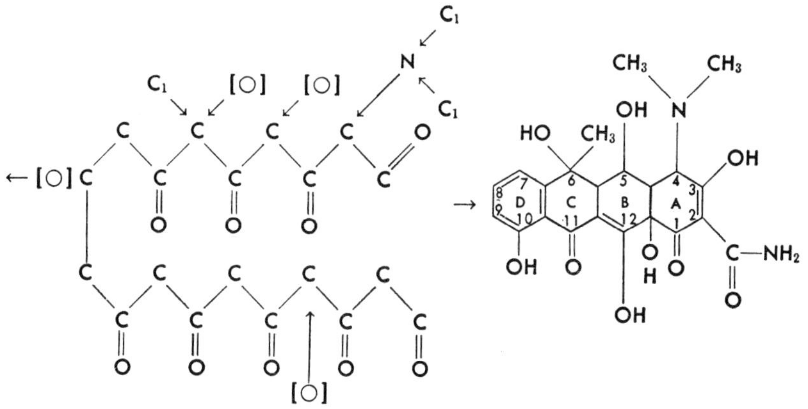

A 6-demethyltetracycline has been isolated from a fermentation broth, and tetracycline itself is a 5-deoxyoxytetracycline as well as a 7-dechlorochlortetracycline; so sometimes some of the steps in the biosynthetic scheme are omitted.

The production by *Streptomyces rimosus* of oxytetracycline-X[1], a modification of Terramycin in which there is an acetyl group instead of a carboxamide group at position 2, supports the acetate theory since terramycin-X is more directly in the line of descent from a polyketomethylene chain (ten head to tail condensed acetate units) than is Terramycin itself.

The dehydro derivatives which have been isolated[2] also may be considered as precursors of the other tetracyclines since the additional double bond may be the (as yet unreduced) result of an aldol type of condensative ring closure with elimination of a water molecule.

More experimental work has been reported on the biosynthetic origin of oxytetracycline than on that of related substances. Addition of $C^{14}H_3$-methionine and 2-C^{14}-acetic acid to oxytetracycline-producing fermentations yields radioactive oxytetracycline (Terramycin). Quantitative degradation and counting studies show that methionine furnishes the C_6-methyl and the N-methyl groups. The radioactivity of the degradation fragments from the molecule which had incorporated 2-C^{14}-acetic acid indicated that most of the molecule is in quantitative agreement with the theoretical requirements for acetate derivation.[3, 4]

Results are entirely consistent with formation of the ring skeleton at least from C_5 to C_{12} by head to tail linkage of acetate units. Glutamic acid has been considered as a possible precursor of part of the A-ring (carboxamide side-chain, carbon atoms 2, 3, 4, 4a and the 4-amino nitrogen) and 2-C^{14}-labeled glutamic acid yielded a labeled oxytetracycline.[5] Later evidence[6] indicates that acetate also is capable of furnishing these carbon atoms although the level of activity in the A-ring seems to be somewhat lower than the theoretical, particularly in Terramycin isolated from older fermentations. The degradation fragments

[1] F. A. Hochstein, M. Schach von Wittenau, Fred W. Tanner, Jr. and K. Murai, *J. Am. Chem. Soc.* 82 (1960). (In press)

[2] J. R. D. McCormick, Philip A. Miller, John A. Growich, Newell O. Sjölander and Albert P. Doerschuk, *ibid.* 80 5572 (1958).

[3] A. J. Birch, J. F. Snell and P. L. Thompson, *ibid.* 82 2402 (1960).

[4] A. J. Birch and P. L. Thompson, *ibid.* 82 (1960). (In press)

[5] J. F. Snell, R. L. Wagner, Jr. and F. A. Hochstein, *Internat. Conf. on Peaceful Uses of Atomic Energy*, 431 (1955); J. F. Snell, Symposium on Uses of Isotopes, Uniontown, Pa., 1957.

[6] A. J. Birch and P. L. Thompson, *J. Am. Chem. Soc.* 82 (1960). (In press)

from this portion of the molecule are not satisfactory for the clarification of the origin of the A-ring. It remains to be seen whether or not a less direct mechanism of acetate incorporation prevails in this area.

The isolation and identification of oxytetracycline-X (2-acetyl-2-decarboxamidooxytetracycline), a lower potency antibiotic, from cultures of *Streptomyces rimosus*, the Terramycin producer, seem to support in a general way the idea of the acetate derivation of ring A. It is tempting to speculate that oxytetra-

cycline-X may be a precursor of oxytetracycline, but this has not been proved.

With the acetate theory as a guide, it is possible to extrapolate some predictions from the tetracyclines isolated and characterized to date. It would seem probable that other mutations of the producing organisms might be obtained in which one minor biosynthetic step is blocked. Thus, retention of an oxygen atom at position 8 might be expected. Similarly, other tetracyclines lacking the C_6-methyl and/or hydroxyl groups, the C_{12a}-hydroxyl group and perhaps the N-methyl groups may be found. It is also possible that glycosides may be isolated as in the pyrromycinones.

The pyrromycinones are produced by streptomyces species, and they bear some resemblance to the tetracyclines. The four linear rings appearing in various states of oxidation and the similarity in the number of carbon atoms make it seem that their biogenetic origin may be similar to that of the tetracyclines. Apparently no experimental work has been published on this point. There is probably a close relationship among the pyrromycinones, rhodomycinones and quinocyclines. All of these pigments are found occasionally as glycosides, but no tetracycline glycosides have been reported yet.

The rhodomycins are a complex of red pigments produced by *Streptomyces purpurascens*. The original complex was separated into four components; rhodomycin A, isorhodomycin A, rhodomycin B and isorhodomycin B. The first three were isolated in the crystalline state. These substances contained nitrogen, and, on mild acid hydrolysis, yielded an amino sugar, rhodosamine, $C_8H_{17}O_3N$, plus the aglycones (rhodomycinones, isorhodomycinones).

The same organism has yielded a number of other pigments which do not contain nitrogen. These also have been designated rhodomycinones. Three of these, β, ϵ and *iso-ϵ* have been obtained crystalline. It has been reported (no experimental details) that a γ-rhodomycinone and six other rhodomycinones have been isolated "in substance" and that three others have been demonstrated by paper chromatography. The rhodomycinones seem to resemble the pyrromycinones, quinocyclines, cinerubins and rutilantinone.

596   **Rhodomycin A** (Hydrochloride), $C_{20}H_{29}O_7N \cdot HCl$, fine, dark red needles, m.p. 193° (dec.) (preheated block).

  Hans Brockmann and Ilse Borchers, *Chem. Ber.* **86** 261 (1953).

597   **Isorhodomycin A** (Hydrochloride), $C_{20}H_{29}O_8N \cdot HCl$ (proposed), m.p. 220°, $[\alpha]_{606-760}^{18}$ +268 ±30° (c 0.1 in methanol).

  Hans Brockmann and Peter Patt, *Chem. Ber.* **88** 1455 (1955).

598   **Rhodomycin B** (Hydrochloride), $C_{19}H_{27}O_7N \cdot HCl$, red prisms, m.p. 180°, $[\alpha]_{606-760}^{18}$ +174 ±10° (c 0.05 in methanol).

  An isorhodomycin B also was present.

  Hans Brockmann and Peter Patt, *Chem. Ber.* **88** 1455 (1955).

599   **β-Rhodomycinone,** $C_{20}H_{14}O_5$ (proposed), dark red needles, m.p. 225°.

  Hans Brockmann and Burchard Franck, *Chem. Ber.* **88** 1792 (1955). (Isolation)

  Hans Brockmann and P. Boldt, *Naturwissenschaften* 44 616 (1957). (Revised empirical formula)

600   **ϵ-Rhodomycinone,** $C_{21}H_{22}O_8$, thick red prisms, m.p. 185° (dec. at 208°)

and

601   **ϵ-Isorhodomycinone,** $C_{20}H_{20}O_9$, dark red leaflets, m.p. 245° (dec.).

Hans Brockmann and Burchard Franck, *Chem. Ber.* **88** 1792 (1955). (Isolation)
Other references:
Hans Brockmann and Klaus Bauer, *Naturwissenschaften* **37** 492 (1950).
Hans Brockmann, Klaus Bauer and Ilse Borchers, *Chem. Ber.* **84** 700 (1951).
Hans Brockmann and Enno Spohler, *Naturwissenschaften* **42** 154 (1955). (Characterization of rhodosamine)
Hans Brockmann, German Patent 913,813 (1954).

602 **7-Chloro-6-demethyltetracycline**, $C_{21}H_{21}O_8N_2Cl$ (isolated as the sesquihydrate), yellow crystals, m.p. 174–178° (dec.), $[\alpha]_D^{25}$ −258° (0.5% in 0.1 N sulfuric acid).

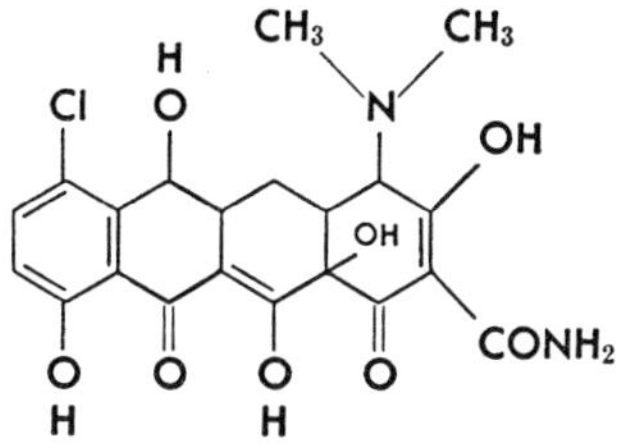

Streptomyces aureofaciens Duggar (mutant)
J. R. D. McCormick, Newell O. Sjölander, Ursula Hirsh, Elmer R. Jensen and Albert P. Doerschuk, *J. Am. Chem. Soc.* **79** 4561 (1957).

603 **6-Demethyltetracycline**, $C_{21}H_{22}O_8N_2Cl$ (isolated as the hydrochloride hemihydrate), yellow crystals, m.p. 203–209° (dec.), $[\alpha]_D$ −259° (c 0.5 in 0.1 N sulfuric acid).

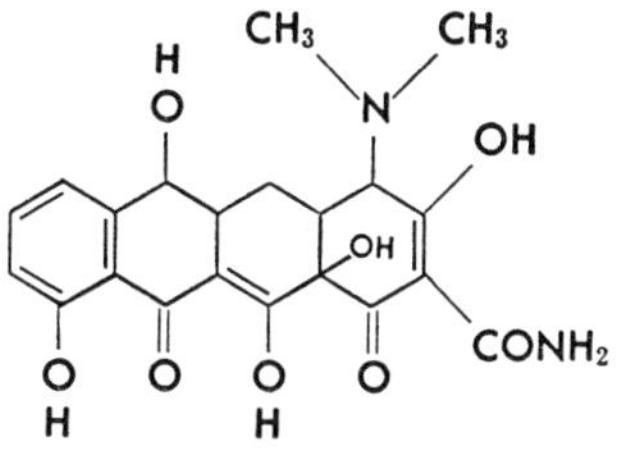

Streptomyces aureofaciens Duggar (mutant)
J. R. D. McCormick, Newell O. Sjölander, Ursula Hirsh, Elmer R. Jensen and Albert P. Doerschuk, *J. Am. Chem. Soc.* **79** 4561 (1957).

604 η-**Pyrromycinone,** $C_{22}H_{16}O_7$, red needles, m.p. 236° (sublimes).

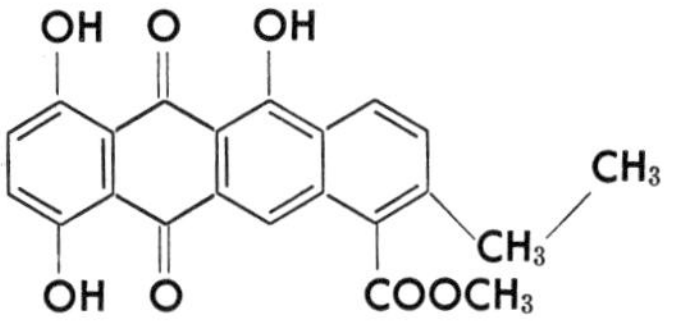

OH O OH

CH₃

CH₃

OH O   COOCH₃

Streptomyces spp.
Hans Brockmann and Werner Lenk, *Chem. Ber.* **92** 1880 (1959). (Structure)
Hans Brockmann and Hans Brockmann, Jr., *Naturwissenschaften* **47** 135 (1960). (Revised structure)

605 ζ-**Pyrromycinone,** $C_{22}H_{20}O_8$, orange-red needles, m.p. 216° (sublimes), $[\alpha]_{Cd}^{20}$ +74 ±6° (in chloroform).

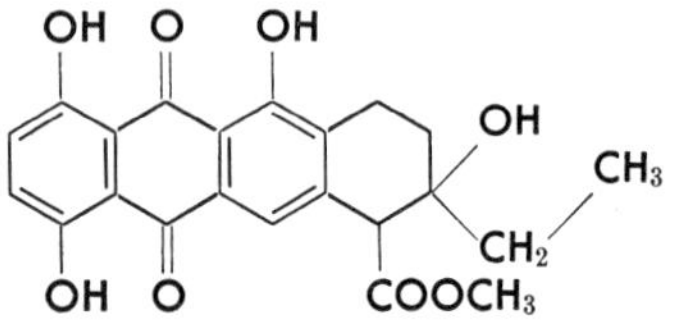

OH O OH

OH

CH₃

CH₂

OH O   COOCH₃

Streptomyces spp.
Brockmann and collaborators have isolated about a dozen pigments of this type from various unclassified streptomycetes.
Hans Brockmann and Burchard Franck, *Chem. Ber.* **88** 1792 (1955).
H. Brockmann, Luis Costa Plà and W. Lenk, *Angew. Chem.* **69** 477 (1957).
H. Brockmann and P. Boldt, *Naturwissenschaften* **44** 616 (1957).
Hans Brockmann and Werner Lenk, *Chem. Ber.* **92** 1880 (1959). (Structure)
Idem., Naturwissenschaften **47** 135 (1960). (Revised structure)

606 ε-**Pyrromycinone** (Rutilantinone), $C_{22}H_{20}O_9$, orange-red needles, m.p. 213°, $[\alpha]_{Cd}^{20}$ +143 ±7° (c 1.0 in chloroform).

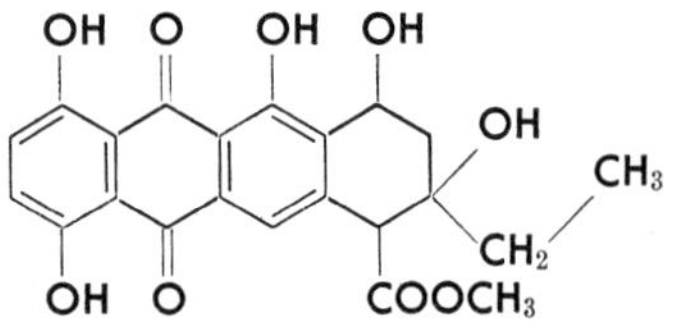

OH O OH OH

OH

CH₃

CH₂

OH O   COOCH₃

Streptomyces spp.

ϵ-Pyrromycinone occurs as such and also as the chromophore of the antibiotics pyrromycin and the cinerubins. It is identical with rutilantinone.

Hans Brockmann and Werner Lenk, *Chem. Ber.* **92** 1880 (1959). (Structure)

Idem., Naturwissenschaften **47** 135 (1960). (Revised structure)

H. Brockmann, H. Brockmann, Jr., J. J. Gordon, W. Keller-Schierlein, W. Lenk, W. D. Ollis, V. Prelog and I. O. Sutherland, *Tetrahedron Letters* No. 8, p. 25 (1960).

W. D. Ollis, I. O. Sutherland and J. J. Gordon, *Tetrahedron Letters* No. 16, p. 17 (1959).

607 **7-Chloro-5a(11a)-dehydrotetracycline,** $C_{22}H_{21}O_8N_2Cl$, $[\alpha]_D^{25}$ 15.5° (c 0.65 in 0.03 N hydrochloric acid).

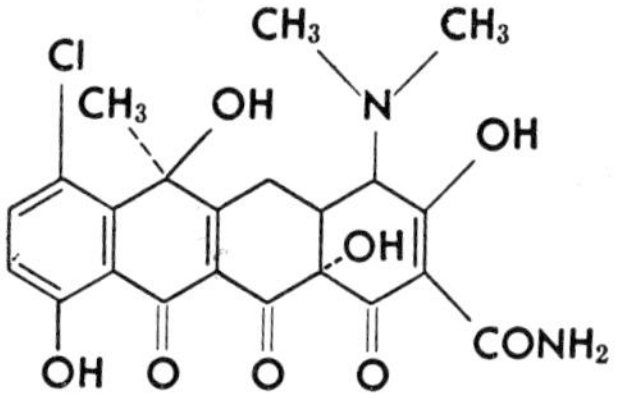

Streptomyces aureofaciens Duggar mutant

The analogous compounds in which the chlorine atom is replaced by H and Br are also claimed.

J. R. D. McCormick, Philip A. Miller, John A. Growich, Newell O. Sjölander and Albert P. Doerschuk, *J. Am. Chem. Soc.* **80** 5572 (1958).

608 **Chlortetracycline** (Aureomycin, Biomycin), $C_{22}H_{23}O_8N_2Cl$, fine yellow crystals, m.p. 168°, $[\alpha]_D^{23}$ −274.9° (in methanol).

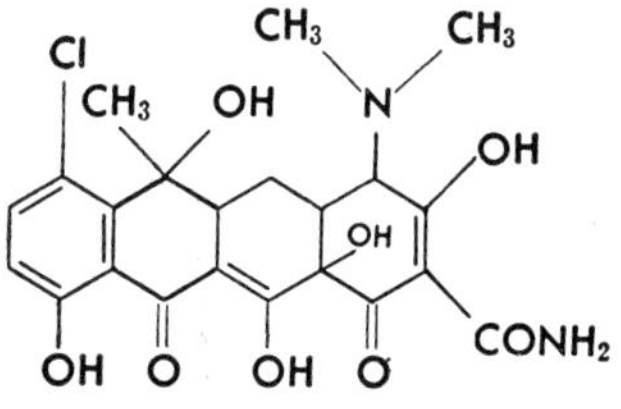

Streptomyces aureofaciens

R. W. Broschard, A. C. Dornbush, S. Gordon, B. L. Hutchings, A. R. Kohler, G. Krupka, S. Kuchner, D. V. Lefemine and C. Pidacks, *Science* **109** 199 (1949). (Isolation)

Benjamin M. Duggar, U. S. Patent 2,482,055 (1949).

C. R. Stephens, L. H. Conover, F. A. Hochstein, P. P. Regna, F. J. Pilgrim, K. J. Brunings and R. B. Woodward, *J. Am. Chem. Soc.* **74** 4976 (1952).

C. W. Waller, B. L. Hutchings, R. W. Broschard, A. A. Goldman, W. J. Stein, C. F. Wolf and J. H. Williams, *ibid.* 74 4981 (1952).

609 Bromotetracycline, $C_{22}H_{23}O_8N_2Br$, m.p. 170–172°, $[\alpha]_D^{20}$ −196° (in 0.1 N hydrochloric acid).

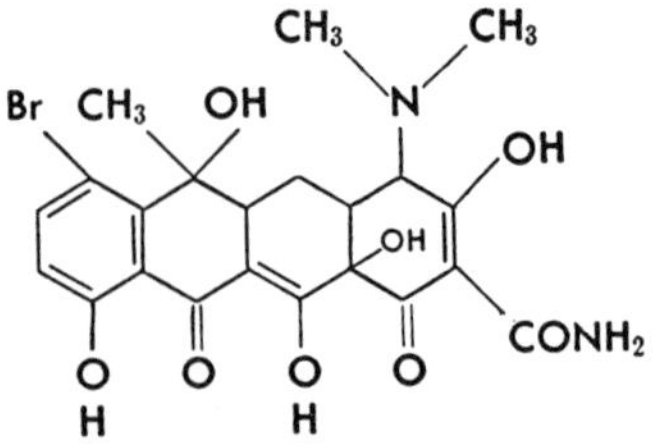

Streptomyces aureofaciens
P. Sensi, G. A. DeFerrari, G. G. Gallo and G. Rolland, *Il Farmaco Ed. sci.* (Pavia) 10 337 (1955).

610 Oxytetracycline (Terramycin), $C_{22}H_{24}O_9N_2$, light-yellow crystals, m.p. (anhydride) ∼185° (dec.), $[\alpha]_D^{25}$ (dihydrate) −196.6° (c 1.0 in 0.1 N hydrochloric acid).

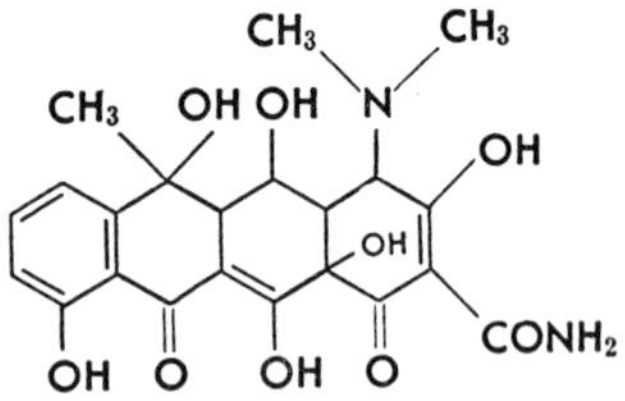

Streptomyces rimosus
A. C. Finlay, G. L. Hobby, S. Y. P'An, P. P. Regna, J. B. Routien, D. B. Seeley, G. M. Shull, B. A. Sobin, I. A. Solomons, J. W. Vinson and J. H. Kane, *Science* 111 85 (1950). (Isolation)

Ben A. Sobin, Alexander C. Finlay and Jasper H. Kane, U. S. Patent 2,516,080 (1950).

Peter P. Regna, I. A. Solomons, Kotaro Murai, Albert E. Timreck, Karl J. Brunings and W. A. Lazier, *J. Am. Chem. Soc.* 73 4211 (1951).

C. R. Stephens, L. H. Conover, F. A. Hochstein, P. P. Regna, F. J. Pilgrim, K. J. Brunings and R. B. Woodward, *ibid.* 74 4976 (1952).

F. A. Hochstein, C. R. Stephens, L. H. Conover, P. P. Regna, R. Pasternack, P. N. Gordon, F. J. Pilgrim, K. J. Brunings and R. B. Woodward, *ibid.* 75 5455 (1953). (Structure)

611 Antibiotic X-340, $C_{23}H_{20}O_6$, yellow needles, m.p. 330° (dec.). An antibiotic isolated from the mycelium of an uniden-

tified streptomycete. The molecular weight was about
390. Contained 3 —OH groups (one acidic) and one
C—CH$_3$ group. Monomethyl derivative with diazomethane. Mono- and tri-acetates were formed, depending on
method. The infrared absorption pattern was similar to
that of Terramycin. The following partial structure was
proposed:

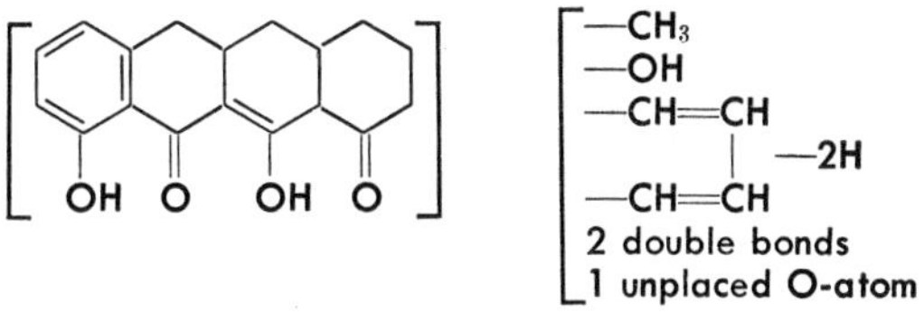

V. C. Vora, K. Shete and M. M. Dhar, *J. Sci. Ind. Research*
(India) **16C** 182 (1957). (Isolation)

612 **2-Acetyl-2-decarboxamidooxytetracycline** (Terramycin-X) (Hydrochloride), C$_{23}$H$_{25}$O$_9$N·HCl, yellow crystals, m.p. 201–
203°, [α]$_D^{25}$ −46.6° (c 0.9 in 0.1 N hydrochloric acid).

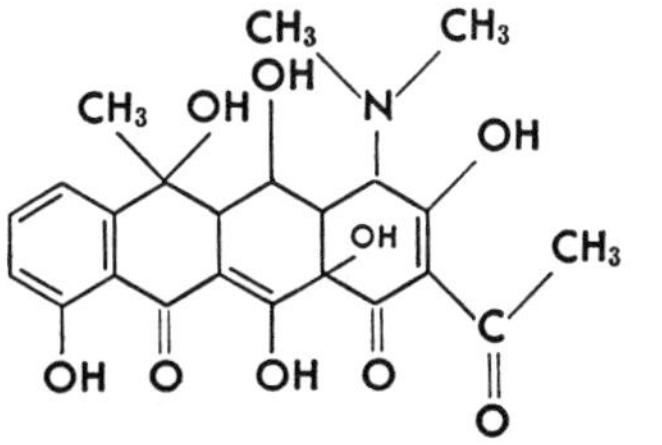

Streptomyces rimosus
F. A. Hochstein, M. Schach von Wittenau, F. W. Tanner, Jr.
and K. Murai, *J. Am. Chem. Soc.* **82** (1960). (In press)

613 **Tetracycline** (Achromycin, Tetracyn, Polycycline, Panmycin),
C$_{22}$H$_{24}$O$_8$N$_2$, yellow crystals, m.p. 170–175° (dec.), [α]$_D^{25}$
−239° (c 1.0 in methanol).

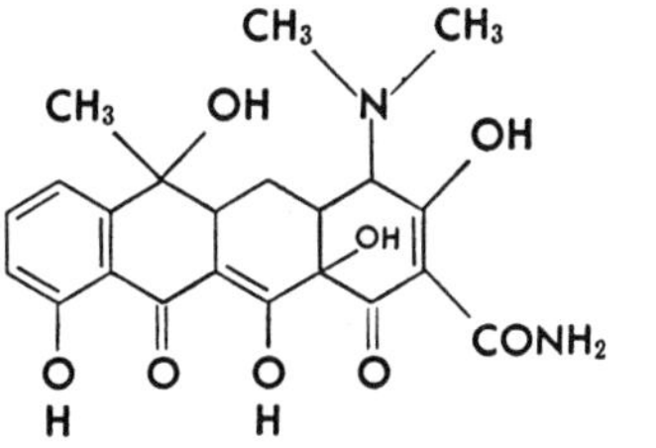

Streptomyces sp.

Tetracycline was first prepared by catalytic dechlorination of chlortetracycline but was later isolated as a primary fermentation product.

P. Paul Minieri, Melvin C. Firman, A. G. Mistretta, Anthony Abbey, Clark E. Bricker, Neil E. Rigler and Herman Sokol, "Antibiotics Annual 1953–1954," Medical Encyclopedia, Inc., New York, p. 81. (Isolation)

614 Quinocyclines (PA-121)

A complex of tetracyclic amphoteric antibiotic yellow pigments, which in some respects resemble nitrogen-containing hydroxyanthraquinones.

Six active components have been separated and analyses and color reactions were determined.

Two components have an aglycone with the probable empirical formula $C_{25}H_{20}O_6N_2$.

Streptomyces sp.

W. D. Celmer, K. Murai, K. V. Rao, F. W. Tanner, Jr. and W. S. Marsh, "Antibiotics Annual 1957–1958," Medical Encyclopedia, Inc., New York, p. 484. (Isolation)

Charles R. Stephens, unpublished. (Empirical formula)

615 η-Pyrromycin, $C_{30}H_{35}O_{11}N$ (Hydrochloride), red crystals, m.p. 162° (dec.), $[\alpha]_{cd}^{20}$ +132 ±27° (c 0.4 in methanol).

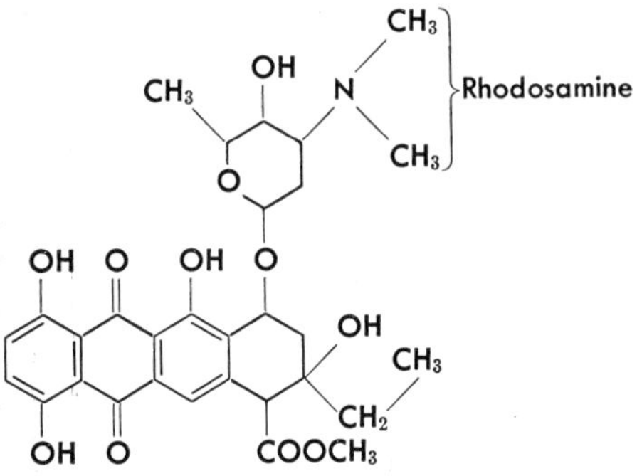

CH₃

OH   N⟩CH₃

CH₃   ⟩Rhodosamine

CH₃

O

OH O OH O

OH

CH₃

CH₂

OH O   COOCH₃

A streptomycete

The relationship to ϵ-pyrromycinone and to the cinerubins should be noted.

Hans Brockmann and Werner Lenk, *Chem. Ber.* 92 1904 (1959). (Structure)

Hans Brockmann and Hans Brockmann, Jr., *Naturwissenschaften* 47 135 (1960).

616 Aklavin, $C_{30}H_{37}O_{11}N$ (Hydrochloride) orange crystals, m.p. 197°.

Amphoteric. Contains an amino sugar, $C_8H_{17}O_4N$, isomeric with mycaminose or amosamine linked glycosidically to the secondary hydroxyl group.

Streptomyces sp.

F. Strelitz, H. Flon, U. Weiss and I. N. Asheshor, *J. Bacteriol.* **72** 90 (1956).

617 Cinerubins

Cinerubins A and B are isomeric red bases, with the empirical formula $C_{44}H_{59}O_{18}N \pm CH_2$. The chromophoric aglycone has been shown to be identical with ϵ-pyrromycinone. Both cinerubins also contain three sugars, two of these being the same in both compounds, but the third one being characteristic. The structures of these sugars have not been reported yet.

Streptomyces antibioticus (Waksman and Woodruff) Waksman et Henrici, *S. galiloeus* Ettlinger *et al.*, *S. niveoruber* Ettlinger *et al.*

Leopold Ettlinger, Ernest Gäumann, Ralf Hütter, Walter Keller-Schierlein, Friederich Kradolfer, Lucien Neipp, Vlado Prelog, Pierre Reusser and Hans Zähner, *Chem. Ber.* **92** 1867 (1959).

14

Aromatic Compounds Not Classified Elsewhere

This chapter includes a heterogeneous group of aromatic compounds which arise from different biosynthetic routes. Cinnamic acid and its derivatives undoubtedly are formed by way of the shikimic acid pathway.[1,2] The occurrence of anisaldehyde and anisic acid derivatives in the same fermentation with methyl p-methoxycinnamate suggests that the former may be degradation products of the latter.

Chloramphenicol, too, has a C_6-C_3 skeleton which seems to relate it to the shikimic acid pathway. It has been shown that p-nitrophenylserinol does not act as a precursor, and, when it is added to fermentations, it is acetylated but not dichloroacetylated. C^{14}-Labeled p-nitrophenylserinol is not incorporated into the chloramphenicol molecule nor is C^{14}-labeled dichloroacetic acid. Thus, what appears to be a logical step in the biosynthesis—the dichloroacetylation of p-nitrophenylserinol—does not occur.[3]

The tricarboxylic acid produced by *Chaetomium indicum* is evidently formed by the condensation of α-ketoglutaric acid with phenylpyruvic acid.

The lichen acids of this chapter show a provocative symmetry, and the incorporation of amino acids into two of them is interesting. The diphenylbutadiene structure has been found also in xanthocillin. Apparently there has been no experimental study of their biogenesis.

[1] Friedrich Weygand and Heinz Wendt, Z. *Naturforsch.* 14b 421 (1959).

[2] T. A. Geissman and T. Swain, *Chem. and Ind.*, 984 (1957).

[3] David Gottlieb, P. W. Robbins and H. E. Carter, *J. Bacteriol.* 72 153 (1956).

618   **Benzoic Acid,** $C_7H_6O_2$, colorless tablets, m.p. 122.5°.

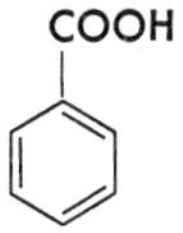

COOH

Yeast
Richard Kuhn and Klaus Schwarz, *Ber.* 74 1617 (1941).

619   **Anisaldehyde,** $C_8H_8O_2$, oily liquid, b.p. 248°, n_D^{13} 1.5764.

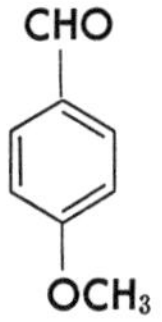

CHO

OCH₃

Trametes suavolens (Linn.) Fr., *Lentinus lepideus,*
Daedalea juniperina
J. H. Birkinshaw, A. Bracken and W. P. K. Findlay,
Biochem. J. 38 131 (1944).
J. H. Birkinshaw and P. Chaplen, *ibid.* 60 255 (1955).

620   *trans*-**Cinnamic Acid,** $C_9H_8O_2$, colorless crystals, m.p. 133°.

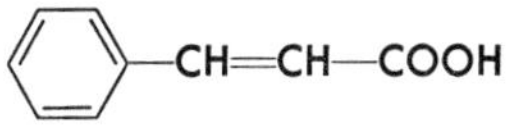

—CH=CH—COOH

Ceratostomella fimbriata (on sweet potato culture)
Takashi Kubota and Keizo Naya, *Chem. and Ind.,* 1427
(1954).

621   *trans*-**Cinnamic Acid Amide,** C_9H_9ON, colorless crystals, m.p.
147–149°.

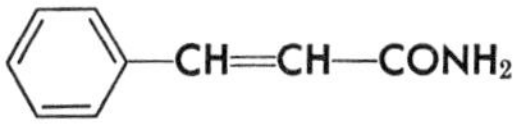

—CH=CH—CONH₂

Streptomyces sp.
Yasuharu Sekizawa, *J. Biochem.* Japan 45 9 (1958). (Isolation)

622   **Methyl Anisate,** $C_9H_{10}O_3$, colorless crystals, m.p. 48°, b.p. 256°.

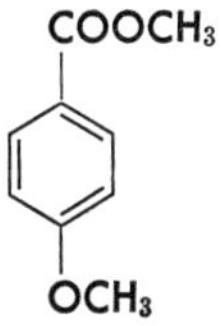

COOCH₃

OCH₃

Trametes suavolens (Linn.) Fr., *Lentinus lepideus*
J. H. Birkinshaw, A. Bracken and W. P. K. Findlay, *Biochem. J.* 38 131 (1944).

623 **Methyl *trans*-Cinnamate,** $C_{10}H_{10}O_2$, clear, pale yellow oil, b.p. 94–110° (2–3 mm.) or white crystals, m.p. 35–37°, n_D^{21} 1.5766

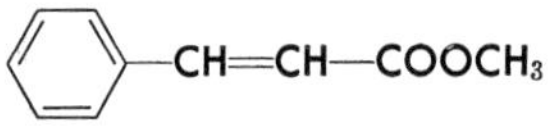

Lentinus lepideus Fr. (artificial medium)
John Howard Birkinshaw and Walter Philip Kennedy Findlay, *Biochem. J.* 34 82 (1940).

624 **Methyl *p*-Coumarate,** $C_{10}H_{10}O_3$, colorless crystals, m.p. 137–139°.

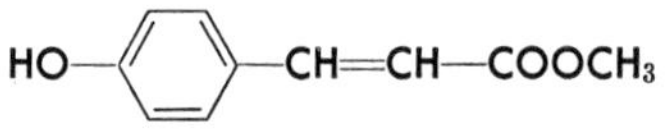

Lentinus lepideus
H. Shimazono and F. F. Nord, *Arch. Biochem. and Biophys.* 78 263 (1958).

625 **Methyl *p*-Methoxycinnamate,** $C_{11}H_{12}O_3$, colorless crystals, m.p. 88°.

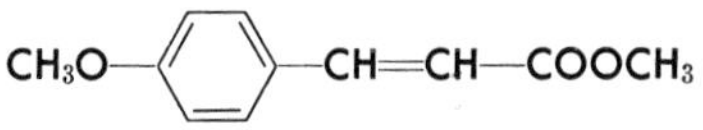

Lentinus lepideus Fr. (artificial medium)
John Howard Birkinshaw and Walter Philip Kennedy Findlay, *Biochem. J.* 34 82 (1940).

626 **Chloramphenicol** (Chloromycetin, Levomycetin), $C_{11}H_{12}O_5N_2Cl_2$, colorless crystals, m.p. 149.7°, $[\alpha]_D^{25}$ −25.5° (in ethyl acetate).

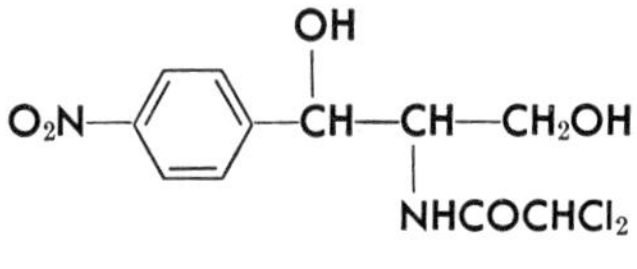

Streptomyces venezuelae
John Ehrlich, Quentin R. Bartz, Robert M. Smith, Dwight A. Joslyn and Paul R. Burkholder, *Science* 106 417 (1947). (Isolation)
John Controulis, Mildred C. Rebstock and Harry M. Crooks, Jr., *J. Am. Chem. Soc.* 71 2463 (1949). (Synthesis)

Loren M. Long and H. D. Troutman, *ibid.* 71 2469 (1949).

627 **1,8-Dimethoxynaphthalene,** $C_{12}H_{12}O_2$, colorless crystals, m.p. 158–161°.

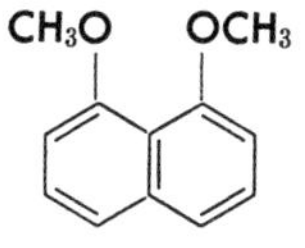

Daldinia concentrica
8-Methoxyl-1-naphthol also was identified (by paper chromatography).

D. C. Allport and J. D. Bu'Lock, *J. Chem. Soc.*, 654 (1960).

628 **4-Carboxy-2-oxo-3-phenylhept-3-enedioic Acid,** $C_{14}H_{12}O_7$, colorless prisms, m.p. 170° (dec.).

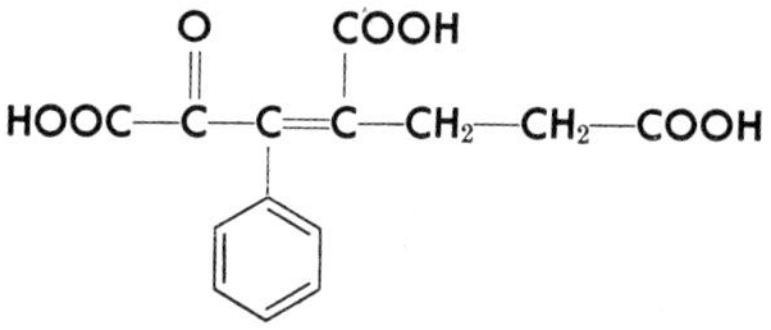

Chaetomium indicum Corda
The yield was 250–500 mg. per liter. In addition to the acid above, two uncharacterized compounds were isolated in smaller quantities: Metabolite A, $C_{26}H_{37}O_6N$, pale yellow needles, m.p. 159°, $[\alpha]_D^{20}$ +11.4° (c 1.022 in chloroform). Yield 1.5–2.0 g. from 100 l. of broth. Soluble in aqueous $NaHCO_3$. Wine red $FeCl_3$ test. Formed an insoluble green-blue copper derivative.

Metabolite B, colorless prisms, m.p. 146°, $[\alpha]_D^{20}$ +120° (c 1.01 in chloroform).

Analysis: C 68.1, H 8.2, N 2.7, C-methyl 12%. Same color tests as A above.

D. H. Johnson, Alexander Robertson and W. B. Whalley, *J. Chem. Soc.*, 2429 (1953).

629 **Pulvic Anhydride,** $C_{18}H_{10}O_4$, yellow needles, m.p. 222–224°.

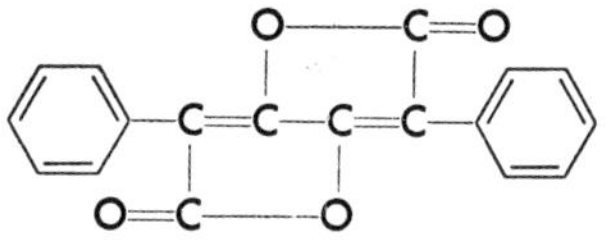

Sticta aurata Ach.

O. Hesse, *J. prakt. Chem.* **170** 334 (1900).

630 Calycin, $C_{18}H_{10}O_5$, orange-red crystals, m.p. 244°.

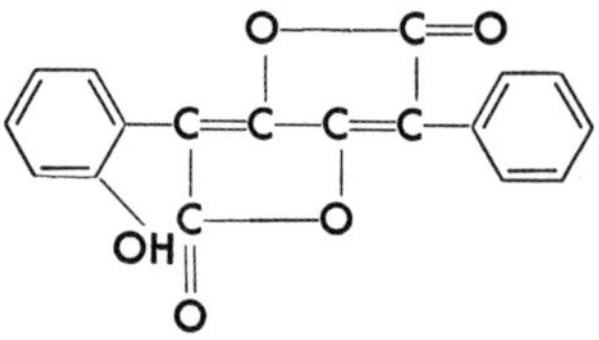

Lepraria candelaris Schaer., *Sticta aurata* Ach. and *Sticta crocata* Ach.

Mitizo Asano and Yukio Kameda, *Ber.* **68** 1568 (1935).

631 Vulpinic Acid, $C_{19}H_{14}O_5$, yellow crystals, m.p. 148°.

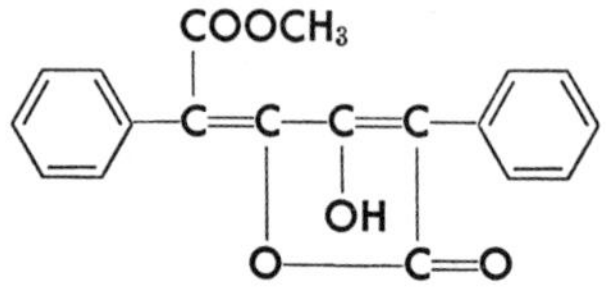

Evernia vulpina L., *Cyphelium chrysocephalum* Ach., *Calicium chlorinum* Körper, *Cetraria juniperina* Fr. var. *tubulosa* Schaer and *Cetraria pinastri* (Scop.)

P. Karrer, K. A. Gehrckens and W. Heuss, *Helv. Chim. Acta* **9** 446 (1926). (Structure)

632 Pinastric Acid (Chrysocetraric Acid), $C_{20}H_{16}O_6$, orange needles, m.p. 200–203°.

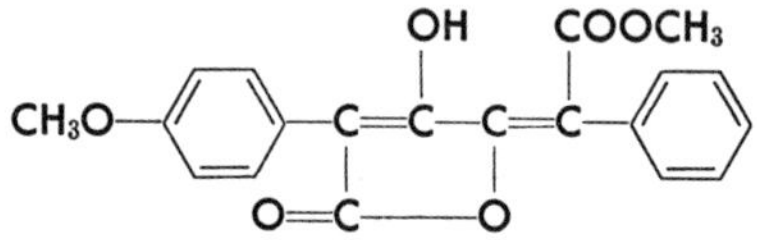

Lepraria flava (Schreber.) f. *quercina, Cetraria pinastri* (Scop.), *Cetraria tubulosa* (Schreb.), *Cetraria juniperina* L. (Ach.)

Mitizo Asano and Yukio Kameda, *Ber.* **68** 1565 (1935). (Structure)

633 Leprapic Acid (Leprapinic Acid, Methyl 2-Methoxypulvinate), $C_{20}H_{16}O_6$, golden plates, m.p. 159°.

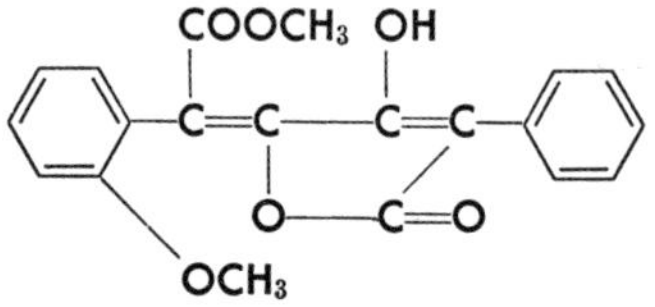

Lepraria citrina
O. P. Mittal and T. R. Seshadri, *J. Chem. Soc.*, 3053 (1955).
(Isolation)
  Idem., ibid., 1734 (1956). (Synthesis)

634 Mycolutein, $C_{22}H_{24}O_6N$ (proposed), bright yellow tablets, m.p. 157°, $[\alpha]_D^{25}$ +54° (c 1 in chloroform).
  Contains an aromatic nucleus. Alkali-unstable. Negative $FeCl_3$. Decolorizes bromine with HBr evolution.
Streptomyces sp.
  Henry Schmitz and Robert Woodside, *Antibiotics and Chemotherapy* 5 652 (1955).

635 Epanorin, $C_{25}H_{25}O_6N$, yellow needles, m.p. 135°, $[\alpha]_D^{26}$ −1.86 ±0.2° (c 6.48 in chloroform).

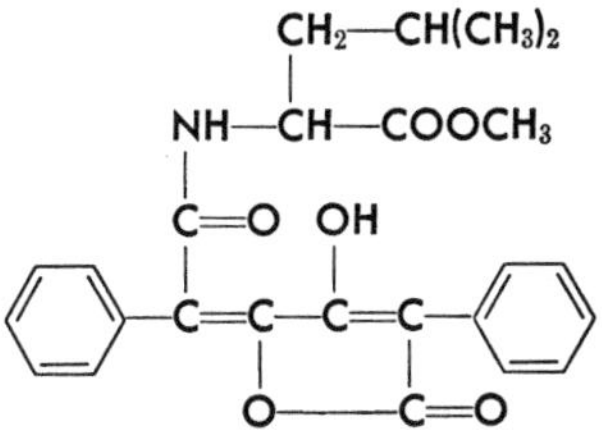

$$CH_2\!-\!CH(CH_3)_2$$
$$NH\!-\!CH\!-\!COOCH_3$$
$$C\!=\!O \quad OH$$

Lecanora epanora Ach.
Zeorin was found in the same extract.
  Robert L. Frank, S. Mark Cohen and James N. Coker, *J. Am. Chem. Soc.* 72 4454 (1950). (Structure and synthesis)

636 Rhizocarpic Acid, $C_{28}H_{23}O_6N$, yellow needles, m.p. 177°, $[\alpha]_D^{20}$ +110.4° ±2.1° (c 1.22 in chloroform).

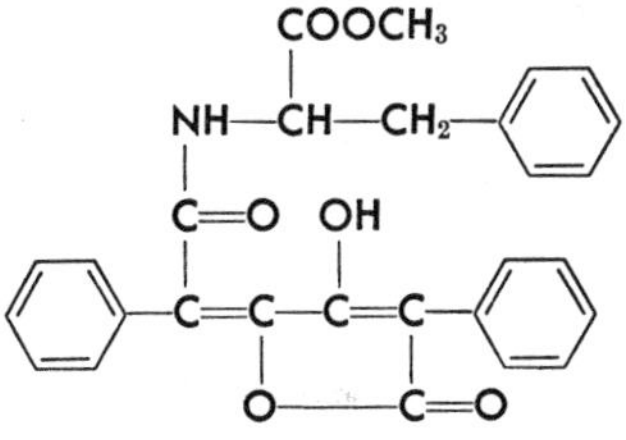

$$COOCH_3$$
$$NH\!-\!CH\!-\!CH_2\!-$$
$$C\!=\!O \quad OH$$

Rhizocarpon geographicum L., *R. viridiatrum* Flk., *Calicium hyperellum* Ach.
  Robert L. Frank, S. Mark Cohen and James N. Coker, *J. Am. Chem. Soc.* 72 4454 (1950). (Synthesis)

15

Amines

Much remains to be learned concerning the earlier stages of nitrogen metabolism in microorganisms. Practically, the ability of certain soil bacteria (in combination with legumes) to fix gaseous nitrogen has been exploited for many years. Research in this area has been reviewed.[1] Ammonia, methane, hydrogen and water probably were present in the atmosphere of the primitive earth, and it has been shown[2] that amino acids can be formed by electric discharges through such mixtures.

While we are primarily concerned in this compilation with metabolites isolated from microorganisms growing in the wild state or cultivated on an essentially glucose medium, the more complex amines are generally only remotely derived from sugar, often by way of the amino acids. A large literature exists on the ability of bacteria to decarboxylate amino acids to amines, these experiments generally involving addition of the amino acid to the medium. It has been shown,[3] however, that many bacteria which produce amines on a casein hydrolysate medium do not do so on a synthetic medium with ammonium salts the only nitrogen source. Studies with Escherichia coli[4] indicate that aspartic acid and alanine and perhaps glutamic acid serve as important nitrogen entry vehicles. These acids can supply the total nitrogen requirement if no ammonium ion is available,

[1] William D. McElroy and Bentley Glass, "Inorganic Nitrogen Metabolism," Johns Hopkins Press, Baltimore, 1956.

[2] Stanley L. Miller, Science 117 528 (1953); idem., J. Am. Chem. Soc. 77 2351 (1955).

[3] H. Proom and A. J. Woiwod, J. Gen. Microbiol. 5 930 (1951).

[4] "Studies of Biosynthesis in E. coli," Carnegie Institute of Washington Publication 607, Washington, 1955.

and, even when it is, much of the cellular nitrogen is derived from them by transamination.

Within the frame of our present endeavor there seems to have been little systematic, comparative study of the amine metabolites of microorganisms. This has been true particularly of the fungi, which generally have been considered to have a poorer nitrogen metabolism than the bacteria. Apparently this situation is being remedied, at least for higher fungi. Recently the amine content of 105 species, representing 18 families of higher fungi, was investigated.[5] It was found that ammonia was distributed universally, and that the ammonia content increased with the age of the fruiting body. Methylamine occurred in 22 species, dimethylamine in 10, trimethylamine in 8, isoamylamine in 19 and β-phenylethylamine in 4. Earlier work was reviewed also, a distinction being made between the amines present in fresh fruiting bodies and those present after autolysis.

Also an exceptionally thorough analysis was made recently of the basic constituents of the fruiting body of a single basidiomycete, *Polyporus sulfureus*.[6] These included amines, basic amino acids, nucleotides and betaines. Many of the simple amines produced by *Claviceps purpurea* have been identified during the extensive studies of ergot, and these are listed in the introduction to the section on ergot alkaloids in the chapter on Heterocycles.

Muscarine, a compound which might have been classified under several different chapter headings, is apparently a derivative of a 1-amino-3,6-desoxyhexose and is probably more directly connected with sugar metabolism than many of the amines listed here.

Amino sugars and other complex amines are listed elsewhere under more appropriate classifications.

It has been shown that putrescine furnishes the 4-carbon atom moiety of spermine and spermidine in *Neurospora crassa*,[7] and that methionine supplies the 3-carbon chain of spermidine in the same organism.[8] It is known that ATP and Mg^{++} are re-

[5] Elard Stein von Kamienski, *Planta* **50** 331 (1958).

[6] P. H. List, *Planta Med.* **6** 424 (1958).

[7] H. Tabor, S. M. Rosenthal and C. W. Tabor, *Federation Proc.* **15** 367 (1956).

[8] Ronald C. Greene, *J. Am. Chem. Soc.* **79** 3929 (1957).

quired. A mechanism such as the one shown here (abbreviated)

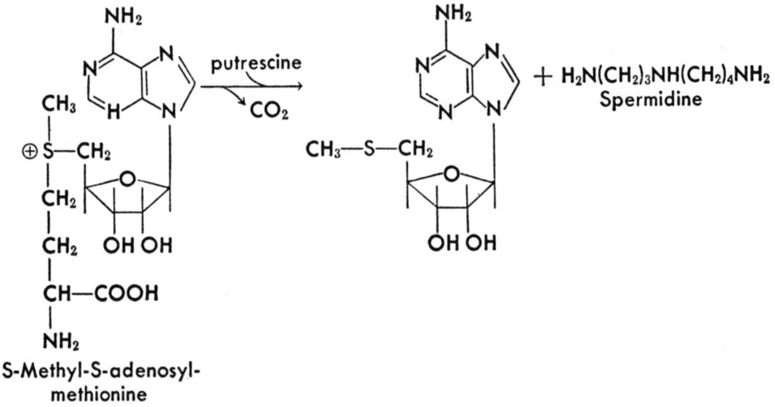

S-Methyl-S-adenosyl-
methionine

may be operative.

637 Ammonia, NH_3, colorless gas.

$$NH_3$$

Widely distributed in the fruiting bodies of the higher fungi and lichens. The content increases with age.

Elard Stein von Kamienski, *Planta* 50 331 (1958).

638 Methylamine, CH_5N, colorless gas.

$$CH_3NH_2$$

Russula (11 spp.), *Lactarius deliciosus, L. vellereus, L. helvus, Boletus edulis, B. appendiculatus, Scleroderma vulgare, Anthurus muellerianus, Mutinus caninus, Trachypus versipellis, Dermocybe (Cortinarius) cinnamomea, Lepiota clypeolaria, Pholiota mutabilis, Sticta fuliginosa, S. sylvatica, Polyporus sulfureus*

Elard Stein von Kamienski, *Planta* 50 331 (1958).

P. H. List, *Planta Med.* 6 424 (1958).

639 Ethylamine, C_2H_7N, volatile liquid, b.p. 16.6°.

$$CH_3CH_2NH_2$$

Claviceps purpurea, Polyporus sulfureus

Maximilian Steiner and Elard Stein von Kamienski, *Naturwissenschaften* 42 345 (1955).

P. H. List, *Planta Med.* 6 424 (1958).

640 Dimethylamine, C_2H_7N, colorless gas, b.p. 7°.

CH₃—NH—CH₃

Phallus impudicus, Clathrus ruber, Russula aurata
Gustav Klein and Max Steiner, *Jahrb. wiss. Bot.* **68** 602
(1928).
*R. sardonia, R. turci, R. lepida, R. cyanoxantha, R.
grisea, R. olivacea, R. vesca, R. alutacea, Sticta sylvatica,
Polyporus sulfureus*
Elard Stein von Kamienski, *Planta* **50** 333 (1958).
P. H. List, *Planta Med.* **6** 424 (1958).

641 Ethanolamine, C_2H_7ON, colorless oil, b.p. 171°, n_D^{20} 1.4539.

HOCH₂CH₂NH₂

Neurospora crassa (and probably in) *Boletus edulis,
B. versipellis, Xerocomus badius, Lepiota clypeoloris,
Pholiota mutabilis, Tricholoma nudum, Russula macu-
lata, R. turci, Lactarius vellercus, Amanita muscaria,
Polyporus sulfureus*
George L. Ellman and Herschel K. Mitchell, *J. Am. Chem.
Soc.* **76** 4028 (1954).
Elard Stein von Kamienski, *Planta* **50** 331 (1958).
P. H. List, *Planta Med.* **6** 424 (1958).

642 Aminoacetone, C_3H_7ON, colorless crystals, m.p. 130.5°.

CH₃COCH₂NH₂

Staphylococcus aureus
W. H. Elliot, *Nature* **183** 1051 (1959).

643 Trimethylamine, C_3H_9N, colorless gas (fishy odor), b.p. 3°.

*Boletus edulis, Ustilago maydis, Phallus impudicus,
Claviceps purpurea, Tilletia laevis, T. tritici, Clathrus
ruber, Russula* spp. *Sticta* spp.
J. Zellner, *Monatsh.* **31** 617 (1910).
William Fielding Hanna, Hubert Bradford Vickery and
George W. Pucher, *J. Biol. Chem.* **97** 351 (1932). (Isolation)
Maximilian Steiner and Elard Stein von Kamienski, *Natur-
wissenschaften* **42** 345 (1955).

644 *n*-Propylamine, C_3H_9N, liquid, b.p. 50°.

$$CH_3CH_2CH_2NH_2$$

Claviceps purpurea, Polyporus sulfureus
Maximilian Steiner and Elard Stein von Kamienski, *Naturwissenschaften* 42 345 (1955).
P. H. List, *Planta Med.* 6 424 (1958).

645 Isopropylamine, C_3H_9N, liquid, b.p. 33°.

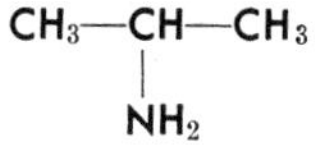

$$CH_3-\underset{\underset{NH_2}{|}}{CH}-CH_3$$

Claviceps purpurea
Maximilian Steiner and Elard Stein von Kamienski, *Naturwissenschaften* 42 345 (1955).

646 Methylaminoethanol, C_3H_9ON, slightly viscous liquid, b.p. 159°.

$$HOCH_2CH_2NHCH_3$$

Neurospora crassa mutant
N. H. Horowitz, *J. Biol. Chem.* 162 413 (1946).

647 *n*-Hexylamine, $C_6H_{15}N$, liquid, b.p. 129°.

$$CH_3(CH_2)_5NH_2$$

Claviceps purpurea
Maximilian Steiner and Elard Stein von Kamienski, *Naturwissenschaften* 42 345 (1955).

648 Isobutylamine, $C_4H_{11}N$, liquid, b.p. 68°.

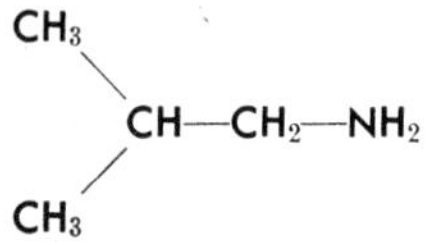

$$\begin{array}{c} CH_3 \\ \diagdown \\ CH-CH_2-NH_2 \\ \diagup \\ CH_3 \end{array}$$

Claviceps purpurea
Maximilian Steiner and Elard Stein von Kamienski, *Naturwissenschaften* 42 345 (1955).

649 1-Amino-2-methyl-2-propanol, $C_4H_{11}ON$, liquid, b.p. 151°.

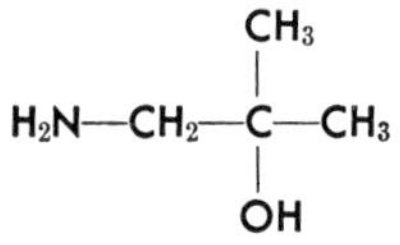

$$H_2N-CH_2-\underset{\underset{OH}{|}}{\overset{\overset{CH_3}{|}}{C}}-CH_3$$

Neurospora crassa

George L. Ellman and Herschel K. Mitchell, *J. Am. Chem. Soc.* **76** 4028 (1954).

650 **Putrescine,** $C_4H_{12}N_2$, crystals, m.p. 27°.

$$H_2NCH_2CH_2CH_2CH_2NH_2$$

Boletus edulis, B. luteus, B. elegans, Amanita muscaria
C. Reuter, *Z. physiol. Chem.* **78** 167, 223 (1912).
Albert Küng, *ibid.* **91** 241 (1914).
Werner Keil and Hans Bartmann, *Biochem. Z.* **280** 58 (1935).

651 **Histamine,** $C_5H_9N_3$, deliquescent needles, m.p. 83° (Hydrochloride) m.p. 244–246° (Picrate) m.p. 160°.

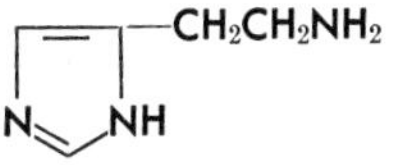

Claviceps purpurea, Coprinus comatis Gray
Paul Heinz List, *Arch. Pharm.* **291** 502 (1958).

652 **Isoamylamine,** $C_5H_{13}N$, liquid, b.p. 95–97°.

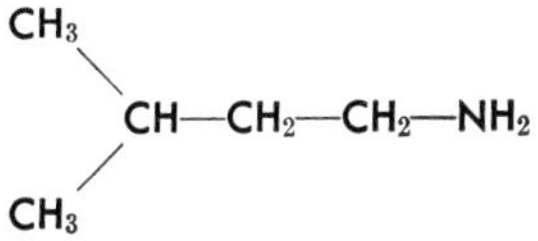

Boletus edulis, B. sanguineus, B. queletii, B. luridus, B. regius, B. appendiculatus, Phallus impudicus, Claviceps purpurea, Amanita phalloides, Marasmium peronatus, Russula foetens, R. turei, R. maulata, Trachypus scaber, Xeroeomus sanguineus, X. subtomentosus, Mutinus caninus, Lycoperdon piriforme, L. gemmatum, Phlegmacium mellioleus, Nematoloma fasciculare, Polyporus sulfureus
Maximilian Steiner and Elard Stein von Kamienski, *Naturwissenschaften* **40** 483 (1953).
Elard Stein von Kamienski, *Planta* **50** 334 (1958).
P. H. List, *Planta Med.* **6** 424 (1958).

653 **Dimethylhistamine,** $C_7H_{13}N_3$ (Dihydrochloride) m.p. 245–250° (dec.).

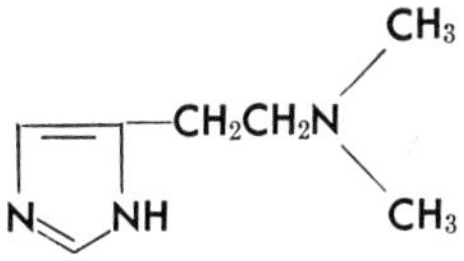

Coprinus comatis Gray
Paul Heinz List, *Arch. Pharm.* 291 502 (1958).

654 Acetylcholine, $C_7H_{17}O_3N$, colorless, hygroscopic powder.

$$(CH_3)_3N—CH_2CH_2OCOCH_3$$
$$\overset{\oplus}{}$$
$$\overset{\ominus}{OH}$$

Streptobacterium plantarum
Acetylcholine is produced also by the ergot fungus, *Claviceps purpurea,* and probably by many other micro-organisms.
Yield: about 160 γ per milliliter from the first organism above.
Adolf Wacker, Adolf Roth, Heinz Sucker and Otto Dann, *Ann.* 601 202 (1957).

655 Spermidine, $C_7H_{19}N_3$, unstable oil, b.p. 128° (14 mm.).

$$H_2N(CH_2)_3NH(CH_2)_4NH_2$$

Yeast, *Neurospora crassa*
Occurs as the phosphate.
H. Tabor, S. M. Rosenthal and C. W. Tabor, *Federation Proc.* 15 367 (1956).
Ronald C. Greene, *J. Am. Chem. Soc.* 79 3929 (1957).

656 β-Phenylethylamine, $C_8H_{11}N$, liquid, b.p. 196–198°.

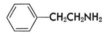

Boletus edulis, B. luteus, Claviceps purpurea, Polyporus sulfureus, Marasmius peronatus, Phlegmacium melliolus, Nematoloma fasciculare, Pholiota mutabilis
C. Reuter, *Z. physiol. Chem.* 78 167 (1912).
Werner Keil and Hans Bartmann, *Biochem. Z.* 280 58 (1935).
Elard Stein von Kamienski, *Planta* 50 335 (1958).
P. H. List, *Planta Med.* 6 424 (1958).

657 Tyramine, $C_8H_{11}ON$, colorless crystals, m.p. 164°. (Picrate), m.p. 206°.

$$HO—\langle\rangle—CH_2CH_2NH_2$$

Coprinus comatis Gray, *Claviceps purpurea*
Paul Heinz List, *Arch. Pharm.* 291 502 (1958).

658 Muscarine, $C_9H_{19}O_2N$, white crystals, Hydrochloride $[\alpha]_D^{20}$ +1.57° (in water).

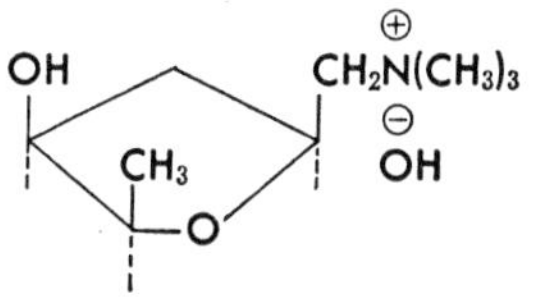

Amanita muscaria

F. Kögl, C. A. Salemink, H. Schouten and F. Jellinck, *Rec. trav. chim.* **76** 109 (1957). (Structure)

E. Hardegger and F. Lohse, *Helv. Chim. Acta* **40** 2383 (1957). (Synthesis and configuration)

P. J. Fraser, *Brit. J. Pharmacol.* **12** 47 (1957). (Pharmacology)

659 Muscaridine, $C_9H_{22}O_2NCl$, isolated as the chloroaurate, $C_9H_{22}AuCl_4O_2N$, m.p. 129–131° (dec.), $[\alpha]_D^{19}$ +20.5° ±0.5° (c 8.3 in water).

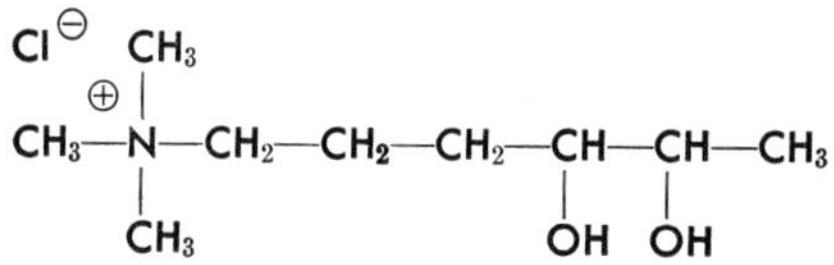

Amanita muscaria L.

F. Kögl, C. A. Salemink and P. L. Schuller, *Rec. trav. chim.* **79** 485 (1960). (Isolation)

C. A. Salemink and P. L. Schuller, *ibid.* **79** 278 (1960). (Synthesis)

660 Spermine, $C_{10}H_{26}N_4$, deliquescent, CO_2-absorbing crystals. Phosphate: m.p. 230–234° (dec.).

$$H_2N(CH_2)_3NH(CH_2)_4NH(CH_2)_3NH_2$$

Yeast, *Neurospora crassa*
Occurs phosphorylated.

H. Tabor, S. M. Rosenthal and C. W. Tabor, *Federation Proc.* **15** 367 (1956).

Ronald C. Greene, *J. Am. Chem. Soc.* **79** 3929 (1957).

661 Bufotenin, $C_{12}H_{16}ON_2$, colorless crystals, m.p. 146°.

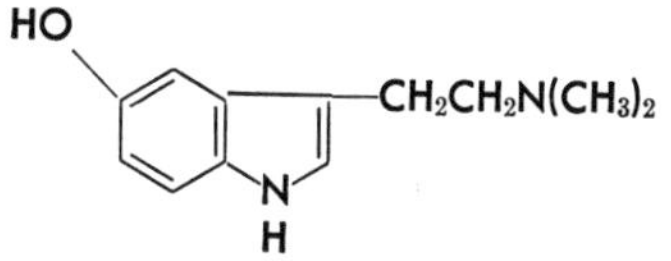

Amanita mappa and certain related species

Bufotenin occurs also in the skin secretions of toads.

Theodor Wieland and Werner Motzel, *Ann.* 581 10 (1953).

662 **Necrosamine,** $C_{20}H_{44}N_2$ (Hydrochloride) crystals, m.p. ~275° (dec.).

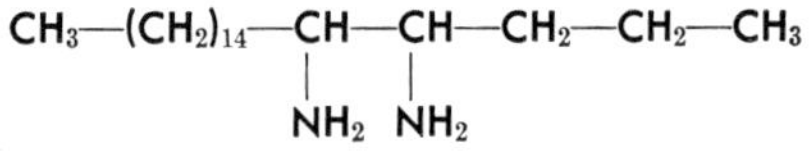

$$CH_3\text{---}(CH_2)_{14}\text{---}CH\text{---}CH\text{---}CH_2\text{---}CH_2\text{---}CH_3$$
$$\underset{NH_2}{|}\quad\underset{NH_2}{|}$$

Escherichia coli

This amine was a component of the phospholipide fraction.

Miyoshi Ikawa, J. B. Koepfli, S. G. Mudd and Carl Niemann, *J. Am. Chem. Soc.* 75 3439 (1953).

16

Amino Acids and Related Compounds

A general review of the intermediary metabolism of amino acids would be disproportionate to the scope of this book. It is only possible to sketch in here some relationships and biosynthetic sequences which may serve as reminders or as guides for the novice.

As in acetate metabolism microorganisms have been used to explore the network of metabolic relationships among the amino acids. Many of these have proved quite general, yet it is only necessary to consider the unusual amino acids which have been isolated from microbial sources to realize the differences from human metabolism.

In this section principally free amino acids are considered. Polypeptides are listed and discussed in the succeeding section. Amino acid isolation and assay formerly were tedious and generally confined to analysis of hydrolysates of total proteins. Paper chromatography and reliable microbiological assays have made possible the separation and assay of the low concentrations of amino acids evolved into fermentation broths.

The older work on fungi has been reviewed.[1] A semiquantitative survey of the free amino acids of a taxonomic range of fungi gave the results shown in Table I[2] on page 300. In general there were found no outstanding differences in the quantities or types of amino acids produced by the different fungi, nor in the types produced by fungi as compared with those of higher plants. The absence of tryptophan in all species examined is noteworthy. Four unidentified compounds were found in various fungi. These were suggested tentatively as

[1] Jackson W. Foster, "Chemical Activities of Fungi," Academic Press, New York, 1949.

[2] R. Close, *Nature* 185 609 (1960).

TABLE I

Free Amino Acids Present in the Hyphal Extract of Certain Fungi

	Pythium ultimum (on Dox)	Phytophthora cactorum	Phycomyces nitens	Thamnidium elegans	Chromocrea spinulosa	Fusarium culmorum	Fusarium javanicum	Stereum purpureum
Aspartic acid	++	++	+++	+++	+++	+++	+++	+++
Glutamic acid	+++	+++	+++	+++	+++	+++	+++	+++
α-Alanine	+	++	+++	+++	++	+++	+++	+++
β-Alanine	-	+++	+++	+	-	-	+	-
γ-Aminobutyric acid	+++	+++	+++	+++	+++	+++	+++	-
Serine	+++	+++	+++	++	+++	+++	+++	+
Glycine	++	+	+++	+	++	-	-	+++
Threonine	++	+++	++	-	++	+++	+++	++
Proline	-	+	-	-	-	-	-	-
Tyrosine	-	-	+++	++	+	-	+	-
Arginine	+++	+++	+++	-	++	+	++	++
Histidine	+++	+++	+	++	+++	-	+	+++
Lysine	-	++	-	-	-	-	-	+++
Phenylalanine	-	-	+	+	+	++	++	-
Leucine and/or iso-leucine	++	-	++	++	++	++	+	+++
Methionine and/or valine	++	++	++	-	++	+	-	++
Ornithine	-	+++	-	-	-	-	+	-
Cysteic acid	++	+	-	+	+++	+++	++	+
Asparagine	++	+++	+++	+++	+++	+++	+++	+++
Glutamine	+++	++	++	++	++	+	++	++
Initial pH	3.7	4.2	4.2	4.2	4.2	4.2	4.2	4.2
Final pH	5.5	4.7	6.7	3.9	5.1	7.0	6.9	6.5
Incubation time (days)	10	29	16	26	14	14	24	19

+++, Strong ninhydrin color; ++, moderate color; +, weak color; −, not detected.

α-aminoadipic acid, 3,4-dihydroxyphenylalanine, ethanolamine and taurine.

The amino acids of some algae have been reported,[3] and also those of *Fusarium lycopersici.*[4] A quantitative study was made of the amino acid composition of *Ustilago maydis* fermentation broth.[5] Of the 3.5 mg. per milliliter of NH_4^+ nitrogen added, 2.9 mg. per milliliter remained extracellular. This extracellular nitrogen contained 1.17 mg. per milliliter of organic nitrogen and 1.74 mg. of residual NH_4^+ nitrogen.

TABLE II

Amino Acid Composition of Ustilago maydis Fermentation Broth

Amino acid*	Unhydrolyzed broth		Hydrolyzed broth	
	μgm /ml.	μgm.N/ml.	μgm./ml.†	μgm.N/ml.†
Lysine	387	64.2	413	79.2
Arginine	997	320.5	1136	365.3
Histidine	155	42.0	182	49.3
Aspartic acid	200	21.0	506	53.2
Glutamic acid	894	85.1	945	90.0
Glycine	200	38.1	295	55.0
Alanine‡			406	63.8
Valine	290	25.7	279	33.4
Leucine	387	41.3	368	39.3
Isoleucine	276	29.5	212	22.7
Serine	276	30.1	307	40.9
Threonine‡			237	27.9
Proline	263	32.0	289	35.2
Phenylalanine	267	22.6	389	33.0
Tyrosine	139	10.7	383	29.6
Tryptophan	40	5.6		
Methionine	65	6.0		
	4.79 mgm.	0.774 mgm.	6.35 mgm.	1.02 mgm.

* The amino acids in the hydrolyzed broth and the basic amino acids in the unhydrolyzed broth were separated chromatographically and assayed colorimetrically. The other amino acids in the unhydrolyzed broth were assayed microbially.

† Values expressed as μgm. per milliliter in terms of original broth.

‡ Valid microbial assays were not obtained.

[3] L. Fowden, *ibid.* **167** 1030 (1951); Borje Wickberg, *Acta Chem. Scand.* 11 506 (1957).

[4] V. Flück and K. H. Richle, *Phytopath. Z.* 24 455 (1955).

[5] Eugene L. Dulaney, E. Bilinski and W. B. McConnell, *Can. J. Biochem. and Physiol.* 34 1195 (1956).

In this case the broth was hydrolyzed and compared with the original to eliminate interference by small peptides in the microbial assays. Tryptophan and methionine were destroyed by the hydrolysis and chromatography procedure and are absent from the second part of the table. It was found that 53% of the extracellular organic nitrogen was represented by free amino acids. Some strains of *Ustilago maydis* produce 200–300 μg. of lysine per milliliter.[6]

A study of the extracellular nitrogen of several molds[7] gave the results in the accompanying table.

TABLE III

Amount of Nitrogen Assimilated Which Appeared in the Medium After Seven Days Growth

Fungus	Nitrogen source	Extracellular nitrogen (as % initially added nitrogen)
Aspergillus niger......................	NH_4^+	7.5
	NO_3^-	3.5
Penicillium chrysogenum................	NH_4^+	20.0
	NO_3^-	7.5
Trichoderma viride....................	NH_4^+	27.0
	NO_3^-	36.0
Botrytis alii..........................	NH_4^+	23.5

The extracellular nitrogen was related to the nitrogen supplied in two cases:

TABLE IV

Formation of Extracellular Nitrogen in Relation to Initially Added Nitrogen Which Disappeared

Fungus	Nitrogen Source	Amount of nitrogen supplied (mg./flask)		
		6.6	13.2	6.6 + 6.6
		Extracellular N as % N assimilated		
Scopulariopsis brevicaulis......	NH_4^-	25.35 ± 5.58	25.80 ± 2.86	
	NO_3^-	20.03 ± 4.47	16.62 ± 2.08	16.50 ± 1.98
Penicillium griseofulvum.......	NO_3^-	13.00 ± 3.35	12.50 ± 0.70	12.34 ± 2.73

[6] M. Richards and R. H. Haskins, *Can. J. Microbiol.* 3 543 (1957).
[7] A. G. Morton and D. Broadbent, *J. Gen. Microbiol.* 12 248 (1955).

In this earlier study most of the extracellular nitrogen appeared to be peptide in nature, yielding some 14 amino acids on hydrolysis. In the one case tested one of the fungi was unable to use the extracellular nitrogen formed, but assimilated the constituent amino acids when these were liberated by acid hydrolysis.

A quantitative report has been made on the free amino acids present in an alcohol extract of *Mucor mucedo*.[8] They were as follows:

TABLE V

Amino Acids Present in 75% Alcohol Extracts of Mucor mucedo (as % Total Nitrogen)

Amino acid	Alcohol extract	Hydrolysate of insoluble residue
Alanine	1.8	6.7
β-Alanine	...	...
Arginine	4.8	12.2
Asparagine	9.5	...
Aspartic acid	22.8	16.4
γ-Aminobutyric acid	6.8	...
Citrulline	...	...
Cystine	...	2.2
Glutamine	15.2	...
Glutamic acid	11.6	35.2
Glycine	1.9	3.8
Histidine	...	1.6
iso-Leucine	1.9	0.7
Leucine	2.4	5.2
Lysine	3.7	3.8
Methionine	0.6	1.1
Proline	1.4	4.2
Phenylalanine	0.9	1.0
Serine	2.4	3.3
Threonine	1.1	2.2
Tyrosine	1.2	2.1
Valine	2.9	4.4

These values were compared with those of other plants over a taxonomic range.

A report of the free amino acids produced by *Penicillium roquefortii* indicated the following to be most prominent:[9]

[8] K. Mansford and R. Raper, *Nature* 174 314 (1954).

[9] J. Koloušek and S. Michalik, *Sbornik Československ. Akad. Zeměděl Ved.* 27A 281 (1954). (*Chem. Abstr.* 50 4295c)

Aspartic Acid	Valine
Glutamic Acid	Methionine
Serine	Leucine
Threonine	Isoleucine
α-Alanine	

The free and combined amino acids of the uredospores of ten wheat rust strains have been determined quantitatively.[10]

The intracellular amino acids of microorganisms have been studied. Gale demonstrated the presence of such a pool in *Streptococcus faecalis*.[11] Gale and Taylor extended the investigation to a variety of bacteria and yeasts with particular attention to lysine and glutamic acid.[12] Fuerst studied several fungi.[13] The free intracellular amino acids of certain strains of *Neurospora crassa* have been explored.[14] The relative quantities of amino acids present varied widely among the various mutants. In all some 35 ninhydrin-positive substances were encountered among the 28 different strains studied. The free amino acids of *Staphylococcus aureus* have been determined, and the ability of bacteria to concentrate amino acids strikingly demonstrated by comparison of the concentrations of internal and external acids.[15]

TABLE VI

Free Amino Acids in Exponentially Growing Staphylococcus aureus Cells Growing in Synthetic Medium

Amino Acid	Quantity (μmole/g.) in internal pool	Ratio of internal to external concentration
Glutamic acid....	39.6	25.4
Aspartic acid....	38	22.6
Proline..........	16.8	23.2
Isoleucine.......	8.3	13.3
Leucine..........	2.6	4.5
Methionine.......	6.7	8.3

[10] M. E. McKillican, *Can. J. Chem.* 38 244 (1960).

[11] E. F. Gale, *J. Gen. Microbiol.* 1 53 (1947).

[12] E. F. Gale and E. S. Taylor, *ibid.* 1 77 (1947); E. S. Taylor, *ibid.* 1 86 (1947).

[13] R. Fuerst and J. Awapara, *Texas Repts. Biol. and Med.* 10 424 (1952).

[14] Robert Fuerst and Robert P. Wagner, *Arch. Biochem. and Biophys.* 70 311 (1957).

[15] R. Hancock, *Biochim. et Biophys. Acta* 28 402 (1958).

TABLE VI—Continued

Free Amino Acids in Exponentially Growing Staphylococcus aureus Cells Growing in Synthetic Medium

Amino Acid	Quantity (μmole/g.) in internal pool	Ratio of internal to external concentration
Alanine	8.1	5.4
Cystine and cysteine	5.5	
Serine	3.4	5.4
Glycine	2.8	2.3
Tyrosine	2.4	3.1
Lysine	2.2	4.6
Arginine	2.2	3.0
Histidine	1.7	2.2
Phenylalanine	1.3	1.8
Threonine	1.0	1.6
Tryptophan	0.3	

All the amino acids found in the internal protein of the cell were present in the internal pool of free amino acids.

A new amino acid, S-methyl-L-cysteine, has been isolated from *Neurospora crassa*.[16]   An isomer of β-methyllanthionine has been isolated from yeast.[17]   Urocanic acid has been detected in *Micrococcus lysodeikticus*.[18]

$$CH_3—S—CH_2—CH—COOH$$
$$\underset{NH_2}{|}$$

S-Methylcysteine

$$HOOC—CH—CH_2—S—CH—CH—COOH$$
$$\underset{NH_2}{|}\qquad\underset{CH_3}{|}\ \underset{NH_2}{|}$$

β-Methyllanthionine

$$HOOC—CH—CH—COOH$$
$$\underset{NH_2}{|}\ \underset{NH_2}{|}$$

α,β-Diaminosuccinic Acid

New, partially characterized α-amino acids have been isolated from boletus and lactarius species.[19, 20, 21] α,β-Diaminosuccinic acid has been isolated from production filtrates of the antibiotic

[16] James B. Ragland and James L. Liverman, *Arch. Biochem. and Biophys.* 65 574 (1956).

[17] Phyllis F. Downey and Simon Black, *J. Biol. Chem.* 228 171 (1957).

[18] Jana Gregoire and Jean Gregoire, *Compt. rend.* 245 2553 (1957).

[19] A. I. Virtanen and O. Ayräpää, *Suomen Kem.* 31B 190 (1958).

[20] Atsushi Komamine and Artturi I. Virtanen, *Acta Chem. Scand.* 13 2141 (1959).

[21] J. Casimir and Artturi I. Virtanen, *ibid.* 13 2139 (1959).

oxytetracycline (*Streptomyces rimosus*).[22]   The structures of certain other unusual amino acids are listed in this section.

Production of glutamic acid by streptomycetes on synthetic medium containing glycine has been investigated.[23]   Yields of extracellular glutamic acid were 0.25–1.75 g. per liter.   It was the only amino acid or nitrogenous material present after four and seven days, but after ten days some alanine, phenylalanine, aspartic acid and glycine appeared.   Strains examined were: *Streptomyces annulatus, S. aureofaciens, S. fradiae, S. olivaceus* and *S. rimosus.*

The high proportions and amounts of L-glutamic acid synthesized by microorganisms have led to the development of an economical process for its commercial production.   Certain micrococcus and bacillus species produce more than a 20% yield (molar basis) from the glucose supplied.[24]   A similar yield of valine has been reported.[25]

L-Lysine is also produced commercially by a direct process (micrococcus, bacillus)[26] and by a two-stage process (*Escherichia coli, Aerobacter aerogenes*),[27] 2,6-diaminopimelic acid being the intermediate in the latter case.

Tryptophan production by *E. coli* and by *Salmonella typhi* has been reported as small unless indole is added.[28]   The indole apparently competitively inhibited tryptophanase.   Many microorganisms are able to synthesize tryptophan from indole and serine.

A survey of 20 genera, 72 species and 334 strains of aerobic bacteria for amino acid accumulation revealed no marked taxonomic difference except that facultative aerobes such as escherichia, aerobacter and bacillus species were superior to obligatory aerobes such as pseudomonas.   Production and accumulation were more dependent on strain and conditions.[29]

The biosynthesis and metabolic interrelationships of amino acids can be considered here only in briefest summary because of the breadth and complexity of the subject.   More thorough re-

[22] F. A. Hochstein, *J. Org. Chem.* 24 679 (1959).

[23] D. Perlman and E. O'Brien, *J. Bact.* 75 611 (1958).

[24] Toshinobu Asai, Ko Aida and Kunio Oishi, *Bull. Agr. Chem. Soc.* (Japan) 21 134 (1957).

[25] Zenjirô Sugisaki, *Nippon Nôgei-kagaku Kaishi* 34 153 (1960).

[26] Shukuo Kinoshita, Kiyoshi Nakayama and Sohei Kitada, *J. Gen. Appl. Microbiol.* 4 128 (1958).

[27] Lester E. Casida, Jr., U. S. Patent 2,711,396 (1956).

[28] P. Fildes, *J. Gen. Microbiol.* 15 636 (1956).

[29] Hiroshi Iizuka and Kazuo Komagata, *Nippon Nôgei-kagashu Kaishi* 34 27 (1960).

views are available[30, 31, 32] and references to some of the vast literature on this subject can be found there.

The occurrence studies cited demonstrate the importance of glutamic acid. It is a constituent of folic acid and related substances, and of glutathione, and various antibiotics. It occurs in the cell wall of bacteria and, as a polypeptide, is the sole capsular substance of certain bacilli. Its wide distribution reflects its cross-roads position in nitrogen metabolism.

Synthesis of glutamic acid by most aerobic microorganisms involves amination of α-ketoglutaric acid (a reversible reaction), thus tying it in with the citric acid cycle. It is a precursor of ornithine, proline and in some cases lysine.

$$HOOC-CH_2-CH_2-\overset{\overset{\displaystyle O}{\|}}{C}-COOH \rightleftharpoons HOOC-CH_2-CH_2-\underset{\underset{\displaystyle NH_2}{|}}{CH}-COOH$$

α-Ketoglutaric Acid   amination   Glutamic Acid

In *E. coli*, at least, the route to ornithine involves N-acetylated intermediates. The intermediates shown accumulate in appro-

$$HOOC-CH_2-CH_2-\underset{\underset{\displaystyle NH_2}{|}}{CH}-COOH$$

Glutamic Acid

reduction ⇅

$$OHC-CH_2-CH_2-\underset{\underset{\displaystyle NH_2}{|}}{CH}-COOH \rightleftharpoons$$ Δ¹-Pyrroline-5-carboxylic Acid

Glutamic Acid Semialdehyde

amination ⇅

$$H_2N-CH_2-CH_2-CH_2-\underset{\underset{\displaystyle NH_2}{|}}{CH}-COOH$$

Ornithine

reduction ⇅

Proline

[30] Bernard D. Davis, *Advances in Enzymol.* 16 247–312 (1955).

[31] Alton Meister, "Biochemistry of the Amino Acids," Academic Press, New York, 1957, pp. 256–394.

[32] Joseph S. Fruton and Sofia Simmonds, "General Biochemistry," John Wiley and Sons, Inc., New York, 1958, pp. 771–896.

priate auxotrophs and can be isolated. This scheme has been found in a variety of molds, yeasts and bacteria.

Ornithine reacts with carbamyl phosphate to form citrulline, an intermediate in the biosynthesis of arginine:

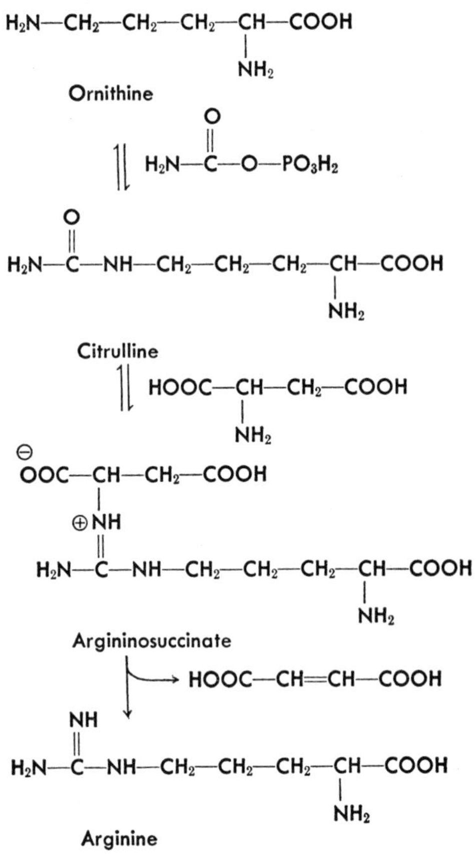

$$H_2N—CH_2—CH_2—CH_2—CH—COOH$$
$$|$$
$$NH_2$$

Ornithine

$$O$$
$$||$$
$$H_2N—C—O—PO_3H_2$$

$$O$$
$$||$$
$$H_2N—C—NH—CH_2—CH_2—CH_2—CH—COOH$$
$$|$$
$$NH_2$$

Citrulline

$$HOOC—CH—CH_2—COOH$$
$$|$$
$$NH_2$$

$$\overset{\ominus}{O}OC—CH—CH_2—COOH$$
$$|$$
$$\overset{\oplus}{N}H$$
$$||$$
$$H_2N—C—NH—CH_2—CH_2—CH_2—CH—COOH$$
$$|$$
$$NH_2$$

Argininosuccinate

$$\longrightarrow HOOC—CH=CH—COOH$$

$$NH$$
$$||$$
$$H_2N—C—NH—CH_2—CH_2—CH_2—CH—COOH$$
$$|$$
$$NH_2$$

Arginine

Arginine can complete the "urea cycle" by losing urea to form ornithine. Enzymes for all these steps have been found in various microorganisms.

Glutamic acid acts as an ammonia carrier by formation of its half amide, glutamine, and in this way contributes nitrogen to the biosynthesis of purines and amino sugars.

Aspartic acid also occupies a central position in nitrogen metabolism. In microorganisms it can be synthesized either by amination of oxaloacetic acid or by the addition of ammonia to fumaric acid, the former process probably being more prevalent.

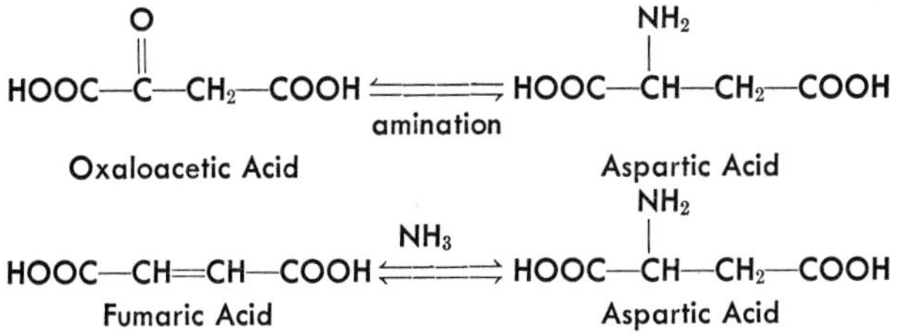

$$\underset{\text{Oxaloacetic Acid}}{HOOC-\overset{\overset{\displaystyle O}{\|}}{C}-CH_2-COOH} \overset{\longrightarrow}{\underset{\text{amination}}{\longleftarrow}} \underset{\text{Aspartic Acid}}{HOOC-\overset{\overset{\displaystyle NH_2}{|}}{CH}-CH_2-COOH}$$

$$\underset{\text{Fumaric Acid}}{HOOC-CH=CH-COOH} \overset{\overset{\displaystyle NH_3}{\longrightarrow}}{\underset{}{\longleftarrow}} \underset{\text{Aspartic Acid}}{HOOC-\overset{\overset{\displaystyle NH_2}{|}}{CH}-CH_2-COOH}$$

Either equation ties aspartic acid in with the citric acid cycle. Like glutamic acid, aspartic acid acts as an ammonia carrier through its half amide, asparagine. One role of aspartic acid was seen above in the biosynthesis of arginine. Aspartic acid has been proved a precursor of pyrimidines in certain microorganisms. It is also a precursor of threonine and of both α- and β-alanines. Separate enzymes control the selective decarboxylations to form the alanines.

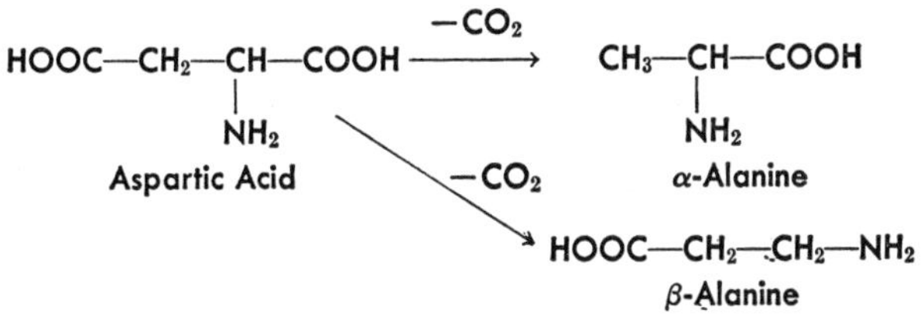

$$\underset{\text{Aspartic Acid}}{HOOC-CH_2-\underset{\underset{\displaystyle NH_2}{|}}{CH}-COOH} \overset{\overset{\displaystyle -CO_2}{\longrightarrow}}{\underset{\displaystyle -CO_2}{\searrow}} \underset{\text{α-Alanine}}{CH_3-\underset{\underset{\displaystyle NH_2}{|}}{CH}-COOH}$$

$$\underset{\text{β-Alanine}}{HOOC-CH_2-CH_2-NH_2}$$

α-Alanine (either isomer) can be synthesized, too, from pyruvic acid by a wide variety of biological systems. Some microorganisms effect this amination directly from ammonia, but the transamination from glutamate is probably more prevalent. Alanine, therefore, is also closely connected with carbohydrate and fat metabolism, and it is used as an energy source by many microbes. Through pyruvate it also may be considered a precursor of glycine, serine, cysteine and of valine, leucine and

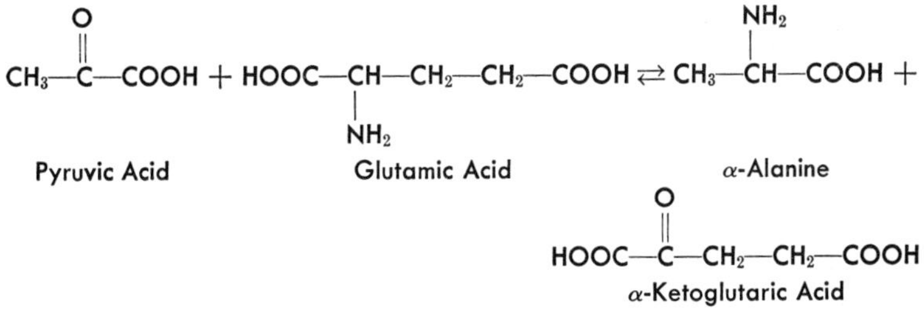

$$\underset{\text{Pyruvic Acid}}{CH_3-\overset{\overset{\displaystyle O}{\|}}{C}-COOH} + \underset{\text{Glutamic Acid}}{HOOC-\underset{\underset{\displaystyle NH_2}{|}}{CH}-CH_2-CH_2-COOH} \rightleftarrows \underset{\text{α-Alanine}}{CH_3-\overset{\overset{\displaystyle NH_2}{|}}{CH}-COOH} +$$

$$\underset{\text{α-Ketoglutaric Acid}}{HOOC-\overset{\overset{\displaystyle O}{\|}}{C}-CH_2-CH_2-COOH}$$

isoleucine. D-Alanine occurs in bacterial cell walls and spores and frequently in antibiotics. Some bacteria even require an exogenous source of D-alanine, particularly on a medium devoid of pyridoxine, since pyridoxal phosphate is a coenzyme for the racemase. β-Alanine is a component of coenzyme A. A related substance, β-nitropropionic acid has been isolated from an aspergillus species.

Glycine and serine are reversibly interconvertible in most organisms, tetrahydrofolic acid transferring the hydroxymethyl group. Glycine also is formed by amination of glyoxylate in some microorganisms.

$$\underset{\text{Glycine}}{\overset{\displaystyle CH_2-COOH}{\underset{\displaystyle NH_2}{|}}} \overset{\text{pyridoxal phosphate}}{\underset{}{\overset{\text{THFA}\cdot CH_2OH}{\rightleftharpoons}}} \underset{\text{Serine}}{\overset{\displaystyle HOCH_2-CH-COOH}{\underset{\displaystyle NH_2}{|}}}$$

$$\underset{\text{Glyoxylic Acid}}{OHC-COOH} \overset{\begin{array}{c}\text{glutamate}\\ \text{or}\\ \text{ammonia}\end{array}}{\rightleftharpoons} \underset{\text{Glycine}}{NH_2-CH_2-COOH}$$

In *E. coli* serine is probably to be regarded as the precursor of glycine. The origin of serine is still obscure. There is a possibility that it may arise from phosphoglyceric acid from the glycolysis scheme:

$$\underset{\substack{\text{3-Phospho-}\\\text{glyceric}\\\text{Acid}}}{\overset{\displaystyle COOH}{\underset{\displaystyle CH_2OPO_3H_2}{\overset{\displaystyle |}{\underset{\displaystyle |}{CH-OH}}}}} \rightleftharpoons \underset{\substack{\text{3-Phospho-}\\\text{hydroxy-}\\\text{pyruvic Acid}}}{\overset{\displaystyle COOH}{\underset{\displaystyle CH_2OPO_3H_2}{\overset{\displaystyle |}{\underset{\displaystyle |}{C=O}}}}} \rightleftharpoons \underset{\substack{\text{Phospho-}\\\text{serine}}}{\overset{\displaystyle COOH}{\underset{\displaystyle CH_2OPO_3H_2}{\overset{\displaystyle |}{\underset{\displaystyle |}{CH-NH_2}}}}} \rightleftharpoons \underset{\text{Serine}}{\overset{\displaystyle COOH}{\underset{\displaystyle CH_2OH}{\overset{\displaystyle |}{\underset{\displaystyle |}{CH-NH_2}}}}}$$

Glycine is a precursor of the porphyrins, purines, glutathione and sarcosine.

Serine contributes the carbon skeleton of cysteine in most organisms. Most microorganisms can use sulfate but not methionine as a sulfur source, while mammals require methionine for this purpose but cannot use sulfate. The conversion route of methionine to cysteine has been worked out for higher animals, but is not entirely understood in microorganisms.

Thiosulfate is used by some molds, and cysteine-S-sulfonate has been found to be an intermediate. Hydrogen sulfide has been reported as a precursor in yeast. Threonine has been isolated as an intermediate to cysteine in a neurospora auxotroph.

Cysteine is a component of glutathione and of penicillin. Methionine is important in transmethylation reactions. The entire topic of one-carbon metabolism cannot be reviewed here. The transfer of methyl groups from methionine to oxygen and nitrogen atoms, and probably to carbon atoms in biosynthetic sequences requires ATP, and the active complex has been identified as S-adenosylmethionine.

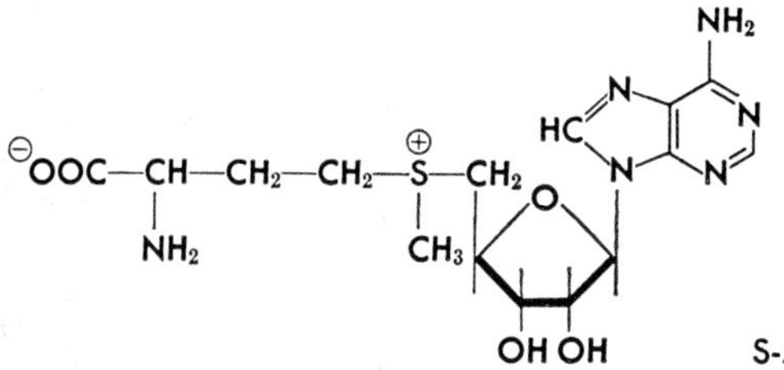

S-Adenosylmethionine

Several labile methyl group compounds (choline, betaine, serine) probably can contribute the methyl group of methionine by way of the proper coenzymes (B_{12}, THFA). Some neurospora mutants have been found which seem to synthesize methionine from cysteine and, ultimately, from aspartic acid. The following scheme has been suggested:

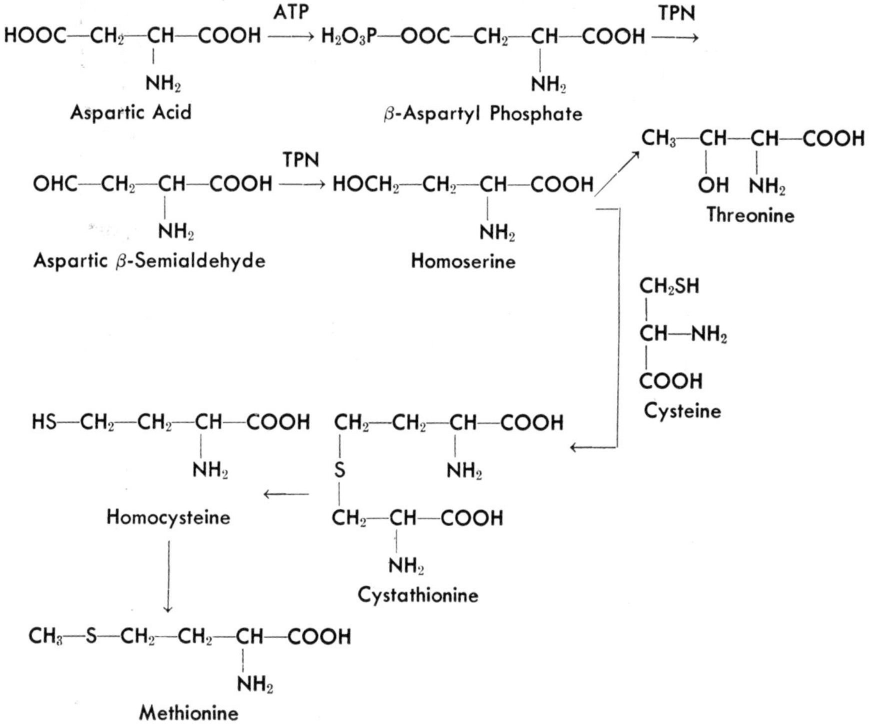

Homoserine also is a precursor of threonine in neurospora mutants, with ATP and pyridoxal phosphate required. Threonine is synthesized by most microorganisms although it is an essential in mammalian diets.

The fact that lysine-requiring neurospora mutants use α-aminoadipic acid makes probable a biosynthetic scheme in which the terminal carboxyl group is reduced and aminated as in the biosynthesis of ornithine from glutamic acid. Some molds even are able to use α-ketoadipic acid, which strengthens the argument. Labeling studies indicate formation of the α-ketoadipic acid by condensation of acetate with either α-ketoglutarate or with the "active succinate" from the citric acid cycle, the acetate carboxyl furnishing the carboxyl group of lysine. Proposed lysine biosynthesis in molds:

$$HOOC-CH_2-CH_2-CO-CoA(COOH)$$

Active Succinate

$$+$$

$$CH_3-CO-CoA$$

Acetate

$$\rightarrow$$

$$HOOC-CH_2-CH_2-CH_2-\overset{\overset{\displaystyle O}{\|}}{C}-COOH$$

α-Ketoadipic Acid

amination $\downarrow \uparrow$

$$HOOC-CH_2-CH_2-CH_2-\underset{\underset{\displaystyle NH_2}{|}}{CH}-COOH$$

$$OCH-CH_2-CH_2-CH_2-\underset{\underset{\displaystyle NH_2}{|}}{CH}-COOH \longleftarrow \text{α-Aminoadipic Acid}$$

α-Aminoadipic Acid
ε-Semialdehyde

| amination
↓

$$H_2N-CH_2-CH_2-CH_2-CH_2-\underset{\underset{\displaystyle NH_2}{|}}{CH}-COOH$$

Lysine

α-Aminoadipic acid is produced by *Penicillium chrysogenum* as a component of a tripeptide isolated from the mycelium. It also occurs as a moiety of the antibiotic synnematin-B (cephalosporin N) produced by the mold *Cephalosporium salmosynnematum*, and it has been isolated from *Aspergillus oryzae*.

α,ε-Diaminopimelic acid is a precursor of lysine in *E. coli* and in many other bacteria. L,L-Diaminopimelic acid is formed in *E. coli* by condensation of pyruvic acid with aspartic acid. Later a specific racemase converts it to the *meso*-form. A complete mechanism for lysine biosynthesis in bacteria has been proposed:

$$
\begin{array}{l}
\text{COOH} \\
|\\
\text{CH---NH}_2 \\
|\\
\text{CH}_2 \\
|\\
\text{COOH}
\end{array}
\quad
\begin{array}{c}
\text{HOOC---CH}_2\text{---CH}_2\text{---COOH} \\
\text{Succinic Acid}
\end{array}
$$

Aspartic Acid

$$
\begin{array}{l}
\text{CH}_3 \\
|\\
\text{C=O} \\
|\\
\text{COOH}
\end{array}
$$

Pyruvic Acid

$\xrightarrow{\text{ATP}}$

$$
\left[
\begin{array}{l}
\text{COOH} \\
|\\
\text{CH---NH---CO---CH}_2\text{---CH}_2\text{---COOH} \\
|\\
\text{CH}_2 \\
|\\
\text{C=O} \\
|\\
\text{CH}_2 \\
|\\
\text{C=O} \\
|\\
\text{COOH}
\end{array}
\right]
\rightarrow
$$

I

$$
\begin{array}{l}
\text{COOH} \\
|\\
\text{CH---NH---CO---CH}_2\text{---CH}_2\text{---COOH} \\
|\\
\text{CH}_2 \\
|\\
\text{CH}_2 \\
|\\
\text{CH}_2 \\
|\\
\text{C=O} \\
|\\
\text{COOH}
\end{array}
$$

II

$$
\xrightarrow{}
\begin{array}{l}
\text{COOH} \\
|\\
\text{CH---NH---CO---CH}_2\text{---CH}_2\text{---COOH} \\
|\\
\text{CH}_2 \\
|\\
\text{CH}_2 \\
|\\
\text{CH}_2 \\
|\\
\text{CH---NH}_2 \\
|\\
\text{COOH}
\end{array}
$$

III

$$
\begin{array}{l}
\text{CH}_2\text{---NH}_2 \\
|\\
\text{CH}_2 \\
|\\
\text{CH}_2 \\
|\\
\text{CH}_2 \\
|\\
\text{CH---NH}_2 \\
|\\
\text{COOH}
\end{array}
\quad \xleftarrow{\text{---CO}_2}
$$

Lysine

$$
\begin{array}{l}
\text{COOH} \\
|\\
\text{CH---NH}_2 \\
|\\
\text{CH}_2 \\
|\\
\text{CH}_2 \\
|\\
\text{CH}_2 \\
|\\
\text{CH---NH}_2 \\
|\\
\text{COOH}
\end{array}
\quad + \quad
\begin{array}{l}
\text{COOH} \\
|\\
\text{CH}_2 \\
|\\
\text{CH}_2 \\
|\\
\text{COOH}
\end{array}
$$

Diaminopimelic Acid   Succinic Acid

Intermediate III has been isolated and identified, and there is some evidence for the existence of II. Rather similar intermediates have been suggested as precursors of 2,6-dipicolinic acid, which is formed in some bacterial spores. Free diaminopimelic

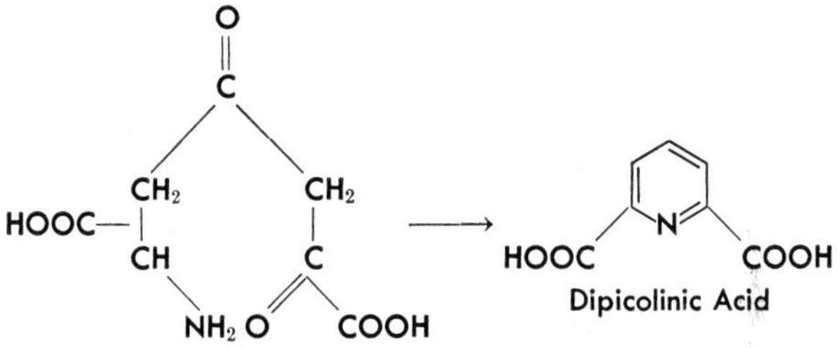

Dipicolinic Acid

acid has been isolated from vegetative cells of such spore-formers. It has never been found in yeasts and molds.

α,ϵ-Diaminopimelic acid replaces lysine in the repeating pentapeptide unit of the bacterial cell wall in *Corynebacterium diphtheriae*, *E. coli* and certain other bacteria (especially gram negatives). Some *E. coli* strains accumulate considerable quantities of diaminopimelic acid, and this faculty has been exploited in a two-step commercial production process.

Many microorganisms metabolize lysine to pipecolic acid, a component of several antibiotics.

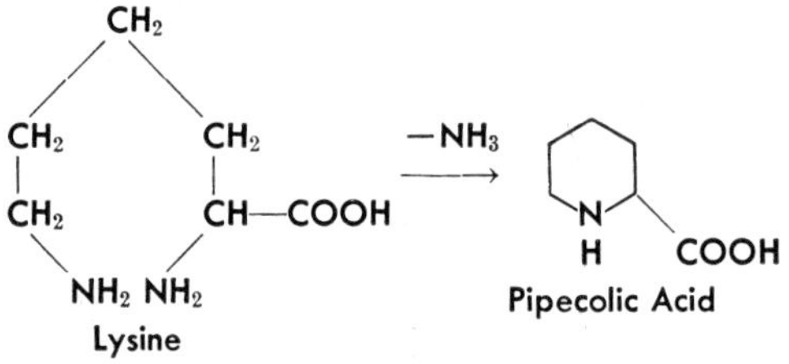

Lysine

Pipecolic Acid

The amino acids discussed to date are closely integrated with carbohydrate and fat metabolism. Those remaining to be considered are more remotely derived.

Valine, isoleucine and leucine are essential to the mammalian diet and are required also by many microorganisms. This seems to indicate enzymatic difficulties in the biosynthesis of these branched-chain amino acids.

Much evidence has accumulated concerning the biosynthesis of valine and isoleucine, and the following pathway is indicated (for valine):

$$CH_3-\overset{\overset{\textstyle O}{\|}}{\underset{\underset{\textstyle ②}{③}}{C}}-\underset{①}{COOH} \longrightarrow CH_3-\overset{\overset{\textstyle O}{\|}}{\underset{④}{C}}-\overset{\overset{\textstyle OH}{|}}{\underset{\underset{\textstyle CH_3}{|②①}}{C}}-COOH$$

Pyruvic Acid CH_3CHO ⑤ ④

⑤ ④

"active acet-aldehyde"

thiamine pyrophosphate

α-Acetolactic Acid   rearrangement

$$CH_3-\overset{\overset{\textstyle O}{\|}}{C}-COOH$$

$$CH_3-\underset{\underset{\textstyle CH_3}{|}}{CH}-\overset{\overset{\textstyle O}{\|}}{C}-COOH \xleftarrow{\;H_2O\;} CH_3-\overset{\overset{\textstyle OH}{|}}{\underset{\underset{\textstyle CH_3}{|}}{C}}-\overset{\overset{\textstyle OH}{|}}{CH}-COOH \xleftarrow[\text{reduction}]{\;TPNH\;} \left[CH_3-\overset{\overset{\textstyle OH}{|}}{\underset{\underset{\textstyle CH_3}{|④}}{C}}-\overset{\overset{\textstyle O}{\|}}{\underset{②}{C}}-\underset{①}{COOH} \right]$$

α-Ketoisovaleric Acid   α,β-Dihydroxy-isovaleric Acid   α-Keto-β-hydroxy-isovaleric Acid

transamination

$$\overset{\textstyle CH_3}{\underset{\textstyle CH_3}{\diagdown\diagup}}CH-\underset{\underset{\textstyle NH_2}{|}}{CH}-COOH$$

Valine

The intermediates, α-acetolactic acid and α,β-dihydroxyisovaleric acid, have been isolated from a variety of microorganisms and are well characterized. α-Keto-β-hydroxyisovaleric acid has not been reported yet, although when it is mixed with enzyme preparations from molds and yeasts together with TPNH, it is reduced to α,β-dihydroxyisovaleric acid. α-Ketoisovaleric acid is aminated by numerous microorganisms.

The scheme for isoleucine is believed to be analogous, but with α-ketobutyric acid replacing pyruvic acid as the initial substance. This four-carbon acid is, in turn, derived from homoserine or threonine, and ultimately from aspartic acid. Some of the steps of the valine and isoleucine syntheses are known to share common enzymes.

Leucine biosynthesis is apparently the same as that of valine up to the final amination step. Leucine, however, requires 3 moles of pyruvate for its 6-carbon atom chain rather than the

2 required by valine. The remaining steps of the proposed leucine biosynthesis in microorganisms are:

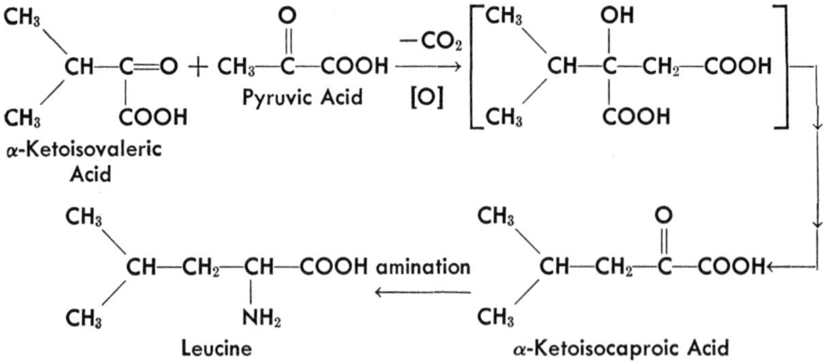

α-Ketoisovaleric Acid

Leucine   amination   α-Ketoisocaproic Acid

This partial scheme is based on labeled media experiments in yeasts, molds and bacteria.

The biogenetic scheme of the aromatic amino acids phenylalanine and tyrosine was briefly outlined in the introduction to the section on simpler alicyclic compounds. The final stages of this route are shown here, beginning with shikimic acid:

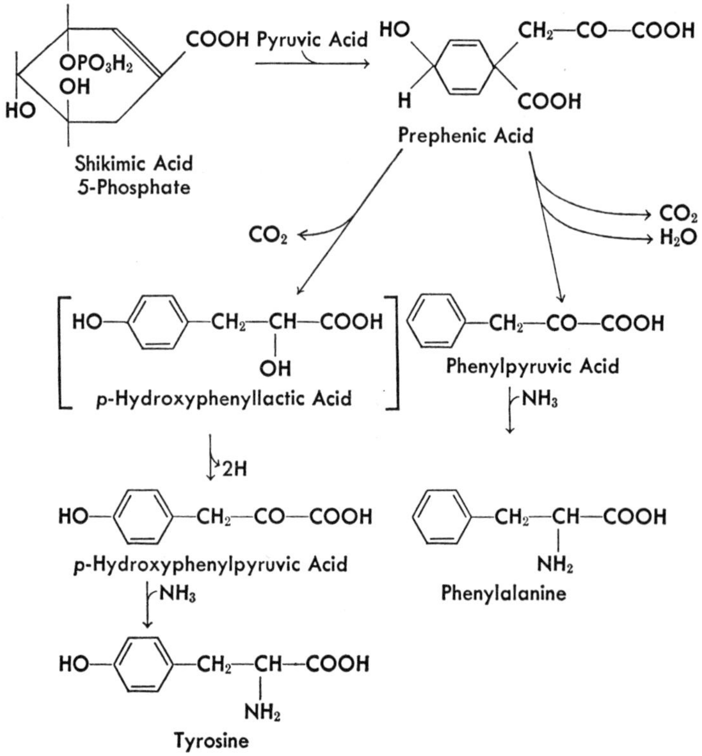

Shikimic Acid
5-Phosphate

Prephenic Acid

p-Hydroxyphenyllactic Acid

Phenylpyruvic Acid

p-Hydroxyphenylpyruvic Acid

Phenylalanine

Tyrosine

The benzene ring of tryptophan also arises from the shikimic acid route. The intermediates are unknown between shikimic acid and the first aromatic member of the sequence, anthranilic acid:

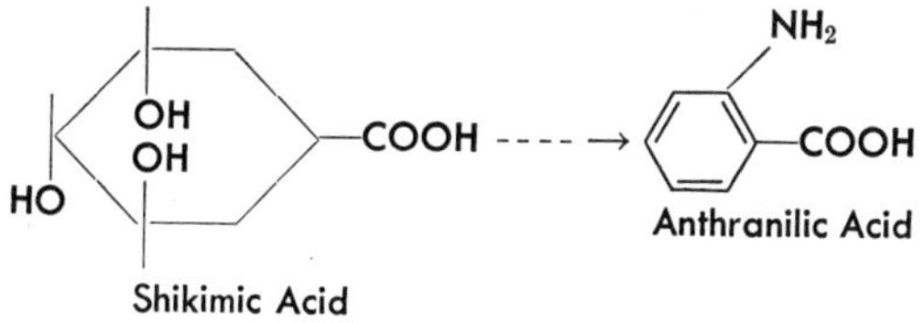

Shikimic Acid

Anthranilic Acid

The remainder of the sequence in its present state of development is as follows:

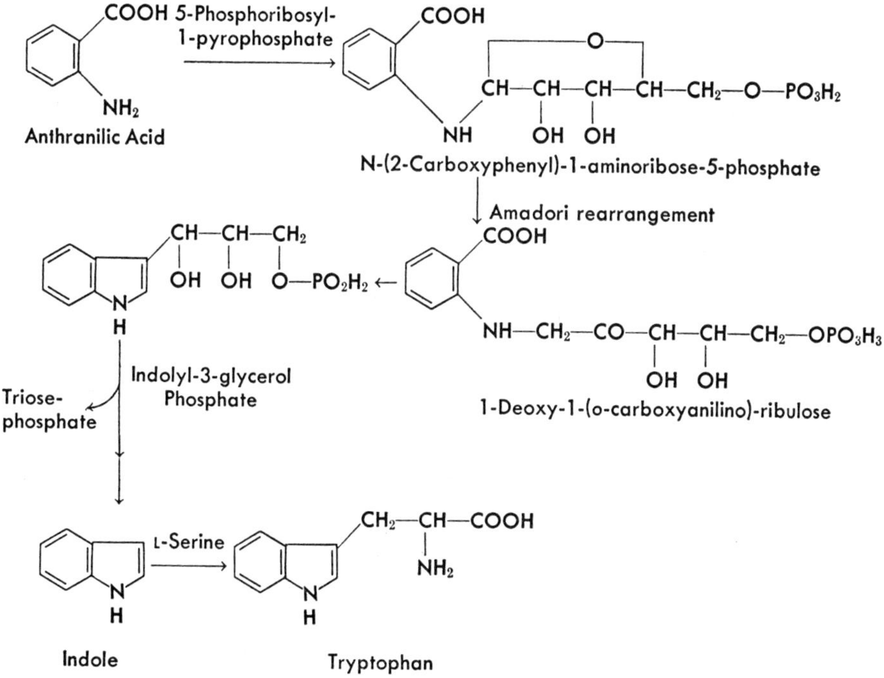

Anthranilic Acid

N-(2-Carboxyphenyl)-1-aminoribose-5-phosphate

Amadori rearrangement

Indolyl-3-glycerol Phosphate

Triose-phosphate

1-Deoxy-1-(o-carboxyanilino)-ribulose

Indole   Tryptophan

There appears to be some question as to whether the Amadori rearrangement product is a bona fide member of this sequence. It has been isolated from *Aerobacter aerogenes* and characterized as derivatives, and it substitutes for anthranilic acid in bacterial mutants requiring the latter.

The anthranilic acid carboxyl group is known to be lost as carbon dioxide during the formation of the pyrrole ring, and the first two carbon atoms of ribose are known to form the 2 and 3 positions of the indole ring. Glucose also can furnish these two carbon atoms. In this connection it should be mentioned that N-fructosylanthranilic acid has been isolated from a yeast. Probably indole never exists in the free state to any appreciable extent during the tryptophan synthesis, but is enzyme-bound.

Ribose contributes also to the biosynthesis of histidine. Here purines are catalytic, furnishing a carbon atom and a nitrogen atom from the pyrimidine ring to form positions 2 and 3 of the histidine ring. The purine is then regenerated by reaction with a C_1 substance. Adenine is the most efficient purine for this purpose. The following scheme has been worked out, largely on the basis of auxotroph work: (P = phosphate, R = ribose).

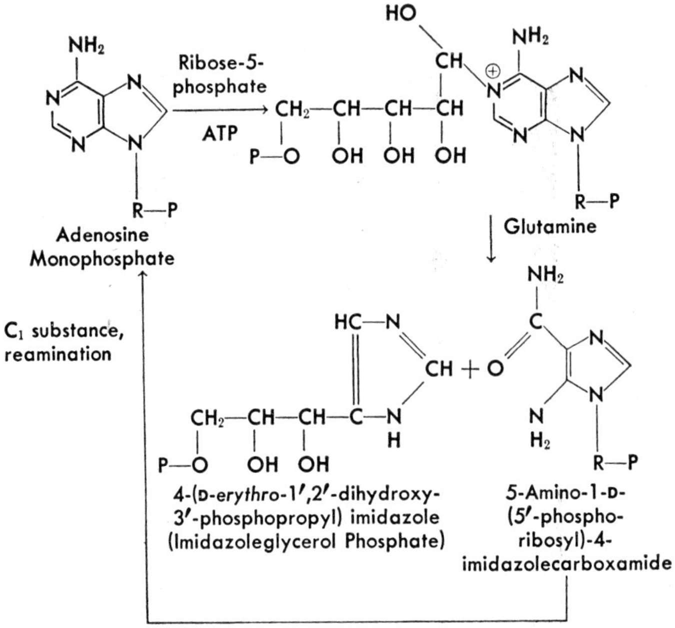

Some chemicals which inhibit purine synthesis also cause accumulation of such intermediates. To continue with the biosynthesis of histidine:

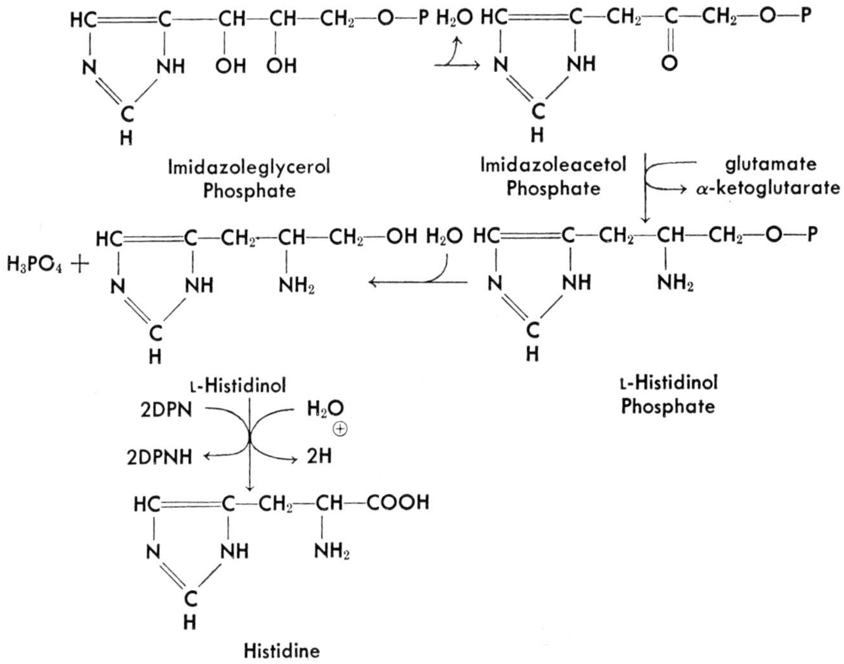

$$HC{=\!=\!=}C{-\!\!}CH{-\!\!}CH{-\!\!}CH_2{-\!\!}O{-\!\!}P \xrightarrow{H_2O} HC{=\!=\!=}C{-\!\!}CH_2{-\!\!}C{-\!\!}CH_2{-\!\!}O{-\!\!}P$$

Imidazoleglycerol
Phosphate

Imidazoleacetol
Phosphate

⎫ glutamate
⎭→ α-ketoglutarate

$$H_3PO_4 + \quad HC{=\!=\!=}C{-\!\!}CH_2{-\!\!}CH{-\!\!}CH_2{-\!\!}OH \xleftarrow{H_2O} HC{=\!=\!=}C{-\!\!}CH_2{-\!\!}CH{-\!\!}CH_2{-\!\!}O{-\!\!}P$$

L-Histidinol

L-Histidinol
Phosphate

2DPN ⎤ ⎡ H₂O
⎦ ⎣ ⊕
2DPNH ← → 2H

$$HC{=\!=\!=}C{-\!\!}CH_2{-\!\!}CH{-\!\!}COOH$$

Histidine

It is interesting that the final stages of this synthesis differ from those in the tryptophan sequence when some of the intermediates are so closely related. Perhaps in some species a lesser difference will be found.

Histidine is converted to ergothioneine in microorganisms by methylation to form hercynine, followed by direct introduction of the thiol group.

663 **Glycine,** $C_2H_5O_2N$, colorless crystals, m.p. ~280–290° (dec.) (rapid heating).

$$H_2N{-\!\!}CH_2{-\!\!}COOH$$

Widely distributed.

664 **Sarcosine,** $C_3H_7O_2N$, colorless crystals, m.p. 212° (dec.).

$$CH_3NHCH_2COOH$$

Cladonia sylvatica
Also a component of the actinomycin antibiotics.
P. Linko, M. Alfthan, J. K. Miettinen and Artturi I. Virtanen, *Acta Chem. Scand.* 7 1310 (1953).

665   L-Alanine, $C_3H_7O_2N$, colorless crystals, m.p. 297° (dec.), $[\alpha]_D^{26}$ +8.5° (9.3% solution of the hydrochloride in water).

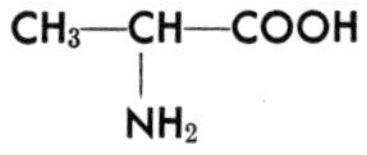

$$CH_3\!-\!CH\!-\!COOH$$
$$|$$
$$NH_2$$

Widely distributed.

666   β-Alanine, $C_3H_7O_2N$, colorless crystals, m.p. 207° (dec.) (preheated bath).

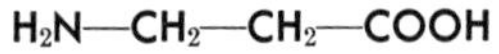

$$H_2N\!-\!CH_2\!-\!CH_2\!-\!COOH$$

Widely distributed.

667   L-Serine, $C_3H_7O_3N$, colorless crystals, m.p. 228° (dec.) (sublimes 150° at 10^{-4} mm. Hg), $[\alpha]_D^{25}$ +14.45° (0.5 g. per 5.6 g. of 1 N hydrochloric acid).

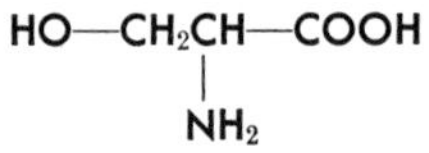

$$HO\!-\!CH_2CH\!-\!COOH$$
$$|$$
$$NH_2$$

Widely distributed.

668   L-Aspartic Acid, $C_4H_7O_4N$, colorless crystals, m.p. 270° (sealed capillary, preheated bath) (dec.), $[\alpha]_D^{24}$ +24.6° (c 2 in 6 N hydrochloric acid).

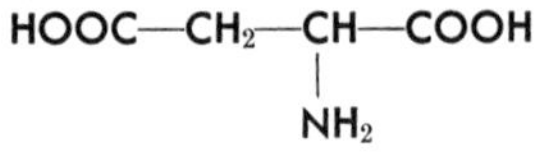

$$HOOC\!-\!CH_2\!-\!CH\!-\!COOH$$
$$|$$
$$NH_2$$

Widely distributed.

669   L-Asparagine, $C_4H_8O_3N_2$, colorless crystals (Monohydrate), m.p. 234°, (dec.) (preheated bath), $[\alpha]_D^{20}$ −5.5° (c 1.3 in water).

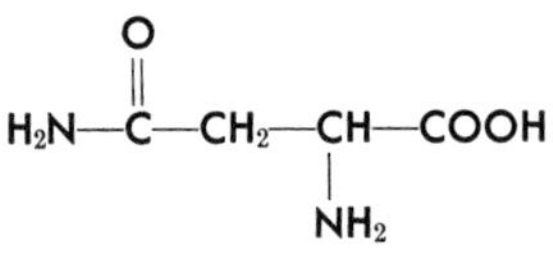

$$O$$
$$\|$$
$$H_2N\!-\!C\!-\!CH_2\!-\!CH\!-\!COOH$$
$$|$$
$$NH_2$$

Widely distributed.

670 *d*-Diaminosuccinic Acid, $C_4H_8O_4N_2$, colorless crystals, m.p. (dec.), 240–290°, $[\alpha]_D^{25}$ +28° (c 2.0 in 5% sodium hydroxide solution).

$$\text{HOOC—CH—CH—COOH}$$
$$\text{NH}_2 \quad \text{NH}_2$$

Streptomyces rimosus

This amino acid sometimes crystallizes from oxytetracycline broth concentrates. The yield is about 250–500 mg. per liter.

F. A. Hochstein, *J. Org. Chem.* 24 679 (1959).

671 O-Carbamyl-D-serine, $C_4H_8O_4N_2$, colorless needles, m.p. 226–234° (dec.), $[\alpha]_D$ −19.6° (c 2 in N hydrochloric acid).

$$\text{O}$$
$$\text{H}_2\text{N—C—O—CH}_2\text{—CH—COOH}$$
$$\text{NH}_2$$

Streptomyces polychromogenes

D-Serine or derivatives is also present in polymyxin, echinomycin, cycloserine and amicetin.

G. Hagemann, L. Pénasse and J. Teillon, *Biochim. et Biophys. Acta* 17 240 (1955).

672 Allantoic Acid, $C_4H_8O_4N_4$, colorless needles, m.p. 165° (dec.).

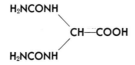

Coprinus miraceus, Collybia dryophila
R. Fosse and A. Brunel, *Compt. rend.* 197 288 (1933).

673 γ-Aminobutyric Acid, $C_4H_9O_2N$, colorless crystals, m.p. 202° (dec.) rapid heating.

$$\text{H}_2\text{N—CH}_2\text{—CH}_2\text{—CH}_2\text{—COOH}$$

Widely distributed.

674 L-(+)-α-Aminobutyric Acid, $C_4H_9O_2N$, colorless crystals, m.p. 270–280° (dec.), $[\alpha]_D^{20}$ +8.0° (c 1.0 in water).

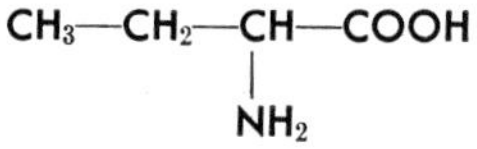

$$CH_3-CH_2-\underset{\underset{NH_2}{|}}{CH}-COOH$$

Escherichia coli, Corynebacterium diphtheriae
A. Polson, *Nature* 161 351 (1948).
Elizabeth Work, *Biochim. et Biophys. Acta* 3 400 (1949).

675 L-Threonine, $C_4H_9O_3N$, colorless crystals, m.p. 255–257° (dec.), $[\alpha]_D^{26}$ −28.3° (c 1.1 in water).

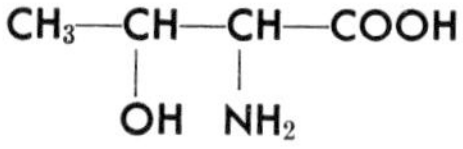

$$CH_3-\underset{\underset{OH}{|}}{CH}-\underset{\underset{NH_2}{|}}{CH}-COOH$$

Widely distributed.

676 S-Methyl-L-cysteine, $C_4H_9O_3NS$, colorless crystals, m.p. ~164° (dec.), $[\alpha]_D^{25}$ +125° (c 2.5 in water).

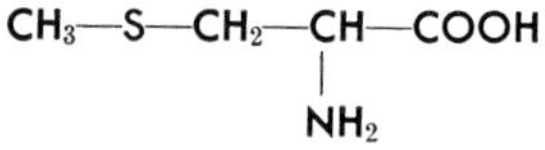

$$CH_3-S-CH_2-\underset{\underset{NH_2}{|}}{CH}-COOH$$

Neurospora crassa
James B. Ragland and James L. Livermore, *Arch. Biochem. and Biophys.* 65 574 (1956). (Isolation from neurospora)
Clayton J. Morris and John P. Thompson, *J. Am. Chem. Soc.* 78 1605 (1956). (Physical properties)

677 4-Imidazolyacetic Acid, $C_5H_6O_2N_2$, colorless needles (Hydrate), m.p. 222° (dec.).

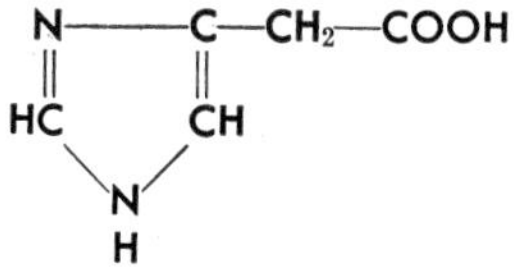

$$\begin{array}{c} N-\!\!\!-\!\!\!-C-CH_2-COOH \\ \| \qquad\quad \| \\ HC \qquad CH \\ \diagdown_{\underset{H}{N}}\diagup \end{array}$$

Polyporus sulfureus
P. H. List, *Planta Med.* 6 424 (1958).

678 Azaserine (Diazoacetyl-L-serine), $C_5H_7O_4N_3$, light yellow-green crystals, dec. 146–162°, $[\alpha]_D^{27.5}$ −0.5° (c 8.46 in water at pH 5.18).

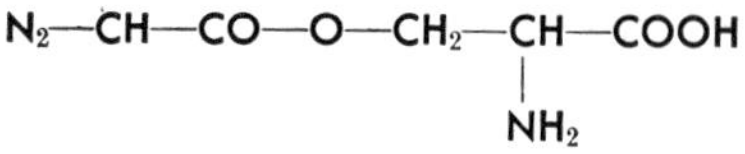

$$N_2-CH-CO-O-CH_2-\underset{\underset{NH_2}{|}}{CH}-COOH$$

An unclassified streptomycete

James A. Moore, John R. Dice, Ernest D. Nicolaides, Roger D. Westland and Eugene L. Wittle, *J. Am. Chem. Soc.* **76** 2884 (1954). (Synthesis)

C. Chester Stock, H. Christine Reilly, Sonja M. Buckley, Donald A. Clarke and C. P. Rhoads, *Nature* **173** 71 (1954).

John Ehrlich, Lucia E. Anderson, George L. Coffey, Arthur B. Hillegas, Mildred P. Knudsen, Harold J. Koepsell, Dorothy L. Kohberger and Julian E. Oyaas, *ibid.* **173** 72 (1954).

Quentin R. Bartz, Carole C. Elder, Roger P. Frohardt, Salvatore A. Fusari, Theodore H. Haskell, Doris W. Johannessen and Albert Ryder, *ibid.* **173** 72 (1954). (Isolation)

679 L-Proline, $C_5H_9O_2N$, colorless crystals, m.p. 220–222° (dec.) (rapid heating), $[\alpha]_D^{25}$ −80° (c 1.0 in water).

$$
\begin{array}{c}
CH_2\text{---}CH_2 \\
|\qquad\quad| \\
CH_2\quad CH\text{---}COOH \\
\diagdown\;\diagup \\
N \\
H
\end{array}
$$

Widely distributed.

680 L-Glutamic Acid, $C_5H_9O_4N$, colorless crystals, m.p. 247° (dec.), $[\alpha]_D^{22.4}$ +31.4° (c 1 in 6 N hydrochloric acid).

$$
\underset{\underset{NH_2}{|}}{HOOC\text{---}CH_2\text{---}CH_2\text{---}CH}\text{---}COOH
$$

Micrococcus varians

A 17% molar yield (from glucose) was reported.

Toshinobu Asai, Ko Aida, Kunio Oishi, *Bull. Agr. Chem. Soc.* (Japan) **21** 134 (1957).

681 L-Glutamine, $C_5H_{10}O_3N_2$, colorless crystals, m.p. 185° (dec.), $[\alpha]_D^{25}$ +5.9° (c 4.0 in water).

$$
\underset{\underset{NH_2}{|}}{H_2N\text{---}\overset{\overset{\displaystyle O}{\|}}{C}\text{---}CH_2\text{---}CH_2\text{---}CH}\text{---}COOH
$$

Widely distributed.

682 L-Valine, $C_5H_{11}O_2N$, colorless crystals, m.p. 315° (dec.) (closed capillary). Sublimes, $[\alpha]_D^{26}$ +14° (c 0.9 in water).

$$
\begin{array}{c}
CH_3 \\
\diagdown \\
\quad CH\text{---}\underset{\underset{NH_2}{|}}{CH}\text{---}COOH \\
\diagup \\
CH_3
\end{array}
$$

Widely distributed.

683 Betaine, $C_5H_{11}O_2N$, white prisms or leaflets, m.p. 293° (dec.).

$$(CH_3)_3\overset{\oplus}{N}-CH_2COO^{\ominus}$$

Aspergillus oryzae, Patella vulgata, Claviceps purpurea (Fries) Tul. and other fungi

Jacqueline Etiènne-Petitfils, *Bull. soc. chim. biol.* 38 1315 (1956).

684 L-Methionine, $C_5H_{11}O_2NS$, colorless crystals, m.p. ~280° (dec.) (sealed capillary), $[\alpha]_D^{25}$ −8° (c 1.0 in water).

$$CH_3S-CH_2CH_2CH-COOH$$
$$|$$
$$NH_2$$

Widely distributed.

685 L-Ornithine, $C_5H_{12}O_2N_2$, colorless crystals, m.p. 140° (subl. 120°), $[\alpha]_D^{25}$ +12° (c 6.5 in water).

$$H_2N-CH_2-CH_2-CH_2-CH-COOH$$
$$|$$
$$NH_2$$

Widely distributed.

686 Choline Sulfate, $C_5H_{13}O_4NS$

$$(CH_3)_3\overset{\oplus}{N}-CH_2CH_2-O-SO_3^{\ominus}$$

Aspergillus sydowi, Penicillium chrysogenum, lichens, yeasts

Choline yields of 6000–7000 μg. per gram of dry cell weight are available in certain Distillers' Dried Solubles.

D. W. Woolley and W. H. Peterson, *J. Biol. Chem.* 122 213 (1937).

J. deFlines, *J. Am. Chem. Soc.* 77 1676 (1955).

687 Imidazoleacetol (Hydrochloride), $C_6H_8O_2N_2 \cdot HCl$, white needles, m.p. 171–174° (dec.).

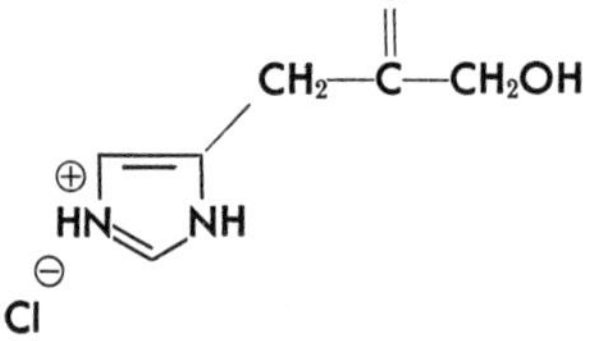

Neuorspora crassa and *E. coli* mutants

Bruce N. Ames, Herschel K. Mitchell and Mary B. Mitchell, *J. Am. Chem. Soc.* 75 1015 (1953).

688   L-**Histidine**, $C_6H_9O_2N_3$, colorless crystals, m.p. 287° (dec.), $[\alpha]_D^{20}$ −39.7° (c 1.13 in water).

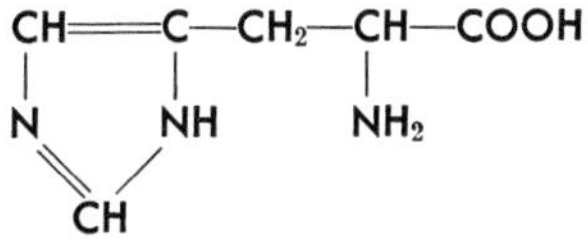

Claviceps purpurea (Fries) Tul.
H. Heath and Jennifer Wildy, *Biochem. J.* 64 612 (1956).

689   **6-Diazo-5-oxo-L-norleucine** (DON), $C_6H_9O_3N_3$, pale greenish yellow crystals, m.p. 145–155° (dec.), $[\alpha]_D^{26}$ +21° (c 5.4 in water).

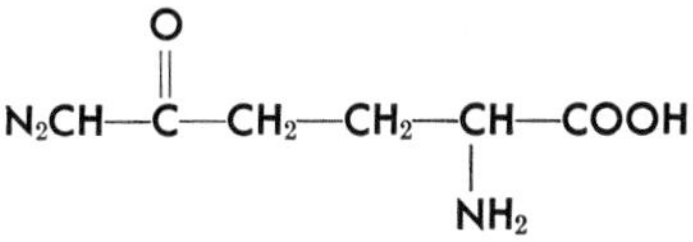

An unclassified streptomycete
Henry W. Dion, Salvatore A. Fusari, Zbigniew L. Jakubowski, John G. Zora and Quentin R. Bartz, *J. Am. Chem. Soc.* 78 3075 (1956). (Isolation and characterization)

690   **Imidazoleglycerol** (Hydrochloride), $C_6H_{10}O_3N_2 \cdot HCl$, colorless crystals, m.p. 103° (dec.), $[\alpha]_D^{25.6}$ +13.3° (c 7.5 in water).

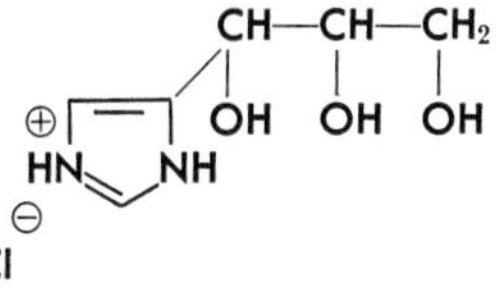

Neurospora crassa mutant
Bruce N. Ames and Herschel K. Mitchell, *J. Biol. Chem.* 212 687 (1955).

691   L-**Histidinol** (Hydrochloride), $C_6H_{11}ON_3 \cdot 2HCl$, colorless crystals, m.p. 194° (dec.).

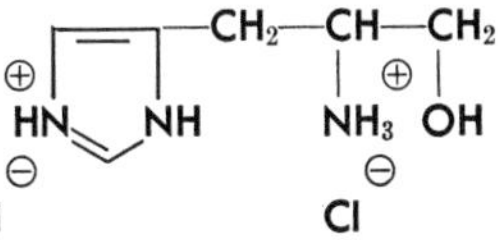

E. coli mutant
Henry J. Vogel, Bernard D. Davis and Elizabeth S. Mingioli, *J. Am. Chem. Soc.* 73 1897 (1951).

692 L-Leucine, $C_6H_{13}O_2N$, colorless crystals, m.p. ~295° (dec.) (sealed tube) (subl. from 140°), $[\alpha]_D^{25}$ −11° (c 2.0 in water).

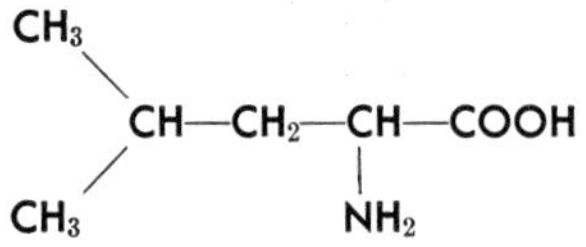

$$CH_3-CH-CH_2-CH-COOH$$
$$CH_3 \qquad \qquad NH_2$$

Widely distributed.

693 L-Isoleucine, $C_6H_{13}O_2N$, colorless crystals, m.p. 284° (dec.) (subl. from 160°), $[\alpha]_D^{20}$ +11° (c 3.0 in water).

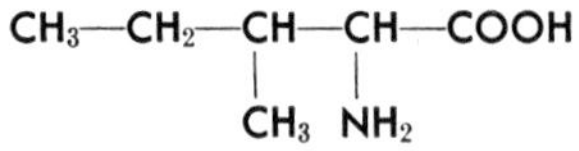

$$CH_3-CH_2-CH-CH-COOH$$
$$CH_3 \ \ NH_2$$

Widely distributed.

694 L-α-Aminoadipic Acid, $C_6H_{11}O_4N$, white crystals, m.p. 206° (dec.).

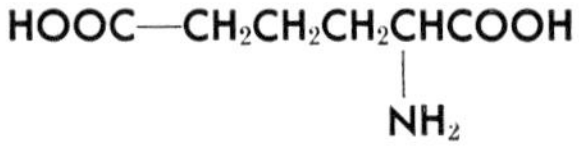

$$HOOC-CH_2CH_2CH_2CHCOOH$$
$$NH_2$$

Aspergillus oryzae
Also a component of several antibiotics.
Emmanuel Windsor, *J. Biol. Chem.* 192 595 (1951).

695 L-Lysine, $C_6H_{14}O_2N_2$, white needles, m.p. 224°.

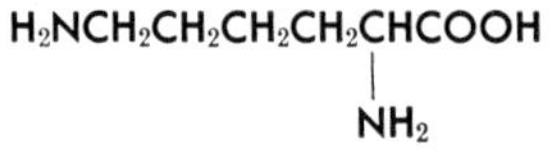

$$H_2NCH_2CH_2CH_2CH_2CHCOOH$$
$$NH_2$$

Ustilago maydis PRL 1092
The yield was 200–300 mg. per liter of free lysine in the broth as determined by a bioassay (not isolated).
M. Richards and R. H. Haskins, *Can. J. Microbiol.* 3 543 (1957).

696 L-Arginine, $C_6H_{14}O_2N_4$, colorless crystals (Dihydrate), m.p. 245° (dec.) (browning above 200°), $[\alpha]_D^{20}$ +13° (c 3.5 in water).

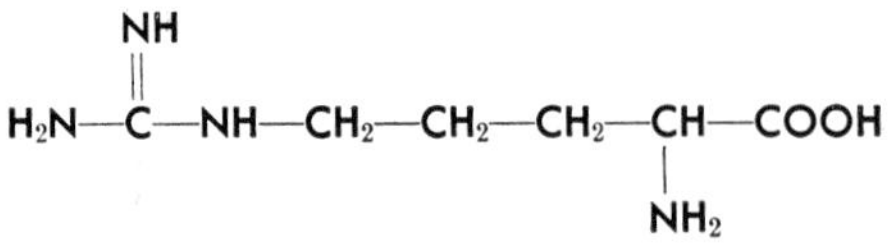

$$NH$$
$$\|$$
$$H_2N-C-NH-CH_2-CH_2-CH_2-CH-COOH$$
$$NH_2$$

Widely distributed.

697 **δ-Oxy-L-lysine** (α,ε-Diamino-δ-hydroxycaproic acid), $C_6H_{14}O_3N_2$.

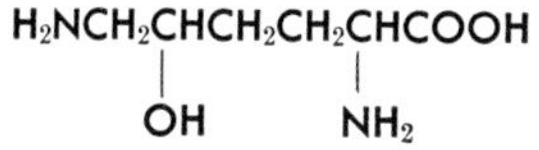
H2NCH2CHCH2CH2CHCOOH
OH
NH2

Mycobacterium phlei

Occurs bound in a phosphatide (yellow powder, m.p. 180–190°), molecular weight about 16,000. It is the sole amino acid, and constitutes about 1% of the phosphatide.

M. Barbier and E. Lederer, *Biochim. et Biophys. Acta* **8** 590 (1952).

698 **Anthranilic Acid,** $C_7H_7O_2N$, leaflets, m.p. 144°.

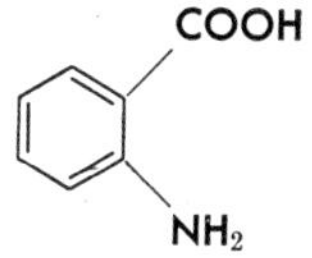
COOH
NH2

Corynebacterium diphtheriae

Detected by paper chromatography.

A. J. Woiwood and F. V. Linggood, *Intern. Congr. Biochem., Abstrs. of Communs.* 1st Congr., Cambridge, England, 320 (1949).

Anthranilic acid has been isolated also from a pseudomonas culture:

Rokuro Takeda and I. Nakanishi, *J. Fermentation Technol.* **37** No. 2 (1959).

It also accumulates in certain bacterial auxotrophs.

699 *p*-**Aminobenzoic Acid,** $C_7H_7O_2N$, yellowish red crystals, m.p. 186°.

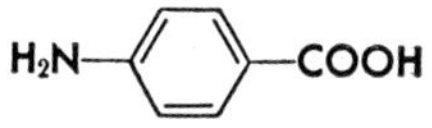
H2N
COOH

Hansenula anomala, Mycotorula lipolytica

Yields about 1 mg. per gram of dry cells.

W. H. Peterson, "Yeasts in Feeding" Symposium, Milwaukee, 1948.

700 **Trigonelline,** $C_7H_7O_2N$, colorless crystals, m.p. (anhyd.) 218° (dec.) (Picrate) m.p. 205° (dec.).

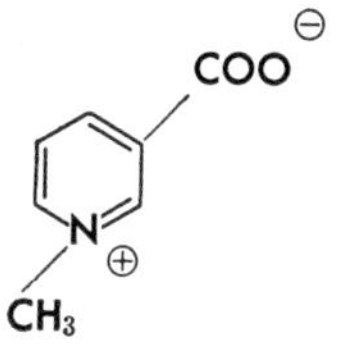
COO
N
CH3

Polyporus sulfureus
P. H. List, *Planta Med.* 6 424 (1958).

701 **Homarine,** $C_7H_7O_2N$ (Hydrochloride), m.p. 170–175° (dec.) (Picrate) m.p. 155–160°.

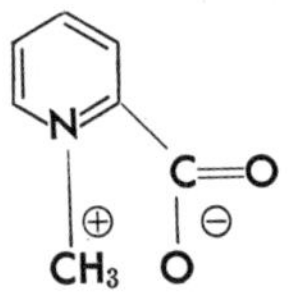
N
C=O
⊕
⊖
CH3
O

Polyporus sulfureus
P. H. List, *Planta Med.* 6 424 (1958).

702 **Stachydrine,** $C_7H_{13}O_2N$, white monohydrated crystals, m.p. (anhydr.) 235° (dec.).

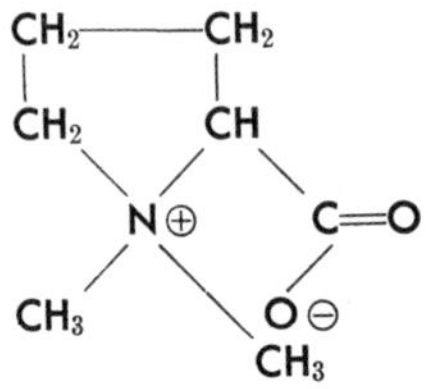
CH2
CH2
CH2
CH
N⊕
C=O
CH3
O⊖
CH3

Aspergillus oryzae, other fungi (in small yields)
R. Takata, *J. Soc. Chem. Ind. Japan* 32 155B (1929).

703 **2,6-Diaminopimelic Acid** (Both L,L- and *meso* forms occur naturally), $C_7H_{14}O_4N_2$, colorless needles, m.p. >305°.

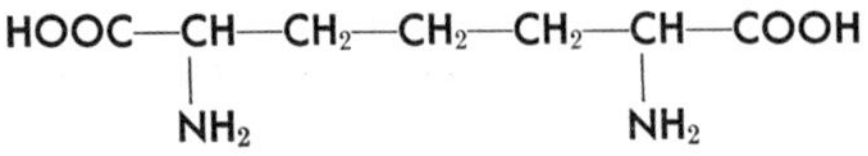
HOOC—CH—CH2—CH2—CH2—CH—COOH
NH2
NH2

Corynebacterium diphtheriae, Mycobacterium tuberculosis, Bacillus anthracis, E. coli mutants
Elizabeth Work, *Biochem. J.* 49 17 (1951).
H. Smith, R. E. Strange and H. T. Zwartouw, *Nature* 178 865 (1956).
Lester E. Casida, Jr., U. S. Patent 2,771,396 (1956).

704 **β-Methyllanthionine,** $C_7H_{14}O_4N_2S$, $[\alpha]_D^{20}$ +37.6° (c 0.5 in 1 N hydrochloric acid).

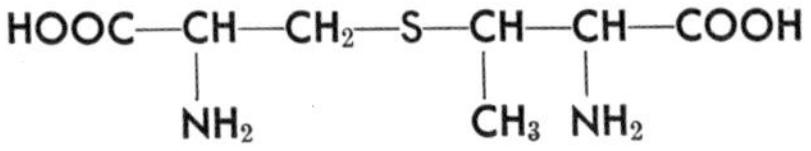
HOOC—CH—CH2—S—CH—CH—COOH
NH2
CH3
NH2

Yeast
This isomer is not the same as the one isolated from

antibiotic hydrolysates. Desulfurization with Raney nickel yields L-alanine and D-α-amino-n-butyric acid.

  Phyllis F. Downey and Simon Black, *J. Biol. Chem.* 228 171 (1957).

705 L-**Phenylalanine,** $C_9H_{11}O_2N$, colorless crystals, m.p. 283° (dec.) (rapid heating), $[\alpha]_D^{20}$ −35° (c 2 in water).

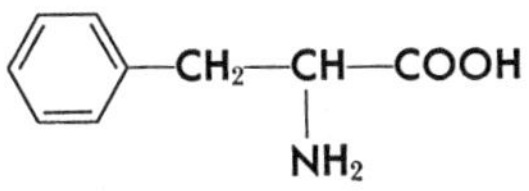

 Widely distributed.

706 L-**Tyrosine,** $C_9H_{11}O_3N$, colorless crystals, m.p. 342–344° (sealed capillary, preheated bath) (dec.), $[\alpha]_D^{22}$ −10.6° (c 4 in 1 N hydrochloric acid).

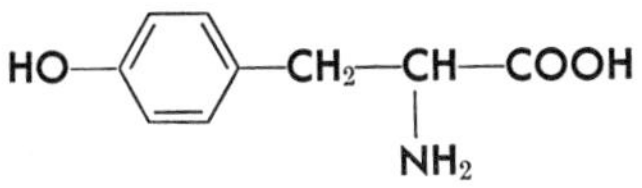

 Widely distributed.

707 **Hercynine** (Histidine Betaine), $C_9H_{15}O_2N_3$, white crystals, no sharp m.p., forms mono- and dipicrates.

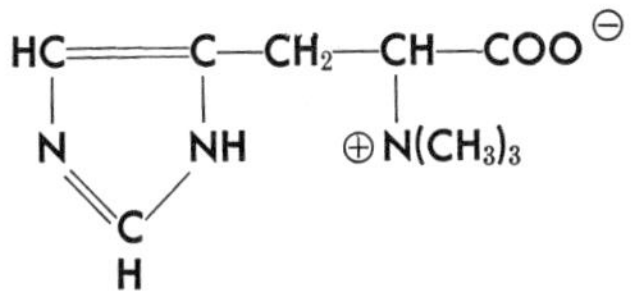

 Amanita muscaria, Agaricus campestris, Boletus edulis Bull., *Polyporus sulfureus*

  Fr. Kutscher, *Zentr. Physiol.* 24 775 (1910).
  R. Engeland and F. Kutscher, *ibid.* 26 569 (1912). (Synthesis)
  Albert Küng, *Z. physiol. Chem.* 91 241 (1914).

708 **Ergothioneine,** $C_9H_{15}O_2N_3S$, colorless crystals, m.p. 290° (dec.), $[\alpha]_D$ +116.5°.

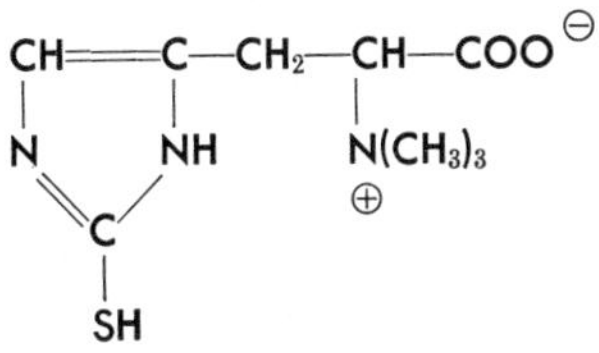

Claviceps purpurea (Fries), Tul. *Coprinus comatus, Mycobacterium tuberculosis*

C. Tanret, *J. pharm. chim.* 30 145 (1909).

H. Heath and Jennifer Wildy, *Biochem. J.* 64 612 (1956). (Biosynthesis)

Paul Heinz List, *Arch. Pharm.* 290 517 (1957).

Dorothy S. Genghof, *Bact. Proc.*, 190 (1960).

709 L-**Tryptophan**, $C_{11}H_{12}O_2N_2$, colorless crystals, m.p. 289° (dec.) (rapid heating), $[\alpha]_D^{23}$ −31.5 (c 1.0 in water).

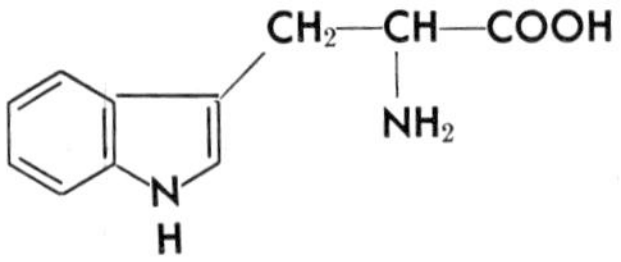

Widely distributed.

710 **Amino Acid from *Lactarius helvus***, $C_{11}H_{18}O_4N_2$, colorless crystals, yellowing near 200° and darkening to 300°. Molecular weight 251 by isothermal distillation. Adds 2 H_2 and 2 Br_2.

Partial structure:

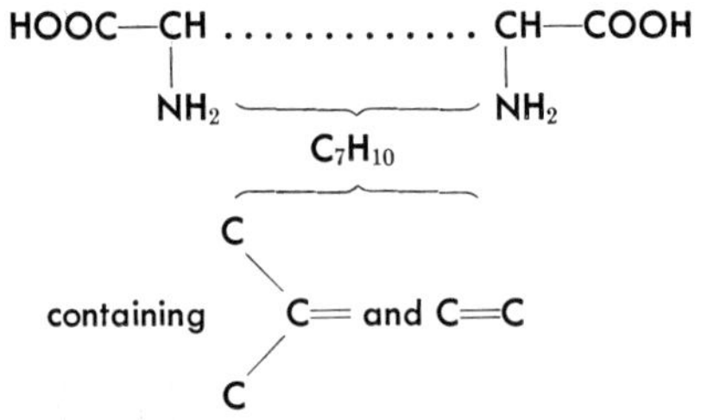

Lactarius helvus

Ateushi Komamine and Artturi Virtanen, *Acta Chem. Scand.* 13 2141 (1959).

J. Casimir and A. I. Virtanen, *ibid.* 13 2139 (1959). (Isolation)

711 **Elaiomycin**, $C_{13}H_{26}O_3N_2$, pale yellow oil, $[\alpha]_D^{26}$ +38.4° (c 2.8 in absolute ethanol).

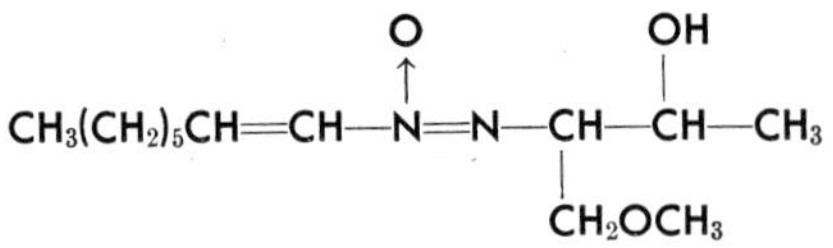

Streptomyces hepaticus

Theodore H. Haskell, Albert Ryder and Quentin R. Bartz, *Antibiotics and Chemotherapy* 4 141 (1954).   (Isolation)

John Ehrlich, Lucia E. Anderson, George L. Coffey, William H. Feldman, Myron W. Fisher, Arther B. Hillegas, Alfred G. Karlson, Mildred P. Knudsen, Jean K. Weston, Anne S. Youmans and Guy P. Youmans, *ibid.* 4 338 (1954).

C. L. Stevens, B. T. Gillis, J. C. French and T. H. Haskell, *J. Am. Chem. Soc.* 78 3229 (1956).   (Structure)

17

Polypeptides and Related Compounds

Polypeptides are often intractable, difficultly crystallizable substances. The newer techniques of chromatography, end-group analysis and electrophoresis have facilitated their investigation.

Most of the polypeptides and related compounds listed in this section are antibiotic isolates. Antibiosis may be a primary or only a secondary function of these materials. Polypeptides, of course, have hormonal and other functions in higher animals. Among microorganisms streptomycetes and bacteria have been the richest sources so far, perhaps in part because they have been examined more extensively for antibiotic activity than other microorganisms.

Special types of polypeptides have been isolated from bacterial cell walls by fragmentation with lysozyme or bacteriophage. They also tend to accumulate when bacteria are inhibited by certain antibiotics. Determination of their structures is beginning to elucidate the nature of the bacterial cell wall as well as the mode of action of the antibiotics involved.

Some attention has been given to intracellular peptides, principally in connection with their role in protein synthesis. The fundamental process of polypeptide and protein biosynthesis is just beginning to yield some of its secrets. Before discussing it, some earlier work on simpler polypeptide biosynthesis will be reviewed.

Glutathione is a widely distributed tripeptide which has a rapid metabolic turnover in yeast and also in mammalian tissues. Partly for this reason it has been suggested as an intermediate in protein biosynthesis, but because of its reversible oxidation-reduction properties, a respiratory role also has been proposed. In fact, it has not been proved satisfactorily that polypeptides serve as direct precursors for protein synthesis in microorganisms, although strepogenins (glutamic acid containing oligopeptides from the enzymic digests of certain proteins) stimulate the growth of some bacteria. There is evidence for the occurrence of independent uptake mechanisms for glycine and glycine peptides in *Lactobacillus casei*.[1]

Glutathione formation takes place in two separate reactions, each involving ATP:[2]

(1) L-Glutamic Acid + L-Cysteine + ATP→
    L-γ-Glutamylcysteine + ADP + H_3PO_4.

(2) L-γ-Glutamylcysteine + Glycine + ATP→
    L-Glutathione + ADP + H_3PO_4.

The biosynthesis of pantothenic acid probably proceeds as follows, the last step also being coupled with ATP cleavage, but with different products:[3, 4]

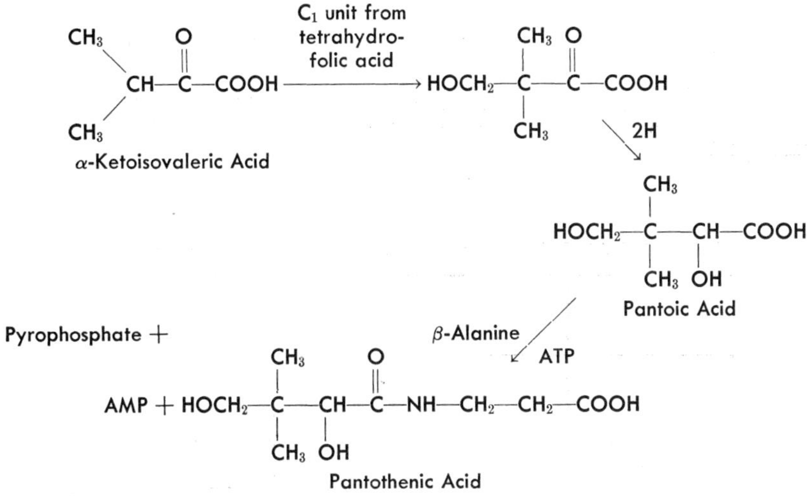

α-Ketoisovaleric Acid

Pantoic Acid

Pyrophosphate +

β-Alanine   ATP

AMP + Pantothenic Acid

---

[1] Franklin R. Leach and Esmond E. Snell, *Biochim. et Biophys. Acta* **34** 292 (1959).

[2] John E. Snoke and Konrad Bloch, *J. Biol. Chem.* **199** 407 (1952); John E. Snoke, *ibid.* **213** 813 (1955); John E. Snoke and Konrad Bloch, *ibid.* **213** 825 (1955); Stanley Mandeles and Konrad Bloch, *ibid.* **214** 639 (1955).

[3] Werner K. Maas and Henry J. Vogel, *J. Bacteriol.* **65** 388 (1953); M. Purko, W. O. Nelson and W. A. Wood, *J. Biol. Chem.* **207** 51 (1954); E. Nelson McIntosh, M. Purko and W. A. Wood, *ibid.*, **228** 499 (1957).

[4] Werner K. Maas, *J. Biol. Chem.* **198** 23 (1952); Akira Matsuyama, *Bull. Agr. Chem. Soc.* (Japan) **21** 47 (1957) and earlier papers in this series; Herbert S. Ginoza and Robert A. Altenbern, *Arch. Biochem. and Biophys.* **56** 537 (1955).

It appears that an adenylic acid-pantoate complex is the intermediate which couples with the enzyme.

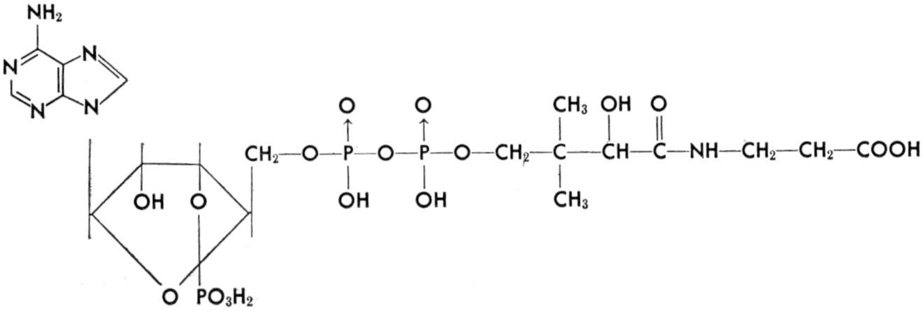

Pantothenylcysteine is a precursor of pantetheine in *Lactobacillus helveticus*.[5]

The red actinomycins were the first antibiotics isolated crystalline from actinomycetes.[6] In the ensuing 20 years about a dozen named species of streptomycetes have been found to produce actinomycins, and probably many other isolates have gone unreported.

TABLE I

Chronological List of Microorganisms Reported to Produce Actinomycins*

Year reported	Name given to microorganism	Actinomycin complex†
1941	Streptomyces antibioticus	A
1946	Non-chromogenic species	A
1947	S. flavus	A (J)
1948	S. parvus	A
	S. flavovirens	—
1949	Streptomyces sp.	B
	S. chrysomallus	C
1951	S. flaveolus	A (J)
	Micromonospora globosa	—
1952	Streptomyces sp.	X

[5] Gene M. Brown, *J. Biol. Chem.* 226 651 (1957).
[6] S. A. Waksman and H. B. Woodruff, *Proc. Soc. Exp. Biol.* 45 609 (1940).

TABLE 1—Continued

Year reported	Name given to microorganism	Actinomycin complex†
1954	S. flavus	X (B)
	S. flavus	X
	S. antibioticus	X
	S. flavus-parvus	X (B)
	S. parvullus	D
	S. cellulosae	—
	S. michiganensis	X
	S. antibioticus	M
1956	Streptomyces sp.	E
	Streptomyces sp.	F
1958	S. fradiae	Z, X

* By courtesy of Dr. H. Boyd Woodruff, Merck, Sharpe and Dohme, and the New York Academy of Science.

† See the discussion of nomenclature preceding the actinomycin entries.

Often these polypeptide pigments occur in closely related complexes, the individual members varying only by slight changes in the side-chains.

The chromophore, actinocinin, resembles that of the ommochromes, a group of insect pigments studied by Butenandt,[7] and it is similar to the pigment cinnabarin from a higher fungus.

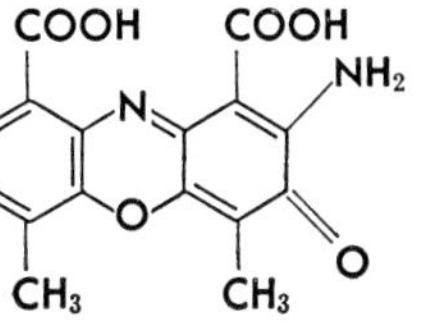

Actinocinin

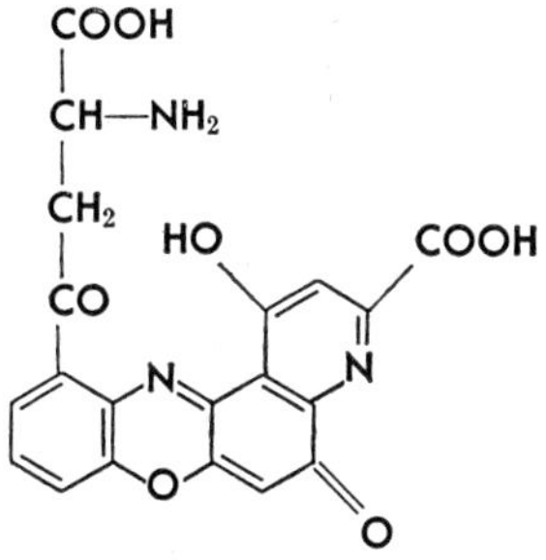

Xanthommatin

[7] Adolph Butenandt, Ulrich Schiedt, Ernst Biekert and Pierre Kornmann, *Ann.* 586 217 (1954); Adolph Butenandt, Ulrich Schiedt and Ernst Biekert, *Ann.* 586 229, 588 106 (1954); Adolph Butenandt, Ulrich Schiedt, Ernst Biekert and R. Jan. T. Cromartie, *Ann.* 590 75 (1954). (Structure)

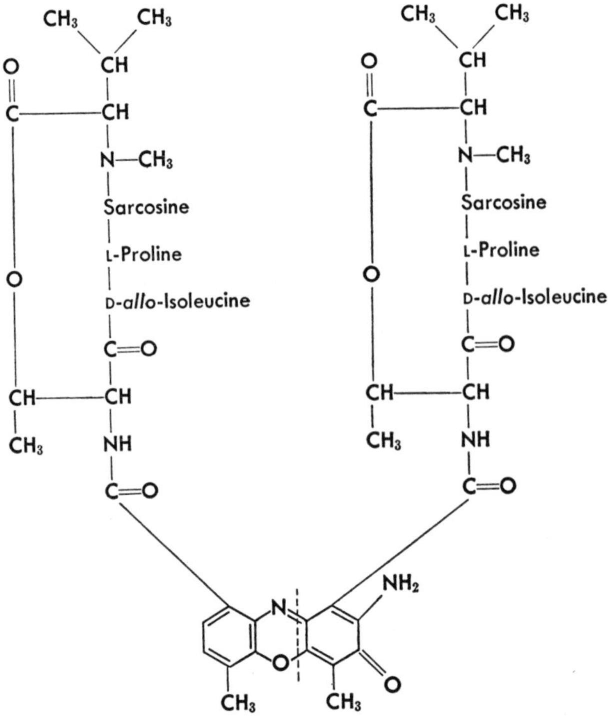

Actinomycin C₃

The dual nature of the actinomycin molecules makes it rather obvious that they must be formed by condensation of two similar halves. Butenandt showed that xanthommatin was derived from tryptophan by feeding experiments with the labeled amino acid. Similarly Katz has shown[8] that actinocinin is derived from tryptophan. Thus the entire actinomycin molecule is composed of amino acid derivatives. In the case of xanthommatin the intermediate is kynurenine, a known degradation product of tryptophan. Kynurenine may also be an intermediate in actinocinin biosynthesis, although the assumed intermediate, 3-oxy-4-methyl-anthranilic acid might equally well arise through a variation in the biosynthetic route to tryptophan.

[8] Edward Katz, N. Y. Acad. Sci. Conference on Actinomycins, March 31 to April 1, 1960. (Unpublished)

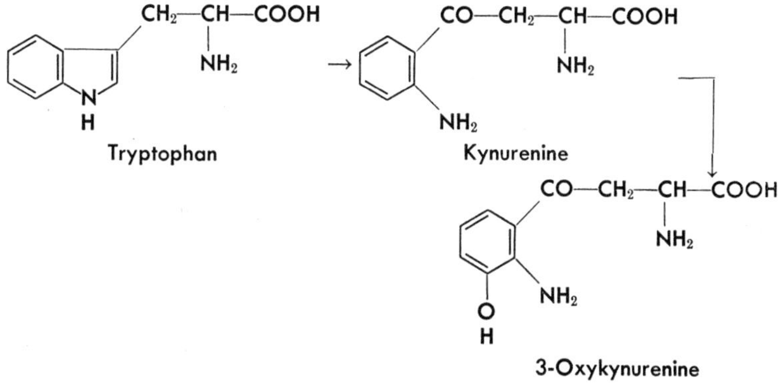

Tryptophan → Kynurenine

3-Oxykynurenine

It is likely that the peptide side-chain is attached before condensation to form the chromophore.

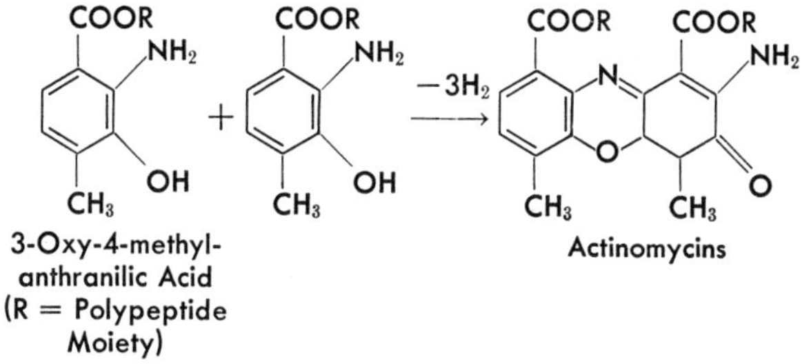

3-Oxy-4-methyl-
anthranilic Acid
(R = Polypeptide
Moiety)

Actinomycins

It is interesting that methyltryptophans (α,5,6-methyls) are inhibitory to actinomycin production. Methionine is probably the donor of the methyl groups in N-methylvaline and sarcosine.[8]

In two streptomycete species D-valine inhibits actinomycin synthesis while L-valine stimulates it, although D-valine is the isomer present in the side-chains.[8] This behavior is reminiscent of the results of similar earlier experiments with penicillin and with valinomycin.

Schmidt-Kastner found that addition of a large quantity of sarcosine to the medium caused replacement of part or all of the side-chain proline by sarcosine. Analogously, addition of isoleucine caused replacement of N-methylvaline by N-methylisoleucine.[9] Since then many new actinomycins have been prepared by addition of various amino acids to the medium. Even

[9] G. Schmidt-Kastner, *Naturwissenschaften* 43 131 (1956).

pipecolic acid can be incorporated.[10] It should be noted that certain amino acid analogues can be incorporated into enzymes and other proteins without impairing their normal functions.[11]

Professor Hans Brockmann and his collaborators at Göttingen, who were primarily responsible for determining the structure of the first well-characterized actinomycin, actinomycin C_3,[12] have succeeded in synthesizing this substance[13] and it should be possible now to prepare an even wider variety of actinomycins.

Valinomycin, shown opposite, can be hydrolyzed to its constituents: L-valine, D-valine, D-α-hydroxyisovaleric acid and L-lactic acid. It has been found[14] that L-valine-1-C^{14} in the medium was incorporated to an equal extent into the D-valyl and L-valyl portions of the molecule, to a lesser extent into the D-α-hydroxyisovaleric acid, and not at all into the lactic acid. D-Valine-1-C^{14} was incorporated only to a slight extent. Similar results have been obtained in studies on the origin of the D-valine moieties in penicillin and in actinomycin.

The co-occurrence of valine with the biosynthetically related α-hydroxyisovaleric acid in several polypeptides is noteworthy. Also conjugated with certain polypeptides are 6-methyloctanoic

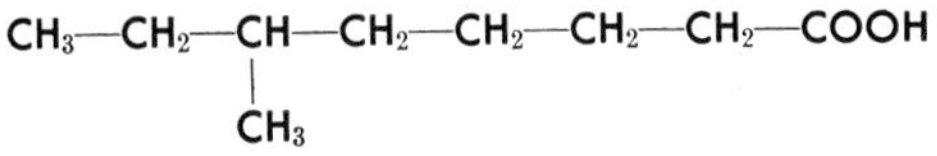

$$CH_3-CH_2-CH-CH_2-CH_2-CH_2-CH_2-COOH$$
$$|$$
$$CH_3$$

6-Methyloctanoic Acid

$$CH_3-CH_2-CH_2-CH_2-CH_2-CH_2-CH_2-CH-CH_2-COOH$$
$$|$$
$$OH$$

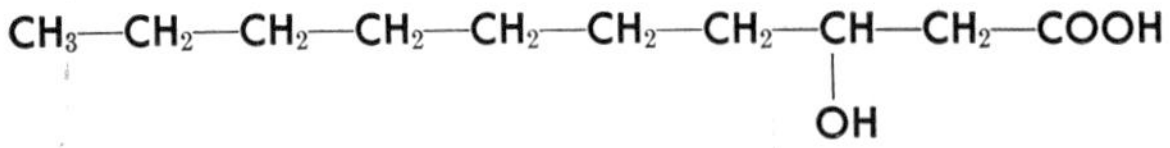

3-Oxydecanoic Acid

acid and 3-oxydecanoic acid. The latter substance has been found conjugated with bacterial carbohydrates too.

[10] Edward Katz and William Goss, *Nature* 182 1668 (1958); S. A. Waksman, E. Katz, W. A. Goss, L. H. Pugh, M. Solvtorowsky, and N. A. Auerbach, *Science* 129 1290 (1959); E. Katz and W. A. Goss, *Biochem. J.* 73 458 (1959); A. W. Johnson and A. B. Mauger, *ibid.* 73 535 (1959); William A. Goss and Edward Katz, *Antibiotics and Chemotherapy* 10 221 (1960).

[11] *E.g.*, Akira Yoshida and Mekoto Yamasaki, *Biochim. et Biophys. Acta* 34 158 (1959).

[12] H. Brockmann, G. Bohnsack, B. Franck, H. Gröne, H. Muxfeldt and C. Süling, *Angew. Chem.* 68 70 (1956); H. Brockmann, N. Grubhofer, H. Kalbe and W. Kass, *Chem. Ber.* 84 260 (1951); H. Brockmann, *Angew. Chem.* 66 1 (1954); H. Brockmann and B. Franck, *ibid.* 68 70 (1956) and other papers in this series.

[13] H. Brockmann, W. Sunderkötter, K. W. Ohly and P. Boldt, *Naturwissenschaften* 47 230 (1960); H. Brockmann and H. Lackner, *ibid.* 47 320 (1960).

[14] J. C. MacDonald, *Can. J. Microbiol.* 6 27 (1960).

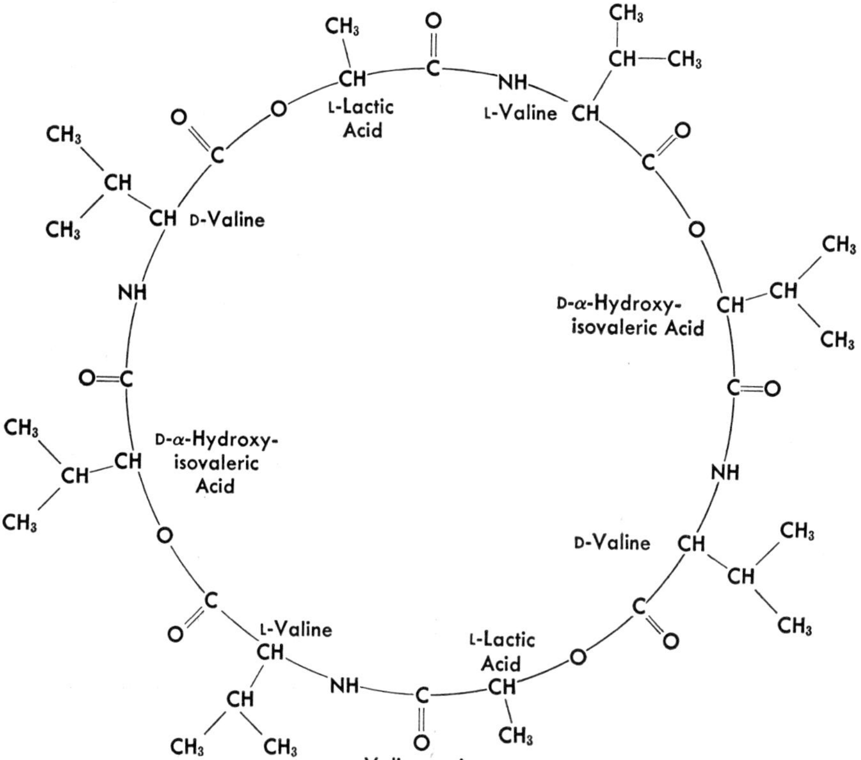

Valinomycin

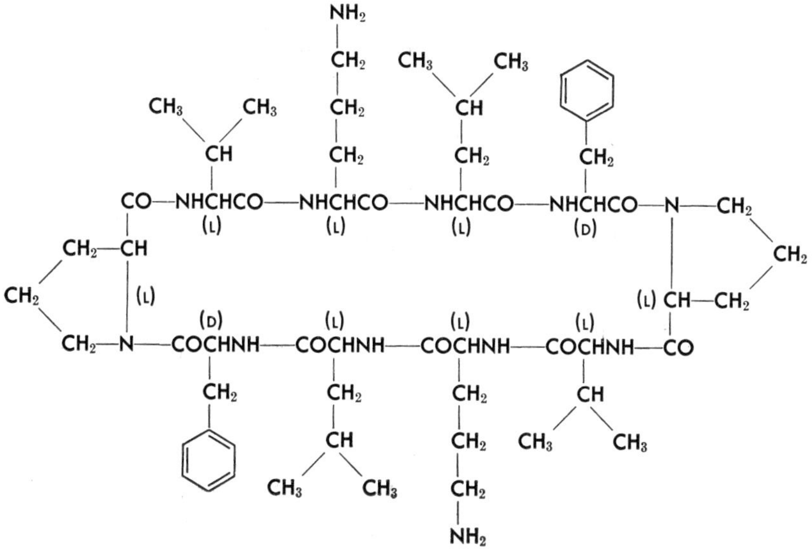

Gramicidin S

The biosynthesis of gramicidin S has been studied.[15] The conclusions were: (a) The five amino acids of the cyclic decapeptide pass through a number of intermediates before or during incorporation. (b) Final formation of gramicidin S is a simple reaction not requiring free amino acids which occurs readily in cell-free suspensions. (c) Three peptides were isolated containing fragments of the amino acid sequences of the antibiotic. These may or may not have been intermediates.

It is possible to extract intracellular peptides with suitable solvents. This has been done with mammalian pituitary tissue,[16, 17] with plant seeds[18] and with yeast[19] and bacteria.[20, 21] In all cases cited care was taken to obviate contamination by fragments of proteolysis. There is some indication that yields are higher from rapidly growing bacteria than from resting cells.

The intracellular peptides of the torula yeast studied were found to be predominantly acidic with glutamic acid the principal amino acid. About 40 peptides were purified in adequate quantity to permit hydrolysis and identification of constituent amino acids. These are tabulated below (x indicates an unidentified ninhydrin-positive substance):

TABLE II

Some Intracellular Peptides of Torula Yeast

Peptide No.	Amino acid content	Peptide No.	Amino acid content
1	Glu, x-6, Gly, Ala, Asp, Arg, Val	21	Glu (Gly, x-3, Ala)
		22	Glu, Gly, Cys (Glutathione)

[15] J. M. Barry and Elizabeth Ishihara, *Nature* 181 1274 (1958).

[16] T. Winnick, R. E. Winnick, R. Acher and C. Fromageot, *Biochim. et Biophys. Acta* 18 488 (1955).

[17] L. K. Ramachandran and T. Winnick, *ibid.* 23 533 (1957).

[18] H. Borriss and G. Schneider, *Naturwissenschaften* 42 103 (1955).

[19] F. Turba and H. Esser, *Biochem. Z.* 327 93 (1956).

[20] G. E. Connell and R. W. Watson, *Biochim. et Biophys. Acta* 24 226 (1957).

[21] R. B. Roberts, P. H. Abelson, D. C. Cowie, E. T. Bolton and R. J. Britten, "Studies of Biosynthesis in *E. coli*," Carnegie Institute, Washington, D. C., 1955.

TABLE II—Continued

Peptide No.	Amino acid content	Peptide No.	Amino acid content
2	Glu, Gly, Ala, Asp, Ser, Val, x-7, Arg	23	Glu, Gly, Ala, His, Arg or. Cys, x-6, Asp, Lys, Val
3	Glu, Gly, Asp, Ala, Thr? x-6, Arg?	24	Glu, Gly, Ala, x-7, x-11, Asp, Ser, Leu, Val, Arg, Lys
4	Glu, Gly, Ala, Thr? Asp, Arg, His, Val, x-5	25	Gly, Glu, x-6, Ser, Ala, His, Val, Leu, Asp
5	Glu, Gly, Ala, His, Asp, x-4	26	Glu, Gly, x-4, Ala, His, Lys,
6	Glu, Gly, Ala, x-5, Asp, Arg, Val, His		Leu
7	Glu, Gly, His, Ala, x-5, Asp, Arg, Val	27	Gly, Ala, Glu, x-4, Val, Arg
8	Glu, Gly, Ala, Asp, x-4, His, Arg	28	Glu, Gly, x-11, Ser, Ala, Arg, Thr, X-7, Asp, Val, Lys
9	Asp, Gly, Glu, Ala, x-5, Val, Arg	29	Glu, Gly, Ser, Ala, x-11, Asp, Thr, Val, Lys, Arg, Leu
10	Ala, Gly, Glu, x-5, x-6, Val	30	Glu, Gly, Ser, Ala, x-8, Asp, Thr, x-11, Val, Leu, Arg
11	x-4, x-7, x-5, Gly, Glu, Ala, Asp	31	Gly, Glu, x-4, Ser, Ala, Asp, Leu
12	Asp (Gly, Glu, Ala, x-5, x-6)	32	Gly, x-5, Glu, Ala, Asp, Arg
13	Glu, Gly, Ala, Asp, x-5	33	Glu, Gly, x-6, Ala, α-But, Leu
14	Glu, Gly, Ala, x-5, x-8, Ser, Asp, Val, Arg?	34	x-3, Ala, Gly, Glu, x-7, Ser, Asp, Val, Arg, Leu
15	Ala, Gly, Glu, x-4, x-6, Asp	35	Gly, Glu, Ala, x-7, Arg, Asp, Val, Leu
16	Glu, Gly, His, Ala, Cys, x-4	36	Arg? x-3, Gly, Glu, Ser., Ala, x-8, x-12, Asp, Thr, Val, Leu
17	Glu, Gly, Cys, x-10, Ala, Ser, x-6, Asp, Arg, Val, Leu	37	Gly, Glu, Ser, Ala, Asp, x-5, Arg, x-9, Thr? Val
18	Glu, Gly, x-9, Ser, Ala, Asp, Thr, Cys? Arg, x-5	38	Gly, Ser, Gly, Ala, Asp, Val, x-6, Thr, Arg, Lys, His, x-12
19	Gly, Glu, x-6, Ala, Ser, Asp, Val, Leu, His	39	Gly, Glu, Ala, x-6, Leu, Val, Thr, Asp, x-11, His, Lys
20	Glu, Gly, Ala, Asp, x-7, Ser, Tyr, Val, Leu, His	40	Gly, Glu, x-5, Ala, α-But, Val

In a similar study with the use of *E. coli* ten intracellular peptides were purified in sufficient amounts to allow amino acid determination.[22] In this case the N-terminal amino acids were

[22] D. Grünberger, Jiřina Černá and F. Šorm, *Experientia* **16** 54 (1960).

distinguished by formation of their dinitrophenyl derivatives. The results are shown in the following table:

TABLE III

Some Intracellular Peptides of Escherichia coli

Peptide No.	Terminal amino acid	(Other amino acids)
1	Glu	(Cys, Gly, Lys)
2	Glu	(Ala, Cys, Gly, Lys)
3	Asp	(Cys, Gly, Lys)
4	Lys	(Ala, Arg, Asp, Cys, Gly, Glu, Ser)
5	Asp	(Arg, Gly, Glu, γ-NH$_2$But, Lys, Val)
6	Ser	(Asp, Gly, Lys)
7	Ala	(Asp, Lys)
8	Glu	(Ala, Asp, Cys, Gly, Lys, Leu, Val)
9	Glu	(Ala, Asp, Lys, Cys, Gly)
10	Glu	(Cys, Gly)

It has been reported that gram-negative bacteria contain much less intracellular free ninhydrin-positive substances than do gram-positive ones.[21]

A basic polypeptide has been extracted from dried cells of the human strain of *Mycobacterium tuberculosis* $H_{37}R_v$, purified, crystallized and quantitatively analyzed for amino acid constituents.[23] The pure peptide showed activity in the tuberculin test at least equal to that of standard old tuberculin. The amino acid content was as follows, subscripts indicating number of moles:

$$\text{Arg}_{10} \text{ His}_1 \text{ Lys}_2 \text{ Phe}_1 \text{ Tyr}_1 \text{ Leu}_3 \text{ Ileu}_2 \text{ Val}_5$$
$$\text{Ala}_9 \text{ Gly}_6 \text{ Glu}_8 \text{ Pro}_5 \text{ Ser}_2 \text{ Thr}_3 \text{ Asp}_6 \text{ Try}_1$$

The molecular weight was calculated to be 7180.

Certain polypeptides accumulate in *E. coli* cells grown in the presence of chloramphenicol (a protein synthesis inhibitor). Two of these have been isolated and purified.[24]

[23] Yuichi Yamamura, Seisi Morizawa, Atsushi Tanaka, and Kenji Shojima, *Proc. Jap. Acad. Sci.* 35 295 (1959); Seisi Morizawa, Atsushi Tanaka, Kenji Shojima and Yuichi Yamamura, *Biochim. et Biophys. Acta* 38 252 (1960).

[24] F. Šorm and Jiřina Černá, *Collection Czechoslov. Chem. Commun.* 25 565 (1960).

Synthesis of the cell wall mucopeptides of staphylococci is unaffected by chloramphenicol, but inhibited (at least indirectly) by penicillin, bacitracin, cycloserine, novobiocin and gentian violet. None of these inhibits protein synthesis.

Penicillin-inhibited *Staphylococcus aureus* accumulates three closely related uridine nucleotides.[25] One of these has been assigned the structure:[26, 27, 28]

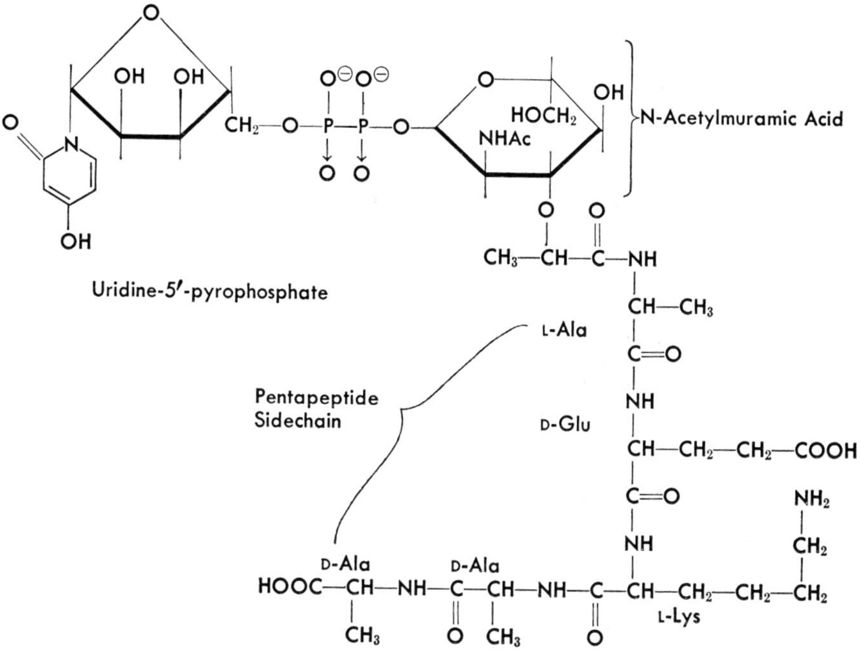

Uridine-5'-pyrophosphate

N-Acetylmuramic Acid

Pentapeptide Sidechain

L-Ala

D-Glu

D-Ala   D-Ala

L-Lys

This fragment may be the repeating unit of an activated cell wall precursor, since the ratio of muramic acid:alanine:glutamic acid:lysine is 1:3:1:1, the same ratio found in lysozyme digests of whole bacteria. In *E. coli* and *Corynebacterium diphtheriae* the lysine in the peptide chain is replaced by its biosynthetic precursor, *meso*-diaminopimelic acid.

[25] J. T. Park and N. J. Johnson, *J. Biol. Chem.* 179 585 (1949).

[26] J. T. Park and J. L. Strominger, *Science* 125 99 (1957).

[27] J. L. Strominger, *J. Biol. Chem.* 234 1520 (1959).

[28] *Idem., Federation Proc.* 18 334 (1959); Eiji Ito and Jack L. Strominger, *J. Biol. Chem.* 235 PC5 (1960).

There is increasing evidence that the antibiotics mentioned, lysozyme and bacteriophages, all bring about a similar result, the accumulation or liberation of a fundamental cell wall unit such as the one shown. Lysozyme and bacteriophages are able to liberate the unit from pre-formed walls, while the antibiotics merely block wall synthesis. Also, the unit obtained by lysozyme or phage action seems to contain glucosamine as well as muramic acid, and sometimes diaminopimelic acid (a lysine precursor) rather than lysine. There is evidence that N-acetyl-D-glucosamine is a direct precursor of muramic acid.

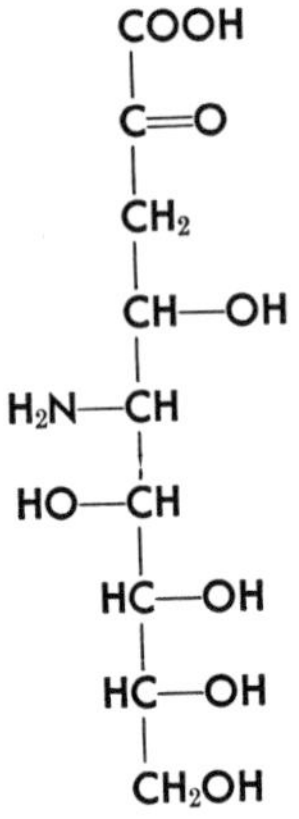

$$
\begin{array}{c}
COOH \\
| \\
C{=}O \\
| \\
CH_2 \\
| \\
CH{-}OH \\
| \\
H_2N{-}CH \\
| \\
HO{-}CH \\
| \\
HC{-}OH \\
| \\
HC{-}OH \\
| \\
CH_2OH
\end{array}
$$

Neuraminic Acid

Several neuraminopeptides have been isolated from an *E. coli* mutant culture, and one of these has been purified.[29] It is composed of N-acetylneuraminic acid, glucosamine, alanine, lysine and glutamic acid.[30]

A model of cell wall structure in gram-positive bacteria has been postulated:[31]

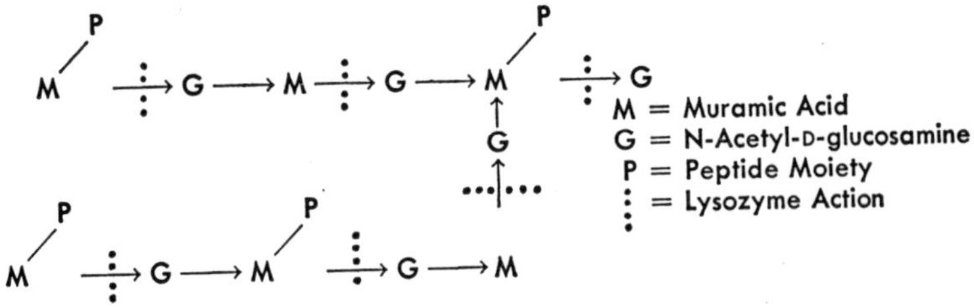

M = Muramic Acid
G = N-Acetyl-D-glucosamine
P = Peptide Moiety
⦙ = Lysozyme Action

[29] P. J. O'Brien and F. Zilliken, *Biochim. et Biophys. Acta* **31** 543 (1959).

[30] E. Kean, Dissertation. (In press)

[31] Friedrich Zilliken, *Federation Proc.* **18** 966–973 (1959).

The spine is composed of alternating muramic acid and N-acetylglucosamine units with branching to adjacent chains from muramic acid, the latter bearing the peptide chain. Penicillin (and perhaps the other antibiotics mentioned) prevents incorporation of M-P units, and cycloserine prevents incorporation of the terminal two D-alanine units into the side-chain. There is evidence that the dipeptide D-alanyl-D-alanine is preformed before attachment to the peptide chain.

A review of the chemistry of bacterial cell walls has been published.[31]

The newer general theory of polypeptide and protein synthesis can be sketched in only briefly here.[32] It is thought that the DNA of the cell nucleus lays out the pattern for replication of the ribosomal RNA, and this pattern is characteristic of each genus, species and type of organism. The ribosomal RNA in turn serves as the template for protein construction. Smaller, more soluble molecules, which seem to be RNA fragments ending in the nucleotide adenylic acid, attach themselves at this end to individual amino acids. This attachment requires an enzyme specific for each of the 20 or more amino acids plus ATP. There is also a different transfer RNA molecule for each amino acid. These activated amino acids can be isolated and purified. In this form the amino acid is able to fit into the proper place on the RNA template, probably due to the unique geometry of a short sequence of nucleotides in the chain. Once attached to RNA, condensation of the amino acids to form polypeptides or proteins is facilitated by the favorable arrangement and proximity of the reacting groups. This scheme is believed to be quite general in metabolism.

A more specific discussion by E. F. Gale of current knowledge about the incorporation of amino acids into bacterial proteins and polypeptides has been published.[33] It is obvious that considerable differences must exist between mechanisms of polypeptide synthesis in microbial and mammalian metabolism in view of the D-amino acids and other abnormal amino acids which occur in microbial polypeptides. It is apparently these differences

[32] Robert B. Loftfield, *Prog. Biophys., Biophys. Chem.* No. 8 348 (1957); F. H. C. Crick, *Symposia of the Society for Exp. Biol.* No. 12 138 (1958); Mahlon B. Hoagland, *Scientific American* 201 55 (1959); Alton Meister, *Rev. Mod. Phys.* 31 210–220 (1959); Leo Szilard, *Proc. Nat. Acad. Sci. U. S.* 46 277 (1960).

[33] "CIBA Lectures in Microbial Chemistry," E. F. Gale, *Synthesis and organization in the bacterial cell,* John Wiley and Sons, New York, 1959, 106 pp.

which are exploited by some of the more successful antibiotics.

Certain compounds listed elsewhere might have been classed as polypeptides. Examples are: penicillins, gliotoxin, certain ergot alkaloids, various diketopiperazines, netropsin, amicetin, Vitamin B_c conjugate and other folic acids.

712 **DL-Fumarylyl Alanine** (Fumaromono-D,L-alanide), $C_7H_9O_5N$, colorless needles, m.p. 229° (dec.).

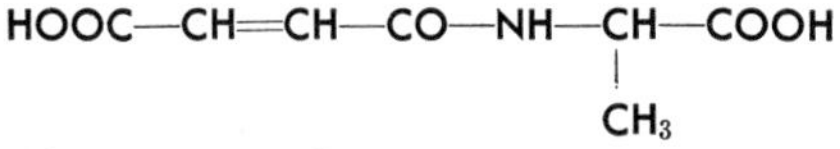
HOOC—CH═CH—CO—NH—CH—COOH
CH3

Penicillium resticulosum

John Howard Birkinshaw, Harold Raistrick and George Smith, *Biochem. J.* 36 829 (1942).

713 **Nocardamin,** $C_8H_{16}O_2N_2$, white needles, m.p. 184°, no optical activity.

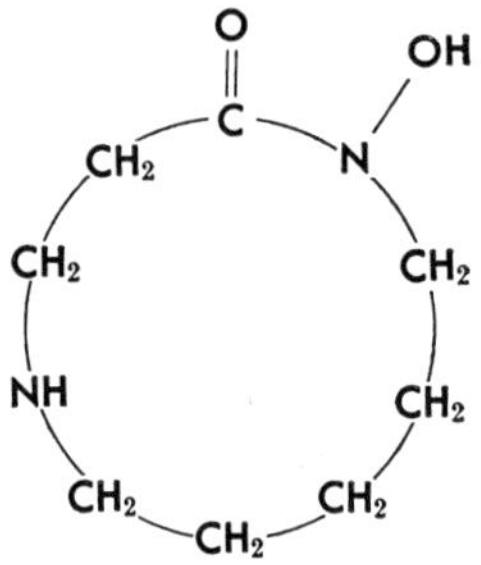
O
OH
C
N
CH2
CH2
CH2
NH
CH2
CH2
CH2
CH2

Actinomyces buchanan

A. Stoll, J. Renz and A. Brack, *Helv. Chim. Acta* 34 862 (1951).

R. F. C. Brown and G. Büchi, unpublished. (Revised structure)

714 **N-Succinyl-L-glutamic Acid,** $C_9H_{13}O_7N$ (Monohydrate), colorless hygroscopic crystals, m.p. 62–64°, $[\alpha]_D^{20}$ −11° (c 1.07 in water).

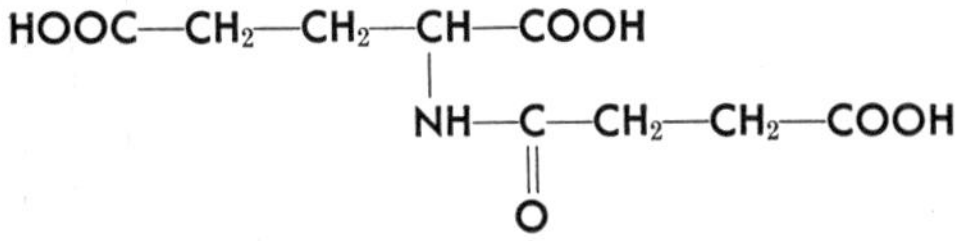
HOOC—CH2—CH2—CH—COOH
NH—C—CH2—CH2—COOH
O

Bacillus megatherium

This substance appears during the sporulating phase before the appearance of dipicolinic acid.

Jean Paul Aubert, Jacqueline Millet, Elisabeth Pineau and Gerard Milhaud, *Compt. rend.* 249 1956 (1959).

715 **Lycomarasmine,** $C_9H_{15}O_7N_3$, white powder, m.p. 227–229 (dec.). Tentative structure:

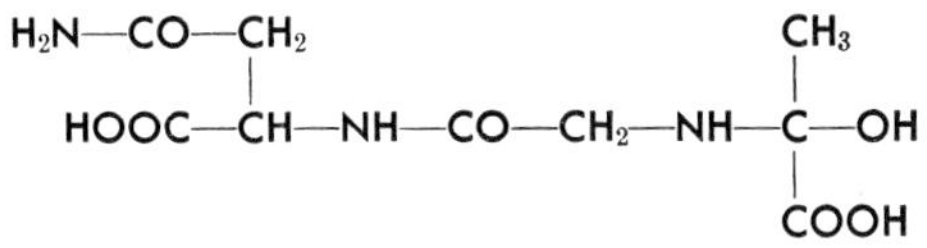

H₂N—CO—CH₂ ... CH₃

HOOC—CH—NH—CO—CH₂—NH—C—OH ... COOH

Fusarium lycopersici Sacc.

This is the toxin of fusarium wilt. A second compound, $C_9H_{12}O_7N_2$, white powder, m.p. 273–276° (dec.), has been isolated from the mother liquors. It is produced in up to three times the yield of lycomarasmine, but is biologically inactive. It is also produced (with evolution of ammonia) by boiling lycomarasmine with water.

The yield of lycomarasmine in the initial isolation was 80–110 mg. per liter.

There is still some dissatisfaction with this structure.

Pl. A. Plattner and N. Clauson-Kaas, *Helv. Chim. Acta* 28 188 (1945). (Isolation)

D. W. Woolley, *J. Biol. Chem.* 176 1291 (1948). (Structure)

M. Brenner, R. Tamm and P. Quitt, *Helv. Chim. Acta* 41 763 (1958). (Criticism of structure)

716 *d*-**Pantothenic Acid,** $C_9H_{17}O_5N$, viscous oil, $[\alpha]_D^{25}$ +37.5° (in water).

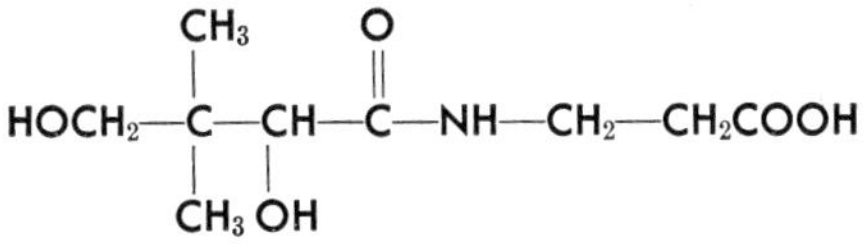

CH₃ ... O

HOCH₂—C—CH—C—NH—CH₂—CH₂COOH

CH₃ OH

Penicillin liquors yield 600–800 μg. per gram of dry cell weight.

Yeasts contain 150–300 μg. per gram of dry cell weight.

D. W. Woolley, *J. Am. Chem. Soc.* 62 2251 (1940). (Synthesis)

Leland A. Underkofler and Richard J. Hickey, "Industrial Fermentations," Chemical Publishing Co., Inc., New York, 1954 Vol. II, J. M. Van Lanen, *Production of vitamins other than riboflavin,* chap. 6, pp. 191–216.

717 Toxin of tobacco wild-fire disease, $C_{10}H_{16}O_6N_2$.
Probable structure:

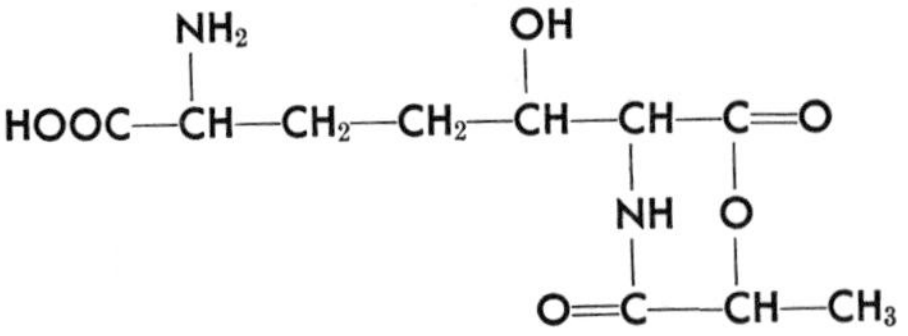

$$\underset{\underset{NH_2}{|}}{HOOC-CH}-CH_2-CH_2-\underset{\underset{NH}{|}}{CH}-\underset{\underset{O}{|}}{\overset{\overset{OH}{|}}{CH}}-C=O$$

$$O=C-CH-CH_3$$

Pseudomonas tabaci
The toxin can by hydrolyzed to lactic acid and the amino acid, tabtoxinin, $C_7H_{14}O_5N_2$, (α,ϵ-diamino-β-hydroxypimelic acid):

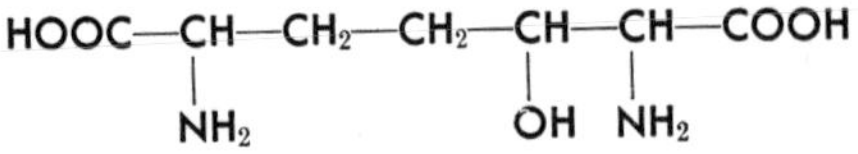

$$\underset{\underset{NH_2}{|}}{HOOC-CH}-CH_2-CH_2-\underset{\underset{OH}{|}}{CH}-\underset{\underset{NH_2}{|}}{CH}-COOH$$

D. W. Woolley, G. Schaffner and Armin C. Braun, *J. Biol. Chem.* **198** 807 (1952). (Isolation)
Idem., ibid. **215** 485 (1955). (Structure)

718 Glutathione (Glutamylcysteinylglycine) $C_{10}H_{17}O_6N_3S$, colorless crystals, m.p. 190–192° (dec.). Unstable. $[\alpha]_{Hg.}^{28.5}$ −9.4° in water, −85° in 10% hydrochloric acid.

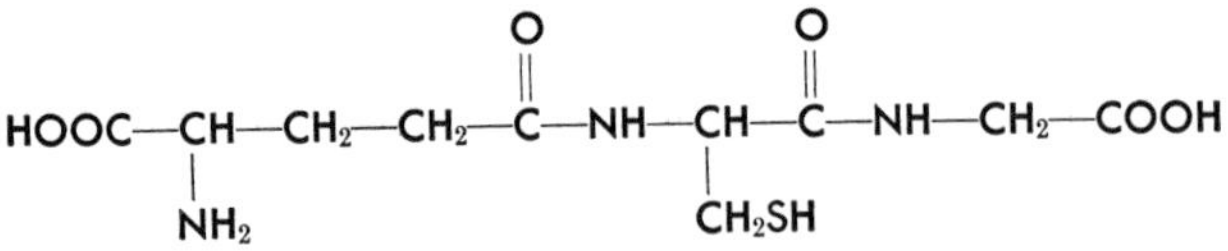

$$\underset{\underset{NH_2}{|}}{HOOC-CH}-CH_2-CH_2-\overset{\overset{O}{||}}{C}-NH-\underset{\underset{CH_2SH}{|}}{CH}-\overset{\overset{O}{||}}{C}-NH-CH_2-COOH$$

Yeasts
F. G. Hopkins, *Biochem. J.* **15** 286 (1921). (Isolation)
Charles Robert Harington and Thomas Hobson Mead, *ibid.* **29** 1602 (1935). (Synthesis)

719 N-Succinyl-L-diaminopimelic Acid, $C_{11}H_{18}O_7N_2$.

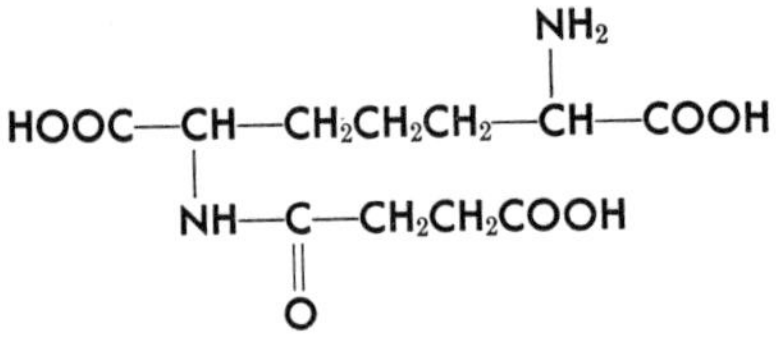

$$\underset{\underset{NH-\overset{\overset{}{}}{C}-CH_2CH_2COOH}{|}}{HOOC-CH}-CH_2CH_2CH_2-\overset{\overset{NH_2}{|}}{CH}-COOH$$

Charles Gilvarg, *Biochim. et Biophys. Acta* **24** 216 (1957).

Lactobacillus bulgaricus Factor (Pantetheine and Pantethine), $C_{11}H_{22}O_4N_2S$ and $C_{22}H_{42}O_8N_4S_2$.

720 Pantetheine: Colorless, hygroscopic, amorphous powder, $[\alpha]_D^{20}$ +12.9° (in water).

$$CH_3 \quad OH$$
$$HOCH_2-\overset{\displaystyle CH_3}{\underset{\displaystyle CH_3}{C}}-CH-CO-NH-CH_2-CH_2-CO-NH-CH_2-CH_2-SH$$

721 Pantethine: viscous oil.

$$[HOCH_2-\overset{\displaystyle CH_3}{\underset{\displaystyle CH_3\ OH}{C}}-CH-CO-NH-CH_2-CH_2-CO-NH-CH_2-CH_2-S-]_2$$

Yeasts, *Ashbya gossypi*, many other microorganisms

William L. Williams, E. Hoff-Jörgensen and Esmond E. Snell, *J. Biol. Chem.* 177 933 (1949).

Esmond E. Snell, Gene M. Brown, Vincent J. Peters, Jean A. Craig, E. L. Wittle, J. A. Moore, V. M. McGlohon and O. D. Bird, *J. Am. Chem. Soc.* 72 5349 (1950).

Vincent J. Peters, Gene M. Brown, William L. Williams and Esmond E. Snell, *ibid.* 75 1688 (1953).

Gene M. Brown and Esmond E. Snell, *ibid.* 75 1691 (1953).

722 Glutathione-Cysteine Disulfide, $C_{13}H_{22}O_8N_4S_2$.

$$H_2N-CH-CH_2-CH_2-CO-NH-CH-CO-NH-CH_2-COOH$$
$$\quad \underset{\displaystyle COOH}{|} \qquad\qquad\qquad \underset{\displaystyle CH_2}{|}$$
$$S-S-CH_2-CH-COOH$$
$$\underset{\displaystyle NH_2}{|}$$

Saccharomyces cerevisiae

Glutathione itself occurs in yeasts. The disulfide above was not isolated.

Arthur H. Livermore and Edward C. Muecke, *Nature* 173 265 (1954).

723 Serratamic Acid, $C_{13}H_{25}O_5N$, colorless crystals, m.p. 138° (dec.), $[\alpha]_D^{20}$ −10.2° (c 5.0 in ethanol).

$$\overset{\displaystyle O}{\overset{\displaystyle \|}{CH_3(CH_2)_6CHCH_2C}}-NH-\overset{\displaystyle CH_2OH}{CH}$$
$$\underset{\displaystyle OH}{|} \qquad\qquad \underset{\displaystyle COOH}{|}$$

Serratia species

Yields as high as 8 g. per liter have been reported. Hydrolysis gives L-serine and (−)-3-oxydecanoic acid. The latter acid also has been found in conjugation with rhamnose and with other amino acids (see Viscosin).

N. J. Cartwright, *Biochem. J.* **60** 238 (1955).

Idem., ibid. **67** 663 (1957). (Structure)

724 δ-(α-Aminoadipyl) cysteinylvaline, $C_{14}H_{25}O_6N_3S$.

$$HOOC-CH-CH_2-CH_2-CH_2-\overset{\overset{O}{\|}}{C}-NH-CH-\overset{\overset{|}{CH_2-SH}}{\underset{\overset{\|}{O}}{C}}-NH-CH-COOH$$

with NH_2 group on the first carbon and $CH(CH_3)_2$ group on the valine carbon

Penicillium chrysogenum

This tripeptide was isolated from the mycelium of the penicillin-producing mold. It may be a penicillin precursor since cyclization in the proper way would yield synnematin-B (cephalosporin-N) which differs from penicillin only in its side-chain. Synnematin never has been isolated from *P. chrysogenum*, however.

H. R. V. Arnstein, D. Morris and E. J. Toms, *Biochim. et Biophys. Acta* **35** 561 (1959).

725 Alazopeptin, $C_{15}H_{21}O_6N_7$, no definite m.p., $[\alpha]_D^{25}$ +9.5° (c 4.7 in water).

A peptide containing 1 mole of α-alanine and 2 moles of 6-diazo-5-oxoaminohexanoic acid (DON) or an isomer.

Streptomyces griseoplanus

S. E. DeVoe, N. E. Rigler, A. J. Shay, J. H. Martin, T. C. Boyd, E. J. Backus, J. H. Mowat and N. Bohonos, "Antibiotics Annual 1956–1957," Medical Encyclopedia, Inc., New York, p. 730.

726 Antibiotic I.C.I. 13,959.

Acid hydrolysis yielded:

α-Aminoisobutyric Acid

$$\underset{CH_3}{\overset{CH_3}{\diagdown}}\underset{NH_2}{\overset{COOH}{\diagup}}C$$

β-Hydroxyleucine

$$CH_3$$
$$\diagdown$$
$$CH\text{---}CH\text{---}CH\text{---}COOH$$
$$\diagup \quad | \quad |$$
$$CH_3 \quad\quad OH \quad NH_2$$

as well as L-leucine, β-alanine and γ-methylproline. The β-hydroxyleucine, which had not been reported previously as a natural product, has either the D- or L-*threo* but not the *erythro* configuration.

A *Paecilomyces* strain

G. W. Kenner and R. C. Sheppard, *Nature* 181 48 (1958).

727 **Viomycin** (Vinactin A, Vinactane, Celiomycin, Viocin), $C_{17\text{-}18}H_{31\text{-}35}O_8N_9$, Sulfate: m.p. (anhydrous) 252° (dec.) (hydrated) 280° (dec.), $[\alpha]_D^{25}$ −32° (c 1 in water). Rotation varies with pH.

A strongly basic polypeptide. The following components have been identified: α,β-diaminopropionic acid, β-lysine, L-serine and a guanidino compound. Salts are neutral.

Streptomyces floridae, S. puniceus, S. vinaceus

A. C. Finlay, G. L. Hobby, F. Hochstein, T. M. Lees, T. F. Lenert, J. A. Means, S. Y. P'An, P. P. Regna, J. B. Routien, B. A. Sobin, K. B. Tate and J. H. Kane, *Am. Rev. Tuberc.* 63 1 (1951).

Quentin R. Bartz, John Ehrlich, James D. Mold, Mildred A. Penner and Robert M. Smith, *ibid.* 63 4 (1951).

Theodore H. Haskell, Salvatore A. Fusari, Roger P. Frohardt and Quentin R. Bartz, *J. Am. Chem. Soc.* 74 599 (1952).

R. L. Mayer, P. C. Eisman and E. A. Konopka, *Experientia* 10 335 (1954).

728 **Phthiomycin**, white powder.

A basic polypeptide resembling viomycin.

Streptomyces luteochromogenes n. sp.

Kenji Maeda, Yoshiro Okami, Ryozo Utahara, Hiroko Kosaka and Hamao Umezawa, *J. Antibiotics* (Japan) 6A 183 (1953).

Yasushi Miyamoto and Kenji Maeda, *ibid.* 7A 17 (1954).

729 **Streptolin A,** $C_{17}H_{31}O_8N_5$ or $C_{24}H_{45}O_{11}N_7$, m.p. 206° (dec.), sulfate $[\alpha]_D^{25}$ −20°.

Streptolins A and B are similar. They resemble streptothricin, viomycin, geomycin and roseothricin in their acid hydrolysates, which contain L-β-lysine, α-D-gulosamine, streptolidine, ammonia and carbon dioxide.

Streptomyces spp.

R. W. Rivett and W. H. Peterson, *J. Am. Chem. Soc.* **69** 3006 (1947). (Isolation)

Edward E. Smissman, Robert W. Sharpe, B. F. Aycock, Eugene E. van Tamelen and W. H. Peterson, *ibid.* **75** 2029 (1953).

Eugene E. van Tamelen and Edward E. Smissman, *ibid.* **75** 2031 (1953).

Eugene E. van Tamelen, John R. Dyer, Herbert E. Carter, Jack V. Pierce and Edward E. Daniels, *ibid.* **78** 4817 (1956).

730 **Noformicin*** (Sulfate), $C_{17}H_{34}O_5N_{10}(SO_4)_2$, m.p. (Hydrochloride) 265° (dec.).

Hydrolysis yields glutamic acid, ammonia and two other ninhydrin-positive compounds which are not ordinary amino acids.

Nocardia formica

Dale A. Harris and H. Boyd Woodruff, "Antibiotics Annual 1953–1954," Medical Encyclopedia, Inc., New York, p. 609.

731 **Streptothricin,** $C_{20}H_{36}O_9N_8$, platelets (Reineckate), m.p. 192–194° (Hydrochloride) $[\alpha]_D^{25}$ −51.3°.

A basic polypeptide.   Hydrolysis yields:

L-β-Lysine:

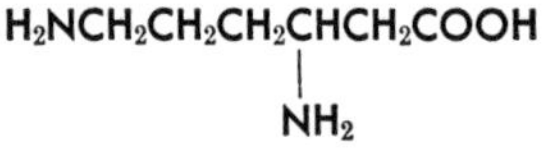

$$H_2NCH_2CH_2CH_2CHCH_2COOH$$
$$|$$
$$NH_2$$

D-Gulosamine:

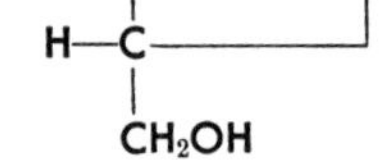

H—C—OH
|
H—C—NH$_2$
|
H—C—OH
| O
HO—C—H
|
H—C
|
CH$_2$OH

Streptolidine:

$$C_6H_{12}N_4O_3$$

Several structures have been proposed for this moiety. See C. Sweeley, Ph.D. Dissertation, Univ. of Illinois, 1955.

* See entry **915** for structure.

It may be identical with the amino acid known as roseonine or geamine.

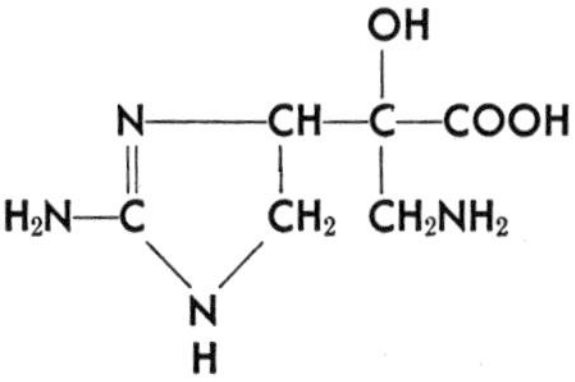

Carbon dioxide and ammonia also have been identified
in hydrolysates.

Streptomyces lavendulae and other streptomyces species

Selman A. Waksman and H. Boyd Woodruff, *Proc. Soc. Exp.
Biol. Med.* 49 207 (1942). (Isolation)

Herbert E. Carter, Walter R. Hearn, Edwin M. Lansford, Jr.,
A. C. Page, Jr., Norman P. Salzman, David Shapiro and W. R.
Taylor, *J. Am. Chem. Soc.* 74 3704 (1952). (Structure)

H. E. Carter, R. K. Clark, Jr., Paul Kohn, John W. Rathrock,
W. R. Taylor, C. A. West, George B. Whitfield and William G.
Jackson, *ibid.* 76 566 (1954).

Koji Nakamishi, Tashito Ito and Yoshimasa Hirata, *ibid.* 76
2845 (1954).

Eugene E. van Tamelen, John R. Dyer, Herbert E. Carter,
Jack V. Pierce and Edward E. Daniels, *ibid.* 78 4817 (1956).

R. Cölln, Ph.D. Dissertation, Göttingen, 1957.

Roseothricins.

A polypeptide antibiotic complex of the streptothricin
type. Acid hydrolysis of **Roseothricin A** yields β-lysine
and roseonine (geamine) I in a 1:1 ratio, an isomer of

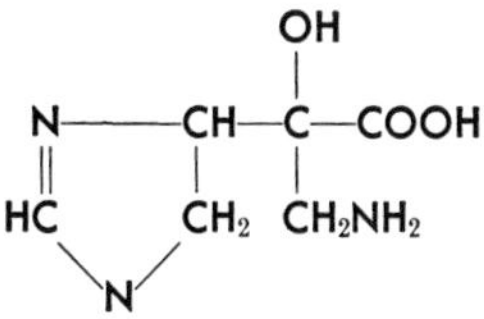

732

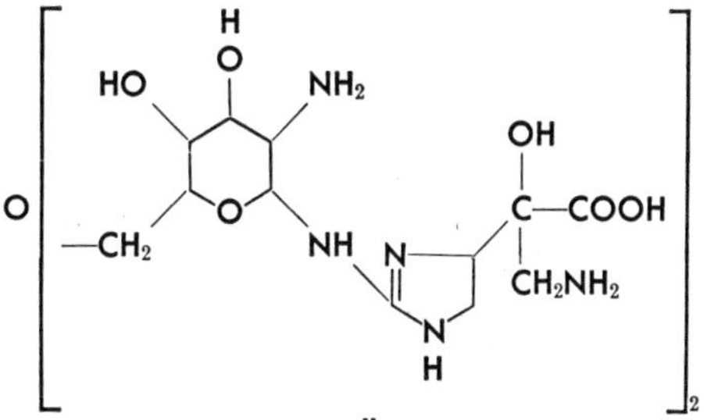

glucosamine, and a substance resistant to further hydrolysis which was assigned structure II.

Streptomyces roseochromogenes
Seigo Hosoya, Momoe Soeda, Nobuhiko Komatsu and Susumu Imamura, *J. Antibiotics* (Japan) 4 79 (1951).
Y. Saburi, *ibid.* 6B 402 (1953).
Tashio Goto, Yosimasa Hirata, Seigo Hosoya and Nabukiko Komatsu, *Bull. Chem. Soc. Japan* 30 304, 729 (1957). (Structure)

733 **Pleocidin,** a hygroscopic white powder.
A polypeptide resembling streptothricin.
S. lavendulae or related sp.
Jesse Charney, Wm. S. Roberts and W. P. Fisher, *Antibiotics and Chemotherapy* 2 307 (1952).

734, 735 **Mycothricins (A and B).**
Basic polypeptides related to streptothricin. Acid hydrolysis yielded β-lysine, (present in streptothricin, pleocidin, geomycin and viomycin), roseonine (geamine) present in streptothricin, geomycin and pleocidin, and serine (present in viomycin).
Streptomyces lavendulae type
G. Rangaswami, C. P. Schaffner and S. A. Waksman, *Antibiotics and Chemotherapy* 6 675 (1956).

736 **Grasseriomycin,** pale yellow hydrochloride, m.p. (Reineckate) 187–190° (dec.). Molecular weight 610.
A polypeptide resembling streptothricin. Negative biuret, Millon, $FeCl_3$. Positive ninhydrin, Molisch, Fehling.
Streptomyces lavendulae, S. griseolavendus
Kasububo Ueda, Youichiro Okimoto, Heiichi Sakai and Kei Arima, *J. Antibiotics* (Japan) 8A 91 (1955).
Yusuke Sumiki, Kinichiro Sakaguchi and Takenori Asai, Japanese Patent 6296 (1957).

737 **Actinorubin** ($C_6H_{14}O_3N_2$ or $C_9H_{22}O_4N_5$) (Helianthate), reddish orange clusters, m.p. 206–214° (dec.).
A basic polypeptide related to streptothricin. Positive biuret, reduces $KMnO_4$, Fehlings solution. Negative Molisch, Sakaguchi.
Streptomyces spp. resembling *S. erythreus, S. fradii, S. albosporeus*
Renate Junowicz-Kocholaty and Walter Kocholaty, *J. Biol. Chem.* 168 757 (1947).

738 Enniatin-B, $C_{22}H_{38}O_6N_2$, colorless needles, m.p. 174°, $[\alpha]_D^{21}$ −106.3° (c 0.695 in chloroform).

Fusaria species
Yield about 0.5 g. per liter.
Pl. A. Plattner and U. Nager, *Experientia* 3 325 (1947).
Pl. A. Plattner, U. Nager and A. Boller, *Helv. Chim. Acta* **31** 594 (1948).
Pl. A. Plattner and U. Nager, *ibid.* 31 665 (1948).

739 Islanditoxin, $C_{24}H_{31}O_7N_5Cl_2$, colorless, amorphous solid, m.p. 258°.

Penicillium islandicum Sopp.

Shingo Marumo and Yusuke Sumiki, *J. Agr. Chem. Soc. Japan* **29** 305 (1955). (Isolation)

Shingo Marumo, *Bull. Agr. Chem. Soc.* (Japan) **19** 258 (1955).

Idem., ibid. **23** 428 (1959). (Structure)

740 Enniatin-A (Lateritiin-I), $C_{24}H_{42}O_6N_2$, colorless needles, m.p. 122°, $[\alpha]_D^{18}$ −91.9° (c 0.926 in chloroform).

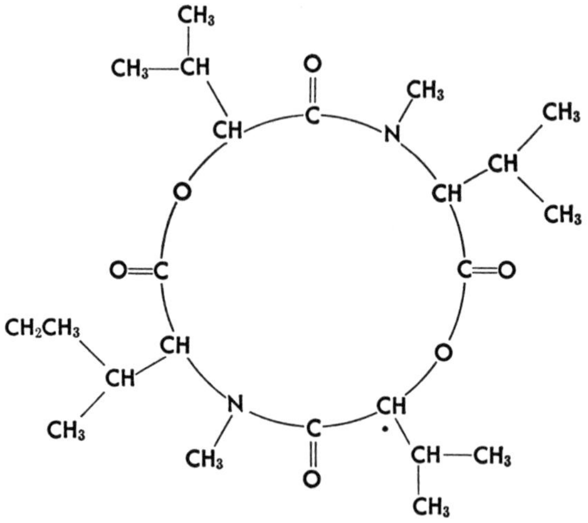

Fusarium orthoceras var. *enniatinum, F. scirpi* Lamb. et Fautr., *F. lateritium*

The yield was about 1 g. per liter.

E. Gaümann, Stephi Roth, L. Ettlinger, Pl. A. Plattner and U. Nager, *Experientia* **3** 202 (1947). (Isolation)

Pl. A. Plattner and U. Nager, *ibid.* **3** 325 (1947).

Pl. A. Plattner, U. Nager and A. Boller, *Helv. Chim. Acta* **31** 594 (1948).

Pl. A. Plattner and U. Nager, *ibid.* **31** 2192, 2203 (1948).

A. H. Cook, S. F. Fox and T. H. Farmer, *J. Chem. Soc.,* 1022 (1949).

741   **Enniatin-C,** $C_{24}H_{42}O_6N_2$, m.p. 123°, $[\alpha]_D^{22}$ −83° (c 1.162 in chloroform).

Proposed structure:

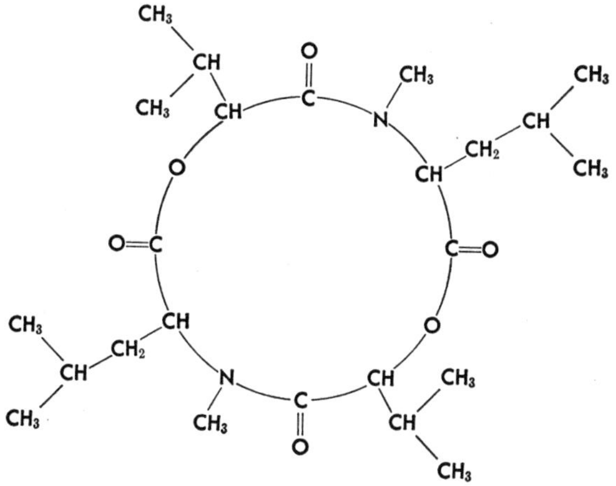

Fusaria species
The yield was about 0.6 g. per liter.
Pl. A. Plattner and U. Nager, *Helv. Chim. Acta* **31** 2203 (1948).

742   **Eulicin,** $C_{24}H_{52}O_2N_8$, m.p. (Helianthate) 139°.

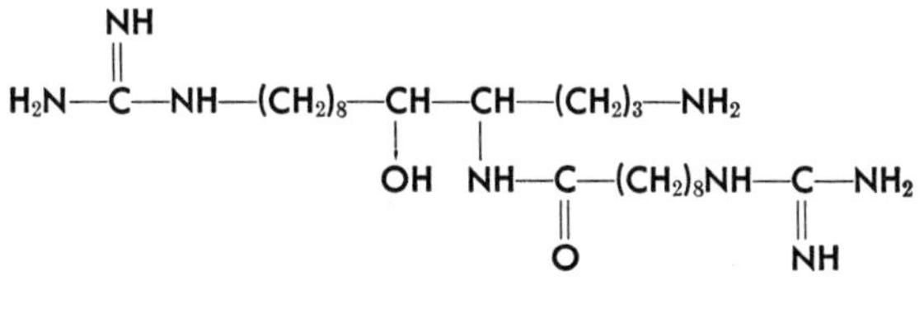

Streptomyces sp. resembling *S. parvus*
An actinomycin and a basic substance also were produced.
Jesse Charney, Roy A. Machlowitz, Frank J. McCarthy, Gertrude A. Rutkowski, Alfred A. Tytell and W. P. Fisher, "Antibiotics Annual 1955–1956," Medical Encyclopedia, Inc., New York, p. 228. (Isolation)
Robert E. Harman, Edward A. Ham, William A. Bolhofer and Norman G. Brink, *J. Am. Chem. Soc.* **80** 5173 (1958). (Structure)

PA 114 Antibiotics.

743 **PA 114A,*** $C_{25}H_{31}O_6N_3$ or $C_{35}H_{42}O_9N_4$ (proposed), colorless needles, m.p. 200° (dec.), $[\alpha]_D^{25}$ −207° (c 0.5 in methanol).
A neutral substance, green $FeCl_3$ test. Negative ninhydrin, carbohydrate tests.

744 **PA 114B,†** $C_{52}H_{63}O_{12}N_9$ (proposed), colorless crystals, m.p. 265° (dec.), $[\alpha]_D^{25}$ −59.7° (c 0.5 in methanol).
A weak acid, red $FeCl_3$ test. Negative ninhydrin, carbohydrate tests, 2,4-DNPH.
Streptomyces olivaceus
Walter D. Celmer and Ben A. Sobin, "Antibiotics Annual 1955–1956," Medical Encyclopedia, Inc., New York, p. 437.

745 **PA 114B-3,** colorless needles, m.p. 207°, $[\alpha]_D^{20}$ −37.2° (in methanol).
A polypeptide antibiotic similar to PA-114B. Analysis: C 62.77, H 6.52, N 12.61.
A *Streptomyces olivaceus* strain
D. C. Hobbs and W. D. Celmer, *Federation Proc.* 18 246 (1959).

746 **Streptogramin,** approximate formula $C_{26}H_{33}O_7N_3$, m.p. 155°, $[\alpha]_D$ −134°.
Neutral compound.
Streptomyces graminofaciens
Jesse Charney, W. P. Fisher, Charles Curran, Roy A. Machlowitz and Alfred A. Tytell, "Antibiotics Annual 1953–1954," Medical Encyclopedia, Inc., New York, p. 171.

Lateritiin Group
Several colorless compounds similar to the enniatins were isolated from fusaria species in England. One of these, lateritiin I, has been shown identical with enniatin A. The others are:

	Name	Suggested formula	Melting point	$[\alpha]_D^{20}$
747	Lateritiin II..............	$C_{26}H_{46}O_7N_2$	125°	−92°
748	Avenacein...............	$C_{25}H_{44}O_7N_2$	139°	−101°
749	Fructigenin..............	$C_{26}H_{44-46}O_7N_2$	129°	−103°
750	Sambucinin..............	$C_{24}H_{42}O_7N_2$	86°	−83°

All these compounds yield D(−)-α-hydroxyisovaleric

* May be identical with staphylomycin M_1, E-129A (ostreogrycin A).

† See addendum for structure.

acid, $C_5H_{10}O_3$, m.p. 65°, $[\alpha]_D^{13}$ $-21°$ (c 1.25 in chloroform), and N-methyl-L-valine on acid hydrolysis.

The enniatins also uniformly contain D(−)-α-hydroxy-isovaleric acid, but each contains a characteristic N-methylamino acid. (*cf.* valinomycin, amidomycin).

A. H. Cook, S. F. Cox, T. H. Farmer and M. S. Lacey, *Nature* **160** 31 (1947).

A. H. Cook, S. F. Cox and T. H. Farmer, *ibid.* **162** 61 (1948).

Idem., J. Chem. Soc., 1022 (1949).

751 Chlorine-containing Peptide, $C_{25}H_{36}O_8N_5Cl_2$, white needles, m.p. 251° (dec.), $[\alpha]_D^{16}$ $-92.9°$ (in methanol).

Positive biuret and Pauly reactions, negative Sakaguchi, Neubauer-Rhode, ninhydrin, Millon reactions.

Acid hydrolysis yielded serine (2 to 3 moles), α-aminobutyric acid (1 mole), β-phenyl-β-aminopropionic acid (1 mole) and an unidentified substance yielding a positive Ehrlich reaction.

Penicillium islandicum Sopp.

Yoshita Kobayashi, Kenji Uraguchi, Takashi Tatsuno, Fuminori Sakai, Michio Tsukioka, Yutaka Sakai, Osamu Yonemitsu, Taiko Sato, Masashi Miyake, Mamoru Saito, Makoto Enomoto, Toshio Shikata and Toshitaka Ishiko, *Proc. Japan Acad.* **34** 736 (1958).

752 Pyridomycin, $C_{26-27}H_{32}O_8N_4$, colorless needles, m.p. 218–222°.

Apparently rather closely related to etamycin. Alkaline fusion yields:

, glycine and HOOC—CHCH—COOH (with CH_2CH_3 and OH substituents)

Acid hydrolysis yields:

, threonine and another degradation product incorporating picoline and glycine

Streptomyces pyridomyceticus

Kenji Maeda, *J. Antibiotics* (Japan) **10A** 94 (1957) and earlier papers in the series.

753 Levomycin, $C_{27}H_{38}O_{10}N_6$ (proposed), colorless crystals, m.p. 222–224°, $[\alpha]_D^{25}$ $-323°$ (c 1 in chloroform).

A polypeptide containing an aromatic group.

Streptomyces sp.

Herbert E. Carter, Carl P. Schaffner and David Gottlieb, *Arch. Biochem. and Biophys.* 53 282 (1954).

754 Staphylomycin M$_1$, C$_{28}$H$_{36}$O$_8$N$_3$ (probable), m.p. 165–167° (dec.), [α]$_D$ −190° ±2° (c 0.5 in ethanol).

A neutral compound. Carbonyl group present. Glycine and proline liberated on acid hydrolysis. Related to PA 114A.*

755 Staphylomycin S, C$_{38-39}$H$_{47-48}$O$_9$N$_6$ (proposed, but see structure below), white crystals, m.p. 240–242° [α]$_D$ −28.0° (c 1.0 in ethanol).

A weak acid. Threonine, norvaline, α-aminobutryic acid, phenylalanine and proline were produced on acid hydrolysis. Related to PA 114B (or identical).

Staphylomycin M$_2$. This third factor has not been obtained pure.

There appears to be a relationship between the staphylomycin complex and streptogramin, etamycin, etc.

Streptomyces sp. resembling *S. virginiae*

H. Vanderhaeghe, P. Van Dijck, G. Parmentier and P. De Somer, *Antibiotics and Chemotherapy* 7 606 (1957).

The probable structure of one of the staphylomycins recently was reported to be:

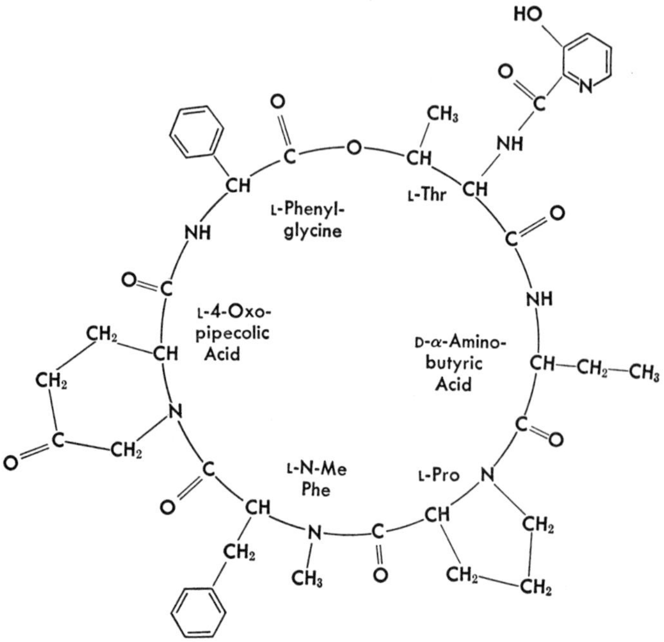

* Identical with PA 114A.

H. Vanderhaege, Abstr. Biochem. Symposium, XVIIth Internat. Congress Pure and Appl. Chem., Munich 1959.

H. Vanderhaege and G. Parmentier, *Bull. Soc. Chim. belges* 68 716 (1959).

756 Phalloidin, $C_{35}H_{46}O_{10}N_8S + 6H_2O$.

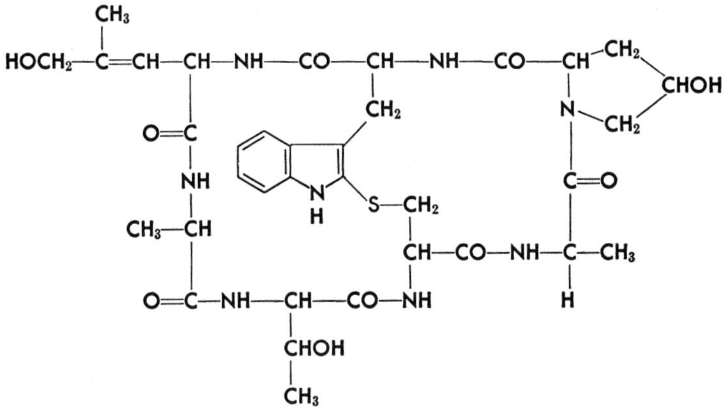

Amanita phalloides

From 100 g. of fresh fungus were obtained 10 mg. of phalloidin, 8 mg. of α-amanitin, 5 mg. of β-amanitin and about 0.5 mg. of γ-amanitin. The amanitins have not been characterized thoroughly, but seem to be related to phalloidin.

Theodor Wieland, *Angew. Chem.* 69 44 (1957).

Theodor Wieland and Werner Schön, *Ann.* 593 157 (1955).

Theodor Wieland and Christoph Dudensing, *ibid.* **600** 156 (1956).

757 Phalloin, $C_{35}H_{46}O_9N_8S$, colorless needles, m.p. 250–280° (dec.). Probable structure:

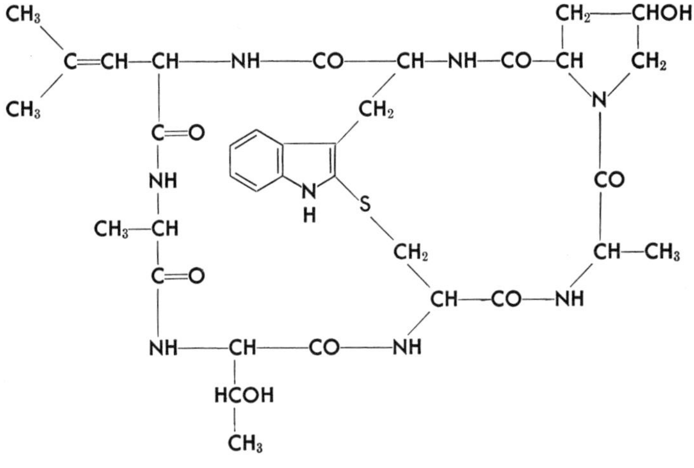

Amanita phalloides
Theodor Wieland and Karl Mannes, *Angew. Chem.* **69** 389 (1957).
Idem., Ann. **617** 152 (1958).

758 **Valinomycin,** $C_{36}H_{60}O_{12}N_4$, colorless platelets, m.p. 190°, $[\alpha]_D^{20}$ +31° (c 1.6 in benzene).

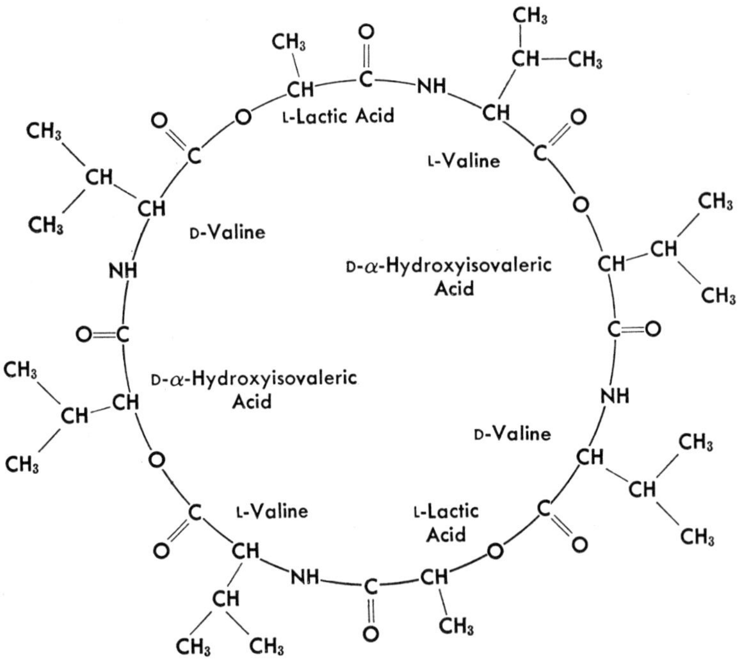

Streptomyces fulvissimus
The yield was about 100 mg. per liter. Acid hydrolysis gives 2 moles of L(+)-valine, 2 moles of D(−)-valine, 2 moles of L(−)-lactic acid and 2 moles of D(−)-α-hydroxyisovaleric acid. (*Cf.* the enniatin and lateritiin groups, and amidomycin.)
H. Brockmann and G. Schmidt-Kastner, *Chem. Ber.* **88** 57 (1955).
Hans Brockmann and Hermann Geeren, *Ann.* **603** 213 (1957).

759 **Viscosin,** $C_{36}H_{66}O_{10}N_6$, amorphous white powder, m.p. 269° (dec.), $[\alpha]_D^{20}$ −162°.

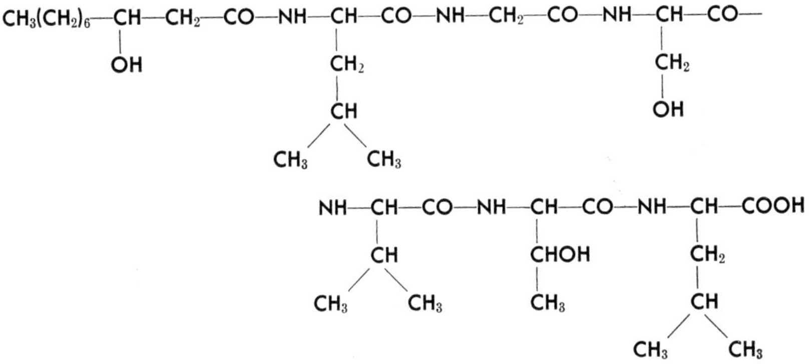

$$CH_3(CH_2)_6-CH-CH_2-CO-NH-CH-CO-NH-CH_2-CO-NH-CH-CO-$$

with branches:
- under first CH: OH
- under fourth CH: CH_2 — CH — (CH_3, CH_3)
- under last CH: CH_2 — OH

$$NH-CH-CO-NH-CH-CO-NH-CH-COOH$$

with branches:
- under first CH: CH — (CH_3, CH_3)
- under second CH: $CHOH$ — CH_3
- under last CH: CH_2 — CH — (CH_3, CH_3)

Pseudomonas viscosa

Mitsuyuki Kochi, Vincent Groupé, Leonora H. Pugh and David Weiss, *Bact. Proc.*, 29 (1951).

Takashi Ohno, Shigeru Tajima and Katsuyuki Toki, *J. Agr. Chem. Soc. Japan* 27 665 (1953).

Doki and Ohno (unpublished). Total structure determination. Reported by S. Otani in a lecture on polypeptide antibiotics in 1957.

Takashi Ohno, Shigeru Tajima and Katsuyuki Toki, *J. Agr. Chem. Soc. Japan* 27 665 (1953).

760 **Bottromycin** (B-Mycin), $C_{38}H_{57-61}O_{7-8}N_7S$, white amorphous material, $[\alpha]_D^{25}$ −14.2° (c 0.5 in 96% ethanol).

Bottromycin is a weakly basic polypeptide. Acid hydrolysis yields six ninhydrin-positive compounds. Two of these are glycine and valine. Two others are new amino acids:

α-Amino-β-phenylbutyric Acid

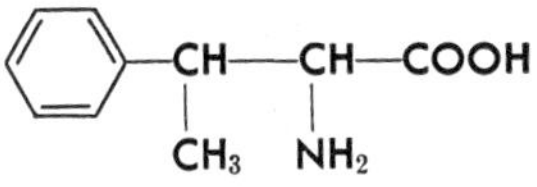

$$\text{(phenyl)}-CH-CH-COOH$$
with CH_3 under first CH and NH_2 under second CH

and

β-(2-Thiazole)-β-alanine

thiazole ring (N, S) attached to
$$CH-CH_2-COOH$$
with NH_2 under CH

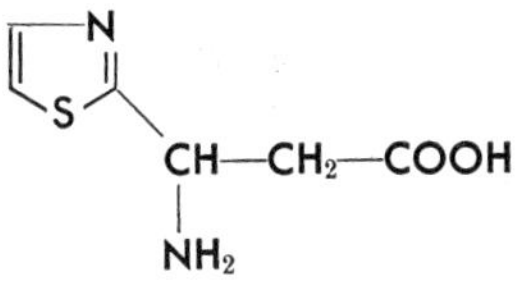

Streptomyces bottropensis

J. M. Waisvisz, M. G. van der Hoeven, J. van Peppen and W. C. M. Zwennis, *J. Am. Chem. Soc.* 79 4520 (1957). (Isolation)

J. M. Waisvisz, M. G. van der Hoeven, J. F. Hölscher and B. te Nijenhuis, *ibid.* 79 4522 (1957).

J. M. Waisvisz, M. G. van der Hoeven and B. te Nijenhuis, *ibid.* 79 4524 (1957). (Structure)

Micrococcins.

761 **Micrococcin,** white needles, m.p. 222–228° (dec.), $[\alpha]_D^{21}$ 116° ±1° (c 5.0 in 90% ethanol), molecular weight >2000.

A *Micrococcus* sp.

T. L. Su, *Brit. J. Exptl. Path.* 29 473 (1948).

N. G. Heatley and Hazel M. Doery, *Biochem. J.* 50 247 (1951).

762 **Micrococcin-P,** white crystals, yellowing in light, m.p. 252° (dec. from 232°), $[\alpha]_D^{21}$ +63.7° (c 1.19 in 90% ethanol), molecular weight ~2200.

Two fragments have been identified as:

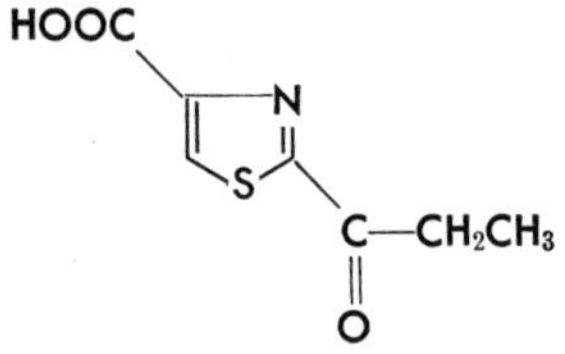

HOOC

C—CH₂CH₃

O

2-Propionylthiazole-4-carboxylic Acid

HOOC

CH₃

CH—CH

NH₂   CH₃

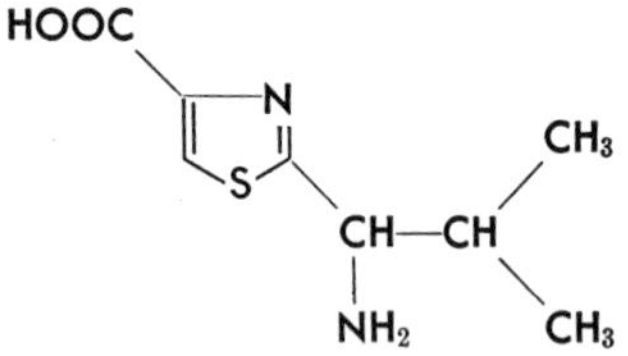

2-(1-Amino-2-methylpropyl)thiazole-4-carboxylic Acid

Acid-catalyzed esterification gave a dimethyl ester, $C_{24}H_{23}O_5N_5S_4$ and a base $C_{16}H_{19}O_3N_3S_3$. Also threonine, ammonia and propionic acid were isolated.

This antibiotic seems to be similar to or identical with the earlier one, but is distinguished by the letter P until identity is proved.

Bacillus pumilis

A. T. Fuller, *Nature* 175 722 (1955). (Isolation)

E. P. Abraham, N. G. Heatley, P. Brookes, A. T. Fuller and James Walker, *ibid.* 178 44 (1956).

P. Brookes, A. T. Fuller and James Walker, *J. Chem. Soc.*, 689 (1957).

763 **Esperin,** $C_{39}H_{67}O_{11}N_5$, colorless crystals, m.p. 238° (dec.), $[\alpha]_D^{15}$ −24° (c 0.66 in methanol).

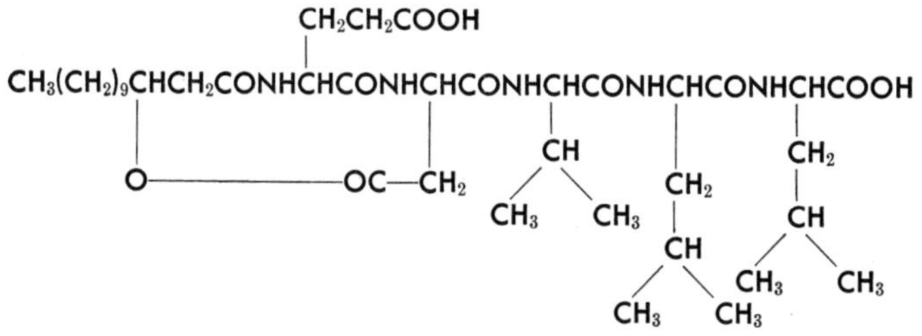
CH2CH2COOH
CH3(CH2)9CHCH2CONHCHCONHCHCONHCHCONHCHCONHCHCOOH
O
OC—CH2
CH
CH3
CH3
CH2
CH
CH3
CH3
CH2
CH
CH3
CH3

Bacillus mesentericus

Hiroshi Ogawa and Teiichiro Ito, *J. Agr. Chem. Soc. Japan* 24 191 (1950). (Isolation)

Idem., ibid. 26 432 (1952).

Idem., Bull. Agr. Chem. Soc. (Japan) 23 536 (1959). (Structure)

764 **Actinochrysin,** $C_{40}H_{57}O_{11}N_7$, a brick red pigment.

Similar to but distinct from actinomycins. A weak base with two acid groups. Molecular weight 811. Soluble in acetone.

Streptomyces chrysomallus

Hans Brockmann and Arnold Bohne, German Patent 912,010 (1954). (*Chem. Abstr.* 52 12334g)

765 **Grisein,** $C_{40}H_{61}O_{20}N_{10}SFe$, red, amorphous powder.

Isolated from acid hydrolysate:

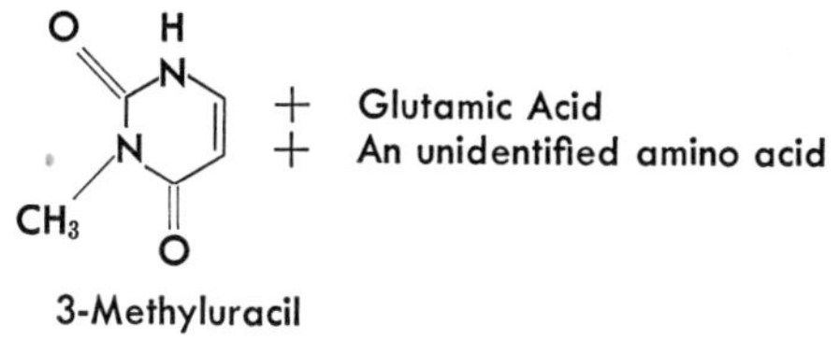
O
H
N
N
CH3
O
+ Glutamic Acid
+ An unidentified amino acid
3-Methyluracil

The iron is Fe^{III} and can be removed and readded to the complex.

Streptomyces griseus

The Russian antibiotic, albomycin, produced by *Streptomyces subtropicus* seems to be similar to or identical with grisein.

Donald M. Reynolds, Albert Schatz and Selman A. Waksman, *Proc. Soc. Exp. Biol.* 64 50 (1947). (Isolation)

Donald M. Reynolds and Selman A. Waksman, *J. Bact.* 55 739 (1948).

Frederick A. Kuehl, Jr., Mary Neale Bishop, Louis Chaiet and Karl Folkers, *J. Am. Chem. Soc.* 73 1770 (1951).

766 Albomycin (Sulfate), red amorphous powder, molecular weight >1300.

Partial Constitution:

Albomycin is a basic, cyclic polypeptide containing iron (~4% by weight). Iron can be removed with acetone (color loss) and restored with $FeCl_3$. Hydrolysis yields: ornithine, serine, glutamic acid, alanine, glycine, proline and one unidentified amino acid.

Streptomyces subtropicus n. sp.

Albomycin may be identical with grisein, produced by *Streptomyces griseus*.

M. G. Brazhnikova, N. N. Lomakina and L. I. Murayeva, *Doklady Akad. Nauk S.S.S.R.* 99 827 (1954).

G. F. Gause, *Brit. Med. J.* 2 1177 (1955).

Yu. O. Sazykin, *Mikrobiologiya* 24 75 (1955).

767 Amidomycin, $C_{40}H_{68}O_{12}N_4$, colorless needles, m.p. 192°, $[\alpha]_D^{26}$ +19.2° (c 1.2 in ethanol).

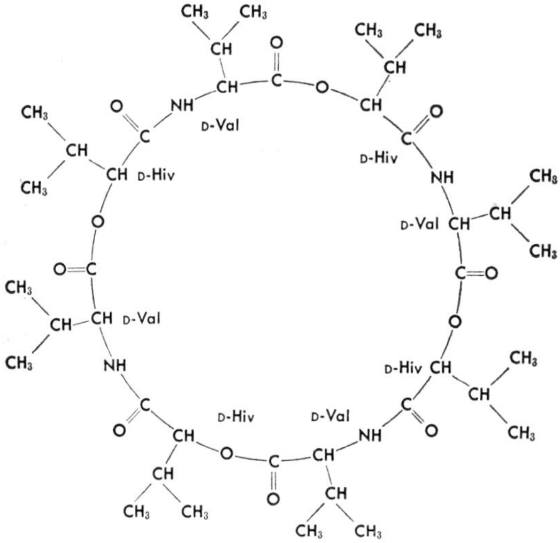

Streptomyces species (PRL 1642)

Amidomycin contains 4 moles each of D(−) valine and D(−) α-hydroxyisovaleric acid. (*Cf.* Valinomycin, lateritiins, enniatins.)

L. C. Vining and W. A. Taber, *Can. J. Chem.* 35 1109 (1957).

768   Toxin of *Helminthosporium victoriae*.

This toxin consists of two loosely connected moieties. The first is a tricyclic secondary amine called victoxinine, and the second a pentapeptide. The intact toxin shows a negative ninhydrin test, and a molecular weight of 800 was assumed.

Victoxinine, $C_{17}H_{29}ON$ (Hydrochloride), colorless needles, m.p. 172°, $[\alpha]_D^{25}$ −78° (c 3.2 in 95% alcohol). Negative U.V.

Pentapeptide:

On acid hydrolysis yielded:

Aspartic acid, glutamic acid, glycine, valine and one of the leucines.

Helminthosporium victoriae

Ross B. Pringle and Armin C. Braun, *Nature* 181 1205 (1958).

769   Telomycin, cream colored amorphous solid.

A polypeptide antibiotic, containing glycine, alanine, threonine and aspartic acid. Molecular weight about 1000. Contains no sulfur. Negative Fehling, ninhydrin, biuret. Similar to etamycin.

Streptomyces sp.

M. Misiek, O. B. Fardig, A. Gourevitch, D. L. Johnson, I. R. Hooper and J. Lein, "Antibiotics Annual 1957–1958," Medical Encyclopedia, Inc., New York, p. 852.

770   Etamycin (Viridogrisein), $C_{44}H_{62}O_{10}N_8$, white crystals, hydrochloride m.p. 163–170° (dec.), $[\alpha]_D^{25}$ conflicting reports.

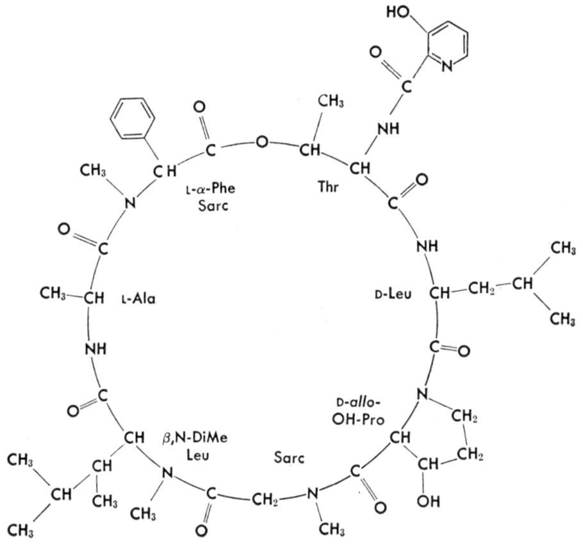

Streptomyces sp. resembling *S. lavendulae*

Cf. Pyridomycin staphylomycin, osteogrycin, PA-114, mikamycin, streptogramin, telomycin, echinomycin.

This class of polypeptides appears to be related biogenically to the actinomycins.

B. Heinemann, A. Gourevitch, J. Lein, D. L. Johnson, M. A. Kaplan, D. Vanas and I. R. Hooper, "Antibiotics Annual 1954–1955," Medical Encyclopedia, Inc., New York, p. 728.

Quentin R. Bartz, Jean Standiford, James D. Mold, Doris W. Johannessen, Albert Ryder, Andrew Maretzki and Theodore H. Haskell, *ibid.*, p. 777.

Theodore H. Haskell, Andrew Maretzki and Quentin R. Bartz, *ibid.*, p. 784.

John C. Sheehan, Hans Georg Zachau and William B. Lawson, *J. Am. Chem. Soc.* 79 3933 (1957). (Structure)

771   Colistin, $C_{45}H_{85}O_{10}N_{13}$.

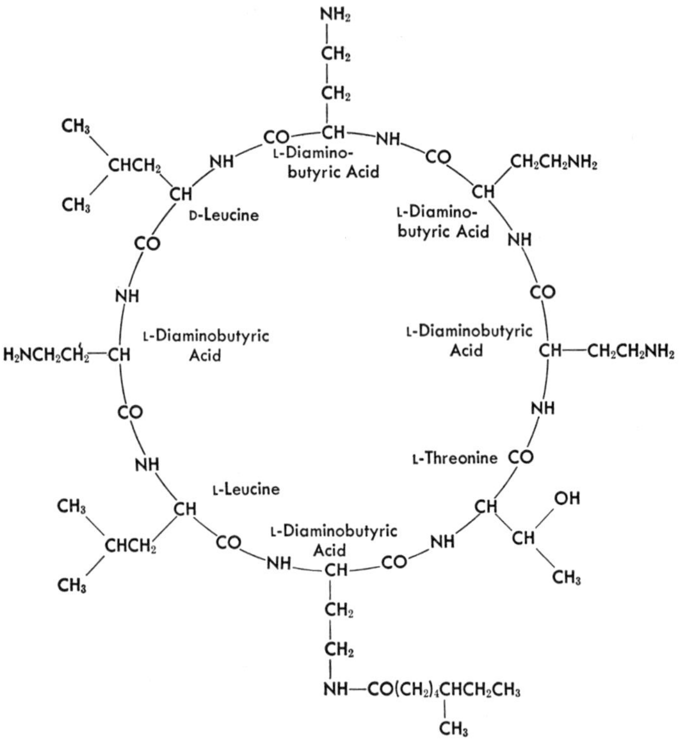

Yasuo Koyama, Akio Kurosasa, Atsushi Tsuchiya and Kinsuke Takakuta, *J. Antibiotics* (Japan) 3 457 (1950).

Taiichi Ito, Sadao Miyamura, Seihachiro Niwayama, Masa-
nobu Oishi, Nobuhiro Igarashi, Hiromichi Hoshino and Shozo
Muto, *ibid.* **7B** 147 (1954).

Yasuo Kayama, Japanese Patent 1546 (1952).

Takeshi Oda, Mitsuhiro Kinoshita, Osamu Yamanaka and
Fumio Ueda, *J. Pharm. Soc. Japan* 74 1234 (1954).

Takeshi Oda and Fumio Ueda, *ibid.* 74 1246 (1954).

772 Mycobactin, $C_{47}H_{75}O_{10}N_5$, microcrystalline white powder with
pale green fluorescence, m.p. 165–166.5°, $[\alpha]_D^{25}$ −19° (c
4.9 in chloroform).

Mycobactin is a weak acid believed to have one of the
following structures:

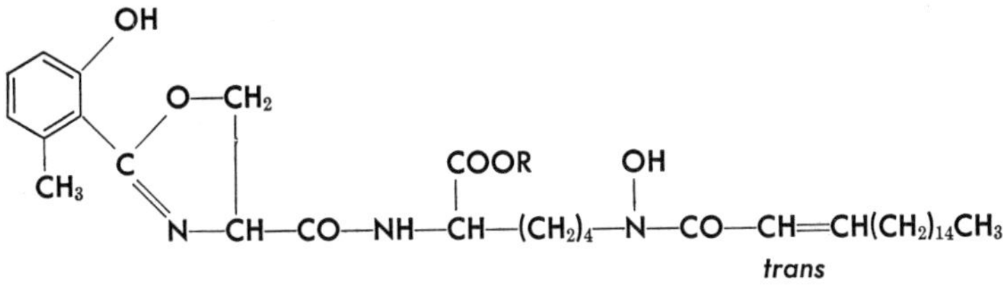

or

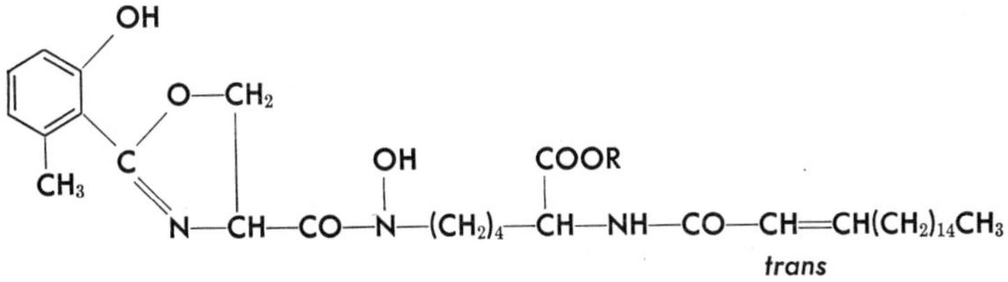

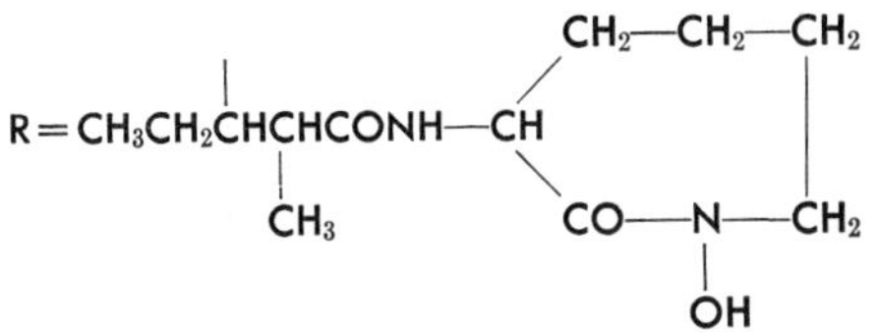

Mycobacterium phlei

The yield was about 67 g. from 41 kg. of moist cells.

G. A. Snow, *J. Chem. Soc.,* 4080 (1954) and earlier papers
in the series.

773 Geomycin $(C_6H_{12}O_2N_2)_{8-10}$, Helianthate red platelets, m.p. 205–
215° (dec.), Hydrochloride $[\alpha]_D^{20}$ +16°.

A basic polypeptide. Acid hydrolysis yields: geamine,
β-lysine, and an amino sugar, plus small amounts of

aspartic acid, glutamic acid, serine, threonine, glycine and alanine.

The structural evidence has been well summarized and a partial structure postulated by R. Cölln, Ph.D. Dissertation, Göttingen, 1957. The partial structure is:

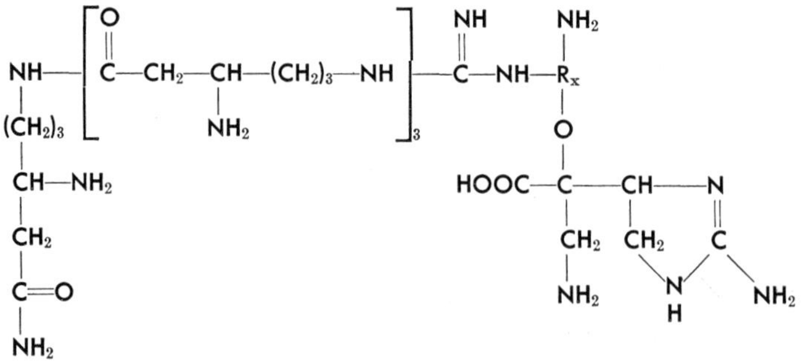

Streptomyces xanthophaeus, n.sp.

Hans Brockmann and Burchard Franck, *Naturwissenschaften* 41 451 (1954).

Hans Brockmann and Hans Musso, *Chem. Ber.* 87 1779 (1954).

Idem., ibid. 88 648 (1955).

774 **Lavendulin** (Helianthate), $C_{49}H_{63}O_{18}N_{13}S$ (proposed), orange crystals, m.p. 212–220° (dec.).

A basic polypeptide. Positive $FeCl_3$, Fehling, biuret, $KMnO_4$. Negative Molisch, Sakaguchi.

Streptomyces sp. similar to *S. lavendulae*

Albert Kelner and Harry E. Morton, *J. Bact.* 53 695 (1947). (Isolation)

Harry E. Morton, *Proc. Soc. Exp. Biol. Med.* 64 327 (1947).

775 **Echinomycin** (X-948),* $C_{50}H_{60}O_{12}N_{12}S_2$, granular, nearly colorless hygroscopic powder, m.p. 217°, $[\alpha]_D$ −310° (c 0.86 in chloroform).

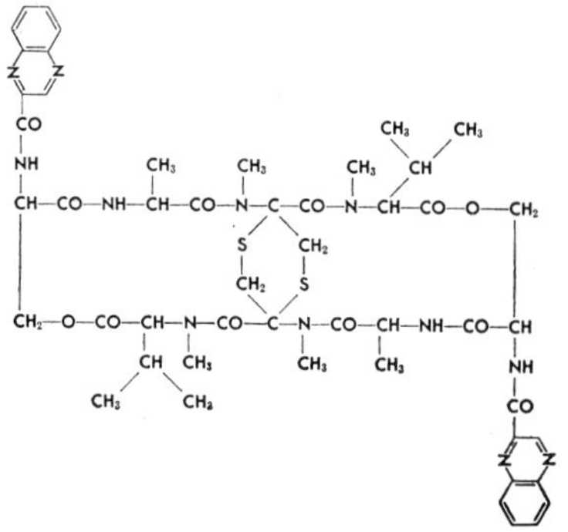

* Antibiotic X-1008 (unclassified) resembles echinomycin.

Streptomyces echinatus n. sp.

R. Corbaz, L. Ettlinger, E. Gaümann, W. Keller-Schierlein, F. Kradolfer, L. Neipp, V. Prelog, P. Reusser and H. Zähner, *Helv. Chim. Acta* **40** 199 (1957). (Isolation)

W. Keller-Schierlein, M. Lj. Mikhailovich and V. Prelog, *ibid.* **42** 305 (1959). (Structure)

Circulins, $C_{53}H_{100}O_{13}N_{16}$ (Sulfate), amorphous solid, m.p. 226–228° (dec.), $[\alpha]_D^{25}$ −61.6°.

776 Circulin A:

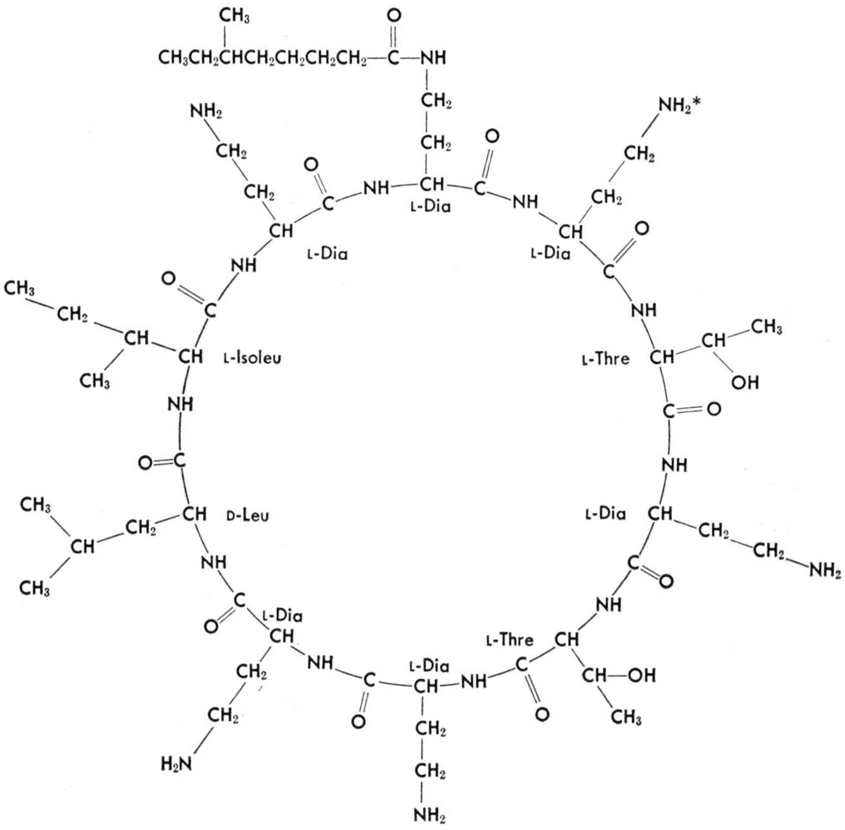

Bacillus circulans

Hydrolysis yields 6 moles of L-α, γ-diaminobutyric acid, 2 moles of L-threonine, 1 mole of D-leucine, 1 mole of L-isoleucine and 1 mole of (+)6-methyloctanoic acid.

777 Circulin B has essentially the same structure, but the 6-methyloctanoic acid moiety is attached at the starred amino group. There may be other similar compounds in the complex also.

F. J. Murray, P. A. Tetrault, O. W. Kaufman, H. Koffler, D. H. Peterson and D. R. Colingsworth, *J. Bact.* **57** 305 (1949).

D. H. Peterson and L. M. Reineke, *J. Biol. Chem.* **181** 95 (1949).

Tashio Kobayashi, J. E. Grady, J. L. Parsons, Henry Koffler and P. A. Tetrault, *Abstr. 133rd Meeting Am. Chem. Soc.,* 25C (1958).

H. Koffler and T. Kobayashi, *Abstr. 4th Intern. Congr. Biochem.,* 9 (1958).

Henry Koffler, *Science* 130 1419 (1959).

778 Fungisporin, $C_{56}H_{72}O_8N_8$, colorless crystals, m.p. 355–360° (dec.) (subl. from 250°), molecular weight 980.
Proposed structure:

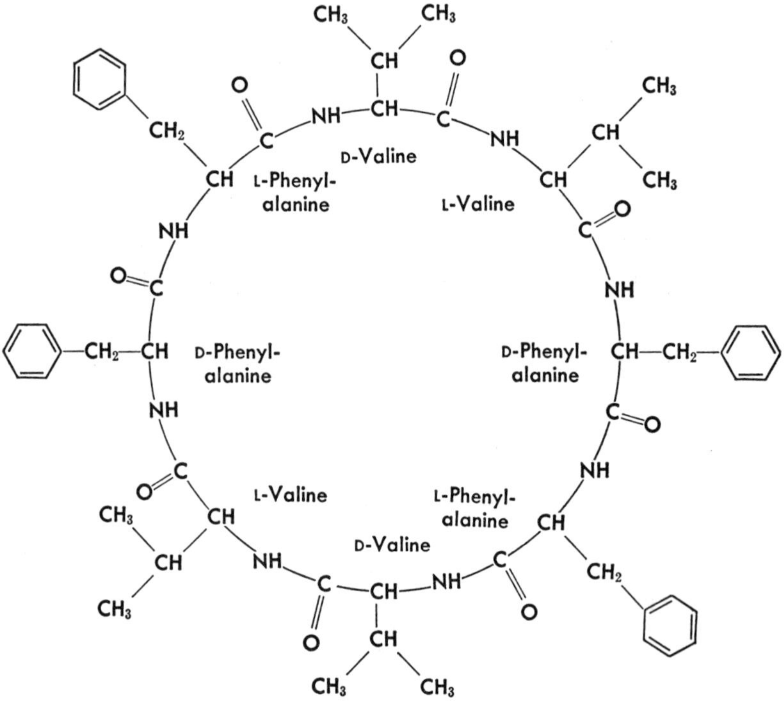

Penicillium and *Aspergillus* spp.

This polypeptide was obtained by destructive distillation of spores, when it separated by sublimation.

U. Sumiki and K. Miyao, *J. Agr. Chem. Soc. Japan* **26** 27 (1952).

Idem., *Bull. Agr. Chem. Soc.* (Japan) **19** 86 (1955).

Kohei Miyao, *ibid.* **24** 23 (1960).

779 **Polypeptin** (formerly called circulin, but not identical with the polypeptide now known as circulin), $C_{56}H_{96}O_{13}N_{12}$, colorless crystals, m.p. 176°, $[\alpha]_D^{20}$ (Sulfate) —93.3° (c 3.0 in 70% isopropyl alcohol).

A basic polypeptide, containing: three α,γ-diaminobutyric acids, one L-threonine, one D-valine, one L-isoleucine, two L-leucines and one D-phenylalanine.

Bacillus krzemieniewski, a *B. circulans* mucoid variant

Stacey F. Howell, *J. Biol. Chem.* **186** 863 (1950).

Werner Hausmann and Lyman C. Craig, *ibid.* **198** 405 (1952).

Polymyxins:

780 **Polymyxin A** (Aerosporin)

781 **Polymyxin B₁**

782 **Polymyxin B₂**

783 **Polymyxin C**

784 **Polymyxin D**

785 **Polymyxin E**

A complex of related polypeptides produced by *Bacillus polymyxa*. Initially five components, A, B, C, D and E were separated. Then B was resolved into two components B_1 and B_2, differing only in the fatty acid moiety. All polymyxins contain L-α, γ-diaminobutyric acid and L-threonine. All but B_2 apparently contain d-6-methyloctanoic acid, and it contains a C-8 acid instead. Polymyxin A has been reported to contain D-leucine but no phenylalanine. It is also known as aerosporin because it is produced by *Bacillus aerosporus*. Polymyxin C contains phenylalanine but no leucine. Polymyxin D contains leucine but no phenylalanine, and it also has been reported to contain D-serine. Polymyxin E has the same qualitative composition as A, but is distinct.

Two alternative structures have been suggested for polymyxin B_1 as the result of degradative studies. These structures are shown here, the amino acids being abbreviated in the following manner:

Dia = α,γ-Diaminobutyric Acid
Thr = Threonine
Phe = Phenylalanine
Leu = Leucine

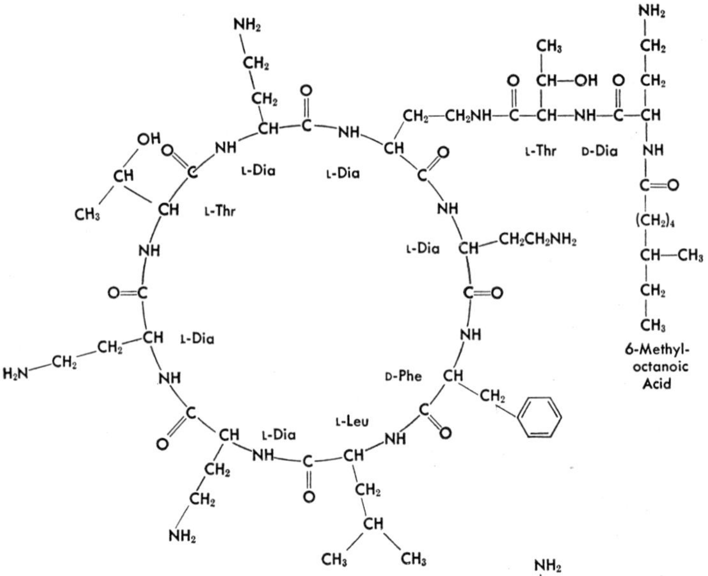

Or

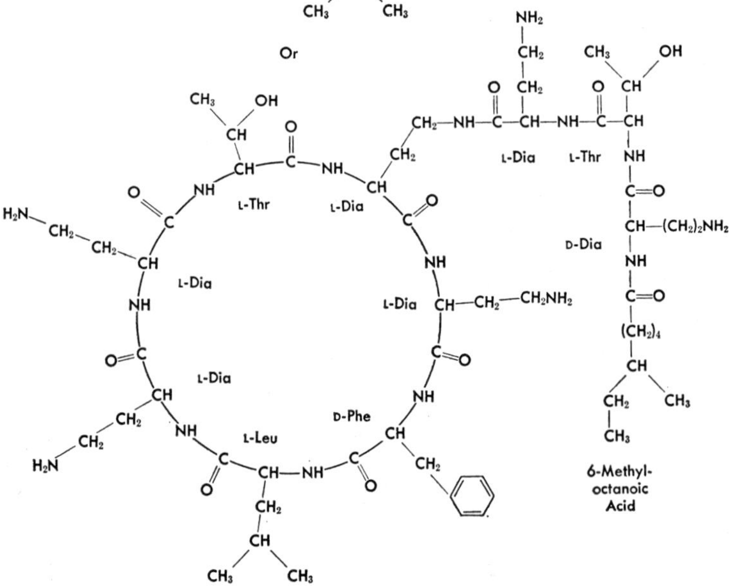

Commercial polymyxin is essentially polymyxin B sulfate, a white powder, m.p. 228–232° (dec.), $[\alpha]_D^{25}$ −45° (c 0.1). The empirical formula of the free base is $C_{56}H_{96-98}O_{13}N_{16}$.

G. C. Ainsworth, A. M. Brown and G. Brownlee, *Nature* **160** 263 (1947). (Isolation)

George Brownlee, *Ann. N. Y. Acad. Sci.* **51** 875 (1949). (Polymyxin A)

P. H. Bell, J. F. Bone, J. P. English, C. E. Fellows, K. S. Howard, M. M. Rogers, R. G. Shepherd and R. Winterbottom, *ibid.* **51** 897 (1949). (Degradations, identification of amino acids)

Tudor S. G. Jones, *ibid.* **51** 909 (1949). (Separations, degradations, identification of amino acids)

J. R. Catch, Tudor S. G. Jones and S. Wilkinson, *ibid.* **51** 917 (1949).

P. P. Regna, I. A. Solomons, B. K. Forscher and A. E. Timreck, *J. Clin. Invest.* **28** 1022 (1949). (Purification of B)

Werner Hausmann and Lyman C. Craig, *J. Am. Chem. Soc.* **76** 4892 (1954). (Resolution of B into two parts)

Werner Hausmann, *ibid.* **78** 3663 (1956). (Proposal of detailed cyclic structures)

Gerard Biserte and Michel Dautrevaux, *Bull. soc. chim. biol.* **39** 795 (1957). (Structure)

Gramicidins.

A mixture of polypeptides produced by *Bacillus brevis* and originally called tyrothricin was separated into two groups, the tyrocidines (about 80%) and the gramicidins (about 20%). Each of these groups has been fractionated further into pure polypeptides.

The original gramicidin consisted of a mixture of three closely related neutral polypeptides. It was assigned an average empirical formula of $C_{148}H_{210}O_{26}N_{30}$, colorless platelets, m.p. 228–231°, $[\alpha]_D^{20}$ +3°.

	Fraction A	Fraction B	Fraction C
D-Leucine	+	+	+
L-Trypotophan	+	+	+
L-Alanine	+	+	+
DL-Valine	+	+	+
Glycine	+	+	+
Phenylalanine		+	−
Tyrosine			+

Rollin D. Hotchkiss and René J. Dubos, *J. Biol. Chem.* 132 791 (1940).

Idem., ibid. 141 155 (1941). (Isolation)

Max Tishler, J. L. Stokes, N. R. Trenner and John B. Conn, *ibid.* 141 197 (1941).

Rollin D. Hotchkiss, *Advances in Enzymol.* 4 153 (1944).

786 Gramicidin J$_2$, C$_{35}$H$_{56}$O$_6$N$_8$.

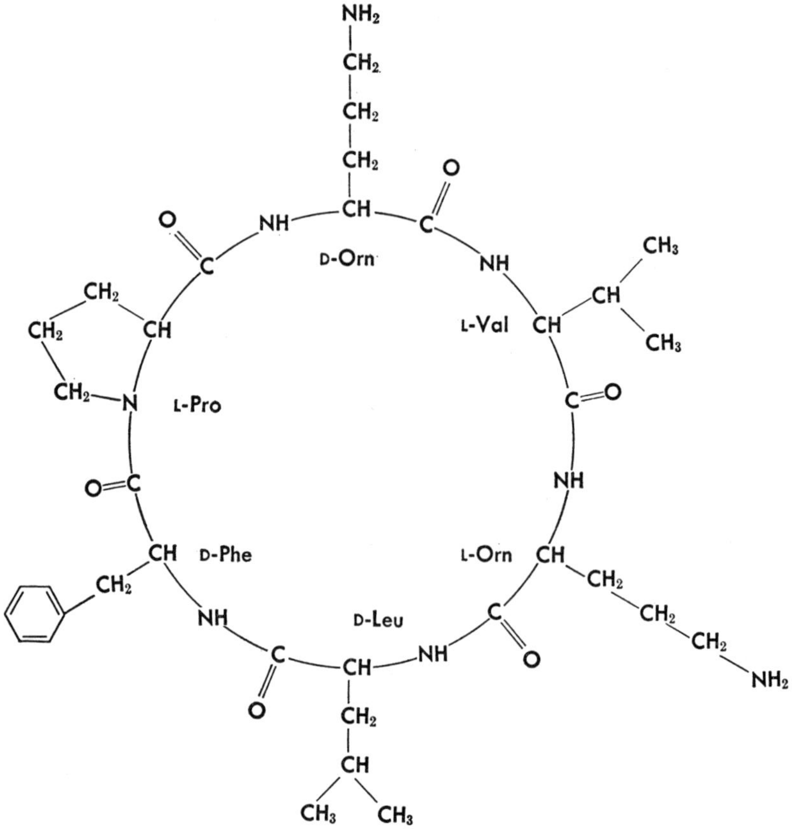

Bacillus brevis

Shokei Otani, H. Nagano and Y. Saito, *Osaka Shiritsu Daigaku Igaku Zasshi* 7 640–650 (1958). (*Chem. Abstr.* 12403g)

787   Gramicidin J$_1$, C$_{44}$H$_{65}$O$_7$N$_9$.

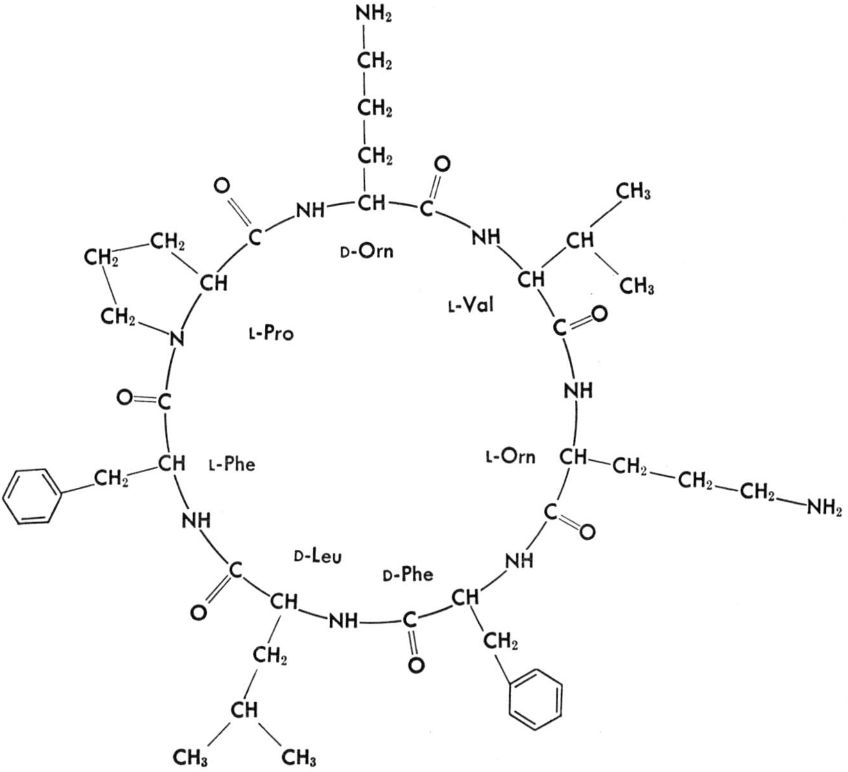

Bacillus brevis
Shokei Otani and Yoshitaka Saito, *Proc. Japan. Acad.* **30** 991 (1954).
Idem., Congr. intern. biochim., Résumés Communs., 3e Congr., Brussels, 88 (1955).

788 Gramicidin S (Gramicidin C), $C_{60}H_{92}O_{10}N_{12}$, colorless needles, m.p. 277° (dec.), $[\alpha]_D^{24}$ −289° ±10° (c 0.43 in 70% ethanol).

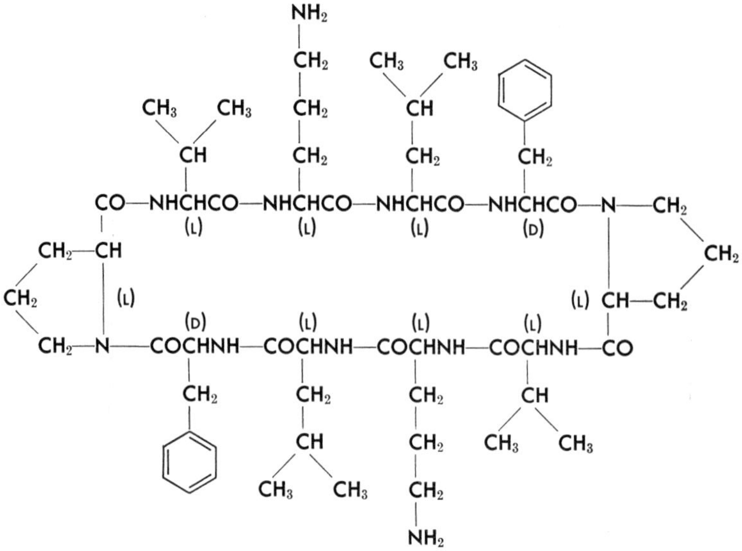

Bacillus brevis var. Gause-Brazhnikova

G. F. Gause and M. G. Brazhnikova, *Am. Rev. Soviet Med.* 2 134 (1944).

R. L. M. Synge, *Biochem. J.* 39 363 (1945). (Characteristics)

F. Sanger, *ibid.* 40 261 (1946).

R. Consden, A. H. Gordon, A. J. P. Martin and R. L. M. Synge, *ibid.* 40 xciii (1946).

Idem., ibid. 41 596 (1947).

Alan R. Battersby and Lyman C. Craig, *J. Am. Chem. Soc.* 73 1887 (1951).

R. Schwyzer and P. Sieber, *Helv. Chim. Acta* 40 624 (1957). (Synthesis)

789 Gramicidin D (Gramicidin Dubos), colorless crystals, m.p. 229° (dec.).

A crystalline component of tyrothricin. A cyclic polypeptide composed of 4 moles of D-Leucine, 4 moles of L-tryptophan, 2 moles of D-Valine, 2 moles of L-Valine, 2 moles of L-alanine, 1 mole of glycine and 1 mole of ethanolamine.

Bacillus brevis

René J. Dubos and Rollin D. Hotchkiss, *J. Exptl. Med.* 73 629 (1941). (Isolation)

A. H. Gordon, A. T. P. Martin and R. L. M. Synge, *Biochem. J.* 37 86 (1943).

Rollin D. Hotchkiss, *Advances in Enzymol.* 4 153 (1944).

R. L. M. Synge, *Biochem. J.* 39 355 (1945).

T. S. Work, *The relation of optical form to biological activity in the amino acid series*, Biochem. Soc. Symposia 1 61 (1948).

790 Racemomycin B, $C_{60}H_{128}O_{32}N_{20}$, white, hygroscopic powder, m.p. 150°, $[\alpha]_D^{19}$ −34° (c 0.5 in water).

A basic antibiotic resembling streptothricin. Acid hydrolysis gives a reducing sugar and carbon dioxide, β-lysine and roseonine in the ratio 2:3:2. Racemomycin B occurs in a complex with two (apparently similar) substances, racemomycins A and C.

Streptomyces racemochromogenus n. sp.

Hyozo Taniyama and Shoji Takemura, *J. Pharm. Soc. Japan* **77** 1210 (1957).

Idem., ibid. **78** 742 (1958).

791 Tyrocidine A, $C_{66}H_{86}O_{13}N_{13}$, colorless needles or rods, m.p. 240–242° (dec.), $[\alpha]_D^{25}$ −111°. A component of the tyrothricin complex.

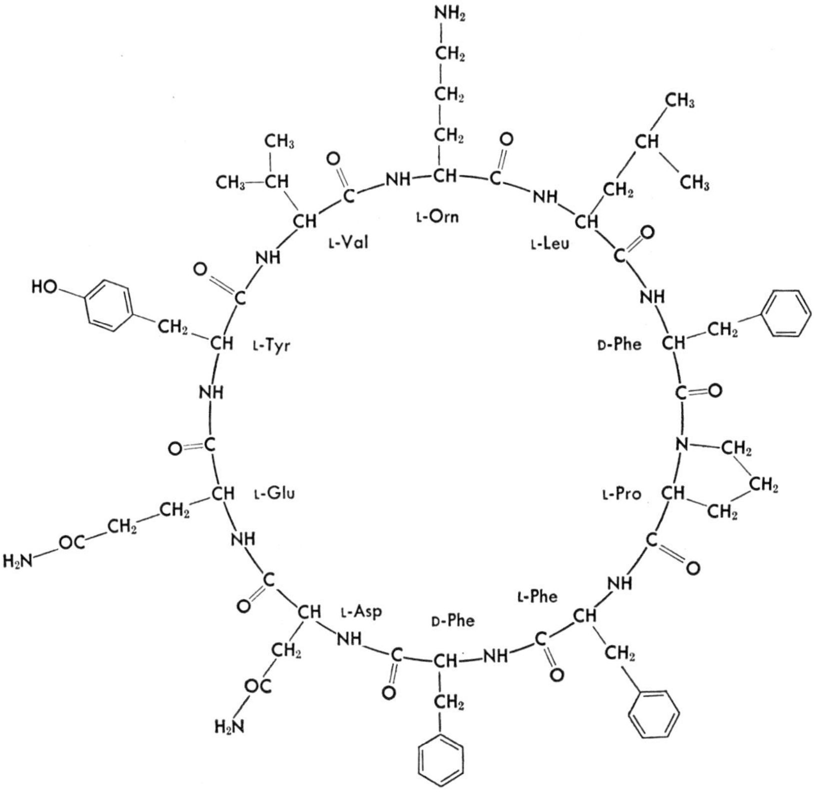

Bacillus brevis

Rollin D. Hotchkiss and René J. Dubos, *J. Biol. Chem.* **132** 791 (1940). (Isolation)

R. L. M. Synge and A. Tiselius, *Acta Chem. Scand.* **1** 749 (1947).

R. L. M. Synge, *Quart. Rev.* **3** 245 (1949). (Review of work to that date)

Alan R. Battersby and Lyman C. Craig, *J. Am. Chem. Soc.* **74** 4019, 4023 (1952). (Separation)

Alejandro Paladini and Lyman C. Craig, *ibid.* **76** 688 (1954). (Structure)

792 Tyrocidine B, $C_{68}H_{88}O_{13}N_{14}$.

A component of the tyrothricin complex.

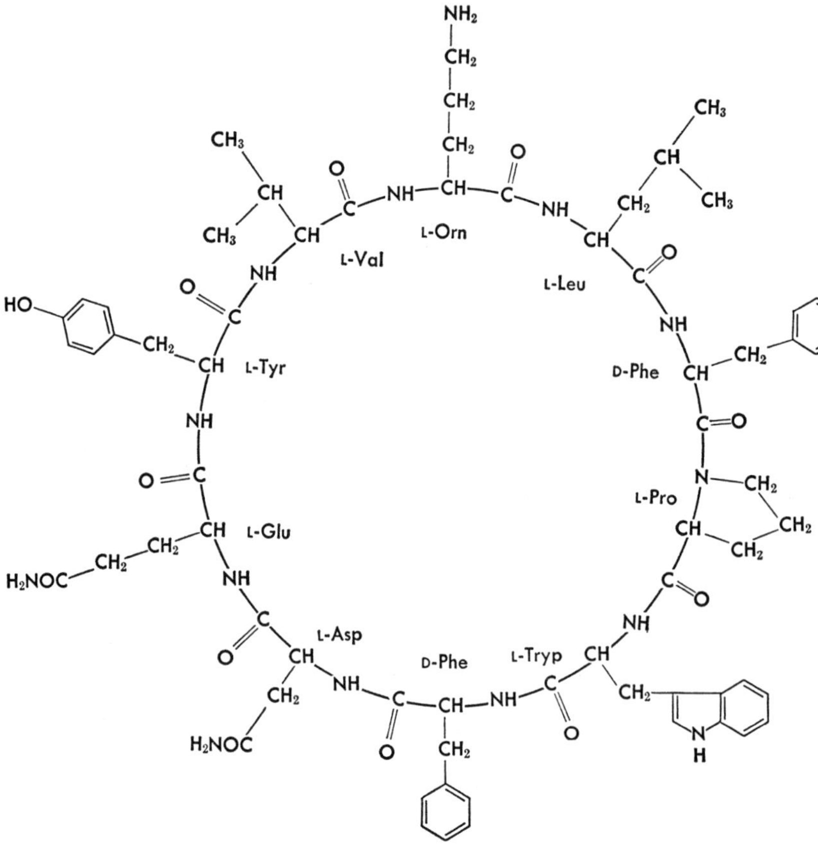

Bacillus brevis
T. P. King and L. C. Craig, *J. Am. Chem. Soc.* **77** 6627
(1955). (Final structure)

Actinomycins.

The nomenclature of the actinomycins is confused because they occur in difficulty separable complex mixtures, several different research groups have investigated them, and, even when pure, one substance cannot be compared with another by techniques as simple as a mixed melting point. This problem has been discussed by Brockmann in a review of the actinomycins.

L. Zechmeister (editor), "Fortschritte der Chemie organischer Naturstoffe" **XVIII**, Hans Brockmann, *The actinomycins,* Springer Verlag, Vienna, 1960.

At first actinomycins A, B and C were isolated, but later these were found to be mixtures. As such complexes were resolved by paper chromatography, Arabic numeral subscripts were attached to the capital Roman letter in order of appearance on the developed chromatogram, the origin on the paper being zero (*e.g.*, C_1, C_2, C_3). When some of the separated actinomycins were resolved even further, a further subdivision in nomenclature was required; so a lower case Roman letter was attached to give, *e.g.*, C_{2a} which appeared between C_2 and C_3. When the X_0 complex at the origin was resolved, a slightly different system was used, Greek letters being attached to the Arabic numeral subscript, *e.g.*, $X_{0\gamma}$ was less polar than $X_{0\beta}$.

Few series are complete because often names have been eliminated due to duplication, further resolution, etc. Thus, a complex designated I was resolved into I_1 and I_2, but these later were shown to be the same as C_1 and C_2 and the I names eliminated.

Still this method of nomenclature does have a rationale, although it may not be readily apparent, and it is used in Germany and in Switzerland.

Other groups continue to refer to various complexes as A, B or D types. These consist essentially of various ratios of actinomycin X_2 and its reduction product, actinomycin C_1, actinomycin D being nearly pure C_1.

The E and F series arose when it was discovered that addition of certain amino acids to the medium in large amounts caused displacement of certain other amino acids in the peptide side-chains, thus creating new "biosynthetic" actinomycins.

Beyond historical interest there seems to be little point in attempting to standardize the nomenclature of actinomycin mixtures. Waksman has proposed that a Roman numeral be assigned to each pure actinomycin, and Johnson's group has taken up this practice, actinomycins II and III being distinct from those characterized elsewhere, while IV is identical with C_1 or D, etc. Brockmann views this as one more contribution to the confusion of the literature and, claiming the right of discoverer of many of the actinomycins, has made the suggestion that no nomenclature system will relieve the confusion unless it makes apparent the amino acid sequences of the side-chains.

Although this does not solve the problem of trivial nomenclature, Brockmann uses a shorthand method of demonstrating the structures of the actinomycins in which a symbol ——< represents the actinocinin moiety, the branches at the right symbolizing the amino and quinonoid carbonyl groups. The abbreviated amino acid names are then attached in proper sequence. In most of the asymmetric actinomycins the chains in which the differing amino acids occur have not yet been specified, and this is indicated by an ⑤-symbol, indicating possible reversal of position.

The structure of actinomycin C_3 (which has been synthesized) is given somewhat more fully to show structural details. The custom of arrangement by empirical formula is ignored here to permit grouping by related structures.

The mitomycins (unclassified) may be actinomycins.

There is an apparent striking biogenetic similarity among the etamycin, staphylomycin, etc. group of polypeptides on the one hand and the actinomycins on the other.

793 Actinomycin C_3 (VII) $C_{64}H_{90}O_{16}N_{12}$, red crystals, m.p. 232–235° (dec.), $[\alpha]_D^{19}$ −321° ±10°.

Below is shown one of the peptide side-chains of actinomycin C_3 to permit comparison with etamycin, etc.

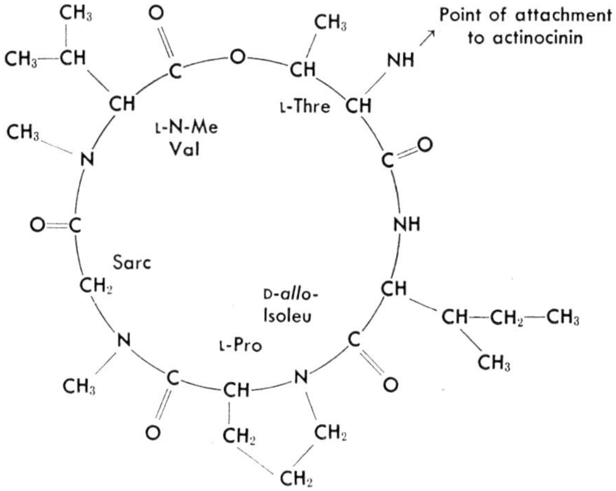

Streptomyces antibioticus, S. chrysomallus

H. Brockmann, G. Bohnsack, B. Franck, H. Gröne, H. Muxfeldt and C. Süling, *Angew. Chem.* **68** 70 (1956) and preceding papers. (Structure)

H. Brockmann, W. Sunderkötter, K. W. Ohly and P. Boldt, *Naturwissenschaften* **47** 230 (1960).

H. Brockmann and L. Lackner, *ibid.*, **47** 230 (1960).

794 Actinomycin C_1 (D,IV,X_1,B_1,I_1) $C_{61}H_{90}O_{16}N_{12}$ red prisms, m.p. 241° (235.5–236.5) (dec.) $[\alpha]_D^{20}$ −349° ±10° (337°).

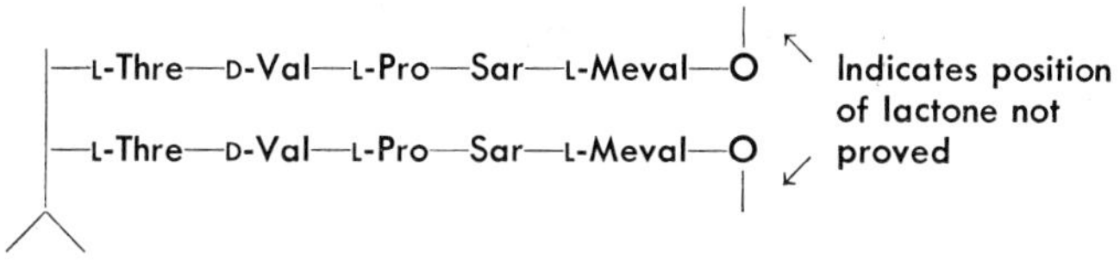

Where

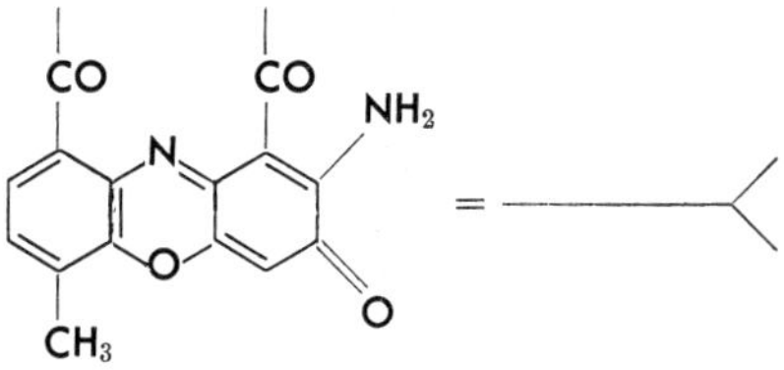

Streptomyces chrysomallus, S. antibioticus; S. parvullus

A. W. Johnson and A. B. Mauger, *Biochem. J.* **73** 535 (1959).

Hans Brockmann and Hans-Sieghard Petras, *Naturwissenschaften* **46** 400 (1959).

Hans Brockmann, P. Boldt and Hans-Sieghard Petras, *ibid.* 47 62 (1960).

795 Actinomycin C$_2$ (VI) C$_{62}$H$_{92}$O$_{16}$N$_{12}$ red crystals, m.p. 237° (dec.), $[\alpha]_D^{19}$ −325° ±10°.

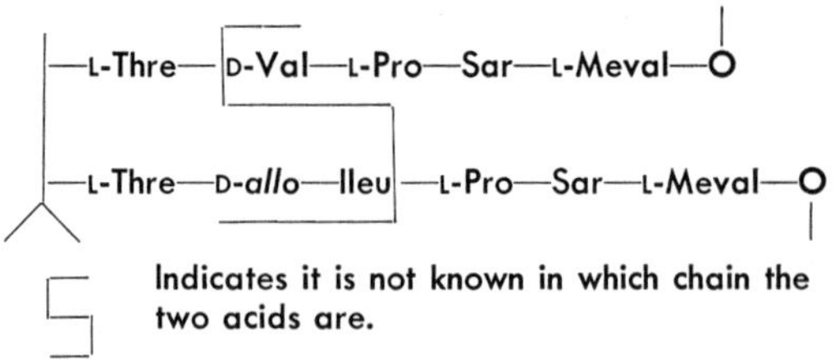

Indicates it is not known in which chain the two acids are.

Streptomyces chrysomallus
A. W. Johnson and A. B. Mauger, *Biochem. J.* 73 535 (1959).
Hans Brockmann and Hans-Sieghard Petras, *Naturwissenschaften* 46 400 (1959).
Hans Brockmann, P. Boldt and Hans-Sieghard Petras, *ibid.* 47 62 (1960).
C$_{2a}$ C$_{62}$H$_{92}$O$_{26}$N$_{12}$ an isomer of C$_2$ found by paper chromatography.
Streptomyces chrysomallus
Hans Brockmann and B. Franck, *ibid.* 47 15 (1960).

796 Actinomycin E$_1$, C$_{64}$H$_{96}$O$_{16}$N$_{12}$.

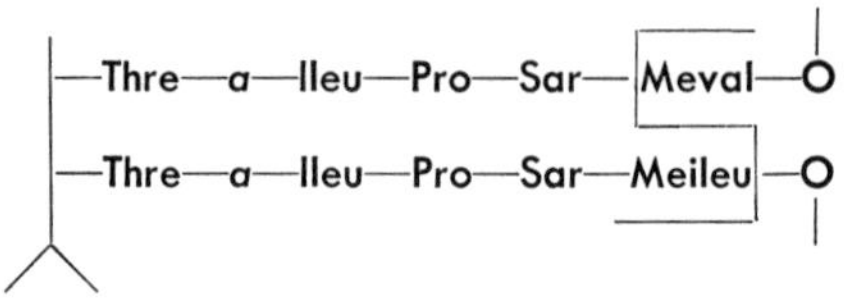

Streptomyces sp.
Günther Schmidt-Kastner, *Naturwissenschaften* 43 131 (1956).

797 Actinomycin E$_2$, C$_{65}$H$_{98}$O$_{16}$N$_{12}$.

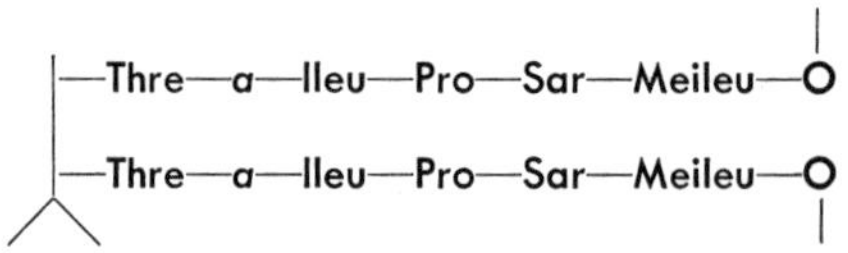

Streptomyces sp.

Günther Schmidt-Kastner, *Naturwissenschaften* 43 131
(1956).

798 Actinomycin F$_1$, C$_{58}$H$_{88}$O$_{16}$N$_{12}$.

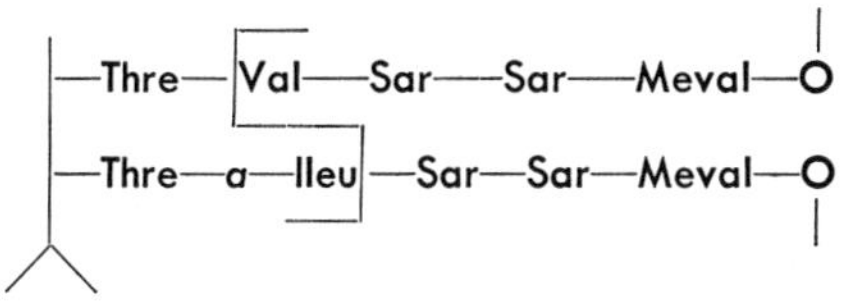

$$
\begin{array}{l}
\text{—Thre—Val—Sar—Sar—Meval—O} \\
\text{—Thre—a—Ileu—Sar—Sar—Meval—O}
\end{array}
$$

Streptomyces sp.
Günther Schmidt-Kastner, *Naturwissenschaften* 43 131
(1956).

799 Actinomycin F$_2$, C$_{60}$H$_{90}$O$_{16}$N$_{12}$.

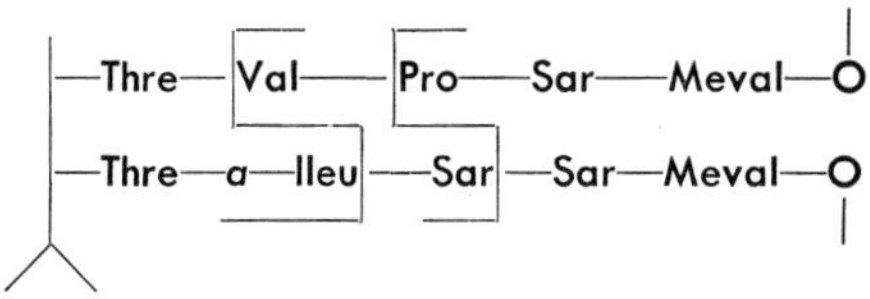

$$
\begin{array}{l}
\text{—Thre—Val—Pro—Sar—Meval—O} \\
\text{—Thre—a—Ileu—Sar—Sar—Meval—O}
\end{array}
$$

Streptomyces sp.
Günther Schmidt-Kastner, *Naturwissenschaften* 43 131
(1956).

800 Actinomycin F$_3$, C$_{59}$H$_{90}$O$_{16}$N$_{12}$.

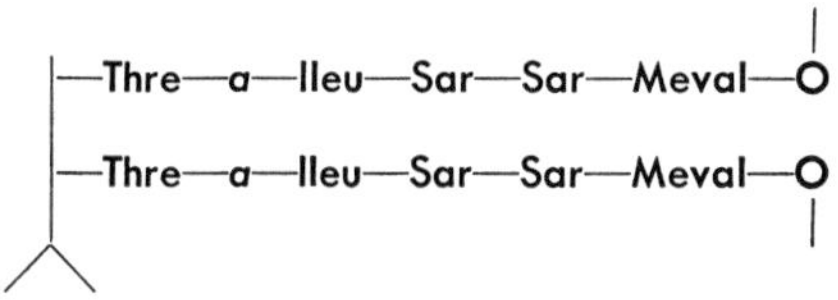

$$
\begin{array}{l}
\text{—Thre—a—Ileu—Sar—Sar—Meval—O} \\
\text{—Thre—a—Ileu—Sar—Sar—Meval—O}
\end{array}
$$

Streptomyces sp.
Günther Schmidt-Kastner, *Naturwissenschaften* 43 131
(1956).

801 Actinomycin F$_4$, C$_{61}$H$_{92}$O$_{16}$N$_{12}$.

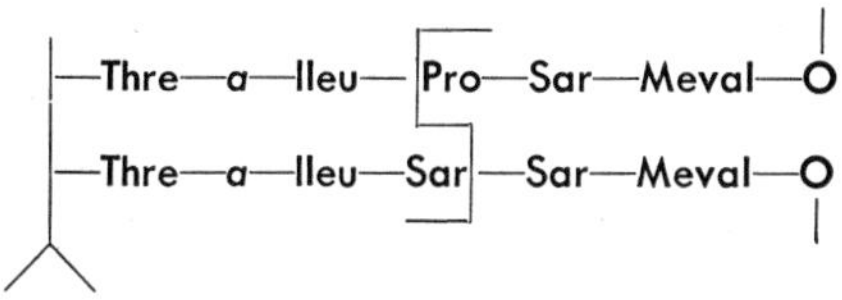

$$
\begin{array}{l}
\text{—Thre—a—Ileu—Pro—Sar—Meval—O} \\
\text{—Thre—a—Ileu—Sar—Sar—Meval—O}
\end{array}
$$

Streptomyces sp.
Günther Schmidt-Kastner, *Naturwissenschaften* 43 131
(1956).

802 Actinomycin X_{1a}, $C_{59}H_{87}O_{17}N_{12}$.

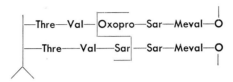

Streptomyces chrysomallus, S. fradiae
Hans Brockmann and H. Gröne, *Chem Ber.* **87** 1036 (1954).

803 Actinomycin X_2 (V, B_2) $C_{61}H_{89}O_{17}N_{12}$ red plates, m.p. 244–246°, $[\alpha]_D^{19}$ −341° ±10°.

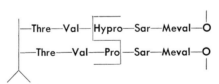

Streptomyces chrysomallus, S. fradiae
Hans Brockmann and Hans Gröne, *Chem. Ber.* **87** 1036 (1954).

804 Actinomycin X_3, needles.
An actinomycin X_3, containing threonine, sarcosine, proline, valine, isoleucine and N-methylvaline, also has been isolated.
H. Brockmann and H. Gröne, *Chem. Ber.* **87** 1036 (1954).
Werner Frommer, *Arch. Mikrobiol.* **34** 1 (1959).

805 Actinomycin $X_{0\beta}$ (I) $C_{61}H_{90}O_{17}N_{12}$ yellow needles, m.p. 245–247, $[\alpha]_D^{20}$ −260° ±10° (c 0.22 acetone).

```
  ┌─Thre─Val─┬Hypro─Sar─Meval─O
  │          │
  ├─Thre─Val─┴Pro─Sar─Meval─O
  │
 /\
```

Streptomyces chrysomallus, S. fradiae
Hans Brockmann, Gottfried Pampus and Jost H. Manegold, *Chem. Ber.* **92** 1294 (1959).
Hans Brockmann and H. Gröne, *Chem Ber.* **87** 1036 (1954).

806   **Actinomycin $X_{o\gamma}$, $C_{59}H_{88}O_{16}N_{12}$.**

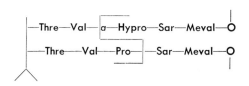

Streptomyces chrysomallus, S. fradiae
Hans Brockmann and Gottfried Pampus, *Angew. Chem.* **67**
519 (1955).
     H. H. Martin and Gottfried Pampus, *Arch. Mikrobiol.* **25**
90 (1956).

807   **Actinomycin $X_{o\delta}$, $C_{64}H_{90}O_{17}N_{12}$.**

```
            —Thre—Val— a —Hypro—Sar—Meval—O
                                             |
            —Thre—Val—Pro —Sar—Meval—O
                                        |
```

Streptomyces chrysomallus, S. fradiae
Same references as Actinomycin $X_{o\gamma}$.

Actinomycins Z.
     All contain the same five amino acids on hydrolysis:
threonine, sarcosine, N-methylalanine, valine and N-
methylvaline.

808   **Actinomycin Z_0,** amorphous orange-red powder, m.p. 250° (dec.).
     Streptomyces fradiae
     R. Bossi, R. Hütter, W. Keller-Schierlein, L. Neipp and
H. Zähner, *Helv. Chim. Acta* **41** 1645 (1958).

809   **Actinomycin Z_1,** orange-red crystals, m.p. 256–260 (dec.), $[\alpha]_D$
−362° (c 0.185 in $CHCl_3$).
     Streptomyces fradiae
     R. Bossi, R. Hütter, W. Keller-Schierlein, L. Neipp and
H. Zähner, *Helv. Chim. Acta* **41** 1645 (1958).

Actinomycins Z_2, Z_3, Z_4, an inseparable mixture, m.p. 256–260°
(dec.), $[\alpha]_D$ −246 (c 0.257 in $CHCl_3$).
     R. Bossi, R. Hütter, W. Keller-Schierlein, L. Neipp and
H. Zähner, *Helv. Chim. Acta* **41** 1645 (1958).

810 **Actinomycin Z₅,** short red staffs, m.p. 261–267 (dec.), $[\alpha]_D$ −284° (c 0.244 in $CHCl_3$).

Streptomyces fradiae

R. Bossi, R. Hütter, W. Keller-Schierlein, L. Neipp and H. Zähner, *Helv. Chim. Acta* 41 1645 (1958).

811 **Actinomycin II,** $C_{57}H_{86}O_{16}N_{12}$ red plates, m.p. 215° $[\alpha]_D^{17}$ −157° (c 0.24 in $CHCl_3$).

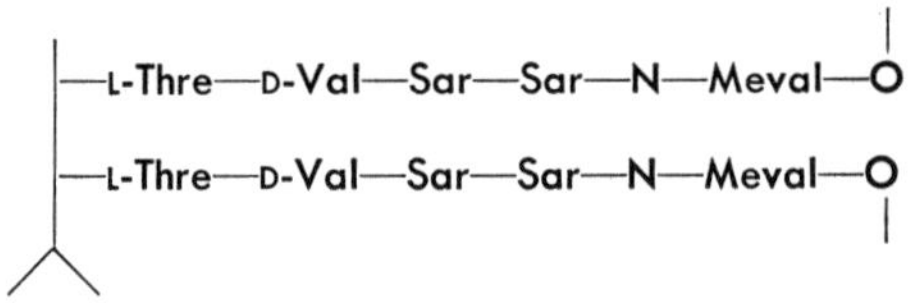

Streptomyces chrysomallus

A. W. Johnson and A. Mauger, *Biochem. J.* 73 535 (1959).

William A. Goss and Edward Katz, *Antibiotics and Chemotherapy* 10 221 (1960).

812 **Actinomycin III,** $C_{59}H_{86}O_{16}N_{12}$ red prisms, m.p. 237°, $[\alpha]_D^{19}$ −205° (c 0.22 in $CHCl_3$).

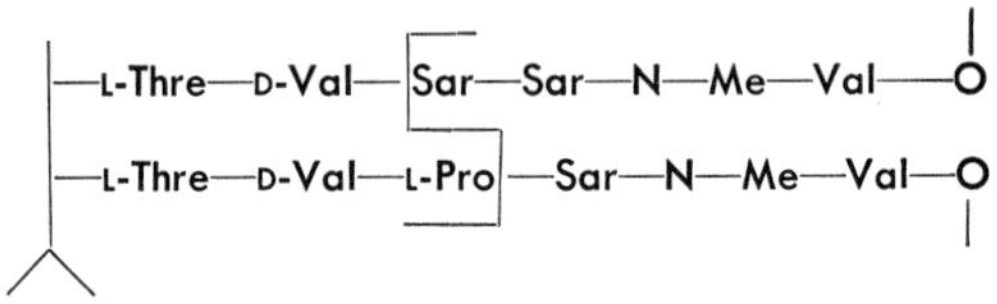

Streptomyces chrysomallus

A. W. Johnson and A. Mauger, *Biochem. J.* 73 535 (1959).

William A. Goss and Edward Katz, *Antibiotics and Chemotherapy* 10 221 (1960).

813   Mycobacillin, $C_{65}H_{85}O_{30}N_{13}$, **colorless needles.**

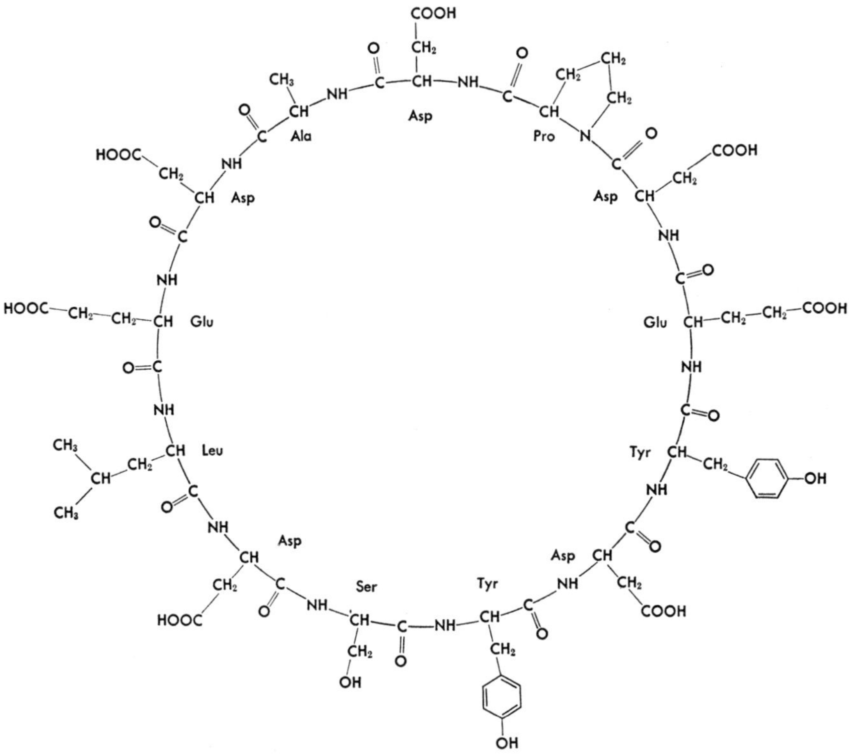

Bacillus subtilis

Hydrolysis yields five aspartic acids, two glutamic acids, two tyrosines, one proline, one serine, one leucine and one alanine. (Unspecified configurations)

S. K. Majumdar and S. K. Bose, *Nature* **181** 134 (1958). (Isolation)

Idem., Biochem. J. **74** 596 (1960). (Structure)

814 **Bacitracin A,** $C_{66}H_{103}O_{16}N_{17}S$, white, hygroscopic, amorphous powder, $[\alpha]_D^{23}$ +5° (±2.5°).

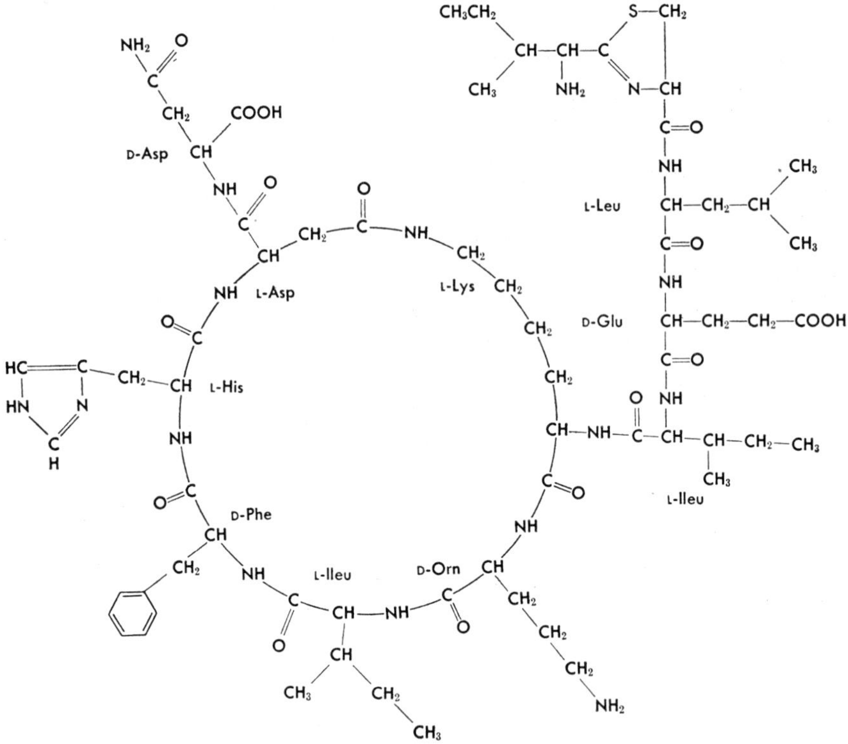

Bacillus subtilis, B. licheniformis

The bacitracins are a difficultly separable polypeptide complex. Bacitracins A, B, C, D, E, F_1, F_2, F_3 and G have been differentiated. The F series may be artifacts. The structure of bacitracin A has received the most attention. In certain of the other bacitracins isoleucine is replaced by valine. The complex from *B. licheniformis* was originally called ayfivin.

I. M. Lockhart, E. P. Abraham and G. G. F. Newton, *Biochem. J.* 61 534 (1955).

J. R. Weisiger, W. Hausmann and L. C. Craig, *J. Am. Chem. Soc.* 77 731, 3123 (1955).

Dorothy Wrinch, *Nature* 179 536 (1957).

E. P. Abraham, "CIBA Lectures in Microbial Biochemistry,"

The bacitracins, John Wiley and Sons, New York, 1957, pp. 1–30.   (A review which also covers the earlier work)

815 **Subtilin,** amorphous white powder, $[\alpha]_D^{23}$ −29° to −35°.

Subtilin is a basic polypeptide, molecular weight 3188, which yields 11 common amino acids, lanthionine:

$$\text{HOOC}-\underset{\underset{\text{NH}_2}{|}}{\text{CH}}-\text{CH}_2-\text{S}-\text{CH}_2-\underset{\underset{\text{NH}_2}{|}}{\text{CH}}-\text{COOH}$$

and a new S-amino acid, probably β-methyllanthionine:

$$\text{HOOC}-\underset{\underset{\text{NH}_2}{|}}{\overset{\text{(L)}}{\text{CH}}}-\text{CH}_2-\text{S}-\underset{}{\overset{\overset{\text{CH}_3(\text{D})}{|}}{\text{CH}}}-\underset{\underset{\text{NH}_2}{|}}{\text{CH}}-\text{COOH}$$

The common amino acids identified are: glycine, alanine, valine, leucine, isoleucine, proline, phenylalanine, tryptophan, lysine, asparagine and glutamic acid.

Bacillus subtilis

Eugene F. Jansen and Doris J. Hirschmann, *Arch. Biochem.* 4 297 (1944).

A. J. Salle and Gregory J. Jann, *Proc. Soc. Exp. Biol.* 60 60 (1945).

W. Steenken, Jr. and E. Wolinsky, *J. Bact.* 57 453 (1949).

J. C. Lewis and N. S. Snell, *J. Am. Chem. Soc.* 73 4812 (1951).

Gordon Alderton, *ibid.* 75 2391 (1953).

Nisins, nearly white needles.

Consist of four active cyclic polypeptides. All contain lanthionine and β-methyllanthionine. These amino acids also occur in the antibiotics, subtilin, cinnamycin and duramycin.

816, 817, 818 **Nisins A, B** and **C** contain leucine and/or isoleucine, valine, alanine, glycine, proline, aspartic acid, histidine, lysine and methionine.

819 **Nisin D** contains glutamic acid, but no valine or methionine.

Nisin A has a molecular weight of ~7000 and also contains serine.

Streptococcus lactis, S. cremoris

N. J. Berridge, G. G. F. Newton and E. P. Abraham, *Biochem. J.* 52 529 (1952).

G. G. F. Newton and E. P. Abraham, *Nature* 171 606 (1953).

G. Cheeseman and N. Berridge, *Biochem. J.* 71 185 (1959).

820 **Duramycin,** colorless amorphous solid, no definite m.p., Hydrochloride: $[\alpha]_D^{25}$ −6.4° (c 3.9 in water).

Duramycin is a polypeptide, containing at least one free amino group and several free carboxyl groups. Acid hydrolysis yielded: lanthionine, β-methyllanthionine, aspartic acid, glutamic acid, glycine, valine, proline, phenylalanine and possibly ornithine and hydroxyproline. Duramycin is related to, but distinct from, cinnamycin.

Streptomyces cinnamoneus f. *azacoluta*

Odette L. Shotwell, Frank H. Stodola, William R. Michael, Lloyd A. Lindenfelser, Robert G. Dworschack and Thomas G. Pridham, *J. Am. Chem. Soc.* 80 3912 (1958).

821 **Cinnamycin.**

A polypeptide containing (probably): glutamic acid, aspartic acid, proline, phenylalanine, valine, arginine, lanthionine and β-methyllanthionine.

Streptomyces cinnamoneus

Robert G. Benedict, William Dvonch, Odette L. Shotwell, Thomas G. Pridham and Lloyd A. Lindenfelser, *Antibiotics and Chemotherapy* 2 591 (1952).

Robert G. Benedict, *Bot. Rev.* 19 229 (1953).

822 **Matamycin,** colorless crystals, m.p. 173° (dec.), $[\alpha]_D^{20}$ +36.6° (c 0.11 in methanol).

An essentially neutral antibiotic of low solubility. Analysis: C 43.95, H 4.06, N 14.45, S 13.57. Halogenfree. Positive Fehlings, Tollens, permanganate, DNPH, and (after hydrolysis) ninhydrin tests. Negative ferric chloride and Sakaguchi tests. A hydrolysate contained: cysteic acid, glycine, serine, alanine, arginine and two other amino acids.

Streptomyces matensis n. sp.

P. Sensi, R. Ballotta and G. G. Gallo, *Antibiotics and Chemotherapy* 9 76 (1959).

An inactive compound, "Compound I," evidently of analogous structure was isolated from the same culture:

823 **Compound I,** colorless crystals, m.p. 189° (dec.), $[\alpha]_D^{20}$ +151.6° (c 0.1 in dioxane).

Analysis: C 45.84, H 3.90, N 14.99, S 14.64. It may be a dehydration product of matamycin.

824   **Comirin,** nearly colorless powder, m.p. 230–235° (dec.).

A polypeptide containing the following amino acids: serine, aspartic acid, glycine, α,γ-diaminobutyric acid, lysine, leucine, isoleucine, tyrosine and arginine. An ether-soluble moiety also was present. Negative ninhydrin, positive biuret. No free amino acid groups.

Pseudomonas antimycetica

W. G. C. Forsyth, *Biochem. J.* 59 500 (1955).

825   **Colimycin.**

A crystalline polypeptide, containing mainly D-leucine and L-threonine.

Bacillus colistinus

P. V. Forni and E. Guidetti, *Minerva med.* II 823 (1956).

826   **Brevin.**

Brevin is a polypeptide containing: aspartic acid, glycine, tyrosine, serine, an unidentified basic substance (and also a fatty acid component?).

Bacillus brevis

Ella M. Barnes and G. G. F. Newton, *Antibiotics and Chemotherapy* 3 866 (1953).

827   **Brevolin,** Hydrochloride yellowish white amorphous, $[\alpha]_D^{26}$ −18.9°.

Brevolin is a polypeptide, probably related to brevin.

Bacillus brevis

Junichi Kawamata and Yutaka Motomura, *J. Antibiotics* (Japan) 7A 25 (1954).

Antibiotics from Yeast.

Two amorphous compounds have been isolated from bakers' yeast. They have antibacterial and antifungal effects, and seem to be cyclic polypeptides. Acid hydrolysis of one of these (Y_1) gave leucine, valine, alanine, glutamic acid and glycine. Acid hydrolysis of Y_2 gave the same amino acids plus γ-aminobutyric acid.

828
829

Werner Motzel and Elton S. Cook, *Nature* 182 455 (1958).

830   **Alvein.**

A basic polypeptide containing arginine.

Bacillus alvei

K. Gilliver, A. M. Holmes and E. P. Abraham, *Brit. J. Exptl. Path.* 30 209 (1949).

831 **Thiostrepton,** colorless crystals, m.p. 246–256° (dec.), $[\alpha]_D^{23}$ −98.5° (c 1 in glacial acetic acid).

A weakly basic polypetide. Probable amino acid content: leucine (or isoleucine), valine, alanine, threonine, proline, lysine, glycine, aspartic acid, glutamic acid, cystine and tryptophan.

Streptomyces sp.

John Vandeputte and James D. Dutcher, "Antibiotics Annual 1955–1956," Medical Encyclopedia, Inc., New York, p. 560.

832 **Antibiotic 899,** reddish yellow amorphous powder, m.p. 115–120°.

A neutral compound with spectra similar to those of streptogramin.

Streptomyces sp. resembling *S. virginiae*

P. De Somer and P. Van Dijck, *Antibiotics and Chemotherapy* 5 632 (1955).

833 **Amphomycin,** colorless crystals, $[\alpha]_D^{25}$ +7.5° ±5 (c 1 in water at pH 6).

An acidic (amphoteric) polypeptide, minimal molecular weight about 1500.

Streptomyces canus

Bernard Heinemann, Murray A. Kaplan, Robert D. Muir and Irving R. Hooper, *Antibiotics and Chemotherapy* 3 1239 (1953).

834 **Aspartocin.**

An acidic polypeptide similar to amphomycin. C 53.2, H 7.6, N 13.2, S 0.42, no halogen. Hydrolyzes to 4 moles of L-aspartic acid, 2 moles of glycine, 1 mole of L-proline, 1 mole of L-valine, α,β-diaminobutyric acid, α-[L],β-methylaspartic acid, D-α-pipecolic acid and an unsaturated fatty acid.

Streptomyces griseus var. *spiralis, S. violaceus*

Yields of 1 to 10 g. per liter were obtained.

A. J. Shay, J. Adam, J. H. Martin, W. K. Hausmann, P. Shu and N. Bohonos, 7th Annual Symposium on Antibiotics, Washington, D. C., 1959.

J. H. Martin and W. K. Hausmann. *J. Am. Chem. Soc.* 82 2079 (1960).

835 **Zaomycin,** m.p. 242–246° (dec.).

A polypeptide resembling amphomycin.

Streptomyces zaomyceticus n. sp.

Yorio Hinuma, *J. Antibiotics* (Japan) 7A 134 (1954).

836   **Bacillomycin** (Fungocin, Bacillomycin R, Bacillomycin A), colorless microcrystals.

An acidic polypeptide, molecular weight ~1000. Analysis: C 52.69, H 7.20, N 12.29. Contains glutamic acid, aspartic acid, serine, threonine and tyrosine. Similar to or identical with eumycin.

Bacillus subtilis

Maurice Landy, Sanford B. Rosenman and George H. Warren, *J. Bact.* 54 24 (1947).

Howard Tint and Wilhelm Reiss, *J. Biol. Chem.* 190 133 (1951).

Robert A. Turner, *Arch. Biochem.* 60 364 (1956).

837   **Bacillomycin B,** amorphous yellow material.

A polypeptide containing glutamic acid, aspartic acid, proline, tyrosine and leucine.

Bacillus subtilis

Isao Shibasaki and Gyozo Terui, *J. Fermentation Technol.* (Japan) 31 339 (1953).

838   **Bacillomycin C.**

A polypeptide containing glutamic acid, aspartic acid, tyrosine, leucine and valine.

Bacillus subtilis

Isao Shibasaki and Gyozo Terui, *J. Fermentation Technol.* (Japan) 32 115 (1954).

839   **Fungistatin.**

An amphoteric polypeptide, containing aspartic acid, lysine, serine, threonine, proline, alanine, isoleucine, valine, tryptophan, tyrosine, other unidentified amino acids. Molecular weight about 2400.

Bacillus subtilis

Gladys L. Hobby, Peter P. Regna, Nancy Dougherty and William E. Steig, *J. Clin. Invest.* 28 927 (1949).

P. P. Regna, R. A. Carboni and W. E. Steig, *Am. Chem. Soc. Meeting-in-Miniature*, Brooklyn (1950).

Robert L. Peck and John E. Lyons, *Ann. Rev. Biochem.* 20 367 (1951).

840   **Bryamycin,** m.p. 223–235° (dec.), $[\alpha]_D^{27}$ −68.5° (c 1 in chloroform).

A polypeptide containing alanine, glycine, isoleucine, threonine, cystine and unidentified compounds.

Streptomyces hawaiiensis n. sp.

M. J. Cron, D. F. Whitehead, I. R. Harper, B. Heinemann and J. Lein, *Antibiotics and Chemotherapy* 6 63 (1956).

841 **Coliformin.**

A polypetide, molecular weight 4000 ± 400, containing glutamic acid, aspartic acid, lysine, valine, leucine, serine, alanine and glycine. Positive Molisch. Contains traces of phosphorus and sulfur.

An *E. coli-Aerobacter aerogenes* type of bacterium

Stig K. L. Freyschuss, Stig O. Pehrson and Borje Steinberg, *Antibiotics and Chemotherapy* 5 218 (1955).

842 **Mycosubtilin,** white crystals, m.p. 256°.

A polypeptide, C 55.31, H 7.61, N 15.15.

Bacillus subtilis

Robert P. Walton and H. Boyd Woodruff, *J. Clin. Invest.* 28 924 (1949).

843 **Grizein** (Helianthate) homogeneous brown powder, m.p. 194–196° (dec.) (hydrochloride) white, hygroscopic powder.

A basic polypeptide complex. Positive biuret, ninhydrin, glucosamine reactions. Negative maltol, histidine, Sakaguchi tests.

Streptomyces griseus-like strains

N. A. Krasilnikov, A. N. Belozerskii, Ya. I. Rautenshtein, A. I. Korenyako, N. I. Nikitina, A. I. Sokolova and S. O. Uryson, *Mikrobiologiya* 26 418 (1957).

Licheniformins, amorphous white powders, no m.p.

844 **Licheniformin A,** hydrochloride: $[\alpha]_D^{20}$ −37.4° (c 1 in chloroform).

845 **Licheniformin B,** hydrochloride: $[\alpha]_D^{20}$ −37.7° (c 1 in chloroform).

846 **Licheniformin C,** hydrochloride: $[\alpha]_D^{20}$ −36.8° (c 1 in chloroform).

A rather high molecular weight polypeptide complex. Negative glucosamine and Molisch. Positive Sakaguchi, biuret.

Licheniformins A and B contain: aspartic acid, glycine, serine, lysine, arginine, valine, proline and phenylalanine.

Bacillus licheniformis

R. K. Callow, R. E. Glover, P. D'Arcy Hart and G. M. Hills, *Brit. J. Exptl. Path.* 28 418 (1947).

R. K. Callow and T. S. Work, *Biochem. J.* 51 558 (1952).

847 Carcinomycin, dark green, amorphous.
>A polypeptide antibiotic.   Sulfur-free.
>*Streptomyces carcinomycicus*
>Shogo Hosotani and Momoe Soeda, Japanese Patent 6893 (1959). (*Chem. Abstr.* 54 831g)

848 Carcinocidin, $[\alpha]_D^{25}$ $-20°$ (c 1 in water).
>A polypeptide antibiotic, containing cystine, lysine, glycine and glutamic acid. Molecular weight >6000.
>*Streptomyces kitazawaensis*
>This organism also produces antimycin A.
>F. Okamoto, Shigeo Kubo, Takahashi Nara and Shiro Tanaka, Jap. Patent Appl. 6894 (1959). (*Chem. Abstr.* 54 832c)

849 Melanomycin (Sodium Salt), brown, amorphous powder.
>A polypeptide antibiotic yielding on hydrolysis: phenylalanine, leucine, valine, proline, alanine, glutamic acid and histidine.
>*Streptomyces melanogenes*
>Fujiki Hata, Ryozo Sugawara, Akihiro Matsumae and Takamoto Sano, Japanese Patent 5899 (1959). (*Chem. Abstr.* 54 833b)

850 Notatin (Penicillin B, Penatin), buff colored powder, water soluble, $[\alpha]_D^{22}$ $-4.8°$ (c 0.012 in water).
>A flavoprotein enzyme (glucose-oxidase), molecular weight about 152,000.
>*Penicillium notatum,* other *Penicillium* spp.
>R. Cecil and A. G. Ogston, *Biochem. J.* 42 229 (1948).

18.

Heterocycles

a. FURANS AND RELATED SUBSTANCES

Apparently there has been no investigation of the biosynthetic origin of the furans listed here, but it is known that furans can be formed in several different ways.

The relationship of furans to sugars is recognized in the designation of the five-membered ring hemi-acetal form of sugars as the furanose form. Dilute acid converts glucose to 5-hydroxymethylfurfural. The latter compound may be a precursor of Sumiki's acid, although the transformations are probably enzymatic. The four carbon atom sugar erythrose also is a likely furan precursor as pointed out by Wenkert.[1]

The furans with carbon chains at the 2-position are obviously terpenoid. Since they were isolated from a sweet potato medium, their direct derivation from glucose cannot be assumed. The simpler substances may arise from oxidation of the more complex.

It is interesting to note that the lactone side-chain of digitoxigenin is derived from acetate rather than from mevalonic acid.[2] Such lactones as well as the related tetronic acids, would seem

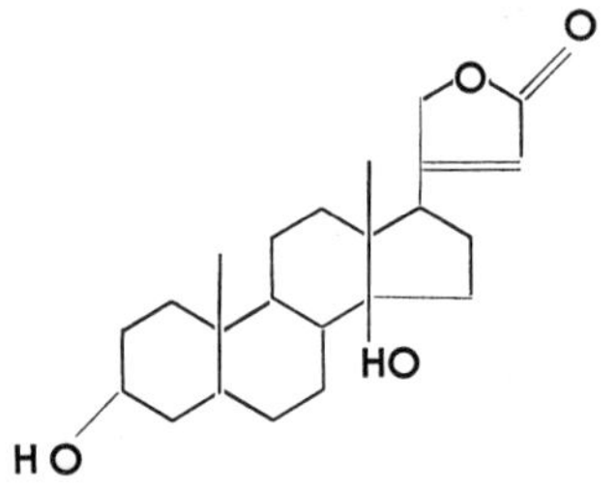

Digitoxigenin

to be potential furan precursors.

[1] Ernest Wenkert, *Experientia* 15 165 (1959).

[2] E. Leete, *Seventh Medicinal Chemistry Symposium of the American Chemical Society,* Kingston, Rhode Island, 1960.

851　Furan-3-carboxylic Acid, $C_5H_4O_3$, colorless crystals, m.p. 121°.

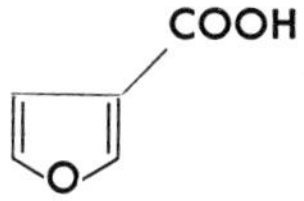

Ceratostomella fimbriata (sweet potato substrate)
Takashi Kubota and Keizo Naya, *Chem. and Ind.*, 1427
(1954).

852　5-Hydroxymethylfuran-2-carboxylic Acid (Sumiki's Acid), $C_6H_6O_4$,
colorless crystals, m.p. 164° (dec.).

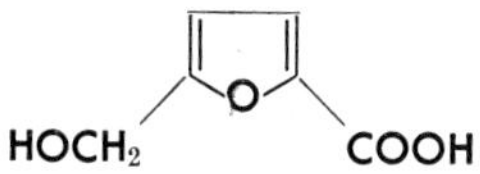

*Aspergillus glaucus, A. clavatus, A. niger, A. oryzae, A.
wentii, Gibberella fujikuroi*
Yusuke Sumiki, *J. Agr. Chem. Soc. Japan* 7 819 (1931).
Akira Kawarada, Nobutaka Takahashi, Hiroshi Kitamura,
Yasuo Seta, Makoto Takai and Saburo Tamura, *Bull. Agr.
Chem. Soc.* (Japan) 19 84 (1955).

853　Ipomeanine, $C_9H_{10}O_3$, oil, b.$_{0.001}$ 74–79°, n_D^{15} 1.4975, $[\alpha]_D$ +3.9°.

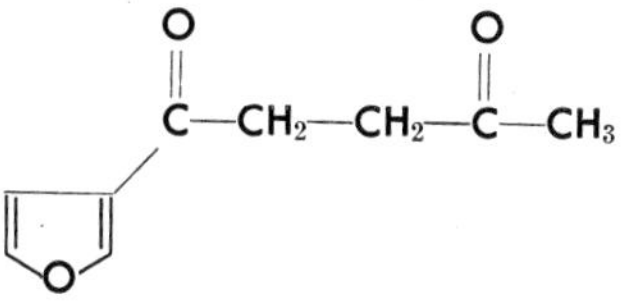

Ceratostomella fimbriata (sweet potato substrate)
Takashi Kubota and Nobutaka Ichikawa, *Chem. and Ind.*,
902 (1954).

854　Batatic Acid, $C_{10}H_{12}O_4$, colorless crystals, m.p. 88.5°, $[\alpha]_D^{10}$
+17.5° (in ethanol).

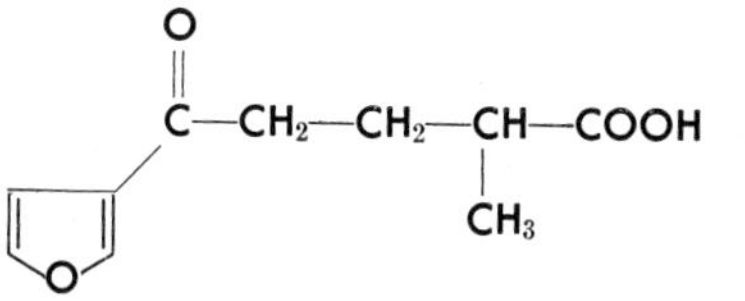

Ceratostomella fimbriata (sweet potato substrate)
Takashi Kubota and Keizo Naya, *Chem. and Ind.*, 1427
(1954).

855 Ipomeamarone, $C_{15}H_{22}O_3$, colorless oil, b.$_{0.001}$ 103°, n_D^{15} 1.4827, $[\alpha]_D^{25}$ +28°.

Ceratostomella fimbriata (sweet potato substrate)

T. Kubota and T. Matsuura, *Chem. and Ind.*, 521 (1956). (Synthesis)

There is a marked resemblance between ipomeamarone and dendrolasin, an oil $C_{15}H_{22}O$, isolated from ants. It is an enantiomer of ngaione, isolated from *Myoporum* spp. (higher plant).

A. Quilico, F. Piozzi and M. Pavan, *Tetrahedron* 1 177 (1957). (Structure)

A. J. Birch, R. A. Massy-Westropp and S. E. Wright, *Chem. and Ind.*, 902 (1954).

Ipomeamarone is thought to be formed by the host (sweet potato) tissue to resist invasion by *Ceratostomella fimbriata*.*

b. DIBENZOFURANS AND RELATED SUBSTANCES

Dibenzofurans constitute a class of natural products found only in lichens. Usnic acid is the most widely distributed dibenzofuran. Its structure, which was controversial for some time, now has been proved by synthesis.[1]

The dibenzofurans are formed from 2 moles of the acetate-derived resorcinolic substances typical of lichens. Results of chemical experiments, including the method of synthesis of usnic acid, make it quite probable that phenol coupling of the sort mentioned in connection with depsides and depsidones also is involved here.[2, 3] Thus,

---

* T. Akazawa, *Arch. Biochem. and Biophys.* **90** 82 (1960).

[1] D. H. R. Barton, A. M. Deflorin, O. E. Edwards and J. B. Hendrickson, *Chem. and Ind.*, 1670 (1955).

[2] D. H. R. Barton and T. Cohen, *Festschr. Arthur Stoll*, 117 (1957).

[3] Holger Erdtman and Carl Axel Wachtmeister, *ibid.*, 144 (1957).

dydymic acid would be formed by coupling of two similar orsellinic acids:

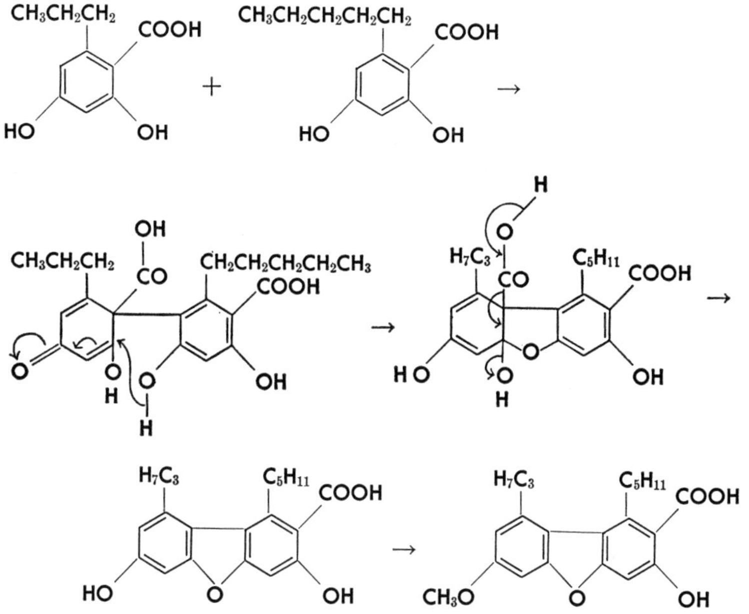

CH₃CH₂CH₂   COOH   CH₃CH₂CH₂CH₂CH₂   COOH

HO   OH   +   HO   OH   →

H_7C_3 C_5H_{11} COOH

H_7C_3 C_5H_{11} COOH

H_7C_3 C_5H_{11} COOH

CH_3O O   OH

Didymic Acid

And in the case of usnic acid:

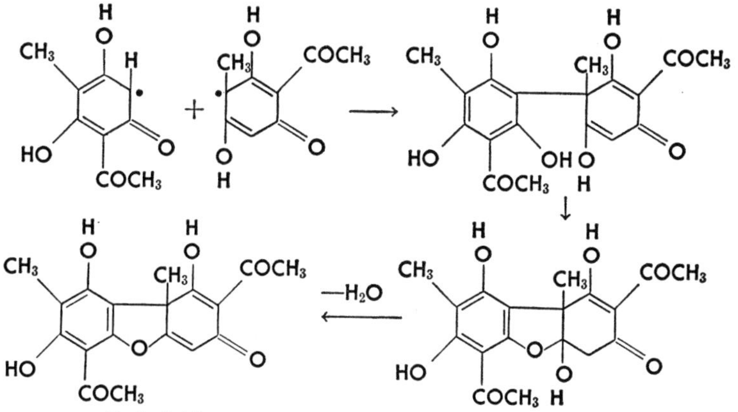

CH_3 COCH₃

HO   COCH₃

Usnic Acid

−H₂O

Formation of the monobenzofuran shown also may involve phenol coupling, if not precisely as indicated at least in the same general fashion:

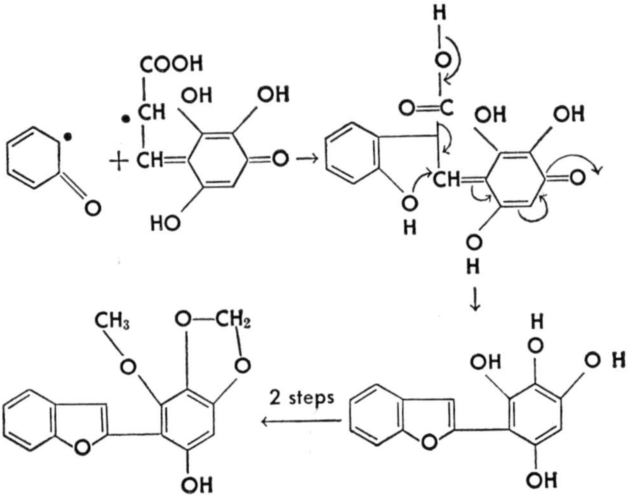

Apparently, many lichens contain an enzyme system which can promote phenolic coupling of this type. Neither the dibenzofurans nor the depsides and depsidones are produced by molds alone (although some of their resorcinolic precursors are), and the algal partners must be required in the coupling process.

856 **Strepsilin,** $C_{15}H_{10}O_5$, colorless crystals, m.p. 324°.

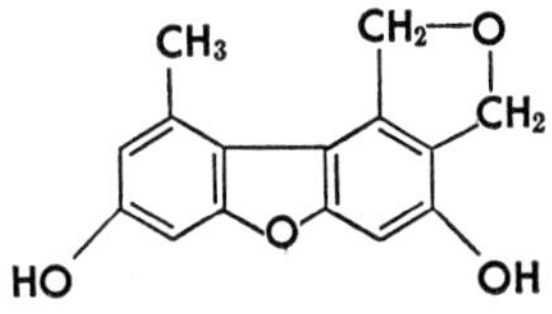

Cladonia strepsilis Wain.
Shoji Shibata, *J. Pharm. Soc. Japan* 64 20 (1944). (Structure)

857 **Porphyrilic Acid,** $C_{16}H_{10}O_7$, colorless needles, m.p. 280–283° (dec.).

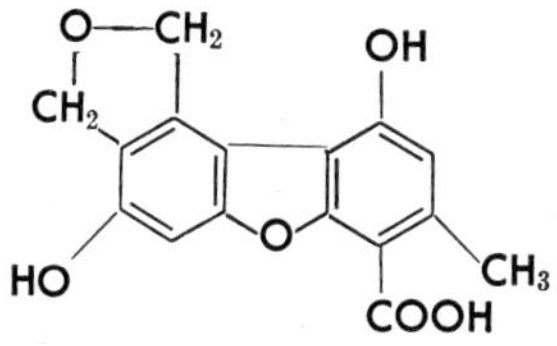

Haematomma coccineum (Dicks.), *H. porphyrium* (Pers.)

Porphyrilic acid occurs together with *l*-usnic acid and atranorin.

Carl Axel Wachtmeister, *Acta Chem. Scand.* **10** 1404 (1956). (Structure)

858 **2-(6-Hydroxy-2-methoxy-3,4-methylenedioxyphenyl)-benzofuran,** $C_{16}H_{12}O_5$, colorless crystals, m.p. 118°.

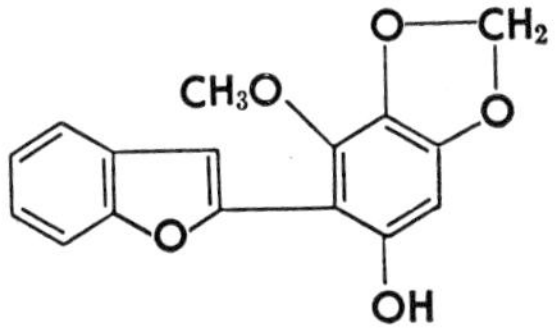

Yeast

A yield of 0.5–2.0 mg. per pound of bakers' yeast was reported.

M. A. P. Meisinger, Frederick A. Kuehl, Jr., E. L. Rickes, Norman G. Brink, Karl Folkers, Martin Forbes, Friederich Zilliken and Paul Gyorgy, *J. Am. Chem. Soc.* **81** 4979 (1959). (Structure)

859 **Pannaric Acid,** $C_{16}H_{12}O_7$, colorless needles, m.p. 243–245°.

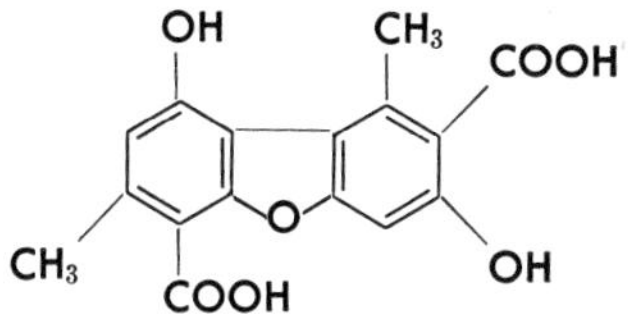

Crocynea membranacea (Dicks.) Zahlbr. = *Pannaria lanuginosa* Ach.

O. Hesse, *J. prakt. Chem.* **70** 1 (1904). (Isolation)

Åkermark H. Erdtman and C. A. Wachtmeister, *Acta Chem. Scand.* 13 1855 (1959). (Structure)

860 *d-* and *l-*Usnic Acid, $C_{18}H_{16}O_7$, yellow crystals, m.p. 203°, $[\alpha]_D^{17}$ (*d*-form) +492°, (*l*-form) −495°. M.p. *d,l*-form 195°.

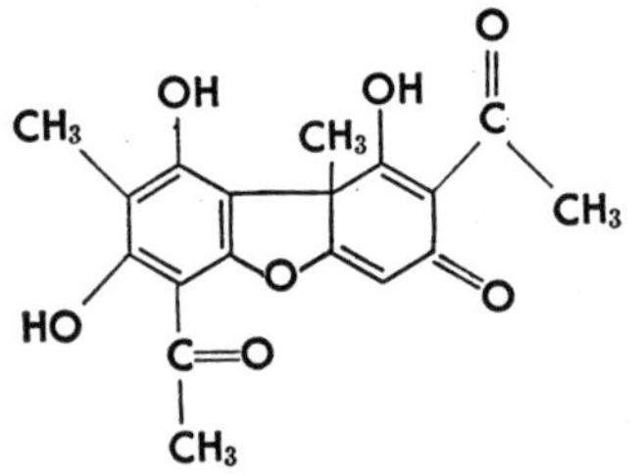

Usnea, Alectoria, Ramalina, Evernia, Cetraria, Parmelia, Cladonia, Lecanora and *Haematomma* species (most yellow lichens). Long known.

Both *d-* and *l*-forms occur in lichens. Relatively high yields are available from some species.

Clemens Schöpf and Friedrich Ross, *Naturwissenschaften* 26 772 (1938).

Idem., Ann. 546 1 (1941). (Structure)

D. H. R. Barton, A. M. Deflorin, O. E. Edwards and J. B. Hendrickson, *Chem. and Ind.,* 1670 (1955). (Synthesis)

861 **Didymic Acid** (Incrassatic Acid), $C_{22}H_{26}O_5$, colorless crystals, m.p. 172°.

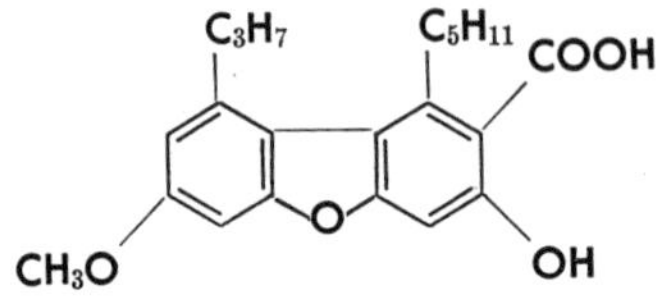

Cladonia species (occurs together with squamatic and barbatic acids)

Yasuhiko Asahina and Masaru Aoki, *J. Pharm. Soc. Japan* 64 41 (1944).

C. PYRANS AND RELATED SUBSTANCES

The γ-Pyrones and Patulin

The biosynthesis of patulin was discussed in the introduction to the chapter on phenolic substances.

Kojic acid has long attracted interest because it is produced in such high yields by certain *Aspergillus* species. Within the past few years isokojic acid and several other related γ-pyrones have been isolated from *Gluconoacetobacter* cultures.

The fungi are able to use pentose and triose substrates as well as glucose, although labeling studies have shown conversion of glucose to kojic acid without cleavage of the 6-carbon chain.[1]

Gluconoacetobacter liquefaciens seems to be more selective in its substrate and uses only glucose, gluconate and 2-ketogluconate. The variety of γ-pyrones produced is useful in deducing the kind of intermediate involved. The foregoing considerations plus the isolation of 2,5-diketogluconic acid from cultures of this bacterium have led to formulation of the following biosynthetic route to the pyrones produced by *Gluconoacetobacter liquefaciens:*[2]

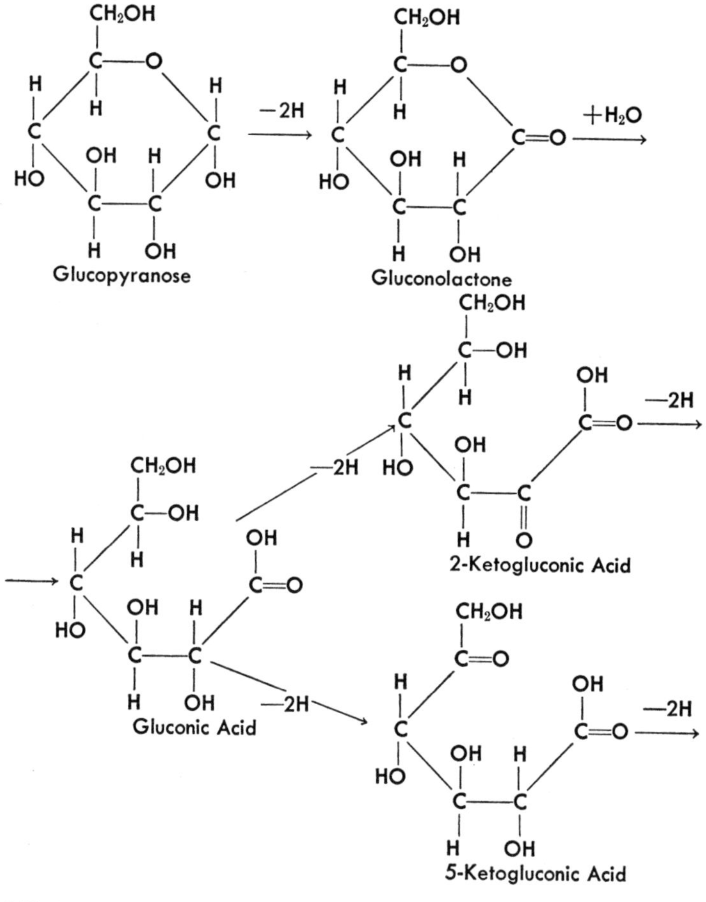

Glucopyranose

Gluconolactone

2-Ketogluconic Acid

Gluconic Acid

5-Ketogluconic Acid

[1] H. R. V. Arnstein and R. Bentley, *Biochem. J.* 62 403 (1956).
[2] Ko Aida, Mitsuko Fujii and Toshinobu Asai, *Bull. Agr. Chem. Soc.* (Japan) 21 30 (1957).

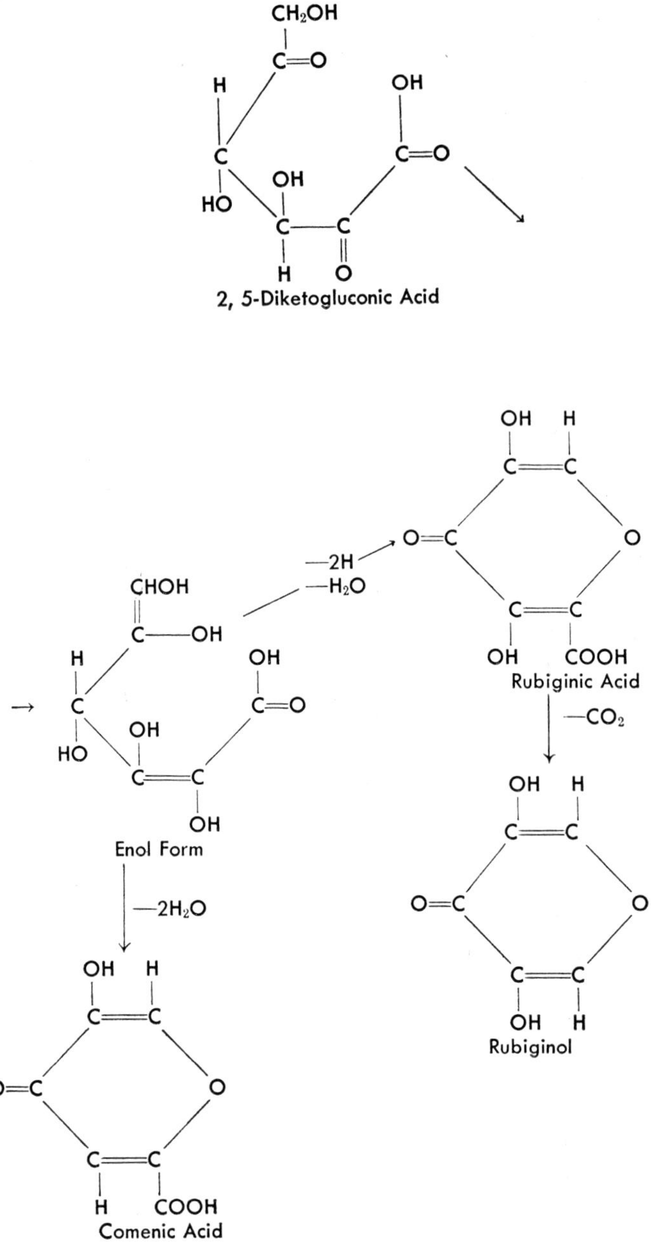

2, 5-Diketogluconic Acid

Enol Form

Rubiginic Acid

$-CO_2$

$-2H$
$-H_2O$

$-2H_2O$

Comenic Acid

Rubiginol

Another bacterial species, *Gluconoacetobacter roseum,* studied by the Japanese, produces kojic and isokojic acids and only from a fructose, sucrose or mannitol substrate. The two products are always found together.   The proposed route by which these two pyrones are formed from fructose by *Gluconoacetobacter roseum* is shown below:[3]

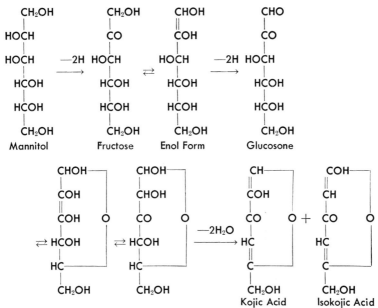

Kojic acid is potentially an inexpensive chemical because of high yields from aspergilli.

862 Rubiginol, $C_5H_4O_4$, colorless plates, m.p. 203.5°.

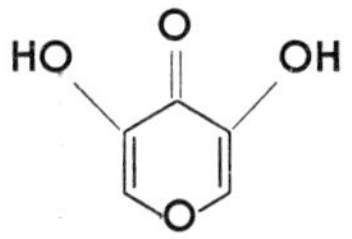

Gluconoacetobacter liquefaciens
A yield of 1.2 g. of rubiginol from 140 g. of glucose substrate was reported.
Ko Aida, *J. Gen. and Appl. Microbiol.* (Japan) 1 30 (1955).

[3] Ko Aida, Mitsuko Fujii and Toshinobu Asai, *Proc. Japan Acad.* **32** 595 (1956).

863 **Comenic Acid,** $C_6H_4O_5$, colorless plates, m.p. 276° (dec.).

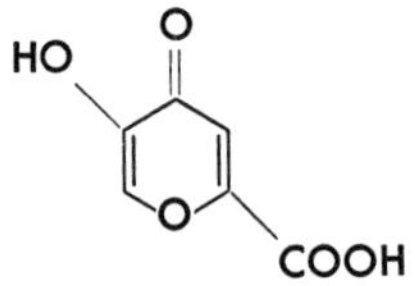

Gluconoacetobacter liquefaciens
A yield of 1.1 g. from 140 g. of glucose has been reported.
Ko Aida, *Bull. Agr. Chem. Soc.* (Japan) **19** 97 (1955).

864 **Rubiginic Acid,** $C_6H_4O_6$, colorless needles, m.p. 230° (dec.).

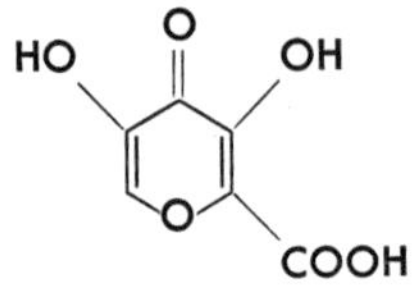

Gluconoacetobacter liquefaciens
Ko Aida, *Bull. Agr. Chem. Soc.* (Japan) **19** 97 (1955).

865 **Kojic Acid,** $C_6H_6O_4$, colorless prisms, m.p. 152°.

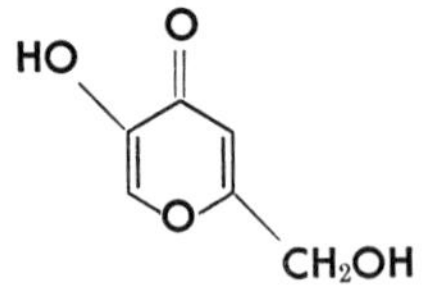

Aspergillus flavus, A. oryzae, A. tamarii, A. glaucus, Gluconoacetobacter roseum (fructose substrate)
High yields (45 g. or more per 100 g. of glucose substrate) are produced by some aspergillus strains.
Leland A. Underkofler and Richard J. Hickey, "Industrial Fermentations," Chemical Publishing Co., Inc., New York, 1954 **Vol. II,** Lewis B. Lockwood, *Ketogenic fermentation processes,* chap. 1, pp. 19–20. (A review)
Andrew Bielik, *Advances in Carbohydrate Chem.* **11** 145 (1956). (A review)

866 **Isokojic Acid,** $C_6H_6O_4$, colorless plates, m.p. 183°.

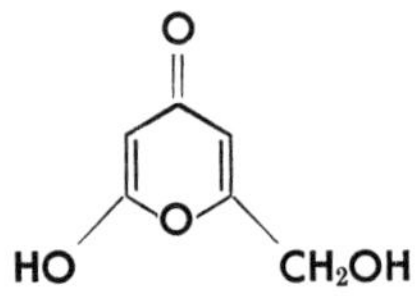

Gluconoacetobacter roseum (fructose substrate)
Isokojic acid was produced together with kojic acid and
an unidentified substance.

Ko Aida, Mitsuko Fujii and Toshinobu Asai, *Proc. Japan.
Acad.* 32 600 (1956).

867 **Patulin** (Clavacin, Clavatin, Claviformin, Penicidin, Expansine,
Mycoin), $C_7H_6O_4$, colorless crystals, m.p. 111°.

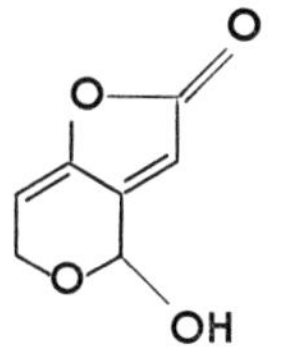

Penicillium patulum Bainier (*P. urticae*), *P. griseofulvum, P. claviforme, P. expansum, P. melinii, P. equi-
num, P. novae-zeelandiae, P. leucopus, Aspergillus clavatus, A. terreus, A. giganteus, Gymnoascus* spp.

H. W. Florey, E. Chain, N. G. Heatley, M. A. Jennings,
A. G. Sanders, E. P. Abraham and M. E. Florey, "Antibiotics,"
Oxford University Press, London, 1949, pp. 223–272. (Re-
views earlier work)

R. B. Woodward and Gurbakhsh Singh, *J. Am. Chem. Soc.*
72 1428 (1950). (Synthesis)

868 **5-Hydroxy-2-methylchromone,** $C_{10}H_8O_3$, yellow needles, m.p. 72–
76°.

Proposed structure:

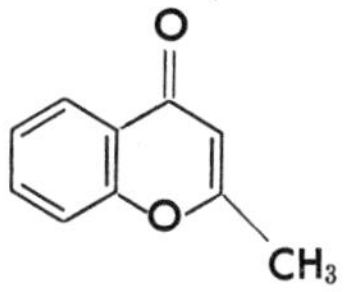

Daldinia concentrica
D. C. Allport and J. D. Bu'Lock, *J. Chem. Soc.*, 654 (1960).

869 **5-Hydroxy-2-methylchromanone,** $C_{10}H_{10}O_3$, pale yellow needles,
m.p. 30–33°.

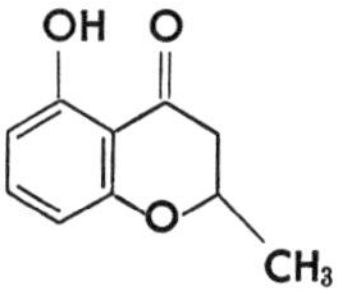

Daldinia concentrica
D. C. Allport and J. D. Bu'Lock, *J. Chem. Soc.*, 654 (1960).

870 **Aureothin,** $C_{22}H_{23}O_6N$, yellow crystals, m.p. 158°.

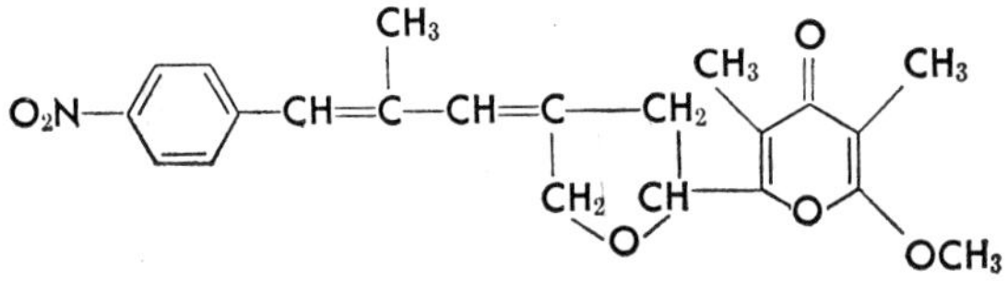

Streptomyces thioluteus

Aureothin occurs as a by-product in the aureothricin fermentation.

Kenji Maeda, *J. Antibiotics* (Japan) **6A** 137 (1953). (Isolation)

Y. Hirata, H. Nakata and K. Yamada, *J. Chem. Soc. Japan* **79** 1390 (1958) and preceding papers. (Structure)

QUINONOID COMPOUNDS.

This section includes a group of colored compounds, many of which have chromophores resembling those of quinones. These unusual substances presented some interesting structural problems. In many cases there was a long time interval between isolation and complete structure determination.

The relationship between fulvic acid and citromycetin is obvious. The relationship of both of these compounds to fusarubin has been pointed out recently.[1] This is less obvious, but a precursor such as (I) was envisaged for all three compounds, the formation of fusarubin involving ring closure at the dotted line.

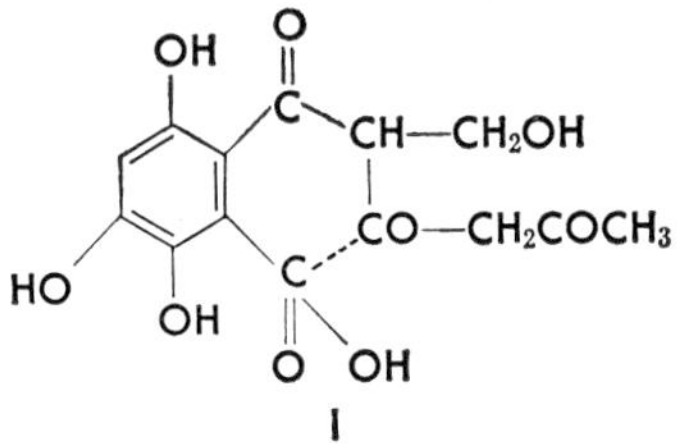

Penicillium griseofulvum, which is one of the producers

[1] F. M. Dean, R. A. Eade, R. A. Moubasher and A. Robertson, *Nature* **179** 366 (1957).

of fulvic acid, also produces a variety of other metabolites, including griseofulvin and mycelianamide. There seems to be no close relationship between these compounds and the three mentioned above, however.

The biosyntheses of sclerotiorin,[2] citromycetin[2] and citrinin[2, 3] have been investigated by using C^{14}-labeled acetate, formate and methionine.

The two studies of citrinin (III) were in agreement, the results of both indicating origin from a 10-carbon atom polyketomethylene chain in the sense of (II).

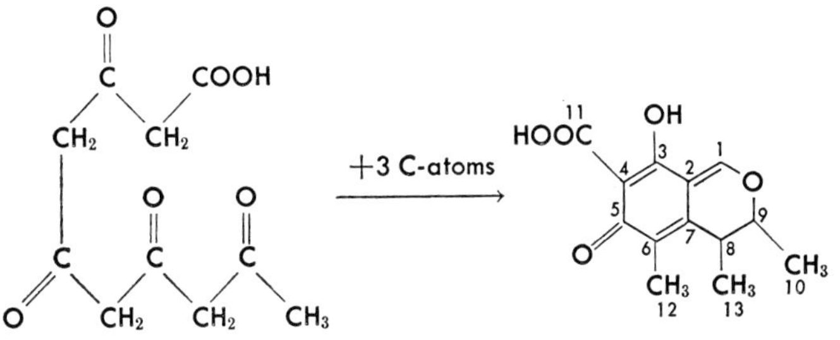

The carbon atoms 11, 12 and 13 in (III) were contributed by methionine or formate.

Sclerotiorin also is acetate derived with contribution of three carbon atoms by formate.

Citromycetin (V) is derived entirely from seven acetic acid units, CH_3—$C^{14}OOH$ (CH_3—$\dot{C}OOH$) and yields the labeling pattern shown below.

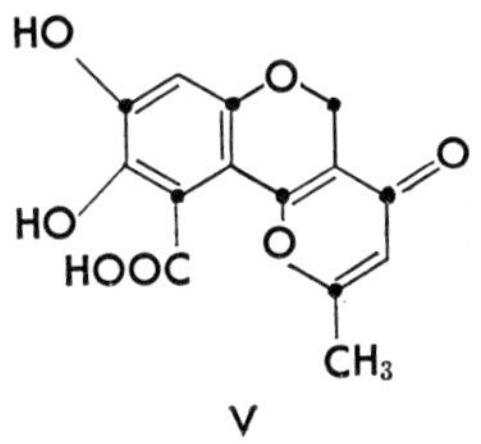

V

It would appear that purpurogenone should also be derived from seven acetate units.

[2] A. J. Birch, P. Fitton, E. Pride, A. J. Ryan, Herchel Smith and W. B. Whalley, *J. Chem. Soc.*, 4576 (1958).

[3] Erwin Schwenk, George J. Alexander, Allen M. Gold and Dean F. Stevens, *J. Biol. Chem.* 233 1211 (1958).

871 **Radicinin,** * $C_{12}H_{12}O_5$, yellow crystals, m.p. 220° (dec.), $[\alpha]_D^{27}$ −217.4° (c 2.37 in pyridine).
Proposed partial structure:

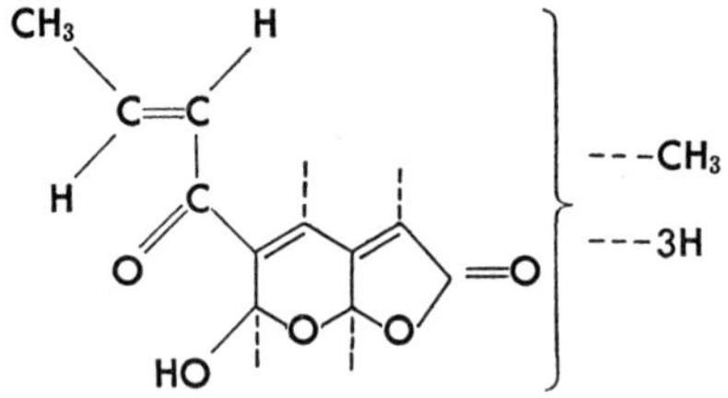

Stemphylium radicinum Sterad (formerly *Alternaria radicina*)
D. D. Clarke and F. F. Nord, *Arch. Biochem. and Biophys.* 59 269, 285 (1955).

872 **Citrinin,** $C_{13}H_{14}O_5$, long yellow prisms, m.p. 179° (dec.), $[\alpha]_D^{20}$ −34.5° (c 0.60 in alcohol).

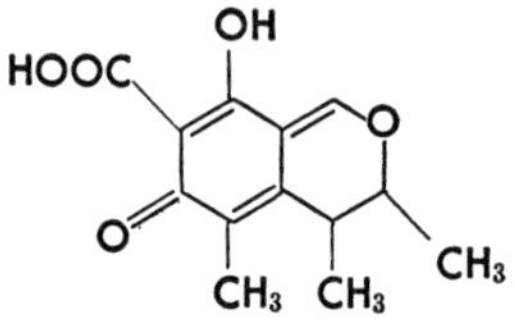

Penicillium citrinum, P. expansum, P. implicatum, P. chrzaszszi, P. citreo-sulfuratum, P. lividum, P. phaeojanthinellum, Aspergillus terreus, A. candidus, A. niveus
A. C. Hetherington and H. Raistrick, *Trans. Roy. Soc.* (London) B220 269 (1931). (Isolation)
D. H. Johnson, Alexander Robertson and W. B. Whalley, *J. Chem. Soc.,* 2971 (1950).
H. H. Warren, Gregg Dougherty and Everett S. Wallis, *J. Am. Chem. Soc.* 71 3422 (1949). (Synthesis)

873 **Citromycetin** (Frequentic Acid), $C_{14}H_{10}O_7$, lemon yellow hydrated needles, m.p. 283–285° (dec.).

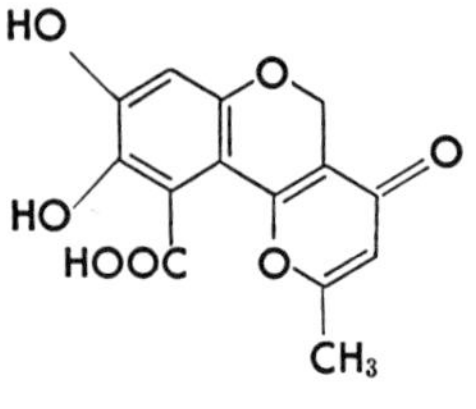

* See entry 413.

Penicillium frequentans, P. roseo-purpurogenum, P. glabrum, P. pfefferianum, Citromyces strains, *Corynebacterium diphtheriae*

A. C. Hetherington and H. Raistrick, *Trans. Roy. Soc.* (London) **B220** 209 (1931). (Isolation)

Alexander Robertson, W. B. Whalley and J. Yates, *J. Chem. Soc.*, 2013 (1951). (Structure)

Michizo Asano and Hideo Takahashi, *J. Pharm. Soc. Japan* **65** 81 (1945). (Isolation from the corynebacterium)

874   **Purpurogenone,** $C_{14}H_{12}O_5$, crimson prisms, m.p. 310° (dec.).

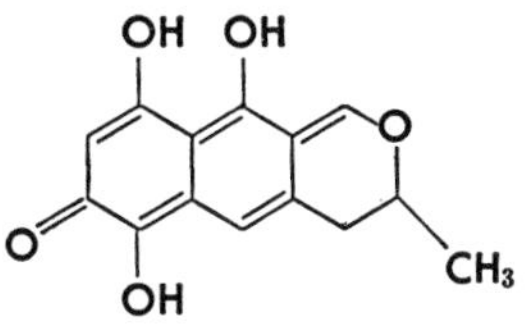

Penicillium purpurogenum Stoll

Yield 8–14 g. of crude pigment from about 250 g. of dry mycelium, which was obtained from about 70 liters of culture solution.

Ergosteryl palmitate, m.p. 104–106°, and mannitol, m.p. 166°, also were isolated from this fermentation.

John C. Roberts and C. W. H. Warren, *J. Chem. Soc.*, 2992 (1955).

875   **Fulvic Acid,** $C_{14}H_{12}O_8$, yellow crystals, m.p. 246° (dec.).

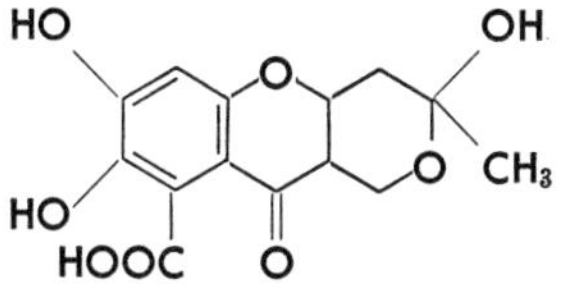

Penicillium flexuosum, P. brefeldianum, P. griseofulvum

876   *P. griseofulvum* produced a **nitrogen-containing compound,** m.p. 165°, in the same broth. *P. brefeldianum*

877   produced a **neutral nitrogen-containing compound,** m.p. 132–135°, in the same culture.

Albert Edw. Oxford, Harold Raistrick and Paul Simonart, *Biochem. J.* **29** 1102 (1935). (Isolation)

F. M. Dean, R. A. Eade, R. A. Moubasher and A. Robertson, *Nature* **179** 366 (1957). (Structure)

878 **Fuscin,** $C_{15}H_{16}O_5$, orange plates, m.p. 230°.

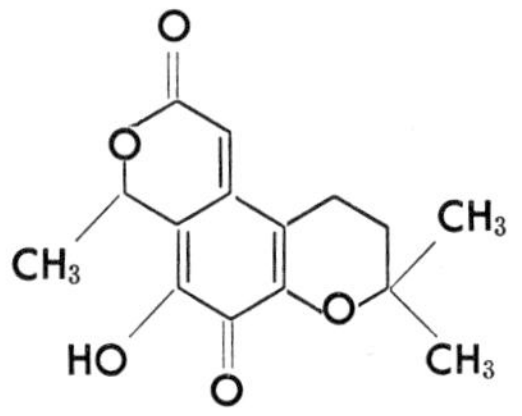

Oidiodendron fuscum Robak

879   A colorless **dihydrofuscin,** m.p. 206°, was also produced.
S. E. Michael, *Biochem. J.* 43 528 (1948). (Isolation)
D. H. R. Barton and J. B. Hendrickson, *J. Chem. Soc.,* 1028
(1956). (Synthesis)

Azaphilones.

     This group of mold pigments, so named because most of
them react avidly with ammonia, includes monascorubrin,
sclerotiorin, rotiorin, rubropunctatin and monascin.
     A. Powell, A. Robertson and W. Whalley, "Chemical Society
Symposia," Special Publication No. 5, The Chemical Society,
London, 1956, p. 27. (Survey of the chemistry of the azaphilones to that date)

880 **Rubropunctatin,** $C_{21}H_{22}O_5$, orange needles, m.p. 156.5° (dec.),
$[\alpha]_D$ −3481° (c 1.07 in chloroform).

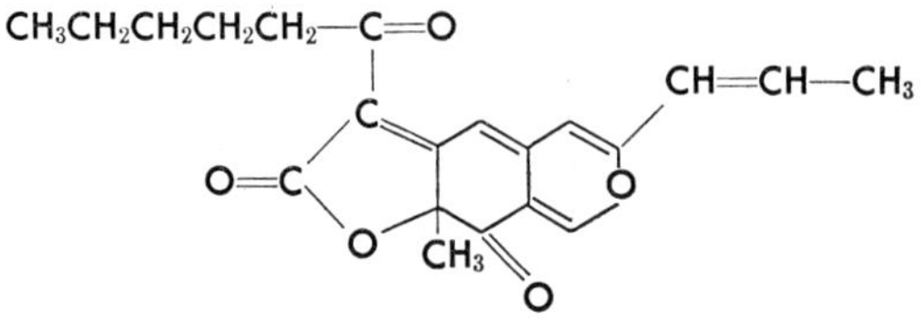

Monascus rubropunctatus Satô
     E. J. Haws, J. S. E. Holker, A. Kelly, A. D. G. Powell and
Alexander Robertson, *J. Chem. Soc.,* 3598 (1959). (Structure)
     A. Powell, Dissertation, Liverpool, 1954. (Isolation)

881 **Sclerotiorin,** $C_{21}H_{22}O_5Cl$, yellow crystals, m.p. 206° $[\alpha]_D$ +500°.

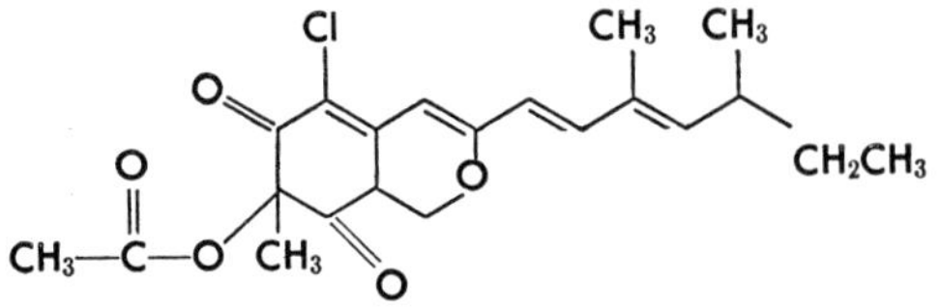

Penicillium sclerotiorum van Beyma, *P. multicolor*
G.M.P., *P. implicatum* Biourge
    Timothy P. MacCurtin and Joseph Reilly, *Biochem. J.* 34
1419 (1940). (Isolation)
    H. C. Fielding, Alexander Robertson, R. B. Traners and
W. B. Whalley, *J. Chem. Soc.*, 1814 (1958).
    F. M. Dean, J. Staunton and W. B. Whalley, *ibid.*, 3004
(1959). (Structure)

882 **Monascin,** $C_{21}H_{26}O_5$, yellow crystals, m.p. 142°, $[\alpha]_D$ +544°.
    Monascus rubriginosus Satô, *M. purpureus* Wentii,
M. rubropunctatus Satô
    Hidijiro Nishikawa, *J. Agr. Chem. Soc. Japan* 8 1007
(1932).
    H. Solomon and P. Karrer, *Helv. Chim. Acta* 15 18 (1932).

883 **Rotiorin,** $C_{23}H_{24}O_5$, red needles, m.p. 246° (dec.) (sublimes),
$[\alpha]_D^{22}$ +5080° (c 0.002 in chloroform).
Tentative structure:

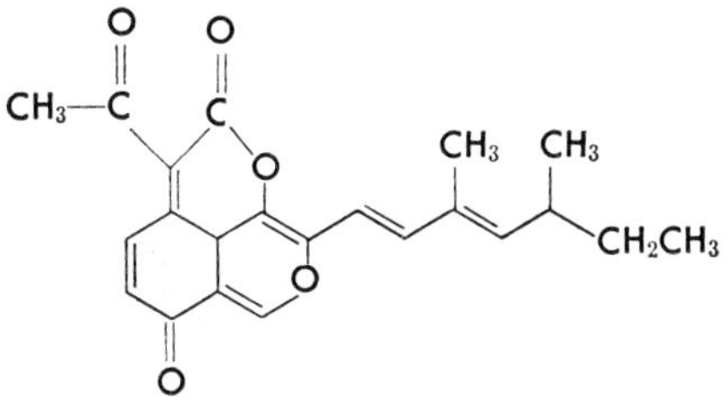

Penicillium sclerotiorum van Beyma
    Eight kilograms of dry mycelium yielded 300–350 g.
of sclerotiorin and 100–150 g. of rotiorin.
    G. B. Jackman, Alexander Robertson, R. B. Traners and
W. B. Whalley, *J. Chem. Soc.*, 1825 (1958). (Structure)

884 **Monascorubrin,** $C_{23}H_{26}O_5$, orange crystals, m.p. 134–136°,
$[\alpha]_{700}^{16}$ −1500° (c 0.1 in ethanol).

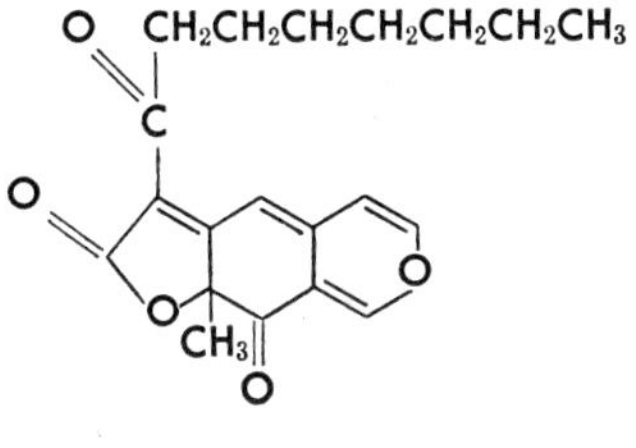

Monascus purpureus Wentii

H. Nishikawa, *J. Agr. Chem. Soc. Japan* 5 1007 (1932).
(Isolation)

K. Nakanishi, M. Ohashi, S. Kumasaki and S. Yamamura,
J. Am. Chem. Soc. 81 6339, 6340 (1959). (Structure)

B. C. Fielding, E. J. Haws, J. S. E. Holker, A. D. G. Powell,
A. Robertson, D. N. Stanway and W. B. Whalley, *Tetrahedron
Letters* No. 5 24 (1960). (Proposed revised structure shown)

885 **Novobiocin** (Streptonivicin, Cathomycin, Albamycin, Sphero-
mycin, Vulcamycin, Crystallinic Acid, Antibiotic PA-93,
Cardelmycin), $C_{31}H_{36}O_{11}N_2$, pale yellow crystals, m.p.
152–156° (dec.) and 174–178° (dec.) (polymorphic),
$[\alpha]_D^{24}$ −63° (c 1 in ethanol).

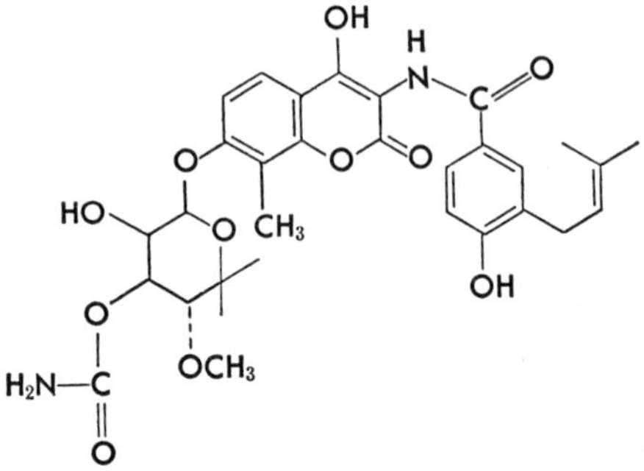

Streptomyces spheroides, S. niveus, S. griseus

Herman Hoeksema, James L. Johnson and Jack W. Hinman, *J. Am. Chem. Soc.* 77 6710 (1955).

Jack W. Hinman, Herman Hoeksema, E. Louis Caron and
W. G. Jackson, *ibid.* 78 1072 (1956).

Clifford H. Shunk, Charles H. Stammer, Edward A. Kaczka,
Edward Walton, Claude F. Spencer, Andrew N. Wilson,
John W. Richter, Frederick W. Holly and Karl Folkers, *ibid.*
78 1770 (1956). (Structure)

Herman Hoeksema, E. Louis Caron and Jack W. Hinman,
ibid. 78 2019 (1956). (Structure)

d. XANTHONES

886 **Ravenelin,** $C_{14}H_{10}O_5$, yellowish crystals, m.p. 267°.

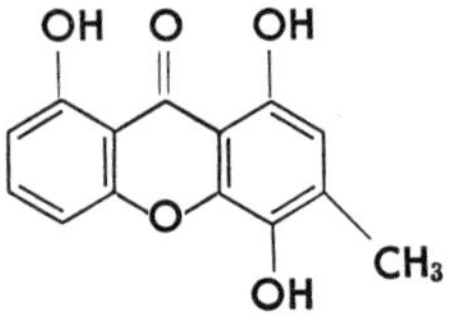

Helminthosporium ravenelii
F. F. Nord and Robert P. Mull, *Advances in Enzymol.* 5 194
(1945). (Synthesis)

887 **Rubrofusarin,** $C_{15}H_{12}O_5$, orange-red needles, m.p. 210°.
Alternative structures:

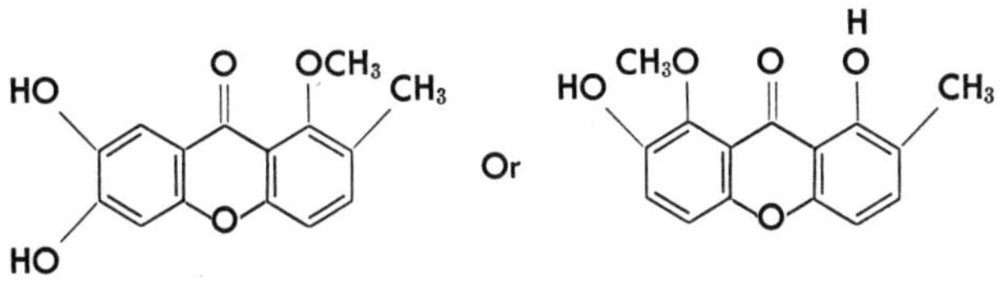

Or

Fusarium culmorum (W.G.Sm.) Sacc., *Fusarium graminearum* Schwabe (*Gibberella saubinettii*)

888   Another pigment, **aurofusarin,*** $C_{30}H_{20}O_{12}$, m.p. >360°
889 and a colorless compound, **culmorin,** $C_{15}H_{26}O_2$, m.p. 175°,
$[\alpha]_D^{20}$ −14.45° were isolated from the same cultures.

Julius Nicholson Ashley, Betty Constance Hobbs and Harold
Raistrick, *Biochem. J.* 31 385 (1937).
Robert P. Mull and F. F. Nord, *Arch. Biochem.* 4 419 (1944).
(Structure)

890 **Asperxanthone,** $C_{16}H_{14}O_5$, yellow needles, m.p. 203°. A 1-hy-
droxydimethoxymethylxanthone which yields nor-rubro-
fusarin on demethylation.
Aspergillus niger (mycelium)
N. A. Lund, Alexander Robertson and W. B. Whalley,
J. Chem. Soc., 2434 (1953).

891 **Lichexanthone,** $C_{16}H_{14}O_5$, yellowish crystals, m.p. 187°.

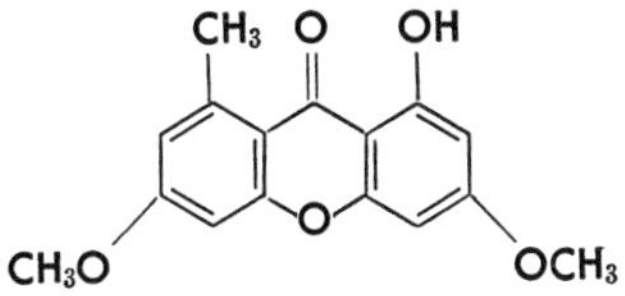

Parmelia formosana Zahlbr.
The yield was about ½ g. from 25 g. of lichen.
Yasuhiko Asahina and Hirashi Nogami, *Bull. Chem. Soc.
Japan* 17 202 (1942).

* See entry 584.

892 Sterigmatocystin, $C_{18}H_{12}O_6$, pale yellow needles, m.p. 246°
(dec.), $[\alpha]_D^{20.5}$ −387° (c 0.424 in chloroform).
Probable structure:

Aspergillus versicolor (Vuillemin) Tiraboschi

J. E. Davies, D. Kirkaldy and John C. Roberts, *J. Chem. Soc.*, 2169 (1960). (Structure)

Abou-Zeid, Dissertation, London, 1953. (Isolation)

J. E. Davies, John C. Roberts and S. C. Wallwork, *Chem. and Ind.*, 178 (1956). (Isolation)

J. H. Birkinshaw and I. M. M. Hammady, *Biochem. J.* **65** 162 (1957). (Isolation)

Yuichi Hatsuda and Shimpei Kuyama, *J. Agr. Chem. Soc. Japan* **28** 989 (1954). (*Chem. Abstr.* **50** 15,522) (Isolation)

e. COMPOUNDS RELATED TO THIOPHENE,

IMIDAZOLE, THIAZOLE

AND ISOXAZOLE.

Some of the commercially important compounds in this section are the antibiotics cycloserine and the penicillins and the vitamins, thiamine and biotin.

Penicillin was discovered by Fleming in 1929, and commercial fermentation techniques were developed during the second World War. Penicillins with several different side-chains were found to be produced by various penicillia and aspergilli, and hundreds of unnatural penicillins were prepared by the addition of side-chain precursors to fermentations.

It was not until 1959, however, that the nucleus common to all penicillins, 6-aminopenicillanic acid, was isolated from fermentations.[1] This discovery has made possible the preparation of a new series of penicillins through

[1] Koichi Kato, *J. Antibiotics* (Japan) **6A** 130, 184 (1953); F. R. Batchelor, F. P. Doyle, J. H. C. Nayler and G. N. Rolinson, *Nature* **183** 257 (1959).

attachment of side-chains by the methods of organic chemistry.

```
HOOC—CH——N——C=O          HOOC—CH——N——C=O
     CH₃  |      |                CH3  |      |           O
          |      |                     |      |           ‖
          C   CH——CH—NH₂              C   CH——CH—NH—C—R
        /  \ /                      /  \ /
     CH₃    S                    CH₃    S
    6-Aminopenicillanic Acid              Penicillins
```

Since 6-aminopenicillanic acid can be isolated from penicillin fermentations in good yields, it is probably an intermediate. Also, the fact that side-chain precursors are so readily incorporated into the molecule indicates attachment of the side-chain to be the final step in penicillin biosynthesis. This is also known to be the rate-limiting step, and, even in commercial fermentations, side-chain precursors are added routinely.

The precursors of the 6-aminopenicillanic acid nucleus have been shown to be (stereospecifically) L-cysteine[2] and L-valine,[3] although additions of these amino acids to fermentations do not cause dramatic improvements in yields or in rates of synthesis. Degradation studies have shown that L-cysteine occurs in the same configuration after incorporation into the penicillin molecule, while valine has been converted to the D-form. Aside from the change in configuration of valine, both amino acids are incorporated intact.

Other substances have been considered as penicillin precursors and intermediates. Among them are penicillamine,[4] β-hydroxyvaline,[3] serine,[2] glycine,[2] homocys-

[2] H. R. V. Arnstein and P. T. Grant, *Biochem. J.* **57** 353, 360 (1954); H. R. V. Arnstein and J. C. Crawhall, *ibid.* **67** 180 (1957); Carl M. Stevens, Edward Inamine and Chester W. Delong, *J. Biol. Chem.* **219** 405 (1956); H. R. V. Arnstein and H. Margreiter, *Biochem. J.* **68** 339 (1958); F. H. Grau and W. J. Halliday, *ibid.* **69** 205 (1957).

[3] H. R. V. Arnstein and Margaret E. Clubb, *ibid.* **65** 618 (1957); Carl M. Stevens and Chester W. Delong, *J. Biol. Chem.* **230** 991 (1958).

[4] Carl M. Stevens, Pran Vohra, Edward Inamine and Oliver A. Roholt, Jr., *ibid.* **205** 1001 (1953).

teine,[5] methionine,[4] glutathione[4] and acetate. Some of these rejected intermediates are shown:

$$
\begin{array}{ccc}
\text{HOOC—CH—NH}_2 & \text{HO—C=O} & \text{HOOC—CH—NH}_2 \quad \text{HO}\diagdown\!\!\text{C=O} \\
\quad\text{CH}_3 \quad\Big| & + \quad \Big|\text{CH—NH}_2 \rightarrow & \quad\text{CH}_3 \quad\Big| \qquad \text{CH}_2\text{—CH—NH}_2 \\
\qquad \text{C} & \quad\text{HOCH}_2 & \qquad \text{C} \\
\text{CH}_3 \quad \text{SH} & & \text{CH}_3 \quad \text{S}
\end{array}
$$

Penicillamine   Serine   β, β-Dimethyllanthionine

$$
\begin{array}{ccc}
\text{HOOC—CH—NH}_2 & \text{HO—C=O} & \text{HOOC—CH—NH}_2 \quad \text{HO}\diagdown\!\!\text{C=O} \\
\quad\text{CH}_2 & + \quad \Big|\text{CH—NH}_2 \rightarrow & \quad\text{CH}_2 \qquad \text{CH}_2\text{—CH—NH}_2 \\
\quad\text{CH}_2 & \quad\text{HOCH}_2 & \quad\text{CH}_2\text{—S} \\
\quad\quad\text{SH} & &
\end{array}
$$

Homocysteine   Serine   Cystathionine

$$
\begin{array}{ccc}
\text{HOOC—CH—NH}_2 & \text{HO—C=O} & \text{HOOC—CH—NH}_2 \quad \text{HO}\diagdown\!\!\text{C=O} \\
\quad\text{CH}_3 \quad\Big| & + \quad \Big|\text{CH—NH}_2 \rightarrow & \quad\text{CH}_3 \quad\Big| \qquad \text{CH}_2\text{—CH—NH}_2 \\
\qquad \text{C} & \quad\text{HS—CH}_2 & \qquad \text{C} \quad \text{S} \\
\text{CH}_3 \quad \text{OH} & & \text{CH}_3
\end{array}
$$

β-Hydroxyvaline   Cysteine   β, β-Dimethyllanthionine

Lanthionine and β-methyllanthionine occur in several other polypeptide antibiotics (subtilin, duramycin, cinnamycin, nisins). Certain of these compounds are incorporated to some extent, but only indirectly.

Some evidence is being accumulated concerning the actual peptide intermediate. The dipeptide L-cystinyl-L-(COOH—C[14]) valine is a better penicillin precursor than L-(COOH—C[14]) valine alone, while the reverse is true for protein synthesis.[6] (L-Cystine can be reduced to L-cysteine by the mold.)

$$
\begin{array}{c}
\text{HOOC—CH—CH}_2\text{—S}\!\vdots\!\text{S—CH}_2\text{—CH—CO—NH—CH—COOH} \\
\quad\quad\text{NH}_2 \qquad\qquad\qquad \text{NH}_2 \qquad\qquad \text{CH} \\
\qquad\qquad\qquad\qquad\qquad\qquad\qquad \text{CH}_3 \quad \text{CH}_3
\end{array}
$$

L-Cystinyl-L-(COOH—C[14]) valine

[5] Carl M. Stevens, Pran Vohra, Joseph E. Moore and Chester W. DeLong, *ibid.* 210 713 (1954).

[6] H. R. V. Arnstein and D. Morris, *Biochem. J.* 71 8p (1959).

The same research group (Arnstein and collaborators) has isolated a tripeptide from the mycelium of the commercial penicillin producer, *Penicillium chrysogenum.*[7] It is δ-(α-aminoadipyl) cysteinylvaline:

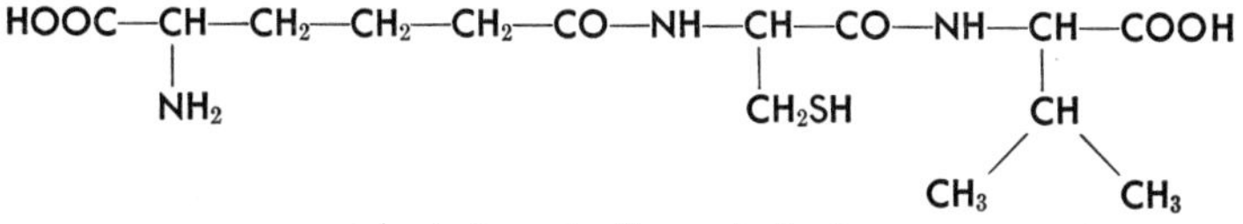

HOOC—CH—CH₂—CH₂—CH₂—CO—NH—CH—CO—NH—CH—COOH

δ-(α-Aminoadipyl) cysteinylvaline

Consistent with the above evidence, this is a cysteinyl-valine. It is not difficult to envisage cyclization to form synnematin B:

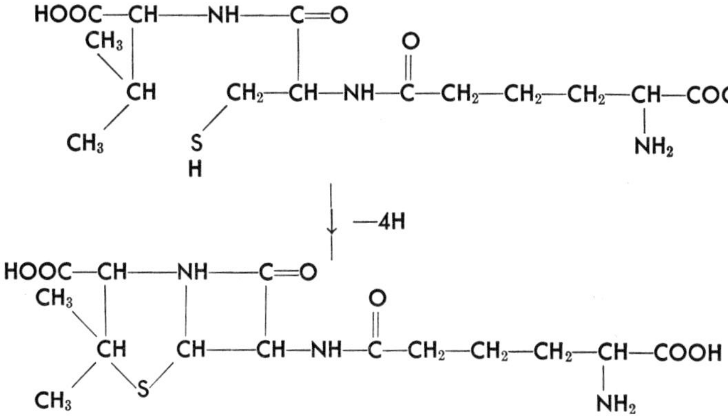

Interesting features of this discovery are, first, that a side-chain is attached before cyclization to form 6-aminopenicillanic acid and, second, that the side-chain is α-aminoadipic acid, the side-chain of synnematin B (cephalosporin N) which is not produced by *Penicillium chrysogenum.* Perhaps side-chain exchange occurs after cyclization. The configurations of the amino acids in the acyclic mycelial peptide have not been reported yet.

The structure of cephalosporin C, a substance related to synnematin B, is known, but has not yet been published.

Two reviews of the biosynthesis of penicillin are cited.[8, 9]

[7] H. R. V. Arnstein, D. Morris and E. Toms, *Biochim. et Biophys. Acta* 35 561 (1959).

[8] A. L. Demain, *Advances in Appl. Microbiol.* 1 23 (1959).

[9] D. Hockenhull, *Prog. in Ind. Microbiol.* 1 1 (1959).

Cycloserine (oxamycin) appears to be a cyclized D-serine amide or hydroxamide. As mentioned elsewhere it is known to inhibit the incorporation of D-alanyl-D-alanine into the cell walls of certain bacteria.

Thiamine is an enzyme prosthetic group of fundamental importance, probably occurring in all living things. Many microorganisms are capable of *de novo* synthesis, although the vitamin is required in mammalian diets. Some microorganisms incapable of total synthesis can couple certain pyrimidine and thiazole precursors, others require only one of the heterocycles preformed, and certain yeasts have a requirement for thiamine itself.

Beyond this little is known about the biosynthesis of thiamine. Other naturally occurring thiazoles (*e.g.* those in certain antibiotics) are known to be derivatives of cysteine. Nakayama has proposed the general scheme:[10]

Cysteine → Thiazolidine-4-carboxylic Acid → 4-Methylthiazole →
4-Methyl-5-(2-hydroxyethyl)-thiazole

on the basis of work with mutants. Some work has been done on the biosynthesis of other pyrimidines, but apparently little on the thiamine constituent.

Bacillus subtilis incorporates formate C^{14} extensively into the pyrimidine, but not the thiazole moiety of thiamine.[11] In this bacterium the pyrimidine moiety of thiamine restores growth and formate incorporation into purines and thymine in amethopterin treated cultures. The thiazole part restores thiamine synthesis, but does not show the additional effects.

It appears now that all enzymes in which thiamine is the active site have the function of decarboxylating α-ketoacids and of cleaving α-diketones or α-hydroxyketones. These functions were illustrated in an earlier section.

Thiamine, unphosphorylated and detached from its apoenzyme, is capable of carrying out some of its coenzyme functions *in vitro* under favorable conditions.[12, 13, 14]

[10] Hideo Nakayama, *Vitamins* (Japan) 11 20, 169 (1956).

[11] Martin J. Pine and Robert Guthrie, *J. Bacteriol.* 78 545 (1959).

[12] Shunzi Mizuhara and Philip Handler, *J. Am. Chem. Soc.* 76 571 (1954).

[13] Emeteria Yatco-Manzo, Frances Roddy, Ralph G. Yount and David E. Metzler, *J. Biol. Chem.* 234 733 (1959).

[14] Ralph G. Yount and David E. Metzler, *ibid.* 234 738 (1959).

By selective synthetic substitutions with blocking groups at various positions in the two heterocycles, the active site of the molecule has been located as the 2-position of the thiazole ring.[15, 16] It is here that pyruvic acid, for example, is decarboxylated to form (still in combination with thiamine pyrophosphate) "active acetaldehyde" and α-ketoglutaric acid to form "active succinate." The active acetaldehyde intermediate was shown in Section 2. It is claimed that this intermediate has been isolated from *Escherichia coli.*[16a]

A thorough review of thiamine is available.[17]

For more than 20 years biotin has been recognized as a dietary requirement in higher animals and yeasts. It was formerly called vitamin H, and animal deficiencies could be induced by feeding raw egg-white. This contains a protein, avidin, which complexes tightly enough with biotin to cause avitaminosis.

The biochemical function and mode of action of biotin long remained obscure. It is now known to be a cocarboxylase or coenzyme component for the transfer of carbon dioxide. Some of the reactions which it catalyzes are:

$$\underset{\text{Pyruvic Acid}}{CH_3-\overset{\overset{\displaystyle O}{\|}}{C}-COOH} \rightleftharpoons \underset{\text{Oxaloacetic Acid}}{HOOC-CH_2-\overset{\overset{\displaystyle O}{\|}}{C}-COOH} \qquad \text{18, 19, 20, 21}$$

$$\underset{\underset{\displaystyle \text{Ornithine}}{\overset{\displaystyle |}{NH_2}}}{HOOC-\overset{\displaystyle |}{C}H-CH_2-CH_2-CH_2-NH_2}$$

$$\underset{\underset{\displaystyle \text{Citrulline}}{\overset{\displaystyle |}{NH_2}}}{HOOC-\overset{\displaystyle |}{C}H-CH_2-CH_2-CH_2-NH-\overset{\overset{\displaystyle O}{\|}}{C}-NH_2} \qquad \text{22, 23}$$

[15] Ronald Breslow, *J. Am. Chem. Soc.* **79** 1762 (1957); **80** 3719 (1958).

[16] Ronald Breslow and Edward McNelis, *ibid.* **81** 3080 (1959).

[16a] Gerald L. Carlson and Gene M. Brown, *J. Biol. Chem.* **235** PC3 (1960).

[17] Paul D. Boyer, Henry Lardy and Karl Myrbäck (Eds.), "The Enzymes" Academic Press, New York, 1960 **Vol. II**, David E. Metzler, *Thiamine coenzymes*, pp. 295–337.

[18] Henry A. Lardy, Richard L. Potter and C. A. Elvehjem, *J. Biol. Chem.* **169** 541 (1947).

$$CH_3-\overset{\displaystyle O}{\overset{\|}{C}}=CH-\overset{\displaystyle O}{\overset{\|}{C}}-CoA \rightleftharpoons HOOC-CH_2-\overset{\displaystyle}{C}=CH-\overset{\displaystyle O}{\overset{\|}{C}}-CoA \quad 24, 25$$

β-Methylcrotonyl CoA β-Methylglutaconyl CoA

$$CH_3CH_2\overset{\displaystyle O}{\overset{\|}{C}}-CoA \rightleftharpoons HOOC-CH_2-CH_2-\overset{\displaystyle O}{\overset{\|}{C}}-CoA \quad 26, 27$$

Propionyl CoA Succinyl CoA

(Intermediates in purine biosynthesis) 28, 29

$$CH_3-\overset{\displaystyle O}{\overset{\|}{C}}-CoA \rightleftharpoons HOOC-CH_2-\overset{\displaystyle O}{\overset{\|}{C}}-CoA \quad 30$$

Acetyl-CoA Malonyl-CoA

[19] William Shive and Lorene Lane Rogers, *ibid.* 169 453 (1947).

[20] Herman C. Lichstein and W. W. Umbreit, *ibid.* 170 329 (1947).

[21] Henry A. Lardy, Richard L. Potter and R. H. Burris, *ibid.* 179 721 (1949).

[22] Patricia R. MacLeod, Santiago Grisolia, Philip P. Cohen and Henry A. Lardy, *ibid.* 180 1003 (1949).

[23] Gladys Feldott and Henry A. Lardy, *ibid.* 192 447 (1951).

[24] Bimal K. Bachhawat, Wm. G. Robinson and Minor J. Coon, *J. Am. Chem. Soc.* 76 3098 (1954); *idem., J. Biol. Chem.* 219 539 (1956).

[25] F. Lynen, J. Knappe, E. Lorch, G. Jütting and E. Ringelmann, *Angew. Chem.* 71 481 (1959).

[26] Henry A. Lardy and Robert Peanasky, *Physiol. Rev.* 33 560 (1953).

[27] Henry A. Lardy and Julius Adler, *J. Biol. Chem.* 219 933 (1956).

[28] Patricia R. MacLeod and Henry A. Lardy, *ibid.* 179 733 (1949).

[29] Albert G. Moat, Charles N. Wilkins, Jr. and Herman Friedman, *ibid.* 223 985 (1956); Albert G. Moat and Floyd Nasuti, *Federation Proc.* 19 313 (1960).

The mode of action of biotin is known now in enough detail to suggest the scheme outlined below. It is still uncertain which nitrogen atom of the biotin molecule participates.[25]

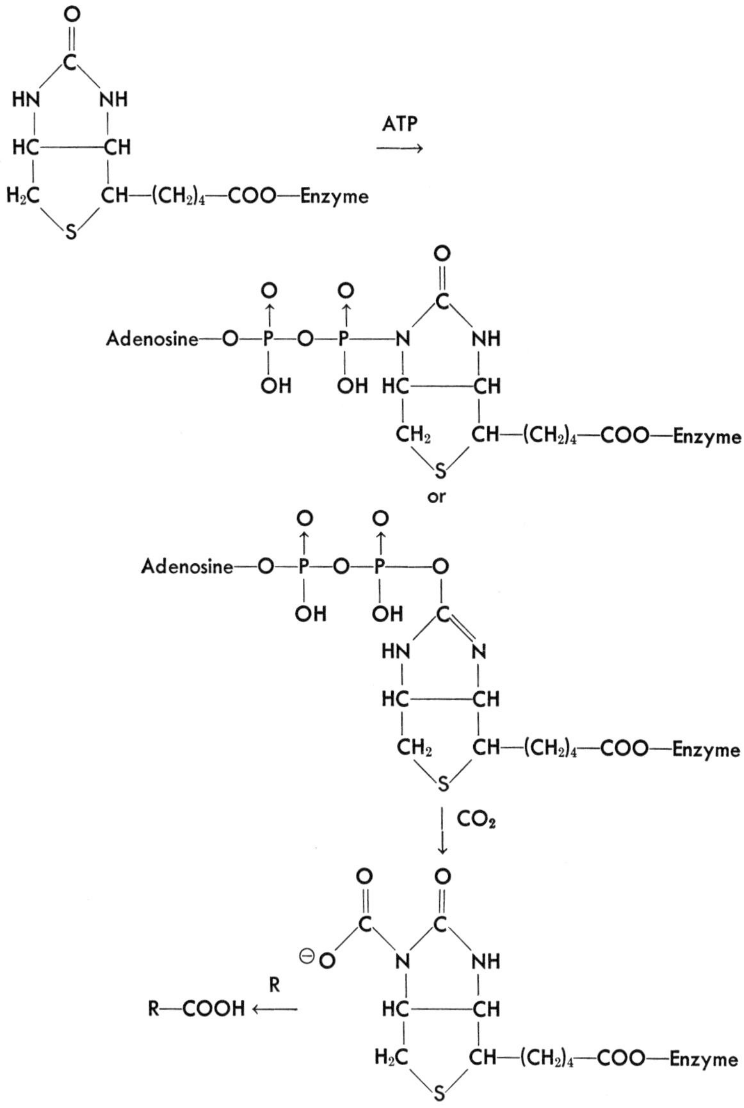

[30] Salih J. Wakil, Edward B. Titchener and David M. Gibson, *Biochim. et Biophys. Acta* **29** 225 (1958); Salih J. Wakil, *J. Am. Chem. Soc.* **80** 6465 (1958).

It is probable that biotin is attached to the enzyme in an amide linkage, perhaps at the ϵ-amino group of a lysine unit. Evidence indicates that a variety of apoenzymes can use biotin as the prosthetic group in reversible carbon dioxide transfer just as a variety of apoenzymes can use riboflavin in reversible hydrogen transfer.

Biocytin is a biotin-lysine conjugate isolated from controlled autolysates of yeast cells.[31, 32]

$$
\begin{array}{c}
O \\
\parallel \\
C \\
HN \quad NH \\
| \quad\quad | \\
HC \longrightarrow CH \quad\quad O \\
| \quad\quad\quad\quad \parallel \\
H_2C \quad CH-(CH_2)_4-C-NH-(CH_2)_4-CH-COOH \\
\diagdown S \diagup \quad\quad\quad\quad\quad\quad\quad\quad | \\
NH_2
\end{array}
$$

Biocytin

$$
\begin{array}{c}
O \\
\parallel \\
C \\
HN \quad NH \\
| \quad\quad | \\
CH \longrightarrow CH \\
| \quad\quad\quad | \\
CH_3 \quad CH_2-(CH_2)_4-COOH
\end{array}
$$

Dethiobiotin

$$
\begin{array}{c}
O \\
\parallel \\
C \\
\quad\quad C \longrightarrow NH \\
| \quad\quad\quad | \\
CH_2 \quad CH-(CH_2)_5-COOH \\
\diagdown S \diagup
\end{array}
$$

Actithiazic Acid

It is better utilized by some microorganisms than is biotin itself.

Actithiazic acid is a biotin antimetabolite.

The biosynthetic origin of biotin remains obscure. Pimelic acid is an effective precursor in biotin-producing organisms. Dethiobiotin is produced by a *Penicillium chrysogenum* mutant, and it may be an intermediate in the biosynthetic scheme at least in this and probably in other microorganisms.[33]

[31] Lemuel D. Wright, Emlen L. Cresson, Helen R. Skeggs, Thomas R. Wood, Robert L. Peck, Donald E. Wolf and Karl Folkers, *ibid.* **74** 1996 (1952).

[32] Donald E. Wolf, John Valiant, Robert L. Peck and Karl Folkers, *ibid.* **74** 2002 (1952).

[33] E. L. Tatum, *J. Biol. Chem.* **160** 455 (1945).

Junipal appears to be related to the acetylenic sub-stances typical of basidiomycetes which were listed in an earlier section. In some way sulfur seems to have been added, in effect across two acetylenic bonds to form a thiophene ring. It has been suggested[34] that junipal and anisaldehyde, occurring in the same culture and with the same number of carbon atoms, may be derivatives of a common acetylenic aldehyde precursor, perhaps C_7H_4O:

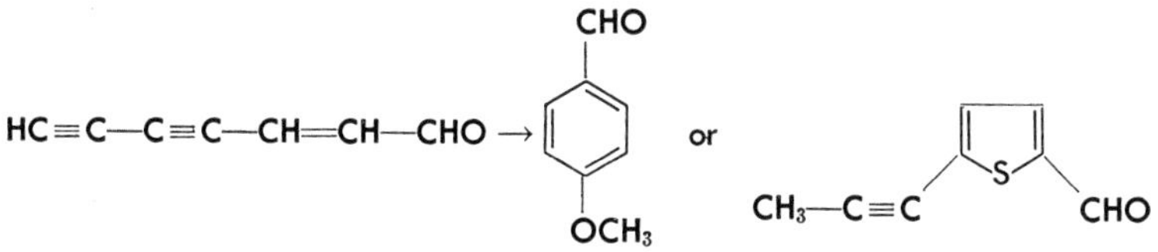

Azomycin seems to incorporate a modified guanidine group.

893 Azomycin (2-Nitroimidazole), $C_3H_3O_2N_3$, white needles, m.p. 283° (dec.).

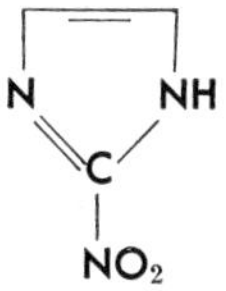

Nocardia sp. resembling *N. mesenterica*
Shoshiro Nakamura and Hamao Umezawa, *J. Antibiotics* (Japan) **8A** 66 (1955) and other papers in this series.

894 Oxamycin (Cycloserine, Orientomycin D-4-Amino-3-isoxazoli-done, PA-94), $C_3H_6O_2N_2$, colorless crystals, m.p. 156° (dec.), $[\alpha]_{5461}$ 25° +137° ±2° (c 5 in 2 N sodium hydrox-ide).

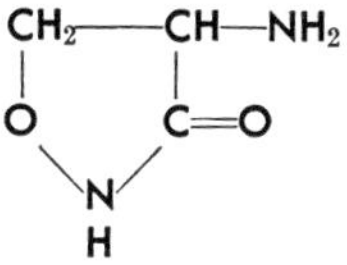

Streptomyces garyphalus, S. orchidaceus, S. lavendulae, S. nagasakiensie nov. sp., *S.* K-300, etc.

[34] J. H. Birkinshaw and P. Chaplen, *Biochem. J.* **60** 255 (1955).

Dale A. Harris, Myrle Ruger, Mary Ann Reagan, Frank J. Wolf, Robert L. Peck, Hyman Wallick and H. Boyd Woodruff, *Antibiotics and Chemotherapy* 5 183 (1955).

Roger L. Harned, Phil Harter Hidy and Eleanore Kropp LaBaw, *ibid.* 5 204 (1955).

Charles H. Stammer, Andrew N. Wilson, Claude F. Spencer, Frank W. Bachelor, Frederick W. Holly and Karl Folkers, *J. Am. Chem. Soc.* 79 3236 (1957). (Synthesis)

895 Junipal, C_8H_6OS, thick, colorless needles, m.p. 80°.

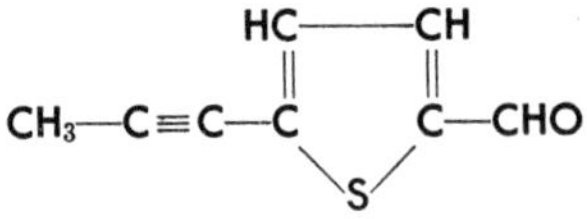

Daedalea juniperina Murr.

J. H. Birkinshaw and P. Chaplen, *Biochem. J.* 60 255 (1955).

896 6-Methoxybenzoxazolidone, $C_8H_7O_3N$, red crystals, m.p. 154°.

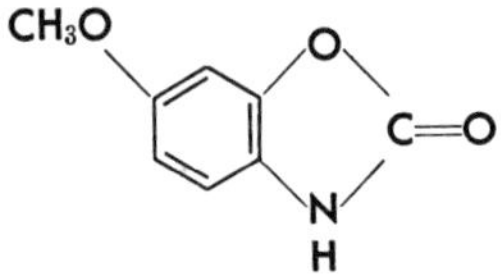

Ustilago maydis (spores)

The same compound has been isolated from young corn plants.

P. H. List, *Arch. Pharm.* 292 452 (1959).

897 6-Aminopenicillanic Acid, $C_8H_{12}O_3N_2S$, colorless crystals, m.p. 208° (dec.).

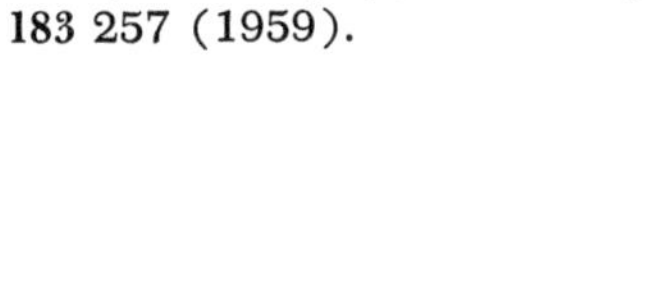

Penicillium chrysogenum

F. R. Batchelor, F. P. Doyle, J. H. C. Nayler and G. N. Robinson, *Nature* 183 257 (1959).

898   5-Amino-4-imidazolecarboxamide Riboside, $C_9H_{14}O_5N_4$, colorless crystals, m.p. 213° (dec., previous browning).

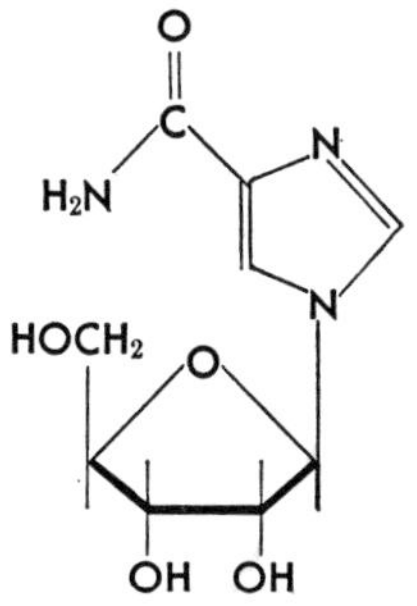

Escherichia coli (sulfonamide–inhibited)

G. Robert Greenberg and Edra L. Spilman, *J. Biol. Chem.* **219** 411 (1956).

899   Actithiazic Acid (Acidomycin, Mycobacidin PA-95), $C_9H_{15}O_3NS$, colorless needles, m.p. 140°, $[\alpha]_D^{25}$ −60° (c 1 in absolute alcohol).

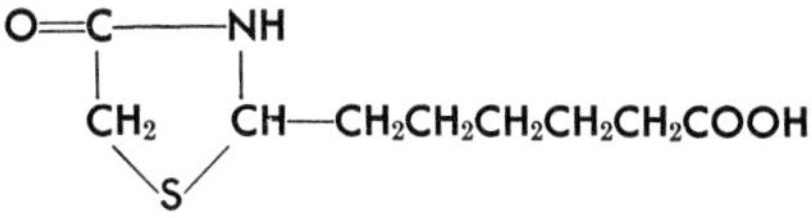

Streptomyces virginiae, S. cinnamonensis, S. lavendulae

Yields of about 0.3 g. per liter have been reported.

Walton E. Grundy, Alma L. Whitman, Elbina G. Rdzok, Edward J. Rdzok, Marjorie E. Hanes and John C. Sylvester, *Antibiotics and Chemotherapy* **2** 399 (1952).

J. R. Schenck and A. F. DeRose, *Arch. Biochem. and Biophys.* **40** 263 (1952).

R. K. Clark, Jr. and J. R. Schenck, *ibid.* **40** 270 (1952).

W. M. McLamore, Walter D. Celmer, Virgil V. Bogert, Frank C. Pennington and I. A. Solomons, *J. Am. Chem. Soc.* **74** 2946 (1952).

B. A. Sobin, *ibid.* **74** 2947 (1952).

W. M. McLamore, Walter D. Celmer, Virgil V. Bogert, Frank C. Pennington, B. A. Sobin and I. A. Solomons, *ibid.* **75** 105 (1953). (Synthesis)

900 **Biotin,** $C_{10}H_{16}O_3N_2S$, colorless needles, m.p. 230–232° (dec.), $[\alpha]_D^{22}$ +92° (c 0.3 in 0.1 N sodium hydroxide).

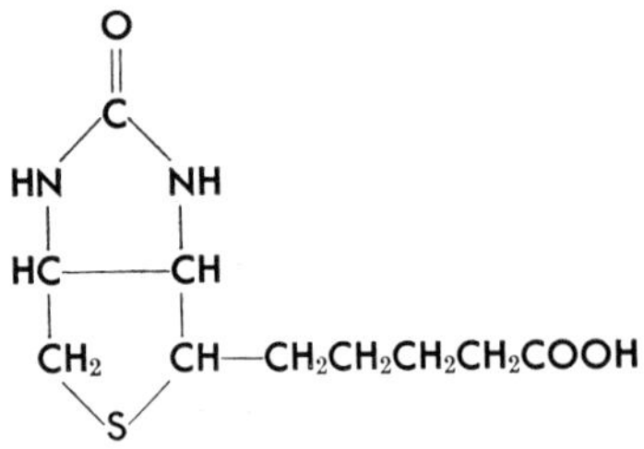

Torula utilis, other yeasts (occurs also in molds and bacteria)

Yields of 0.5–3.6 μg. per gram of dry cell weight are obtained from *Torula utilis.*

Leland A. Underkofler and Richard J. Hickey, "Industrial Fermentations," Chemical Publishing Co., Inc., New York, 1954 **Vol. II,** J. M. Van Lanen, *Production of vitamins other than riboflavin,* chap. 6, pp. 191–216. (A review)

901 **Biotin-l-sulfoxide,** $C_{10}H_{16}O_4N_2S$, colorless crystals, m.p. 238–243°, $[\alpha]_D^{20}$ −40° (in 0.1 N sodium hydroxide).

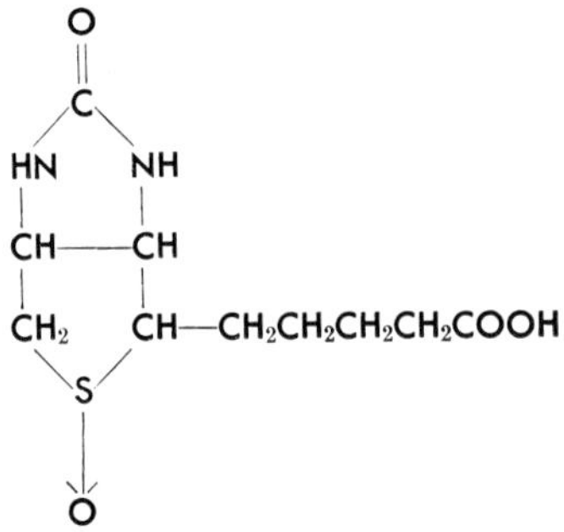

Aspergillus niger

Lemuel D. Wright and Emlen L. Cresson, *J. Am. Chem. Soc.* **76** 4156 (1954).

Lemuel D. Wright, Emlen L. Cresson, John Valiant, Donald E. Wolf and Karl Folkers, *ibid.* **76** 4160, 4163 (1954). (Isolation and characterization)

902 Dethiobiotin (Desthiobiotin, 5-Methyl-2-oxo-4-imidazolidineca-
proic Acid), $C_{10}H_{18}O_3N_2$, colorless needles, m.p. 156–158°,
$[\alpha]_D^{21}$ +10.7° (c 2.0 in water).

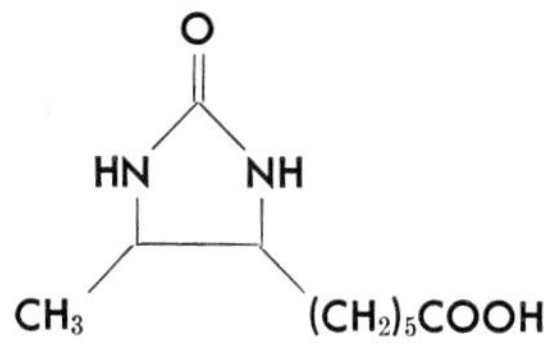

Penicillium chrysogenum
E. L. Tatum, *J. Biol. Chem.* 160 455 (1945).

903 Thiamin (Vitamin B_1, Aneurin) (Chloride Hydrochloride),
$C_{12}H_{18}ON_4Cl_2S$, colorless needles, m.p. ~250° (dec.).

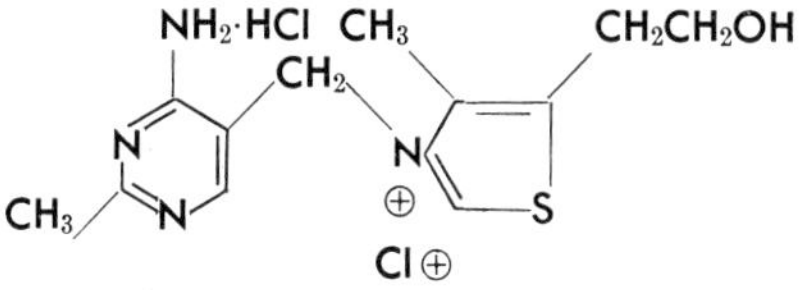

Most yeasts, molds and bacteria
Yields of 120–200 μg. per gram of dry primary-grown
yeast cells can be obtained. Much higher yields (600–
1200 μg. per gram) can be obtained if all that is required
is coupling of supplied precursors.
Leland A. Underkofler and Richard J. Hickey, "Industrial
Fermentations," Chemical Publishing Co., Inc., New York,
1954 **Vol. II,** J. M. Van Lanen *Production of vitamins other
than riboflavin,* chap. 6, pp. 191–216. (A review)

904 Cocarboxylase (Cozymase II, Vitamin B_1-diphosphate, Thiamin
diphosphate,   Aneurindiphosphate)   (Hydrochloride),
$C_{12}H_{18}O_7N_4SP_2 \cdot HCl$, nearly colorless needles, m.p. 242–
244° (dec.).

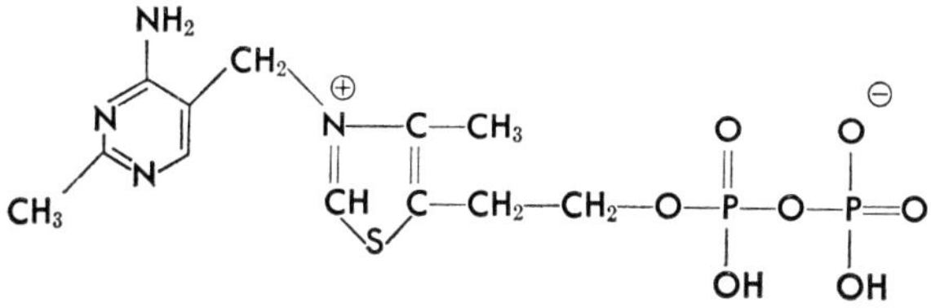

Yeast

K. Lohmann and Ph. Schuster, *Biochem. Z.* 294 188 (1937). (Isolation)

Kurt G. Stern and Jesse W. Hofer, *Science* 85 483 (1937). (Synthesis)

905 **Synnematin-B** (Cephalosporin N, Salmotin), $C_{14}H_{21}O_6N_3S$, barium salt, $[\alpha]_D^{20}$ +187° (c 0.6 in water).

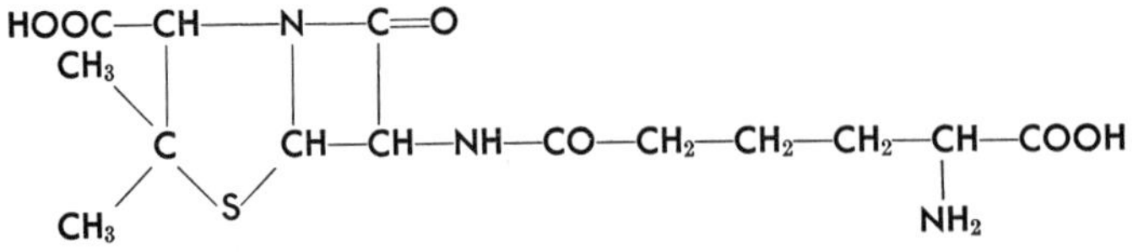

Cephalosporium salmosynnematum

E. P. Abraham, "CIBA Lectures in Microbiol. Biochemistry," *Biochemistry of some peptide and steroid antibiotics,* John Wiley and Sons, New York, 1957. (A review)

Natural Penicillins. General formula:

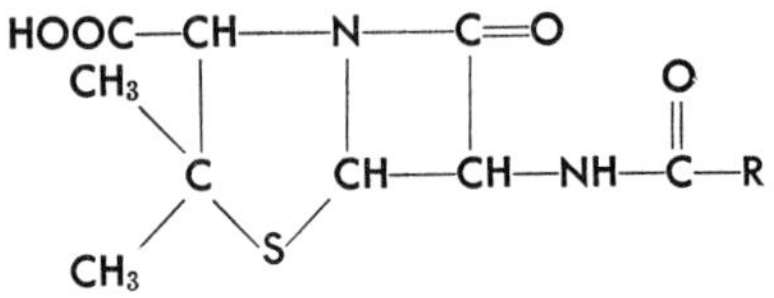

906 **Penicillin G,** $C_{16}H_{18}O_4N_2S$, colorless prisms, m.p. (Na salt) 215° (dec.), $[\alpha]_D^{25}$ +305° (c 0.821 in water).

R = Benzyl —CH₂⁻

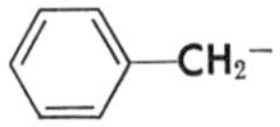

907 **Penicillin K,** $C_{16}H_{26}O_4N_2S$, colorless prisms (Na salt), $[\alpha]_D^{25}$ +258° (c 0.43 in water).

R = *n*-Heptyl $CH_3(CH_2)_6^-$

908 **Penicillin X,** $C_{16}H_{18}O_5N_2S$, colorless crystals, m.p. (Na salt) 228–235° (dec.), $[\alpha]_D$ +267° (c 0.525 in water).

R = *p*-Hydroxybenzyl HO——CH₂⁻

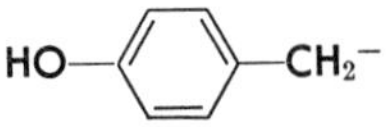

909 **Gigantic Acid** (Dihydro F), $C_{14}H_{22}O_4N_2S$ (Na salt), colorless crystals, m.p. 188° (dec.), $[\alpha]_D^{23}$ +319° (c 1 in water).

R = *n*-Amyl $CH_3(CH_2)_4^-$

910   Penicillin F (Flavicidin, Flavicin) $C_{14}H_{20}O_4N_2S$, m.p. (Na salt) 204° (dec.), $[\alpha]_D^{20-25}$ +276–316° (c 0.821 in water).

R = n-Pentenyl $CH_3CH_2-CH=CH-CH_2-$

The Δ^3-pentenyl variant is also known.

Penicillium species, especially *P. chrysogenum* and *P. notatum* Westling, and aspergillus species, especially *A. flavus* from which Penicillin F was obtained.

H. Clarke, J. Johnson and R. Robinson, "The Chemistry of Penicillin," Princeton University Press, Princeton, 1949. (A review)

911   Cephalosporin C, proposed molecular formula $C_{16}H_{21}O_8N_3S$, Na salt: $[\alpha]_D^{20}$ +103°.

Structural features:

Acid hydrolysis yields 1 D-α-aminoadipic acid, 1 CO_2 and 2 NH_3. No penicillamine is produced in contrast to cephalosporin N.

Cephalosporium salmosynnematum

G. G. F. Newton and E. P. Abraham, *Biochem. J.* 62 651 (1956).

912   Biocytin, $C_{16}H_{28}O_4N_4S$, colorless crystals, m.p. 228–230° (dec.) (245–252°).

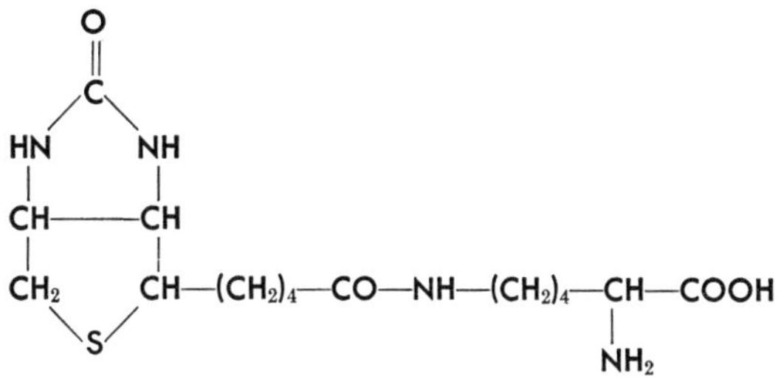

Yeast

Lemuel D. Wright, Emlen J. Cresson, Helen R. Skeggs, Thomas R. Wood, Robert L. Peck, Donald E. Wolf and Karl Folkers, *J. Am. Chem. Soc.* 72 1048 (1950). (Isolation)

Robert L. Peck, Donald E. Wolf and Karl Folkers, *ibid.* 74 1999 (1952). (Structure)

Donald E. Wolf, John Valiant, Robert L. Peck and Karl Folkers, *ibid.* 74 1002 (1952). (Synthesis)

f. PYRROLES, PORPHYRINS AND RELATED COMPOUNDS

Pyrroles occur rather frequently as microorganism metabolites. They are constituents of porphyrins, of vitamin B_{12}, of certain bacterial pigments, and of some compounds which have been considered as antibiotics.

More has been published concerning the biosynthesis of the complex substances because of their more general import in biological systems, but it is tempting to speculate on the origins of the simpler compounds even though little evidence is yet available.

Holomycin is the simplest of three similar substances produced by streptomycetes, although the structures of aureothricin and thiolutin were determined earlier. The skeletons of glycine and cysteine are perceptible within the holomycin molecule, and, superficially, it seems that a biosynthetic route related to the following might take place:

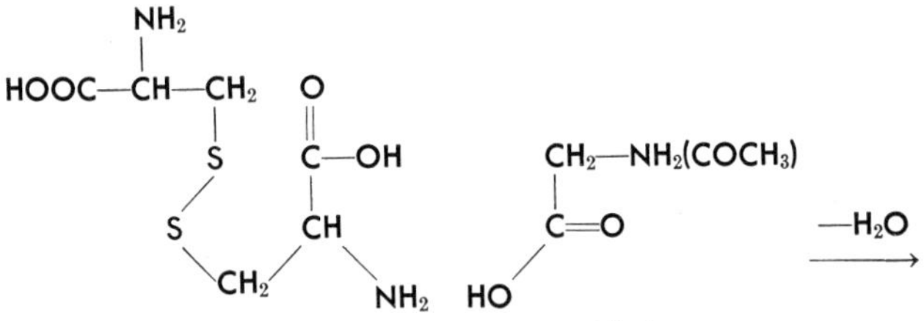

Cystine   Glycine

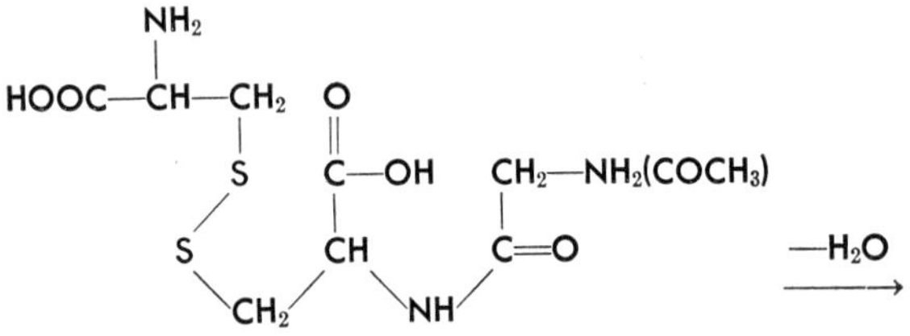

$-H_2O$

I

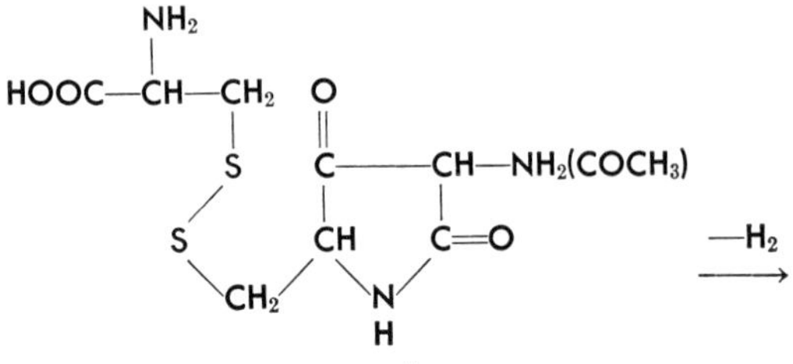

$-H_2O$

II

$-H_2$

$$
\begin{array}{c}
\text{NH}_2 \\
|
\end{array}
$$

HOOC—CH—CH$_2$ O
       | ||
       S   C———CH—NH$_2$(COCH$_3$)
     / | | →→
    S   C   CO
     \CH⁄ \N⁄
             H

III

    S
   / \
S   C═══CH—NH—CO—CH$_3$
| |
CH══C   C═O   + Serine or Alanine
    \N⁄
     H

Holomycin

A glycylcystine intermediate I is reminiscent of the peptide intermediate now implicated in the biosynthesis of penicillin.[1] It is known that there has been some academic interest in the origin of these compounds, however, and since no publications have been forthcoming, perhaps the problem is more complicated.

Pyoluteorin, with a carbonyl group at the two position of the pyrrole moiety, suggests an origin in the glutamate → proline pathway, perhaps from δ^1-pyrroline-5-carboxylic acid, although the chlorination of the ring may indicate a less obvious derivation. The pyrrolidine moiety of the plant alkaloid, nicotine, has been shown to be biosynthesized from glutamate.[2]

The origins of prodigiosin and netropsin are not obvious. Some work has been done on prodigiosin.[3, 4] Glycine-2-C^{14} was incorporated into prodigiosin, but 5-aminolevulinic acid-5-C^{14} was not.[4] This apparently distinguishes the method of biosynthesis from that of the porphyrins. Moreover, C^{14}-labeled L-proline was found to be several times more efficient as a prodigiosin precursor in *Serratia marcescens* than glycine, while the reverse is

[1] H. R. V. Arnstein, D. Morris and E. Toms, *Biochim. et Biophys. Acta* 35 561 (1959).

[2] Thomas Griffith, Kenneth P. Hellman and Richard U. Byerrum, *J. Biol. Chem.* 235 800 (1960).

[3] R. Hubbard and C. Rimington, *Biochem. J.* 46 220 (1950).

[4] Gerald S. Marks and Lawrence Bogorad, *Proc. Nat. Acad. Sci.* 46 25 (1960).

true in heme synthesis (in rats).[5] The biosynthesis at least seems to be related to the metabolism of 5-carbon units such as proline, ornithine and glutamic acid. It was further proposed[4] that the methoxyl group in one pyrrole ring indicated derivation from hydroxyproline, and that the colorless C_{10} pyrrolic substance, which is thought to be a prodigiosin precursor,[6] was also probably derived from two C-5 units and that the *n*-amyl side-chain also might be a rudimentary C-5 amino acid chain. In this connection, the isolation of a C_{25} "prodigiosin-like pigment"[7] from a streptomycete should be mentioned. While all of the proposals made are not entirely compatible with the revised structure published since,[8] the basic tenets seem to be sound.

Orange and blue variants of prodigiosin occur. The latter, which are less soluble, may be metal chelates.

Some work also has been done on the biosynthesis of the pyrrolic pigments of *Bacillus bruntzii,* and glycylglycine was found to be a better precursor than glycine and a number of other peptides.[9]

It is safe to say that natural pyrroles are formed by a variety of methods. Demonstration of the participation of erythrose in the shikimic acid biosynthetic route has inspired the admonition that erythrose and its 4-C-atom derivatives should not be ignored as possible precursors of furans and pyrroles.[10]

Because of their importance in photosynthesis, in hemoglobin, in cytochromes and peroxidases and in the chromophore of vitamin B_{12}, there has been much investigation of the general mode of biosynthesis of porphyrins. It is likely that a similar method is operative in all cases.

Porphyrins are present in yeasts, molds and bacteria.

[5] David Shemin and D. Rittenberg, *J. Biol. Chem.* **166** 621 (1946).

[6] Ursula V. Santer and Henry J. Vogel, *Biochim. et Biophys. Acta* **19** 578 (1956).

[7] F. Arcamone, A. DiMarco, M. Ghione and T. Scotti, *Giorn. microbiol.* **4** 77 (1957).

[8] Harry H. Wasserman, James A. McKeon, Lewis Smith and Peter Forgione, *J. Am. Chem. Soc.* **82** 506 (1960).

[9] J. G. Marchal and S. Baldo, *Trav. lab. microbiol. fac. pharm.* (Nancy) No. **18** 187 (1956).

[10] Ernest Wenkert, *Experientia* **15** 166 (1959).

The photosynthetic bacteria, grown aerobically in light, are a rich source, and so are corynebacteria. Part of the biosynthetic pathway to the porphyrins has been explored in photosynthetic bacteria, and it is thought to be of general significance:[11, 12]

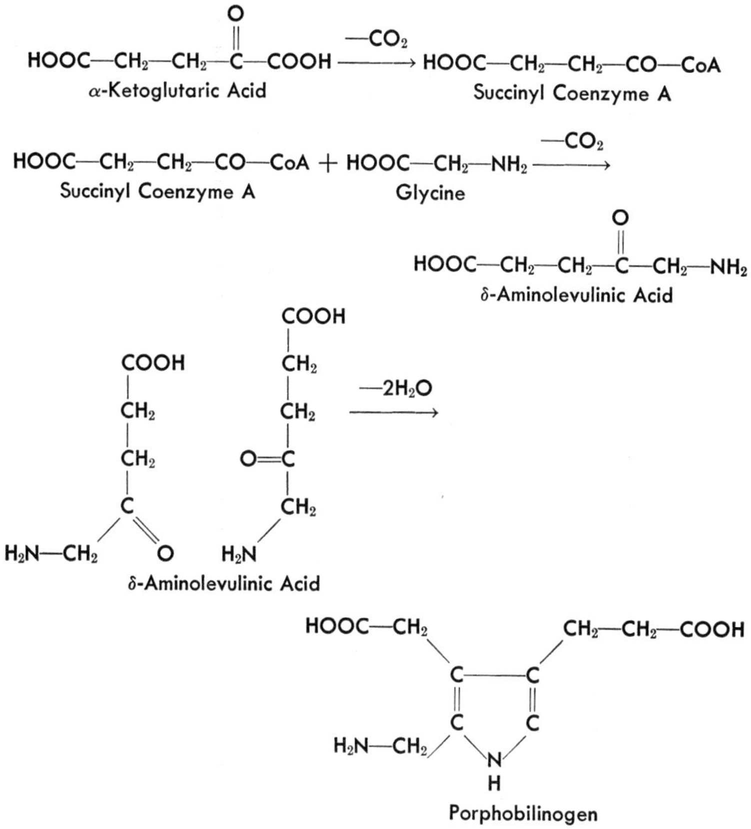

$$\text{HOOC—CH}_2\text{—CH}_2\text{—C(=O)—COOH} \xrightarrow{\text{—CO}_2} \text{HOOC—CH}_2\text{—CH}_2\text{—CO—CoA}$$

α-Ketoglutaric Acid   Succinyl Coenzyme A

$$\text{HOOC—CH}_2\text{—CH}_2\text{—CO—CoA} + \text{HOOC—CH}_2\text{—NH}_2 \xrightarrow{\text{—CO}_2}$$

Succinyl Coenzyme A   Glycine

$$\text{HOOC—CH}_2\text{—CH}_2\text{—C(=O)—CH}_2\text{—NH}_2$$

δ-Aminolevulinic Acid

δ-Aminolevulinic Acid $\xrightarrow{\text{—2H}_2\text{O}}$

Porphobilinogen

Pyridoxal phosphate is required as a co-factor (glycine activator) in the glycine-succinyl-COA condensation.[12] Porphobilinogen then condenses to form coproporphyrin and protoporphyrin. In certain photosynthetic bacteria,

[11] June Lascelles, *Biochem. J.* 62 78 (1956); *idem., Abstracts of the Gordon Conference on Metabolism,* 1957.

[12] Goro Kikuchi, Abhaya Kumar, Phyllis Talmadge and David Shemin, *J. Biol. Chem.* 233 1214 (1958).

such as *Rhodopseudomonas spheroides*, the following sequence has been shown:

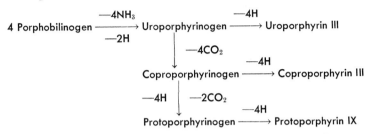

The reduced precursors may be the biologically active species, and the porphyrins by-products stabilized by oxidation.[11]

Higher animals (as well as microorganisms) are capable of porphyrin synthesis, and, in fact, the above work with photosynthetic bacteria was based on earlier labeling experiments in animals,[13] and porphobilinogen was first isolated from the urine of humans with acute porphyria.[14]

Widely occurring enzymes convert porphobilinogen to uroporphyrins, but it is difficult to isolate and identify the intermediates.   Apparently they are quite transitory. Some interesting speculations have been published concerning their nature.[15, 16]   The Wittenberg hypothesis, based on the known transformations of porphobilinogen by chemicals and enzymes, the extensive labeling studies that have been published, and on the construction of models, is outlined in the following series of equations:

[13] David Shemin and D. Rittenberg, *J. Biol. Chem.* **166** 621, 627 (1946); Norman S. Radin, D. Rittenberg and David Shemin, *ibid.* **184** 745 (1950); Jonathan Wittenberg and David Shemin, *ibid.* **185** 103 (1950); David Shemin and Jonathan Wittenberg, *ibid.* **192** 315 (1951); Helen M. Muir and A. Neuberger, *Biochem. J.* **47** 97 (1950); David Shemin, Charlotte S. Russell and Tessa Abramsky, *J. Biol. Chem.* **215** 613 (1954); K. D. Gibson, W. G. Lauer and A. Neuberger, *Biochem. J.* **70** 71 (1958); K. D. Gibson, A. Neuberger and J. J. Scott, *ibid.* **61** 618 (1955); J. E. Falk, E. I. B. Dresel, A. Benson and B. C. Knight, *ibid.* **63** 87 (1956); E. I. B. Dresel and J. E. Falk, *ibid.* **63** 388 (1956).

[14] R. G. Westall, *Nature* **170** 614 (1952); G. H. Cookson and C. Rimington, *Biochem. J.* **57** 476 (1954).

[15] David Shemin, *Harvey Lectures* **50** 258 (1956).

[16] Jonathan B. Wittenberg, *Nature* **184** 876 (1959).

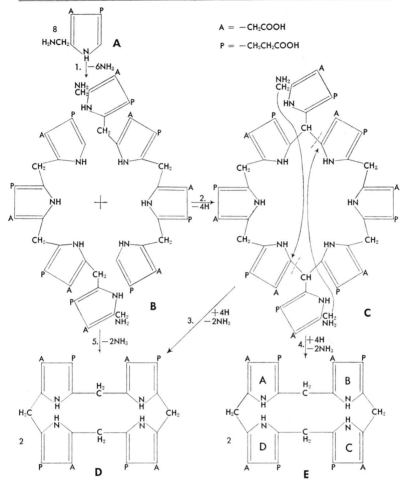

$$A = -CH_2COOH$$
$$P = -CH_2CH_2COOH$$

Bogorad found[17] that the enzyme porphobilinogen de-aminase converts porphobilinogen (**A**) to uroporphyrinogen (**D**). Because a second enzyme, uroporphyrinogen isomerase, has as its only substrate (not **D**) a product of the action of porphobilinogen deaminase on (**A**), there must have been one or more colorless intermediates. The intermediates must be convertible, spontaneously or under the continuing influence of porphobilinogen deaminase,

[17] Lawrence Bogorad, *J. Biol. Chem.* 233 501, 510, 516 (1958).

to (**D**) (reaction 5). The linear tetrapyrrole (**B**) shown is the intermediate proposed by Wittenberg.

The enzyme, uroporphyrinogen isomerase, acting on porphobilinogen, yields uroporphyrinogen III (**E**) as its first detectable product. Wittenberg proposed that the function of this enzyme is to condense 2 molecules of (**B**) (reaction 2), creating the cyclic octapyrrole (**C**). Model studies indicate that such an intermediate could fold and undergo rearrangement, spontaneously or under continued enzyme influence, to yield 2 molecules of uroporphyrinogen III (**E**) (reaction 4).

The over-all result of this reaction sequence would be the interchange of the pyrrole moieties destined to form rings D of the porphyrins between two tetrapyrroles, with consequent reversal of the positions of the D rings relative to the other pyrrole rings of the tetrapyrroles.

This hypothesis seems to be in accord with all other known evidence concerning porphyrin biosynthesis, and it would account for their peculiar asymmetry. Many references to related work are cited by Wittenberg. It is notable that appropriate dipyrromethanes were not converted to porphyrinogens or porphyrins by porphobilinogen deaminase.[18]

Vitamin B_{12} is the only vitamin produced exclusively by microorganisms, although not all microbes are capable of elaborating it. Most seem to form little more than enough for their own slight requirements, the best organisms for primary production by fermentation being: *Streptomyces olivaceus, S. griseus, Propionibacterium shermanii* and *Bacillus megatherium.*

The nucleus of vitamin B_{12} differs somewhat from that of porphyrins and is called the corrin ring:[55]

[18] D. S. Hoare and H. Heath, *Biochim. et Biophys. Acta* **39** 167 (1960).

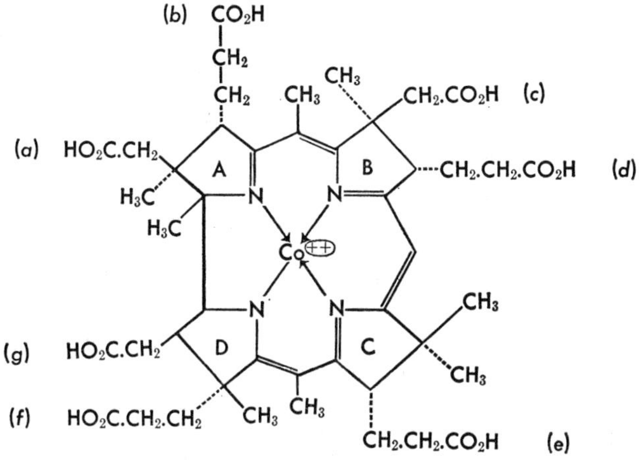

Cobyrinic Acid

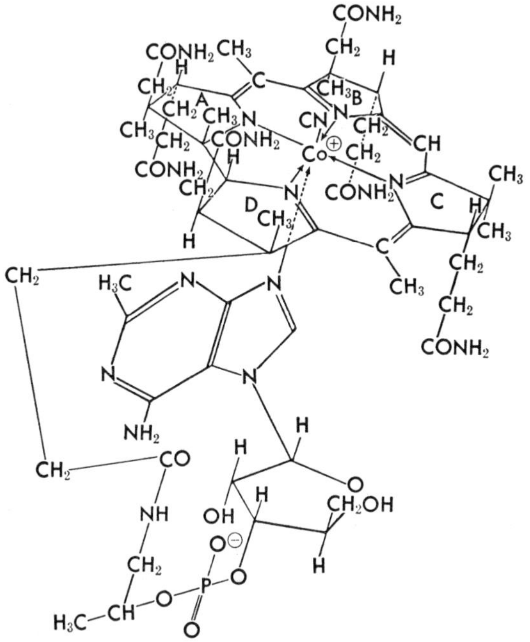

α-(5,6-Dimethylbenzimidazolyl) cobamide Cyanide

The nucleotide-free carboxylic acid form is called co-byrinic acid, the carboxyl groups (amides, etc.) being lettered as shown. When the aminopropanol group is incorporated by amide linkage at the f-position, the name is modified to cobinic acid (all carboxyl groups as amides = cobinamide), and when ribose is incorporated, the name is modified to cobamic acid (cobamide). The name of the heterocycle is then inserted at the beginning with the suffix -yl. Thus, vitamin B_{12} is correctly named: α-(5,6-dimethylbenzimidazolyl) cobamide cyanide.

The two principal moieties are called the planar group and the nucleotide, and these are essentially perpendicular in relative steric arrangement.

A number of analogues of vitamin B_{12} have been isolated from natural sources. These sources include B_{12} fermentations, the rumen or the gut of various animals and sewage sludge. The naturally occurring analogues are listed below by trivial name, together with the characteristic heterocycle of the nucleotide.

TABLE I

Naturally Occurring Vitamin B_{12} Analogues

Name	Nucleotide base	Reference
Vitamin B_{12}	5,6-Dimethylbenzimidazole	
Pseudo (ψ)-Vitamin B_{12}	Adenine	19, 20, 21, 22, 23
Factor A	2-Methyladenine	20, 21, 22, 23
Factor B (Etiocobalamine)	No nucleotide	21, 24, 25, 26
Factor C (Guanosine Diphosphate Factor B)	Guanine	21, 24, 25, 27, 37
Factor D*	Unknown	21, 22
Factor E*	Unknown	22
Factor F	2-Methylmercaptoadenine(?)	21, 22, 25
Factor G	Hypoxanthine	22
Factor H	2-Methylhypoxanthine	22
Factor I (B_{12} factor$_{III}$)	5-Hydroxybenzimidazole	22, 28, 29
Factors J, K, L, M	Unknown	30
—————	Unknown purine base (?)	31
—————— (May be factor F)	2-Methylmercaptoadenine	32
—————— (May be factor C)	Guanine	27
Factor "A" Ribose Phosphate	No base	33
Factor V_{1a} (Cobyrinic Acid a, b, c, d, e, g-hexaamide)	No base	34, 35
Factor V_{1b} (Cobyrinic Acid Pentamide)	No base	34, 35
—————	5-Methylbenzimidazole	36
—————	Benzimidazole	36†

* Not crystalline.   † About 17 other cobamides were detected in this study.

Besides the natural analogues, many vitamin B_{12} variants have been prepared by addition of analogues of the

[19] H. W. Dion, D. G. Calkins and J. J. Pfiffner, *J. Am. Chem. Soc.* 74 1108 (1952).

[20] J. E. Ford, E. S. Holdsworth, S. K. Kon and J. W. G. Porter, *Nature* 171 148 (1953).

[21] H. G. Heinrich (Editor), "Vitamin B_{12} and Intrinsic Factor, First European Symposium, Hamburg, 1956." M. E. Coates and S. K. Kon, Ferdinand Enke, Stuttgart, 1956, p. 72.

[22] F. B. Brown, J. C. Cain, Dorothy E. Gant, T. F. J. Parker and E. Lester Smith, *Biochem. J.* 59 82 (1955).

[23] H. W. Dion, D. G. Calkins, and J. J. Pfiffner, *J. Am. Chem. Soc.* 76 948 (1954).

[24] S. K. Kon, Biochem. Symposium No. 13, p. 17 (1955).

[25] H. G. Heinrich (Editor), "Vitamin B_{12} and Intrinsic Factor, First European, Hamburg, 1956." J. W. S. Porter, Ferdinand Enke, Stuttgart, 1956, p. 43.

[26] J. B. Armitage, J. R. Cannon, A. W. Johnson, T. F. J. Parker, E. Lester Smith, W. H. Stafford and A. R. Todd, *J. Chem. Soc.,* 3849 (1953).

[27] R. Barchielli, G. Boretti, P. Julita, A. Migliacci and A. Minghetti, *Biochim. et Biophys. Acta* 25 452 (1957).

[28] Wilhelm Friedrich and Konrad Bernhauer, *Chem. Ber.* 89 2030 (1956).

[29] Wilhelm Friedrich and Konrad Bernhauer, *Angew. Chem.* 65 627 (1953).

[30] Clifford H. Shunk, Franklin M. Robinson, James F. McPherson, Marjorie M. Gasser and Karl Folkers, *J. Am. Chem. Soc.* 78 3228 (1956).

[31] G. E. W. Wolstenholm and Maeve O'Connor (Eds.), CIBA Foundation Symposium on "The Chemistry and Biology of Purines," E. Lester Smith, *The chemistry of new purines in the B_{12} series of vitamins,* Little, Brown & Co., Boston, 1957, pp. 160–168.

[32] Wilhelm Friedrich and Konrad Bernhauer, *Chem. Ber.* 90 1966 (1957).

[33] Hanswerner Dellweg and Konrad Bernhauer, *Arch. Biochem. and Biophys.* 69 74 (1957).

[34] Konrad Bernhauer, Hanswerner Dellweg, Wilhelm Friedrich, Gisela Gross and F. Wagner, *Z. Naturforsch.* 156 336 (1960).

[34a] K. Bernhauer, H. W. Dellweg, W. Friedrich, G. Gross, F. Wagner, and P. Zeller, *Helv. Chim. Acta* 43 693 (1960).

[35] Konrad Bernhauer, Elisabeth Becher, Gisela Gross and Georg Wilharm, *Biochem. Z.* 332 562 (1960).

[35a] K. Bernhauer, F. Wagner and P. Zeller, *Helv. Chim. Acta* 43 696 (1960).

[36] Wilhelm Friedrich and Konrad Bernhauer, *Chem. Ber.* 91 2061 (1958).

[37] G. Boretti, A. DiMarco, T. Fuoco, M. P. Marnati, A. Migliacci and C. Spalla, *Biochim. et Biophys. Acta* 37 379 (1960).

nucleotide base to fermentations. A review[38] lists about 50 such compounds, some of which have vitamin activity.

There seems to be a fundamental similarity in the biosynthetic routes to vitamin B_{12} and the porphyrins. C^{14}-Labeled glycine or δ-aminolevulinic acid are heavily incorporated.[39] Threonine furnishes the aminopropanol moiety as demonstrated by incorporation of the amino acid labeled with N^{15}.[40] There seems to be no information yet on the biosynthetic origin of the dimethylbenzimidazole moiety.

Red cobamide-containing polypeptides have been isolated from microorganisms, and some of these can replace cobamide in deficient microorganisms, and in the oral treatment of pernicious anemia.[41, 42]

Cobamides have been implicated in several metabolic processes.[43] In *Escherichia coli* mutants they seem to assist in the formation and transfer of methionine methyl groups[44] (folic acid is also required). They are thought to be involved in the reduction of disulfides to thiols.[45] In

[38] D. Perlman, *Advances in Appl. Microbiol.* 1 87–112 (1952). (A review)

[39] David Shemin, John W. Corcoran, Charles Rosenblum and Ian M. Miller, *Science* 124 272 (1956); John W. Corcoran and David Shemin, *Biochim. et Biophys. Acta* 25 661 (1957).

[40] Alvin I. Krasna, Charles Rosenblum and David B. Sprinson, *J. Biol. Chem.* 225 745 (1957).

[41] H. G. Wijmenga, J. Lens and A. Middlebeek, *Chem. Weekblad* 45 342 (1949); H. G. Wijmenga and B. Hurenkamp, *ibid.* 47 217 (1951); H. G. Wijmenga and W. L. C. Veer, *ibid.* 48 33 (1952); H. G. Wijmenga, K. W. Thompson, K. G. Stern and D. J. O'Connell, *Biochim. et Biophys. Acta* 13 144 (1954); H. G. Wijmenga, J. Lens and S. J. Geerts, *Acta Haematol.* 11 372 (1954).

[42] K. Hausmann, *Lancet* 257 962 (1949); K. Hausmann and K. Mulli, *Acta Haemotol.* 1 345 (1952); *idem.*, *Lancet* 262 185 (1952); K. Hausmann, *Klin. Wochschr.* 31 1017 (1953); K. Hausmann, L. Ludwig and K. Mulli, *Acta Haemotol.* 10 282 (1953); K. Mulli and O. J. Schmid, *Z. Vitamin-, Hormon-u. Fermentforsch.* 8 225 (1956); J. G. Heathcote and F. S. Mooney, *Lancet* 274 982 (1958).

[43] R. D. Williams (Ed.), "The Biochemistry of Vitamin B_{12}," June Lascelles and M. J. Cross, *The function of vitamin B_{12} in microorganisms*, Biochemical Society Symposia No. 13, Cambridge University Press, London, 1955, pp. 109–123.

[44] C. W. Helleiner and D. D. Woods, *Biochem. J.* 63 26p (1956).

[45] J. W. Dubnoff and E. Bartroy, *Arch. Biochem. and Biophys.* 62 86 (1956); Chiun T. Ling and Bacon F. Chow, *J. Biol. Chem.* 206 797 (1954).

Lactobacillus leichmannii they are required for the reduction of formate to the methyl group of thymine by a pathway not involving methionine nor a hydroxymethyl intermediate.[46] In the same organism they have been reported necessary for the synthesis of deoxyribose.[47]

The isolation of actual coenzyme forms of cobamides has permitted more precise determination of some functions which are known to be direct. Barker and collaborators found that cell-free extracts of the anaerobe *Clostridium tetanomorphum* metabolized glutamate in a way different from the citric acid cycle, catalyzing the equilibrium:

$$HOOC-CH_2-CH_2-CH-COOH \rightleftharpoons HOOC-CH-CH-COOH$$

	NH_2		CH_3 NH_2
	Glutamic Acid		β-Methylaspartic Acid

$$HOOC-CH$$
$$\parallel$$
$$CH_3-C-COOH$$

Mesaconic Acid

An orange form of pseudovitamin B_{12} was isolated and found to be required for the first step.[48] (It is noteworthy that β-methylaspartic acid occurs in the polypeptide antibiotic, aspartocin.) The entire nature of this coenzyme is still unknown, but the nucleotide base is known to be adenine. Also a second mole of adenine nucleoside is present, bound in such a way as to affect radically the corphyrin spectrum, and cleavable by photolysis. The nucleoside apparently is attached to cobalt, replacing the cyano group. It contains an unusual sugar.[49]

In this isomerization there are two possible migrating

[46] James L. Dinning, Barbara K. Allen, Ruth Young and Paul L. Day, *J. Biol. Chem.* 233 674 (1958).

[47] Mancourt Downing and B. S. Schweigert, *J. Biol. Chem.* 220 521 (1956); W. T. Wong and B. S. Schweigert, *Proc. Soc. Exptl. Biol. Med.* 94 455 (1957).

[48] H. A. Barker, H. Weissbach and R. D. Smyth, *Proc. Nat. Acad. Sci. U. S.* 44 1093 (1958).

[49] H. A. Barker, R. D. Smyth, H. Weissbach, J. I. Toohey, J. N. Ladd and B. E. Volcani, *J. Biol. Chem.* 235 480 (1960); H. Weissbach, J. N. Ladd, B. E. Volcani, R. D. Smyth and H. A. Barker, *ibid.* 235 1462 (1960); J. N. Ladd, H. P. C. Hogenkamp and H. A. Barker, *Biochem. and Biophys. Res. Comms.* 2 143 (1960).

groups as shown below. A labeling experiment has shown that

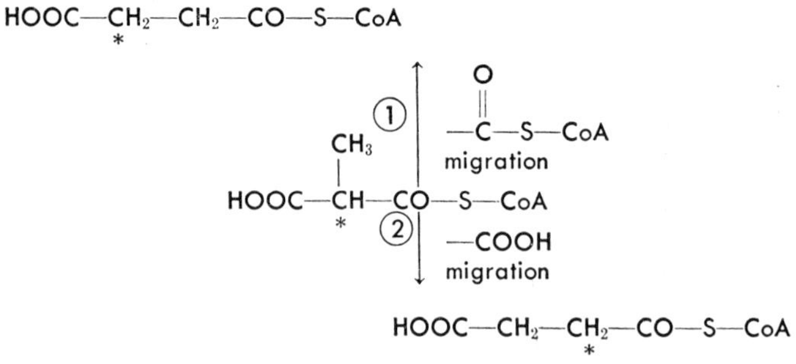
HOOC—CH2—CH2—CO—S—CoA
O
—C—S—CoA
migration
CH3
HOOC—CH—CO—S—CoA
—COOH
migration
HOOC—CH2—CH2—CO—S—CoA

① is the actual process.[50] A free radical mechanism was proposed in which the Co^{+++} of the cobamide coenzyme initiates the one-electron transfer:

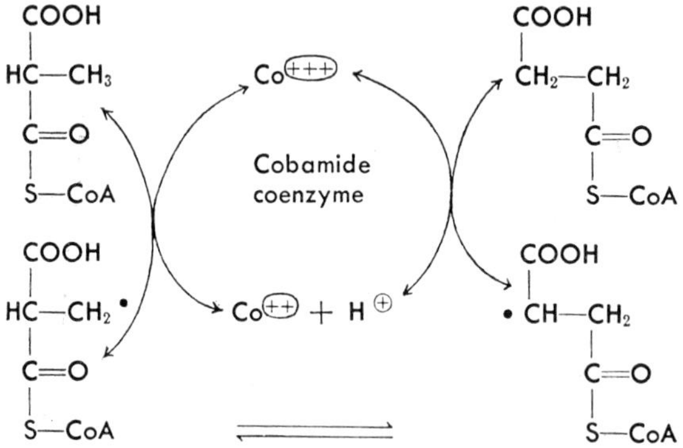
COOH
HC—CH3
C=O
S—CoA
Co+++
Cobamide
coenzyme
COOH
CH2—CH2
C=O
S—CoA
COOH
HC—CH2•
C=O
S—CoA
Co++ + H+
COOH
• CH—CH2
C=O
S—CoA

This is analogous to a rearrangement reported earlier by Urry and Kharasch.[51]

The same organism (*Clostridium tetanomorphum*) was found capable of producing coenzymes containing the benzimidazole and dimethylbenzimidazole forms of vitamin B_{12}.[52] The dimethylbenzimidazole coenzyme has been found[53] to promote the equilibrium rearrangement previously known to exist:[54]

[50] H. Eggerer, P. Overath and F. Lynen, *J. Am. Chem. Soc.* 82 2643 (1960).

[51] W. H. Urry and M. S. Kharasch, *ibid.* **66** 1438 (1944).

[52] H. Weissbach, J. Toohey and H. A. Barker, *Proc. Nat. Acad. Sci.* 45 521 (1959).

[53] E. R. Stadtman, P. Overath, H. Eggerer and F. Lynen, *Biochem. and Biophys. Res. Comms.* 2 1 (1960); Joseph R. Stern and Daniel L. Friedman, *ibid.* 2 82 (1960); Shantov Gurnani, S. P. Mistry and B. Connor Johnston, *Biochim. et Biophys. Acta* 38 187 (1960).

[54] Robert W. Swick and Harland G. Wood, *Proc. Nat. Acad. Sci. U. S.* 46 28 (1960).

$$\underset{\text{Succinyl Coenzyme A}}{\text{HOOC—CH}_2\text{—CH}_2\text{—CO—CoA}} \rightleftharpoons \underset{\text{Methylmalonyl Coenzyme A}}{\text{HOOC—}\overset{\displaystyle CH_3}{\underset{|}{C}}\text{H—CO—CoA}}$$

The final step in the conversion of succinate to propionate is the biotin-dependent decarboxylation:[53]

$$\underset{\text{Methylmalonyl Coenzyme A}}{\text{HOOC—}\underset{\underset{\displaystyle CH_3}{|}}{\text{CH}}\text{—CO—CoA}} \xrightleftharpoons{\quad -CO_2 \quad} \underset{\text{Propionyl Coenzyme A}}{\text{CH}_3\text{—CH}_2\text{—CO—CoA}}$$

The total process can be written:

(1) Acetyl CoA + Succinate $\rightleftharpoons$ Succinyl CoA + Acetate

(2) Succinyl CoA $\xrightleftharpoons{\text{B}_{12} \text{ coenzyme}}$ Methylmalonyl CoA

(3) Methylmalonyl CoA + Biotinenzyme $\rightleftharpoons$ CO$_2$ Biotinenzyme + Propionyl CoA

(4) Propionyl CoA + Acetate $\rightleftharpoons$ Acetyl CoA + Propionate

Perhaps it is significant that propionibacteria are relatively rich sources of vitamin B_{12} and of biotin. This scheme also shows how propionic acid can be oxidized by entry into the carboxylic acid cycle.

The precise mechanism by which these interesting rearrangements are promoted by the B_{12} coenzymes remains to be determined. It has been pointed out[53] that, in effect, what is accomplished is a transpropionation.

A monograph on vitamin B_{12} has been published.[55]

The cytochromes are heme proteins important in electron transport. The most studied is cytochrome c. The commonest source is muscle, but yeast cytochrome c has been crystallized.[56] Classification is made by spectrum, and the proteins are species specific.

The prosthetic group of cytochrome c is protoporphyrin IX bound firmly to the apoenzyme by covalent bonds between the thiol groups of cysteine and the vinyl groups of the porphyrin.[57] Four of the iron coordination bonds are

[55] E. Lester Smith, "Vitamin B$_{12}$," John Wiley & Sons, Inc., New York, 1960.

[56] Bunji Hagihara, Takekazu Horio, Kazuo Okunuki, Jinpei Yamashita and Mitsuhiro Nozaki, *Nature* 178 629 (1956).

[57] K. Zeile and H. Meyer, *Hoppe-Seylers Z. physiol. Chem.* 262 178 (1939); H. Theorell, *Enzymologia* 6 88 (1939); Karl-Gustav Paul, *Acta Chem. Scand.* 5 389 (1951).

to porphyrin nitrogen, the other two to histidyl residues in the protein.

Proteolytic enzyme degradation of cytochrome c has yielded the polypeptide fragment in the vicinity of the porphyrin, and the amino acid sequence has been determined. It is thought to be:[58]

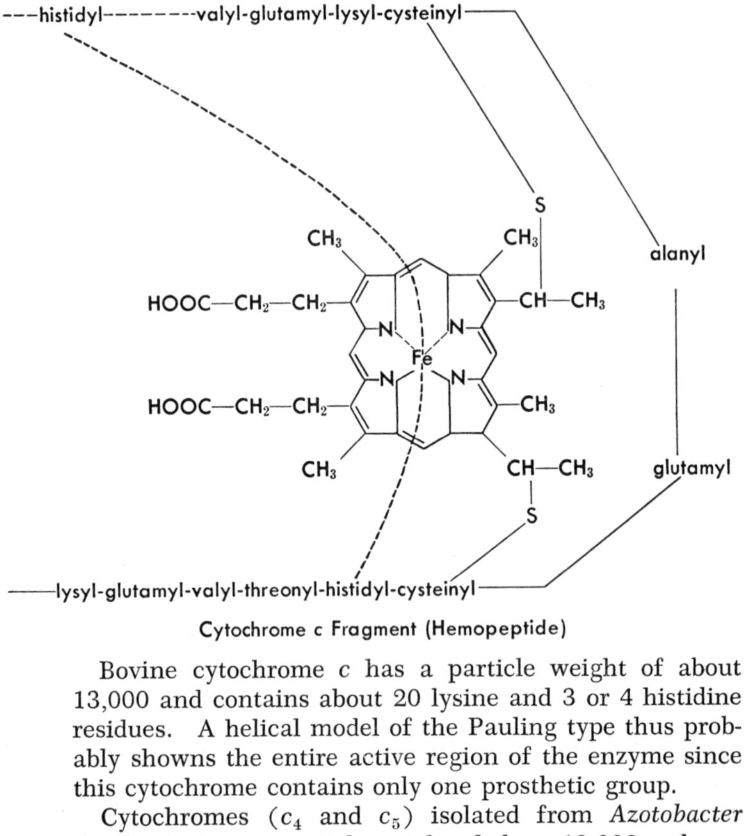

Cytochrome c Fragment (Hemopeptide)

Bovine cytochrome c has a particle weight of about 13,000 and contains about 20 lysine and 3 or 4 histidine residues. A helical model of the Pauling type thus probably showns the entire active region of the enzyme since this cytochrome contains only one prosthetic group.

Cytochromes (c_4 and c_5) isolated from *Azotobacter vinelandii* have a particle weight of about 12,000 and contain 0.46% iron, so that superficially they resemble mammalian cytochrome c.[59] In a comparative study of mammalian and bacterial (*Pseudomonas aeruginosa*) cyto-

[58] Hans Tuppy and G. Bodo, *Monatshefte Chem.* 85 1024, 1182 (1954); Hans Tuppy and Sven Paleus, *Acta Chem. Scand.* 9 353, 365 (1955).

[59] A. Tissieres, *Biochem. J.* 64 582 (1956).

chrome c rather minor spectral differences were noted, but there were gross differences in the amino acid composition of the protein.[60] The prosthetic group of cytochrome a_2 from *Aerobacter aerogenes* has been purified but not crystallized.[61] Strict anaerobes such as clostridia seem to lack cytochromes, and some lactobacilli seem to use flavins instead.

Reviews of the role of cytochromes in electron transport have been published.[62, 63, 64, 65] This process is shown in outline in the accompanying diagram.

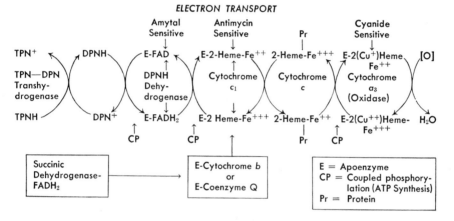

The role of lipides and quinones in electron transport has been discussed.[66] The mechanism of coupled phosphorylation is not understood in detail, but can be represented as follows:

[60] Martin D. Kamen and Yoshiro Takeda, *Biochim. et Biophys. Acta* 21 518 (1956).

[61] J. Barrett, *Biochem. J.* 64 626 (1956).

[62] Albert L. Lehninger, *The Harvey Lectures*, 49 176–215 (1955); *idem., Scientific American* 202 102–118 (1960).

[63] Britton Chance and G. R. Williams, *Advances in Enzymol.* 17 65–130 (1956).

[64] Joseph S. Fruton and Sofia Simmons, "General Biochemistry," John Wiley and Sons, New York, 1958, pp. 284–386.

[65] David E. Green and Johan Jarnefelt, *Perspectives in Biol. and Med.* 2 163–184 (1959).

[66] D. E. Green and R. L. Lester, *Federation Proc.* 18 987–1000 (1959).

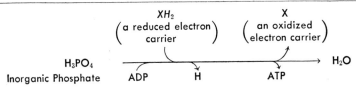

Some electron transport poisons are shown. Many other poisons also act by interfering somehow with the function of the electron transport enzymes.

A lucid, if rather popularized, exposition has been published of the energy relationships in cell respiration, as well as the gross cell structure involved.[67]

913 **Holomycin** (Des-N-methylthiolutin), $C_7H_6O_2N_2S_2$, orange-yellow leaflets, m.p. 264–271° (dec.).

Streptomyces griseus (Krainsky) Waksman et Henrici
L. Ettlinger, E. Gäumann, R. Hütter, W. Keller-Schierlein, F. Kradolfer, L. Neipp, V. Prelog and H. Zähner, *Helv. Chim. Acta* **42** 563 (1959).

914 **Thiolutin** (Acetopyrrothine, Farcinicin), $C_8H_8O_2N_2S_2$, yellow crystals, m.p. 260–270° (dec.).

[67] Albert L. Lehninger, *Scientific American* **202** 102–117 (1960).

Streptomyces albus
Walter D. Celmer, Fred W. Tanner, Jr., M. Harfenist, T. M. Lees and I. A. Solomons, *J. Am. Chem. Soc.* **74** 6304 (1952).
Walter D. Celmer and I. A. Solomons, *ibid.* **77** 2861 (1955). (Structure)

915 **Noformicin,** $C_8H_{15}ON_5$, Dihydrochloride m.p. 265° (dec.), $[\alpha]_D^{25}$ +7.0° (c 1.0 in water).

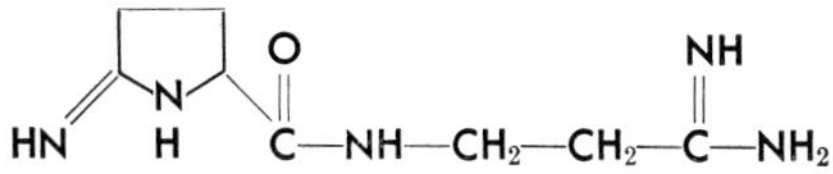

Nocardia formica
Reed A. Gray, *Phytopathology* **45** 281 (1955).
Robert L. Peck, Henry M. Shafer and Frank J. Wolf, U. S. Patent 2,804,463 (1957).

916 **Aureothricin** (Propiopyrrothine), $C_9H_{10}O_2N_2S_2$, yellow crystals, m.p. 256° (dec.).

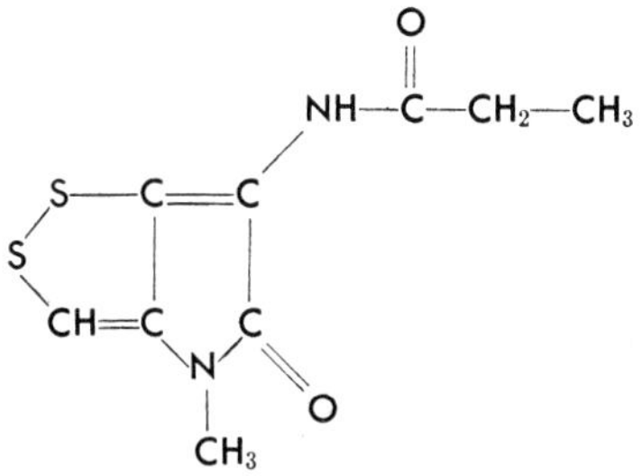

Streptomyces celluloflavus n. sp.
Haruo Nishimura, Toshiaki Kimura and Masa Kuroya, *J. Antibiotics* (Japan) **6A** 57 (1953).
Walter D. Celmer and I. A. Solomons, *J. Am. Chem. Soc.* **77** 2861 (1955). (Structure)

917 **Pyoluteorin,** $C_{11}H_7O_3NCl_2$, m.p. 174° (dec.).
Partial structure:

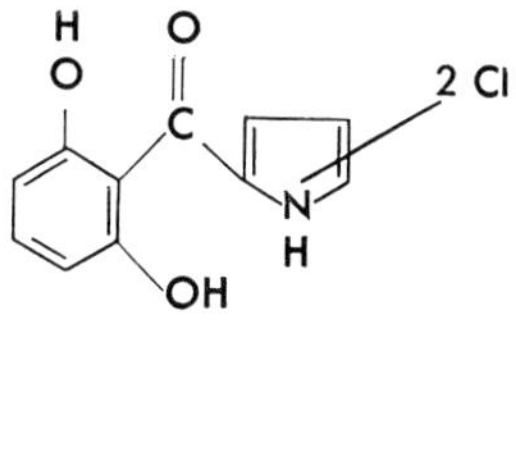

Pseudomonas aeruginosa
Rokuro Takeda, *J. Am. Chem. Soc.* 80 4749 (1958). (Structure)

918 Netropsin (Congocidine, Sinanomycin, T1384), $C_{18}H_{26}O_3N_{10}$, the hydrochloride crystallizes as colorless, hygroscopic prisms, m.p. 168–172° (dec.).

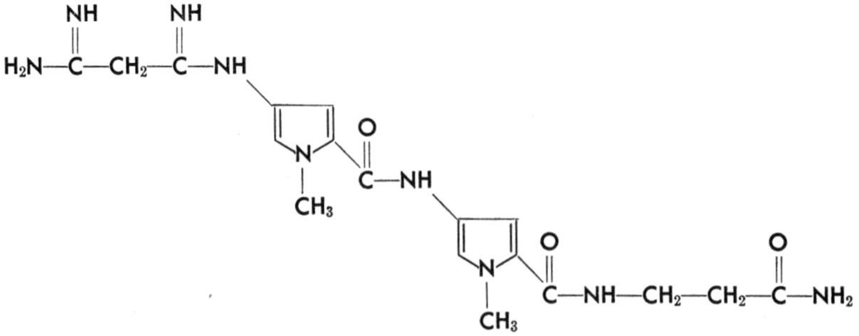

Streptomyces netropsis, S. chromogenes n.sp., *S. ambofaciens* n. sp.
A. C. Finlay, F. A. Hochstein, B. A. Sobin and F. X. Murphy, *J. Am. Chem. Soc.* 73 341 (1951).
E. E. van Tamelen and A. D. G. Powell, *Chem. and Ind.*, 365 (1957). (Structure)

919 Prodigiosin, $C_{20}H_{25}ON_3$, red crystals with a green reflex, m.p. 151.5–152.9° (dec.).
Alternative structures: *

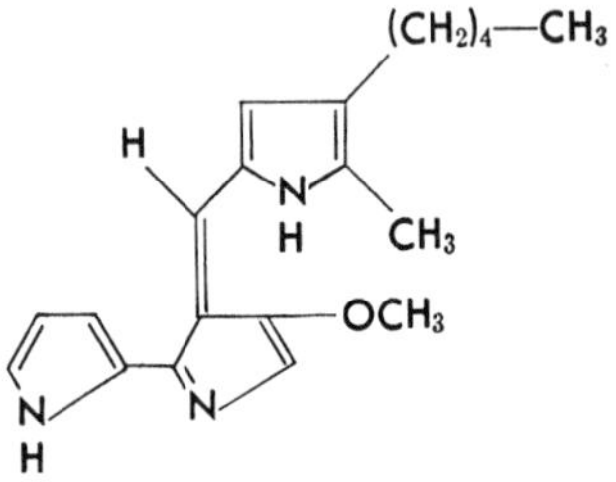

or

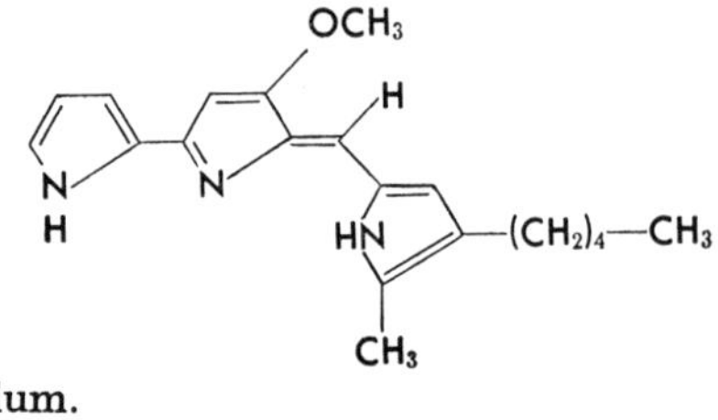

* See addendum.

Serratia marcescens (Bacillus prodigiosum), S. marino-rubrum

Fritz Wrede and Alexander Rothhaas, Z. *physiol. Chem.* **226** 95 (1934).

Other metabolites which have been isolated from cultures of *Serratia marcescens* are:

920   A "prodigiosin precursor," $C_{10}H_{10}O_2N_2$, colorless needles, m.p. > 250° (dec.).

921   A colorless, crystalline compound, not an antibiotic, $C_{34}H_{62}O_{10}N_3$, m.p. 153°.

922   An amide, $C_{24}H_{33}O_2N_7$.
Palmitic acid.
Three other red, one orange and one blue pigments.
A polypeptide, marcescin.
A polysaccharide.
Fritz Wrede and Alexander Rothhaas, Z. *physiol. Chem.* **226** 95 (1934).
Ursula V. Santer and Henry J. Vogel, *Biochim. et Biophys. Acta* 19 578 (1956).
O. M. Efimenko, G. A. Kuznetsova and P. A. Yakimov, *Biokhimiya* 21 416 (1956).
A. J. Castro, J. F. Deck, M. T. Hugo, L. R. Williams and M. R. Zingg, *J. Org. Chem.* 23 1232 (1958).
A. J. Castro, A. H. Corwin, F. J. Waxham and A. L. Beilby, *ibid.* 24 455 (1959).
Doris P. Courington and T. W. Goodwin, *J. Bacteriol.* **70** 568 (1955).
Harry H. Wasserman, James E. McKeon, Lewis Smith and Peter Forgione, *J. Am. Chem. Soc.* 82 506 (1960). (Structure shown above)
A. Treibs and R. Galler, *Angew. Chem.* 70 57 (1958).

923   Celesticetin, $C_{24}H_{36}O_9N_2S$, hygroscopic glass, m.p. (Oxalate): 147–152°, $[\alpha]_D^{24}$ +126.6° (c 0.5 in chloroform), $[\alpha]_D^{24}$ (Oxalate) 106.6° (c 0.5 in water).
Proposed Structure:

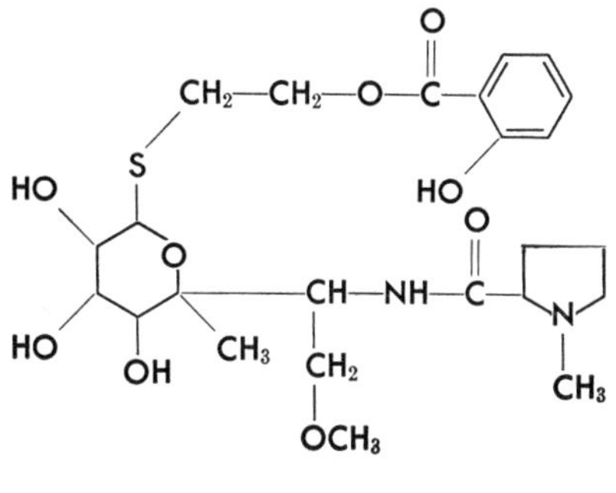

Streptomyces celestis n. sp., resembling *S. glaucus*

C. DeBoer, A. Dietz, J. R. Wilkins, C. N. Lewis and G. M. Savage, "Antibiotics Annual 1954–1955," Medical Encyclopedia, Inc., New York, p. 831.

Herman Hoeksema, Glen F. Crum and William H. DeVries, *ibid*. p. 837.

Clarence DeBoer, Alma Dietz and Herman Hoeksema, U. S. Patent 2,928,844 (1960). (Structure)

924 Prodigiosin-like Pigment, $C_{25}H_{35}ON_3$, orange crystals, partial melting 147–149°, resolidification, melting 203°.

Streptomycete related to *S. ruber* (Krainsky, Waksman and Henrici) and *S. roseodiastaticus*, Waksman and Lechevalier

F. Arcamone, A. DiMarco, M. Ghione and T. Scotti, *Giorn. microbiol.* 4 77 (1957).

925 Hematin, $C_{34}H_{32}O_4N_4Fe^{\oplus}OH^{\ominus}$.

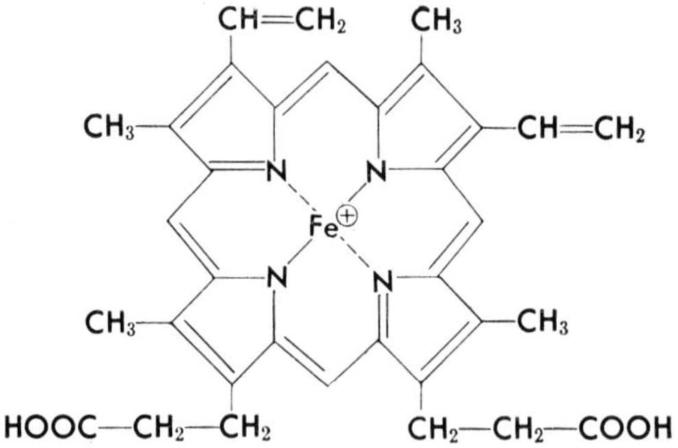

Saccharomyces anamensis

H. Fischer and F. Schwerdtel, *Z. physiol. Chem.* 175 248 (1928).

926 Protoporphyrin, $C_{34}H_{34}O_4N_4$, deep red crystals, m.p. >300°.

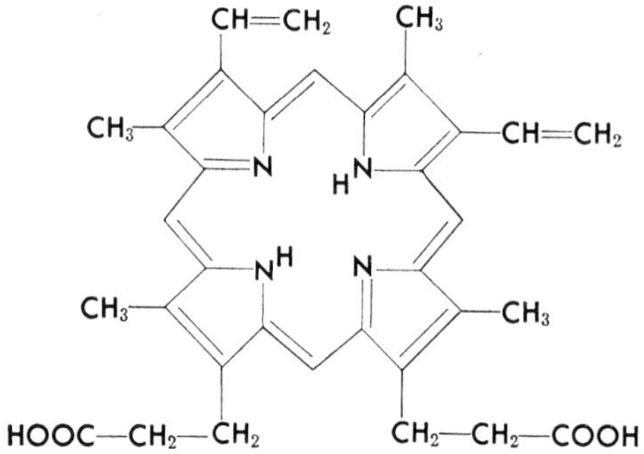

Yeasts, *Rhodopseudomonas spheroides,* other photosynthetic bacteria
    Hans Fischer and Hermann Fink, Z. *physiol. Chem.* **140** 57 (1924).

927 Coproporphyrin I, $C_{36}H_{38}O_8N_4$.

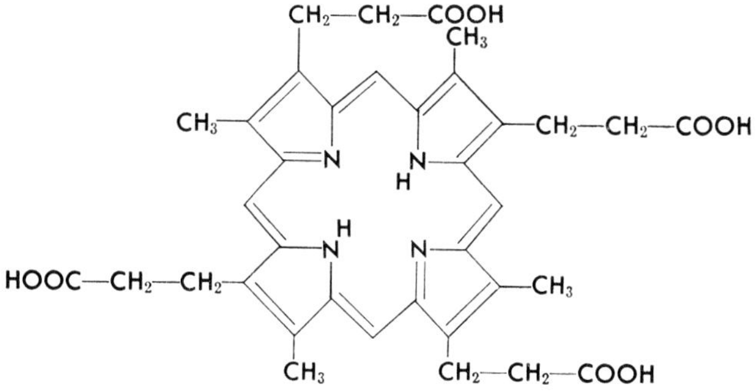

Saccharomyces cerevisiae, S. anamensis, other yeasts, *Aspergillus oryzae,* photosynthetic bacteria
    Hans Fischer and Hermann Fink, Z. *physiol. Chem.* **150** 243 (1925).

928 Coproporphyrin III, $C_{36}H_{38}O_8N_4$, dark red crystals.

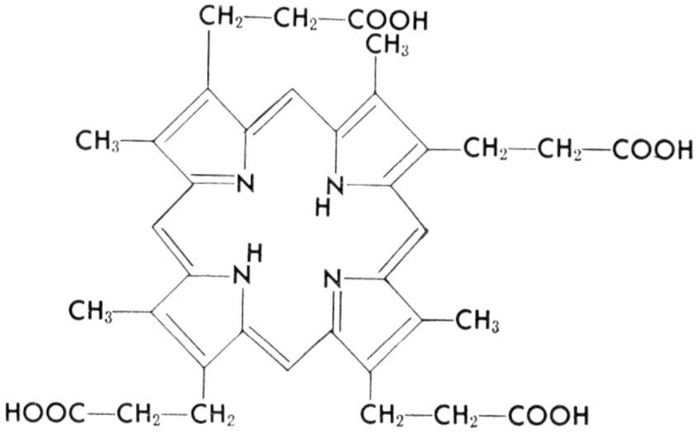

Mycobacterium tuberculosis var. *hominis, Rhodopseudomonas spheroides, Corynebacterium diphtheriae*
    M. O'L. Crowe and A. Walker, *Brit. J. Exptl. Path.* **32** 1 (1951).
    C. M. Todd, *Biochem. J.* **45** 386 (1949).

929   Uroporphyrin III, $C_{40}H_{38}O_{16}N_4$.

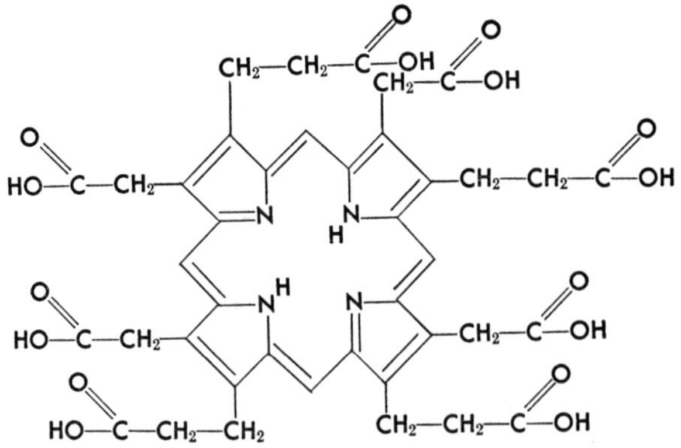

Rhodopseudomonas spheroides

June Lascelles, *Abstracts Gordon Research Conference, Vitamins and Metabolism* (1958). (Detection)

H. Fischer and H.-J. Hofmann, *Z. physiol. Chem.* 246 15 (1937); H. Fischer and A. Müller, *ibid.* 246 31 (1937). (Structure)

930   **Bacteriochlorophyll a,** $C_{55}H_{74}O_6N_4Mg$, amorphous, slow decomposition above 94°.

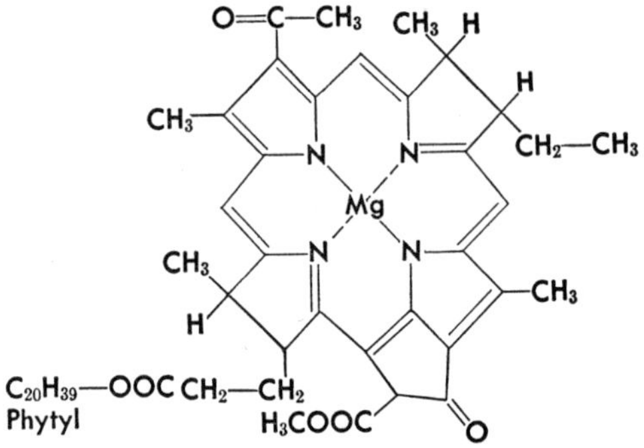

Rhodospirillum rubrum, R. fulvum, Rhodopseudomonas spheroides, Thiocystis violacea, other *Rhodovibrio* spp. and sulfur and chlorobacteria

Hans Fischer and Robert Lambrecht, *Z. physiol. Chem.* 249 1 (1937).

Hans Fischer, Robert Lambrecht and Hellmuth Mittenzwei, *ibid.* 253 1 (1938).

John W. Weigl, *J. Am. Chem. Soc.* 75 999 (1953).

A. Seybold and G. Hirsch, *Naturwissenschaften* 41 258 (1954.)

931 Vitamin B$_{12}$ (Cyanocobalamin, α-(5,6-Dimethylbenzimidazolyl) cobamide cyanide), $C_{63}H_{88}O_{14}N_{14}PCo$, dark red crystals which blacken near 212° and do not melt below 320°, $[\alpha]_{6563}^{23}$ −59 ±9° (dilute aqueous solution).

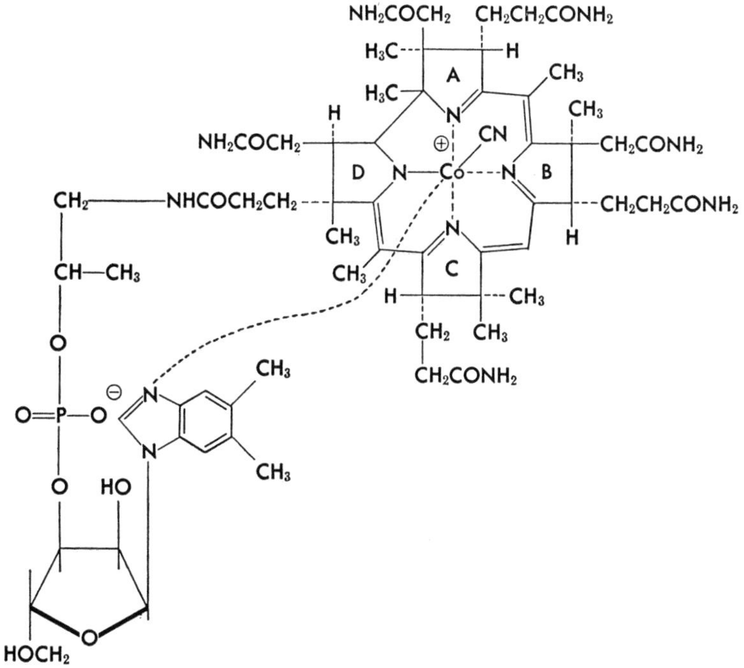

Vitamin B$_{12}$ activity has been detected in fermentation broths from many microorganisms, *e.g. Streptomyces griseus, S. antibioticus, S. roseochromogenes, Mycobacterium smegmatis, Lactobacillus arabinosus,* propionibacteria. Crystalline material has been isolated from some of these. For primary fermentations, *Streptomyces olivaceus* is probably the best producer (3.3 mg. per liter).

Dorothy Crowfoot Hodgkin, Jennifer Kamper, Maureen MacKay and Jenny Pickworth, *Nature* 178 64 (1956). (Structure)

W. H. Sebrell, Jr. and Robert S. Harris, "The Vitamins," Robert S. Harris, Donald E. Wolf, Karl E. Folkers, H. M. Wuest, Thomas H. Jukes and William L. Williams, *Vitamin B$_{12}$,* Academic Press Inc., New York, 1954 Vol. I Chap. 3, pp. 396–524. (A review)

Leland A. Underkofler and Richard J. Hickey, "Industrial Fermentations," Chemical Publishing Co., Inc., New York, 1954 Vol. II, J. M. VanLanen, *Production of vitamins other than riboflavin,* chap. 6, pp. 207–8.

932   Factor B is vitamin B_{12} from which the nucleotide moiety has been removed. It has been isolated from fermentations, from rumen contents, from sewage, and it can be prepared chemically from vitamin B_{12}.

E. Lester Smith, "Vitamin B_{12}," John Wiley and Sons, Inc., New York, 1960, 196 pp. (A monograph)

This monograph also explains the new nomenclature system for B_{12} and related compounds.

Other intermediates in the biosynthesis of vitamin B_{12} by *Propionibacterium shermanii* have been detected:

Konrad Bernhauer, Elisabeth Becher, Gisela Gross and Georg Wilharm, *Biochem. Z.* 332 562 (1960).

K. Bernhauer, Hw. Dellweg, W. Friedrich, G. Gross, F. Wagner and P. Zeller, *Helv. Chim. Acta* 43 693 (1960).

K. Bernhauer, F. Wagner and P. Zeller, *ibid.* 43 696 (1960).

g. INDOLES

The indole nucleus occurs in microorganisms in such forms as tryptophan, one of the less abundant amino acids, in bacterial pigments such as violacein and indigo and in amines from higher fungi such as serotonin and psilocybin, which have strong physiological effects in higher animals. The indole nucleus is incorporated also into bizarre fungal metabolites such as echinulin and gliotoxin, into the mushroom poisons, such as phalloidin, and into the ergot alkaloids listed in the following section.

One route to indole and to tryptophan was outlined in the section on amino acids. This is the pathway discovered by Yanofsky and confirmed and elaborated in his and other laboratories.[1] Anthranilic acid from the shikimic acid route combines with ribose phosphate, cyclization occurs to form the pyrrole ring, a triose phosphate is elimi-

---

[1] C. Yanofsky, *Biochim. et Biophys. Acta* 16 594 (1955); *idem.,* *J. Biol. Chem.* 223 171 (1956); F. Gibson, M. Jones and H. Taltscher, *Biochem. J.* 64 132 (1956); P. A. Trudinger, *ibid.* 62 480 (1956); F. Lingens and H. Hellmann, *Angew. Chem.* 69 97 (1957); L. W. Parks and H. C. Douglas, *Biochim. et Biophys. Acta* 23 207 (1957); J. Gots and S. Ross, *ibid.,* 24 429 (1957); C. Yanofsky and M. Rachmeier, *ibid.* 28 640 (1958).

nated and the indole so formed combines with L-serine to form L-tryptophan:

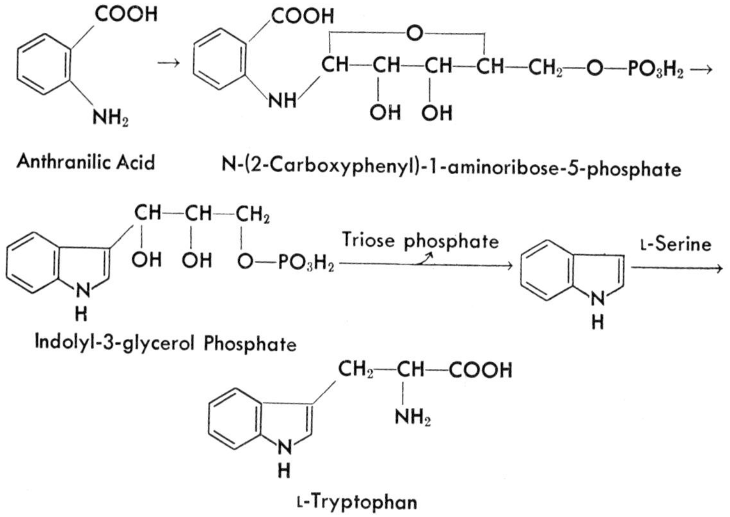

Anthranilic Acid   N-(2-Carboxyphenyl)-1-aminoribose-5-phosphate

Indolyl-3-glycerol Phosphate

L-Tryptophan

N-Fructosylanthranilic acid has been isolated from a yeast, and it may be another intermediate in indole synthesis. In this case a tetrose would be eliminated. If pentoses and hexoses can both be used in reactions with anthranilic acid, perhaps tetroses can be as well. This possibility is emphasized by Wenkert[2] in a discussion of alkaloid biosynthesis. A reaction of this sort might explain the frequent occurrence in nature of indole derivatives with two carbon atom side-chains in the 3-position. In other words the indole biosynthesis could be generalized:

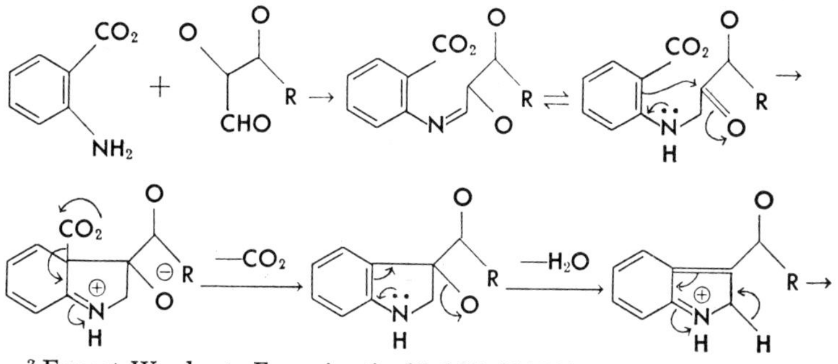

[2] Ernest Wenkert, *Experientia* **15** 165 (1959).

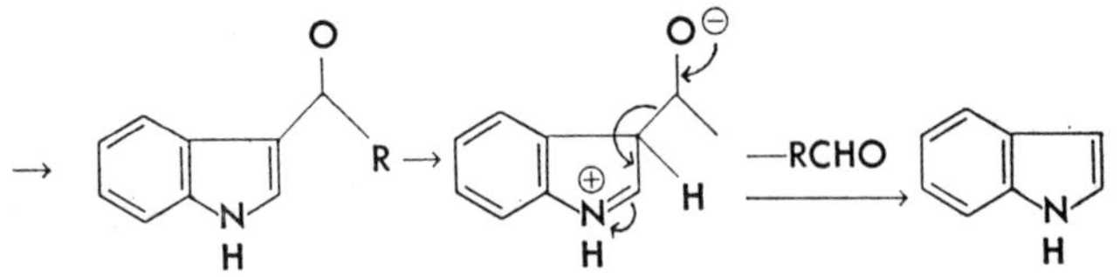

in which R—CH—CH—CHO is any of several sugars.
      | |
      OH OH

It may be that other derivatives of anthranilic acid can participate in this route, too. For example 5-hydroxyanthranilic acid would give rise to the 5-oxyindole derivatives found in nature. It is notable that this acid is a growth promoter for an *Escherichia coli* mutant.[3]

Ascorbigen, a bound form of ascorbic acid isolated from plants of the cabbage family, has one of the structures:[4]

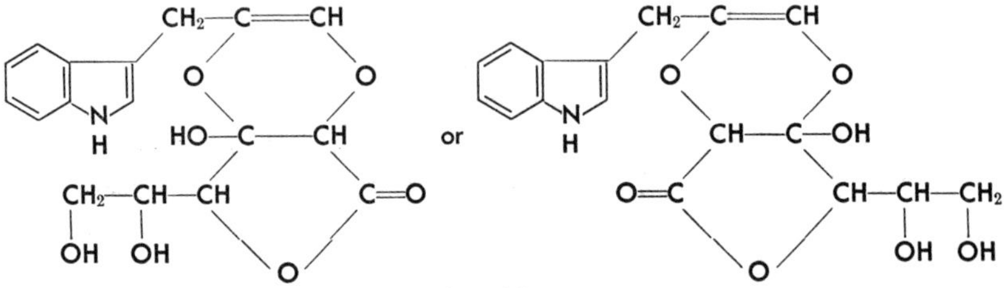

Ascorbigen
(alternate structures)

The presumptive precursor is 3-indolylacetol, analogous to an intermediate in histidine biosynthesis, and it is interesting to speculate as to whether this is an offshoot of the biosynthetic route to tryptophan or whether it is formed by way of tryptophan.

The mold product, echinulin, has an unusual structure, apparently involving the indole synthesis, terpenoid and amino acid precursors. Gliotoxin, on the other hand, is almost entirely derived from amino acids, and it could have been classified as a polypeptide. C^{14}-Labeling studies have demonstrated the following biosynthetic pathway for gliotoxin:[5]

[3] H. Niemer and A. Oberdorfer, Z. *physiol. Chem.* **308** 51 (1957).
[4] Z. Prochazka, V. Sanda and F. Sorm, *Coll. Czech. Chem. Comm.* **22** 654 (1957).
[5] J. A. Winstead and R. J. Suhadolnik, *J. Am. Chem. Soc.* **82** 1644 (1960); R. J. Suhadolnik, A. Fischer and J. Wilson, *Federation Proc.* **19** 8 (1960).

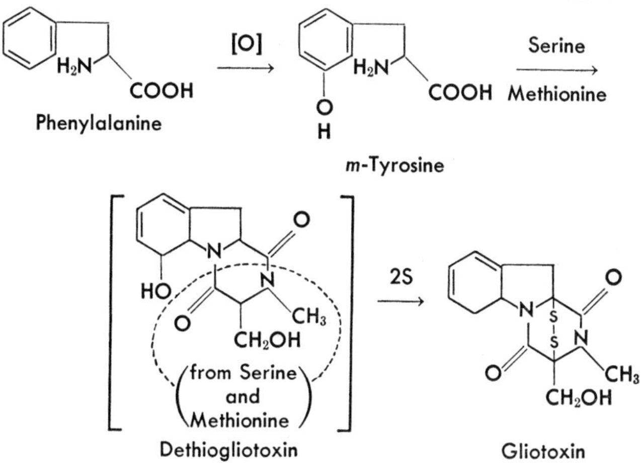

Phenylalanine → [O] → m-Tyrosine → Serine / Methionine

Dethiogliotoxin → 2S → Gliotoxin

Methionine was the most efficient source of the N-methyl group, the β-carbon of serine being about one third as effective. Both of the amino acid skeletons were incorporated intact when furnished, and m-tyrosine could also be used as a precursor.

933   **Indole**, C_8H_7N, colorless leaflets, m.p. 52°.

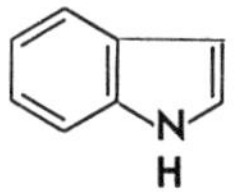

Escherichia coli mutants, yeasts, *Treponema* spp.
P. A. Trudinger, *Biochem. J.* 62 480 (1956).
Charles Yanofsky, *J. Biol. Chem.* 223 171 (1956).
F. Gibson, Marjorie J. Jones and H. Teltscher, *Biochem. J.* 64 132 (1957).
L. W. Parks and H. C. Douglas, *Biochim. et Biophys. Acta* 23 207 (1957).
Michel Moureau and W. Aladame, *Ann. inst. Pasteur* 88 231 (1955).

934   **Indole-3-acetic Acid** (Rhizopin), $C_{10}H_9O_2N$, colorless plates, m.p. 164°.

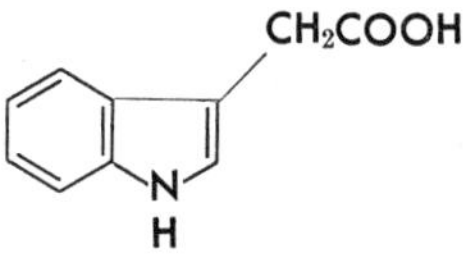

Rhizopus suinus, R. nigricans, Aspergillus niger, Peni-

cillium notatum, Absidia ramosa, Boletus edulis, Yeasts
Niels Nielsen, *Biochem. Z.* 237 244 (1931); 249 196 (1932).
Fritz Kögl and D. G. F. R. Kostermans with A. J. Haagen-
Smit and H. Erxleben, Z. *physiol. Chem.* 228 113 (1934).
Kenneth V. Thimann, *J. Biol. Chem.* 109 279 (1935).
Donald J. Cram and Max Tishler, *J. Am. Chem. Soc.* 70
4238 (1948). (Isolation)
Ryuichi Honda, Japanese Patent 603 (1950).

935 **Serotonin** (5-Hydroxytryptamine), $C_{10}H_{12}ON_2$ (Hydrochloride),
colorless crystals, m.p. 167°.

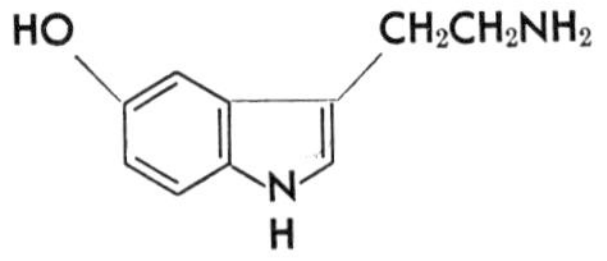

Panaeolus campanulatus
Demonstrated by paper chromatography only.
Varro E. Taylor, Jr., *Science* 128 718 (1958).

936 **Psilocin,** $C_{12}H_{16}ON_2$, colorless crystals, m.p. 173–176° (dec.).

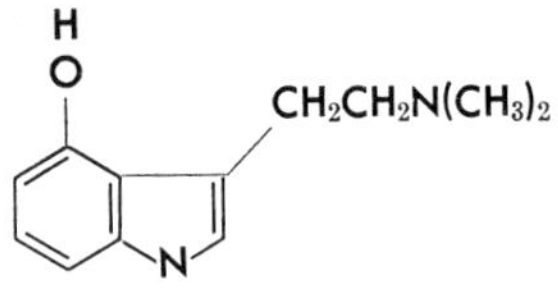

Psilocybe species
Psilocin is a minor constituent of the mushrooms which
contain psilocybin.
A. Hofmann and F. Troxler, *Experientia* 15 101 (1959).

937 **Psilocybin,** $C_{12}H_{17}O_4N_2P$, colorless crystals, m.p. 185–195°
(dec.).

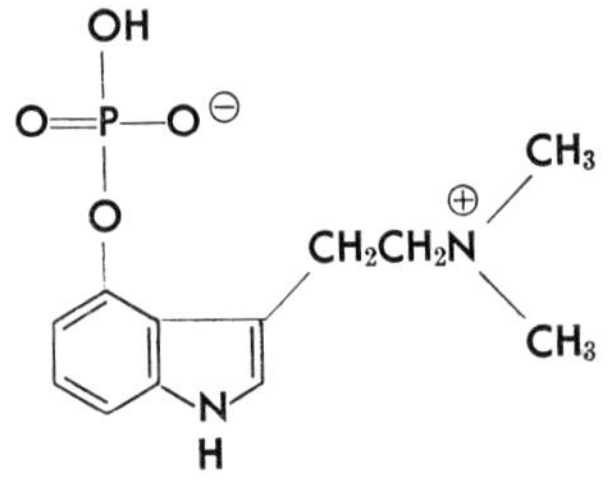

Psilocybe mexicana Heim, *P. caerulescens* Murr. var.
Mazecatorum Heim, *P. aztecorum* Heim, *P. sempervirens*
Heim et Cailleux, *P. zapotecorum* Heim, *Stropharia cubensis* Earle

A. Hofmann, R. Heim, A. Brack and H. Kobel, *Experientia*
14 107 (1958).

A. Hofman, A. Frey, H. Ott, Th. Petrzilka and F. Troxler,
ibid. **14** 397 (1958). (Synthesis)

938 Gliotoxin (Aspergillin), $C_{13}H_{14}O_3N_2S_2$, m.p. 195° (dec.), $[\alpha]_D^{25}$
−290° ±10° (c 0.078 in ethanol).

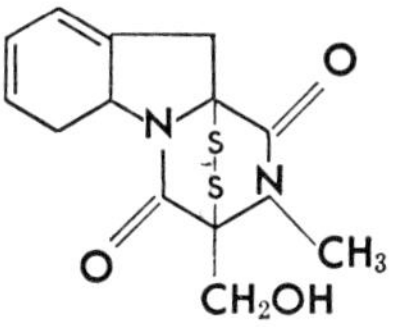

*Trichoderma viride, Aspergillus fumigatus, Penicillium
terlikowski* Zaleski, *P. cinerascens, P. jenseni, Gliocladium
fimbriatum*

The yield of gliotoxin and its acetate from *P. terlikowski*
Zaleski was reported as about 100 mg. per liter.

John R. Johnson, William F. Bruce and James D. Dutcher,
J. Am. Chem. Soc. **65** 2005 (1943) and other papers in this
series.

Malcolm R. Bell, John R. Johnson, Bernard S. Wildi and
R. B. Woodward, *J. Am. Chem. Soc.* **80** 1001 (1958). (Structure)

939 Gliotoxin Acetate, $C_{15}H_{16}O_5N_2S_2$, pale yellow rhombic crystals,
m.p. 159°, $[\alpha]_D^{19}$ −197° (c 0.600 in chloroform).

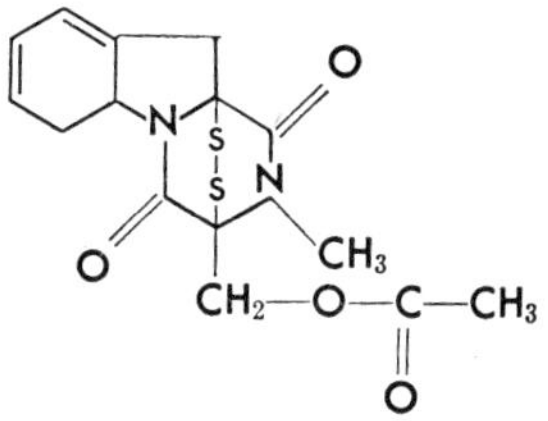

Penicillium terlikowski Zaleski

John R. Johnson, Aklaq R. Kidwai and John S. Warner, *J.
Am. Chem. Soc.* **75** 2110 (1953).

940 **Indigo**, $C_{16}H_{10}O_2N_2$, blue powder with a coppery luster, sublimes.

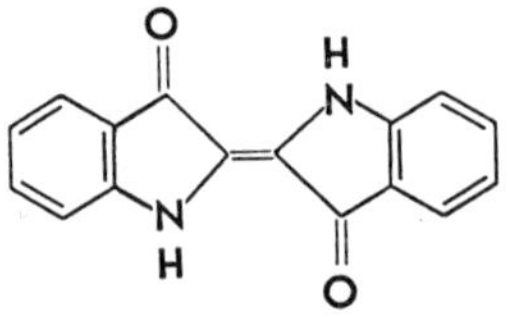

Schizophyllum commune mutant
Ammonium ion was the only nitrogen source.
Philip G. Miles, Henning Lund and John R. Raper, *Arch. Biochem. and Biophys.* 62 1 (1956).

941 **Chetomin**, $C_{16}H_{17}O_4N_3S_2$ (proposed), amorphous white powder, m.p. 218–220° (dec.), [α]$_D^{22}$ +360° (c 1 in chloroform).
A neutral compound. Positive indole, Hopkins-Cole, negative biuret, Millon.
Chaetomium cochlioides
Walton B. Geiger, Jean E. Conn and Selman A. Waksman, *J. Bacteriol.* 48 531 (1944). (Isolation)
Walton B. Geiger, *Arch. Biochem.* 21 125 (1949).

942 **Violacein**, $C_{20}H_{13}O_3N_3$, violet-black microcrystals, m.p. >350° (dec.).

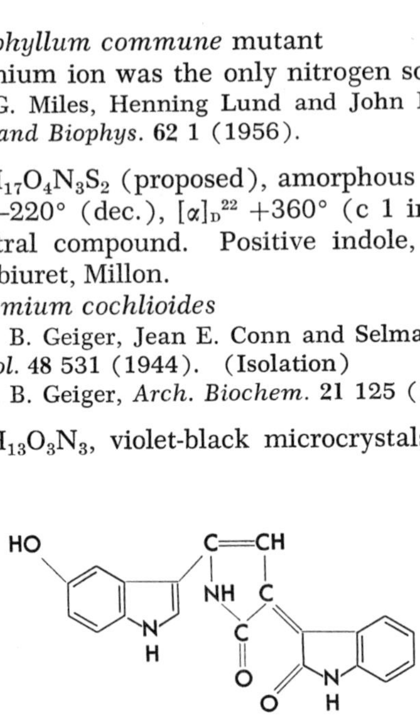

Chromobacterium violaceum
F. M. Strong, *Science* 100 287 (1944).
R. T. S. Beer, *Angew. Chem.* 69 676 (1957).
J. A. Ballantine, C. B. Barrett, R. J. S. Beer, B. G. Boggiano, K. Clarke, Stephen Eardley, B. E. Jennings and Alexander Robertson, *J. Chem. Soc.*, 2222 (1957) and preceding papers in this series.
J. A. Ballantine, R. T. S. Beer, D. J. Crutchley, G. M. Dodd and D. R. Palmer, *J. Chem. Soc.*, 2292 (1960). (Synthesis)
R. D. Demoss and N. R. Evans, *J. Bacteriol.* 79 729 (1960). (Biosynthesis)

943   **Echinulin**, $C_{28}H_{37}O_2N_3$, white needles, m.p. 242°.
      Probable structure:

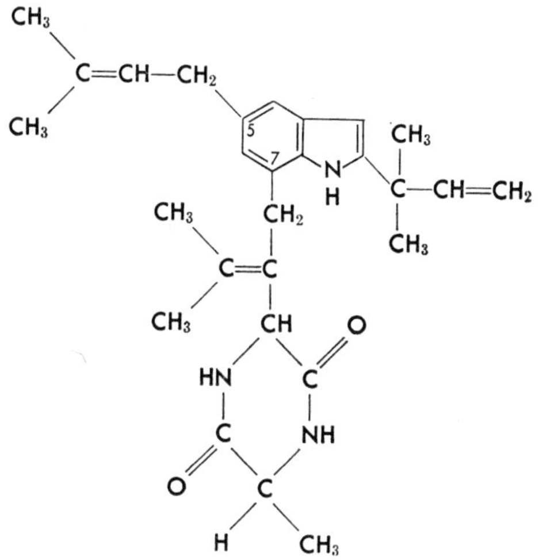

Aspergillus glaucus types, A. echinulatus, A. chevalieri
About 200 g. of pure material were obtained from 5 kg.
of dry mycelium.   Auroglaucin and flavoglaucin were
isolated from the same source.

A. Quilico and L. Panizzi, *Ber.* **76B** 348 (1943).   (Isolation)

Adolfo Quilico, Cesare Cardini and Franco Piozzi, *Gazz.
Chim. ital.* **86** 211 (1956).   (Structure)

Ziro Kitamura, Uzukiko Kurimoto and Matatsugu Yoko-
yama, *J. Pharm. Soc. Japan* **76** 972 (1956).

C. Cardani, G. Casnati, F. Piozzi and A. Quilico, *Tetrahedron
Letters* No. 16 1 (1959).   (Structure)

h. ERGOT ALKALOIDS

The constituents of the sclerotia of the fungus *Claviceps
purpurea* (Fries) Tul., a cereal parasite, have been extensively studied.   Some of the alkaloids are used in medicine
for their oxytocic properties and to relieve migraine.

Ergocristine, ergokryptine and ergocornine (and their
isomers) constitute a closely related complex formerly
thought to be homogeneous and called ergotoxine.   Besides the alkaloids which are shown in the succeeding

pages, many other chemicals have been identified. Among them are:

Ergothioneine	Leucine	Clavicepsin
Histidine	Ammonia	Ergosterol
Tyrosine	Methylamine	Oils
Betaine	Trimethylamine	Lactic Acid
Choline	Ethylamine	Succinic Acid
Acetylcholine	n-Propylamine	Oxalic Acid
Cadaverine	iso-Propylamine	Citric Acid
Putrescine	iso-Butylamine	Formic Acid
Agmatine	iso-Amylamine	Ethanol
Histamine	n-Hexylamine	Furfural
Tyramine	β-Phenylethylamine	Acetaldehyde
Valine	Mannitol	Acetone
		Ergoflavine and other pigments

Careful work has shown that many of the alkaloids produced in the natural state can be produced in artificial culture as well.[1, 2, 3] Total alkaloid yields of 1000–1500 mg. per liter of culture fluid have been obtained exclusive of mycelial alkaloids.[1]

The conventional ergot alkaloids contain the lysergic acid moiety I or isolysergic acid, the stereoisomer at position 8.

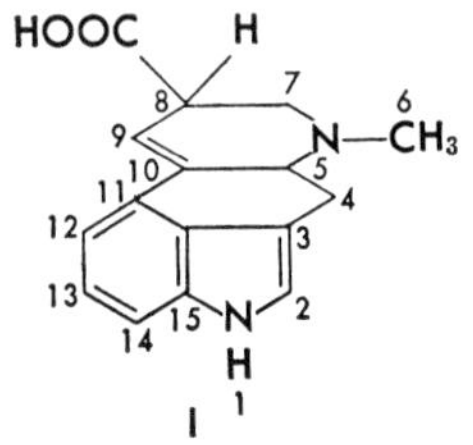

[1] A. Hofmann, R. Brunner, H. Kobel and A. Brack, *Helv. Chim. Acta* **40** 1358 (1957).

[2] W. A. Taber and L. C. Vining, *Can. J. Microbiol.* **3** 55 (1957).

[3] Ervin Gláz, *Acta Pharm. Hung.* **25** 11 (1955).

A number of different hypotheses have been advanced concerning the biosynthetic origin of the ergot alkaloids. These are outlined below:

(1) van Tamelen (1953):[4]

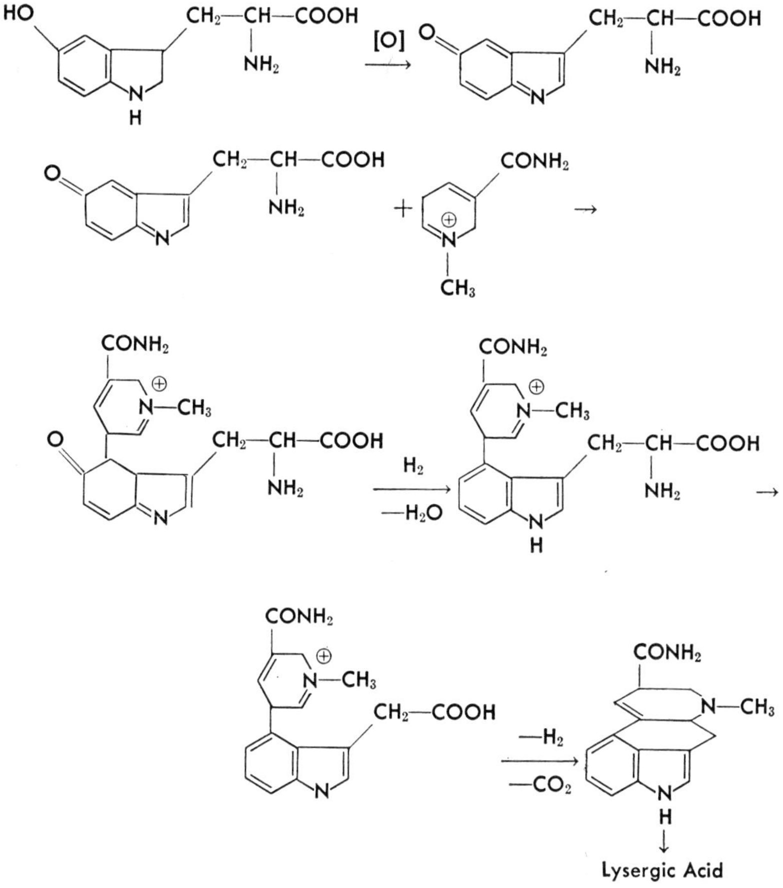

HO [indoline ring] $CH_2-CH-COOH$, NH_2 $\xrightarrow{[O]}$ O= [indole ring] $CH_2-CH-COOH$, NH_2

O= [indole ring] $CH_2-CH-COOH$, NH_2 +   [pyridinium ring] $CONH_2$, $N^{\oplus}$, CH_3 $\rightarrow$

[dihydropyridine ring $CONH_2$, $N^{\oplus}-CH_3$] O= [indole ring] $CH_2-CH-COOH$, NH_2 $\xrightarrow[-H_2O]{H_2}$ [ring $CONH_2$, $N^{\oplus}-CH_3$] [indole ring H] $CH_2-CH-COOH$, NH_2 $\rightarrow$

[ring $CONH_2$, $N^{\oplus}-CH_3$] [indole ring] CH_2-COOH $\xrightarrow[-CO_2]{-H_2}$ [ring system $CONH_2$, $N-CH_3$, indole N H]

Lysergic Acid

$\oplus$

(2) Harley-Mason (1954):[5]

[4] Eugene van Tamelen, *Experientia* 9 457 (1953).
[5] J. Harley-Mason, *Chem. and Ind.*, 251 (1954).

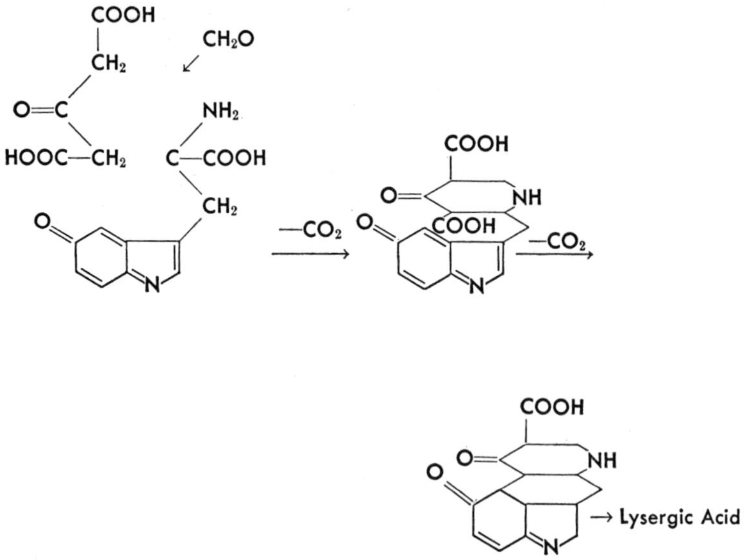
CH_2O
$-CO_2$
$-CO_2$
→ Lysergic Acid

(3) Wendler (1954):[6]

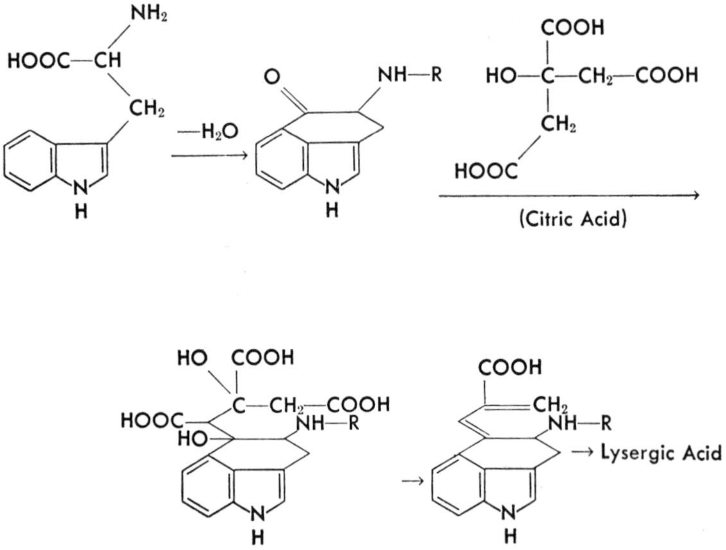
$-H_2O$
(Citric Acid)
→ Lysergic Acid

[6] N. L. Wendler, *Experientia* **10** 338 (1954).

(4) Robinson (1955):[7]

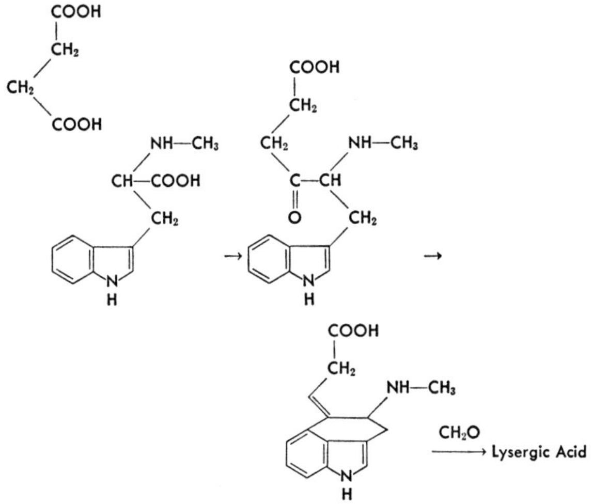

COOH
|
CH₂
|
CH₂
|
COOH

NH—CH₃
|
CH—COOH
|
CH₂

→

COOH
|
CH₂
|
CH₂
|
C—CH—NH—CH₃
‖ |
O   CH₂

→

COOH
|
CH₂
|
CH—NH—CH₃
|
CH₂

CH₂O
———→ Lysergic Acid

(5) Feldstein (1956):[8]

NH₂
/
HOOC—CH
|
CH₂

→

O   NH₂
‖
(ring)

α-Keto-
———→
glutaric Acid

COOH
|
O   CH₂
‖ |
HOOC—C—C   NH₂

—CO₂
———→

COOH
|
CH₂
|
HOOC—C   NH₂

CH₂O
———→ Lysergic Acid
—CO₂
+CH₃

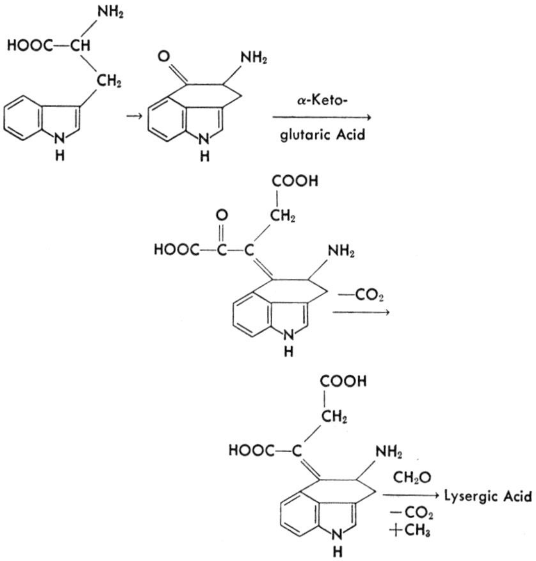

[7] Sir Robert Robinson, "The Structural Relations of Natural Products," Oxford University Press, Oxford, 1955.
[8] A. Feldstein, *Experientia* 12 475 (1956).

(6) Birch (1958),[9] Mothes, *et al.* (1958):[10]

Each of these hypotheses has had its votaries, but now experimental work is beginning to accumulate. There have been conflicting results, partly because some experimenters have injected labeled precursors into infected rye plants, while others added them to cultures grown on artificial medium.

The 5-hydroxytryptophan proposals have been criticized[7] because no 5-hydroxyindole analogues of lysergic acid have been found in nature, and because (obviously the devices of organic chemists) they suffer from some rather improbable biological intermediates. Brady has found that in artificial culture tryptophan was an efficient precursor for the clavine alkaloids, while 5-hydroxytryptophan was not.[11]

By using parasitic cultures one group reported good incorporation of β-C^{14}-tryptophan,[10] while another reported[12] only weak labeling of the alkaloids isolated from the sclerotia.

By use of a cell homogenate technique, it was found that alanine and phenylalanine were incorporated into ergotamine and the ergotoxine complex, but not into ergonovine, which suggests that these amino acids are precursors of the peptide structure of the water-insoluble

[9] G. E. Wolstenholme and Cecilia M. O'Connor, CIBA Foundation Symposium on "Amino Acids and Peptides with Antimetabolic Activity," A. J. Birch and Herchel Smith, *Oxidative formation of biologically active compounds from peptides,* Little, Brown and Co., Boston, 1958, pp. 254–256.

[10] K. Mothes, F. Weygand, D. Gröger and H. Grisebach, Z. *Naturforsch.* 13b 41 (1958).

[11] Lynn Robert Brady, *Dissertation Abstr.* 20 2526 (1960).

[12] R. J. Suhadolnik, L. M. Henderson, J. B. Hanson and Y. H. Loo, *J. Am. Chem. Soc.* 80 3153 (1958).

ergot alkaloids.[13] C_{14}-Labeled indole and serine, alone or together, were not incorporated.

Another artificial culture study in which the *Claviceps purpurea* culture was grown saprophytically on a simple galactose, ammonium succinate, mineral salts, biotin medium to which D,L-β-C^{14}-tryptophan was added, found that the tryptophan was an efficient precursor.[14] Labeling was about the same throughout the range of alkaloids isolated, thus suggesting a common biogenesis. Supplementation with L-tryptophan increased the yield and caused the formation of elymoclavine and agroclavine, which were not formed otherwise.

Another (non-tracer) experiment in artificial culture showed no increase in total alkaloid production on supplementation with either tryptophan, hydroxytryptophan, indole, 5-hydroxyindole or serotonin.[15]

The consensus of the labeling experiments seems to be, however, that tryptophan is a rather direct precursor of the lysergic acid skeleton.

Apparently there is no good evidence yet concerning the origin of the remainder of the skeleton. The isoprenoid precursor hypothesis is under investigation.[9, 16] This proposal is buttressed by the structure of the mold metabolite, echinulin, which has an indole nucleus bearing isoprenoid attachments.

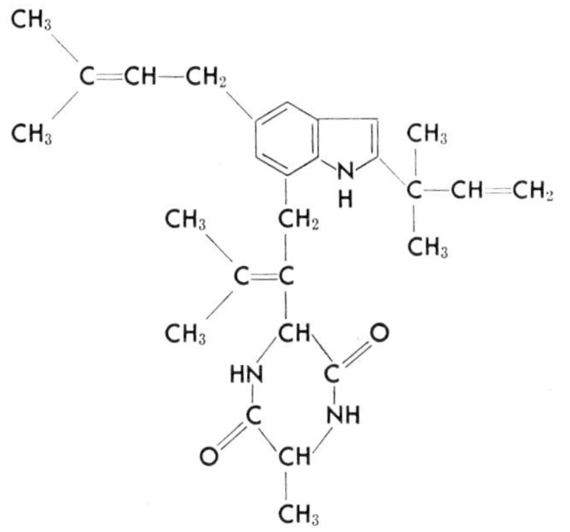

Echinulin

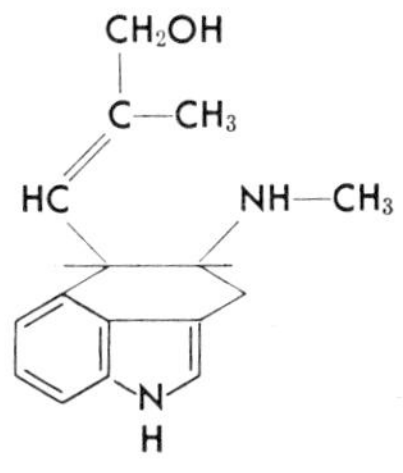

Chanoclavine

[13] Aro Garo Paul, *Dissertation Abstr.* 17 2143 (1957).

[14] W. A. Taber and L. C. Vining, *Chem. and Ind.* 1218 (1959).

[15] Ross M. Baxter, S. I. Kandel and A. Okany, *Nature* 185 241 (1960).

[16] A. J. Birch, B. J. McLoughlin and Herchel Smith, *Tetrahedron Letters* No. 7 1 (1960).

It is also supported by the structure of chanoclavine, which seems to be not too remotely derived from such an intermediate.

A thorough review of the chemistry of the ergot alkaloids has been published.[17]

944 **Agroclavine,** $C_{16}H_{18}N_2$, colorless crystals, m.p. 210–212° (dec.), $[\alpha]_D^{20}$ −183° (c 1 in pyridine).

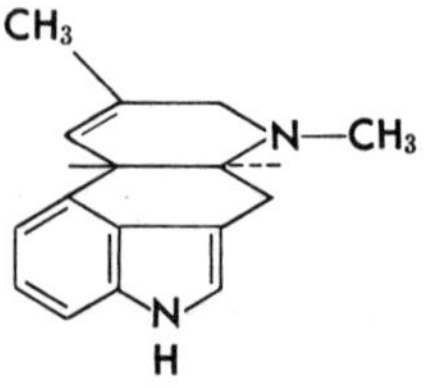

Claviceps purpurea (Fries) Tul.
A. Hofmann, R. Brunner, H. Kobel and A. Brack, *Helv. Chim. Acta* 40 1358 (1957).

945 **Setoclavine,** $C_{16}H_{18}ON_2$, colorless crystals, m.p. 229–234° (dec.), $[\alpha]_D^{20}$ +174° (c 1 in pyridine).

946 **Isosetoclavine** (Triseclavine), $C_{16}H_{18}ON_2$ (stereoisomer of setoclavine), colorless crystals, m.p. 234–237° (dec.), $[\alpha]_D^{20}$ +107° (c 1 in pyridine).

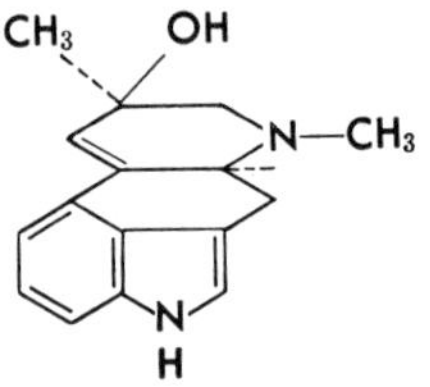

Clavicepts purpurea (Fries) Tul.
A. Hofmann, R. Brunner, H. Kobel and A. Brack, *Helv. Chim. Acta* 40 1358 (1957).

[17] Arthur Stoll, *Fortschr. Chem. org. Naturstoffe* 9 114–170 (1952).

947   **Elymoclavine,** $C_{16}H_{18}ON_2$, colorless crystals, m.p. 245–247° (dec.), $[\alpha]_D^{20}$ −152° (c 1 in pyridine).

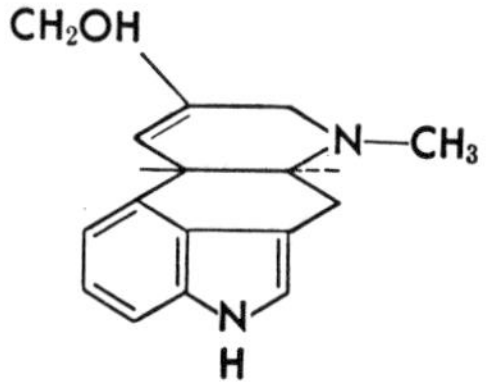

Claviceps purpurea (Fries) Tul.
A. Hofmann, R. Brunner, H. Kobel and A. Brack, *Helv. Chim. Acta* **40** 1358 (1957).

948   **Penniclavine,** $C_{16}H_{18}O_2N_2$, colorless crystals, m.p. 222–225° (dec.), $[\alpha]_D^{20}$ +153° (c 1 in pyridine).

949   **Isopenniclavine,** $C_{16}H_{18}O_2N_2$ (stereoisomer of penniclavine), colorless crystals, m.p. 163–165° (dec.), $[\alpha]_D^{20}$ +146° (c 1 in pyridine).

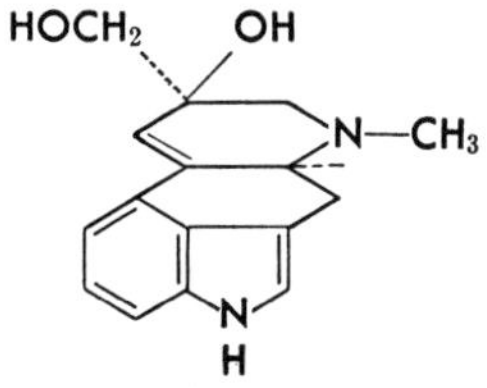

Claviceps purpurea (Fries) Tul.
A. Hofmann, R. Brunner, H. Kobel and A. Brack, *Helv. Chim. Acta* **40** 1358 (1957).

950   **Dihydroagroclavine** (Festuclavine), $C_{16}H_{20}N_2$, colorless crystals, m.p. 242° (dec.), $[\alpha]_D^{20}$ −69° (c 0.5 in chloroform).

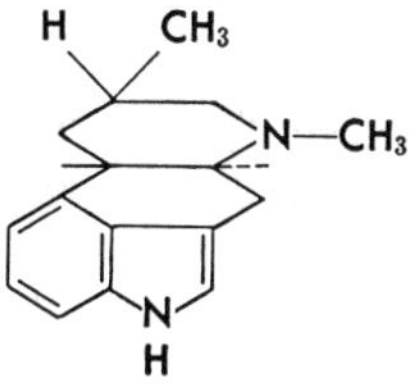

Claviceps purpurea (Fries) Tul.

Matazo Abe, *Ann. Rept. Takeda Res. Lab.* 10 73, 83, 90, 110, 126, 129, 145, 152, 167, 171, 179, 190, 205, 210 (1951).

Matazo Abe, Togo Yamano, Yoshiharu Kôzu and Mitsugu Kusumoto, *J. Agr. Chem. Soc. Japan* 24 416, 471 (1951); 25 458 (1952); 27 18, 613, 617 (1953).

Matazo Abe *ibid.* 28 44, 501 (1954).

Matazo Abe, Togo Yamano, Yochiharu Kozu and Mitsugi Kusumoto, *ibid.* 29 364 (1955).

Matazo Abe, Saburo Yamatodani, Togo Yamano and Mitsugi Kusumoto, *Bull. Agr. Chem. Soc.* (Japan) 19 92 (1955).

Saburo Yamatodani and Matazo Abe, *ibid.* 19 94 (1955).

951 **Pyroclavine,** $C_{16}H_{20}N_2$, colorless crystals, m.p. 204° (dec.), $[\alpha]_D^{20}$ −90° (c 0.2 in pyridine).

and

952 **Costaclavine,** $C_{16}H_{20}N_2$, colorless crystals, m.p. 182° (dec.), $[\alpha]_D^{20}$ +44° (c 0.2 in pyridine).

These are thought to be isomers of dihydroagroclavine.

Claviceps purpurea (Fries) Tul.

Matazo Abe, Saburo Yamatodani, Togo Yamano and Mitsugi Kusumoto, *Bull. Agr. Chem. Soc.* (Japan) 20 59 (1956).

953 **Dihydroelymoclavine,** $C_{16}H_{20}ON_2$, colorless crystals, m.p. 210° (dec.), $[\alpha]_D^{28}$ −167° (c 0.16 in chloroform).

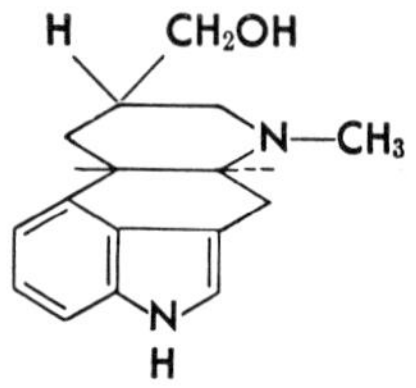

Claviceps purpurea (Fries) Tul.

See references under dihydroagroclavine.

954 Chanoclavine (Secaclavine), $C_{16}H_{20}ON_2$, colorless crystals, m.p. 220–222° (dec.), $[\alpha]_D^{20}$ −240° (c 1 in pyridine).

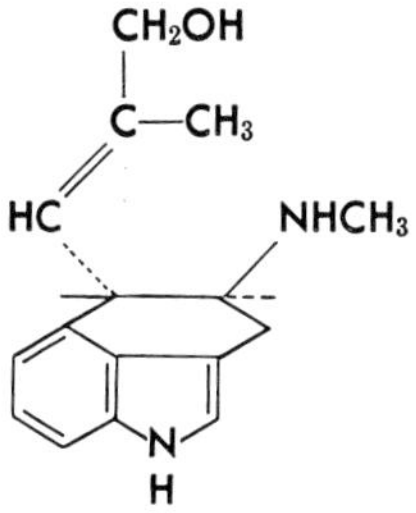

$$CH_2OH$$
$$|$$
$$C-CH_3$$

HC   NHCH₃

N
H

Claviceps purpurea (Fries) Tul.
A. Hofmann, R. Brunner, H. Kobel and A. Brack, *Helv. Chim. Acta* 40 1358 (1957).

Matazo Abe, Togo Yamano, Saburo Yamatodani, Yoshiharu Kozu, Mitsugi Kusumoto, Hajime Komatsu and Saburo Yamada, *Bull. Agr. Chem. Soc.* (Japan) 23 246 (1959).

955 Ergobasine (Ergometrine, Ergonovine, Ergotocine, Ergostetrine, Ergotrate, Ergoclinine), $C_{19}H_{23}O_2N_3$, colorless crystals, m.p. 162°, $[\alpha]_D^{20}$ +90° (c 1 in water).

956 Ergobasinine, $C_{19}H_{23}O_2N_3$ (stereoisomer of ergobasine), colorless crystals, m.p. 196°, $[\alpha]_D^{20}$ +414° (c 1 in chloroform).

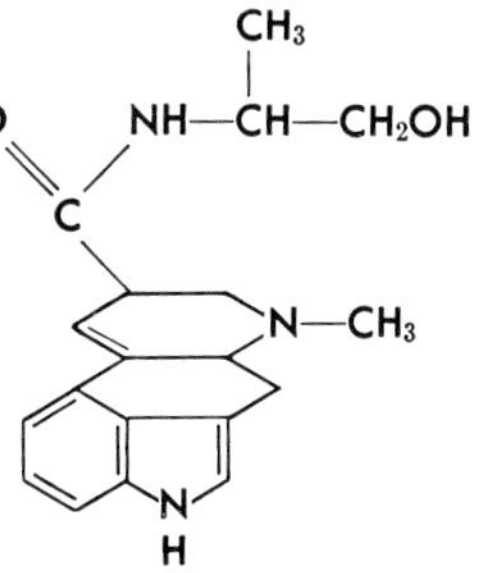

$$CH_3$$
$$|$$
O   NH—CH—CH₂OH

C

N—CH₃

N
H

Claviceps purpurea (Fries) Tul.
Walter A. Jacobs and Lyman C. Craig, *Science* 82 16 (1935). (Structure)

957 **Ergosecalinine,** $C_{24}H_{28}O_4N_4$, colorless crystals, m.p. 217° (dec.), $[\alpha]_D^{18}$ +298° (c 0.2 in chloroform).

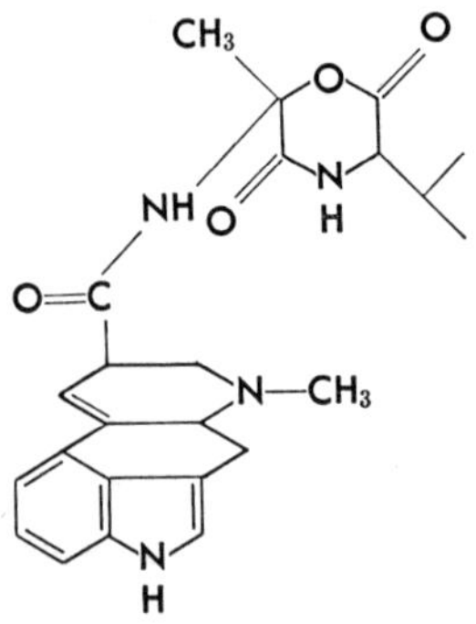

Claviceps purpurea
Matazo Abe, Togo Yamano, Saburo Yamatodani, Yoshiharu Kozu, Mitsugi Kusumoto, Hojime Komatsu and Saburo Yamada, *Bull. Agr. Chem. Soc.* (Japan) **23** 246 (1959).

958 **Ergosine,** $C_{30}H_{37}O_5N_5$, colorless crystals, m.p. 228° (dec.), $[\alpha]_D^{20}$ −179° (c 1 in chloroform).

959 **Ergosinine,** $C_{30}H_{37}O_5N_5$ (stereoisomer of ergosine), colorless crystals, m.p. 228° (dec.), $[\alpha]_D^{20}$ +420° (c 1 in chloroform).

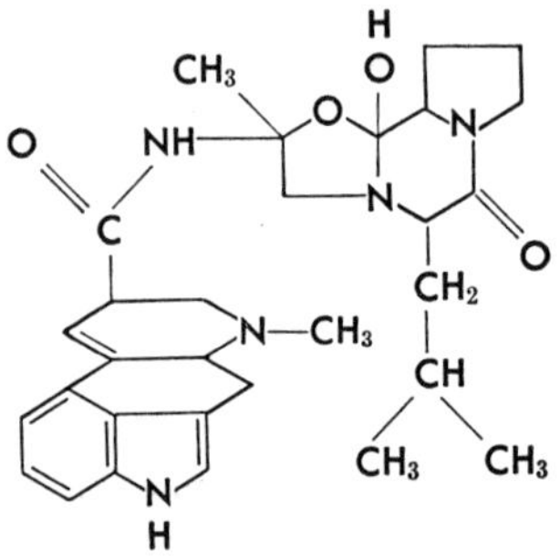

Claviceps purpurea (Fries) Tul.

A. Stoll, A. Hofmann and Th. Petzilka, *Helv. Chim. Acta* 34
1544 (1951). (Structure)

960 **Ergocornine,** $C_{31}H_{39}O_5N_5$, colorless crystals, m.p. 182–184°
(dec.), $[\alpha]_D^{20}$ −188° (c 1 in chloroform).

961 **Ergocorninine,** $C_{31}H_{39}O_5N_5$ (stereoisomer of ergocornine), colorless crystals, m.p. 228° (dec.), $[\alpha]_D^{20}$ +409° (c 1 in chloroform).

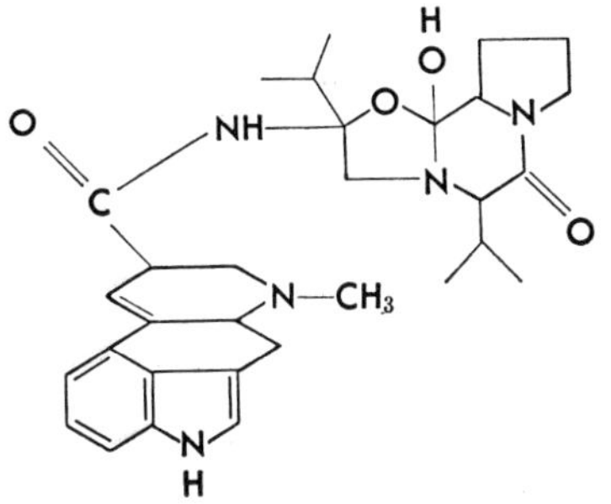

Claviceps purpurea (Fries) Tul.
A. Stoll, A. Hofmann and Th. Petzilka, *Helv. Chim. Acta*
34 1544 (1951). (Structure)

962 **Ergokryptine,** $C_{32}H_{41}O_5N_5$, colorless crystals, m.p. 212–214°
(dec.), $[\alpha]_D^{20}$ −187° (c 1 in chloroform).

963 **Ergokryptinine,** $C_{32}H_{41}O_5N_5$ (stereoisomer of ergokryptine) colorless crystals, m.p. 240–242° (dec.), $[\alpha]_D^{20}$ +408° (c 1 in
chloroform).

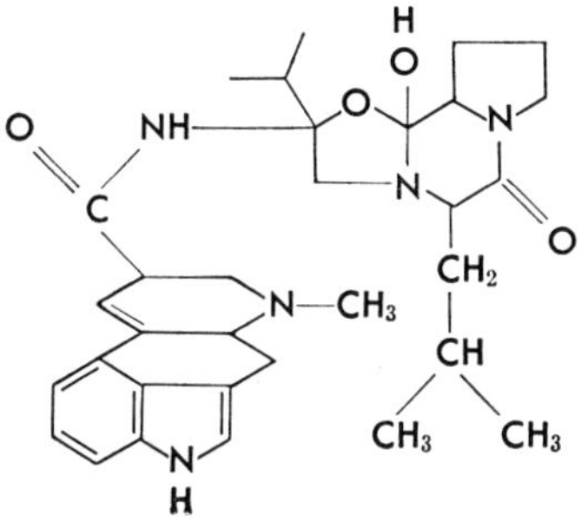

Claviceps purpurea (Fries) Tul.
A. Stoll, A. Hofmann and Th. Petzilka, *Helv. Chim. Acta*
34 1544 (1951). (Structure)

964 **Ergotamine,** $C_{33}H_{35}O_5N_5$, colorless prisms, m.p. 212–214° (dec.),
$[\alpha]_D^{20}$ −160° (c 1 in chloroform).

965 **Ergotaminine,** $C_{33}H_{35}O_5N_5$ (stereoisomer of ergotamine), colorless plates, m.p. 241–243° (dec.), $[\alpha]_D^{20}$ +369° (c 0.5 in
chloroform).

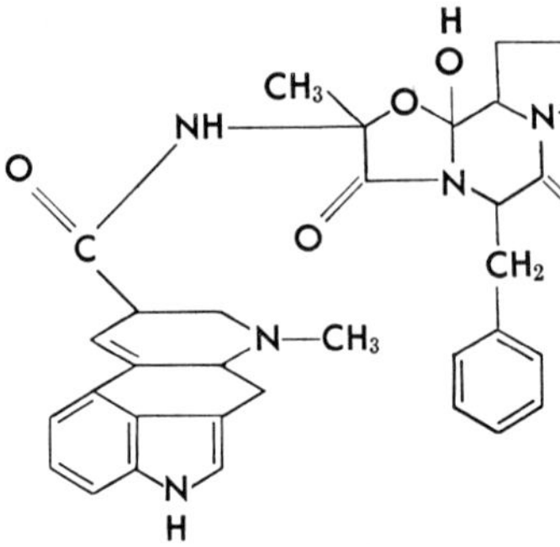

Claviceps purpurea (Fries) Tul.
Walter A. Jacobs and Lyman C. Craig, *J. Org. Chem.* 1 245
(1936).
Arthur Stoll, *Helv. Chim. Acta* 28 1283 (1945).

966 **Ergocristine,** $C_{35}H_{39}O_5N_5$, colorless crystals, m.p. 165–170°
(dec.), $[\alpha]_D^{20}$ −183° (c 1 in chloroform).

967 **Ergocristinine,** $C_{35}H_{39}O_5N_5$ (stereoisomer of ergocristine), m.p.
226° (dec.), $[\alpha]_D^{20}$ +336° (c 1 in chloroform).

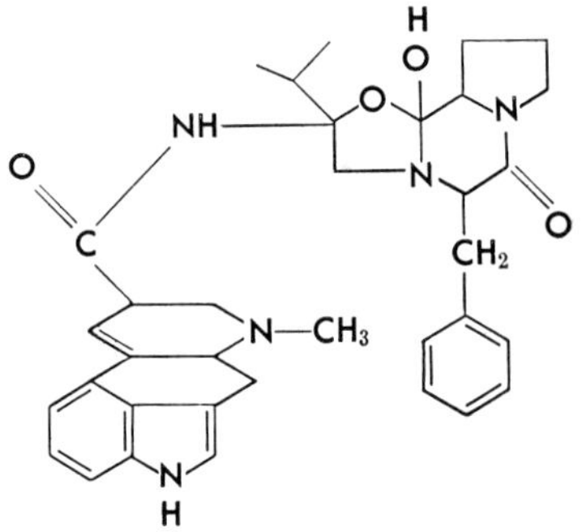

Claviceps purpurea (Fries) Tul.
A. Stoll, A. Hofmann and Th. Petzilka, *Helv. Chim. Acta*
34 1544 (1951). (Structure)

i. PYRIDINES

Few pyridines are listed, but two of these, nicotinic acid
and pyridoxine, are vitamins. Fusaric acid is a wilt toxin,
and 2,6-dipicolinic acid appears in conspicuous quantities
in bacterial spores.

Dipicolinic acid[1, 2, 3, 4] probably is formed by cyclization
of α,ϵ-diaminopimelic acid, a lysine precursor and cell wall
constituent of some bacteria:

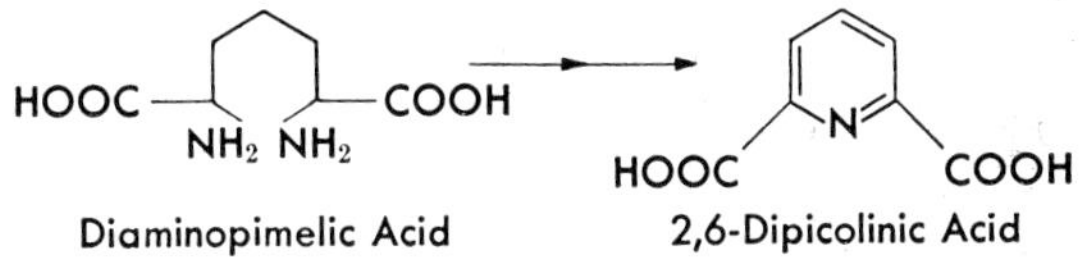

HOOC —⟨ ⟩— COOH   ⟶   ⟨N⟩
        NH$_2$ NH$_2$ HOOC   COOH

Diaminopimelic Acid   2,6-Dipicolinic Acid

The metabolic significance, if any, is unknown. In *Bacillus sphaericus* diaminopimelic acid is present in spores
and not in vegetative cells, but in many bacteria it is present in both.

Fusaric and dehydrofusaric acids are by-products of the
gibberellin fermentation and are produced by fusarium
types. These include plant pathogens, and fusaric acid
solutions sprayed on healthy plants of the usual host
cause wilting typical of infection. Apparently no study
has been made of the mode of biogenesis.

Nicotinic acid in its coenzyme forms occurs in all living
cells where it is essential in hydrogen and electron transport. It is used by a variety of apoenzymes as the prosthetic group for various dehydrogenase reactions. It is
much less tightly bound to the protein than, for example,
flavine adenine dinucleotide, perhaps to facilitate move-
ment of the available supply among the apoenzymes in
need of it.

Some of the many microbial reactions known to require
diphosphopyridine nucleotide (DPN) or triphosphopyridine nucleotide (TPN) are:

[1] Joan F. Powell, *Biochem. J.* 54 210 (1953).
[2] J. J. Perry and J. W. Foster, *J. Bacteriol.* 72 295 (1956).
[3] William K. Harrell and Emil Mantini, *Can. J. Microbiol.* 3 735
(1957).
[4] Joan F. Powell and R. E. Strange, *Biochem. J.* 65 700 (1957).

$$\text{CH}_3\text{CH}_2\text{OH} \rightleftharpoons \text{CH}_3\text{CHO (in yeast)}$$
$$\text{R---CHO} \rightleftharpoons \text{R---COOH (in yeast)}$$
$$\text{Glutathione---SH} \rightleftharpoons \text{Glutathione---S---S---Glutathione (in yeast)}$$
$$\text{Isocitrate} \rightleftharpoons \text{Oxalosuccinate (bacteria, yeast)}$$
$$\text{D-Glucopyranose-6-phosphate} \rightleftharpoons \text{6-Phospho-D-gluconolactone (yeast)}$$

$$\text{L-Glutamate} \rightleftharpoons \alpha\text{-Ketoglutarate} + \text{NH}_4^{\oplus} \text{ (bacteria)}$$
$$\text{D-Glyceraldehyde-3-phosphate} + \text{Phosphate} \rightleftharpoons \text{D-1,3-Diphosphoglyceric}$$
$$\text{Acid (yeast)}$$

Some of these reactions occur quite generally. Occasionally DPN and TPN are interchangeable, although one or the other is used more efficiently.

Direct transfer of hydrogen between the substrate and the 4-position of the nicotinamide moiety of DPN (in the presence of yeast alcohol dehydrogenase) has been demonstrated, and the stereochemistry of this reaction studied in exquisite detail by means of deuterated substrate:[5, 6]

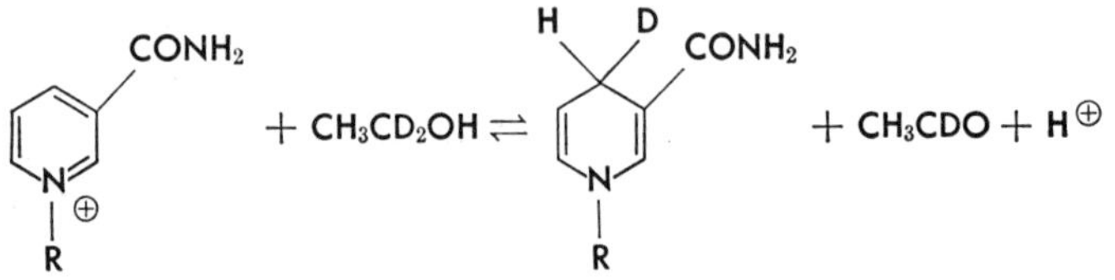

(R = the rest of the DPN molecule)

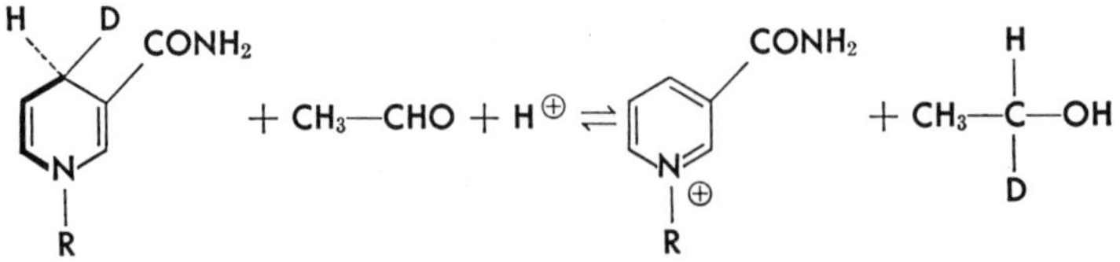

In the second equation the deuterium atom is removed exclusively, leaving deuterium-free DPN. This indicates a marked steric effect, since the deuterium atom projects from one side of the molecule. Moreover, a single stereoisomer of deuterated ethanol is produced.

Speculations have been made concerning the precise nature of the coenzyme-apoenzyme-substrate-metal ion complex. One model[7] is shown below:

[5] Harvey F. Fisher, Eric E. Conn, Birgit Vennesland and F. H. Westheimer, *J. Biol. Chem.* 202 687 (1953).

[6] H. Richard Levy, Frank A. Loewus and Birgit Vennesland, *J. Am. Chem. Soc.* 79 2949 (1957).

[7] Kurt Wallenfels and Horst Sund, *Biochem. Z.* 329 59 (1957).

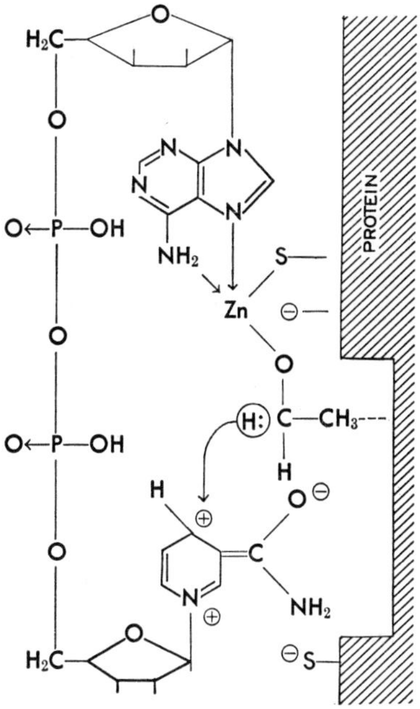

The fact that alcohol and lactic acid dehydrogenases all have been found to contain 2 or 4 DPN molecules has also inspired the hypothesis that hydrogen transfer might require a pair of adjoining prosthetic groups in a scheme such as:

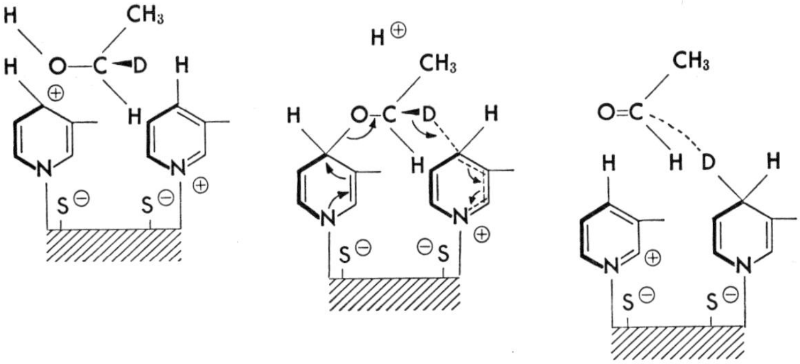

in which a deuterated substrate is shown for clarity.[8] A more detailed discussion has been published of the stereo-

[8] Jan van Eys, Anthony San Pietro and Nathan O. Kaplan, *Science* **127** 1443 (1958).

chemistry of microbiological reactions with emphasis on those promoted by dehydrogenases.[9]

The biosynthesis of nicotinic acid has been studied in several different biological systems. In neurospora (and in mammals) tryptophan is the source with 3-oxyanthranilic acid a proved intermediate.[10, 11, 12, 13, 14, 15] The remaining stages of this route are obscure, although α-aminomethyl-α,β-*trans*-γ,δ-*cis*-muconic acid may be an intermediate.[16] It has been shown to be a precursor of nicotinic acid for the bacterium *Xanthomonas pruni*. If it proves to be generally significant, then the following scheme can be written:

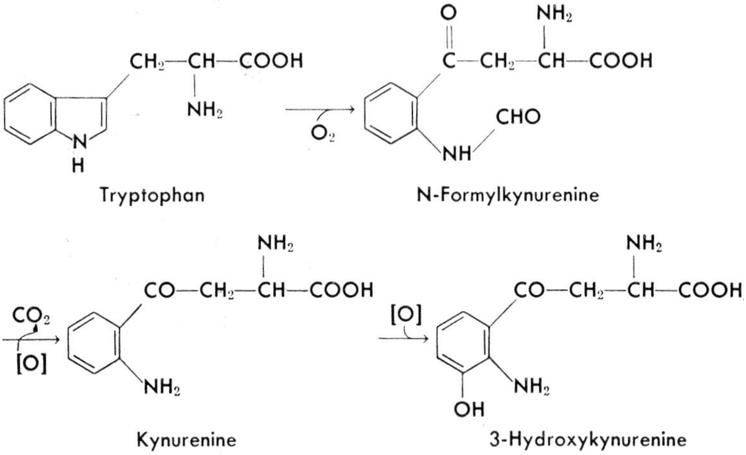

Tryptophan   N-Formylkynurenine

Kynurenine   3-Hydroxykynurenine

[9] G. E. W. Wolstenholme and Cecilia M. O'Connor (Eds.), CIBA Foundation Study Group No. 2, "Steric Course of Microbiological Reactions," Little, Brown and Company, Boston, 1959, 115 pp.

[10] W. A. Krehl, L. J. Teply, P. S. Sarma and C. A. Elvehjem, *Science* 101 489 (1945).

[11] Fred Rosen, Jesse W. Huff and William A. Perlzweig, *J. Biol. Chem.* 163 343 (1946).

[12] G. S. Beadle, H. K. Mitchell and J. F. Nye, *Proc. Nat. Acad. Sci.* 33 155 (1947).

[13] Francis A. Haskins and Herschel K. Mitchell, *ibid.* 35 500 (1949).

[14] Irving L. Miller and Edward A. Adelberg, *J. Biol. Chem.* 205 691 (1953).

[15] William B. Jakoby and David M. Bonner, *ibid.* 205 699, 709 (1953).

[16] J. O. Harris and F. Binns, *Nature* 179 475 (1957).

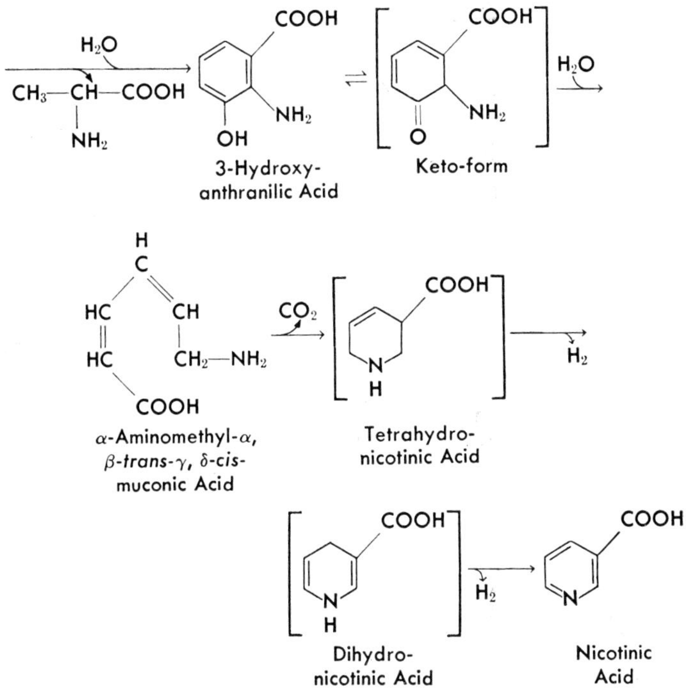

3-Hydroxy-
anthranilic Acid

Keto-form

α-Aminomethyl-α,
β-trans-γ, δ-cis-
muconic Acid

Tetrahydro-
nicotinic Acid

Dihydro-
nicotinic Acid

Nicotinic
Acid

A different method of biosynthesis exists in *Escherichia coli* and *Bacillus subtilis* since tryptophan is not used. Investigation of this route has not progressed so far, but glycerol is capable of supplying all carbon atoms, as are glyceric acid and dihydroxyacetone (but not pyruvate). Succinate, malate, fumarate and oxaloacetate also were used. Ribose and adenine were required, which suggests direct synthesis of the coenzyme.[17]

[17] Manuel V. Ortega and Gene M. Brown, *J. Am. Chem. Soc.* 81 4437 (1959).

The various forms of pyridoxine are:

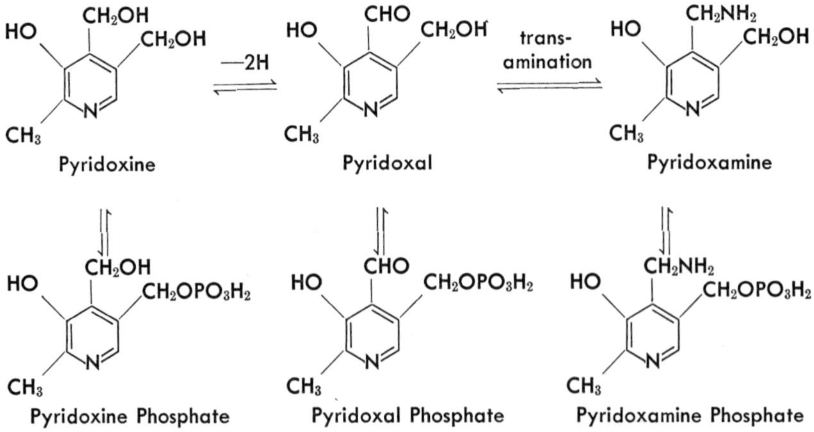

Pyridoxine   Pyridoxal   Pyridoxamine

Pyridoxine Phosphate   Pyridoxal Phosphate   Pyridoxamine Phosphate

Virtually nothing is known concerning the biogenesis of pyridoxine. Since catabolism often furnishes clues useful in the study of biosynthesis, it should be noted that oxidative bacteria degrade pyridoxine as follows:[18]

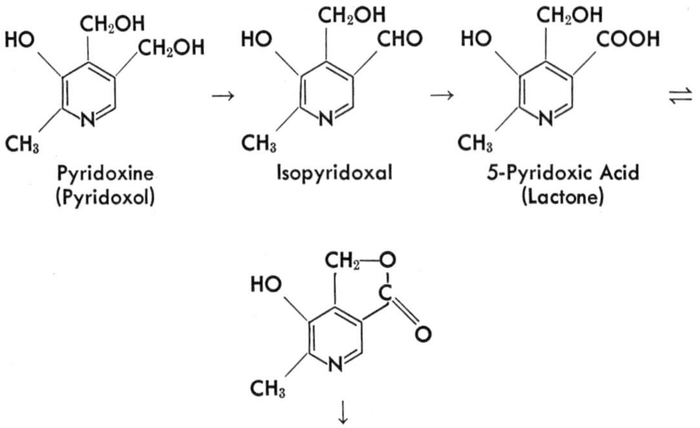

Pyridoxine (Pyridoxol)   Isopyridoxal   5-Pyridoxic Acid (Lactone)

[18] Victor W. Rodwell, Benjamin E. Volcani, Miyoshi Ikawa and Esmond E. Snell, *J. Biol. Chem.* 233 1548 (1958); Miyoshi Ikawa, Victor W. Rodwell and Esmond E. Snell, *ibid.* 233 1555 (1958).

$$\overset{\downarrow}{CH_2OH}$$

α-Hydroxymethyl-α'-
(N-acetylaminomethylene)-
succinic Acid

Acid hydrolysis converts the acyclic product to paraconic acid.

Functions of the vitamin are better understood. The names pyridoxine or vitamin B_6 commonly are used in a general sense to refer to the group. Pyridoxal 5-phosphate is the actual prosthetic group in most enzymic reactions. It is a component of transaminases, amino acid decarboxylases, tryptophan synthetase, amino acid racemases, threonine synthetase (homoserine isomerase), δ-aminolevulinate synthetase, phosphorylase and various other enzymes which manipulate amino acids. More thorough discussions of functions of this important vitamin can be found in reviews.[19, 20]

Some pyridoxal-catalyzed reactions can be carried out in aqueous solution without the apoenzymes if heat and the proper metal ions (Al^{+++}, Fe^{++}, Cu^{++}) are supplied. Mechanisms which have been proposed for three such reactions are outlined in the following equations:[21, 22, 23, 24]

[19] Esmond E. Snell, *Vitamins and Hormones* 16 77 (1958).

[20] Paul D. Boyer, Henry Lardy and Karl Myrbäck, (Eds.) "The Enzymes," Alexander E. Braunstein, *Pyridoxal phosphate,* Academic Press, New York, 1960, pp. 113–184.

[21] David E. Metzler, Miyoshi Ikawa and Esmond E. Snell, *J. Am. Chem. Soc.* 76 648 (1954).

[22] J. B. Longenecker and Esmond E. Snell, *ibid.* 79 142 (1957).

[23] W. Terry Jenkins and Irwin W. Sizer, *ibid.* 79 2655 (1957).

[24] D. S. Hoare and Esmond E. Snell, Proc. Internat. Sympos. Enz. Chem., Tokyo and Kyoto, Pergamon Press, London, 1957, p. 142.

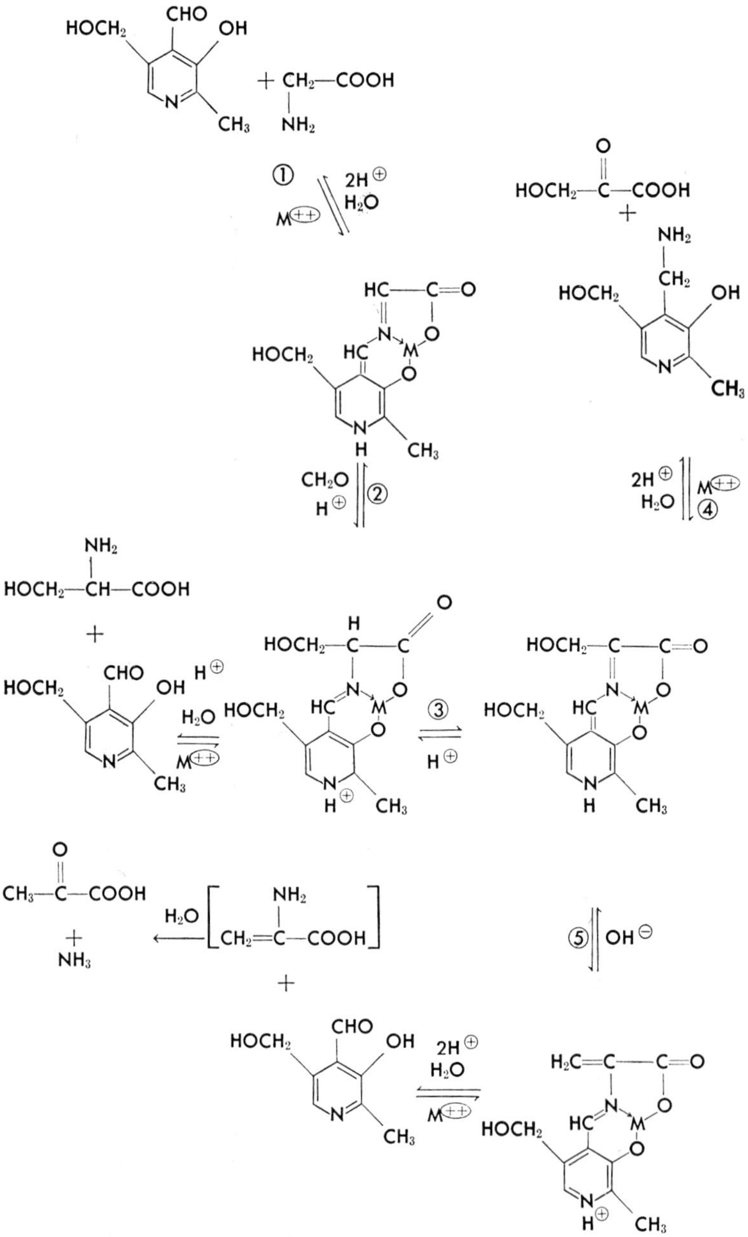

HOCH₂ — CHO OH — CH₃ (pyridine ring)

$+ \ CH_2—COOH$ with NH_2

① 2H⊕ / H₂O
M⊕⊕

$HOCH_2—\overset{O}{\overset{\|}{C}}—COOH$
$+$
NH_2
CH_2
HOCH₂ ... OH ... CH₃

HC — C=O
N — M — O
HOCH₂ HC ... CH₃ (ring with N, H)

CH₂O / H⊕ ②

2H⊕ / H₂O ④ M⊕⊕

NH_2
$HOCH_2—CH—COOH$

$+$

HOCH₂ CHO OH H⊕ / H₂O M⊕⊕ CH₃ (ring)

$HOCH_2—\overset{H}{C}—\overset{O}{C}$
N — M — O
HOCH₂ HC ... CH₃ (ring, H⊕)
③

$HOCH_2—C—C=O$
N — M — O
HOCH₂ HC ... CH₃ (ring)

$CH_3—\overset{O}{\overset{\|}{C}}—COOH$
$+$
NH_3

H₂O ← $\left[CH_2=\overset{NH_2}{C}—COOH \right]$

$+$

⑤ OH⊖

HOCH₂ CHO OH 2H⊕ / H₂O M⊕⊕ CH₃ (ring)

$H_2C=C—C=O$
N — M — O
HOCH₂ HC ... CH₃ (ring, H⊕)

M = Metal: ①,② = Aldol formation and cleavage
③,④ = Transamination
③,⑤ = α, β-Elimination

Attachment to the apoenzyme *in vivo* was assumed to be at the pyridine nitrogen atom. Spectral data from such model systems, however, when applied to purified enzymes, indicate that pyridoxal phosphate is bound to the apoenzyme as a Schiff base in glutamate-aspartate aminopherase[23] and in homoserine deaminase-cystathionase.[25] In crystalline muscle phosphorylase pyridoxal is bound to the apoenzyme, probably at a lysine ε-amino group, as an aldamine, involving an additional side-chain of the protein (perhaps —SH).[26, 27]

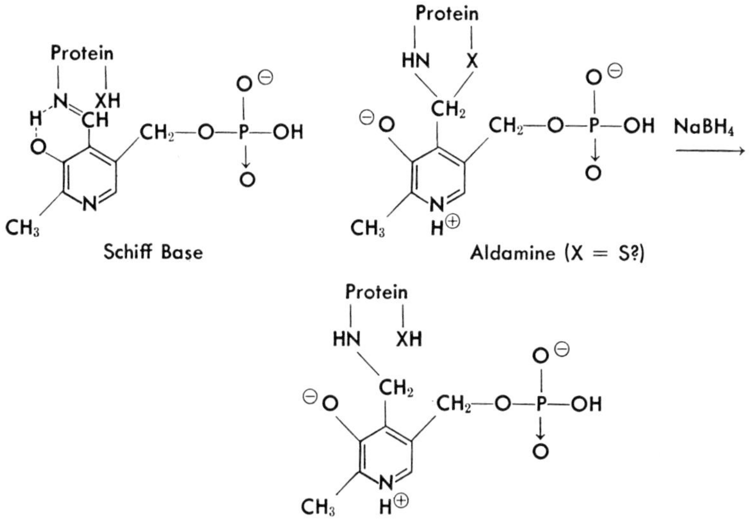

Schiff Base

Aldamine (X = S?)

Reduced Enzyme

Glutamate-aspartate aminopherase contains 2 moles of bound pyridoxal phosphate and muscle phosphorylase 4. It is rather surprising to find the vitamin in an enzyme, such as the latter, unrelated to its ordinary function. Doubt has been cast on its function as a prosthetic group in phosphorylase by several experiments, one of them the reduction shown, which should have inactivated the pyridoxal, but which did not inactivate the enzyme.[28] It

[25] Yoshihiko Matsuo and David M. Greenberg, *J. Biol. Chem.* **230** 545, 561 (1958); *idem., ibid.* **234** 507, 516 (1959).

[26] Alan B. Kent, Edwin G. Krebs and Edmond H. Fischer, *J. Biol. Chem.* **232** 549 (1958).

[27] Barbara Illingworth, Hendrik S. Jansz, David H. Brown and Carl F. Cori, *Proc. Nat. Acad. Sci.* **44** 1180 (1958).

[28] Edmond H. Fischer, Alan B. Kent, Eloise R. Snyder and Edwin G. Krebs, *J. Am. Chem. Soc.* **80** 2906 (1958).

may be that it serves a structural or other function here.

D-Cycloserine has been reported to inhibit aspartate aminopherase, indole synthetase and D-alanine-D-glutamate aminopherase in some bacteria.[29, 30] Aspartic analogues, such as diaminosuccinic acid and hydroxyaspartic acid also are effective inhibitors of the first enzyme above.[31]

It has been suggested that pyridoxine may be implicated in the active transport of amino acids across cell walls.[32]

968 2, 6-Dipicolinic Acid, $C_7H_5O_4N$, colorless needles, m.p. 236° (dec.).

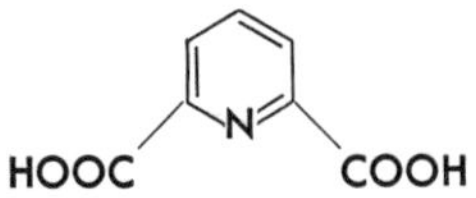

Bacillus megatherium, B. cereus var. *terminalis, B. sphaericus* types

Occurs as the calcuim salt in spores.

Joan F. Powell, *Biochem. J.* 54 210 (1953).

William K. Harrell and Emil Mantini, *Can. J. Microbiol.* 3 735 (1957).

Joan F. Powell and R. E. Strange, *Biochem. J.* 65 700 (1957).

969 Pyridoxal-5′-phosphate $C_8H_{10}O_6NP$

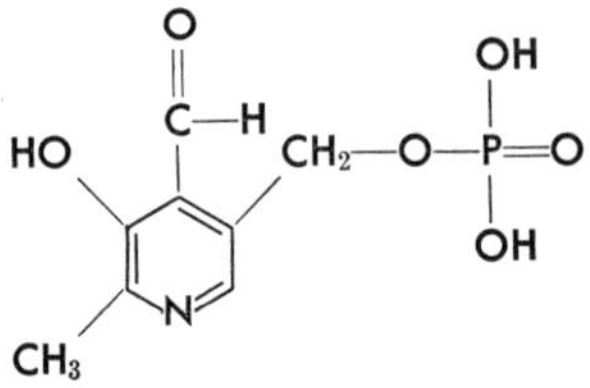

Yeasts, molds, bacteria (widely distributed)

[29] Takakazu Aoki, *Kekkaku* 32 544, 605 (1957). (*Chem. Abstr.* 52 7427g).

[30] N. K. Kochetkov, R. M. Khomutov, M. J. Karpeiskii, E. I. Budovskii and E. S. Severin, *Doklady Akad. Nauk S.S.S.R.* 126 1132 (1959).

[31] Mario Garcia-Hernandez and Ernest Kun, *Biochim. et Biophys. Acta* 24 78 (1957).

[32] Halvor N. Christensen, Thomas R. Riggs and Barbara R. Coyne, *J. Biol. Chem.* 209 413 (1954); Halvor N. Christensen and Thomas R. Riggs, *ibid.* 220 265 (1956).

I. C. Gunsalus, W. D. Bellamy and W. W. Umbreit, *J. Biol. Chem.* 155 685 (1944).

Dorothea Heyl, Eileen Luz, Stanton A. Harris and Karl Folkers, *J. Am. Chem. Soc.* 73 3430 (1951). (Synthesis)

970 Pyridoxine (Vitamin B$_6$), C$_8$H$_{11}$O$_3$N, colorless needles from acetone, m.p. 160° (sublimes).

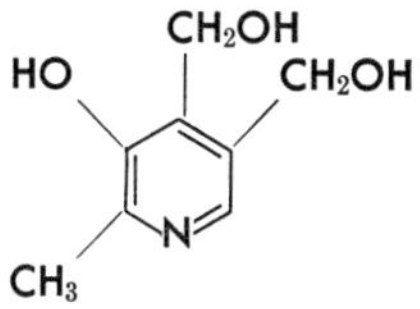

Yeasts, molds.

Yields of 82–114 μg. per gram (dry basis) have been reported from penicillin broth filtrates.

Yields of 23–100 μg. per gram of dry cells have been reported from brewers' yeast.

Leland A. Underkofler and Richard J. Hickey, "Industrial Fermentations," Chemical Publishing Co., Inc., New York, 1954 **Vol. II**, J. M. VanLanen, *Production of vitamins other than riboflavin*, Chap. 6, pp. 191–216. (A review)

971 Ethyl Hydrogen 2, 6-Dipicolinate, C$_9$H$_9$O$_4$N, colorless crystals, m.p. 121.5°.

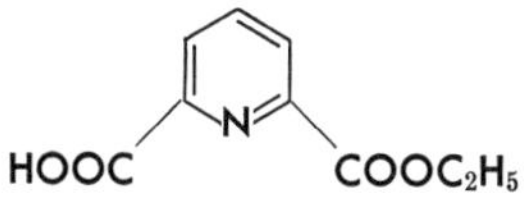

Bacillus cereus var. *mycoides* (spores)
J. J. Perry and J. W. Foster, *J. Bacteriol.* 72 295 (1956).

972 Dehydrofusaric Acid, C$_{10}$H$_{11}$O$_2$N, colorless crystals, m.p. 118°.

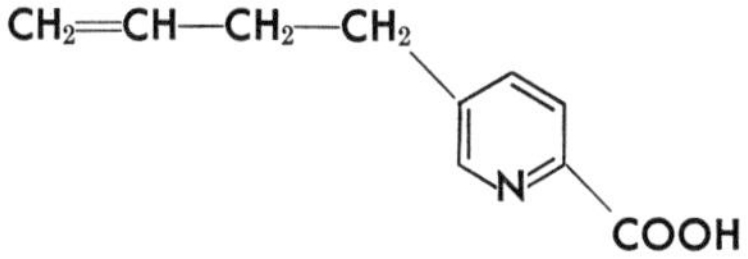

Gibberella fujikuroi Saw.
Ernst Gäumann, *Phytopathology* 47 342 (1957).
C. A. Stoll and J. Renz, *Phytopathol. Z.* 27 380 (1957).
John Frederick Grove, P. W. Jeffs and T. P. C. Mulholland, *J. Chem. Soc.,* 1236 (1958).

973 Fusaric Acid, $C_{10}H_{13}O_2N$, colorless crystals, m.p. 100°.

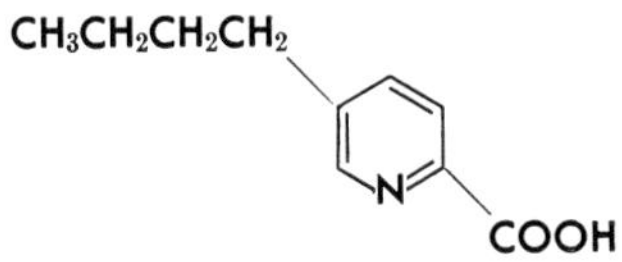

$$CH_3CH_2CH_2CH_2$$

COOH

Gibberella fujikuroi (Saw.) Wr., *Fusarium heterosporum* Nees, *F. bulbigenum* Cke. *et* Mass. var. *lycopersici* (Bruchi) Wr. *et* Rg., *F. vasinfectum* Atk., *F. orthoceras* App. *et* Wr., *Nectria cinnabarina* (Tode) Fr.

Yields of about 0.5 g. per liter have been reported.

Teijiro Yabuta, Katsuji Kambe and Takeshi Hayashi, *J. Agr. Chem. Soc. Japan* 10 1059 (1934).

John Frederick Grove, P. W. Jeffs and T. P. C. Mulholland, *J. Chem. Soc.,* 1236 (1958).

974 Coenzyme III (Nicotinamide Ribose 5′-Diphosphate), $C_{11}H_{16}O_{11}N_2P_2$.

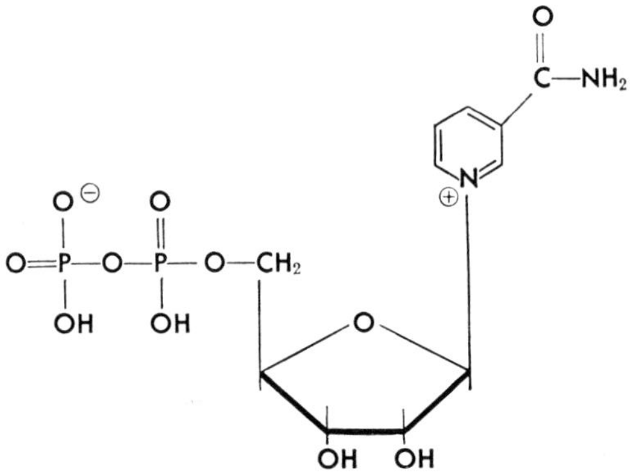

O
||
C—NH₂

O=P—O—P—O—CH₂
OH   OH

OH   OH

Yeast

Nicotinic acid nucleotides also have been isolated from yeast.

Thomas P. Singer and Edna B. Kearney, *Biochim. et Biophys. Acta* 11 290 (1953).

975 Diphosphopyridinenucleotide (DPN), $C_{21}H_{27}O_{14}N_7P_2$.

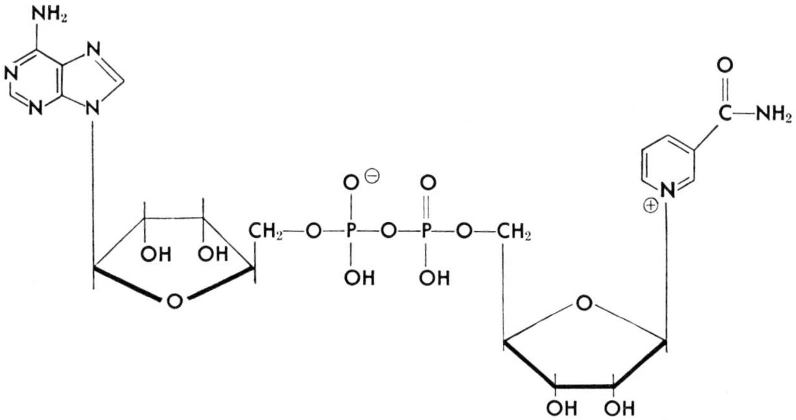

Yeasts, molds (widely distributed)
H. von Euler, P. Karrer and B. Brecker, *Helv. Chim. Acta*
19 1060 (1936). (Structure)
G. A. LePage, *J. Biol. Chem.* **168** 623 (1947).

976 Triphosphopyridinenucleotide (TPN, Codehydrase II), $C_{21}H_{28}$-
$O_{17}N_7P_3$.

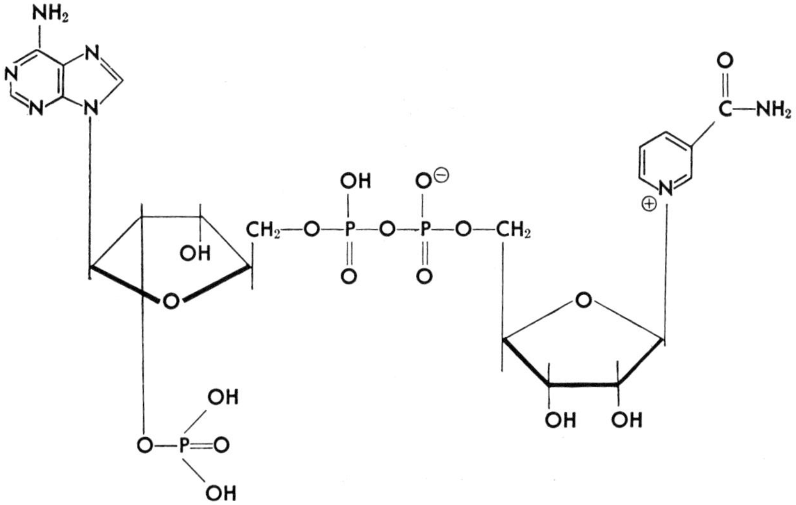

Yeasts, molds, etc.
Otto Warburg, Walter Christian and Alfred Griese,
Biochem. Z. **279** 143 (1935); **282** 157 (1935). (Isolation)

H. von Euler and F. Schlenk, *Z. physiol. Chem.* **246** 64
(1937). (Structure)
   Arthur Kornberg and W. E. Pricer, Jr., *J. Biol. Chem.* **186**
557 (1950).

j. QUINOLINES

Quinolines are produced by bacteria and molds, but apparently none has been reported from streptomycetes or
lichens. A complex of seven related 4-oxyquinolines is
elaborated by the oxidative bacterium *Pseudomonas aeruginosa* (*Bacillus pyocyaneus*). These are commonly
called "pyo" compounds.
   Evidently no investigations have been made on the
mode of biosynthesis of microbial quinolines. The isolation of anthranilic acid and of 2-*n*-heptyl-3-oxy-4-quino-
lone from "pyo" fermentation broths is suggestive, however.[1] It seems probable that the "pyo" compounds could

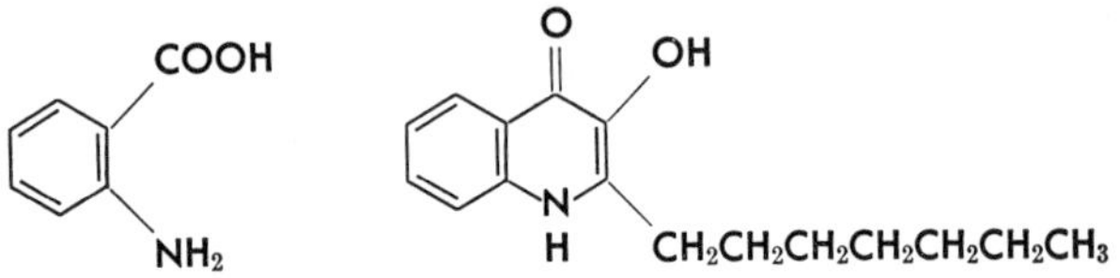

Anthranilic
Acid

2-*n*-Heptyl-3-oxy-4-quinolone

be formed essentially by condensation of anthranilic acid
or a biosynthetic precursor with a fatty acid or a fatty
acid precursor:

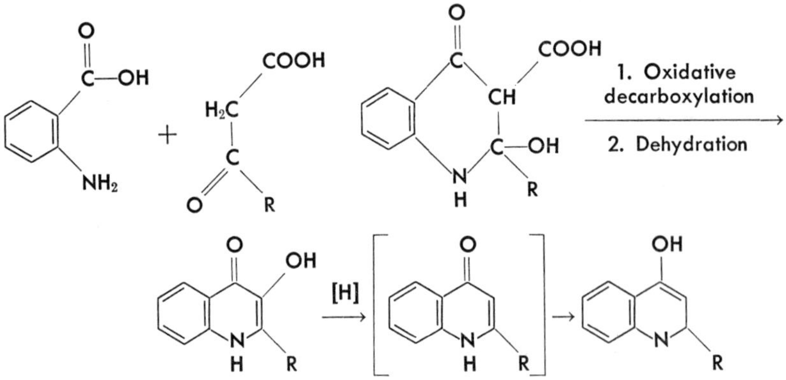

1. Oxidative
decarboxylation

2. Dehydration

[1] Rokuro Takeda, *J. Fermentation Technol.* **37** 59 (1959).

Oxidative decarboxylation would then yield an intermediate of the type isolated, and a one-stage reduction the 4-oxyquinolines. The N-oxides might be formed later by post-oxidation. Quinolines are known to be quite susceptible to N-oxidation by peroxides or oxygen.

The structure of the mold product, viridicatin, has been verified by synthesis, while that of cyclopenin is still uncertain. It would appear that these substances are also derivatives of anthranilic acid. In this case, condensation probably occurs with an earlier member of the shikimic acid pathway, perhaps prephenic acid or phenylpyruvic acid:

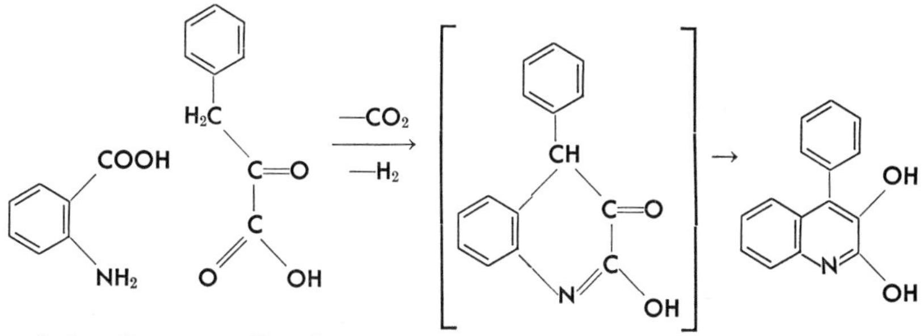

Anthranilic   Phenylpyruvic   Viridicatin
   Acid   Acid

Such condensations have been suggested to explain the origin of certain oxyquinoline plant alkaloids.[2]

There is, of course, a possibility for 4-oxyquinoline formation by way of tryptophan and kynurenine:

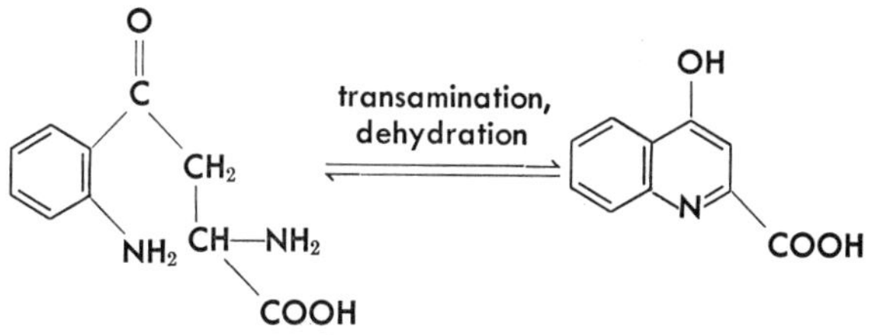

Kynurenine

This seems to be an unnecessarily indirect route, but all of the schemes shown here await experimental test.

[2] Ernest Wenkert, *Experientia* 15 165 (1959).

977 **Viridicatin,** $C_{15}H_{11}O_2N$, colorless needles, m.p. 268°.

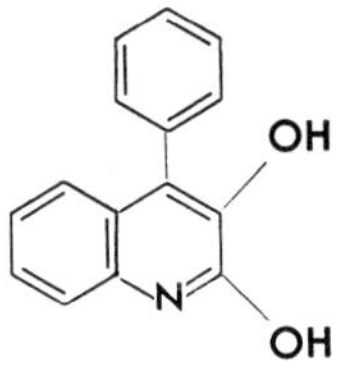

Penicillium viridicatum Westling, *P. cyclopium* Westling
See under cyclopenin.
A. Bracken, Anna Pocker and H. Raistrick, *Biochem. J.* 57 587 (1954). (Synthesis)

978 **2-*n*-Heptyl-4-oxyquinoline,** $C_{16}H_{21}ON$, colorless crystals, m.p. 146°.

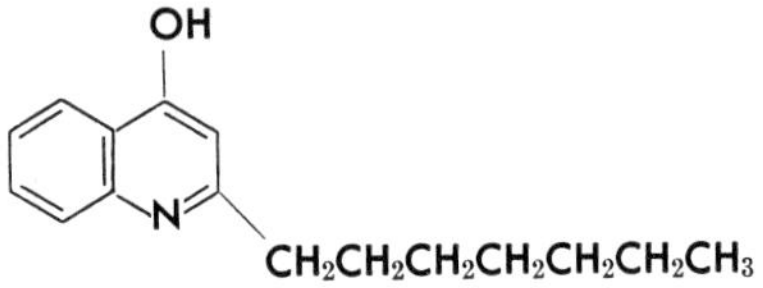

Pseudomonas aeruginosa
These quinoline derivatives are called "pyo" compounds.
Ibert C. Wells, *J. Biol. Chem.* 196 331 (1952). (Synthesis)

979 **2-*n*-Heptyl-3-oxy-4-quinolone,** $C_{16}H_{21}O_2N$.

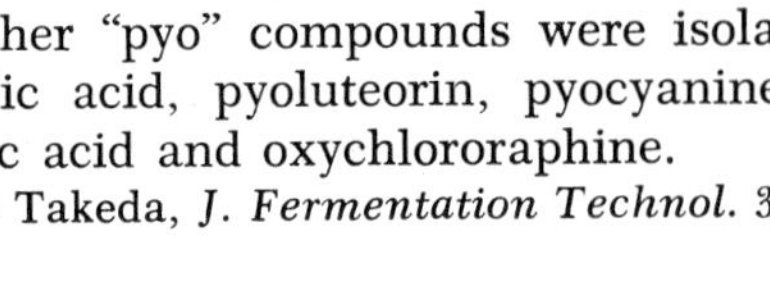

Pseudomonas aeruginosa strain T-359
The other "pyo" compounds were isolated as well as anthranilic acid, pyoluteorin, pyocyanine, phenazine-1-carboxylic acid and oxychlororaphine.
Rokuro Takeda, *J. Fermentation Technol.* 37 59 (1959).

980 **2-*n*-Heptyl-4-oxyquinoline N-oxide,** $C_{16}H_{21}O_2N$, colorless leaflets, m.p. 158–160°.

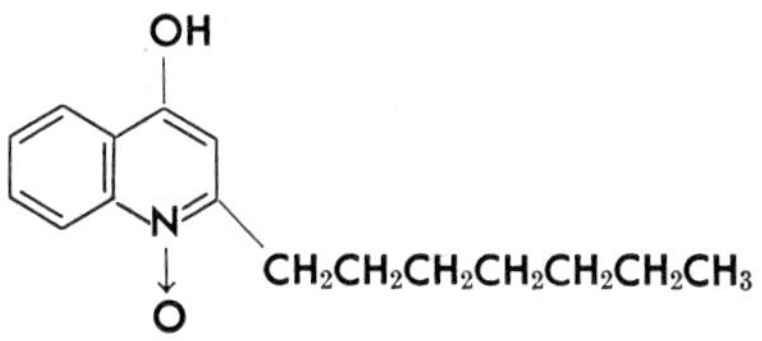

Pseudomonas aeruginosa
J. W. Cornforth and A. T. James, *Biochem. J.* **63** 124 (1956). (Synthesis)

981 **Cyclopenin,** $C_{17}H_{14}O_3N_2$, colorless tablets, m.p. 207°, $[\alpha]_D^{20}$ −306° (c 1.0 in ethanol).
Proposed structures:

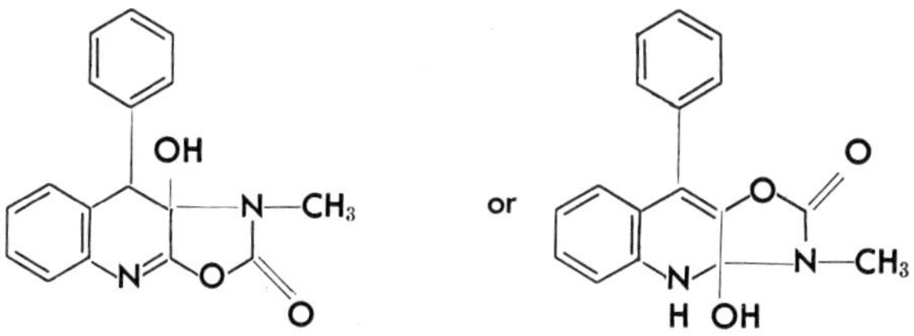

Penicillium cyclopium Westling
Usually viridicatin is produced by the same organism. Palitantin and frequentin are also produced by *P. cyclopium*
A. Bracken, Anna Pocker and H. Raistrick, *Biochem. J.* **57** 587 (1954).

982 **2-(*n*-Δ¹-Nonenyl)-4-oxyquinoline,** $C_{18}H_{23}ON$, colorless crystals, m.p. 153°.

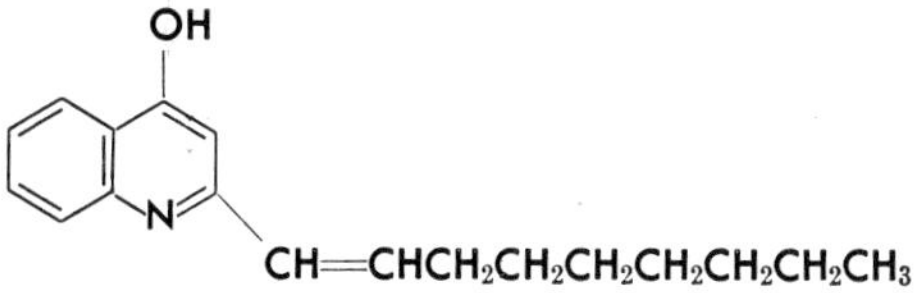

Pseudomonas aeruginosa
Ibert C. Wells, *J. Biol. Chem.* **196** 331 (1952). (Synthesis)

983 **2-*n*-Nonyl-4-oxyquinoline,** $C_{18}H_{25}ON$, colorless crystals, m.p. 139°.

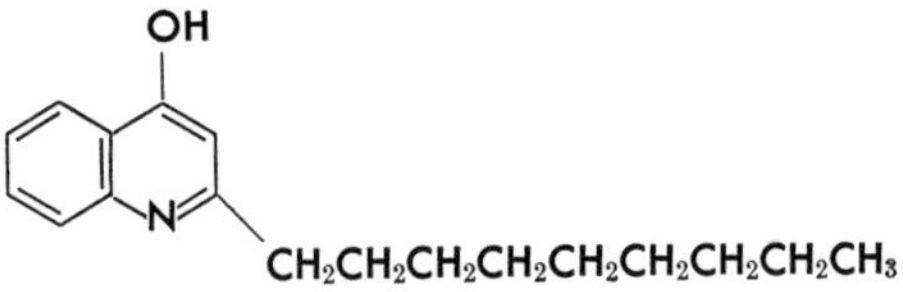

OH

$CH_2CH_2CH_2CH_2CH_2CH_2CH_2CH_2CH_3$

Pseudomonas aeruginosa
Ibert C. Wells, *J. Biol. Chem.* **196** 331 (1952). (Synthesis)

984 **2-*n*-Nonyl-4-oxyquinoline N-Oxide,** $C_{18}H_{25}O_2N$, colorless leaflets, m.p. 148°.

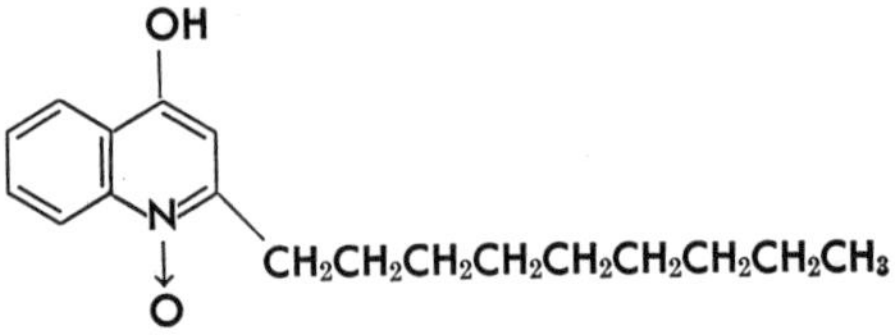

OH

$CH_2CH_2CH_2CH_2CH_2CH_2CH_2CH_2CH_3$

O

Pseudomonas aeruginosa
J. W. Cornforth and A. T. James, *Biochem. J.* **63** 124 (1956). (Synthesis)

985 **2-*n*-Undecyl-4-oxyquinoline N-Oxide,** $C_{20}H_{29}O_2N$, colorless leaflets, m.p. 148.5°.

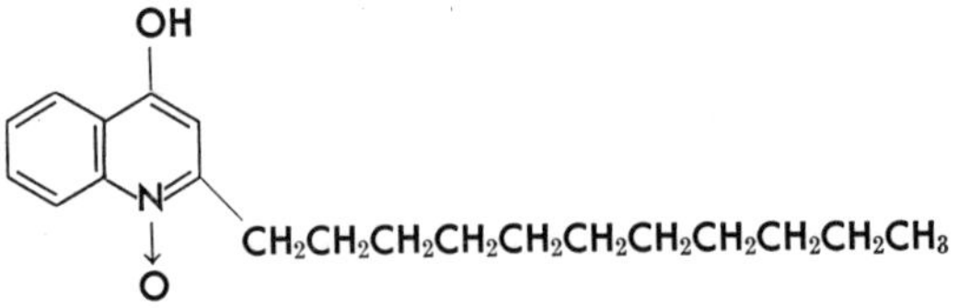

OH

$CH_2CH_2CH_2CH_2CH_2CH_2CH_2CH_2CH_2CH_2CH_3$

O

Pseudomonas aeruginosa
J. W. Cornforth and A. T. James, *Biochem. J.* **63** 124 (1956). (Synthesis)

k. PYRAZINES, DIKETOPIPERAZINES

Diketopiperazines are produced by molds, yeasts and lichens, but none has been reported from bacteria. Besides those listed in this section, others are classified elsewhere, for example, echinulin and gliotoxin under indoles. Flavacol and pulcherriminic acid seem to be derived from leucine, the echinulin moiety from leucine and alanine, aspergillic acid from leucine and isoleucine, the mycelianamide moiety from tyrosine and alanine, picrorocellin from phenylalanine, and gliotoxin from phenylalanine and serine. It might be mentioned that we have isolated from a *Rhizopus nigricans* culture a diketopiperazine which is a derivative of isoleucine and valine (unpublished).

Dehydration, dehydrogenation, oxidation and N- or O-methylation sometimes occur to obscure the origin to some degree. Aromatization to a pyrazine has taken place in flavacol and pulcherriminic acid, aspergillic acid, a dihydropyrazine, representing an intermediate oxidation state. Formation of pulcherriminic acid might be represented as follows:

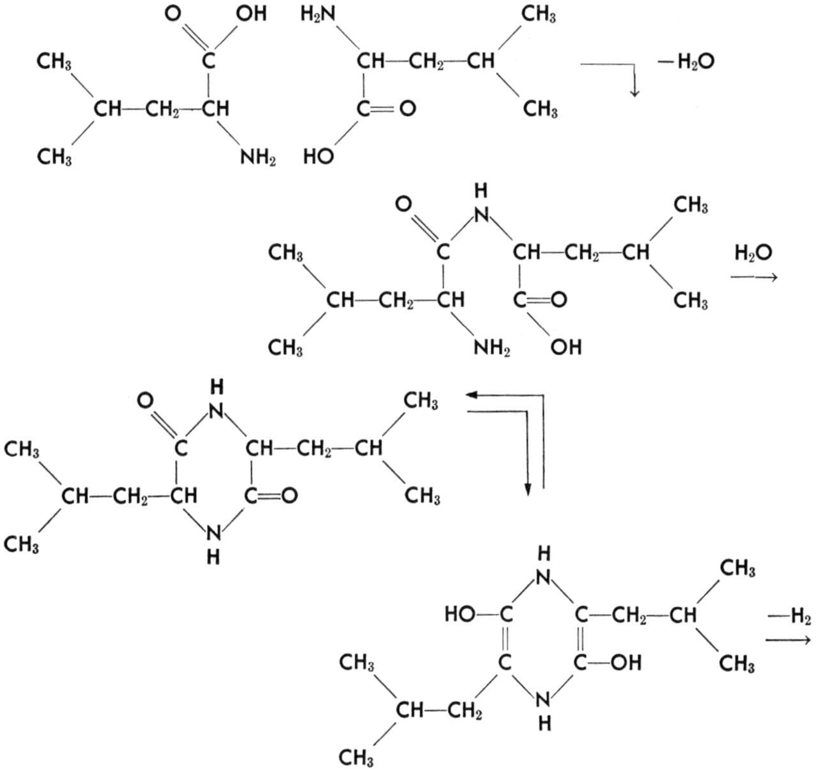

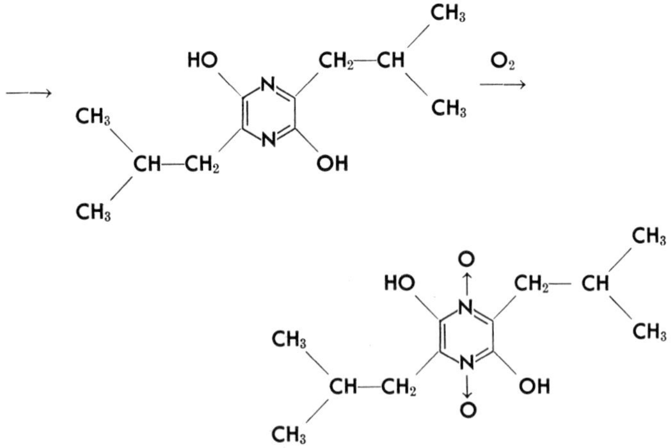

The structures shown:

$$\text{HO}-\underset{\begin{array}{c}\text{CH}-\text{CH}_2\\ |\\ \text{CH}_3\end{array}}{\overset{\begin{array}{c}\\ \text{CH}_2-\text{CH}\\ |\\ \text{CH}_3\end{array}}{\text{pyrazine}}}-\text{OH} \xrightarrow{O_2}$$

The addition of sulfur across the diketopiperazine ring in gliotoxin is interesting.

986 Flavacol, $C_{12}H_{20}ON_2$, colorless needles, m.p. 147–149°.

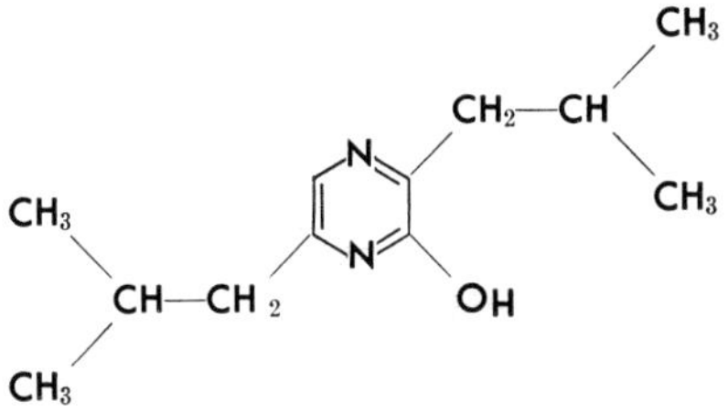

Aspergillus flavus

George Dunn, G. T. Newbold and F. S. Spring, *J. Chem. Soc.* 2586 (1949). (Synthesis)

987 Aspergillic Acid, $C_{12}H_{20}O_2N_2$, pale yellow needles, m.p. 97–99°, $[\alpha]_D^{25} +13.4°$ (c 1 in ethanol).

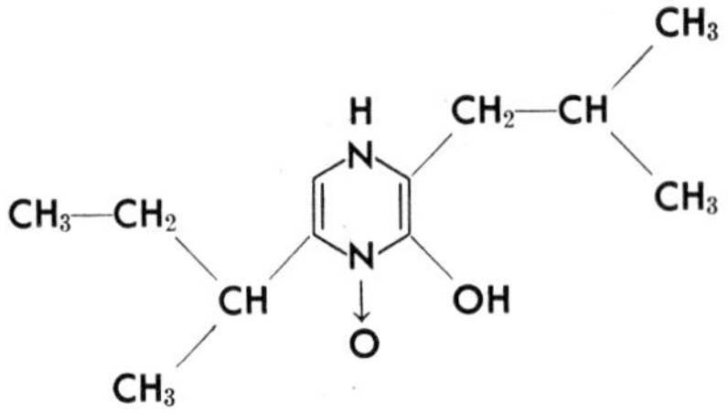

Aspergillus flavus

James D. Dutcher, *J. Biol. Chem.* **232** 785 (1958).

988 Granegillin, $C_{12}H_{20}O_2N_2$, pale yellow needles, m.p. 99–100°, optically inactive, the crystals have a characteristic odor (as does Aspergillic Acid).

The only important difference in properties between granegillin and aspergillic acid is the lack of optical activity in the former, and the two compounds may be identical.

A mold resembling *Aspergillus flavus*

A. Csillag, *Acta Microbiol.* (Hungary) 1 321 (1954); Abstr. in *Bull. Hyg.* **30** 159 (1955).

989 Hydroxyaspergillic Acid, $C_{12}H_{20}O_3N_2$, nearly colorless needles, m.p. 148–150°, $[\alpha]_D^{25}$ +36° (c 1 in ethanol).

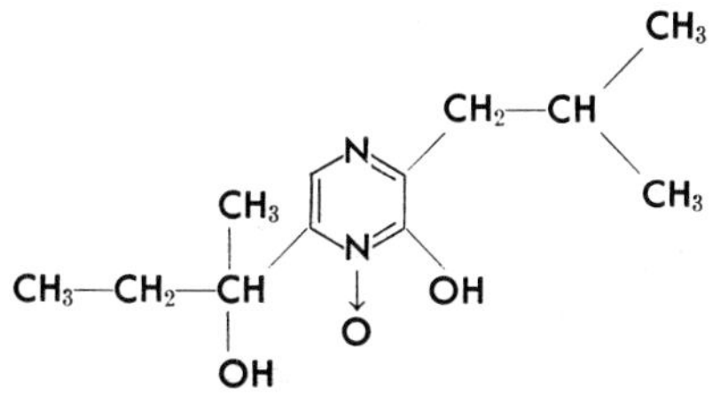

Aspergillus flavus
James D. Dutcher, *J. Biol. Chem.* **232** 785 (1958).

990 Neohydroxyaspergillic Acid, $C_{12}H_{20}O_3N_2$, colorless crystals, m.p. 164–166°, $[\alpha]_D^{25}$ −58° (c 1.01 in ethanol).
Aspergillus sclerotiorum
A yield of about 300 mg. per liter was obtained.
Ulrich Weiss, Frieda Strelitz, Helen Flon and Igor N. Asheshov, *Arch. Biochem. and Biophys.* 74 150 (1958).

991 Pulcherriminic Acid, $C_{12}H_{20}O_4N_2$, m.p. 173°.

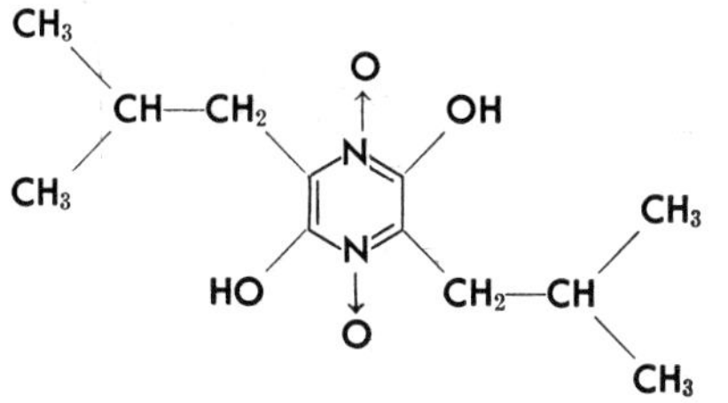

Candida pulcherrima (Lindner) Windisch
This compound was isolated as a red, iron-complexed

pigment called pulcherrimin, which probably has the structure:

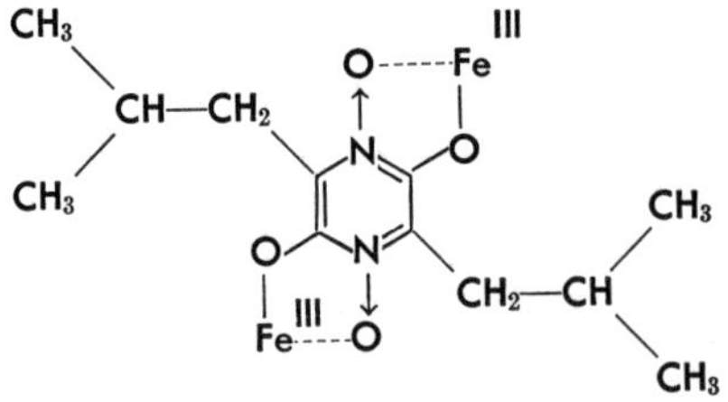

The yield was 30 mg. of pulcherrimin per gram of dry cells.

A. J. Kluyver, J. P. van der Walt and A. J. van Triet, *Proc. Nat. Acad. Sci. U. S.* 39 583 (1953).

A. H. Cook and C. A. Slater, *J. Chem. Soc.*, 4130, 4133, (1956). (Structure)

992 **Picrorocellin,** $C_{20}H_{22}O_4N_2$, colorless prisms, m.p. 192–194°, $[\alpha]_D$ +12.5°.

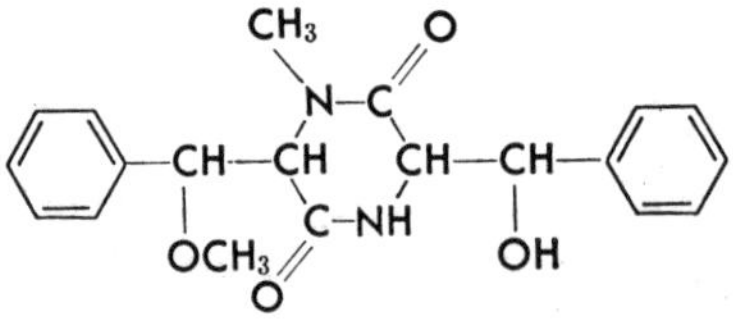

Roccella fuciformis Ach.

Martin Onslow Forster and William Bristow Saville, *J. Chem. Soc.*, 816 (1922).

993 **Mycelianamide,** $C_{22}H_{28}O_5N_2$, colorless leaflets, m.p. 170–172° (dec.), $[\alpha]_{5461}^{19}$ −217° (c 0.869 in chloroform).

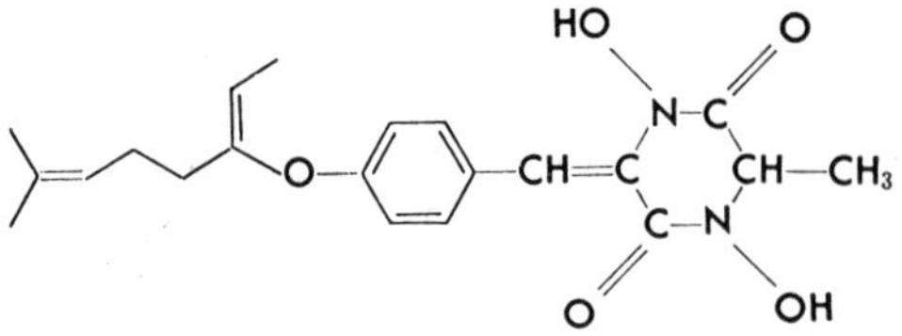

Penicillium griseofulvum

A. J. Birch, R. A. Massy-Westropp and R. W. Rickards, *J. Chem. Soc.*, 3717 (1956).
A. J. Birch, *Proc. Chem. Soc.*, 233 (1957).

l. PHENAZINES AND PHENOXAZONES

The phenazine bacterial pigments have been known for many years. Pyocyanine was probably isolated in the early 1860's, and oxychlororaphine was synthesized in 1930. New pigments of this type continue to be reported, usually from pseudomonas species, but also from streptomycetes. Pyocyanine is responsible for the blue-green color of pus, since *Pseudomonas aeruginosa* is a skin parasite, and certain other blue or green stains on natural materials have been identified with phenazine pigments.

The phenazine bacterial pigments have been reviewed,[1] and this introduction will be confined to a few remarks on biosynthesis. Actually, there is as yet little to be said on this subject. Several studies have been made concerning medium requirements and improvements for optimum pigment production in both growing[2] and stationary cultures.[3] In growing cultures a yield of 231 mg. of pyocyanine per liter was obtained on a medium containing glycerol, D,L-alanine, L-leucine and magnesium, calcium, phosphate, sulfate and ammonium ions.

In resting cultures glutamic acid and γ-aminobutyric acid were found to be the best substrates, yielding about 250 mg. of pyocyanine per liter. Pigment production was slow and inhibited by respiratory poisons (cyanide, azide) but not by fluoride.

These results are not very helpful in speculations on the biosynthetic intermediates.

Viewed in aggregate there is a noticeable recurrence of either hydroxyl or carboxyl groups at the 1-position, the 9-position or the 6-position of the phenazine nucleus.

[1] G. A. Swan and D. G. I. Felton, "Phenazines," Interscience Publishers, Inc., New York, 1957, pp. 174–191.
[2] M. O. Burton, J. J. R. Campbell and B. A. Eagles, *Can. J. Res.* 26C 15 (1948); M. O. Burton, B. A. Eagles and J. J. R. Campbell, *ibid.* 25C 121 (1947); G. Young, *J. Bacteriol.* 54 109 (1947); Esther Hellinger, *J. Gen. Microbiol.* 5 633 (1951).
[3] N. Grossowicz, Peyuta Hayat and Y. S. Halpern, *J. Gen. Microbiol.* 16 576 (1957).

This is reminiscent of the phenoxazones such as cinna-

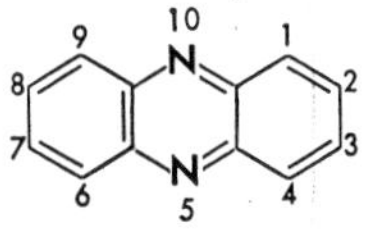

Phenazine 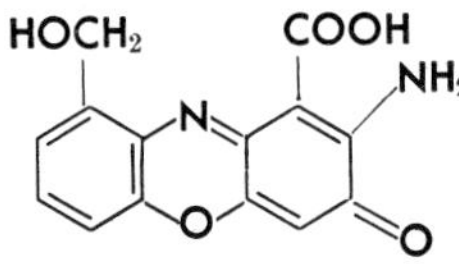   Cinnabarin 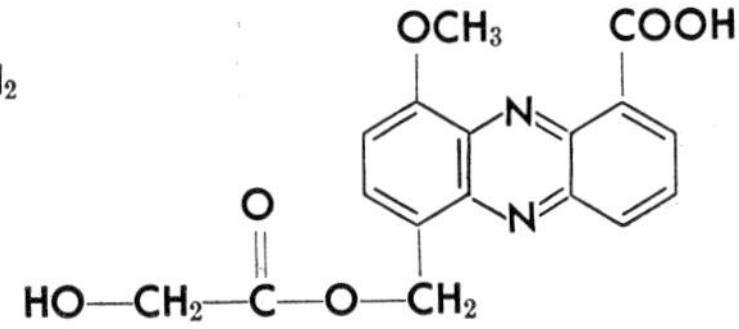   Griseolutein A

barin and actinocinin. The analogy perhaps can be developed farther, since a streptomycete pigment has been
found with an amino group in the 2-position.

The resemblance is sufficient to suggest anthranilic acid
or related substances as intermediates in the biosynthesis
of phenazines. Oxidative decarboxylations of aromatic
acids to phenols are not unknown among obligate aerobes
of the type that produce phenazines. Also 3-oxyanthra-
nilic acid might account for some of the phenolic hydroxyl
groups.

As for the coupling reaction, perhaps something akin
to phenolic-free radical coupling takes place. Photoirra-
diation of aniline at low temperatures has been reported
to produce phenazine.[4] Also tetraphenylhydrazine heated
to 90° apparently dissociates to a free radical which rearranges to (among other things) a dihydrophenazine.[5]

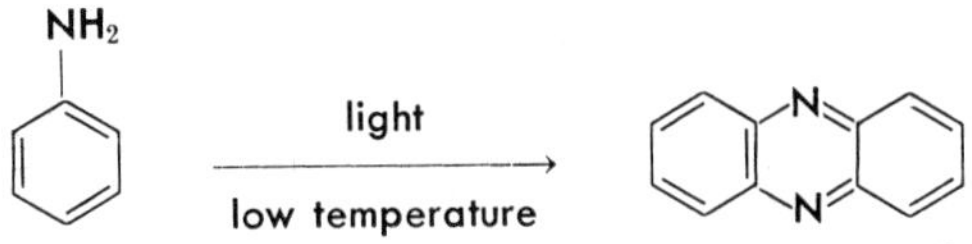

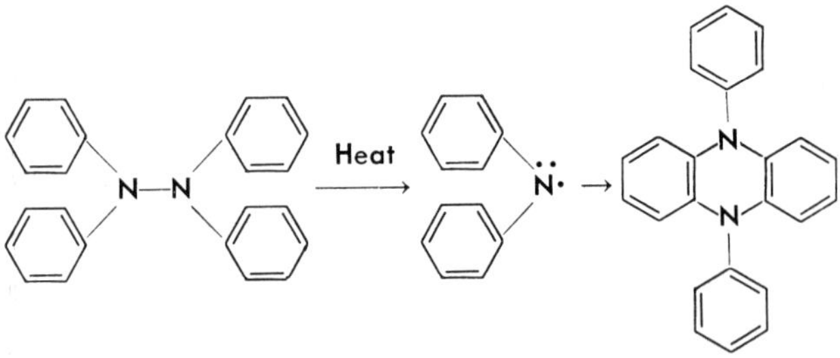

[4] A. N. Terenin, *Acta Physicochim. S.S.S.R.* 13 1 (1940); *Chem. Abstr.* 35 1701 (1941).

[5] G. W. Wheland, "Advanced Organic Chemistry," John Wiley and Sons, Inc., New York, 1949, pp. 727–728.

Atmospheric oxidation is enough to cause phenazine formation from 3,4-diaminoguaiacol.[6] This is a favorable case for free radical stabilization.

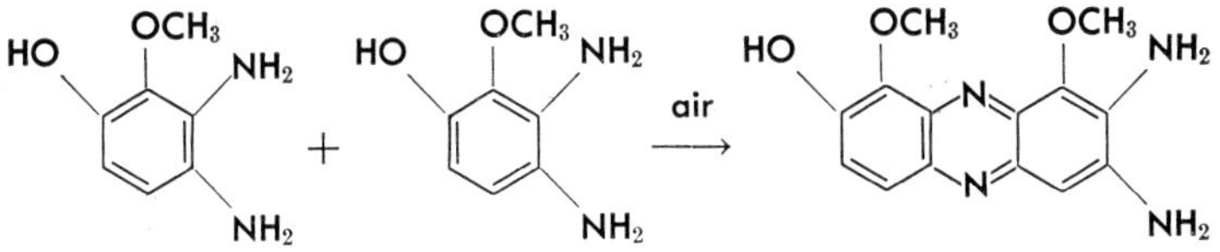

This argument of course is speculative.

994 **1-Phenazinol** (1-Hydroxyphenazine, Hemipyocyanine), $C_{12}H_8$-ON_2, orange crystals, m.p. 157° (sublimes).

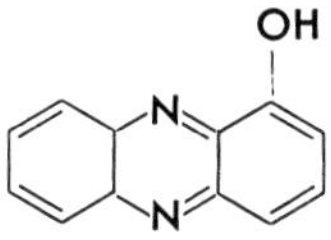

Pseudomonas aeruginosa
Fritz Wrede and E. Strack, Z. *physiol. Chem.* **177** 177 (1928).
G. M. Badger, R. S. Pearce and R. Pettit, *J. Chem. Soc.* 3204 (1951).
Walter S. Moos and John W. Rowen, *Arch. Biochem. and Biophys.* 43 88 (1953).

995 **1,6-Dihydroxyphenazine,** $C_{12}H_8O_2N_2$, golden yellow prisms, m.p. 274°.

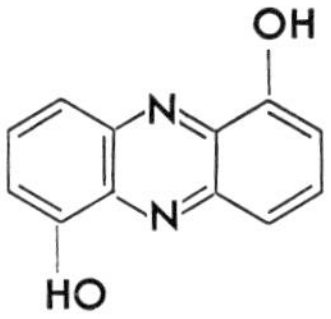

Streptomyces thioluteus
Hideshi Akabori and Michikazu Nakamura, *J. Antibiotics* (Japan) **12A** 17 (1959).

[6] Fr. Fichter and Julius Schwab, *Ber.* 39 3339 (1906).

996 **Iodinin** (1,6-Phenazinediol-5,10-dioxide), $C_{12}H_8O_4N_2$, purple crystals with a coppery glint, m.p. 236° (dec.).

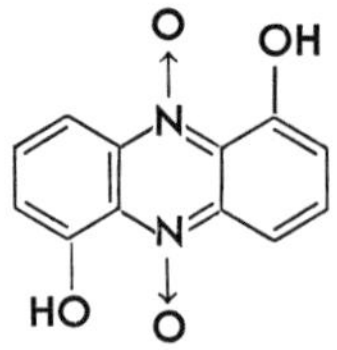

Chromobacterium iodinum
G. R. Clemo and A. F. Daglish, *J. Chem. Soc.*, 1481 (1950).

997 **Phenazine-1-carboxylic Acid,** $C_{13}H_8O_2N_2$, greenish yellow needles, m.p. 242°.

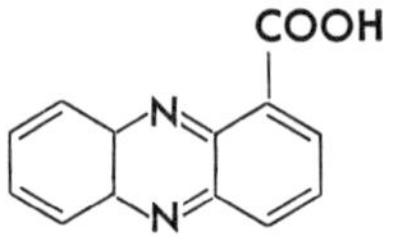

Pseudomonas aureofaciens Kluyver, *Streptomyces misakiensis, Calonectria*
Yields of about 1 g. per liter have been mentioned. The streptomycete produced another phenazine, $C_{17}H_{16}N_2O_2$, called tubermycin A. A pigment closely related to phenazine-1-carboxylic acid was also isolated by Kluyver from the pseudomonas organism.
A. J. Kluyver, *J. Bacteriol.* **72** 406 (1956).
Wm. C. Haynes, Frank H. Stodola, Joan M. Locke, Thomas G. Pridham, Howard F. Conway, Virgil E. Sohns and Richard W. Jackson, *ibid.* **72** 412 (1956).
Kiyoshi Isono, Kentaro Anzai and Saburo Suzuki, *J. Antibiotics* (Japan) **11A** 264 (1959).

998 **Oxychlororaphine,** $C_{13}H_9ON_3$, yellow needles, m.p. 237° (sublimes in the absence of O_2, giving yellow crystals, m.p. 241°).

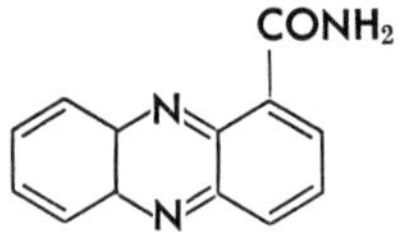

Pseudomonas chlororaphis
Fritz Kögl and J. J. Postowsky, *Ann.* **480** 280 (1930). (Synthesis)

999 Chlororaphine, green crystals, m.p. (in the absence of O_2) 225° (dec.) (in the presence of O_2 sublimes at 210°, giving a yellow sublimate).

Chlororaphine in the crystalline state is a molecular compound of phenazine-1-carboxamide and its dihydro derivative in the ratio of 3:1.

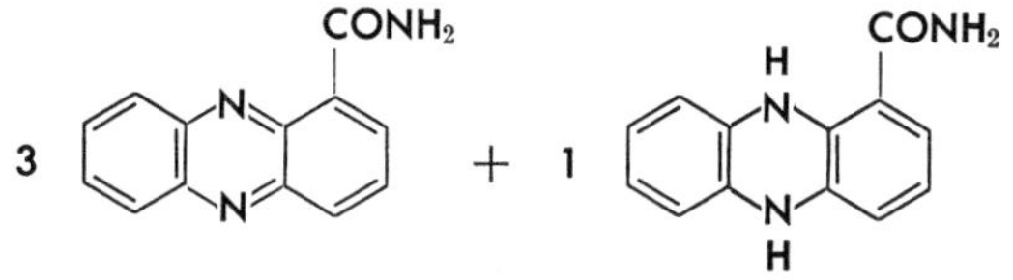

Charles Dufraisse, André Etienne and Edmond Toromanoff, *Compt. rend.* 235 920 (1952).

But in solution in the pH range 1.75–10.85 (particularly at lower pH) chlororaphine exists largely in the semi-quinone form:

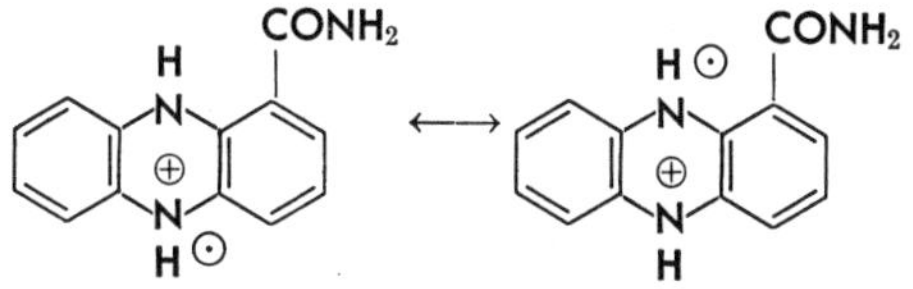

Carlo Cattaneo, Guido Sartori and M. Morellini, *Gazz. chim. ital.* 77 381 (1947).

Pseudomonas chlororaphis
Fritz Kögl and J. J. Postowsky, *Ann.* 480 280 (1930).

1000 Pyocyanine, $C_{13}H_{12}N_2O$, dark blue needles, m.p. 133°, decomposes to 1-phenazinol on standing in light and air.

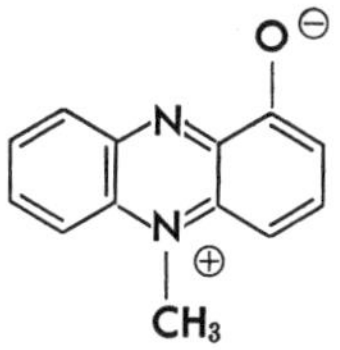

Pseudomonas aeruginosa (Bacillus pyocyaneus), Cyanococcus chromospirans
Heinz Hilleman, *Ber.* 71B 46 (1938). (Structure)
G. Farber, *Sbornik Ceskoslov. Akad. Zemedelske* 23 355 (1951); *Chem. Abstr.* 45 9605 (1951).

1001 Cinnabarin (Polystictin), $C_{14}H_{10}O_5N_2$, red needles, m.p.: dec. >320°.

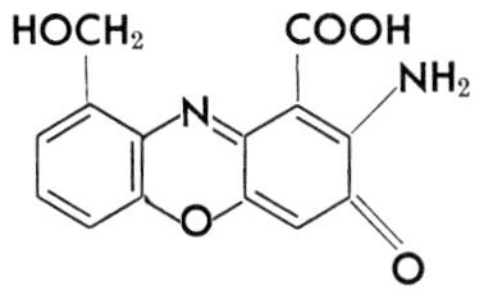

Coriolus sanguineus Fr. [= *Polyporus cinnabarinus* Fr. = *P. sanguineus* Fr. = *P. coccineus* Fr. = *P. puniceus* Kalch. = *Polystictus cinnabarinus* (Jacq.) = *P. sanguineus* L. = *P. semisanguineus* Lloyd = *Trametes cinnabarina* (Jacq.) Fr.]

About 100 mg. of red pigment were obtained from 55 g. of mycelium.

Jarl Gripenberg, *Acta Chem. Scand.* 5 590 (1951).

G. W. K. Cavill, B. J. Ralph, J. R. Tetaz and R. W. Werner, *J. Chem. Soc.*, 525 (1953).

Jarl Gripenberg, *Acta Chem. Scand.* 12 603 (1958). (Structure)

The same phenoxazone chromophore which occurs in cinnabarin and the actinomycins has been found in certain insect pigments called ommatins, *e.g.* xanthommatin:

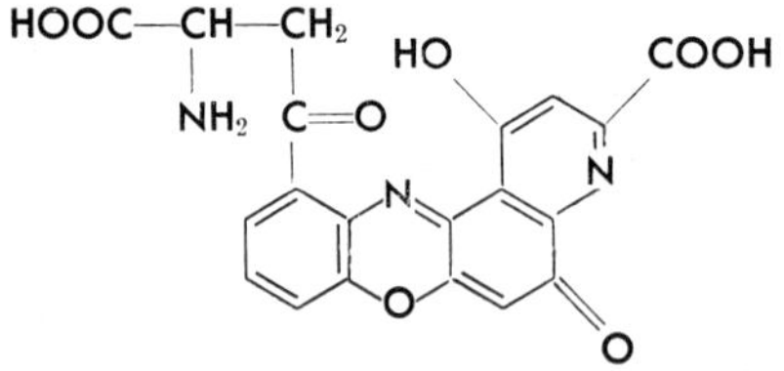

Adolf Butenandt, Ulrich Schiedt, Ernst Bickert and R. Jan. T. Cromartie, *Ann.* 590 75 (1954).

1002 Pigment A, $C_{14}H_{11}O_2N_3 \cdot 2H_2O$, red crystals, dec. without melting. Tentative structure:

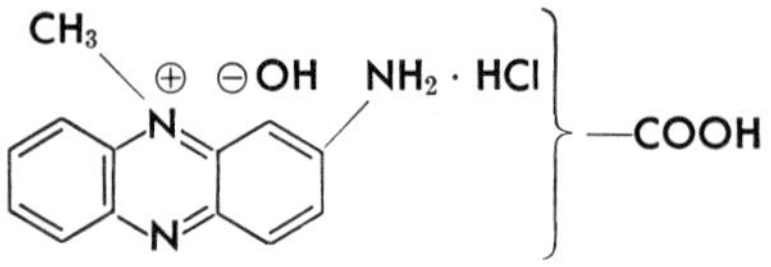

Yield 12–20 mg. per liter
and

1003   **Pigment B,** $C_{15}H_{15}O_6N_3S$ (may also be hydrated), red crystals, dec. without melting.

An acidic pigment similar to A in structure, but with an additional methyl group and a sulfo group. Yield 30–40 mg. per liter.

Both produced by a red strain of *Pseudomonas aeruginosa*.

F. G. Holliman, *Chem. and Ind.*, 1668 (1957).

1004   **Griseolutein A,** $C_{17}H_{14}O_6N_2$, reddish yellow needles, m.p. 193° (dec.).

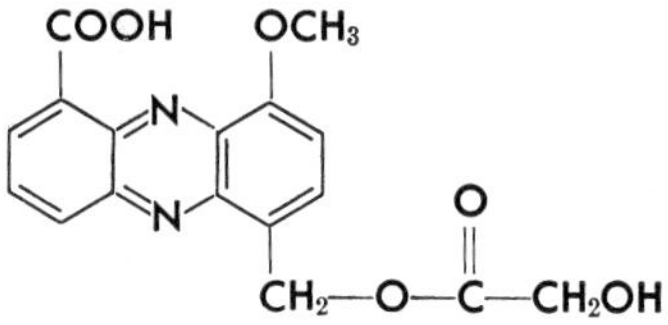

COOH   OCH₃

$CH_2—O—\overset{\overset{\displaystyle O}{\|}}{C}—CH_2OH$

Streptomyces griseoluteus

Shoshiro Nakamura, *Chem. and Pharm. Bull.* (Japan) **6** 547 (1958).

1005   **Griseolutein B,** $C_{17}H_{16}O_6N_2$, pale yellow crystals, darkening from 150°, dec. above 220°. Griseolutein B is a phenazine with the following proposed structure:

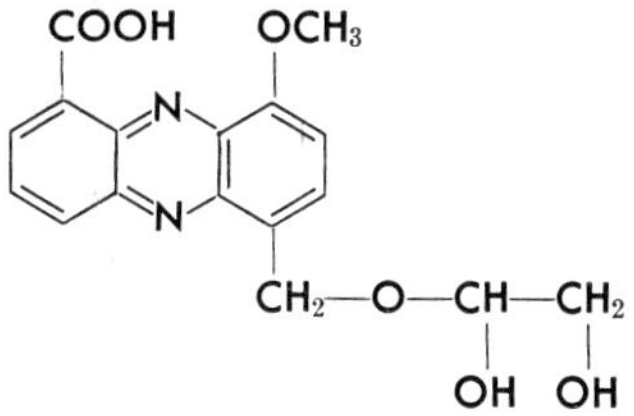

COOH   OCH₃

$CH_2—O—CH—CH_2$

OH OH

Streptomyces griseoluteus n. sp.

Hamao Umezawa, Seiki Hayano, Kenji Maeda, Yasuo Ogata and Yoshiro Okami, *J. Antibiotics* (Japan) 4 34 (1951).

Teisuke Osato, Kenji Maeda and Hamao Umezawa, *ibid.* **7A** 15 (1954).

Shoshiro Nakamura, Kenji Maeda, Teisuke Osato and Hamao Umezawa, *ibid.* **10A** 265 (1957).

Shoshiro Nakamura, *Chem. and Pharm. Bull.* (Japan) **6** 547 (1958).

m. PYRIMIDINES

Pyrimidines are fundamental components of living cells. They have long been recognized as constituents of nucleic acids, and more recently other functions have been discovered.

Microorganisms are rather rich in nucleoproteins. Yeast, which has been a common experimental source, contains about 4 percent of its dry weight in nucleic acids, and bacteria up to 15 percent. Bacteriophages are largely nucleoprotein, and certain plant viruses entirely. By contrast, thymus gland, one of the richer animal tissue sources, contains only about 3 percent.

The protein moieties often are relatively low in molecular weight, some of them qualifying as large peptides, and they generally seem to be rich in basic amino acids. The total nucleoprotein molecular weights, however, are very high—often running to many millions. The complexity of the nucleic acid moiety varies with the complexity of the species. Since the DNA carries the genetic information, it might be expected to be more complex and higher in molecular weight for the human species than, for example, in a simple plant virus.

Two types of nucleic acids have been distinguished, both widely distributed. Ribose nucleic acid (RNA) and deoxyribose nucleic acid (DNA) have been mentioned earlier in connection with their roles in protein synthesis and genetics.

Neither of these substances has been obtained entirely pure, but newer techniques such as electrophoresis and paper chromatography have permitted refinements. The important purine and pyrimidine components of RNA are adenine, guanine, cytosine and uracil. In DNA thymine takes the place of uracil, and 5-methylcytosine is a minor

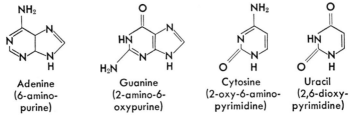

Adenine
(6-amino-
purine)

Guanine
(2-amino-6-
oxypurine)

Cytosine
(2-oxy-6-amino-
pyrimidine)

Uracil
(2,6-dioxy-
pyrimidine)

component in some species.

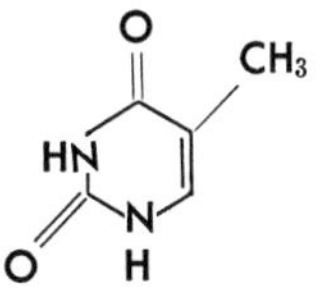

Thymine
(2,6-dioxy-5-
methylpyrimidine)

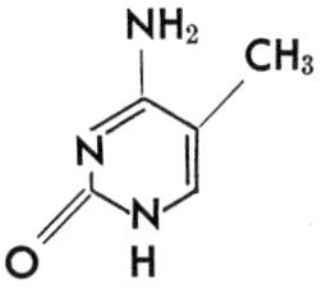

5-Methyl
cytosine
(2-oxy-5-methyl-
6-aminopyrimidine)

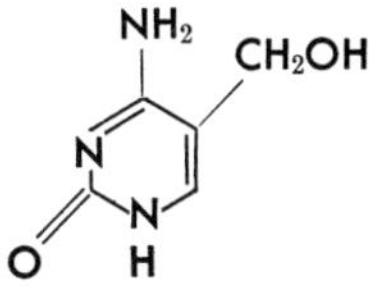

5-Hydroxymethyl
cytosine
(2-oxy-5-hydroxy-
methyl-6-amino-
pyrimidine)

In some *Escherichia coli* bacteriophages the 5-methylcytosine is replaced by 5-hydroxymethylcytosine. A substance believed to be 5-ribosyluracil has been isolated in considerable quantities from yeast RNA.

The united pyrimidine and ribose moieties are called nucleosides, and the phosphorylated nucleosides are called nucleotides.

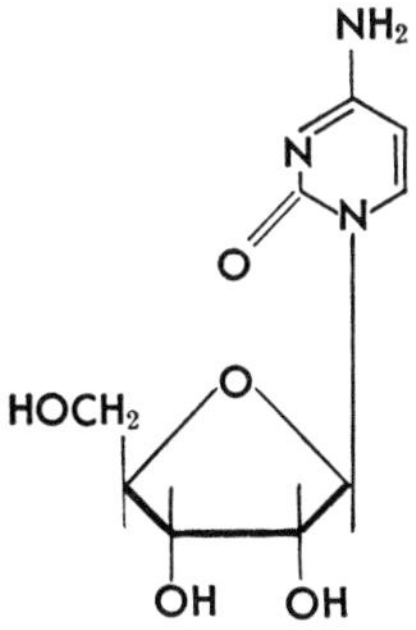

Cytidine
(a nucleoside)

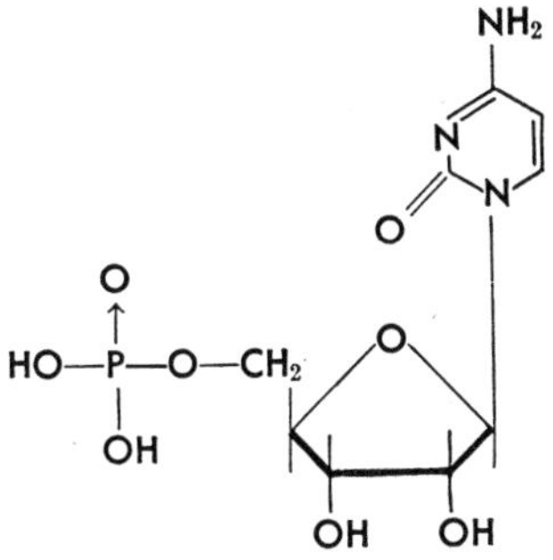

Cytidylic Acid
(a nucleotide)

The nucleic acids are, then, polymeric nucleotides, a free phosphoric acid function being esterified by a free pentose alcohol group.

In neither RNA nor DNA are the four main heterocyclic components present in equimolar quantities, and, moreover, there is of course species variation. For example, yeast DNA contains more adenine and thymine than guanosine and cytosine, while the reverse is true for some bacteria. The molar sum of the purines generally equals that of the pyrimidines, and, more specifically, the number of moles of adenine present equals the number of moles of thymine, and the cytosine (and methylcytosine) equals the guanine.

There is good evidence now that most DNA is composed

of a helical coil of paired strands, the strands and coils being associated by hydrogen bonding, *e.g.*, between the amino group of adenine and the carbonyl group of thymine.[1] This structure is supported by roentgen ray diffraction data, by acid-base titration studies and by light-scattering measurements on solutions. There are some recent indications, however, that single-stranded DNA does exist in some cases.

Tobacco mosaic virus, a crystalline substance which has been investigated extensively, consists of a single strand of RNA coiled within a protein sheath. The degree of organization (non-covalent bonding) in the nucleic acid moieties of nucleoproteins has been studied.[2] In some instances the nucleic acids seem to be less organized in the intact protein than in the free state.

Pyrimidine nucleotides also serve as coenzymes in a number of biological reactions. Thus uridine nucleotide is important in the enzymic manipulation of sugars. In recent years, uridine-5'-diphosphate sugar esters have been isolated from a variety of animal, plant and microbial sources.

Confining our attention to microorganisms, uridine diphosphate glucose, UDP-galactose, UDP-acetylglucosamine as well as uridine triphosphate (UTP) and uridine-diphosphate (UDP) have been isolated from yeast.[3, 4, 5] The same substances have been isolated from *Penicillium chrysogenum* mycelium.[6] Other free nucleotides identified from the mold were: diphosphophyridine nucleotide (DPN), cytidine-5'-monophosphate (CMP), adenosine-5'-monophosphate (AMP), triphosphopyridine nucleotide (TPN), guanosine-5'-monophosphate (GMP), inosine-5'-monophosphate (IMP), uridine-5'-monophosphate (UMP),

[1] J. D. Watson and F. H. C. Crick, *Nature* 171 737, 964 (1953).

[2] F. Bonhoeffer and H. K. Schachman, *Biochem. and Biophys. Res. Comms.* 2 366 (1960).

[3] R. Caputto, Luis F. Leloir, C. E. Cardini and A. C. Paladini, *J. Biol. Chem.* 184 333 (1950); E. Cabib, Luis F. Leloir and C. E. Cardini, *ibid.* 203 1055 (1953).

[4] S. H. Lipton, S. A. Morell, Alexander Frieden and Robert M. Bock, *J. Am. Chem. Soc.* 75 5449 (1953).

[5] Hanns Schmitz, *Biochem. Z.* 325 555 (1954).

[6] A. Ballio, C. Casinovi and G. Serlupi-Crescenzi, *Biochim. et Biophys. Acta* 20 414 (1956).

adenosine-5'-diphosphate (ADP), guanosine-5'-diphosphate mannose (GDPM), adenosine-5'-triphosphate (ATP) and guanosine-5'-triphosphate (GTP).

The UTP is an intermediate in the formation of the diphosphate:[7, 8]

UTP + Sugar-1-phosphate $\rightleftharpoons$ UDP-Sugar + Pyrophosphate

Once in the form of UDP esters, sugars are susceptible to a variety of enzymic transformations, some of which were mentioned in the section on polypeptides. For example, 4-epimerization may be caused:[3, 9]

UDP-Glucose $\rightleftharpoons$ UDP-Galactose

and

UDP-D-Xylose $\rightleftharpoons$ UDP-L-Arabinose

Since there is a DPN requirement in these reactions, it is likely that the 4-hydroxyl group of the sugar is oxidized to a ketone, then reduced stereospecifically. Isotope work supports this hypothesis.[10, 11, 12] UDPG can be oxidized also to UDP-glucuronate:[13, 14]

$$\text{UDP-Glucose} \xrightarrow[\text{H}_2\text{O}]{\text{2DPN}} \xleftarrow[\text{2DPNH}]{\text{3H}^{\oplus}} \text{UDP-Glucuronic Acid}$$

A yeast enzyme catalyzes the reaction:[15, 16]

UDP-Glucose + Glucose-6-phosphate $\longrightarrow$ Trehalose Phosphate + UDP

Similarly, di- and polysaccharides seem to be formed

[7] Paul E. Trucco, *Arch. Biochem. and Biophys.* 34 482 (1951).

[8] Agnete Munch-Petersen, Herman M. Kalckar, Enrico Cutolo and Evelyn E. B. Smith, *Nature* 172 1036 (1953).

[9] Luis F. Leloir, *Arch. Biochem. and Biophys.* 33 186 (1951).

[10] Arthur Kowalsky and Daniel E. Koshland, *Biochim. et Biophys. Acta* 22 575 (1956).

[11] Laurens Anderson, Aurora M. Landel and Donald F. Diedrich, *ibid.* 22 573 (1956).

[12] Herman M. Kalckar and Elizabeth S. Maxwell, *ibid.* 22 589 (1956).

[13] V. Ginsburg, E. F. Neufeld and W. Z. Hassid, *Proc. Nat. Acad. Sci. U. S.* 42 333 (1956); V. Ginsburg, *J. Biol. Chem.* 232 55 (1958).

[14] Evelyn E. B. Smith, Agnete Munch-Petersen and George T. Mills, *Nature* 172 1038 (1953).

[15] E. Cabib and Luis F. Leloir, *J. Biol. Chem.* 231 259 (1958).

[16] Luis F. Leloir and E. Cabib, *J. Am. Chem. Soc.* 75 5445 (1953).

in this way. Involvement in chitin (*Neurospora crassa*)[17] and cellulose (*Acetobacter xylinum*)[18] biosynthesis has been shown with labeled UDP-acetylglucosamine and UDP-glucose, respectively, and work with tritium-labeled substrates and cell-free extracts of group A streptococci has shown involvement in hyaluronate biosynthesis.[19] Other evidence indicates involvement in glucuronide[20, 21] and glycogen[22, 23] formation in animals, and glucoside[24, 25] formation in plants. UMP,[26] UDP, UTP[27, 28] and UDP-glucose[29, 30] have been synthesized chemically.

Several cytidine nucleotides have been isolated from natural sources.[31, 32, 33] CDP-Choline and CDP-ethanolamine have been isolated from animals,[33] plants and yeasts[34]

[17] Luis Glaser and David H. Brown, *Biochim. et Biophys. Acta* **23** 449 (1957); *idem., J. Biol. Chem.* **228** 729 (1957).

[18] Luis Glaser, *Biochim. et Biophys. Acta* **25** 436 (1957); *idem., J. Biol. Chem.* **232** 627 (1958).

[19] Alvin Markovitz, J. A. Cifonelli and Albert Dorfman, *Biochim. et Biophys. Acta* **28** 453 (1958).

[20] Evelyn E. B. Smith and George T. Mills, *Biochim. et Biophys. Acta* **13** 386 (1954).

[21] G. J. Dutton and I. D. E. Storey, *Biochem. J.* **57** 275 (1954); **59** 279 (1955).

[22] Luis F. Leloir and C. E. Cardini, *J. Am. Chem. Soc.* **79** 6340 (1957); L. F. Leloir, J. M. Olavarria, Sara H. Goldemberg and H. Carminatti, *Arch. Biochem. and Biophys.* **81** 508 (1959).

[23] P. W. Robbins, R. R. Traut and F. Lipmann, *Proc. Nat. Acad. Sci. U. S.* **45** 6 (1959).

[24] G. Jacobelli, M. J. Tabone and D. Tabone, *Bull. soc. chim. biol.* **40** 955 (1958).

[25] C. E. Cardini and L. F. Leloir, *Nature* **182** 1446 (1958).

[26] Alexander R. Todd, "Methods in Enzymology" (S. P. Colowick and N. O. Kaplan, Editors) Academic Press, New York, 1957 **3** p. 811.

[27] R. B. Hurlbert, *ibid.,* p. 785.

[28] G. W. Kenner, A. R. Todd and F. J. Weymouth, *J. Chem. Soc.,* 3675 (1952); N. Annand, V. M. Clark, R. H. Hall and A. R. Todd, *ibid.,* 3665 (1952).

[29] G. W. Kenner, A. R. Todd and R. F. Webb, *ibid.,* 2843 (1954).

[30] Robert Warner Chambers, J. G. Moffatt and H. G. Khorana, *J. Am. Chem. Soc.* **79** 4240 (1957); J. G. Moffatt and H. G. Khorana, *ibid.* **80** 3756 (1958).

[31] Rolf Bergquist and Adam Deutsch, *Acta Chem. Scand.* **7** 1307 (1953).

[32] Hanns Schmitz, Robert B. Hurlbert and Van R. Potter, *J. Biol. Chem.* **209** 41 (1954).

[33] Eugene P. Kennedy and Samuel B. Weiss, *J. Am. Chem. Soc.* **77** 250 (1955); *idem., J. Biol. Chem.* **222** 193 (1956).

[34] Irving Lieberman, L. Berger and W. Theodore Gimenez, *Science* **124** 81 (1956).

and seem to be nearly ubiquitous, although so far they have not been reported from other microorganisms. CDP-Glycerol and CDP-ribitol have been isolated only from lactobacilli,[35] but probably such substances will be found elsewhere.

CDP-Choline and CDP-ethanolamine are coenzymes essential to the biosynthesis of lecithin and phosphotidyl-ethanolamine.[33] The stages in the biosynthesis of lecithin may be outlined:

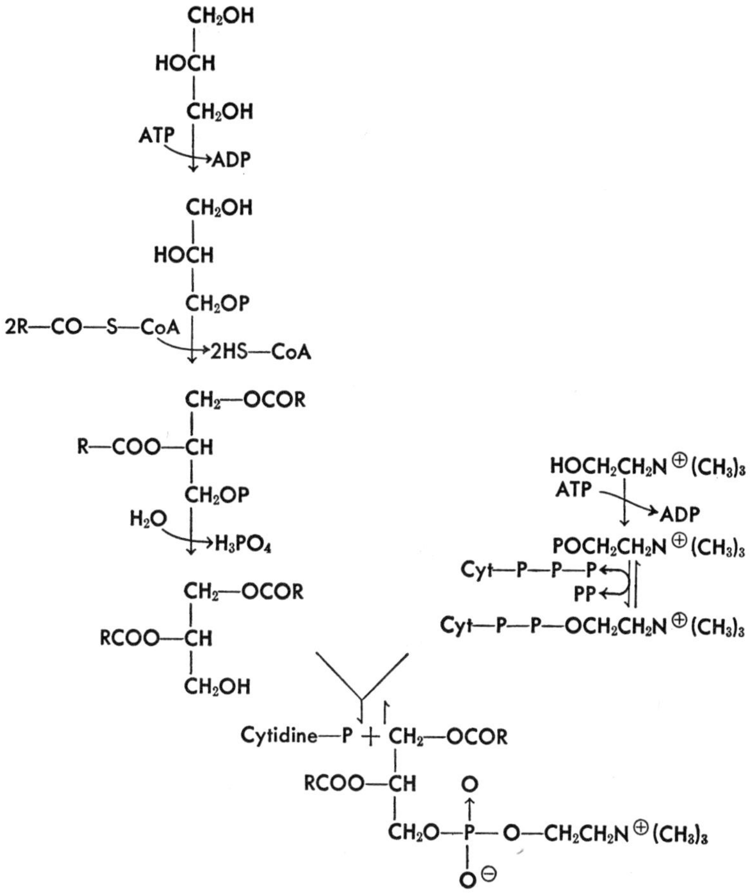

CH_2OH
|
$HOCH$
|
CH_2OH

ATP |
$\searrow$ ADP

CH_2OH
|
$HOCH$
|
CH_2OP

$2R-CO-S-CoA$ |
$\searrow$ 2HS—CoA

CH_2-OCOR
|
$R-COO-CH$
|
CH_2OP

H_2O |
$\searrow$ H_3PO_4

CH_2-OCOR
|
$RCOO-CH$
|
CH_2OH

$HOCH_2CH_2N^{\oplus}(CH_3)_3$

ATP
$\searrow$ ADP

$POCH_2CH_2N^{\oplus}(CH_3)_3$

Cyt—P—P—P
PP

Cyt—P—P—OCH$_2$CH$_2$N$^{\oplus}$(CH$_3$)$_3$

Cytidine—P + CH_2-OCOR
|
$RCOO-CH$ O
| ↑
$CH_2O-P-O-CH_2CH_2N^{\oplus}(CH_3)_3$
|
$O^{\ominus}$

The cytidine monophosphate can then be rephosphoryl-

[35] J. Baddiley and A. P. Mathias, *J. Chem. Soc.*, 2723 (1954); J. Baddiley, J. G. Buchanan, B. Cares, A. P. Mathias and A. R. Sanderson, *Biochem. J.* 64 599 (1956).

ated to the triphosphate by ATP, making the process a catalytic one.

The function of the CDP-ribitol and CDP-glycerol in *Lactobacillus arabinosus* seems to be to donate these two reduced sugar phosphates in the formation of polymers. These ribitol-glycerol-phosphate polymers are components of the cell walls of bacteria. Several references are given in Appendix A to structural studies on these substances.

Biosynthesis of the pyrimidines seems to take a similar course in microorganisms and in higher animals. So many workers have contributed to our knowledge of this scheme that referencing cannot be included, but in outline what is now believed to be the important pathway is shown below:

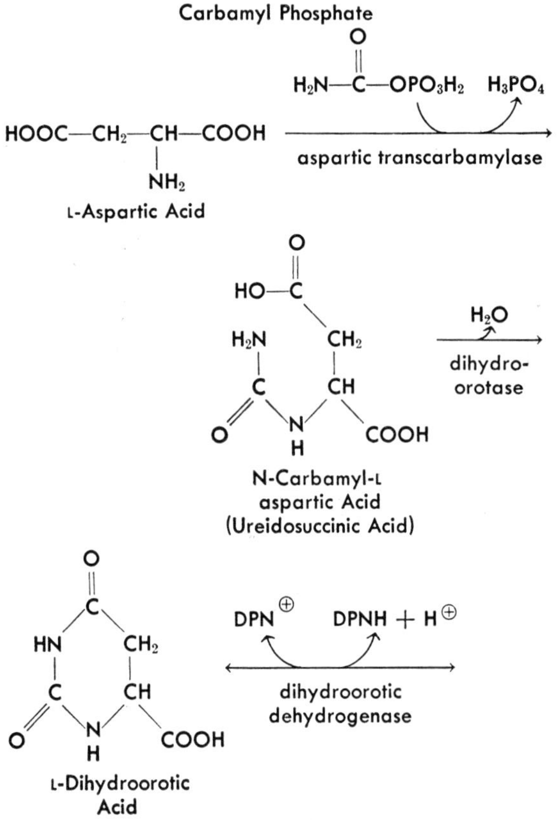

Carbamyl Phosphate

$$\underset{\text{aspartic transcarbamylase}}{\text{HOOC—CH}_2\text{—CH—COOH} \xrightarrow{\hspace{2cm}} \underset{}{}}$$

NH$_2$

L-Aspartic Acid

$H_2N\text{—C—OPO}_3H_2 \quad H_3PO_4$

N-Carbamyl-L
aspartic Acid
(Ureidosuccinic Acid)

dihydro-
orotase

L-Dihydroorotic
Acid

DPN$^{\oplus}$ DPNH + H$^{\oplus}$

dihydroorotic
dehydrogenase

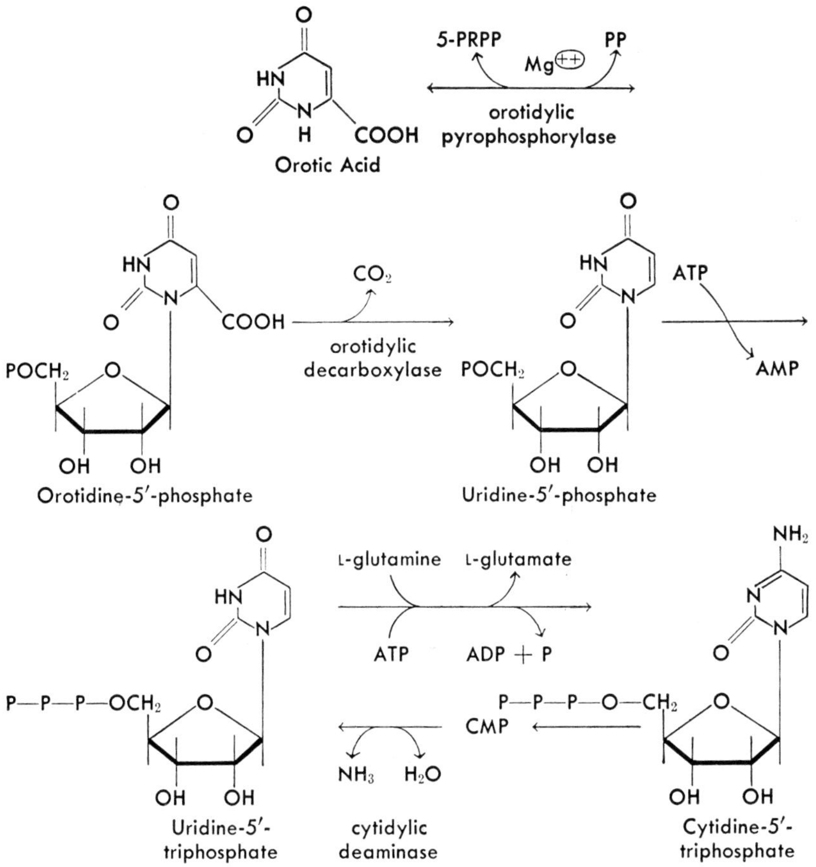

O

HN

O   H   COOH

Orotic Acid

5-PRPP   PP

$Mg^{\oplus\oplus}$

orotidylic
pyrophosphorylase

O

HN

O   COOH

POCH₂   O

OH   OH

Orotidine-5'-phosphate

CO_2

orotidylic
decarboxylase

O

HN

O

POCH₂   O

OH   OH

Uridine-5'-phosphate

ATP

AMP

O

HN

O

P—P—P—OCH₂   O

OH   OH

Uridine-5'-
triphosphate

L-glutamine   L-glutamate

ATP   ADP + P

NH_3 H_2O

cytidylic
deaminase

CMP

NH₂

N

O   N

P—P—P—O—CH₂   O

OH   OH

Cytidine-5'-
triphosphate

The biosynthesis of the deoxyribonucleotides may proceed similarly as far as uridine-5'-phosphate. Direct transfer into the deoxyribose series (*i.e.* removal of the 2'-hydroxyl from the ribose moiety) can then occur, or hydrolysis to the pyrimidine base and subsequent reaction with 2-deoxyribose-1-phosphate can take place.

There has been much interest in the origin of the 5-methyl group in thymine (5-methyluracil). The occurrence of 5-hydroxymethylcytosine in some species suggested donation (in that series) by a tetrahydrofolic acid derivative. Isotope experiments indicate that the α-C-atom of glycine, the β-C-atom of serine and the C-atom of formate can all serve as donors at least indirectly.[36, 37] There is a vitamin B_{12} requirement for the conversion of formate to the thymine methyl group in *Lactobacillus leichmannii,* and the pathway does not involve methionine or a hydroxymethyl group.[38] It has been suggested that since vitamin B_{12} coenzymes are required to promote the equilibrium

$$HOOC-CH_2-CH_2-\underset{\underset{NH_2}{|}}{CH}-COOH \rightleftharpoons HOOC-\underset{\underset{CH_3}{|}}{CH}-\underset{\underset{NH_2}{|}}{CH}-COOH$$

Glutamic Acid β-Methylaspartic Acid

β-methylaspartic acid may replace aspartic acid as an intermediate in thymine biosynthesis.[39]

An alternate pathway of pyrimidine biosynthesis involving dihydrouracil, a member of the catabolic route, has been suggested.[40]

4,5-Dihydrouracil   4,5-Diaminouracil

The entire subject of the enzymic synthesis of pyrimidines has been reviewed.[41]

4,5-Diaminouracil has been detected as a metabolite of *Eremothecium ashbyii* and suggested as an intermediate in riboflavin biosynthesis.[42]

[36] David Elwyn and David B. Sprinson, *J. Biol. Chem.* **207** 467 (1954); idem., *J. Am. Chem. Soc.* **72** 3317 (1950).

[37] J. R. Totter, Elliott Volkin and C. E. Carter, *J. Am. Chem. Soc.* **73** 1521 (1951); J. R. Totter and Audrey N. Best, *Arch. Biochem. and Biophys.* **54** 318 (1955).

[38] James S. Dinning, Barbara K. Allen, Ruth Young and Paul L. Day, *J. Biol. Chem.* **233** 674 (1958).

[39] H. D. Isenberg, E. Seifter and J. I. Berkman, *Biochim. et Biophys. Acta* **39** 187 (1960).

[40] Lewis C. Mokrasch and Santiago Grisolia, *Biochim. et Biophys. Acta* **27** 227 (1958).

[41] Peter Reichard, *Advances in Enzymology* **21** 263–294 (1959).

[42] T. W. Goodwin and D. H. Treble, *Biochem. J.* **67** 10p (1957).

1006 **Uracil,** $C_4H_4O_2N_2$, colorless needles, m.p. ~335° (dec.).

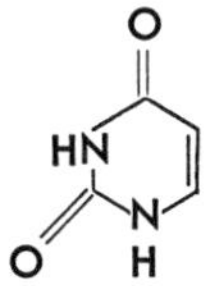

Agaricus nebularis, yeasts
Nils Löfgren, Björn Lüning and Harry Hedström, *Acta Chem. Scand.* **8** 670 (1954).

1007 **Cytosine,** $C_4H_5ON_3$, large colorless crystals, m.p. ~320° (dec.).

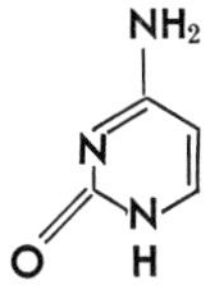

Agaricus nebularis
Nils Löfgren, Björn Lüning and Harry Hedström, *Acta Chem. Scand.* **8** 670 (1954).

1008 **4,5-Diaminouracil,** $C_4H_6O_2N_4$, has been shown to be a metabolite of *Eremothecium ashbyii* by trapping with diacetyl.

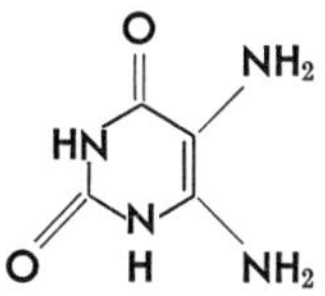

T. W. Goodwin and D. H. Treble, *Biochem. J.* **67** 10p (1957).

1009 **Uridine,** $C_9H_{12}O_6N_2$, colorless crystals, m.p. 165°, $[\alpha]_D^{20}$ +6.4° (10°) (in water).

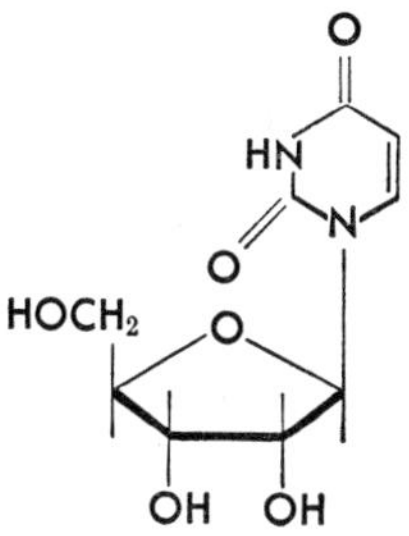

Yeast
Hellmut Bredereck, Annelise Martini and Friedrich Richter,
Ann. 74 694 (1941).
Hubert S. Loring and James McT. Ploeser, *J. Biol. Chem.*
178 439 (1949).

1010 **Cytidine,** $C_9H_{13}O_5N_3$, colorless needles, m.p. 225–230° (dec.),
$[\alpha]_D^{20}$ +29.6° (in water).

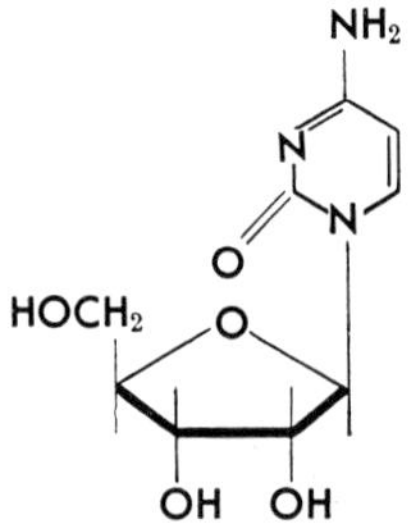

Yeast
Hellmut Bredereck, Annelise Martini and Friedrich Richter,
Ann. 74 694 (1941).

1011 **Uridine-3′-phosphate** (Uridylic Acid), $C_9H_{13}O_9N_2P$, colorless
prisms, m.p. 200° (dec.), $[\alpha]_D$ +9.5 to 14.5° (in water).

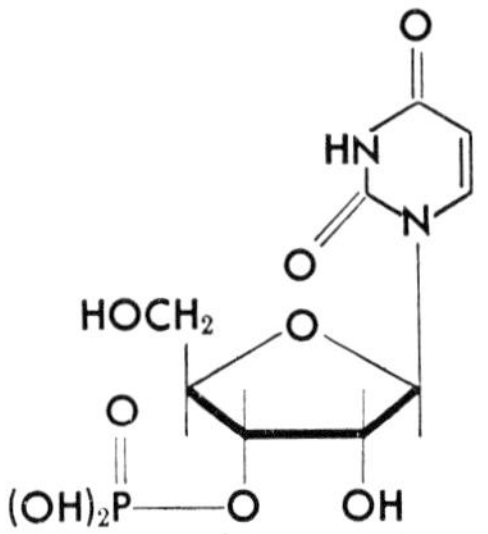

Yeast
The 5′-di- and triphosphates also have been isolated
from microorganisms.
Hellmut Bredereck and Gerd Richter, *Ber.* 71B 718 (1938).
W. E. Cohn and C. E. Carter, *J. Am. Chem. Soc.* 72 2606
(1950).
A. M. Michelson and A. R. Todd, *J. Chem. Soc.*, 2476 (1949).

1012 Cytidine-2′-phosphate (Cytidylic Acid) $C_9H_{14}O_8N_3P$, colorless crystals, m.p. 238–240° (dec.), $[\alpha]_D$ +20.7° (c 1.0 in water).

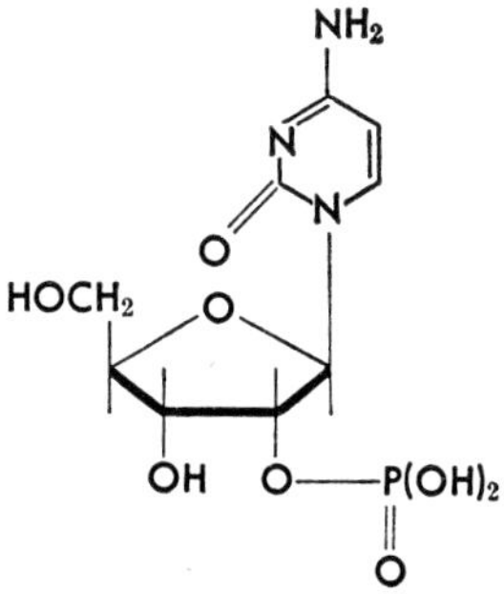

Yeast

Hubert S. Loring, Nydia G. Luthy, Henry W. Bortner and Luis W. Levy, *J. Am. Chem. Soc.* **72** 2811 (1950).

Hubert S. Loring and Nydia G. Luthy, *ibid.* **73** 4215 (1951).

1013 Cytidine-3′-phosphate (Cytidylic Acid), $C_9H_{14}O_8N_3P$, colorless tablets, m.p. 230–234° (dec.), $[\alpha]_D$ +49°. (c 0.5 in water).

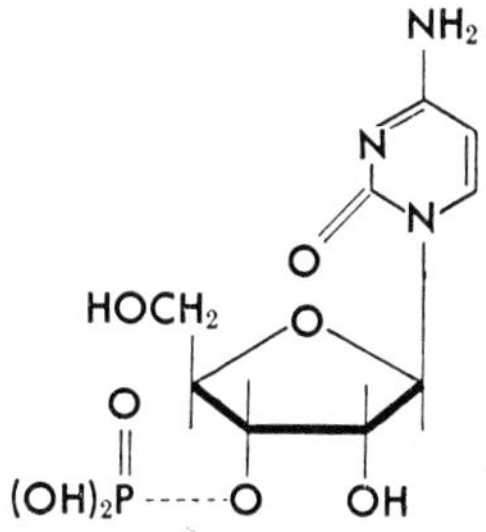

Yeast

The 5′-di- and triphosphates also have been isolated from microorganisms.

Hubert S. Loring, Nydia G. Luthy, Henry W. Bortner and Luis W. Levy, *J. Am. Chem. Soc.* **72** 2811 (1950).

Hubert S. Loring and Nydia G. Luthy, *ibid.* **73** 4215 (1951).

1014 **Orotidine** (Orotic Acid Riboside), $C_{10}H_{12}O_8N_2$, cyclohexylamine salt, m.p. 183°.

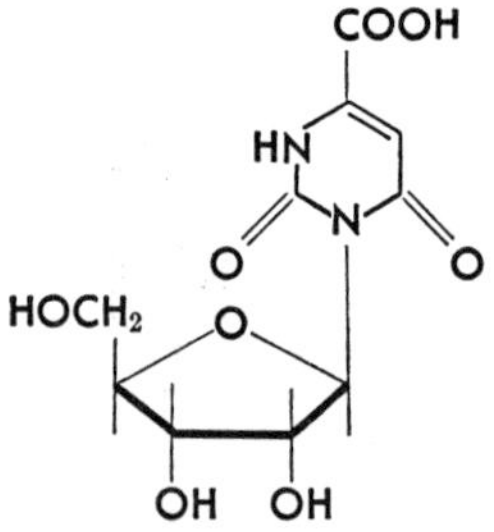

Neurospora crassa mutant
A. Michael Michelson, William Drell and Herschel K. Mitchell, *Proc. Nat. Acad. Sci. U. S.* **37** 396 (1951).

1015 **Cytidine Diphosphate Glycerol,** $C_{12}H_{21}O_{12}N_3P_2$.

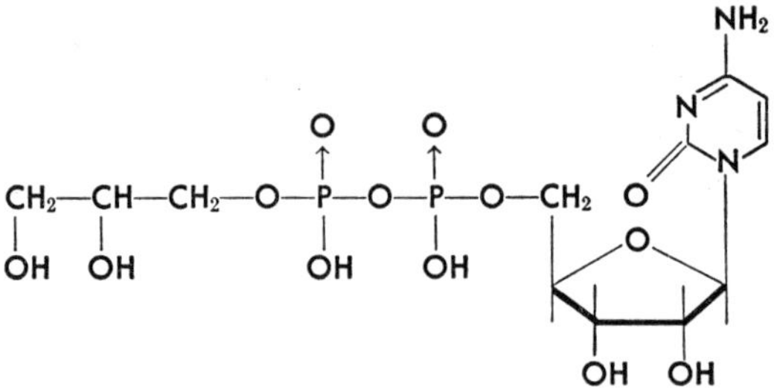

Lactobacillus arabinosus
J. Baddiley and R. P. Mathias, *J. Chem. Soc.*, 2723 (1954).
J. Baddiley, J. G. Buchanan, B. Cares, A. P. Mathias and A. R. Sanderson, *Biochem. J.* **64** 599 (1956).

1016 **Cytidine-5'-diphosphatecholine** (CDP-Choline), $C_{13}H_{24}O_{11}N_4P_2$, amorphous white, hygroscopic powder.

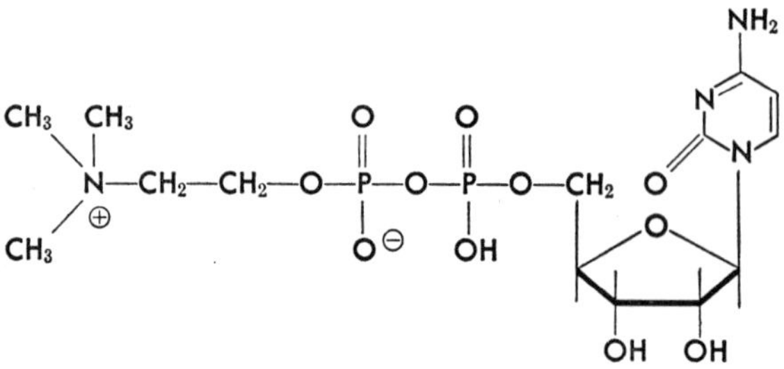

Yeast

This compound is a biogenetic precursor of the lecithins and cephalins.

Irving Lieberman, L. Berger and W. Theodore Gimenez, *Science* **124** 81 (1956).

Eugene P. Kennedy and Samuel B. Weiss, *J. Biol. Chem.* **222** 193 (1956).

1017   Cytidine Diphosphate Ribitol, $C_{14}H_{25}O_{15}N_3P_2$.

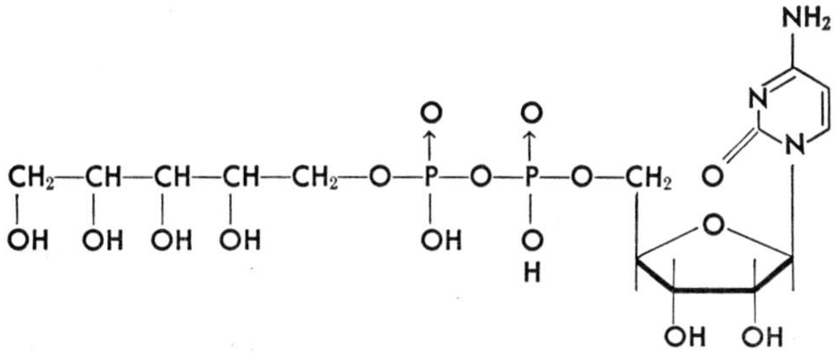

Lactobacillus arabinosus

J. Baddiley and A. P. Mathias, *J. Chem. Soc.,* 2723 (1954).

J. Baddiley, J. G. Buchanan, B. Cares, A. P. Mathias and A. R. Sanderson, *Biochem. J.* **64** 599 (1956).

1018   Uridinediphosphateglucose (UDPG), $C_{15}H_{24}O_{17}N_2P_2$.

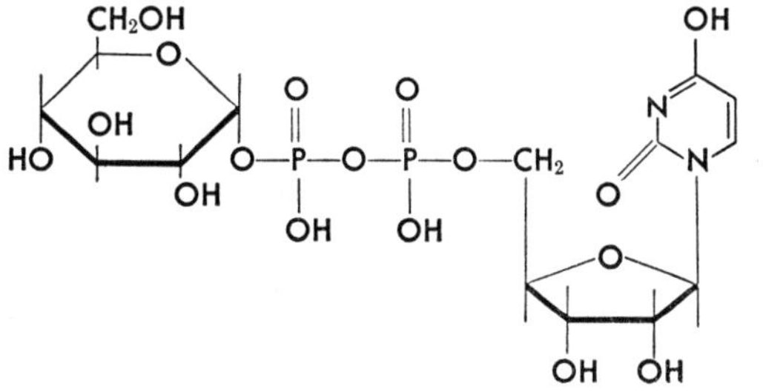

Yeast, molds

A uridinediphosphateacetylglucosamine also has been isolated from yeast.

R. Caputto, Luis F. Leloir, C. E. Cardini and A. C. Paladini, *J. Biol. Chem.* **184** 333 (1950).

E. Cabib, Luis F. Leloir and C. E. Cardini, *ibid.* **203** 1055 (1953).

J. G. Moffatt and H. G. Khorana, *J. Am. Chem. Soc.* **80** 3756 (1958). (Synthesis)

1019 **Thymidine Diphosphate Rhamnose,** $C_{16}H_{26}O_{14}N_2P_2$.

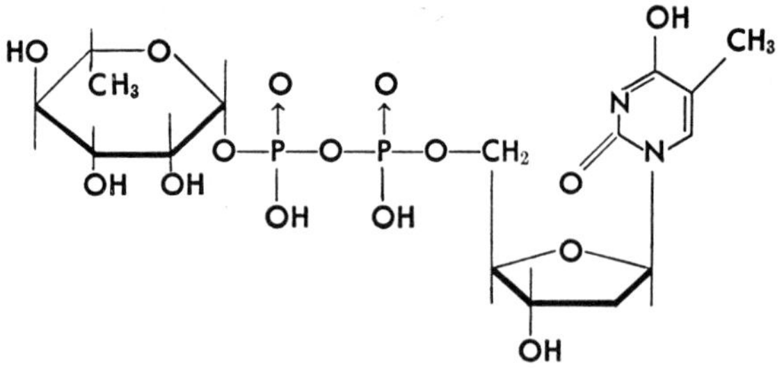

Lactobacillus acidophilus
Reiji Okazaki, *Biochem. and Biophys. Res. Comms.* 1 34 (1959).

1020 **Plicacetin** (Amicetin B), $C_{25}H_{35}O_7N_5$, colorless needles, m.p. 182–184° from H_2O—CH_3OH, $[\alpha]_D^{26}$ +181° (c 2.7 in methanol).

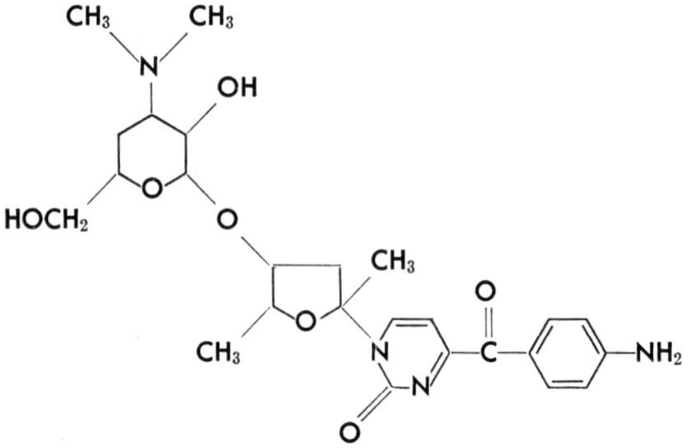

Streptomyces plicatus
Theodore H. Haskell, Albert Ryder, Roger P. Frohardt, Salvatore A. Fusari, Zbigniew L. Jakubowski and Quentin R. Bartz, *J. Am. Chem. Soc.* 80 743 (1958).

1021 **Bamicetin**, $C_{28}H_{40}O_9N_6$, white microcrystals, m.p. 240° (dec.), $[\alpha]_D^{26}$ +123° (c 0.5 in 0.1 N hydrochloric acid).
Partial Structure:

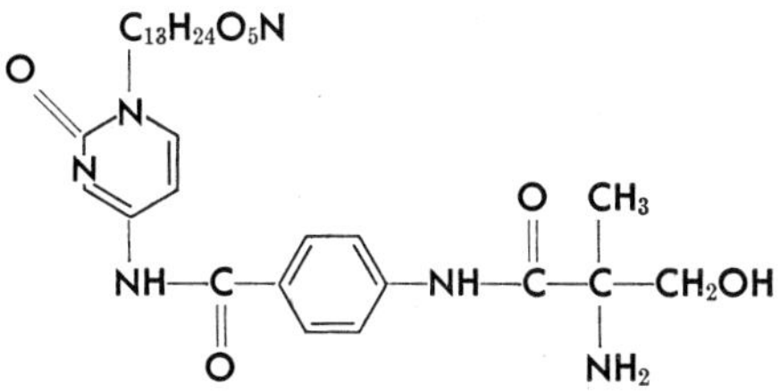

Streptomyces plicatus
Theodore H. Haskell, Albert Ryder, Roger P. Frohardt, Salvatore A. Fusari, Zbigniew L. Jakubowski and Quentin R. Bartz, *J. Am. Chem. Soc.* 80 743 (1958).

1022 **Amicetin** (Sacromycin, Allomycin), $C_{29}H_{42}O_9N_6$, colorless needles, m.p. 165–169°, $[\alpha]_D^{24}$ +116.5° (c 0.5 in 0.1 N hydrochloric acid).

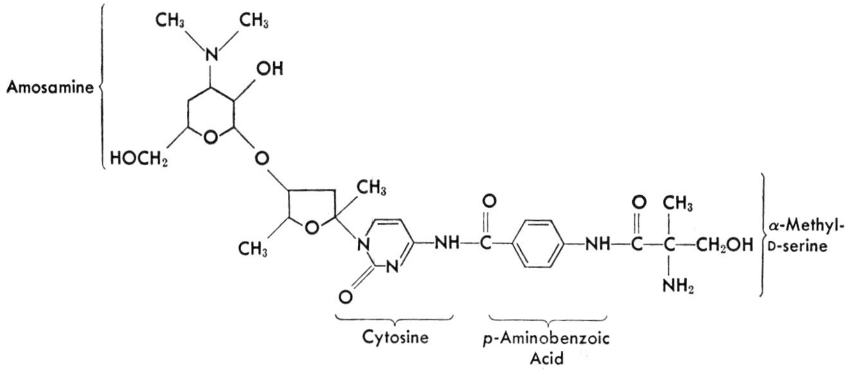

Streptomyces vinaceus-drappus, S. fasciculatus, S. sindenensis, S. plicatus
Edwin H. Flynn, J. W. Hinnan, E. L. Caron and D. O. Woolf, Jr., *J. Am. Chem. Soc.* 75 5867 (1953).

Calvin L. Stevens, Robert J. Gasser, Tapan K. Mukherjee and Theodore H. Haskell, *ibid.* 78 6212 (1956).

n. PURINES

The nature of nucleic acids and the participation of purines in their structure were discussed in the preceding section. The process of oxidative phosphorylation also was mentioned although it is not yet entirely understood. In this process inorganic phosphate ions disappear during biological oxidation of substrates and become bound in adenosine triphosphate (ATP), the universal storage molecule for chemical energy within cells. Many examples of ATP as an energy donor were seen in earlier sections.

Adenosine polyphosphates have other functions, most of them concerned with the activation and transfer of various chemical moieties with formation of new chemical bonds. ATP, for example, can donate phosphate or pyrophosphate groups to form new phosphate esters. Two such known reactions are:

$$\text{Glucose} + \text{ATP} \xrightleftharpoons[\text{hexokinase}]{\text{Mg}^{\oplus\oplus}} \text{Glucose-6-phosphate} + \text{ADP}$$

and

$$\text{Ribose-5-phosphate} + \text{ATP} \xrightleftharpoons[\substack{\text{phosphoribose}\\\text{pyrophosphokinase}}]{\text{Mg}^{\oplus\oplus}} \text{Ribose-5-phosphate-l-pyrophosphate} + \text{AMP}$$

Adenosine-3'-phospho-5'-phosphosulfate has been established as activated sulfate,[1,2] and it has been used in the formation of sulfate esters of a number of phenols and

[1] Robert S. Bandurski, Lloyd G. Wilson and Craig L. Squires, *J. Am. Chem. Soc.* 78 6408 (1956).

[2] P. W. Robbins and Fritz Lipmann, *ibid.* 78 2652, 6409 (1956).

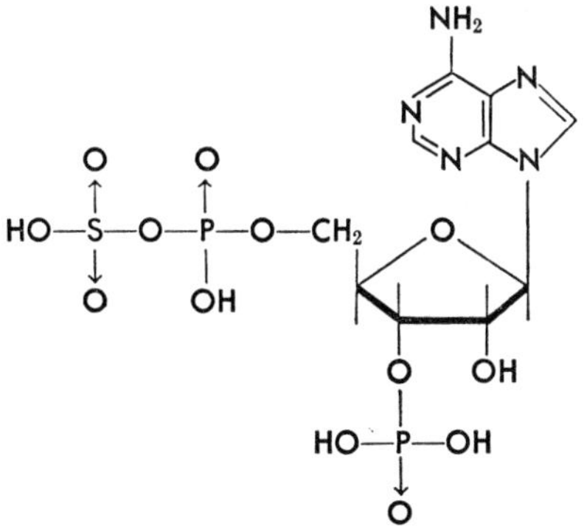

Adenosine-3'-phospho-
5'-phosphosulfate

alcohols in the presence of sulfokinases. The generality
of the sulfate transfer mechanism has been demonstrated
in yeast, neurospora and liver.

The recognition of S-adenosylmethionine as the active
complex in methyl group transfer from methionine (and
perhaps in its biosynthesis) was noted in the section on
amino acids.

In the section on aliphatic acids an ATP requirement
was noted in the formation of acyl coenzyme A. A number of acyl adenylates have been prepared or isolated
from natural sources.[3, 4, 5] These can be converted enzymically into acyl coenzyme As. The general structure
of these activated acids is:

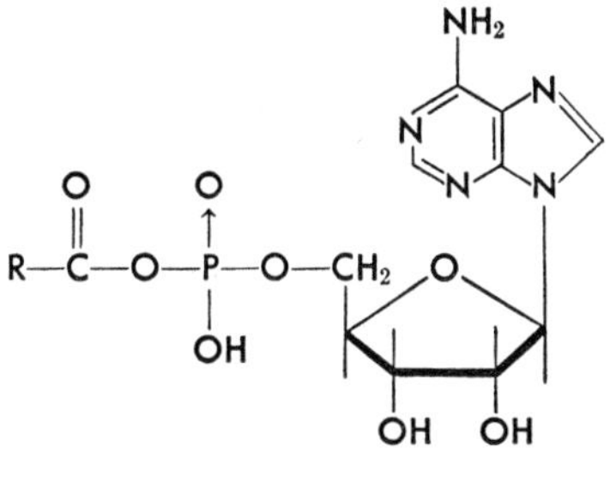

Acid Anhydrides of
Adenosine-5'-phosphate

[3] Paul Berg, *ibid.* **77** 3163 (1955).
[4] Preston T. Talbert and F. M. Huennekens, *ibid.* **78** 4671 (1956).
[5] C. H. Lee Peng, *Biochim. et Biophys. Acta* **22** 42 (1956).

In the same section the mediation of ATP in the formation of active carbon dioxide was seen:

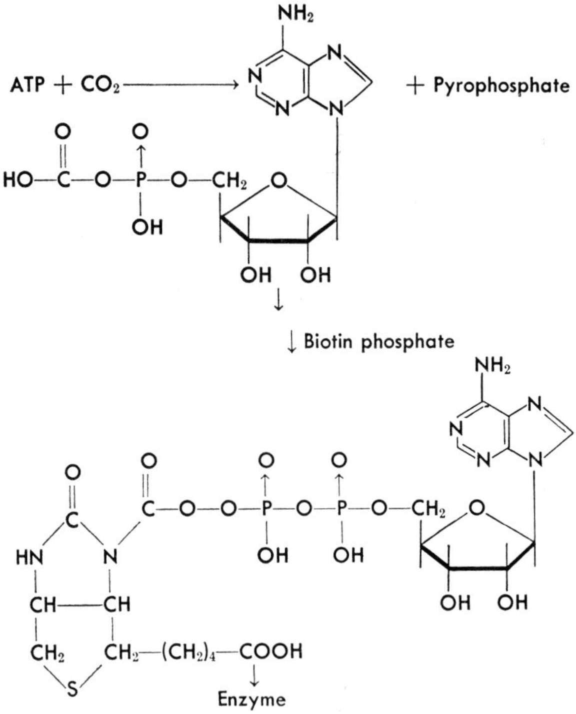

$$ATP + CO_2 \longrightarrow$$ + Pyrophosphate

↓ Biotin phosphate

Possible intermediate in
formation of activated
carbon dioxide

Synthetic adenosyl-5′-phosphoryl carbonate has been prepared.[6]

The role of adenine nucleotide as the terminal or ac-
tivating nucleotide of transfer RNA in protein synthesis
was mentioned in the amino acid section.

[6] B. K. Bachhawat, J. F. Woessner and M. J. Coon, *Federation
Proc.* 15 214 (1956).

Finally, the occurrence of the adenine nucleotide moiety in various other coenzymes (coenzyme A, flavine-adenine dinucleotide, DPN, etc.) should not be forgotten. The functions of these coenzymes are considered elsewhere.

Adenine polyphosphates, then, are so ubiquitous and so metabolically important that they nearly all have been encountered prior to this point in our discussions of microbial metabolism.

Guanosine polyphosphates, too, are widespread, and they seem to be able to duplicate some of the less specific functions of those of adenine. One reaction in which a guanine polyphosphate is known to participate is:[7]

α-Ketoglutaric Acid + DPN$^{\oplus}$ + CoA-SH $\rightarrow$
$\qquad\qquad$ Succinyl-S-CoA + DPNH + H$^{\oplus}$ + CO_2
Succinyl-S-CoA + Guanosine Diphosphate + H_3PO_4 $\rightleftarrows$
$\qquad\qquad$ Succinic Acid + CoA-SH + GTP

The enzyme catalyzing this reaction has been isolated only from tissues of higher animals, and there is evidence that in *Escherichia coli* at least the adenine nucleotide seems to be involved.[8]

Guanosine and inosine nucleotides also participate in the formation of phosphoenolpyruvate from oxaloacetate:[9]

Oxaloacetic Acid + GTP $\rightleftarrows$ Phosphoenolpyruvic Acid + GDP + CO_2

but again this has been shown only in animal tissues.

The general function of GTP as an energy source in the amination of inosinic acid during adenine biosynthesis will be seen later.

Guanosine diphosphate mannose has been isolated

---

[7] D. R. Sanadi, David M. Gibson, Padmasini Ayengar and Miriam Jacob, *J. Biol. Chem.* **218** 505 (1956).

[8] Roberts A. Smith, Irma F. Frank and I. C. Gunsalus, *Federation Proc.* **16** 251 (1957).

[9] M. F. Utter and K. Kurahashi, *J. Biol. Chem.* **207** 821 (1954).

from yeast[10] and a penicillium mold[11] as well as from higher animals, and it probably occurs in plants. Guano-

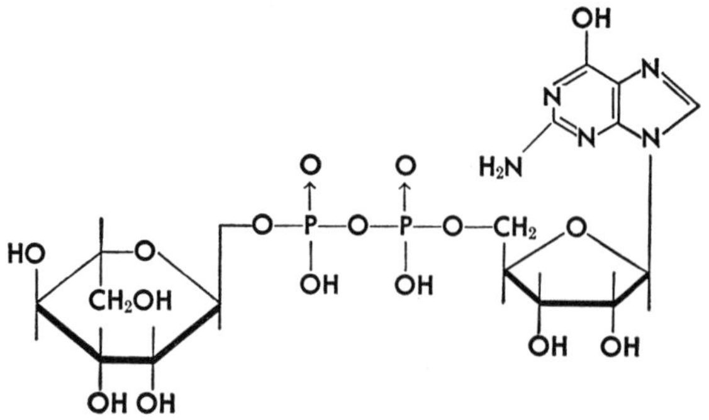

Guanosine Diphosphate Mannose

sine diphosphate fucose has been isolated from *Aerobacter aerogenes*,[12] and this organism has an enzyme which converts GDP-mannose to GDP-fucose. This conversion requires TPNH and must involve several steps to accomplish the requisite epimerizations and reduction of the terminal carbon atom. The functions of these guanosine derivatives are unknown, but yeast elaborates a mannan, and fucose is a proven constituent of bacterial polysaccharides (as well as blood group specific polysaccharides in higher animals). This may then be a form in which sugars are modified and transported for incorporation into polysaccharides.

A substance of the vitamin B_{12} group isolated from *Nocardia rugosa* has been identified as guanosine diphosphate factor B, *i.e.* a guanosine-5'-pyrophosphoric ester of factor B in which ribose is linked to N-9 of guanine (partial structure shown).[13]

[10] E. Cabib and Luis F. Leloir, *ibid.* **206** 779 (1954).

[11] A. Ballio, C. Casinovi and G. Serlupi-Crescenzi, *Biochim. et Biophys. Acta* **20** 414 (1956).

[12] V. Ginsburg and H. N. Kirkman, *J. Am. Chem. Soc.* **80** 3481, 4426 (1958).

[13] R. Barchielli, G. Boretti, A. DiMarco, P. Julita, A. Migliacci, A. Minghetti and C. Spalla, *Biochem. J.* **74** 382 (1960).

Guanosine Diphosphate
Factor B
(Factor B = Vitamin B_{12}
minus the
dimethylbenzimidazole
nucleotide moiety)

This substance has been suggested as an intermediate near the end of the vitamin B_{12} synthesis just prior to introduction of the dimethylbenzimidazole nucleotide.

There is evidence that labeled guanine is an isotopic precursor of riboflavin in *Eremothecium ashbyii*. Adenine also is a precursor of this vitamin. In each case the C_8 atom is lost. In the case of adenine, at least, the pyrimidine ring is incorporated intact into riboflavin[14] although pyrimidines such as uracil and thymine are ineffective precursors.[15]

Inosine is an intermediate in the biosynthesis of adenine and guanine, but beyond the phosphoenol pyruvate formation and some of the less specific reactions of the purine nucleotides (phosphate transfer, etc.) few functions have been discovered.

The purine nucleotides have been reviewed.[16, 17, 18, 19, 20, 21]

[14] Walter S. McNutt, Jr., *J. Biol. Chem.* 219 365 (1956).

[15] John A. MacLaren, *J. Bacteriol.* 63 233 (1952).

[16] Paul D. Boyer, Henry Lardy and Karl Myrbäck, "The Enzymes" Vol. II, Robert M. Bock, *Adenine nucleotides and properties of pyrophosphate compounds*, Academic Press, New York, 1960, pp. 3–27.

[17] *Ibid.*, Merton F. Utter, *Guanosine and inosine nucleotides*, pp. 75–87.

[18] Jack L. Strominger, *Physiol. Rev.* 40 55–111 (1960).

[19] J. Baddiley and J. G. Buchanan, *Quart. Rev.* 12 152–172 (1958).

[20] Standish C. Hartman and John M. Buchanan, *Advances in Enzymology* 21 199–261 (1959). (Copyright 1959 by Interscience Publishers, Inc., New York)

[21] G. E. W. Wolstenholme and Cecilia M. O'Connor (Eds.), "CIBA Foundation Symposium on the Chemistry and Biology of Purines," J. M. Buchanan, J. G. Flaks, L. C. Hartman, B. Levenberg, L. N. Lukens and L. Warren, *The enzymatic synthesis of inosinic acid de novo*, Little, Brown and Co., Boston, 1957, pp. 233–255.

The general scheme of purine biosynthesis is understood now. It is outlined in the following equations:[22]

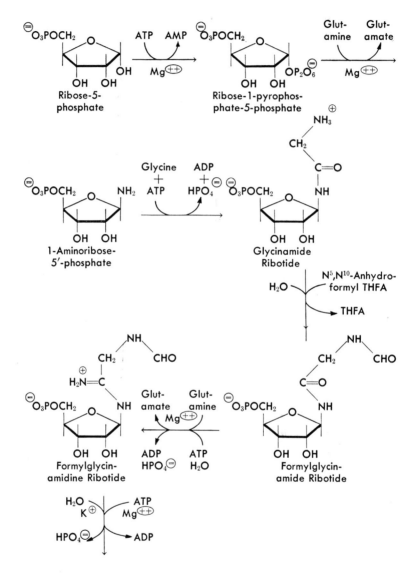

[22] Reproduced from reference 20.

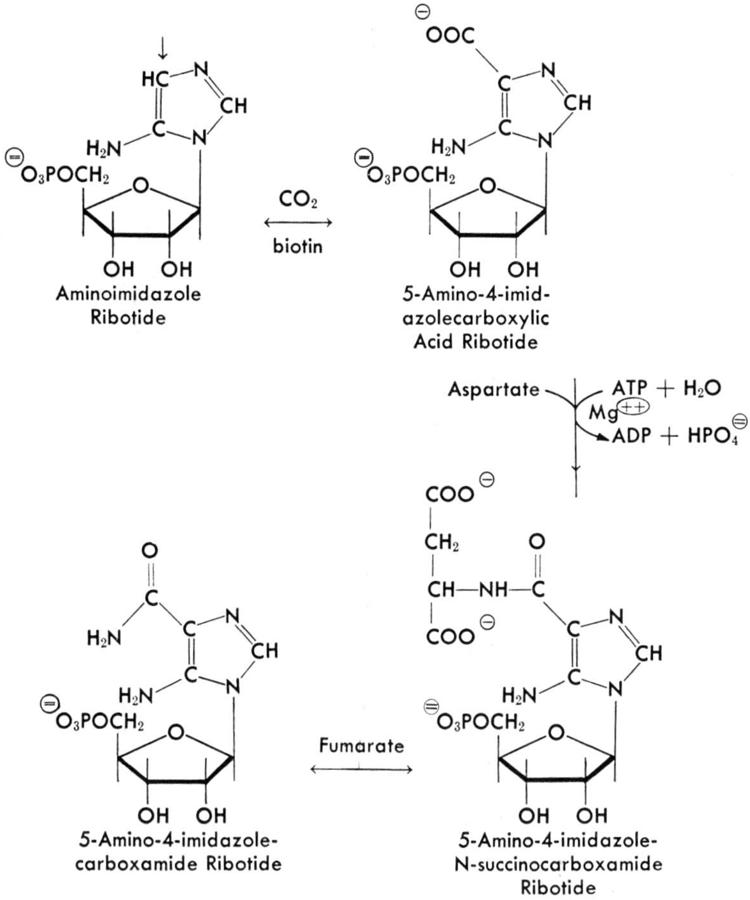

Aminoimidazole Ribotide → (CO₂, biotin) → 5-Amino-4-imidazolecarboxylic Acid Ribotide → (Aspartate; ATP + H₂O, Mg²⁺; ADP + HPO₄⁻) → 5-Amino-4-imidazole-N-succinocarboxamide Ribotide → (Fumarate) → 5-Amino-4-imidazole-carboxamide Ribotide

Sulfanilamide and other sulfa drugs inhibit the growth of many bacteria by interfering with the incorporation of p-aminobenzoic acid into the folic acid coenzymes (p-aminosalicylic acid, etc., may do the same in mycobacteria), and E. coli cultures so inhibited accumulate isolable quantities of 5-amino-4-imidazolecarboxamide ribotide.[23]

[23] Joseph S. Gots and Edith G. Gollub, Proc. Nat. Acad. Sci. U. S. 43 826 (1957).

Azaserine, a glutamine antagonist, inhibits purine synthesis in some bacteria, and causes accumulation of formylglycinamide ribotide in *E. coli*.[24] Another antibiotic, 6-diazo-5-oxo-L-norleucine, also inhibits purine biosynthesis at this stage. Purine-requiring mutants of *E. coli* and *A. aerogenes* accumulate the following compounds or derivatives: aminoimidazole,[25] 5-aminoimidazolecarboxamide,[26] 5-amino-4-imidazole-N-succinocarboxamide[23] and xanthine.[27] Yeast grown on a biotin-deficient medium gives off aminoimidazole riboside and hypoxanthine.[28]

Cell-free extracts of *Neurospora crassa* are able to promote all the reactions shown in the biosynthetic scheme above. All these facts as well as other evidence indicate that this is the principal biosynthetic route to purines in bacteria and fungi, and probably is quite general.

Inosinic acid is an intermediate in the biosynthetic route to the other purines as shown in the formula sequence on page 533.

Extracts of *Aerobacter aerogenes* convert inosinic acid to xanthylic acid, and there is other evidence that the final stages of purine biosynthesis follow this route in many bacteria and fungi as well as in animal cells.

Other references can be found in some of the reviews of this subject.[20, 21]

There are indications that methylated purines may be minor constituents of yeast and bacterial nucleic acids. Traces of 6-methylaminopurine, 6-hydroxy-2-methylaminopurine and 1-methylguanine were detected in yeast RNA.[29] Small amounts of 6-methylaminopurine, 6,6-di-

[24] A. J. Tomisek, H. J. Kelley and H. E. Skipper, Abstr., 128th Meeting, Am. Chem. Soc., 5C, Minneapolis, Sept., 1955.

[25] Samuel H. Love and Joseph S. Gots, *J. Biol. Chem.* 212 647 (1955).

[26] Joseph S. Gots, *ibid.* 228 57 (1957).

[27] Boris Magasanik, H. S. Moyed and Lois B. Gehring, *ibid.* 226 339 (1957).

[28] D. P. Lones, C. Rainbow and J. D. Woodward, *J. Gen. Microbiol.* 19 146 (1958).

[29] Max Adler, Bernard Weissmann and Alexander B. Gutman, *J. Biol. Chem.* 230 717 (1958).

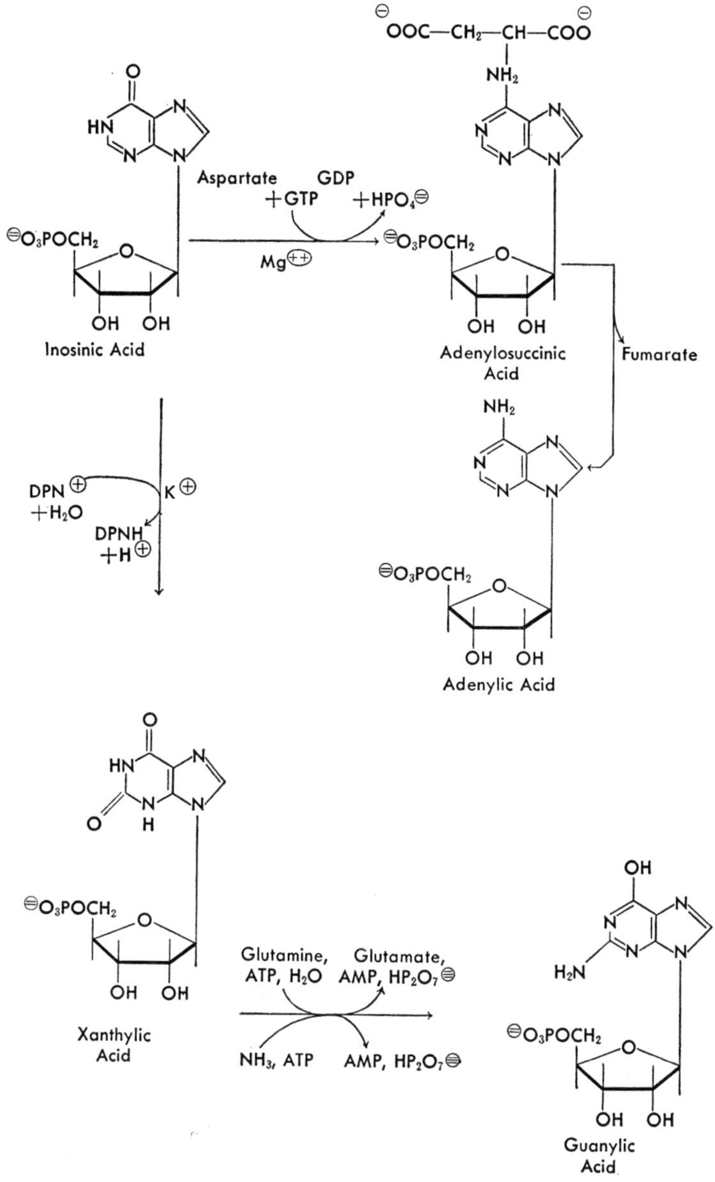

$$\overset{\ominus}{OOC}-CH_2-CH-\overset{\ominus}{COO}$$

$$\underset{NH_2}{|}$$

Aspartate   GDP

$+GTP$ $+HPO_4^{\ominus}$

$Mg^{\oplus\oplus}$

$\ominus O_3POCH_2$

OH   OH

Inosinic Acid

$\ominus O_3POCH_2$

OH   OH

Adenylosuccinic
Acid

Fumarate

$DPN^{\oplus}$
$+H_2O$

$K^{\oplus}$

$DPNH$
$+H^{\oplus}$

NH_2

$\ominus O_3POCH_2$

OH   OH

Adenylic Acid

$\ominus O_3POCH_2$

OH   OH

Xanthylic
Acid

Glutamine,   Glutamate,
ATP, H_2O AMP, $HP_2O_7^{\ominus}$

NH_3, ATP   AMP, $HP_2O_7^{\ominus}$

OH

H_2N

$\ominus O_3POCH_2$

OH   OH

Guanylic
Acid

methylaminopurine and 2-methyladenine have been found in bacterial RNA.[30]

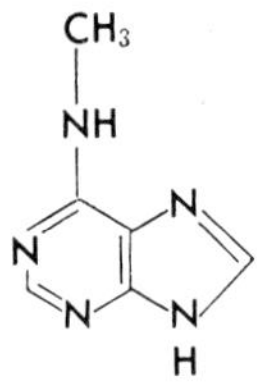

6-Methylamino-purine 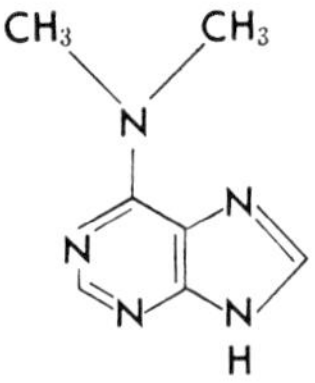   6-Dimethylamino-purine 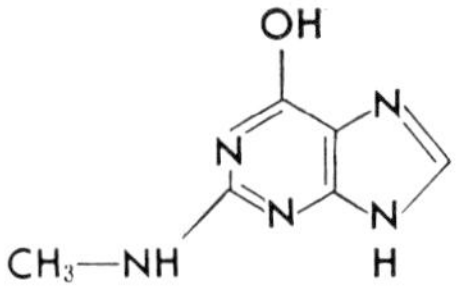   2-Methylamino-6-hydroxy purine

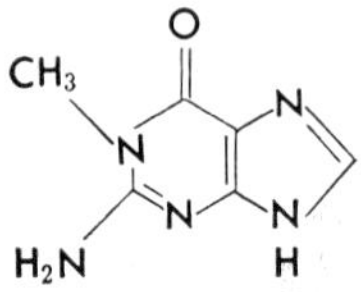

1-Methylguanine 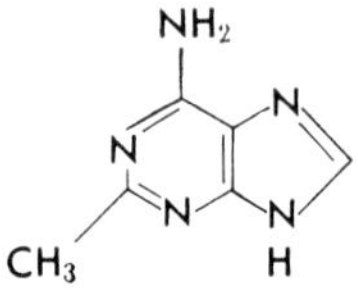   2-Methyladenine 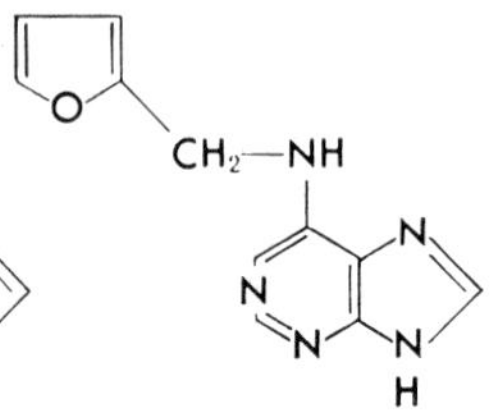   Kinetin

Kinetin is a substance isolated from yeast which stimulates cell division in plant tissues. Work on kinetin and related compounds has been reviewed.[31]

Several antibiotics contain the purine nucleus. Some of these have excited interest as purine analogues for tumor inhibition, but they are all toxic. Puromycin is an inhibitor of protein synthesis.[32] The interference has been shown to occur at the last stage—that is the exchange of the activated amino acid between transfer–RNA and the growing protein chain.

[30] J. W. Littlefield and D. B. Dunn, *Biochem. J.* **68** 8P (1958); *idem., Nature* **181** 254 (1958).

[31] E. R. Squibb Lectures on Chemistry of Microbial Products, "Topics in Microbial Chemistry," John Wiley and Sons, New York, 1958, F. M. Strong, *Kinetin and kinins*, pp. 98–158.

[32] Michael Yarmolinsky and Gabriel de la Haba, *Chem. and Eng. News* April 25, 1960.

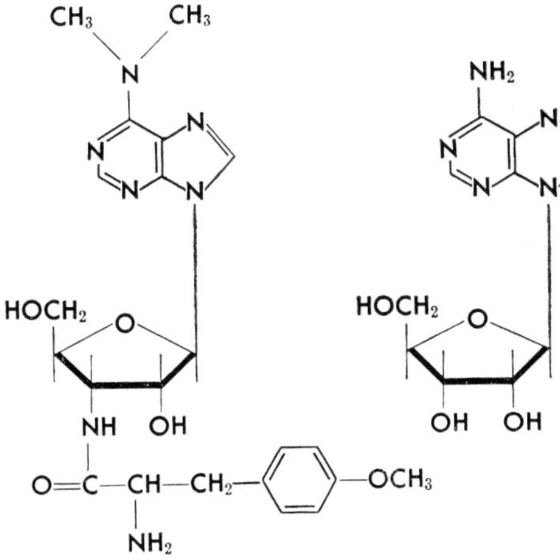

Puromycin

Adenine
Nucleoside

Substitution of other amino acids for the *p*-methoxy-phenylalanine moiety gives analogues which still inhibit protein synthesis, although the free nucleoside moiety is a less effective inhibitor. The similarity in structure suggests competition with adenine nucleoside.

Functions of coenzyme A have been discussed throughout the appropriate sections. The biosyntheses of the various moieties of the molecule also have been considered with the possible exception of β-aminoethanethiol, which is derived from cysteine.

The biosynthetic union of these moieties, originally studied in animal tissues, follows the probable course:

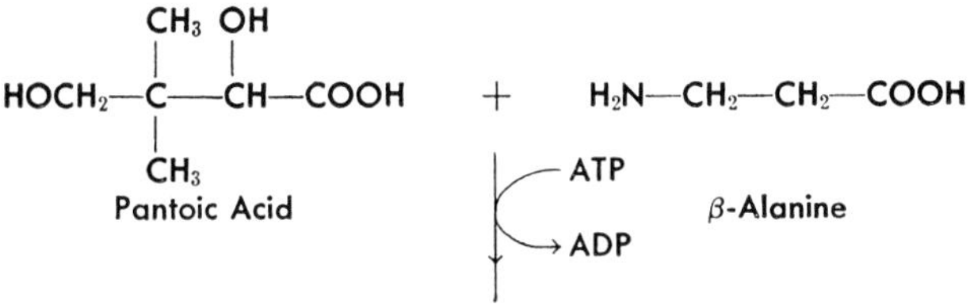

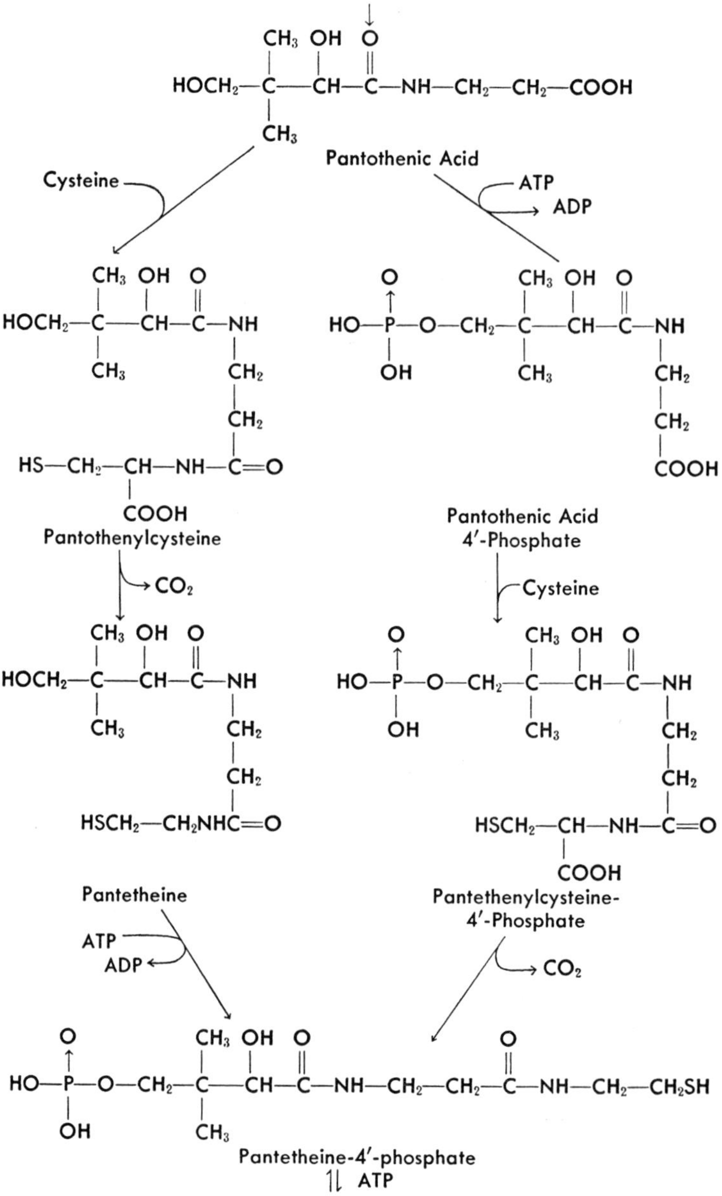

CH₃ OH O
HOCH₂—C—CH—C—NH—CH₂—CH₂—COOH
CH₃

Pantothenic Acid

Cysteine

ATP
ADP

CH₃ OH O
HOCH₂—C—CH—C—NH
CH₃ CH₂
CH₂
HS—CH₂—CH—NH—C=O
COOH
Pantothenylcysteine

CO₂

O CH₃ OH O
HO—P—O—CH₂—C—CH—C—NH
OH CH₃ CH₂
CH₂
COOH
Pantothenic Acid
4'-Phosphate

Cysteine

CH₃ OH O
HOCH₂—C—CH—C—NH
CH₃ CH₂
CH₂
HSCH₂—CH₂NHC=O
Pantetheine

ATP
ADP

O CH₃ OH O
HO—P—O—CH₂—C—CH—C—NH
OH CH₃ CH₂
CH₂
HSCH₂—CH—NH—C=O
COOH
Pantethenylcysteine-
4'-Phosphate

CO₂

O CH₃ OH O
HO—P—O—CH₂—C—CH—C—NH—CH₂—CH₂—C—NH—CH₂—CH₂SH
OH CH₃
Pantetheine-4'-phosphate
ATP

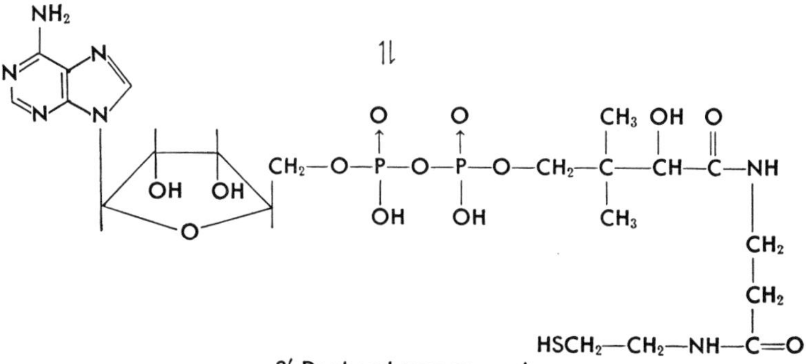

3'-Dephosphocoenzyme A
↓ ATP
Coenzyme A

Most of these intermediates have been identified in microorganisms, *e.g. Streptobacterium plantarum.*[33] Pantothenic acid is required by some microorganisms, but probably not by man, perhaps because of the excess produced by *E. coli* and other intestinal microbes.

A number of higher fungi and molds have been examined thoroughly for nucleotide content. Some of the organisms which have been studied are: *Penicillium chrysogenum,*[34] *Aspergillus oryzae,*[35] *Polyporus squamosus,*[36] *Amanita muscaria,*[36] *Lycoperdon pratense,*[36] *Hypholoma capnoides,*[36] *Armillaria mellea,*[36] *Pholiota squarrosa,*[36] *Lactarius vellereus,*[36] *Lactarius turpis,*[36] *Torulopsis utilis,*[37] *Micrococcus lysodeikticus,*[38] *Coprinus comatis,*[39] and *Polyporus sulfureus.*[40]

[33] Theodor Wieland, Walter Maul and Ernst Friedrich Möller, *Biochem. Z.* **327** 85 (1955).

[34] A. Ballio, C. Casinovi and G. Serlupi-Crescenzi, *Biochim. et Biophys. Acta* **20** 414 (1956); Alessandro Ballio and Giovanni Serlupi-Crescenzi, *Nature* **179** 154 (1957).

[35] Kazuo Okunuki, Kozo Iwasa, Fumio Imamoto and Tadoyoshi Higashiyama, *J. Biochem.* (Tokyo) **45** 795 (1958).

[36] Rolf Bergkvist, *Acta Chem. Scand.* **12** 1549, 1554 (1958).

[37] D. Gilbert and E. Yemm, *Nature* **182** 1745 (1958).

[38] J. V. Scaletti, *Dissertation Abstr.* **17** 1191 (1957).

[39] Paul Heinz List, *Arch. Pharm.* **291** 502 (1958).

[40] *Idem., Planta Med.* **6** 424 (1958).

1023 Hypoxanthine, $C_5H_4ON_4$.

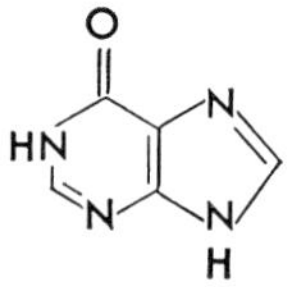

Amanita muscaria, Boletus edulis, Agaricus nebularis, Polyporus sulfureus

E. Buschmann, *Pharm. Post* 45 453 (1912). (*Chem. Abstr.* 6 2485)

E. Winterstein, C. Reuter and R. Korolev, *J. Chem. Soc.* 104 I 433 (1913).

Nils Löfgren, Björn Lüning and Harry Hedström, *Acta Chem. Scand.* 8 670 (1954).

Paul Heinz List, *Planta Med.* 6 424 (1958).

1024 Xanthine, $C_5H_4O_2N_4$, colorless crystals, m.p. 220° (dec.).

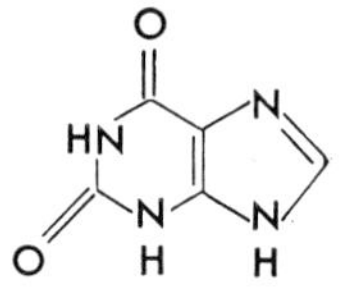

Amanita muscaria

E. Buschmann, *Pharm. Post* 45 453 (1912). (*Chem. Abstr.* 6 2485)

1025 Uric Acid, $C_5H_4O_3N_4$, colorless crystals, m.p. >400° (dec.).

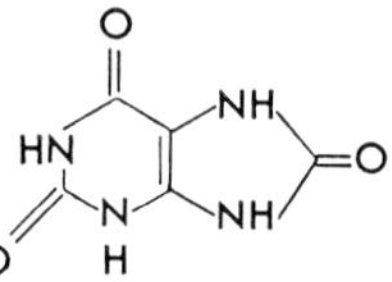

Aspergillus oryzae

Miazuko Sumi, *Biochem. Z.* 195 161 (1928).

1026 Adenine, $C_5H_5N_5$ (Trihydrate), colorless needles, m.p. 360–365° (dec.) (subl. from 220°) (Picrate), dec. 280°.

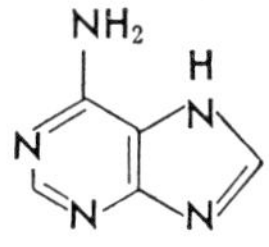

Coprinus comatis Gray, *Boletus edulis, Polyporus sul-fureus*

Paul Heinz List, *Arch. Pharm.* **291** 502 (1958).

E. Winterstein and C. Reuter, *Centr. Bakt. Parasitenk. II Abt.* **34** 566 (1912). (*Chem. Abstr.* **6** 3279)

Paul Heinz List, *Planta Med.* **6** 424 (1958).

1027 Guanine, $C_5H_5ON_5$, (Picrate) dec. from 190°.

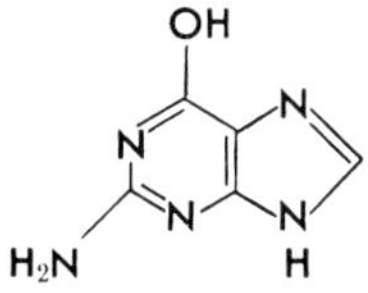

Coprinus comatis Gray, *Boletus edulis*

Paul Heinz List, *Arch. Pharm.* **291** 502 (1958).

E. Winterstein, C. Reuter and R. Korolev, *J. Chem. Soc.* **104** I 433 (1913).

1028 Heteroxanthine, $C_6H_6O_2N_4$, colorless crystals, m.p. ~380° (dec.).

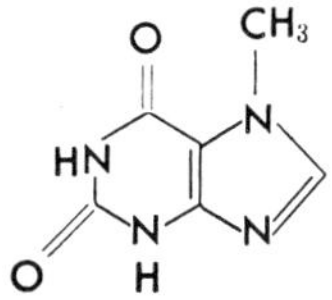

Yeast

P. W. Wiardi and B. C. P. Jansen, *Rec. trav. chim.* **53** 205 (1934).

1029 Toxoflavin, $C_6H_6O_2N_4$, yellow crystals, m.p. 171°.

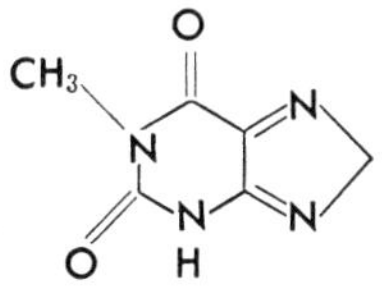

Pseudomonas cocovenenans

A. G. van Veen and W. K. Mertens, *Proc. Acad. Sci. Amsterdam* **36** 666 (1933). (Isolation) (*Chem. Abstr.* **27** 5771)

A. G. van Veen and J. K. Baars, *Rec. trav. chim.* **57** 248 (1938). (Structure)

1030 Kinetin (6-Furfurylaminopurine), $C_{10}H_9ON_5$, colorless prisms, m.p. 265° (sealed tube to prevent sublimation).

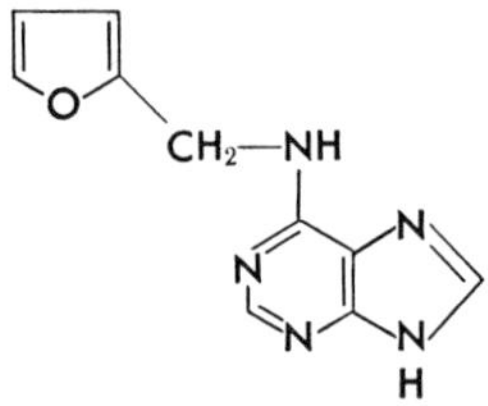

Yeast extracts

E. R. Squibb Lectures on Chemistry of Microbial Products, "Topics in Microbial Chemistry," John Wiley and Sons, New York, 1958, F. M. Strong, *Kinetin and kinins*, pp. 98–157.

1031 Nebularine (9-(β-D-Ribofuranosyl) purine), $C_{10}H_{12}O_4N_4$, colorless prisms, m.p. 181°, $[\alpha]_D^{25}$ −48.6° (c 1 in water).

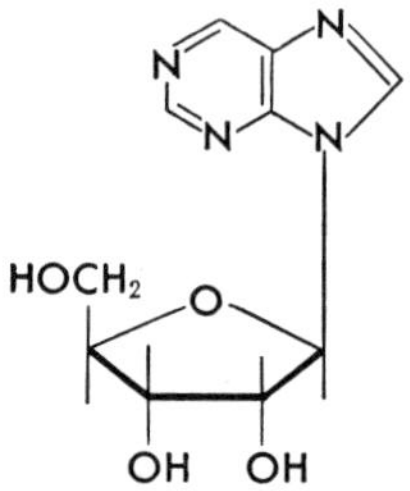

Agaricus (Clitocybe) nebularis Batsch.

Lars Ehrenburg, Harry Hedström, Nils Löfgren and Bertil Takman, *Svensk Kem. Tidskr.* **58** 269 (1946).

Nils Löfgren, Björn Lüning and Harry Hedström, *Acta Chem. Scand.* **8** 670 (1954).

David I. Magrath and George Bosworth Brown, *J. Am. Chem. Soc.* **79** 3252 (1957). (Synthesis)

1032 Cordycepin, $C_{10}H_{13}O_3N_5$, colorless needles, m.p. 225°, $[\alpha]_D^{20}$ −47° (in water).

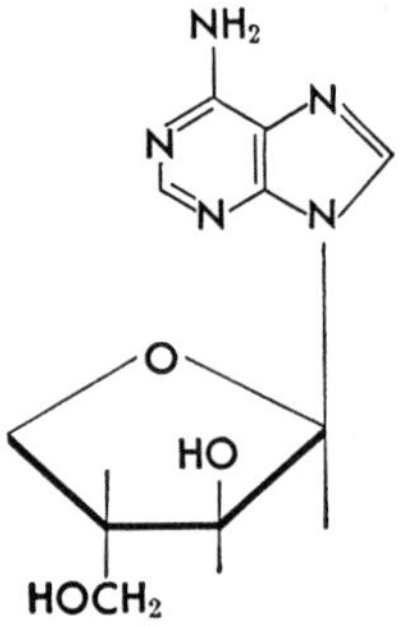

Cordyceps militaris (Linn.) Link

K. G. Cunningham, S. A. Hutchinson, William Manson and F. S. Spring, *J. Chem. Soc.*, 2299 (1951).

H. R. Bentley, K. G. Cunningham and F. S. Spring, *ibid.*, 2301 (1951). (Structure)

1033 **Adenosine,** $C_{10}H_{13}O_4N_5$, needles, m.p. 229°, $[\alpha]_D^{20}$ −60 to −63° (in water).

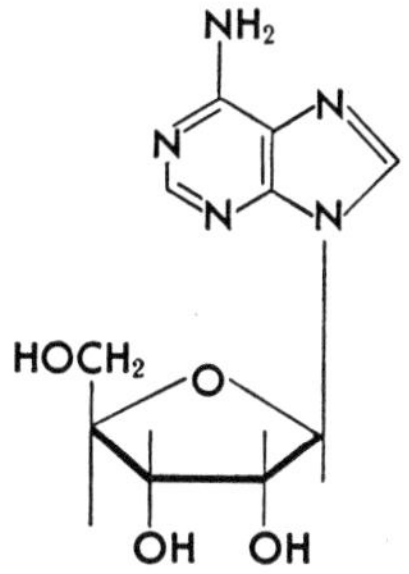

Agaricus nebularis

Nils Löfgren, Björn Lüning and Harry Hedström, *Acta Chem. Scand.* 8 670 (1954).

1034 **Guanosine,** $C_{10}H_{13}O_5N_5$, colorless crystals, m.p. 237° (dec.), $[\alpha]_D^{20}$ −60° (in 0.1 N sodium hydroxide).

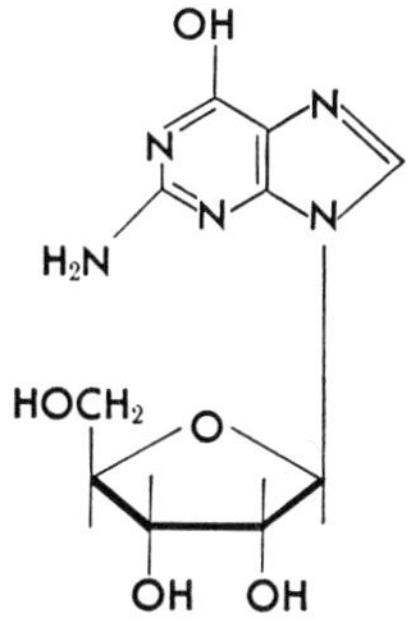

Yeast

Hellmut Bredereck, Annelise Martini and Friedrich Richter, *Ber.* **74B** 694 (1941).

1035 **Inosine-5'-phosphate** (Inosinic Acid), $C_{10}H_{13}O_8N_4P$, a syrup.

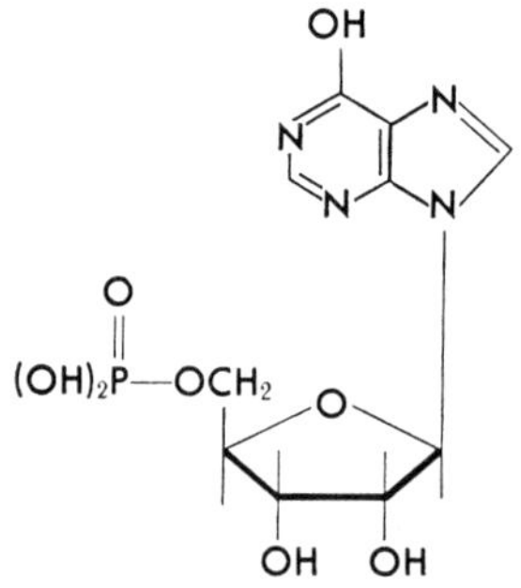

Yeast, *Penicillium chrysogenum*
The 5'-diphosphate also has been isolated.
E. Cabib, Luis F. Leloir and C. E. Cardini, *J. Biol. Chem.* **203** 1055 (1953).
A. Ballio, C. Casinovi and G. Serlupi-Crescenzi, *Biochim. et Biophys. Acta* **20** 414 (1956).

1036 **Adenosine-2'-phosphate** (Adenylic Acid a), $C_{10}H_{14}O_7N_5P$, colorless crystals, m.p. 187° (dec.).

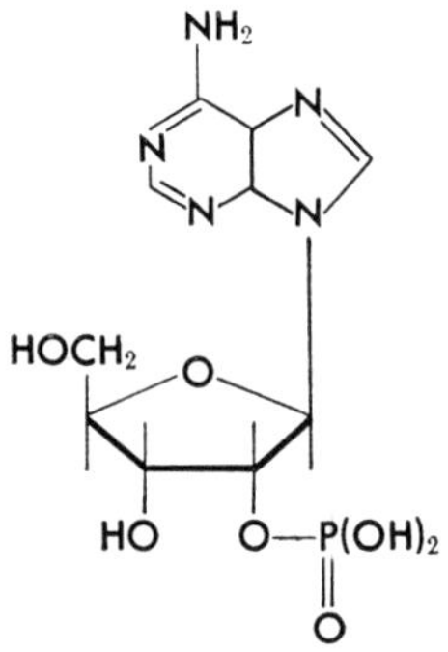

Yeast
D. M. Brown, G. D. Fasman, D. I. Magrath, A. R. Todd, W. Cochran and M. M. Woolfson, *Nature* **172** 1184 (1953).
C. E. Carter, *J. Am. Chem. Soc.* **72** 1466 (1950).
Joseph X. Khym, David G. Doherty, Elliot Volkin and Waldo E. Cohn, *ibid.* **75** 1262 (1953).
D. M. Brown and A. R. Todd, *J. Chem. Soc.,* 44 (1952).

1037 **Adenosine-3′-phosphate** (3-Adenylic Acid, Yeast Adenylic Acid),
$C_{10}H_{14}O_7N_5P$, colorless crystals, m.p. 191–195° (dec.),
$[\alpha]_D^{20}$ −66° (c 2 in 5% sodium hydroxide).

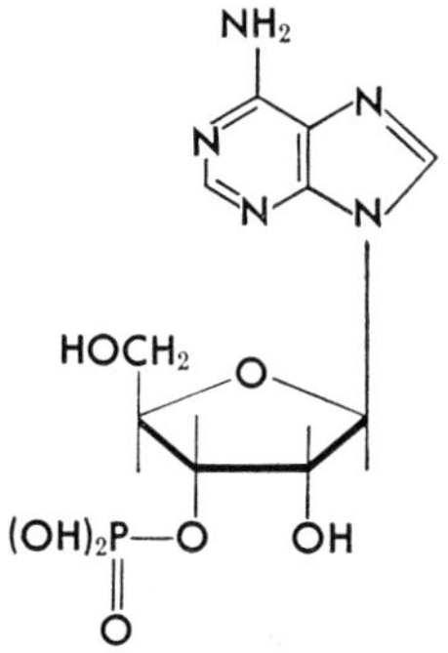

Yeast, *Penicillium chrysogenum*
H. Steudel and E. Peiser, Z. *physiol. Chem.* **127** 262 (1923).
D. A. Kita and W. H. Peterson, *J. Biol. Chem.* **203** 861
(1953).

1038 **Adenosine-5′-phosphate** (Muscle Adenylic Acid), $C_{10}H_{14}O_7N_5P$,
colorless crystals, m.p. 178°, $[\alpha]_D^{25}$ −50° (in formamide).

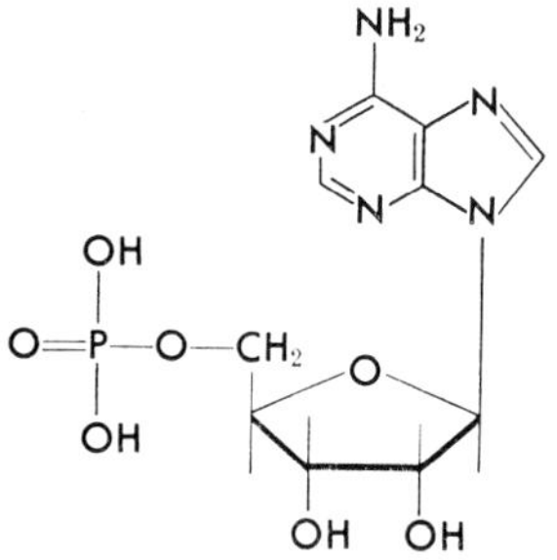

Yeasts, *Lactobacillus arabinosus, Penicillium chryso-
genum*
The 5′-diphosphate (ADP) also has been isolated from
microorganisms.
E. Cabib, Luis F. Leloir and C. E. Cardini, *J. Biol. Chem.*
203 1055 (1953).
J. Baddiley and A. C. Mathias, *J. Chem. Soc.*, 2723 (1954).
A. Ballio, C. Casinovi and G. Serlupi-Crescenzi, *Biochim. et
Biophys. Acta* **20** 414 (1956).

1039   Guanosine-3′-phosphate (Guanylic Acid), $C_{10}H_{14}O_8N_5P$, colorless crystals, $[\alpha]_D$ −7.5° to −13.5° (in water).

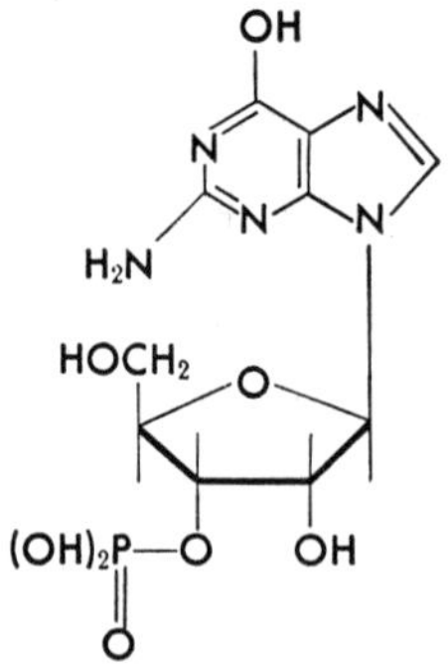

Yeast

The 5′-di- and triphosphates also have been isolated from microorganisms.

Walter Jones and M. E. Perkins, *J. Biol. Chem.* 62 557 (1925).

1040   Adenosine-5′-triphosphate (ATP), $C_{10}H_{16}O_{13} N_5P_3$.

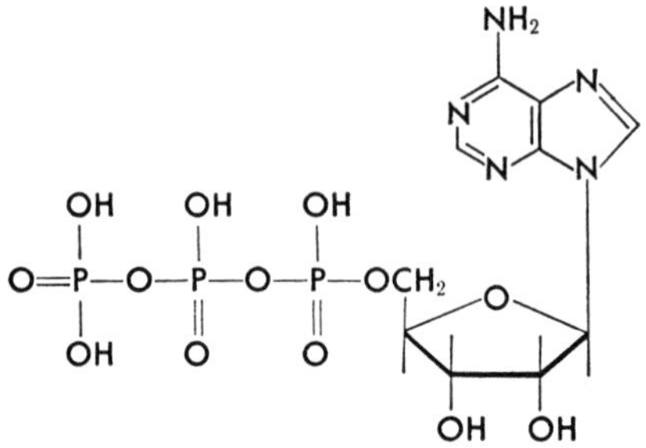

Yeasts, molds, bacteria, etc. (widely distributed)

Th. Wagner-Jauregg, *Z. physiol. Chem.* 238 129 (1936). (Isolation)

G. A. LePage and W. W. Umbreit, *J. Biol. Chem.* 148 255 (1943).

D. A. Kita and W. H. Peterson, *ibid.* 203 861 (1953).

A. Endō, *Ann. Report Takamine Lab.* 11 45 (1959).

1041 **Angustmycin A,** $C_{11}H_{13}O_4N_5$, colorless needles, m.p. (anhydr.) 169.5° (dec.), $[\alpha]_D^{18}$ +48.3°.

Probable structure:

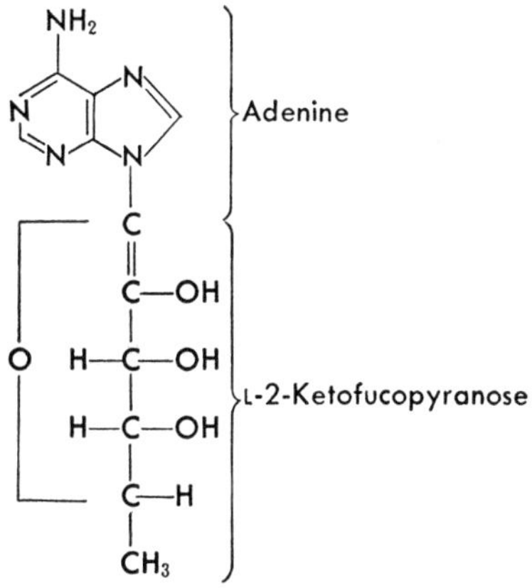

Streptomyces hygroscopicus

Hsü Yüntsen and Hiroshi Yonehara, *Bull. Agr. Chem. Soc.* (Japan) 21 261 (1957).

Hsü Yüntsen, Kazuhiko Ohkuma, Yoshio Ishii and Hiroshi Yonehara, *J. Antibiotics* (Japan) 9A 195 (1956). (Isolation and characterization)

Hsü Yüntsen, *ibid.* 11A 79 (1958). (Structure)

1042 **Angustmycin C** (Psicofuranine), $C_{11}H_{15}O_5N_5$, colorless crystals, m.p. 202–204°, $[\alpha]_D^{19}$ −71.1° (c 1.8 in pyridine).

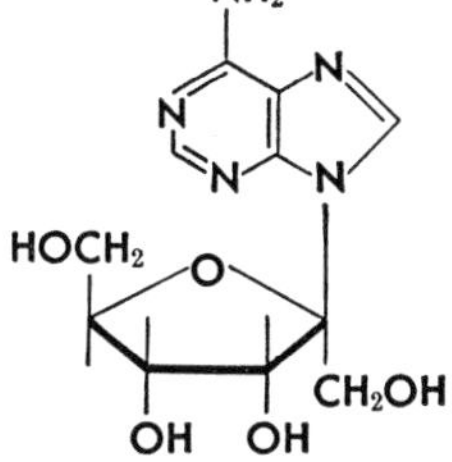

Streptomyces hygroscopicus var. *angustmyceticus*

Hsü Yüntsen, *J. Antibiotics* (Japan) 11A 244 (1958). (Structure)

1043 **Nucleocidin,** $C_{11}H_{16}O_8N_6S$, colorless crystals, no definite m.p., $[\alpha]_D^{24.5}$ $-33.3°$ (c 1.05 in 1:1 ethanol, 0.1 N hydrochloric acid).

Partial structure:

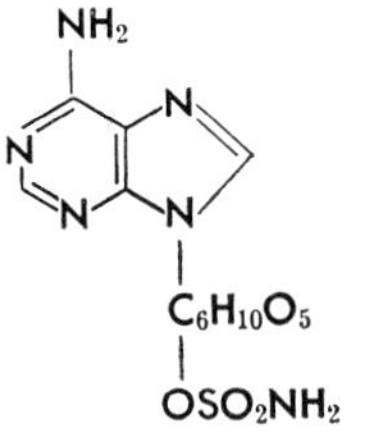

NH₂ ... C₆H₁₀O₅ ... OSO₂NH₂   C₆H₁₀O₅ is an unusual reducing sugar.

Streptomyces calvus

S. O. Thomas, V. L. Singleton, J. A. Lowery, R. W. Sharpe, L. M. Pruess, J. N. Porter, J. H. Mowat and N. Bohonos, "Antibiotics Annual 1956–1957," Medical Encyclopedia Inc., New York, p. 716. (Isolation)

C. W. Waller, J. B. Patrick, W. Fulmor and W. E. Meyer, *J. Am. Chem. Soc.* **79** 1011 (1957). (Structure)

1044 **Adenylosuccinic Acid,** $C_{14}H_{18}O_{11}N_5P$, no properties listed.

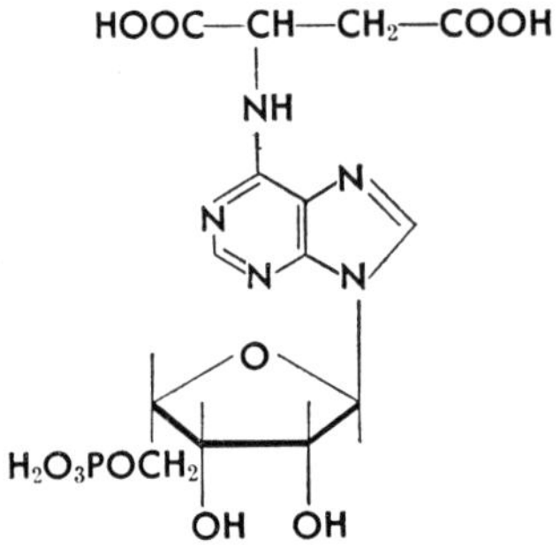

HOOC—CH—CH₂—COOH ... NH ... H₂O₃POCH₂ ... OH OH

Penicillium chrysogenum (mycelium)

About 16 known derivatives of adenine, guanine, cytidine, uracil, etc., also were detected in this study.

Alessandro Ballio and Giovanni Serlupi-Crescenzi, *Nature* **179** 154 (1957).

1045 Diadenosinetetraphosphate, $C_{20}H_{28}O_{19}N_{10}P$, $[\alpha]_{5446}^{20}$ −39.2° (in N sulfuric acid).

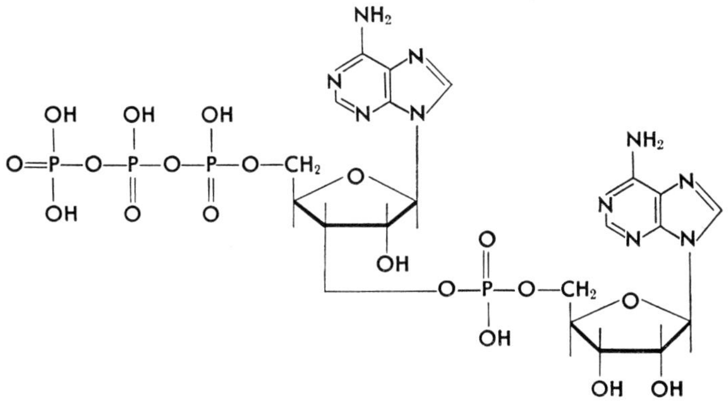

Yeast

W. Kiessling and O. Meyerhof, *Naturwissenschaften* **26** 13 (1938).

1046 Coenzyme A, $C_{21}H_{36}O_{16}N_7SP_3$, white amorphous powder.

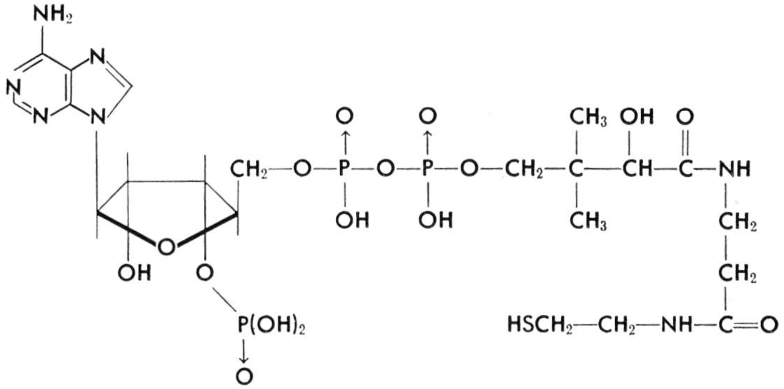

Occurs widely in microorganisms and higher animals. Yeast and certain streptomycetes were early sources.

F. M. Strong, "Squibb Lectures on the Chemistry of Microbial Products," *Coenzyme A and related compounds*, John Wiley and Sons, Inc., New York, 1956, pp. 44–98. (This review lists 117 earlier references.)

J. G. Moffatt and H. G. Khorana, *J. Am. Chem. Soc.* **81** 1265 (1959). (Synthesis)

1047 **Puromycin,** $C_{22}H_{29}O_5N_7$, white crystals, m.p. 175.5–177° (uncorr.), $[\alpha]_D^{25}$ −11° (c 1 in ethanol).

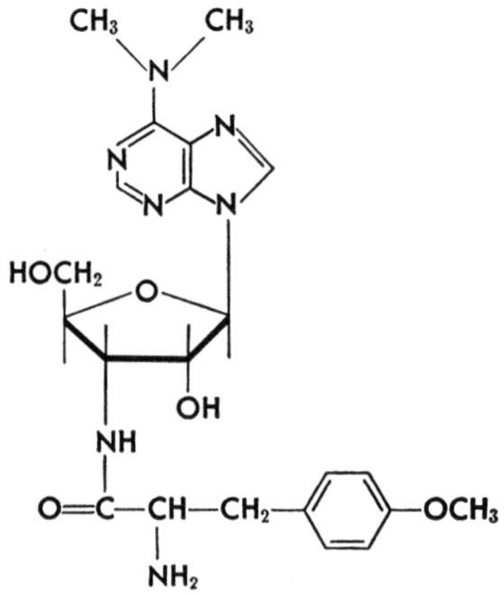

Streptomyces albo-niger

J. W. Porter, R. I. Hewitt, C. W. Hesseltine, G. Krupka, J. A. Lowery, W. S. Wallace, N. Bohonos and J. H. Williams, *Antibiotics and Chemotherapy* **2** 409 (1952).

Coy W. Waller, Peter W. Fryth, Brian L. Hutchings and James H. Williams, *J. Am. Chem. Soc.* **75** 2025 (1953). (Structure)

B. R. Baker, Robert E. Schaub, Joseph P. Joseph and James H. Williams, *ibid.* **77** 12 (1955). (Synthesis)

0. PTERIDINES AND FLAVINES

Pteridines (pterins), originally discovered in insects, occur widely, and several have been isolated from microbial sources. The most important of these from the metabolic standpoint is folic acid. This substance, or group of related substances, is a vitamin for most mammals and plants and for some microorganisms unable to produce it. Pure folic acid first was isolated from liver and from yeast. The triglutamyl form was isolated from a corynebacterium, and the heptaglutamyl derivative, first isolated from yeast, since has been found in a variety of microorganisms. The reason for the polypeptide chains is not clear. These forms are as effective as folic acid in higher animals, but are not so active as folic acid for the bacteria ordinarily used in bioassays.

The functions of folic acid as a B-vitamin have been investigated extensively and are now largely understood. Some of these have been encountered earlier in our discussions, but the role of folic acid derivatives in one-carbon metabolism has not been considered as such.

In its coenzyme form folic acid is attached to a protein apoenzyme, probably at the glutamic acid moiety, and the pteridine ring is reduced. One of these pteroproteins has been crystallized.[1] The "active formate" form of the coenzyme has been shown to be N^{10}-formyltetrahydrofolic acid,[2, 3, 4] and the "active formaldehyde" form probably is N^5,N^{10}-methylenetetrahydrofolic acid.[5, 6, 7, 8]

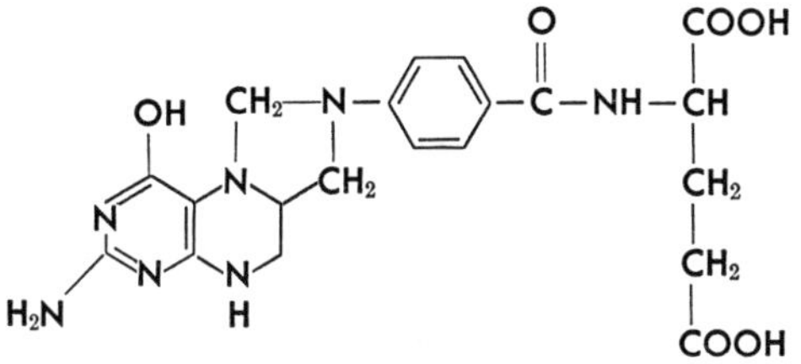

"Active Formaldehyde" N^5, N^{10}-
Methylenetetrahydrofolic Acid

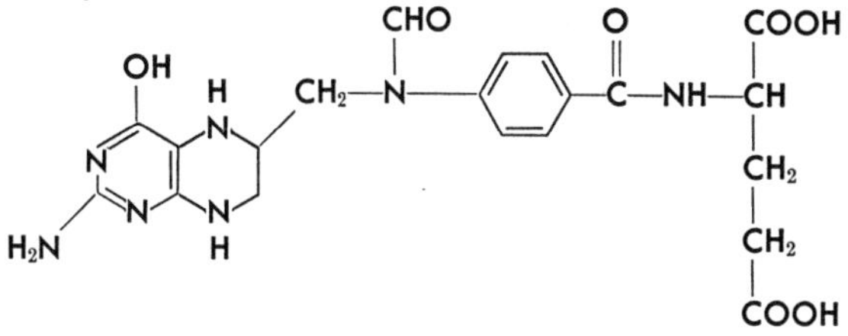

"Active Formate"
N^{10}-Formyltetrahydrofolic Acid

[1] Jesse C. Rabinowitz and W. E. Pricer, Jr., *Federation Proc.* **17** 293 (1958).

[2] H. M. Rauen and Lothar Jaenicke, *Z. physiol. Chem.* **293** 46 (1953).

[3] Lothar Jaenicke, *Biochim. et Biophys. Acta* **17** 588 (1955).

[4] H. M. Rauen, *Biochem. Z.* **328** 562 (1957).

[5] R. L. Blakley, *Biochem. J.* **58** 448 (1954).

[6] Roy L. Kisliuk, *J. Biol. Chem.* **227** 805 (1957).

[7] M. J. Osborn and F. M. Huennekens, *Biochim. et Biophys. Acta* **26** 646 (1957).

[8] F. M. Huennekens and M. J. Osborn, *Advances in Enzymology* **21** 370 (1959).

The two forms are interconvertible and this oxidation-reduction equilibrium probably is mediated by an enzyme with triphosphopyridine nucleotide (TPN) as the prosthetic group.

Formate added as a substrate is, then, activated in this way. The N^{10}-formyl group also can be furnished by glycine, either by way of glyoxylic acid[9, 10] or by way of δ-aminolevulinic acid.[11, 12, 13] The equations are:

$$H_2N\text{—}CH_2\text{—}COOH \underset{\text{ination}}{\overset{\text{transam-}}{\rightleftharpoons}} OHC\text{—}COOH \overset{[O]}{\longrightarrow}$$

Glycine   Glyoxylic Acid

$$CO_2 + N^{10}\text{-Formyltetrahydrofolic Acid}$$

and

$$H_2N\text{—}CH_2\text{—}\overset{O}{\overset{\|}{C}}\text{—}CH_2\text{—}CH_2\text{—}COOH \overset{NH_3}{\rightleftharpoons} H\text{—}\overset{O}{\overset{\|}{C}}\text{—}\overset{O}{\overset{\|}{C}}\text{—}CH_2\text{—}CH_2\text{—}COOH$$

δ-Aminolevulinic Acid   α-Ketoglutaraldehyde

$$\overset{[O]}{\rightleftharpoons} HOOC\text{—}CH_2\text{—}CH_2\text{—}COOH + N^{10}\text{-Formyltetrahydrofolic Acid}$$

Succinic Acid

Once formed "active formate" is the formylating agent in certain metabolic reactions. The important formylations by this agent which have been discovered to date are the two formylations already noted in the biosynthetic route to the purines. Thus glycineamide ribotide is formylated to furnish C-8 of the purine nucleus and, later, 5-amino-4-imidazolecarboxamide ribotide is formylated to furnish C-2 of the purine nucleus.

[9] Henry I. Nakada and Sidney Weinhouse, *Arch. Biochem. and Biophys.* 42 257 (1953).

[10] Sidney Weinhouse in W. D. McElroy and H. B. Glass (Editors), "Amino Acid Metabolism," Johns Hopkins Press, Baltimore, 1955, pp. 637–57.

[11] David Shemin, *ibid.*, p. 727.

[12] David Shemin, Tessa Abramsky and Charlotte S. Russell, *J. Am. Chem. Soc.* 76 1204 (1954).

[13] Irving Weliky and David Shemin, *Federation Proc.* 16 268 (1957).

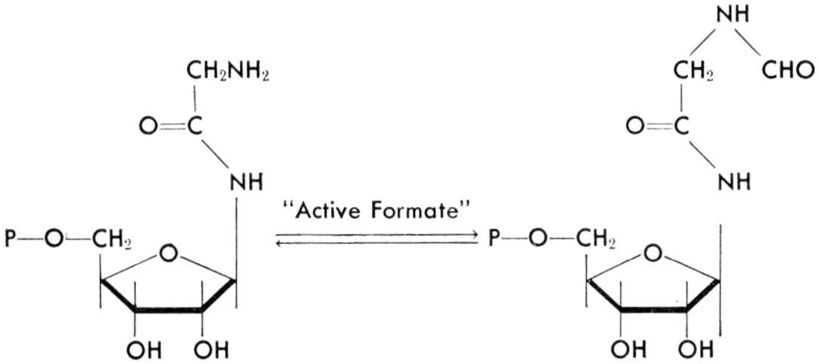

Glycineamide
Ribotide

Formylglycineamide
Ribotide

and

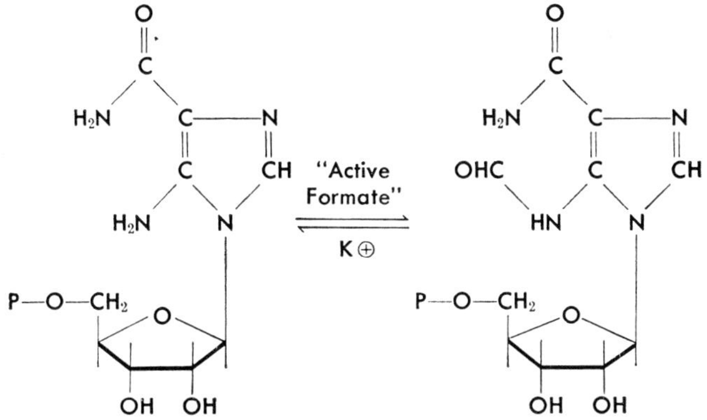

5-Amino-4-imidazole-
carboxamide Ribotide

5-Formamido-4-imidazole-
carboxamide Ribotide

As was seen in the biosynthesis of histidine the N-1 and C-2 atoms of the purine nucleus are donated to this amino acid during its formation so that

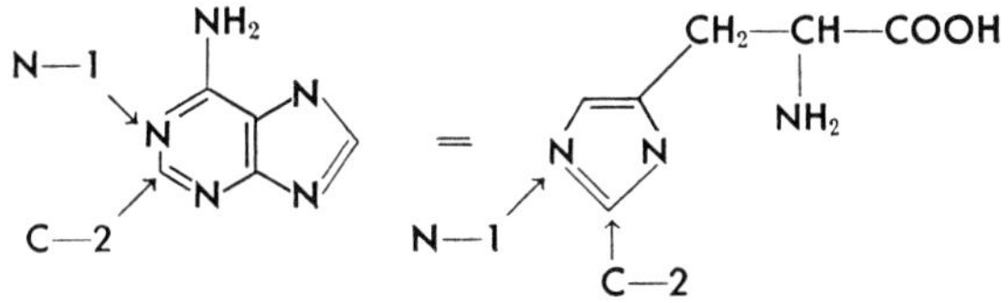

Adenine

Histidine

indirectly, at least, these atoms too are furnished by the coenzyme.

The "active formaldehyde" form of the coenzyme is intermediate in the interconversion of glycine and serine:

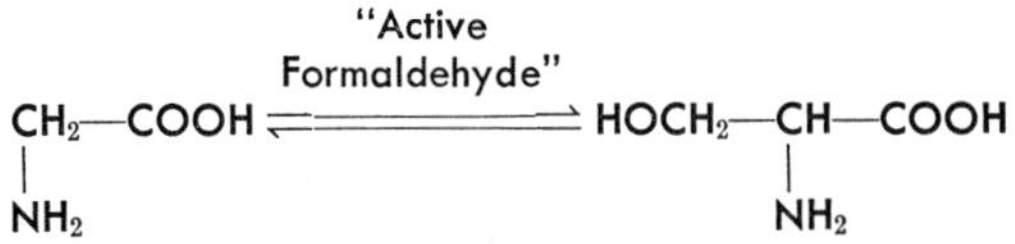

The large literature on this subject has been reviewed.[8]

The "active formaldehyde" form may also be considered to be a methyl group donor, although much remains to be learned about the mechanisms of these donations. In the biosynthesis of thymine from uracil, serine, formaldehyde or formate are more effective precursors of the introduced methyl group than is methionine, and this precursor effect is inhibited by folic acid antagonists.[8] Actually, the acceptor is probably not uracil, but deoxyuridine or deoxyuridylic acid:

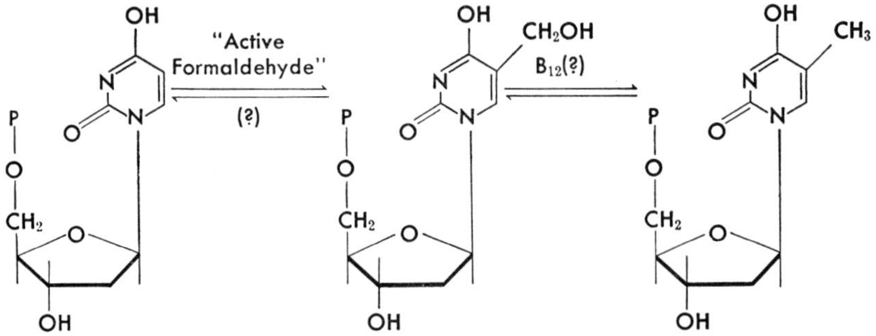

2′-Deoxyuridine-   2′-Deoxy-5-methylol-   Thymidine-
5′-phosphate   uridine-5′-phosphate   5′-phosphate

The occurrence of 5-hydroxymethylcytosine in some species has been cited as suggestive of formation of a hydroxymethyl intermediate in this way, at least in the cytosine series.[14, 15] On the other hand it has been reported that in *Lactobacillus leichmannii* there is a vitamin B_{12} requirement for the conversion of formic acid to the thymine methyl group, and that the route does not involve either methionine or a hydroxymethyl group.[16]

[14] Seymour S. Cohen and Lawrence L. Weed, *J. Biol. Chem.* **209** 789 (1954).

[15] Maurice Green and Seymour S. Cohen, *ibid.* **225** 387 (1957).

[16] James S. Dinning, Barbara K. Allen, Ruth Young and Paul L. Day, *ibid.* **233** 674 (1958).

The synthesis of the labile methyl group of methionine has been shown to involve a one-carbon unit at the formaldehyde oxidation level, and the "active formaldehyde" form of the coenzyme has been implicated.[17, 18] Here, again, not everything is known. The following route has been suggested:[8, 19]

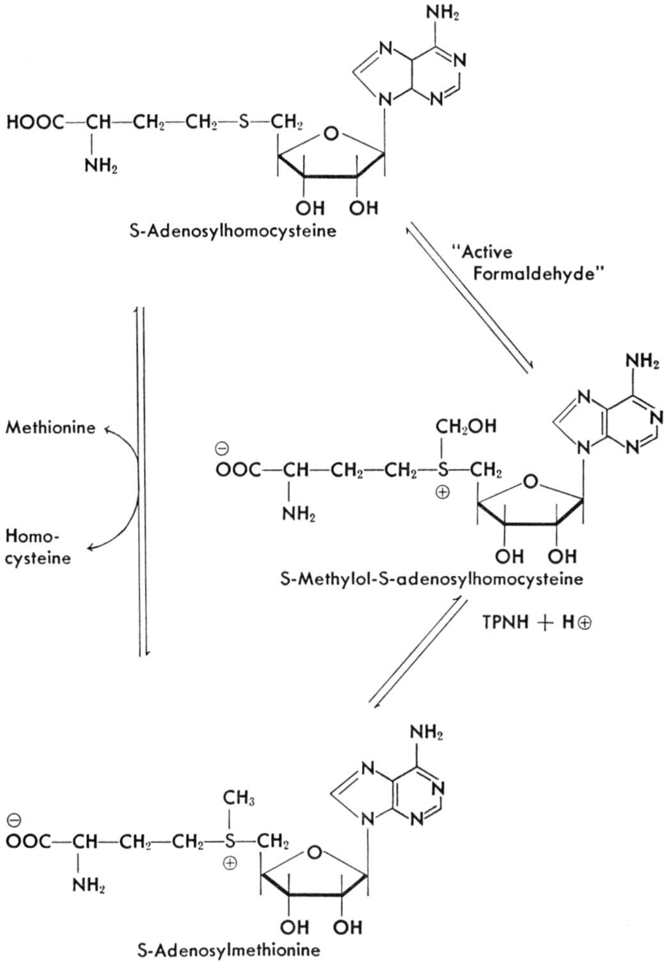

$HOOC-CH-CH_2-CH_2-S-CH_2$
$\quad\quad\quad |$
$\quad\quad\quad NH_2$

S-Adenosylhomocysteine

"Active Formaldehyde"

Methionine

$OOC-CH-CH_2-CH_2-\overset{+}{S}-CH_2$
$\ominus\quad\quad |\quad\quad\quad\quad\quad\quad |$
$\quad\quad\quad NH_2\quad\quad\quad\quad CH_2OH$

Homo-cysteine

S-Methylol-S-adenosylhomocysteine

TPNH + H⊕

$OOC-CH-CH_2-CH_2-\overset{+}{S}-CH_2$
$\ominus\quad\quad |\quad\quad\quad\quad\quad\quad |$
$\quad\quad\quad NH_2\quad\quad\quad\quad CH_3$

S-Adenosylmethionine

[17] David Elwyn, Arthur Weissbach and David B. Sprinson, *J. Am. Chem. Soc.* **73** 5509 (1951).

[18] David B. Sprinson in W. D. McElroy and H. B. Glass (Editors), "Amino Acid Metabolism," Johns Hopkins Press, Baltimore, 1955, p. 608.

[19] Audrey Stevens and W. Takami, *Federation Proc.* **17** 316 (1958).

In an *Escherichia coli* mutant requiring either methionine or vitamin B_{12} for growth methionine synthesis from homocysteine and serine was stimulated by addition of vitamin B_{12}.[20, 21] This suggests that again vitamin B_{12} may be involved in methyl group synthesis.

There is some evidence (from higher animals) that there is a folic acid requirement for the introduction into aminoethanol of some, if not all, of the methyl groups of choline.[22, 23]

Little is known about the biosynthesis of pteridines in microorganisms. There are suggestions that both pteridines and flavines are related to the purines in this respect.

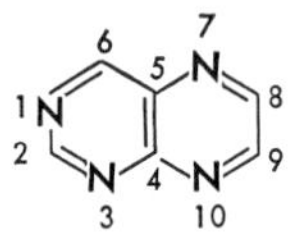

Pteridine

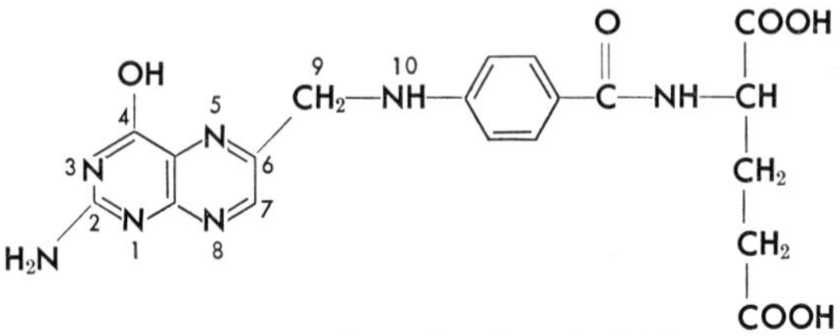

Pteroyl-L-glutamic Acid
(Folic Acid)

Labeled molecule studies with butterflies indicate that carbon atoms 4 and 5 of the pteridine ring in leucopterin and xanthopterin are derived from glycine (4 from the glycine carboxyl group and 5 from the α-carbon atom).[24]

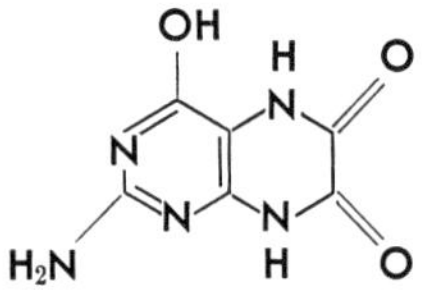

Leucopterin 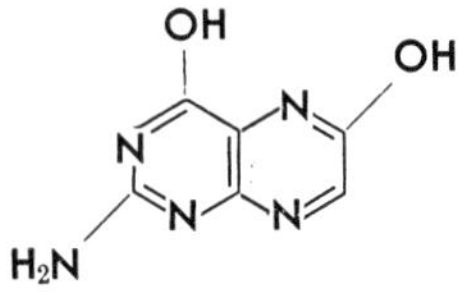   Xanthopterin

The C-6 position seems to be furnished from carbon dioxide and the C-2 position from formate, reminiscent of the purines. Carbon atoms 8 and 9 of the pteridine nucleus

[20] C. W. Helliner and D. D. Woods, *Biochem. J.* **63** 26 p (1956).
[21] R. L. Kisliuk and D. D. Woods, *J. Gen. Microbiol.* **18** xv (1957).
[22] Jacob A. Stekol, Sidney Weiss and Ethyl I. Anderson, *J. Am. Chem. Soc.* **77** 5192 (1955).
[23] R. Venkataraman and D. M. Greenberg, *ibid.* **80** 2025 (1958).
[24] F. Weygand and M. Waldschmidt, *Angew. Chem.* **67** 328 (1955).

(in leucopterin from butterflies) are furnished quite directly by glucose. Over 50 percent of the activity of D-glucose-1-C[14] was found in these two positions, and acetate was excluded as a direct precursor of this part of the molecule.[25]

A sugar origin for this part of the pteridine ring is suggested, too, by the natural occurrence of such substances as erythropterin and biopterin, although, in these cases,

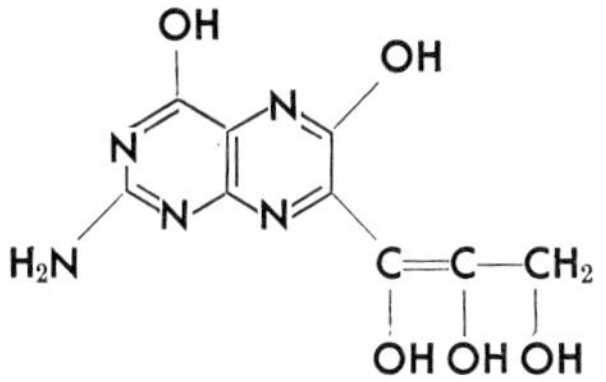

Erythropterin 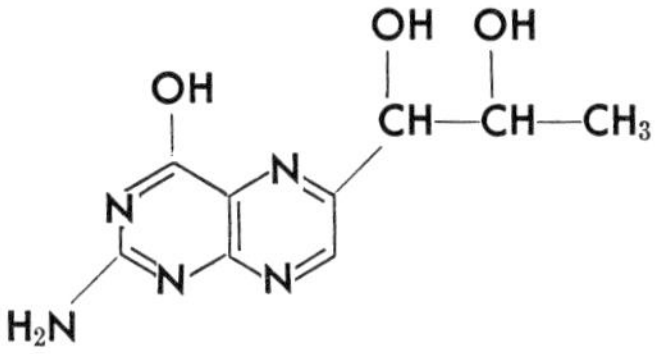   Biopterin

pentoses would be expected. Both erythropterin and biopterin, incidentally, occur as glycosides. If a precursor such as this were assumed, it would relate these substances closely with the riboflavin structure. There is experimental support for the assumption of the pyrimidine shown as a riboflavin precursor.[26]

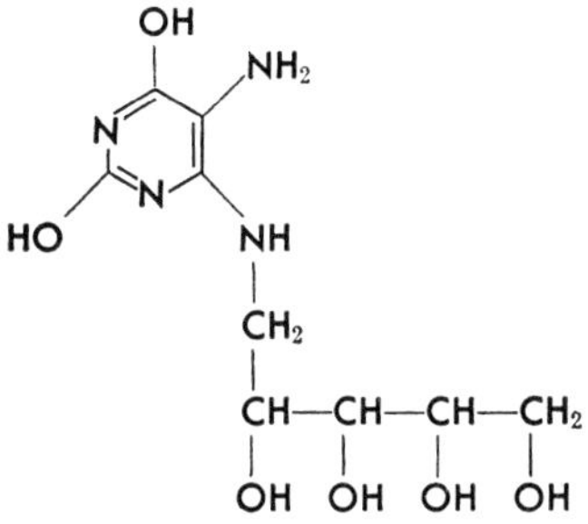

Assumed pteridine   Riboflavin
precursor

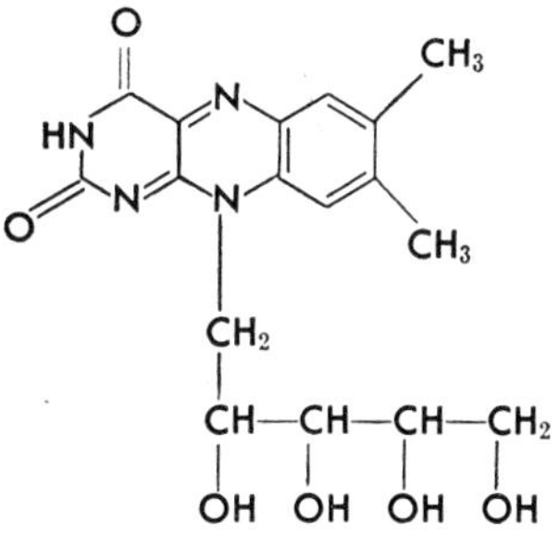

Many pteridine derivatives related to the pteridine

[25] F. Weygand, H.-J. Schliep, H. Simon and G. Dahms, *ibid.* 71 522 (1959).

[26] Toyokazu Kishi, Mitsuko Asai, Toru Masuda and Satoru Kuwada, *Chem. and Pharm. Bull.* (Japan) 7 515 (1959).

moiety of folic acid have been isolated from non-microbial species. This subject has been reviewed.[8, 27]

Labeled xanthopterin was converted to 5-formyl-5,6–7,8-tetrahydropteroic acid by *Enterococcus stei, Streptococcus fecalis, E. coli* and *Pichia membranaefaciens.*[27a] Folic acid was not formed even when *p*-aminobenzoic acid was added to the medium. Cell extracts of these microorganisms produced folic acid principally.

The assembly of the three moieties of folic acid into the complete molecule has been studied. *Lactobacillus arabinosus* contains enzymes able to couple 2-amino-4-hydroxy-pteridine-6-carboxaldehyde or the corresponding alcohol with *p*-aminobenzoic acid.[28]

2-Amino-4-hydroxy-
pteridine-6-carboxaldehyde

2-Amino-4-hydroxy-6-
hydroxymethylpteridine

These pteridines are even more effective precursors in their reduced forms. Many other pteridines tested were not used. ATP (and Mg^{++}) was required. Its role is unknown, although phosphorylation of the alcohol of the pteridine hydroxymethyl group might be necessary to activate it for coupling.

p-Aminobenzoic acid was more effective than *p*-aminobenzoylglutamic acid in this coupling reaction in *E. coli*,[29] although *Mycobacterium avium* was able to use the peptide.[30] Apparently adenylo-*p*-aminobenzoic acid was an intermediate in the latter organism (ATP and CoA were required).

The origin of *p*-aminobenzoic acid was considered in an earlier section. It has been known for some time that the anti-infective sulfonamide drugs function by interfering

[27] J. J. Pfiffner and O. D. Bird, *Ann. Rev. Biochem.* 25 416–419 (1956).

[27a] F. Korte and Gotthard Synnatschke, *Ann.* 628 153 (1959).

[28] T. Shiota, *Arch. Biochem. and Biophys.* 80 155 (1959).

[29] Gene M. Brown, *Federation Proc.* 18 19 (1959).

[30] H. Katunuma, Abstr. 32nd Congr. Japanese Biochem. Assoc., Kyoto, July 1957.

with the incorporation of *p*-aminobenzoic acid into folic acid. Enzyme studies (*E. coli* extracts) now seem to have narrowed this to inhibition of the coupling of the pteridine moiety with *p*-aminobenzoic acid,[31] although in the *Mycobacterium avium* study inhibition of peptide formation by prevention of adenylo-*p*-aminobenzoic acid formation was suggested.

Investigation of the biosynthesis of riboflavin is facilitated by the existence of the two microorganisms, *Eremothecium ashbyii*, a yeast, and *Ashbya gossypii*, a mold, which are prodigious producers of this vitamin, evolving large quantities into the culture medium.

Besides riboflavin several other substances have been isolated from riboflavin fermentations. The structures of these metabolites suggest that they may be biosynthetic precursors of the vitamin.

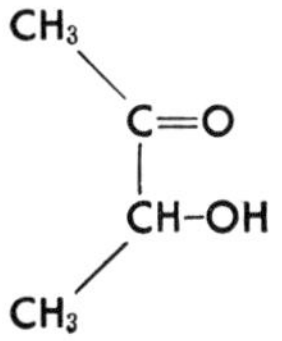

Acetoin 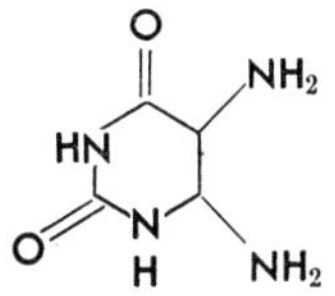   4,5-Diaminouracil 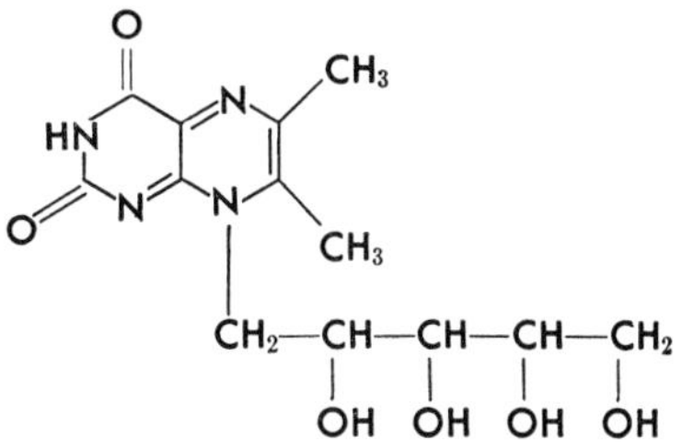   6,7-Dimethyl-8-(D-1'-ribityl)-lumazine
                                         G-Compound (green fluorescence)

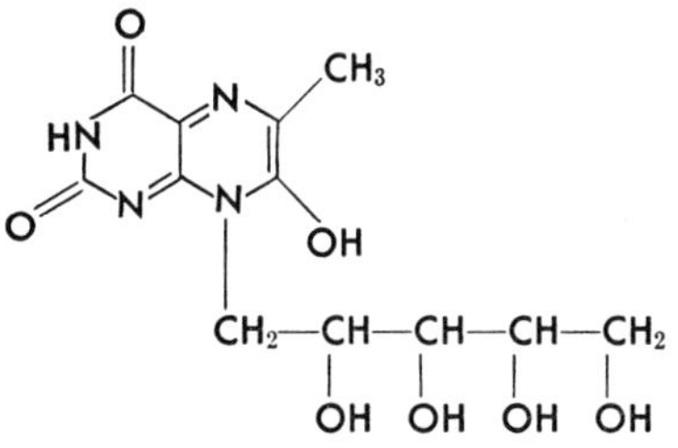

6-Methyl-7-oxy-8-(D-1'-ribityl)-lumazine   Riboflavin
V-Compound (violet fluorescence)

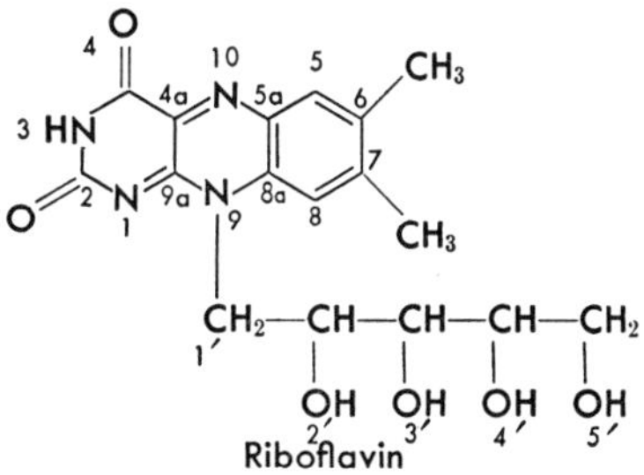

They are shown in the accompanying formulas.

Addition of purines to cultures of growing riboflavin producers increases the yield of riboflavin.[32] C^{14}-8-Labeled adenine contributes no radioactivity to the riboflavin mole-

[31] Gene M. Brown, *Physiol. Revs.* **40** 359 (1960).
[32] John A. MacLaren, *J. Bacteriol.* **63** 233 (1952).

cule,[33] but C-4 of the purine nucleus is equivalent to C-4a in riboflavin, and C-5 of purine to C-9a of riboflavin.[34] The C-4 of riboflavin is furnished by carbon dioxide (*cf.* C-6 in purines), and C-2 from formate (*cf.* C-2 in purines). These relationships are shown in generalized diagram.

Sources of the Carbon Atoms in Purines, Pteridines and Flavines

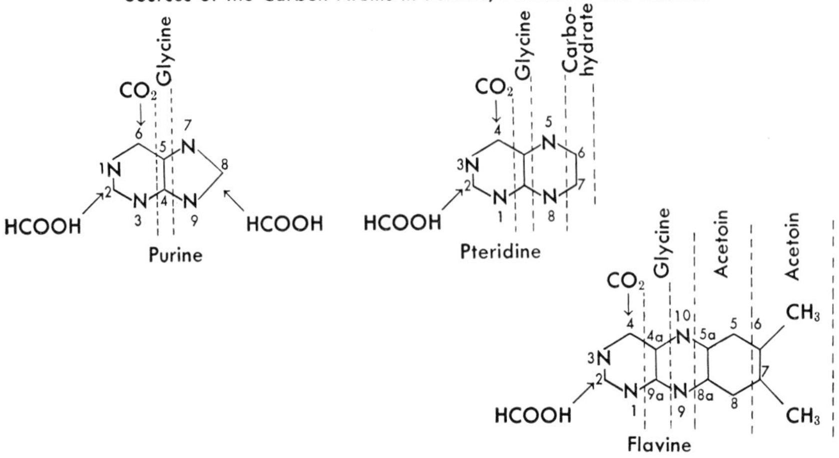

Purine

Pteridine

Flavine

The pyrimidine rings in all these systems seem to have a common origin, and perhaps purines are precursors of the other two classes of heterocycles.

Guanine-5-C^{14} was converted to labeled riboflavin and to labeled G-compound by *Eremothecium ashbyii, Ashbya gossypii, Candida flareri, C. guilliermondii* and *C. parapsilopsis*.[35] Pyrimidines and pteridines were not used directly, and, when labeled G-compound was added to growing cultures, it was not converted to riboflavin by *E. ashbyii* nor was labeled 4,5-diaminouracil. V-Compound was shown to be formed rather easily from G-compound by air oxidation of a stored alkaline solution. While G-compound was not used by growing whole cells, cell-free extracts of *E. ashbyii, Ashbya gossypii, Mycobacterium smegmatis* and *M. avium* were able to incorporate it into the riboflavin molecule.[36, 37]

[33] Walter S. McNutt, *J. Biol. Chem.* 210 511 (1954).

[34] G. W. E. Plaut, *ibid.* 208 513 (1954).

[35] Friedhelm Korte, Hans Ulrich Aldag, Gerhard Ludwig, Wilfried Paulus and Klaus Störiko, *Ann.* 619 70 (1958).

[36] Friedhelm Korte and Hans Ulrich Aldag, *Ann.* 628 144 (1959).

[37] G. F. Maley and G. W. E. Plaut, *J. Am. Chem. Soc.* 81 2025 (1959).

Adenine was found to be a more efficient precursor for riboflavin than G-compound in C^{14}-labeling studies,[38] and guanine and xanthine have been found more efficient than adenine.[39]

Acetate[40] and shikimic acid[41] have been shown to be improbable direct precursors of the A ring of riboflavin. Acetoin has been isolated from riboflavin fermentations[42] and is a normal metabolite of these organisms and of other yeasts. On the basis of chemical studies this substance (or near derivatives) was proposed as a precursor of the A ring of riboflavin.[38, 43] It has been confirmed that acetoin is an efficient biological precursor of the vitamin[41] although intermediates cannot be ruled out entirely.

At present, then, the following biosynthetic scheme seems indicated:

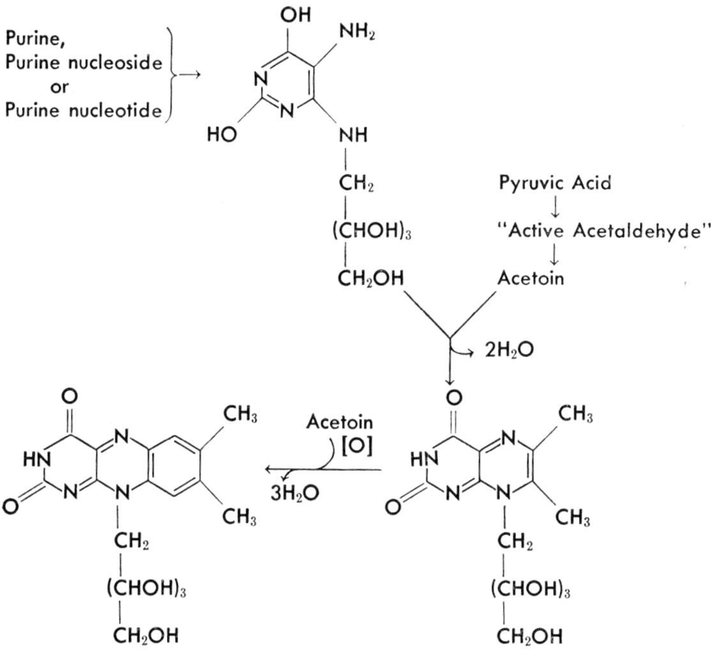

[38] R. Cresswell and H. Wood, *Proc. Chem. Soc.,* 386 (1959).

[39] E. G. Brown, T. W. Goodwin and S. Pendleton, *Biochem. J.* 68 40 (1955).

[40] G. W. E. Plaut, *J. Biol. Chem.* 211 111 (1954).

[41] T. W. Goodwin and D. H. Treble, *Biochem. J.* 70 14 p (1958).

[42] Toru Masuda, *Pharm. Bull.* (Japan) 5 136 (1957).

[43] A. J. Birch and C. J. Moye, *J. Chem. Soc.,* 412 (1957); 2622 (1958).

The occurrence of V-compound could be explained as due to a side-reaction in which pyruvate rather than acetoin reacted with the pyrimidine, or it may merely be an oxidation product of G-compound. The close relationship between pyruvate, active acetaldehyde and acetoin, which is mediated by thiamine, has been discussed in an earlier section.

The origin of the ribityl group remains obscure. It is yet to be shown whether this moiety is derived from the ribose of the purine nucleosides or whether it is formed in some other way. Some work has been done on this facet of the biosynthesis.[33, 44, 45, 46]

Riboflavin is phosphorylated by ATP to give riboflavin-5'-phosphate, a coenzyme form. This, in turn, can react again with ATP in the presence of the appropriate enzyme to form flavine-adenine dinucleotide, the other co-

$$\text{Riboflavin} + \text{ATP} \xrightarrow{\text{Mg}^{++}} \text{Riboflavin-5'-phosphate} + \text{ADP}$$
$$\text{Riboflavin-5'-phosphate} + \text{ATP} \rightleftharpoons \text{Flavine-adeninedinucleotide} + \text{Pyrophosphate}$$

enzyme form. Flavine-adenine dinucleotide (FAD) is produced commercially in Japan from *E. ashbyii* mycelium.

The principal point of attachment of flavinemononucleotide (FMN) to the apoenzyme seems to be the phosphate group. There may be involvement of the 3-imino group also. FAD is the most prevalent coenzyme form, although FMN occurs in rather large proportions in some microor-

[44] G. W. E. Plaut and Patricia L. Broberg, *J. Biol. Chem.* 219 131 (1956).

[45] Edna B. Kearney and Sasha Englard, *ibid.* 193 821 (1951).

[46] Anthony W. Schrecker and Arthur Kornberg, *ibid.* 182 795 (1950).

ganisms. Obligate anaerobes contain relatively large quantities of flavoproteins. Surveys have been made of the flavine content of microorganisms not used in commercial production.[47, 48] There is variation in the tightness of binding of the coenzyme, and the modes of attachment are not entirely understood.

One of the functions of the flavine enzymes has been mentioned already, namely, the dehydrogenation of reduced DPN in the respiratory chain. Sites of DPNH formation were seen earlier, particularly in the glycolysis route and the citric acid cycle. The enzyme succinic dehydrogenase is a flavoprotein, and the $FADH_2$ formed in this reaction also is fed into the respiratory chain. Besides the direct net synthesis of 2 moles of ATP during glycolysis and of 1 mole of ATP in the citric acid cycle, the remaining energy released during glucose catabolism is transferred in the form of hydrogen or electrons to enzymes with TPN, DPN or FAD as prosthetic groups.

These reduced enzymes are, in turn, oxidized by the metal ion-porphyrin enzymes, which are oxidized by gaseous oxygen. When two hydrogen atoms are passed along the entire respiratory chain, water is formed as well as 3 more molecules of ATP.

The exact number of particles in the chain is not entirely clear, and there are variations with different organisms. In lactobacilli, for example, flavines seem to replace heme proteins in electron transport.[48a] Also obscure is the exact manner in which ATP is formed during respiration and the precise way in which hydrogen is transferred from one coenzyme to the next. There has been interesting speculation in this area of biophysics.

The respiratory chain can be shown in a simplified form as in the accompanying diagram.[49]

[47] J. L. Peel, *Biochem. J.* 69 403 (1958).

[48] Chester DeLuca, Morton M. Weber and Nathan O. Kaplan, *J. Biol. Chem.* 223 559 (1956).

[48a] Cornelius F. Strittmatter, *Federation Proc.* 17 318 (1958).

[49] Albert L. Lehninger, *Scientific American* 202 102 (1960).

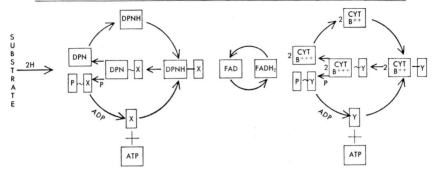

The natures of the entities X, Y and Z are mysterious. If they are assumed to possess nucleophilic groups such as R—S⁻, R—COO⁻ or $H_2PO_4^-$, then one scheme has been advanced to show how the requisite energy-rich bonds could be formed in DPNH, FADH and Ferricytochrome a_3.[50] The coupling methods and resonance systems involved are shown in the diagram:

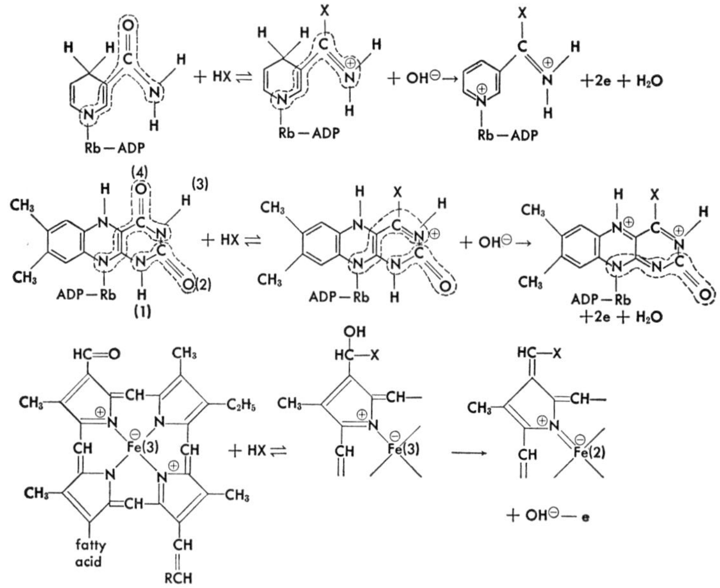

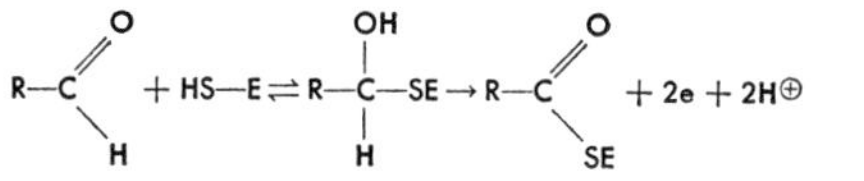

[50] Paul E. Glahn and Sigurd O. Nielsen, *Nature* 183 1578 (1959).

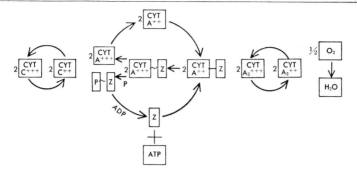

Another hypothesis assumes close approach of DPNH and riboflavin in parallel planes with interposition of inorganic phosphate, held perhaps by hydrogen bonding, *e.g.* to the amide moiety of nicotinamide.[51] These geometrical and chemical relationships can be represented as follows:

[51] Barbro Grabe, *Biochim. et Biophys. Acta* **30** 560 (1958).

When an electron is transferred from the N-atom of the reduced pyridine ring to an unoccupied π-orbital of the isoalloxazine ring of FAD, the N-atom assumes a positive charge, which is neutralized by attraction of a proximate, ionized phosphate hydroxyl oxygen. The increased electron density on the O-atom at position 2 in the riboflavin nucleus might cause formation of a bond to phosphorus as shown in the activated complex above, the reaction being:

$$\text{DPNH} + \text{FAD} + \text{H}_2\text{O}_3\text{PO}^{\ominus} + \text{H}^{\oplus} \rightleftharpoons \text{DPN}^{\oplus} + \text{H}_2\text{O}_3\text{P}\text{—FADH} + \text{OH}^{\ominus}$$

When this substance is oxidized by the subsequent carrier (probably a cytochrome), two electrons, perhaps dislocalized π-electrons, are withdrawn from the FAD-complex thus permitting dissociation of a proton and activation of the phosphoryl group. In the presence of ADP, then, ATP could be formed according to the equation:

$$\text{FADH—PO}_3\text{H}_2 + \text{ADP} + 2\text{Fe}^{\oplus\oplus\oplus} \rightleftharpoons \text{FAD} + \text{H}^{\oplus} + \text{ATP} + 2\text{Fe}^{\oplus\oplus}$$

Other flavoprotein dehydrogenase substrates are: aldehydes, α-amino acids, α-hydroxy acids, purines, fatty acid-coenzyme A esters and certain amines. Flavine enzymes also participate in bacterial hydrogenase systems, in nitrate reduction and assimilation by fungi and higher plants and in photosynthesis and bioluminescence. There is currently much study of flavoprotein reactions, which can often be followed by spectrophotometry and EPR techniques.

Reviews of the flavine coenzymes and their biosynthesis are available.[52, 31]

1048 **Xanthopterin,** $C_6H_5O_2N_5$, yellow amorphous substance, isolated as barium or sodium salts.

[52] Paul D. Boyer, Henry Lardy and Karl Myrbäck (Eds.), "The Enzymes" Vol. II, 2nd ed., Helmut Beinert, *Flavin coenzymes,* Academic Press, New York, 1960, pp. 340–416.

Mycobacterium tuberculosis
Also occurs as a butterfly wing pigment.

Marguerite O'L. Crowe and Amy Walker, *Brit. J. Exptl. Pathol.* **35** 18 (1954). (Isolation from this organism)

Robert Purrmann, *Ann.* **546** 98 (1940), **548** 284 (1941). (Synthesis)

1049 **Pterin-like Substance.**

By paper chromatographic comparisons this purple fluorescent substance was shown to be similar to or identical with 2-amino-4,7-dihydroxypteridine-6-acetic acid ($C_8H_7O_4N_5$).

Aspergilli

Yasuyuki Kaneko, *J. Agr. Chem. Soc. Japan* **31** 122 (1957).

1050 **Erythropterin,** $C_9H_9O_5N_5$, deep red crystals from 0.01 N hydrochloric acid.

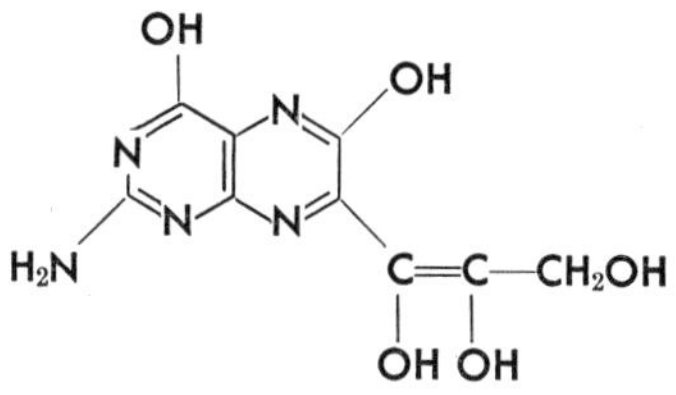

Mycobacterium tuberculosis var. *hominis, M. lacticola*

M. O'L. Crowe and A. Walker, *Science* **110** 166 (1949).

Rudolf Tschesche and Frederic Vester, *Chem. Ber.* **86** 454 (1953).

1051 **Biopterin,** $C_9H_{11}O_3N_5$, pale yellow crystals, m.p. 250–280° (dec.), $[\alpha]_D^{25}$ −50° (in 0.1 N hydrochloric acid).

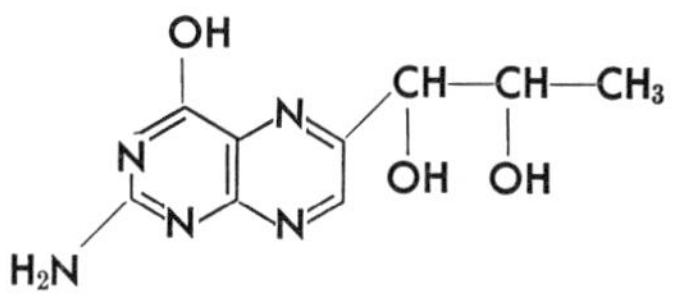

Yeast, *Ochromonas malhamensis*

E. L. Patterson, H. P. Broquist, Alberta M. Albrecht, M. H. von Saltza and E. L. R. Stokstad, *J. Am. Chem. Soc.* **77** 3167 (1955).

1052 **V-Compound** (8-Ribityl-6-methyl-7-oxylumazine, Compound A), $C_{12}H_{16}O_7N_4$, colorless crystals, m.p. 263° (dec.), $[\alpha]_D^{20}$ +4.5° (c 3.3 in water) +11.45° (in 0.1 N sodium hydroxide solution).

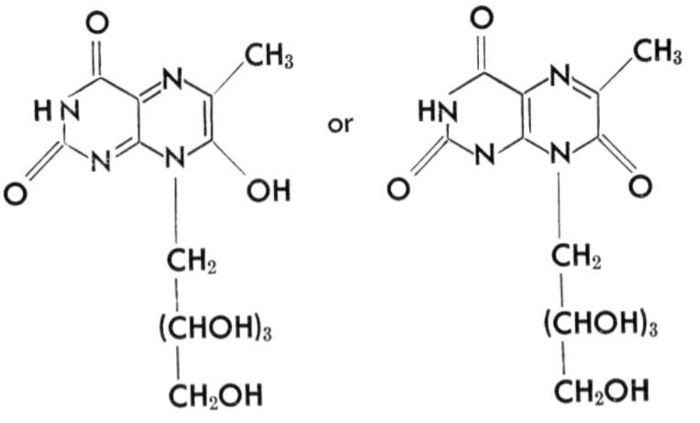

Eremothecium ashbyii
Toru Masuda, Toyokazu Kishi and Mitsuko Asai, *Chem. and Pharm. Bull* (Japan) **6** 291 (1958). (Structure)
Toru Masuda, Toyokazu Kishi, Mitsuko Asai and Satoru Kuwada, *ibid.* **7** 361, 366 (1959). (Synthesis)
Walter S. McNutt, *J. Am. Chem. Soc.* **82** 217 (1960).

1053 **G-Compound** (8-Ribityl-6,7-dimethyllumazine), $C_{13}H_{18}O_6N_4$, light yellow needles, m.p. 273° (dec.), $[\alpha]_D^{20}$ −164°.

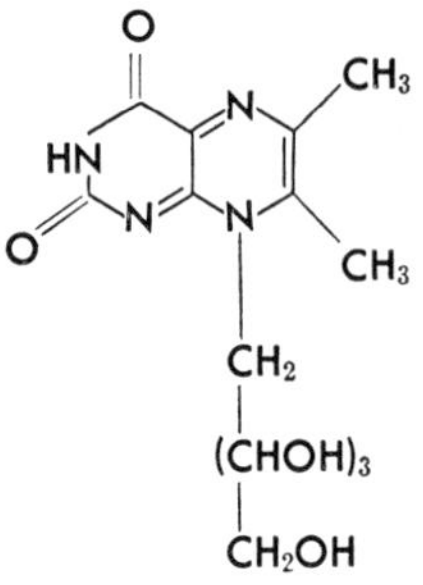

Eremothecium ashbyii

1054 **l-3-Oxykynurenine**, $C_{10}H_{12}O_4N_2$

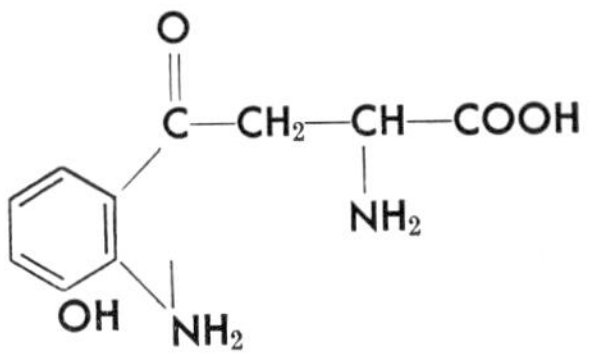

was isolated from the same culture. This metabolite resembles 3-oxyanthranilic acid, known to be a biosynthetic precursor of nicotinic acid.

Toru Masuda, *Pharm. Bull.* (Japan) 4 71 (1956). (Isolation)

Idem., ibid. 5 28 (1957). (Structure)

Toru Masuda, Toyokazu Kishi, Mitsuko Asai and Satoru Kuwada, *Chem. and Pharm. Bull.* (Japan) 7 361 (1959). (Synthesis)

1055 **Rhizopterin** (N^{10}-Formylpteroic Acid) (*Streptococcus lactis* R Factor) (SLR Factor), $C_{15}H_{12}O_4N_6$, light yellow crystals, m.p. >300°.

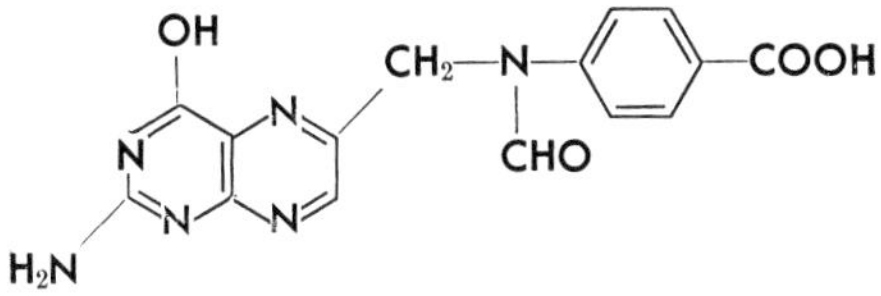

Rhizopus nigricans

Edward L. Rickes, Louis Chaiet and John C. Keresztesy, *J. Am. Chem. Soc.* 69 2749 (1947).

Donald E. Wolf, R. Christian Anderson, Edward A. Kaczka, Stanton A. Harris, Glen E. Arth, Philip L. Southwick, Ralph Mozingo and Karl Folkers, *ibid.* 69 2753 (1947). (Synthesis)

1056 **Riboflavin** (Vitamin B_2), $C_{17}H_{20}O_6N_4$, yellow-orange microcrystalline powder, m.p. ~280° (rapid heating), $[\alpha]_D^{25}$ −112° to −122° (50 mg. in 2 ml. of 0.1 N alcoholic sodium hydroxide diluted to 10 ml. with water).

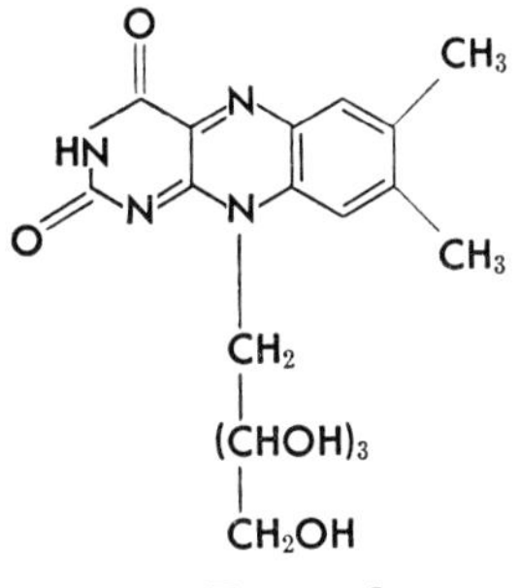

Ascomycetes such as *Eremothecium ashbyii* and *Ashbya gossypi* produce high yields.

Leland A. Underkofler and Richard J. Hickey, "Industrial Fermentations," Chemical Publishing Co., Inc., New York, 1954 **Vol. II**, Richard J. Hickey, *Production of riboflavin by fermentation*, Chap. 5, pp. 157–190. (A review)

1057 Riboflavin-5′-phosphate, $C_{17}H_{21}O_9N_4P$, yellow microcrystals.

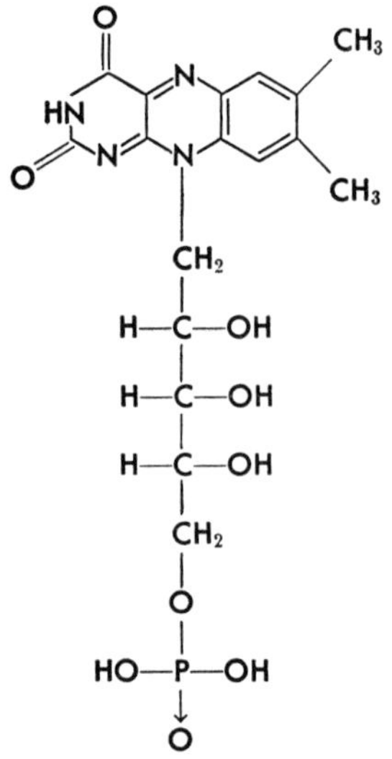

Yeast
Otto Warburg and Walter Christian, *Biochem. Z.* 254 438 (1932); 258 496 (1933); 263 228 (1933). (Isolation)
H. S. Forrest and A. R. Todd, *J. Chem. Soc.*, 3295 (1950). (Synthesis)

1058 Folic Acid (Pteroylglutamic Acid Folacin, Vitamin B_c), $C_{19}H_{19}$-O_6N_7, pale yellow-orange needles, which char above 250°.

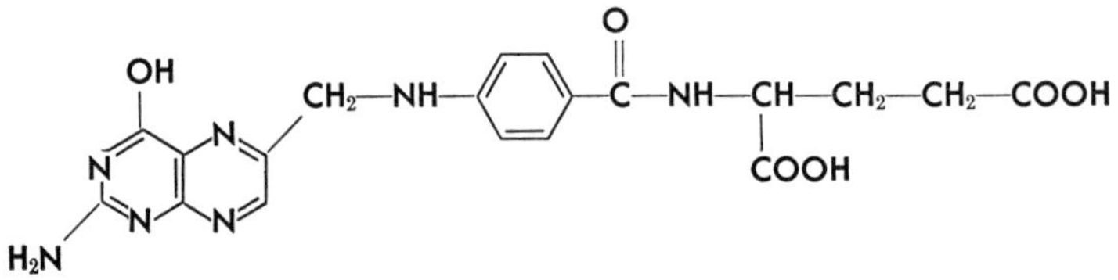

Yeasts and certain higher fungi
Yields of 19–80 μg. per gram of dry cell weight are obtained from brewers' yeast.
Leland A. Underkofler and Richard J. Hickey, "Industrial Fermentations," Chemical Publishing Co., Inc., New York, 1954 **Vol. III**, J. M. Van Lanen, *Production of vitamins other than riboflavin*, Chap. 6, pp. 191–216. (A review)

1059   **Citrovorum Factor** (Folinic Acid-SF, Leucovorin, N^5-Formyltet-
rahydrofolic Acid) $C_{20}H_{23}O_7N_7$ (Trihydrate): Buff crystals, m.p. 248–250° (dec.), $[\alpha]_D^{25}$ +16.76 (c 3.52 on
anhydrous basis in 5% sodium bicarbonate solution).

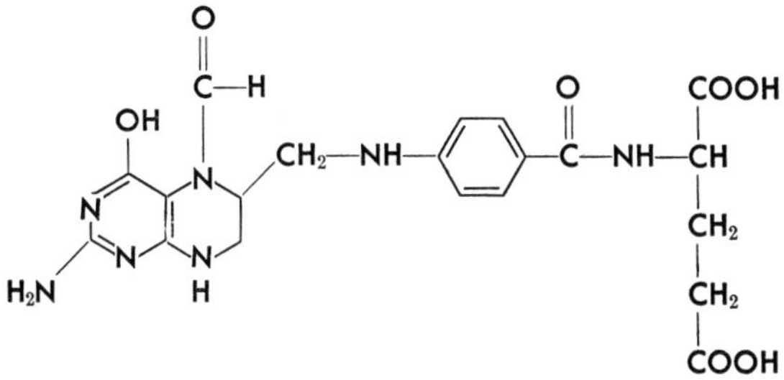

Yeasts (probably widely distributed)
The corresponding compound with the formyl group
transferred to the amine group of the p-aminobenzoic acid
moiety (N_{10}) is also known.
   C. H. Hill and M. L. Scott, *J. Biol. Chem.* 196 195 (1952).
(Isolation from brewers' yeast)
   A. G. M. Sjöström and L. E. Ericson, *Acta Chem. Scand.* 7
870 (1953).   (Isolation from eight lichens)
   Donna B. Cosulick, Barbara Roth, James M. Smith, Jr.,
Martin E. Hultquist and Robert P. Parker, *J. Am. Chem. Soc.*
74 3252 (1952).   (Structure)

1060   **Flavine-Adenine-Dinucleotide,** $C_{27}H_{33}O_{15}N_9P_2$, amorphous white
powder.

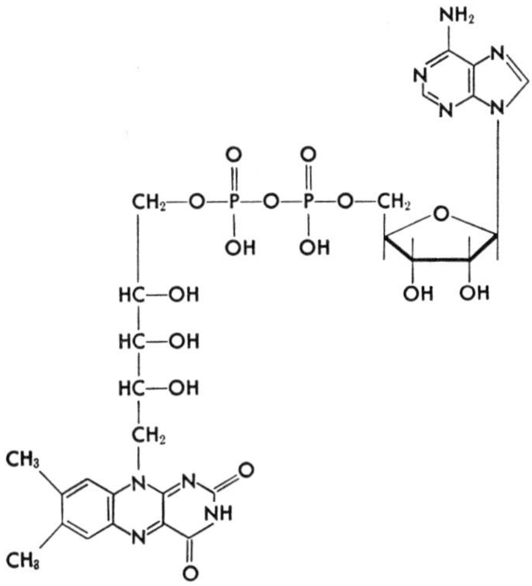

Yeasts, molds, bacteria (widely distributed)

Otto Warburg and Walter Christian, *Biochem. Z.* 298 150 (1938). (Isolation)

S. M. H. Christie, G. W. Kenner and A. R. Todd, *Nature* 170 924 (1952).

Idem., J. Chem. Soc., 46 (1954). (Synthesis)

J. G. Moffatt and H. G. Khorana, *J. Am. Chem. Soc.* 80 3756 (1958). (Synthesis)

1061 **Fermentation "Lactobacillus casei" Factor** (Teropterin, Pteroyl-γ-glutamyl-γ-glutamylglutamic Acid), $C_{29}H_{33}O_{12}N_9$.

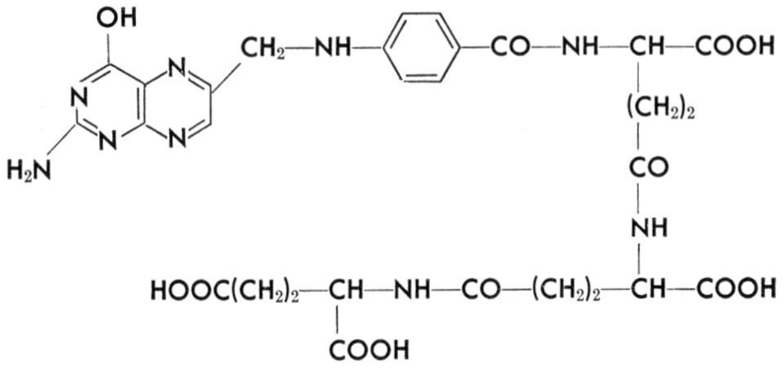

Corynebacterium sp.

Brian L. Hutchings, E. L. R. Stokstad, Nestor Bohonos, Nathan Sloane and Y. Subbarow, *Ann. N. Y. Acad. Sci.* 48 265 (1946). (Isolation)

J. H. Boothe, J. H. Mowat, B. L. Hutchings, R. B. Angier, C. W. Waller, E. L. R. Stokstad, J. Semb, A. L. Gazzola and Y. Subbarow, *J. Am. Chem. Soc.* 70 1099 (1948).

J. H. Boothe, J. Semb, C. W. Waller, R. B. Angier, J. H. Mowat, B. L. Hutchings, E. L. R. Stokstad and Y. Subbarow, *ibid.* 71 2304 (1949). (Synthesis)

1062 **Vitamin B$_c$ Conjugate** (Pteroylhexaglutamylglutamic Acid), $C_{49}H_{61}O_{24}N_{13}$.

The structure is like that of the preceding formula, but with four more glutamic acid units in the polypeptide side-chain.

Bacteria, yeasts, molds (widely distributed among microorganisms)

P. R. Burkholder, Ilda McVeigh and Katherine Wilson, *Arch. Biochem.* 7 287 (1945).

J. J. Pfiffner, D. G. Calkins, E. S. Bloom and B. L. O'Dell, *J. Am. Chem. Soc* 68 1392 (1946). (Structure)

1063 Pteridine pigment.

A pigment which fluoresces under U.V. light is produced by *Microsporum* species (some of which cause ringworm). This pigment has been isolated and purified to some extent. The infrared spectrum indicates that it is a pteridine, probably trisubstituted, and possibly 2-NH$_2$ (or —OH), 4—OH and 6—CH$_2$OH substituted.

Microsporum gypseum, M. canis

Frederick T. Wolf, Ernest A. Jones and Helene A. Nathan, *Nature* **182** 475 (1958).

19.

Unclassified Metabolites

1064 Aburamycin (M5-18903), yellow crystals, m.p. 163–165° (169–171°), $[\alpha]_D^{20}$ +24.56° (c 1 in methanol) $[\alpha]_D^{25}$ −29° (c 0.5 in methanol).

Absorbs 2 moles of H_2. Acetylates (m.p. acetate = 205–207°). A weakly acidic antibiotic, apparent molecular weight 1295. Aburamycin and M5-18903 appear to be optical antipodes of the same compound.

Streptomyces spp.

Haruo Nichimura, Toshiaki Kimura, Katsuya Tawara, Kunio Sasaki, Kiyoshi Nakajima, Noboru Shimaoka, Saburo Okamoto, Masafumi Shimohira and Jun Isono, J. *Antibiotics* (Japan) 10A 205 (1957).

Richard M. Gale, Marvin M. Hoehn and Mack H. McCormick, "Antibiotics Annual 1958–1959," Medical Encyclopedia, Inc., New York, p. 489.

1065 Actinobolin, $C_{13}H_{20-22}O_6N_2$, amorphous hygroscopic white powder, $[\alpha]_D^{26}$ (Sulfate) +54.5° (c 1 in water).

An amphoteric antibiotic. Forms an acetate: m.p., partial m. at 130°, resolidified 145°, dec. 263–266°, $[\alpha]_D^{26}$ +58° (c 1 in water). Positive ninhydrin, ferric chloride, $KMnO_4$, Fehlings, iodoform tests. Absorbs no hydrogen.

Streptomyces sp.

Theodore H. Haskell and Quentin R. Bartz, "Antibiotics Annual 1958–1959," Medical Encyclopedia, Inc., New York, p. 505.

1066 Actinoleukin $(C_9H_{12}O_3N_2)_n$, colorless crystals, m.p. 191° (dec.).

Analysis: C 55.53, H 6.05, N 14.05
          55.68,   5.98,   14.01

Negative biuret, ninhydrin, Tollens, Fehling. Positive $FeCl_3$.

Streptomyces aureus
Masahiro Ueda, Yukio Tanigawa, Yoshiro Okami and Hamao
Umezawa, *J. Antibiotics* (Japan) **7A** 125 (1954).

1067 **Akitamycin,** $[\alpha]_D^{25}$ +158° (c 0.5 in dimethylformamide), U.V.
291, 303.5, 319 mμ. Tetraene, C 57.26, H 7.68, N 1.64.
Streptomyces akitaensis
J. Antibiotics (Japan) **12B** 293, 295, 297 (1959).

1068 **Albidin,** $C_5H_4O_2$ (proposed), red needles, not melting below
380°.
Unstable. Most stable below pH 3.
Penicillium albidum
P. J. Curtis and J. F. Grove, *Nature* **160** 574 (1947).
P. J. Curtis, H. G. Hemming and C. H. Unwin, *Brit. Mycol.
Soc. Trans.* **34** 332 (1951).

1069 **Albofungin,** bright yellow powder, dec. 190°, U.V. 240, 255, 305,
375 mμ. Contains C, H, N, O.
Streptomyces albus var. *fungus*
A. S. Chochlov, *Czech. Symposium on Antibiotics* (Prague),
154 (1959).

1070 **Albomycetin,** $C_{32}H_{54}O_9N$ (proposed), colorless crystals, m.p.
166°.
A basic substance precipitated by ammonium reineck-
ate. Positive Fehlings, Tollens, cherry colored Elson-
Morgan. Negative $FeCl_3$, Sakaguchi, Molisch, Millon.
May be a macrolide.
Streptomyces albus
Bunji Takahashi, *J. Antibiotics* (Japan) **7A** 149 (1954).

1071 **Alboverticillin** (Hydrochloride), colorless, amorphous, $[\alpha]_D^{20}$
−33.5° (c 1.0 in water).
Negative U.V., Tollens, Molisch, Benedict, maltol, Elson-
Morgan, biuret, Millon, Sakaguchi, anthrone and $FeCl_3$.
Positive ninhydrin, Fehling.
Streptomyces sp.
Kenji Maeda, Sinichi Kondo, Kofumi Ohi, Hiroko Kondo,
E. Lin Wang, Yasusuke Osato and Hamao Umezawa, *J. Anti-
biotics* (Japan) **11A** 30 (1958).

1072 **Aliomycin,** yellowish brown powder. Contains C, H, N, O, S.
Pentaene. U.V. 321, 330, 351 mμ.
Positive Fehling (on heating, weakly positive Molisch,
red purple in concentrated H_2SO_4).
Streptomyces acidomyceticus

Seizi Igarasi, Koichi Ogata and Akira Miyake, *J. Antibiotics* (Japan) **9B** 101 (1956).

1073 **Allomycin,*** $C_{29}H_{44}O_9$, crystalline, m.p. 237–239° (dec.) $[\alpha]_D^{17}$ −118.8 ± 0.5° (c 0.98 in 0.1 N hydrochloric acid).

Streptomyces sindenensis

Koichi Nakazawa, Shigehiro Fujii, Michitaka Inoue, Hiroshi Hitomi, Ohira Miyake and Jyuzo Kaneko, *J. Antibiotics* (Japan) **7B** 168 (1954).

Sueo Tatsuoka, Koichi Nakazawa, Michitaka Inoue and Shigehiro Fujii, *J. Pharm. Soc. Japan* **75** 1206 (1955).

1074 **Alternarine,** colorless needles, m.p. 230°.

Alternaria solani

Herman Darpoux, Albert Faivré-Amiot and Louis Roux, *Compt. rend.* **230** 993 (1950).

1075 **Althiomycin,** $C_{15}H_{14}N_4S_2O_6$, colorless crystals, m.p. 172–174° (dec.) (browning from 120–160°), $[\alpha]_D^{20}$ +20.3 (c 1.33 in methyl cellosolve).

Unstable at pH <5.0 or >7.0.

A streptomycete

Hiroshi Yamaguchi, Yuya Nakayama, Keiichi Takeda, Kosaku Tawara, Kenji Maeda, Tomio Takeuchi and Hamao Umezawa, *J. Antibiotics* (Japan) **10A** 195 (1957).

1076 **Anisomycin** (PA-106, PA-107), $C_{14}H_{19}O_4N$, white needles, m.p. 140°, $[\alpha]_D^{25}$ −45° ± 3° (c 1.0 in chloroform).

Streptomyces griseolus, other *Streptomyces* spp.

Ben A. Sobin and Fred W. Tanner, Jr., *J. Am. Chem. Soc.* **76** 4053 (1954).

Fred W. Tanner, Jr., B. A. Sobin and J. F. Gardocki, "Antibiotics Annual 1954–1955" Medical Encyclopedia, Inc., New York, p. 809.

1077 **Antibiotic A 246,**† $C_{41}H_{66-70}O_{14}$, crystalline, m.p. 235° (dec.), $[\alpha]_D^{20}$ −160° (c 0.2 in methanol).

Reacts with HIO_4.

Streptomyces sp.

M. L. Dhar, V. Thaller and M. C. Whiting, *Proc. Chem. Soc.*, 148 (1958).

1078 **Antibiotic B-456,** m.p. 176° (dec.), $[\alpha]_D^{16}$ −22.9°.

C 57.52, H 6.67, N 11.12

Positive biuret, Millon. Negative Molisch, Benedict, Fehling.

* See amicetin.

† Identical with lagosin, entry 229.

Valine, leucine, proline, aspartic, glutamic, D-tyrosine and ornithine produced after hydrolysis.
Bacillus subtilis
Yuzuru Tanaka, *J. Antibiotics* (Japan) **9B** 1 (1956).

1079 **Antibiotic C-159,**
U.V. 260–280, 345 mμ in aqueous solution.
C 58.7, H 7.4, N 9.9, O 24.0
Inhibits growth of organisms containing glycine, alanine, threonine, aspartic acid.
Streptomyces canus
Bristol Laboratories, British Patent 814,794 (1959).

1080 **Antibiotic D-13,** dense crystals, m.p. 243°.
C 56.91, H 6.97, O 22.61, N 13.51.
Streptomyces vinaceus-drappus
Upjohn Co., British Patent 708,686 (1954).

1081 **Antibiotic E-212,** colorless needles, m.p. 233–234°.
U.V. 235, 273 mμ in 0.1 N hydrochloric acid. C 49.14, H 4.34, N 23.77, O 22.55
Negative ninhydrin, biuret, Fehling, $FeCl_3$, Molisch, Millon and Ehrlich.
Streptomyces sp. like *S. albus*
Ko Kikuchi, *J. Antibiotics* (Japan) **8A** 145 (1955).

1082 **Antibiotic LA-7017,** greenish yellow powder, m.p. 154–157° (dec.), $[\alpha]_D^{25}$ −155° (c 0.4 in ethanol).
Contains only C, H, O (C 56.99, H 7.18). Contains two acidic groups, Equiv. Wt. = 1180. Decolorized $KMnO_4$. Negative Fehling's test.
Streptomyces sp. 7017
P. Sensi, A. M. Greco and H. Pagani, *Antibiotics and Chemotherapy* **8** 241 (1958).

1083 **Antibiotic M-4209,** $C_{40-42}H_{67-71}O_{16}N$, white crystals m.p. 210–214° (dec.), $[\alpha]_D^{25}$ −54 ± 2° (c 1 in methanol), U.V. 240, 330 mμ.
Methoxyl, acetyl and iso-valeryl groups present.
Streptomyces hygroscopicus
James D. Dutcher, John Vandeputte, Sidney Fox and L. J. Heuser, *Antibiotics and Chemotherapy* **3** 910 (1953).

1084 **Antibiotic WC 3628,** $C_{42}H_{73}O_{16}N$, white crystals, m.p. 220–222° (Kofler), $[\alpha]_D^{22}$ −57 ± 3° (c 0.5 in ethanol).

Streptomyces sp. WC 3628
McCormick, Canadian Patent 513,324 (1955).

1085 **Antibiotic T,** trichothecin-like, crystalline prisms, m.p. 126°, $[\alpha]_D^{20}$ +135° (c 1 in chloroform).
A basidiomycete.
E. T. Glaz, Eszter Scheiber, J. Gyimesi, I. Horwath, Katalin Steczek, A. Szentirmai and G. Bohus, *Nature* 184 908 (1959).

1086 **Antibiotic X-206,** $C_{46}H_{80}O_{13}$, colorless crystals, m.p. 126–128°, $[\alpha]_D^{29}$ +15.0° (c 2.0 in methanol).
Streptomyces sp.
Julius Berger, A. I. Rachlin, W. E. Scott, L. H. Sternbach and M. W. Goldberg, *J. Am. Chem. Soc.* 72 5295 (1951).

1087 **Antibiotic X-464,** $C_{25}H_{40}O_7$, white crystals, m.p. 172–174° (dec.), $[\alpha]_D^{27}$ +65.9° (c 2.0 in methanol).
Streptomyces sp.
Julius Berger, A. I. Rachlin, W. E. Scott, L. H. Sternbach and M. W. Goldberg, *J. Am. Chem. Soc.* 73 5295 (1951).

1088 **Antibiotic X-537A,** $C_{34}H_{52}O_8$, colorless crystals, m.p. 100–109°, $[\alpha]_D^{26}$ −7.2° (c 1.0 in alcohol), U.V. 317, 249 mμ in isopropyl alcohol.
Positive $FeCl_3$ test.
Streptomyces sp.
Julius Berger, A. I. Rachlin, W. E. Scott, L. H. Sternbach and M. W. Goldberg, *J. Am. Chem. Soc.* 73 5295 (1951).

1089 **Antibiotic X-1008,** $C_{29}H_{38}O_7N_6S$, cube-like crystals, m.p. 209–216° (dec.), $[\alpha]_D^{27}$ −282° (c 1 in chloroform).
Resembles echinomycin
Streptomyces sp.
J. Berger, E. R. LaSala, W. E. Scott, B. R. Meltsner, L. H. Sternbach, S. Kaiser, S. Teitel, E. Mack and M. W. Goldberg, *Experientia* 13 434 (1957).

1090 **Antibiotic from** *B. cepae*, colorless crystals, m.p. 185° (dec.) C 40.8, H 5.3.
Bacillus cepae
Isolated from rotting onion.
M. Fiuczek, *Med. Doswiadczalna i Mikrobiol.* 2 175 (1950).
(*Biol. Abstr.* 26 3975).

1091 **Antibiotic from** *B. pumilis*, $C_8H_9N_2O_2S$, white crystals, m.p. 252°.
Negative ninhydrin.

Bacillus pumilis
A. T. Fuller, *Nature* 175 722 (1955).

1092 Antibiotic from *Monosporium bonorden,* $C_{17}H_{16}O_7$, colorless
crystals, m.p. 193.5°, $[\alpha]_D^{20}$ +203° (in chloroform).

Two phenolic hydroxyl groups, one active hydrogen on
an aromatic ring, one double link in a side-chain and a
free carboxyl group present.

Molecular structure may be closely related to the structure proposed for mycophenolic acid.

Monosporium bonorden
P. Delmotte and J. Delmotte-Plaquee, *Nature* 171 344
(1953).

1093 Antibiotic from *Penicillium spinulosum,* fine white needles,
m.p. 183–185°.

Penicillium spinulosum
Shegejii Kondo and Bunji Takahashi, *J. Penicillin* (Japan),
1 147 (1947).

1094 Antibiotic from *S. abikoensis,* yellow powder. Heptaene. U.V.
242, 358, 400 mμ in ethanol.   Actinoleukin in mycelium.

Streptomyces abikoensis
Masahiro Ueda and Hamao Umezawa, *J. Antibiotics* (Japan) 9A 86 (1956).

1095 Antibiotic from *S. fungicidicus.* U.V. 290, 303, 317 mμ. Similar
to fungicidin or rimocidin.

Positive Fehling, Molisch, Negative Millon, Sakaguchi,
Schiff, Tollens, $FeCl_3$.   Blue with $FeCl_3$-K ferricyanate;
decolorizes $KMnO_4$.

Streptomyces fungicidicus
Hamao Umesawa, Yoshio Okami and Ryozo Utahara, Japanese Patent 5744 (1956).

1096 Antibiotic from *S. griseus.* Heptaene. U.V.   359–362, 378–
382, 401–405 mμ.

Streptomyces griseus
Richard A. Pledger and Hubert Lechevalier, "Antibiotics
Annual 1955–1956," Medical Encyclopedia, Inc., New York,
p. 249.

1097 Antibiotic 26/1, yellow crystalline. Heptaene. U.V. 359, 380,
404 mμ in ethanol.

Alcohol solution turns violet with H_2SO_4; decolorizes
$KMnO_4$.   Negative biuret and ninhydrin.

Actinomyces globisporus
V. A. Tsyganov, P. N. Golyakov, A. M. Bezborodov, V. P.
Namestnikova, G. V. Khopko, S. N. Solov'ev, M. A. Malyshkina
and L. O. Bol'shakova, *Antibiotiki* 4 21 (1959).

1098 **Antibiotic 446,** white crystalline powder, m.p. 81–87°, $[\alpha]_D^{22}$
−82° (c 0.5 in ethanol). U.V. 230–231, 280 mμ.
C 60.47, H 7.99, N 2.02
Negative Fehling.
Nocardia mesenterica
Masahiro Ueda and Hamao Umezawa, *J. Antibiotics* (Japan) 8A 164 (1955).

1099 **Antibiotic 720-A,** * $C_{28}H_{40}O_9N_2$, white needles, m.p. 139.5–140°,
$[\alpha]_D^{18}$ +73.5° (c 1.0 in acetone) U.V. 227, 346 mμ.
Positive FeCl$_3$; negative Molisch, ninhydrin, biuret,
Ehrlich and 2:4 DNPH.
Streptomyces n. sp.
Yoshio Sakagami, Setsuo Takeuchi, Hiroshi Yonehara,
Heüchi Sakai and Matao Takashima, *J. Antibiotics* (Japan)
9A 1 (1956).

1100 **Antibiotic 587/13,** Hydrochloride
C 39.5, H 6.97, N 15.7, Cl 16.75
Streptomyces lavendulae
D. M. Trakhtenberg, V. M. Baikina, E. I. Rodionovskaya,
I. M. Prosnyakova, O. A. Kalinovskii, Yu V. Zakharova and
A. A. Khokhlov, *Antibiotiki* (U.S.S.R.) 4 9 (1959).

1101 **Antibiotic 1037,** crystalline needles, m.p. 283–289°, $[\alpha]_D^{35}$ −51°.
C 49.33–49.47, H 4.56–4.90, N 23.75–24.14, no halogen or sulfur
Streptomyces sp.
Hiroshi Yamamoto, Shigehiro Fujii, Koichi Nakazawa,
Akira Miyake, Hiromu Hitomi and Masahiko Imanishi, *Ann.
Repts. Takeda Research Lab.* 16 26 (1957).

1102 **Antibiotic 6270,** † $C_{29}H_{37}N_6SO_{6-7}$, crystalline.
Streptomyces flavochromogenes
M. G. Brazhnikova, Czech. Symposium on Antibiotics
(Prague), 140 (1959).

1103 **Antibiotic 6706,** ‡ $C_{26-27}H_{32}O_8N_4$, colorless needles, m.p. 214–216°, U.V. 304 mμ.
Gives negative FeCl$_3$, Fehling, Tollens, ninhydrin and
Millon tests.

* See entry 269 (antimycin A$_1$).
† Cf. entry 1089.
‡ See pyridomycin, entry 752.

Streptomyces sp.

Masahiko Kuraya, Bunji Takahashi, Yorio Hinuma, Takaaki Yashima, Kenzo Watanabe, Masa Kuroya and Susumu Hamada, J. Antibiotics (Japan) 7A 58 (1954).

1104 Antifungal Substance, colorless needles, m.p. 283–289°, $[\alpha]_D^{35}$ −51°.

A water-soluble compound similar to toyokamycin and monilin.　Analysis:　C　49.33–49.47, H　4.56–4.90, N 23.75–24.14.

Streptomyces sp.

Hiroshi Yamamoto, Shigehiro Fujii, Koichi Nakazawa, Akira Miyake, Hiromu Hitomi and Masahiko Imanishi, Takeda Kenkyusho Nempo 16 26 (1957).

1105 Antifungal substance produced by Streptomyces strain No. 1037. Crystalline needles, m.p. 283–289°, $[\alpha]_D^{35}$ −51°.　C 49.33–49.47 H 4.56–4.90 N 23.75–24.14, no halogen or sulfur.

It seems to belong to the same group of substances as toyokamycin and monilin.

Hiroshi Yamamoto, Shigehiro Fujii, Koichi Nakazawa, Akira Miyake, Hiromu Hitomi and Masahiko Imanishi, Ann. Rept. Takeda Research Lab. 16 26 (1957).

1106 Argomycin, $C_{25}H_{43}O_7N$, m.p. 164°, $[\alpha]_D^{25}$ +8.2° (in ethanol). May be a macrolide.

Streptomyces griseolus

Toji Hata, Yoshimoto Sano, Hideo Tatsuta, Ryozo Sugawara, Akihiro Matsumae and Kokichi Kanamori, J. Antibiotics (Japan) 8A 9 (1955).

1107 Aspelein, $C_{29}H_{20}O_{10}$, dark red plates, no m.p.

This pigment contained two hydroxyl groups (diacetate, yellow crystals, m.p. 276–285°) and an alkoxyl group. Spectra described.

Aspergillus elegans

P. E. Gregoire, Bull. soc. chim. biol. 33 1681 (1951).

Aterrimins—complex containing aterrimins A and B, exhibiting characteristics of a lactone; contain C, H and O and have no definite m.p.

1108 Aterrimin A, $[\alpha]_D^{20}$ +245° in ethanol.　U.V. 277, 287, 310–325 mμ in absolute alcohol C. 65.5 H 7.8 O 26.7 (by difference).

1109   Aterrimin B, $[\alpha]_D^{20}$ +342° in ethanol. U.V. same as A. C 69.7
        H 8.05 O 22.25 (by difference).
        Bacillus subtilis var. *aterrimus*
        Gordon Alderton and Neva S. Snell, U. S. Patent 2,850,427
        (1958).

1110   **Aureolic Acid,** Mg salt: $(C_{56\text{-}60}H_{96\text{-}104}O_{29\text{-}31})_2Mg$, yellow crystals,
        $[\alpha]_D$ +68° (c 1 in methanol).
        A weak acid, green $FeCl_3$ test, negative Fehlings,
        anthrone.
        Streptomyces sp.
        Walton E. Grundy, Alma W. Goldstein, Charles J. Rickher,
        Marjorie E. Hanes, Halleck B. Warren, Jr. and John C. Sylves-
        ter, *Antibiotics and Chemotherapy* 3 1215 (1953).

1111   **Azalomycin B,** $C_{14}H_{24}O_5$, white needles, 185–187° (dec.) $[\alpha]_D^{25}$
        −48° (c 1.0 in methanol). U.V. 252.5 mμ.
        Streptomyces hygroscopicus
        Manoru Arai, *J. Antibiotics* (Japan) 13A 51 (1960).

1112   **Azalomycin F,** $C_{30}H_{50}O_{10}N_2$, white needles, m.p. 125–127° (dec.)
        $[\alpha]_D^{22}$ +46° (c 1.0 in methanol).
        U.V. resembles that of musarin and hygrostatin. I.R.
        differs.
        Positive ninhydrin, negative $FeCl_3$, Molisch, anthrone
        and Millon.
        Streptomyces hygroscopicus
        H. D. Tresner and E. J. Backus, *Appl. Microbiol.* 4 243
        (1956).
        S. A. Waksman and A. T. Henrici, Bergey's "Manual of
        Determinative Bacteriology," 1957, pp. 796–797.
        Mamoru Arai, *J. Antibiotics* (Japan) 13A 51 (1960).

1113   **Baccatine A,** $C_{26}H_{48}O_6N_2$ (proposed). Colorless crystals, m.p.
        135°. Mol. Wt. ~480.
        May be a depsipeptide (peptolide).
        Gibberella baccata.
        Jean Guérillot-Vinet, A. Guérillot-Vinet, Lucien Guyot, Jac-
        ques Montégut and Louis Roux, *Compt. rend.* 230 1424 (1950).
        M. M. Shemyakin, *Angew. Chem.* 72 342 (1960).

1114   **Bacilipin A,** sheaves of needles, m.p. 76–78°.
        C 42.6, H 6.3, N 2.5, Ba 24.6.
        Negative Molisch, 2,4-DNPH, $AgNO_3$.
        Positive Br_2.

1115   **Bacilipin B,** crystals, m.p. 105°.

C 52.45, H 6.75, N 2.09, Ba 21.6

Gave same tests as Bacilipin A.

Both A and B gave positive ninhydrin after hydrolysis.

Bacillus subtilis

G. G. F. Newton, *Brit. J. Exptl. Biol.* **30** 306 (1949).

1116   **Bacilysin,** white powder containing C, H, O and N.

Gives a positive ninhydrin; negative biuret and Molisch tests.

Produced by the soil bacillus NTCC 7197.

E. P. Abraham and H. W. Florey, "Antibiotics," **Vol. I** *Antibiotics from bacteria in the genus bacillus,* Oxford University Press, London, 1949 Chap. 10, pp. 457–458.

1117   **Biformyne 1** (Biformin), $C_9H_{20}O_2$, white crystalline solid, m.p. 40–43°, U.V. 276, 278, 291 mμ in alkali.

Polyporus biformis

Marjorie Anchel and Marvin P. Cohen, *J. Biol. Chem.* **208** 319 (1954).

1118   **Blasticidin A,** C_{46-52}, H_{8-12} N_{4-7}, light yellow powder, m.p. 197–201°. U.V. 216 mμ. Soluble in H_2O.

1119   **Blasticidin B,** colorless liquid, b.p. 36° (0.001 mm.). Insoluble in H_2O.

1120   **Blasticidin C,** red-brown powder. Insoluble in H_2O.

Streptomyces griseochromogenes

Kazuo Fukunaga, Tomomasa Misato, Itaru Iskii and Masaru Asakawa, *Bull. Agr. Chem. Soc.* (Japan) **19** 181 (1955).

1121   **Blasticidin-S,** $C_{14}H_{20}O_5N_6$, white needles, m.p. 235° (dec.), $[\alpha]_D^{11}$ +108.4° (c 1.0 in water).

A basic antibiotic (forms a picrate).

Negative $FeCl_3$, Fehling, Tollens, Millon, Ehrlich, Sakaguchi, Molisch, biuret, ninhydrin, aldehyde and ammoniacal $AgNO_3$ tests. Blasticidin-S is a member of a complex with at least three other components, blasticidins A, B and C.

Streptomyces griseochromogenes

Setsuo Takeuchi, Kosei Hirayama, Kazaburo Ueda, Heiichi Sakai and Hiroshi Yonehara, *J. Antibiotics* (Japan) **11A** 1 (1958).

1122 **Borrelidin,** $C_{28}H_{43}O_6N$, m.p. 145°, $[\alpha]_D^{27}$ −28° (in ethanol).
An acidic compound.
Streptomyces rochei
J. Berger, L. M. Jampolsky and M. W. Goldberg, *Arch. Biochem.* 22 476 (1949).

1123 **Caerulomycin,** $C_{12}H_{11}O_2N_3$, colorless needles, m.p. 175°.
Red $FeCl_3$ test. Contains one methoxyl group.
Streptomyces caeruleus
A. Funk and P. V. Divekar, *Can. J. Microbiol.* 5 317 (1959).

1124 **Camphomycin,** white needles, m.p. ∼149°. Positive Nessler and Tollens.
Streptomyces rutgersensis var. *castelarense*
Augusto P. Cercos, *Rev. argentian agron.* 20 53 (1953).

1125 **Candidulin,** $C_{11}H_{15}O_3N$, white needles, m.p. 88°, $[\alpha]_D^{24}$ +15° ± 2° (c 1 in chloroform).
A neutral, non-aromatic substance. Negative ninhydrin, 2,4-DNPH, $FeCl_3$.
Aspergillus candidus
P. G. Stansly and N. H. Ananenko, *Arch. Biochem.* 23 256 (1949).

1126 **Canescin,** $C_{15}H_{14}O_7$, white needles, m.p. 201–202° (dec.).
Purple color with $FeCl_3$ in ethanol.
Penicillium canescens
Yield 30–110 mg. per liter.
P. W. Brian, H. G. Hemming, J. S. Moffatt and C. H. Unwin, *Trans. Brit. Mycol. Soc.* 36 243 (1953).

1127 **Cardinophyllin** (Carzinophilin), potassium salt: colorless needles, m.p. 220° (dec.).
Contains C, H, O, N. Positive xanthoprotein, negative ninhydrin, diphenylamine. Negative resorcinol, Millon, Liebermann.
Streptomyces sahachiroi
Toju Hata, Fumiwaka Koga, Yoshimoto Sano, Kokichi Kanamori, Akihiro Matsumae, Ryozo Sugawara, Tadashi Hoshi and Tatsuo Shima, *J. Antibiotics* (Japan) 7A 107 (1954).
Fujiki Hata and Takamoto Sano, Japanese Patent 7590 (1956).

1128 **Carzinophilin A,** colorless needles, m.p. 217–222° (dec.), $[\alpha]_D^{28}$ +57.8° (in chloroform).
Positive ninhydrin, 2,4-DNPH, bromine uptake, an-

throne, Baeyer, xanthoproteic.   Unstable in aqueous solution.

Streptomyces sahachiroi n. sp.

Hideo Kamada, Shigetoshi Wakaki, Yasuo Fujimoto, Keitaro Tomioka, Satoshi Ueyama, Hakudai Marumo and Keizo Uzu, *J. Antibiotics* (Japan) **8A** 187 (1955).

1129 Cerevioccidin, $C_{22}H_{39}O_4N_5$, colorless needles, m.p. 249° (dec.).

Negative biuret, ninhydrin, Fehling, Sakaguchi, Tollens, glucosamine.   Positive Janovsky.

Streptomyces sp. resembling *S. cacaoi*

Satoru Yamashita, Teruzo Sawazaki, Makoto Kawasaki, Goto Nakamura, Kentaro Anzai, Kiyoshi Isono, Yoshiko Serizawa, Yoshiko Sekiyama and Saburo Suzuki, *J. Antibiotics* (Japan) **8A** 42 (1955).

Chlamydosporin, complex of two closely related antibiotics produced by the fungus *Fusarium* MLF 1230 found in insects and their larvae.

1130 Chlamydosporin A, light brown amorphous substance insoluble in water.

1131 Chlamydosporin B, colorless, crystalline, soluble in water.

Both contain 4.3% N but no sulfur.

Albert Faivré-Amiot, Hermon Darpoux and Louis Roux, *Compt. rend.* **235** 912, 982 (1952).

1132 Chromomycin A$_3$ (main component of complex), $C_{22\text{-}23}H_{32\text{-}34}O_{11}$, yellow powder, m.p. 183° (dec.), $[\alpha]_D^{20}$ −26° (c 1 in ethanol).

May be related to the actinomycins.

Streptomyces griseus No. 7

Yoshitomo Aramaki, Junmei Watanabe, Ichiro Ishikawa, Akira Miyake, Homu Ito, Koichi Nakazawa, Koichi Ogata, Motoo Shibata, Masaji Igarashi and Kazuo Tanabe, *Ann. Repts. Takeda Research Lab.* **14** 60 (1955).

Tatsuoka *et al., Gann.* **49** Suppl. 23 (1958).

S. Wakaki *et al., Antibiotics and Chemotherapy* **8** 228 (1958).

Motoo Shibata, Kazuo Tanabe, Yoshio Hamada, Koiti Nakazawa, Akira Miyake, Hiroshi Hitoma, Masuo Miyamoto and Komei Mizuno, *J. Antibiotics* (Japan) **13B** 1 (1960).

1133 Chrysergonic Acid, $C_{32}H_{30\text{-}32}O_{14}$, fine yellow needles, m.p. 268–270° from chloroform (250–257° from acetic acid), $[\alpha]_D^{20}$ −3° → +34° (in pyridine).

Claviceps purpurea

A. Stoll, J. Renz and A. Brack, *Helv. Chim. Acta* 35 2022 (1952).

1134 **Chrysomycin,** $C_{22}H_{20}O_7$ (proposed), greenish yellow crystals, m.p. 255–260° (dec.), $[\alpha]_D^{22}$ +16° (c 1 in acetic acid).
Neutral, photosensitive compound. Takes up $4H_2$ with loss of color.
Streptomyces sp.
Frieda Strelitz, Helen Flon and Igor V. Asheshov, *J. Bacteriol.* 69 280 (1955).

1135 **Clitocybin,** colorless crystals, m.p. 77°.
Clitocybe candida
A. Charles Hollande, *Compt. rend.* 221 361 (1945); 228 1758 (1949).

1136 **Coelicolorin,** purplish red powder, 142–146°.
Streptomyces coelicolor
Yuichi Hatsuta, *J. Antibiotics* (Japan) 2 276 (1949).

1137 **Collinomycin,** orange prisms, m.p. 280°.
Streptomyces collinus (mycelium)
Hans Brockmann and Karl-Heinz Renneberg, *Naturwissenschaften* 40 166 (1953).

1138 **Compound $C_{11}H_{20}O_9N_2$.**
A basic red pigment, yellow in alkaline, red in acid solutions. Positive Bayer, diazo tests.
Inocybe patoullardii Bres.
Helmut Müller, Dissertation, Würzburg, 1959.

1139 **Cosynthetic Factor-1** $C_{14-15}H_{17}O_7N_3$, crystalline. An acidic compound, Mol. Wt. 340–360.
Thought to be a cofactor in the biosynthesis of tetracyclines.
Streptomyces aureofaciens strain W-5, *S. albo-niger*, *S. griseus*, *S. albas*, *S. platensis*, *S. hygroscopicus*, *S. rimosus*
Jerry Robert Daniel McCormick, Nancy Hazlett Arnold, Ursula Hirsch, Philip Andrew Miller and Newell Oscar Sjölander, Union of South Africa Patent Application 59–2174 (1959).

1140 **Croceomycin,** $C_{22}H_{18}O_6$, m.p. 325° (subl. 240° at 1–2 mm.), $[\alpha]_D^{18}$ −32 ±4°.
Forms a triacetate. Diazomethane adds two methyl groups.
Streptomyces arabicus

Motoo Shibata, Koichi Nakazawa, Akira Miyake, Michitaka Inoue and Akira Akabori, *Takeda Kenkyusho Nempo* 16 32 (1957). (*Chem. Abstr.* 52 10279e)

1141 **Cyanomycin,** $C_{15}H_{12}N_2O_2$ (proposed), dark blue needles, m.p. 128° (dec.).

A basic antibiotic pigment with pH-indicating properties, apparently distinct from other known pigments. Aureothricin occurs in the same culture.

Streptomyces strain No. 4738

Masanao Funaki, Fumiyasu Tsuchiya, Kiyoharu Maeda and Takeshi Kamiya, *J. Antibiotics* (Japan) 11A 143 (1958).

1142 **Datemycin,** $C_{58}H_{102}O_6N_4$, colorless powder, m.p. 197° (dec.), $[\alpha]_D^{15}$ −43.7° (c 1 in water).

U.V. maximum at 247 mμ. Negative ninhydrin $\dfrac{6N\ HCl}{100°,\ 10\ hrs.}$ > positive ninhydrin. Negative Hopkins-Cole, xanthoprotein, Sakaguchi, Millon, Elson-Morgan, Molisch, Fehling, silver mirror tests.

"M-14" strains

Masahiko Kuroya and Yasuo Koyama, Japanese Patent 6648 (1959).

1143 **Desertomycin,** $C_{33}H_{60-62}O_{14}N$, snow white crystals, m.p. 189°.

Positive ninhydrin, C-methyl. Acetylates, hydrogenates, decolorizes bromine or permanganate.

A crystalline antifungal agent, flavofungin, has been isolated from the same culture.

Streptomyces flavofungini

J. Úri and I. Béhési, *Nature* 181 908 (1958).

J. Úri, R. Bognár and B. Varga, *ibid.* 182 401 (1958).

1144 **Diaporthin,** $C_{13}H_{14}O_3$, white crystals, m.p. 91.5–92.5° $[\alpha]_D^{25}$ +58° (c 1 in chloroform).

Endothia parasitica

A. Neelameghan, *Hindustan Antibiotics* 2 13 (1959).

1145 **Diplococcin,** antibacterial substance elaborated by certain milk streptococci. In the same category as the sulfur-free polypeptides, gramicidin and tyrocidine. Unlike these polypeptides diplococcin contains arginine residues, shows no tendency to crystallize and is obviously of greater molecular complexity.

C 50.5, H 7.3, N 13.1, no sulfur.

Streptomyces lactis
A. E. Oxford, *Biochem. J.* 38 178 (1944).
Idem., ibid. 39 xiii (1945).

1146 **Distamycin A,** pure white powder, basic, forms salts.
Positive biuret test.
CIBA, Australian Patent 28,469 (1957).

1147 **D-Substance,** white needles, m.p. 124–125°.
Highly toxic.
Streptomyces flavus O-2
Isao Takahashi, *J. Antibiotics* (Japan) 6A 117 (1953).

1148 **Elaiophylin** $(C_6H_{10}O_2)_n$, no N, S, X, white crystals, m.p. 178–183° (dec.) $[\alpha]_D^{20}$ −49° (in chloroform).
Streptomyces melanosporus (sine *melanosporofaciens*)
F. M. Arcamone, C. Bertazzoli, M. Ghione and T. Scotti, *Giorn. microbiol.* 7 207 (1959).

1149 **Endosubtilysin,** yellow powder, soluble in alcohol and chloroform. Forms a water-soluble sodium salt. Appears to be an organic acid.
Bacillus subtilis
Louis de Saint-Rat and Henry R. Olivier, *Compt. rend.* 222 297 (1946).

1150 **Enteromycin,** m.p. 167–168°, U.V. 282 mμ.
C 38.2, H 4.62, N 4.3.
Streptococcus albireticuli
Teisuke Osato, Masahiro Ueda, Setsuko Fukuyama, Koki Yagishita, Yoshiro Okami and Hamao Umezawa, *J. Antibiotics* (Japan) 8A 105 (1955).

1151 **Ergochrysin,** $C_{28}H_{28}O_{12}$, yellow-golden leaflets, m.p. 266° from chloroform (242–244° from alcohol-pyridine).
Claviceps purpurea
C. Jacoby, *Arch. exp. Pathol. Pharmakol.* 39 85 (1897).
Werner Bergmann, *Ber.* 65 1486, 1489 (1932).

1152 **Ergoflavin,** $C_{30}H_{26}O_{14}$, yellow needles, m.p. 350° (dec.) from methanol or dioxane, $[\alpha]_D^{21}$ +37.5° (c 1.236 in acetone).
Structural features determined:
4 phenolic hydroxyls
2 alcoholic hydroxyls
2 carbonyls
2 γ-lactones
Claviceps purpurea

The yield is 1–2% of the weight of the dry sclerotia.
G. Eglinton, F. E. King, G. Lloyd, J. W. Loder, J. R. Marshall, Alexander Robertson and W. B. Whalley, *J. Chem. Soc.*, 1833 (1958).

The relationship of ergoflavin to the other yellow pigments, secalonic acid, ergochrysin, chrysergonic acid, sclererythrin, scleroxanthin, sclerocristallin and ergoxanthin (some of them identical) is discussed in the above paper as well as in an earlier paper by:
Albert Freeborn, *Pharm. J.* 88 568 (1912).
A. Stoll, J. Renz and A. Brack, *Helv. Chim. Acta.* 35 2022 (1952).

1153   **Estin,** $C_{16}H_{14}O_6Cl_2$, m.p. 223°.
Contains two methoxyl groups. A second and similar compound, Nordin, is produced with it. A 143 mg. sample of the mixture was obtained from 1480 ml. of culture solution.
Penicillium paxilli var. *echinulatum*
Eitaro Komatsu, Japanese Patent 4799 (1953).

1154   **Eumycetin,** fine white needles, m.p. 148–150°.
Positive $FeCl_3$, negative biuret, ninhydrin, Molisch, Fehling.
Streptomyces sp. similar to S. *purpurochromogenes*
Edwin A. Johnson and Kenneth L. Burdon, *J. Bacteriol.* 51 591 (1946).

1155   **Eumycin,** amorphous precipitate, heat-stable in acid, unstable in alkaline solutions above pH 8.0.
Bacillus subtilis
Edwin A. Johnson and Kenneth L. Burdon, *J. Bacteriol.* 51 591 (1946).

1156   **Exfoliatin,** $C_{27}H_{40}O_{16}Cl$, colorless needles, m.p. 172°.
Positive $FeCl_3$, Molisch, Negative Fehling.
Streptomyces exfoliatus
Hamao Umezawa, Kiyoshi Oikawa and Motoko Suzuki, *J. Antibiotics* (Japan) 5 466 (1952).

1157   **Fairodin,** crystalline, m.p. 237–239° (dec.) $[\alpha]_D^{25}$ −102° (c 1 in water).
C 59.6, H 6.7, N 14.3.
Bacillus brevis

S. Oya, Japanese Patent Application SHO 32–3997 (1957).

1158 **Fermicidin,** $C_{14}H_{21}O_4N$, colorless needles, m.p. 96°, $[\alpha]_D^{18}$ +52.3° ±1.5° (c 0.65 in water).
Streptomyces sp. similar to *S. griseolus*
Seizi Igarasi and Shozo Wada, *J. Antibiotics* (Japan) **7B** 221 (1954).

1159 **Fermizin,** $C_{14}H_{21}O_4N$, needles, m.p. 96–98°.
An antifungal agent.
Streptomyces griseus
About 10 g. were obtained from 100 l. of fermentation broth. Apparently identical with fermicidin.
Koichi Ogata, Masaji Igarashi and Shozo Wada, Japanese Patent Application 6150 (1958).

1160 **Fervenulin,** $C_7H_7O_2N_5$, yellow crystals, m.p. 178–179° (dec.). Mol. Wt. 193. Acid-stable, base-labile. U.V. peaks at 275, 239 mμ.
Streptomyces fervens
T. E. Eble, E. C. Olson, C. M. Large and J. W. Shell, 7th Annual Symposium on Antibiotics, Washington, D. C., 1959.

1161 **Flavensomycin,** pale yellow crystals, m.p. 152°.
A water soluble compound containing nitrogen but not sulfur or halogen. Some carbohydrates tests were positive. U.V. maximum at 251 mμ.
Streptomyces tanaschiensis type
R. Craveri and G. Giolitti, *Nature* **179** 1307 (1957).

1162 **Flavucidin,** $C_{34}H_{55}NO_9$, colorless needles, m.p. 144–145°, $[\alpha]_D^{20}$ 94°, U.V. 275 mμ.
Positive Molisch. Negative ninhidrin.
Streptomyces sp. No. 14420
Motoo Shibata, Koichi Nakazawa, Akira Miyake, Michitaka Inoue, Jiro Terumichi and Hiroshi Kawashima, *Ann. Rept. Takeda Research Lab.* **17** 16 (1958).

1163 **Folimycin,** m.p. 163–164° (dec.) agricultural antifungal antibiotic.
Streptomyces nayagawaensis n. sp.
Hiroichi Yamamoto, Koiti Nakazawa, Satoshi Horii and Akira Miyake, *J. Agr. Chem. Soc. Japan* **34** 268 (1960).

1164 **Fomecin A,** $C_8H_8O_5$, m.p.: dec. >160°.
Weakly acidic, thermostable, alkali labile.
Fomes (Polyporus) juniperinus

Marjorie Anchel, Annette Hervey and William J. Robbins, *Proc. Nat. Acad. Sci. U. S.* **38** 655 (1952).

1165 Fuscomycin, m.p. 180° (dec.).
Streptomyces fuscus
Fujiki Hata and Keigen Sano, Japanese Patent 5046 (1953).

1166 Glutinosin, $C_{48}H_{60}O_{16}$ (proposed), colorless plates, gradual dec. to 300°, $[\alpha]_D^{20} \sim +54°$ (c 0.2 in benzene).
Metarrhizium glutinosum
P. W. Brian and J. C. McGowan, *Nature* **157** 334 (1946).

1167 Grisamine, $C_{28}H_{38}O_{10}N_6$ or $C_{20}H_{30}O_7N_4$ (proposed), colorless needles, m.p. 167–170°.
Negative Fehling, $FeCl_3$, Sakaguchi, ninhydrin, biuret.
Streptomyces sp. similar to *S. griseoflavus*
Teruzo Sawazaki, Goto Nakamura, Makato Kawasaki, Satoru Yamashita, Kiyoshi Isono, Kentaro Anzai, Yoshiko Serizawa, Yoshiko Sekiyama and Saburo Suzuki, *J. Antibiotics* (Japan) **8A** 39 (1955).

1168 Griseoflavin, colorless needles, m.p. 210–215° (dec.).
Not precipitated by peptide reagents. Negative carbohydrate and amino sugar tests, $FeCl_3$.
Streptomyces griseoflavus
Yoshio Waga, *J. Antibiotics* (Japan) **6A** 66 (1953).

1169 Griseoviridin, $C_{22}H_{29}O_7N_3S$ (proposed), colorless crystals, m.p. (polymorphic) 158–166°, 194–200°, 230°, 240° (dec.), $[\alpha]_D^{27} -237°$ (c 0.5 in methanol).
Neutral compound. Negative $FeCl_3$, Sakaguchi, positive Bayer. Gives cystine on acid hydrolysis. Further structural features are suggested in the last reference below.
Streptomyces griseus, S. griseoviridus n. sp.
Quentin R. Bartz, Jean Standiford, James D. Mold, Doris W. Johannessen, Albert Ryder, Andrew Maretzki and Theodore H. Haskell, "Antibiotics Annual 1954–1955," Medical Encyclopedia, Inc., New York, p. 777.
John Ehrlich, George L. Coffey, Myron W. Fisher, Margaret M. Galbraith, Mildred Penner Knudsen, Raymond W. Sarber, A. S. Schlingman, Robert M. Smith and Jean K. Weston, *ibid.*, p. 790 (1954–1955).
Lucia E. Anderson, John Ehrlich, Sung Huang Sun and Paul R. Burkholder, *Antibiotics and Chemotherapy* **6** 100 (1956).

D. E. Ames, R. E. Bowman, J. F. Cavalla and D. D. Evans, *J. Chem. Soc.*, 4260 (1955).
D. E. Ames and R. E. Bowman, *ibid.*, 4264 (1955).

1170 **Helenine.**
An unstable, little characterized antiviral agent. A ribonucleoprotein.
Penicillium funiculosum
Richard E. Shope, *J. Exp. Med.* 97 601, 639 (1953).
U. J. Lewis, Edward L. Rickes, Laurella McClelland and Norman G. Brick, *J. Am. Chem. Soc.* 81 4115 (1959).

1171 **Heliomycin,** needles, chars >300°, complex U.V., Mol. Wt. 235. Positive $FeCl_3$ and Millon.
May be a polypeptide.
Actinomyces flavochromogenes var. *heliomycini*
M. G. Brazhnikova, T. A. Uspenskaya, L. B. Sokolova, T. P. Preobrazhenskaya, G. F. Gauze, R. S. Ukholina, V. A. Shorin, O. K. Rossolimo and T. P. Vertogradova, *Antibiotiki* 3 29 (1958).

1172 **Hirsutic Acid C,** $C_{15}H_{20}O_4$ (proposed), colorless crystals, m.p. 179.5°, $[\alpha]_D^{20}$ +11.9° (in absolute ethanol).
A group of acidic materials. Hirsutic acid C has been best characterized. It is a monobasic acid, only slightly soluble in H_2O, soluble in most organic solvents. Negative 2,4-DNPH, $FeCl_3$, Fehling. White precipitate with Br water.
Stereum hirsutum
N. G. Heatley, M. A. Jennings and H. W. Florey, *Brit. J. Exp. Path.* 28 35 (1947).

1173 **Hygroscopin A,** $C_{13}H_{24}O_3N_2$, oil, b.p. 64° (0.003 mm.), n_D^{13} 1.4830, $[\alpha]_D^{14}$ 84.7° (in methanol).

1174 **Hygroscopin B,** $C_{15}H_{28}O_3N_2$, oil, b.p. 70° (0.008 mm.), n_D^{14} 1.4935, $[\alpha]_D^{14}$ −38.8° (in ethanol).
Streptomyces hygroscopicus
Koichi Nakazawa, Kinzo Oki, Isao Tadokoro, Mikio Honjo, Hiroshi Hitomi and Jisaburo Ueyanagi, *J. Agr. Chem. Soc. Japan* 28 296 (1954).
Sueo Tatsuoka, Akira Miyake, Mikio Honjo, Hiroshi Hitomi, Jisaburo Ueyanagi, Masuo Miyamoto, Koiti Nakazawa and Kinzo Oki, *J. Antibiotics* (Japan) 7B 329 (1954).

1175 Hygrostatin, light yellow powder, m.p. 129–131° (dec.), $[\alpha]_D^{20}$ +43° (c 1.21 in methanol).

Contains nitrogen, but no sulfur or halogen. U.V. at 240 mμ.

Streptomyces hygrostaticus

Kenzo Furushiro, Kiyotake Shimizu, Heiichi Sakai, Masayuki Minoyata and Toshio Fujisawa, Iyaku, *Shigen Kankyusho Nempo* 24–39 (1958). (*Chem. Abstr.* 54 10048b)

1176 Illudin M, $C_{21}H_{22}O_7$, prismatic rods in ethanol, m.p. 216° (cor.). $[\alpha]_D^{20}$ −126° in ethanol. Mol. Wt. 386. U.V. 247, 330 mμ in 95% ethanol.

Contains two acidic groups and an α,β-unsaturated carbonyl group.

Yield 0.08 g. per liter.

1177 Illudin S, $C_{15}H_{22}O_4$, crystalline, m.p. 124–125°. Mol. Wt. 264. U.V. 235, 328 mμ in 95% ethanol.

Yield 0.33 g. per liter.

Clitocybe illudens

Marjorie Anchel, Annette Hervey and William J. Robbins, *Proc. Nat. Acad. Sci. U. S.* 36 300 (1950); 38 927 (1952).

A third, antibiotically inactive substance, $C_{10}H_{16}O_4$ or $C_{15}H_{24}O_6$, crystals, m.p. 72–74°, $[\alpha]_D^{20}$ −107° (in absolute ethanol) occurred in the same culture.

1178 Imoticidin, m.p. 245° (darkening from 210°).

An antibiotic isolate, C 64.71, H 9.50, N 0.0, H_2O 7.63. Mol. Wt. 532–553.

Streptomyces albus

Tadao Inouye, Yasuhiro Okamoto and Yosikazu Nishikado, *Ber. Ohara Inst. Landwirtsch. Biol., Okayama Univ.* 11 95 (1959). (In English)

1179 Indigoidine, deep blue pigment, no melting point.

Low solubility in most solvents. Soluble in dilute hydrochloric acid. Analysis of partially purified compound: C 47.74, H 3.82, N 17.95. Formed a red crystalline acetate, m.p. >300° (dec.), but more soluble: C 49.63, H 3.98, N 16.05, acetyl 16.9. A red benzoate was also prepared.

Corynebacterium insidiosum (McCulloch) Jensen, *Pseudomonas indigofera, Erwinia chrysanthemi, Arthrobacter* sp.

B. Elazari-Volcani, *Arch. Mikrobiol.* **10** 343 (1939).
D. A. Kuhn and M. P. Starr, *Bacteriol. Proc.* **58** (1956).
Mortimer P. Starr, *Arch. Mikrobiol.* **30** 325 (1958).

1180   Isorhodomycin A,* $C_{20}H_{29}O_8N$ or $C_{21}H_{31}O_8N$, hydrochloride: deep red prisms, m.p. 220°, $[\alpha]_{6060\text{-}7600}^{18}$ +268° ±30° (c 1 in methanol).

Occurs with rhodomycin A.

Either compound on mild hydrolysis yields a water-soluble, N-containing moiety and a water-insoluble chromophore.

Streptomyces purpurascens

Hans Brockmann and Peter Patt, *Chem. Ber.* **88** 1455 (1955).

1181   **Itaconitin,** yellow needles, m.p. 169°.

Negative Beilstein, fuchsin, xanthogen, Legal, Ehrlich, Liebermann, $FeCl_3$ tests.   Decolorized bromine and $KMnO_4$.   Formed an acetate, semicarbazone and 2,4-DNPH.   Hydrogenated to hexahydroitaconitin.

Aspergillus itaconicus

Kono Kinoshita and Shoichi Nakajima, *Hoshi Yakka Daigaku Kiyo* **7** 17 (1958).

1182   **Laterosporin**

Appeared to be a peptide.   Isolated as a hydrochloride. Soluble in water.   Tendency to precipitate out of solution in NaCl solution or in 0.2 M phosphate buffer.

Bacillus laterosporus

Ella M. Barnes, "Antibiotics," **Vol. II** *Antibiotics from bacteria in the genus bacillus,* Oxford University Press, London, 1949, Chap. 10 appendix, pp. 1540–1541.

1183   **Latumcidin** (Sulfate), $C_{11}H_{13}O_2N \cdot H_2SO_4$, white needles, m.p. 140°, $[\alpha]_D^{21}$ +148.9° (c 0.1 in 0.1 N sodium hydroxide).

A basic, unstable, antifungal agent.   Positive diazo, Baeyer, bromine.   Negative $FeCl_3$, Fehling, Tollens, Ehrlich, Sakaguchi, ninhydrin, biuret, Molisch.

Somewhat resembles eulicin, and abikoviromycin.

Streptomyces reticuli var. *latumcidus*

Yoshio Sakagami, Ichiro Yamaguchi, Hiroshi Yonehara, Zoichiro Okimoto, Sadazi Yamanouchi, Kazuo Takiguchi and Heiichi Sakai, *J. Antibiotics* (Japan) **11A** 6 (1958).

* Identical with entry 597.

1184   **Lenamycin,** $C_4H_4O_3N_2$ or $C_4H_4O_2N_2$ (proposed), colorless crystals, m.p. 202–207° (dec.) optically inactive.

Apparently an α,β-unsaturated amide. Negative ninhydrin, biuret, anthrone, $FeCl_3$, Sakaguchi, Elson-Morgan, nitro and oxime tests.

A streptomycete

The yield was 72 mg. from 5 l. of broth. Occurs together with *trans*-cinnamic acid amide and ethoxyethene-1,2-dicarboamide.

Yasuharu Sekizawa, *J. Biochem.* (Japan) 45 159 (1958).

1185   **Lenzitin,** colorless needles, m.p. 166°.

Contains C, H, O only. Positive $FeCl_3$, $KMnO_4$.

Lenzites sepiaria (Wulf)

M. Litvinov and E. Moiseeva, *Priroda* 1 60 (1951).

1186   **Litmocidin,** m.p. 144–146° (dec.).

An acid-base indicator. Decolorized by bisulfite or zinc dust, color restored by air oxidation.

Proactinomyces cyaneus var. *antibioticus*

G. F. Gause, *J. Bacteriol.* 51 649 (1946).

M. G. Brazhnikova, *ibid.* 51 655 (1946). (Isolation)

1187   **Longisporin,** $C_{36}H_{58}O_{10}$, crystals, m.p. 99–101°, $[\alpha]_D$ +2.62°.

Alkaline hydrolysis yields a hydroxy acid $C_{10}H_{16}O(OH)$ (COOH). It was suggested that the antibiotic is a cyclic ester of three such acid units.

Actinomyces longispori

G. P. Menshikov and M. M. Rubinshtein, *Zhur. Obshchei Khim.* 26 2035 (1956).

1188   **Lustericin,** $C_{40}H_{64}O_{13}$, white crystals, m.p. 130° $[\alpha]_D^{20}$ 0°, mol. wt. 130.

Streptomyces sp.

Motoo Shibata, Koichi Nakazawa, Michitaka Inoue, Jiro Terumichi and Akira Miyake, *Ann. Rept. Takeda Research Lab.* 17 19 (1958).

1189   **Lycopersin,** $C_{20}H_{15}O_8$, bright red needles, darkens from 250°, dec. 305°.

Fusarium lycopersici, F. vasinfectum

G. Kreitman and F. F. Nord, *Arch. Biochem.* 21 457 (1949).

Gerald Kreitman, Oldrich K. Sebek and F. F. Nord, *ibid.* 28 77 (1950).

1190 Malucidin, complex yeast protein, soluble in water, not coagulable, not dialyzable. Contains organic phosphorus to which its activity can be related.

The protein is combined with RNA, while the latter by itself has very little, if any, antibacterial property.

Brewers' and bakers' yeasts

I. A. Parfentjev, *Federation Proc.* 16 428 (1957).

1191 **Marasmic Acid,** $C_{16}H_{20}O_4$ (proposed) colorless needles, m.p. 174° (sealed tube), $[\alpha]_D^{25}$ 176° (c 1.4 in acetone).

A monobasic acid with reducing properties. Negative $FeCl_3$, Br_2 in CCl_4. Forms a 2,4-dinitrophenylhydrazone.

Marasmius conigenus

Frederick Kavanagh, Annette Hervey and William J. Robbins, *Proc. Nat. Acad. Sci. U. S.* 35 343 (1949).

1192 **Marcomycin,** $C_{17}H_{30}O_9N_2$, white crystals, m.p. 160–180° (dec.).

Streptomyces hygroscopicus

German Patent 1,027,846 (1958).

1193 **Megacidin,** $C_{24}H_{38}O_{10}$ (proposed), colorless crystals, m.p. 162–164°, $[\alpha]_D$ −51° (c 0.958 in ethanol).

A neutral compound with an easily saponifiable ester or lactone group.

Also isolated from the same fermentation were: L-leu-
1194 cyl-L-proline anhydride, m.p. 158–165°, $[\alpha]_D$ −128° (c
1195 0.968 in ethanol) and L-leucyl-L-leucine anhydride.

Streptomyces sp.

L. Ettlinger, E. Gäumann, R. Hütter, W. Keller-Schierlein, F. Kradolfer, L. Neipp, V. Prelog, P. Reusser and H. Zähner, *Monatsh. Chem.* 88 989 (1957).

1196 **Melanosporin,** $C_{56-63}H_{105-117}O_{20-22}N_3$, yellowish white amorphous solid, m.p. 132–134°, $[\alpha]_D^{20}$ +30° (c. 1.57 in methanol).

Strong acid hydrolysis yields three ninhydrin-positive compounds. Negative $FeCl_3$. Positive ninhydrin.

Streptomyces melanosporus (*sine melanosporofaciens*) n. sp.

F. M. Arcamone, C. Bertazzoli, M. Ghione and T. Scotti, *Giorn. microbiol.* 7 207 (1959).

1197 **Mesenterin,** colorless needles, m.p. 122–126°.

A basic compound, analysis: C 65.82, H 7.10, N 8.66. Positive Molisch, negative ninhydrin, biuret, Fehling, $FeCl_3$.

Occurs with azomycin and antibiotic 446.
Nocardia mesenterica
Masahiro Ueda and Hamao Umezawa, *J. Antibiotics* (Japan) **8A** 164 (1955).

1198 **Metabolite,** $C_{24}H_{50}O_2$, colorless crystals, m.p. 82°.
Negative Liebermann-Burchard, $KMnO_4$, tetranitromethane tests.
Amanita phalloides
Heinrich Wieland and Gustav Coutelle, *Ann.* 548 270 (1941).

1199 **Metabolite of** *Coprinus comatis,* $C_{12}H_{16}ON_2S$, m.p. 157°.
A basic compound, containing a phenolic hydroxyl group. Positive Millon, Pauly diazo tests. Raney nickel desulfurization gave a compound, m.p. 250° (dec.).
Coprinus comatis Gray
Paul Heinz List, *Arch. Pharm.* **291** 502 (1958).

1200 **Metabolite from** *Curvularia lunata,* $C_{14}H_{18}O_5$, colorless needles, m.p. 195°.
Insoluble in aqueous sodium carbonate, soluble in aqueous sodium hydroxide. Brown color with alcoholic ferric chloride.
Curvularia lunata
Also isolated from the same culture were mannitol and a trace of crystalline material, m.p. 176–178° (dec.).
T. Krishna Murty and S. Sankara Subramanian, *Indian J. Pharm.* **20** 72 (1958).

1201 **Metamycin,** white crystals, m.p. 173° (dec.) $[\alpha]_D^{589}$ +36.6 (c 0.11 in methanol) U.V. 237, 305–307 mμ in 0.1 N sodium hydroxide.
C 43.95, H 4.06, N 14.45, S 13.57.
Positive Fehling, Tollens, Br_2, decolorization of permanganate, 2,4-DNPA tests. Negative $FeCl_3$ and Sakaguchi tests.
Streptomyces matensis
P. Sensi, R. Ballotta and G. G. Gallo, *Antibiotics and Chemotherapy* **9** 76 (1959).

1202 **Microcin A,** neutral, reddish violet in color, separated at pH 7.0.

1203 **Microcin B,** acidic, yellowish red, slightly soluble in water separated at pH 2.0.
Both give negative Molisch and $FeCl_3$; vary from micromonosporin in activity, have much resistance to U.V.

Micromonospora sp.

Tomotsune Taira and Shigehiro Fujii, *J. Antibiotics* (Japan) 5 187 (1952).

1204 **Mikamycin A,** $C_{31}H_{39}O_9N_3$, yellowish white crystals, m.p. 147–152° (dec.), $[\alpha]_D^{28}$ −152° (c 0.5 in methanol).

Apparently identical with the principal active component of the streptogramin and antibiotic No. 899 complexes.

A neutral antibiotic. Negative ninhydrin, biuret, glucosamine, maltol and Millon. Green-black $FeCl_3$. Brown precipitate with the Tollens reagent. Positive Benedict. Forms a 2,4-DNPH.

Streptomyces mitakaensis

Mamoru Arai, Keiko Karasawa, Shoshiro Nakamura, Hiroshi Yonehara and Hamao Umezawa, *J. Antibiotics* (Japan) 11A 14 (1958).

Mamoru Arai, Koichi Okabe, Hiroshi Yonehara and Hamao Umezawa, *ibid.* 11A 21 (1958).

Koichi Okabe, *ibid.* 12A 86 (1959).

1205 **Mikamycin B,** $C_{45}H_{58}O_{11}N_8$ (proposed), white platelets, m.p. 160°, dec. 262°, $[\alpha]_D^{15}$ −61.3° (c 1.0 in methanol).

Similar to PA-114 B in physical and chemical properties but differs from staphylomycin S. It is thought to be different from both.

Gives a positive $FeCl_3$. Negative Ehrlich, biuret, Fehling, Tollens, nearly negative ninhydrin.

Streptomyces mitakaensis

Kiyoshi Watanabe, Hiroshi Yonehara, Nobuo Tanaka and Hamao Umezawa, *J. Antibiotics* (Japan) 12A 112 (1959).

Koyoshi Watanabe, *ibid.* 13A 57 (1960).

Mitomycins.

1206
1207
1208
1209
1210
1211
1212
1213

A complex from which several compounds were isolated: colorless fractions W-1 (m.p. 148°), W-2 (m.p. 138°) and W-3 (m.p. 187°). Pigmented fractions A (red crystals) m.p. 167°, B (violet crystals), C (bluish violet crystals), Y (yellow crystals) m.p. 180–240° (dec.) and R (red-brown amorphous powder). Pigmented fractions are antibiotic.

1214 **Mitomycin C,** $C_{54}H_{61}O_{19}N_{13}$ (tentative), deep bluish violet crystals, m.p.: no melting or dec. noted below 360°.

Positive $FeCl_3$, Fehling, biuret, Ehrlich, decolorization of permanganate. Negative Benedict, Tollens, ninhydrin, Milton, Raymond. Mol. Wt. ~1120.

The mitomycins may be related to the actinomycins.

Streptomyces caespitosus

S. Wakaki, H. Marumo, K. Tomioka, G. Shimizu, E. Kato, H. Kamada, S. Kudo and Y. Fugimoto, *Antibiotics and Chemotherapy* 8 228 (1958).

Toju Hata, Yoshimoto Sano, Ryozo Sugawara, Akihiro Matsumae, Kokichi Kamamori, Tatsuo Shima and Tadashi Hoshi, *J. Antibiotics* (Japan) 9A 141 (1956).

1215 **Moldin,** gives positive Molisch and $FeCl_3$ but negative biuret, ninhydrin, Tollens, Fehling and Sakaguchi tests.

Streptomyces sp. res. *S. phalochromogenus*

Kenji Maeda, Yoshiro Okami, Osamu Taya and Hamao Umezawa, *J. Antibiotics* (Japan) 5 465 (1952).

1216 **Monilin,** $C_{15}H_{20}O_3N_6$, colorless needles, m.p. 235–238° (dec.). An antifungal compound. Positive ninhydrin.

Streptomyces sakaiensis

Shigehiro Fujii, Hiromu Hitomi, Masahiko Imanishi and Koichi Kakazawa, *Ann. Rept. Takeda Research Lab.* 14 8 (1955).

1217 **Musarin** $(C_{35}H_{60}O_{14}N_2)_n$ (proposed), Mol. Wt. ~5000, yellow powder, m.p. 170° (dec.), $[\alpha]_D^{20}$ +35.1° ±1.6° (c 1.21 in methanol).

An acidic substance.

Streptomyces sp.

H. R. V. Arnstein, A. H. Cook and Margaret S. Lacey, *J. Gen. Microbiol.* 2 111 (1948).

1218 **Mutomycin,** $C_7H_{11-12}O_2$, white crystalline powder, m.p. 141.5–142°.

Actinomyces atroolivaceus var. *mutomycini*

G. F. Gauze, T. S. Maksimova, O. L. Popova, M. G. Brazhnikova, T. A. Uspenskaya and O. K. Rossolimo, *Antibiotiki* U.S.S.R. 4 20 (273 in English) (1959).

1219 **Mycelin,** m.p. 263° (dec.).

Water insoluble, contains no nitrogen or sulfur. Negative Molisch. Flavomycin is produced by the same organism. Mycelin has antifungal properties.

Streptomyces roseoflavus

Kazuyoshi Aiso, Tadashi Arai, Kazuhiro Washida and Tei Tanaami, *J. Antibiotics* (Japan) 5 217 (1952).

1220 **Mycelin-IMO,** yellow crystalline, m.p. 214–222° (dec.), $[\alpha]_D^{21}$ +70 ±2 (c 1 in 1,4-dioxane) U.V. 243, 294, 335, 355, 373 mμ. Mol. Wt. 335, C 71.29, H 5.96, N 11.31.

Streptomyces diastatochromogenes

Koichi Ogata, Masaji Igarashi, Akira Miyake and Hiroichi Yamamoto, Japanese Patent 5898 (1957).

1221 **Mycorhodin,** bright red needles, m.p. 200–202° (dec.) U.V. 420, 471, 250 mμ in ethanol.   C 58.7 H 5.2 N 2.1.

Mol. Wt. 698, 635.

Acid-base indicator.

Streptomyces sp.

M. Misiek, A. Gourevitch, B. Heinemann, M. J. Cron, D. F. Whitehead, H. Schmitz, I. R. Hooper and J. Lein, *Antibiotics and Chemotherapy* **9** 280 (1959).

1222 **Mycospocidin** $(C_{20}H_{32}O_9N_2)_n$, colorless crystals, dec. 233°, $[\alpha]_D^{26}$ +56° (c 1 in pyridine).

Negative ninhydrin, biuret, Tollens, Fehling, ferric chloride tests.   Positive diazo reaction.

Acid hydrolysis yielded two ninhydrin-positive substances, one perhaps being glycine.

Streptomyces bobiliae

Shoshiro Nakamura, Mamoru Arai, Keiko Karasawa and Hiroshi Yonehara, *J. Antibiotics* (Japan) **10A** 248 (1957).

1223 **Mycothricin,** colorless crystals, complex consists of strong organic bases.

Negative ninhhydrin, biuret, Fehling, Tollens, Molisch, Millon, maltol and Sakaguchi.

Streptomyces lavendulae

G. Rangaswami, *Hindustan Antibiotics Bull.* **2** 46 (1959).

1224 **Mycoticin,** $C_{18}H_{30}O_5$ (proposed), yellow crystals.

Contains a hydroxyl group, has reducing properties, fluoresces under U.V.

Streptomyces ruber

Ruth C. Burke, Jacob H. Swartz, S. S. Chapman and Wei-Yuan Huang, *J. Invest. Dermatol.* **23** 163 (1954).

1225 **Nigericin,** $C_{39}H_{69}O_{11}$, colorless needles, m.p. 246–254°.

A monobasic acid.

Streptomyces sp. resembling *S. violaceaniger*

Roger L. Harned, Phil Harter Hidy, Cyril J. Corum and Kenneth L. Jones, *Antibiotics and Chemotherapy* **1** 594 (1951).

1226 **Nocardianin,** $C_{65-67}H_{96-104}O_{15}N_{18}$, red prisms, m.p. 228–235° (dec.), $[\alpha]_D^{25}$ −223° (c 0.3 in methanol).
Negative biuret, ninhydrin.
Nocardia sp.
I. R. Bick, Gregory J. Jann and Donald J. Cram, *Antibiotics and Chemotherapy* 2 255 (1952).

1227 **Nocardorubin,** crimson powder, darkens from 180° (dec.).
Nocardia narasinoensis
J. Antibiotics (Japan) **8B** 253 (1955).

1228 **Nonactin,** $C_{30}H_{48}O_9$, colorless crystals, m.p. 147°, optically inactive.
Slight U.V. at 264 mμ (log ϵ = 1.5 in ethanol). Inert to chemicals and microbes.
Streptomyces spp. which produce cycloheximide.
R. Corbaz, L. Ettlinger, E. Gaümann, W. Keller-Schierlein, F. Kradolfer, L. Neipp, V. Prelog and H. Zähner, *Helv. Chim. Acta* 38 1445 (1955).

1229 **Nordin,** $C_{18}H_{16}O_8Cl_2$, m.p. 134–136°.
Occurs with estin (q.v.).
Penicillium paxilli var. *echinulatum*
Eitaro Komatsu, Japanese Patent 4799 (1953).

1230 **Nudic Acid A,** $C_{14}H_{20}O_3$ (proposed), colorless crystals, m.p. 123.5°.
No reducing properties. Takes up bromine.
Tricholoma nudum
H. W. Florey, E. Chain, N. G. Heatley, M. A. Jennings, A. G. Sanders, E. P. Abraham and M. E. Florey, "Antibiotics," Oxford University Press, London, 1949, p. 358.

1231 **Nybomycin,** $C_{16}H_{14}O_4N_2$, colorless crystals, which darken at 330° without melting.
Negative ninhydrin, biuret, $FeCl_3$; sugar tests, Ehrlich, KM_nO_4, Br_2.
Streptomyces sp.
Frieda Strelitz, Helen Flon and Igor N. Asheshov, *Prac. Nat. Acad. Sci. U. S.* 41 620 (1955).
T. E. Eble, G. A. Boyack, C. M. Large and W. H. De Vries, *Antibiotics and Chemotherapy* 8 627 (1958).

1232 **Oligomycin A,** $C_{24}H_{40}O_6$, colorless crystals, m.p. 140° (dec.), 150° (dec.) (polymorphic), $[\alpha]_D^{23}$ −54.5° (c 4.40 in dioxane).

Mol. Wt. $= 424$. Absorbs 2 moles H_2. Four active H. Five C—CH_3 groups. Forms a diacetate.

1233 **Oligomycin B,** $C_{22}H_{36}O_6$, colorless crystals, m.p. 160°, 169° (polymorphic), $[\alpha]_D^{23.5}$ $-49.5°$ (c 1.03 in methanol). Mol. Wt. $= 396$. Four active H. Five C—CH_3 groups. Forms a diacetate.

1234 **Oligomycin C,** $C_{28}H_{46}O_6$, colorless crystals, m.p. 198–200°, $[\alpha]_D^{23}$ $-80.7°$ (c 3.70 in dioxane).
Contains six C—CH_3 groups.
Streptomyces sp. (may be *S. diastatochromogenes*)
Robert M. Smith, William H. Peterson and Elizabeth McCoy, *Antibiotics and Chemotherapy* 4 962 (1954).
Satoru Masamune, J. M. Sehgal, E. E. van Tamelen, F. M. Strong and W. H. Peterson, *J. Am. Chem. Soc.* 80 6092 (1958).

1235 **Ophiobalin,** $C_{28}H_{32}O_4$, white prisms, m.p. 181–182°.
Ophiobalus miyabeanus
A. Neelameghan, *Hindustan Antibiotics* 2 13 (1959).

1236 **Oregonensin,** $C_{20}H_{32}O_8$ (proposed), colorless needles, m.p. 82°. A neutral substance. Positive 2,4-DNPH.
Ganoderma oregonense
H. W. Florey, E. Chain, N. G. Heatley, M. A. Jennings, A. G. Sanders, E. P. Abraham and M. E. Florey, "Antibiotics," Oxford University Press, London, 1949, p. 362.

1237 **Oryzacidin** (Oryzasizine), $C_8H_{13}O_5N$, colorless, hygroscopic needles, m.p. 162° (dec.), $[\alpha]_D$ $-138°$.
β-Nitropropionic acid also occurs free in the culture broth.
Aspergillus oryzae
Chujiro Shimoda, *J. Agr. Chem. Soc. Japan* 25 254 (1951).
Seiji Nakamura and Chuji Shimoda, *ibid.* 28 909 (1954).

1238 **PA-128,** $C_{37-46}H_{61-75}O_{13-16}N$, light yellow rectangular plates, m.p. 143° $[\alpha]_D^{25}$ $-2.0°$ (c 1 in methanol).
Negative $FeCl_3$, no colors in aqueous base nor concentrated H_2SO_4. Positive 2,4-DNPH, decolorizes Br_2 water and permanganate. Takes up >6 mM of hydrogen per gram of antibiotic.
Unclassified *Streptomycete*
Koppaka V. Rao and John E. Lynch, *Antibiotics and Chemotherapy* 8 437 (1958).

1239 **PA-132,** $C_{16}H_{18-20}O_5$, free acid is a colorless amorphous powder, $[\alpha]_D^{25}$ $-161°$ (c 1.0 in methanol). Handled as the benzylamine salt: white crystals, m.p. 128–131°, $[\alpha]_D^{25}$ $-130°$ (c 1.0 in methanol).

A lactonic acid containing two C-methyl groups. Decolorizes bromine or permanganate. Negative $FeCl_3$, Fehling, 2,4-DNPH, Tollens, $AgNO_3$ and NaOI.

Streptomyces sp.

B. Kenneth Koe, Ben A. Sobin and Walter D. Celmer, "Antibiotics Annual 1956–1957," Medical Encyclopedia, Inc., New York, p. 672.

1240 **Phagolessin A 58,** light yellow hygroscopic powder.

Negative $FeCl_3$, biuret, Millon and ninhydrin test.

Streptomyces sp.

Igor N. Asheshov, Freda Strelitz and Elizabeth A. Hall, *Antibiotics and Chemotherapy* 2 366 (1952).

1241 **Phalamycin,** $C_{36}H_{41}O_{14}N_9S$ (proposed), colorless crystals, no sharp m.p.

Positive $FeCl_3$, Br_2 absorption. Has primary or secondary alcohol groups.

Streptomyces noursei variant

Rachel Brown, *N. Y. State Dept. Health, Ann. Rept. Div. Labs and Research* 18 (1956). (*Chem. Abstr.* 51 16672e)

1242 **Phalofacin** gives positive $FeCl_3$ but negative biuret, Millon, ninhydrin, Molisch, Tollens and Sakaguchi tests.

Streptomyces sp. res. *S. aureus*

Kenji Maeda, Yoshiro Okami, Osamu Taya and Hamao Umezawa, *J. Antibiotics* (Japan) 5 465 (1952).

1243 **Phleomycin,** $C_{53}H_{93}O_{32}N_{17}$, white to pale green amorphous powder, isolated as a blue monocopper complex. U.V. 244, 295–300 mμ.

Gives positive ninhydrin and diazo tests. Negative Fehling, Tollens, Sakaguchi and Molisch.

Streptomyces verticillis

Tomohisa Takita, Kenji Maeda and Hamao Umezawa, *J. Antibiotics* (Japan) 12A 111 (1959).

Tomohisa Takita, *ibid.* 12 285 (1959).

1244 **Phytonivein,** $C_{29}H_{46}O_2$, colorless needles, m.p. 138°.

Fusarium bulbigenum

The watermelon wilt toxin.

Isamu Hirose and Seiyo Aoe, *Ann. Phytopathol. Soc. Japan* 19 162 (1955). (*Chem. Abstr.* 50 14058g)

Isamu Hirose and S. Nishimura, *Nippon Nogêi-kagaku Kaishi* 30 528 (1956).

1245 **Piricularin,** $C_{17}H_{14}N_2O_3$ or $C_{18}H_{14}N_2O_3$, colorless crystals, m.p. 73.5°, $[\alpha]_D^{28}$ −19°.

Absorbs 4 moles of hydrogen over platinum catalyst, contains two phenolic or enolic hydroxyls, no methoxyl. Reacts with 3 moles of 2,4-dinitrophenylhydrazine. Has 1 N-methyl, no NH or NH_2. λ max. in H_2O = 240 mμ. $E_{1cm.}^{1\%}$ 2824. A toxin of rice blast disease.

Piricularia oryzae

Kinjiro Tamari and Jun Kaji, *Nippon Nogêi-kagaku Kaishi* 31 387 (1957).

1246 **Pleomycin,** $C_{14}H_{12}O_8$, rectangular plates from ethanol, m.p. 235°, U.V. 270, 330, 340 mμ in 0.13 M phosphate buffer.

Streptomyces pleofaciens

Roy A. Machlowitz, Jesse Charney, Alfred A. Tytell and W. P. Fisher, "Antibiotics Annual 1954–1955," Medical Encyclopedia, Inc., New York, p. 806.

1247 **Pleuromutilin** (Drosophilin B), $C_{22}H_{34}O_5$, colorless crystals, m.p. 170°, $[\alpha]_D^{24}$ +20° (c 3.0 in absolute ethanol).

Forms a diacetate, non-phenolic, probably has a lactone ring, forms a hydrazone.

Pleurotus mutilus

Marjorie Anchel, *J. Biol. Chem.* 199 133 (1952).

1248 **Pleurotin,** $C_{20}H_{22}O_5$, yellow-amber needles, m.p. 220–215° (dec.), $[\alpha]_D^{23}$ −20° (c 0.59 in chloroform).

A neutral, photosensitive compound. Negative $FeCl_3$, oxidized KI.

Pleurotus griseus

William J. Robbins, Frederick Kavanaugh and Annette Hervey, *Proc. Nat. Acad. Sci. U. S.* 33 171 (1947).

1249 **Pluramycin A,** orange needle crystals, dec. from 177°, U.V. 208, 245 (265–270) mμ in ethanol.

C 66.63, H 6.30, N 3.66

Negative $FeCl_3$, Fehling, Tollens and 2,4-DNPH.

1250 **Pluramycin B,** reddish brown powder, possible neutral substance. The pluramycins may be related to the actinomycins.

Tomio Takeuchi, Kazuo Nitta and Hamao Umezawa, *J. Antibiotics* (Japan) **9A** 22 (1956).

Kenji Maeda, Tomio Takeuchi, Kazuo Nitta, Koki Yagishita, Ryozo Utahara, Teisuke Osato, Masahiro Ueda, Shinichi Kondo, Yoshiro Okami and Hamao Umezawa, *ibid.* **9A** 75 (1956).

1251 Poin, crystals, m.p. 142–143°.
C 59.70, H 7.77, O 32.53
Fusarium sporotrichiella var. *poae*
O. K. Élpidina, *Antibiotiki* U.S.S.R. 4 46 (273 in English) (1959).

1252 Primycin, $C_{19}H_{37}O_7N$, white microcrystals, m.p. 166–168° (dec.). No reducing properties. Can be acetylated. Strong Sakaguchi test.
An unclassified actinomycete
T. Vályi-Nagy, J. Úri and I. Szilágy, *Nature* 174 1105 (1954).

1253 Psalliotin, crystalline, water soluble, inactivated by bright light.
Psalliota xanthoderma
Nancy Atkinson, *Nature* 174 598 (1954).
Idem., Australian Patent 20,272,156 (1957).

1254 Pulvilloric Acid, buff colored needles, turning bright yellow in air.
An acidic, antifungal antibiotic, containing only C, H, O. Blue $FeCl_3$, negative Tollens. Yield 600 mg. per liter.
Penicillium pulvillorum Turfitt
P. W. Brian, P. J. Curtis, H. G. Hemming and G. L. F. Norris, *Brit. Mycol. Soc. Trans.* 40 369 (1957).

1255 Pumilin, lemon-yellow crystals, m.p. >360°.
Negative $FeCl_3$, copper-red in 5 N hydrochloric acid.
Bacillus pumilis
0.7 g. was obtained from 500 gal. of broth.
D. S. Bhate, *Nature* 175 816 (1955).

1256 Racemomycin A

1257 Racemomycin B,* $C_{60}H_{128}O_{32}N_{20}$, white powder, m.p. (Hydrochloride) 175° (dec.), $[\alpha]_D^{19}$ −45° (c 0.5 in water).
Positive Molisch, Elson-Morgan and biuret. Negative Sakaguchi, maltol, $FeCl_3$, 2,4 DNPH and Fehling. Yields β-lysine and roseonine on hydrolysis.

1258 Racemomycin C, isolated in a small amount as a salt (m.p. 210°).

* See entry **790.**

Streptomyces racemochromogenes n. sp.

Hyozo Taniyama and Shoji Takemura, *J. Pharm. Soc. Japan* **77** 1210, 1217 (1957); **78** 742 (1958).

1259 **Ractinomycin A,** $C_{33}H_{30}O_{14}N_3$, orange needles, m.p. browns ~157°, blackens at 205°.

Negative ninhydrin, biuret, Sakaguchi, Millon. Positive Tollens, Molisch, $FeCl_3$. Decolorizes $KMnO_4$. Decolorized by H_2O_2. Alkali-unstable. Turns purple above pH 6.5. Contains no amino acids.

1260 **Ractinomycin B,** reddish orange needles, m.p. 172–175° (dec.).

Negative $FeCl_3$.

The ractinomycins are said to resemble the actinomycins in some respects.

Streptomyces sp. similar to *S. phaeochromogenes*

Ryozo Utahara, Hideo Oyagi, Koki Yagishita, Yoshiro Okami and Hamao Umezawa, *J. Antibiotics* (Japan) **8A** 132 (1955).

Ryozo Utahara, *ibid.* **10A** 115 (1957).

S. Wakiki *et al.*, *Antibiotics and Chemotherapy* **8** 228 (1958).

1261 **Raisnomycin,** dark yellow basic material, insoluble in water. The hydrochloride and disulfate are slightly soluble. The impure material does not have an end absorption in U.V.

Streptomyces kentuckensis

Fred S. Barr and Paul E. Carman, *Antibiotics and Chemotherapy* **6** 286 (1956).

1262 **Rammacin,** $C_{26}H_{43}O_8$, crystalline, m.p. 235°, Mol. Wt. 499.

Negative Br_2; positive benzenoid.

Streptomyces sp.

K. Ahmad and M. F. Islam, *Nature* **176** 646 (1955).

1263 **Ramycin** (Mol. Wt. 478, contains only carbon, hydrogen and oxygen), colorless plates, m.p. 158° (dec.), optically inactive.

Structural features:

A non-phenolic hydroxy acid with one or more carbon-carbon double bonds.

Mucor ramannianus

P. J. van Dijck and P. deSomer, *J. Gen. Microbiol.* **18** 377 (1958).

1264 **Raromycin,** m.p. 211–213° C 57.97, H 8.46, N 0.44, O 33.13 by difference.

Streptomyces sp.
Nabuo Tanaka, Hisaji Yamazaki, Koichi Okabe and Hamao Umezawa, *J. Antibiotics* (Japan) 10A 189 (1957).

1265 Roseomycin, crystalline helianthate, m.p. 211–216° (dec.) and reineckate m.p. 114° (dec.).
Positive Molisch, Tollens, indole, glucosamine and Fehling.
Negative maltol, biuret, ninhydrin and Sakaguchi.
Streptomyces roseochromogenes
Nakao Ishida, *J. Antibiotics* (Japan) 3 845 (1950).

1266 Rhizobacidin, crystalline, m.p. 215–220° (dec.). Contains C, H, O and N but not S. Positive biuret, xanthoproteic, ninhydrin and Sakaguchi. Negative Ehrlich, Molisch and FeCl$_3$.
Bacillus subtilis
Carlos Casas-Campillo, *Ciencia* (Mexico) 11 21 (1951).

1267 Rhodocidin, red powder, U.V. shows a broad peak at 500–530 mμ. Soluble in water and organic solvents.
Streptomyces phoenix
Jesse Charney, Roy A. Machlowitz, W. S. Roberts and W. P. Fisher, *Antibiotics and Chemotherapy* 3 788 (1953).

Ristocetins (Spontins, Ristins).
Two closely related amphoteric antibiotics containing amino and phenolic groups and sugars. Each contains four reducing sugars: glucose, mannose, rhamnose and D-arabinose.
Negative biuret, Sakaguchi, maltol. Positive phosphomolybdic acid test for phenols, ninhydrin (after acid hydrolysis), anthrone. Mol. Wt. 2500–5000. Contain C, H, O, N, S.

1268 Ristocetin A (Sulfate): $[\alpha]_D^{25}$ −120–133° (in water).

1269 Ristocetin B (Sulfate): $[\alpha]_D^{25}$ −144–149° (in water).
Nocardia lurida
Julian E. Philip, Jay R. Schenck and Martha P. Hargie, "Antibiotics Annual 1956–1957," Medical Encyclopedia, Inc., New York, p. 699.

1270 Rotaventin, white crystals, m.p. 170–175° (dec.).
Streptomyces reticuli
Nobukiko Komatsu and Momoe Soeda, *Japan. J. Exp. Med.* 21 279 (1951).

1271 **Rubromycin,** thin square rods, m.p. 215° (dec.) U.V. 518–520, 546, 584 mμ.

C 60.30, H 4.26, O 33.91

Contains no N (differing from rhodomycin). Differs from rhodomycetin in that the latter is found in the culture solution; the present compound is in the mycelium.

Streptomyces collinus n. sp.

Hans Brockman and Karl Heinz Renneberg, *Naturwissenschaften* 40 59 (1953).

1272 **Ruticin,** orange needle-like crystals, U.V. 227, 262, 364 mμ.

Streptomyces res. *S. rutgersensis*

W. P. Fisher, Jesse Charney, Ray A. Machlowitz, James E. Blair and Alfred A. Tytell, "Antibiotics Annual 1953–1954," Medical Encyclopedia, Inc., New York, p. 174.

1273 **Sarcidin,** m.p. 274–275° (dec.).

C 41.89, H 5.02, N 21.82 and a qualitative sulfur test.

Tamio Takeuchi, Kazuo Nitta and Hamao Umezawa, *J. Antibiotics* (Japan) 6A 31 (1953).

1274 **Secalonic Acid,** $C_{31}H_{30\text{-}32}O_{14}$, lemon-yellow needles, m.p. 244–250° from chloroform, $[\alpha]_D^{20}$ −81° (acetone), −66° (chloroform), −198° → −59° (pyridine).

Claviceps purpurea

F. Kraft, *Arch. Pharm.* 244 336 (1906).

A. Stoll, J. Renz and A. Brack, *Helv. Chim. Acta* 35 2022 (1952).

1275 **Seligocidin,** crystalline powder, U.V. 304 mμ in ethanol.

Positive Sakaguchi and ninhydrin; negative biuret.

Streptomyces res. *S. roseochromogenes*

Shoshiro Nakamura, Kenji Maeda, Yoshiro Okami and Hamao Umezawa, *J. Antibiotics* (Japan) 7A 57 (1954).

1276 **Sirenin,** $C_{21}H_{36}O_7N$.

Mol. Wt.: found 386, calculated 414. Contains a lactone ring, a carbonyl group and a —C≡C— or —C≡N— bond. The absence of hydroxyl and carboxyl groups and of aromatic rings was ascertained.

Allomyces species

Sirenin is a sex hormone of this water-mold.

Leonard Machlis, *Nature* 181 1790 (1958).

1277   **Sporidesmin** (probably) $C_{19}H_{21}O_6N_3S_2Cl \cdot CCl_4$, colorless crystals (carbon tetrachloride solvate) sintering from 109° → resin → 125° semi-solid → meniscus at 130–134°, $[\alpha]_D^{20}$ −19° (c 2.2 in methanol).

Other formulae without chlorine are not excluded, since the solvent-free compound has not been isolated. The compound is a toxin in animals.

Sporidesmium bakeri Syd.

R. L. M. Synge and E. P. White, *Chem. and Ind.*, 1546 (1959).

1278   **Streptocardin**, Crystalline, U.V. 365 (242) (252) mμ in phosphate buffer (pH 6) forms water-soluble alkali salts.

Streptomyces sp., Nocardia sp.

W. P. Fisher, Roy A. Machlowitz, Alfred A. Tytell and Jesse Charney, "Antibiotics Annual 1953–1954," Medical Encyclopedia, Inc., New York, p. 177.

1279   **Streptolydigin**, $C_{32}H_{46}O_9N_2$ (or $C_{35}H_{50}O_{10}N_2$), m.p. 144–150° (dec.), $[\alpha]_D^{25}$ −93° (c 1.6 in chloroform).

An enolic acid. Positive $FeCl_3$, iodoform. Negative biuret, ninhydrin, Fehling, Molisch. Reacts with Br_2 in CCl_4.

Streptomyces lydicus

T. E. Eble, C. M. Large, W. H. DeVries, G. F. Crum and J. W. Shell, "Antibiotics Annual 1955–1956," Medical Encyclopedia, Inc., New York, p. 893.

Streptovaricin (Dalacin). A complex consisting of at least five active closely related components. These were separated by countercurrent distribution into Streptovaricins:

1280   **A,** $C_{34}H_{47-49}O_{13}N$, yellow crystals, m.p. 182–184°, $[\alpha]_D^{24}$ +454° ($CHCl_3$).

1281   **B,** $C_{34}H_{47-49}O_{13}N$, yellow crystals, m.p. 195–200°, $[\alpha]_D^{24}$ +168° ($CHCl_3$).

1282   **C,** $C_{34}H_{47-49}O_{13}N$, yellow crystals, m.p. 168–171°, $[\alpha]_D^{24}$ +317° ($CHCl_3$).

1283   **D,** yellow crystals, m.p. 115–118°, $[\alpha]_D^{24}$ +102° ($CHCl_3$).

1284   **E,** yellow crystals, m.p. 102–105°, $[\alpha]_D^{24}$ +6.13° ($CHCl_3$).

Streptomyces spectabilis
Paul Siminoff, Robert M. Smith, Walter T. Sokolski and
G. M. Savage, *Am. Rev. Tuberc. Pulmonary Diseases* 75 576
(1957).
George B. Whitfield, Edward C. Olson, Ross R. Herr, John A.
Fox, Malcolm E. Bergy and Gerald A. Boyack, *ibid.* 75 584
(1957).
Upjohn Co., British Patent 811,757 (1959).

1285 **Streptozotacin,** $C_{14}H_{17}O_{12}N_5$, m.p. 115–125° (dec.).
Probably still a mixture. Base-unstable neutral
substance. Seems to contain the partial structure

$$R-C\overset{\displaystyle O}{\underset{\displaystyle N}{\Big\langle}} \begin{matrix} \\ N=O. \\ CH_3 \end{matrix}$$

Alkaline treatment liberates diazo-
methane.
Streptomyces achromogenes
R. R. Herr, T. E. Eble, M. E. Bergy and H. K. Jahnke, 7th
Annual Symposium on Antibiotics, Washington, D. C., 1959.

1286 **Substance 1404,** yellow crystalline, Hexaene. M.p. 210–220°
(dec.), $[\alpha]_D^{21}$ +67.5 ±2.0° (c 1 in dioxane).
Contains N 10.47, no sulfur, no halogen.
Streptomyces diastatochromogenes (Mycelium)
Masaji Igarashi, Koichi Ogata and Akira Miyake, *J. Anti-
biotics* (Japan) 8B 113 (1955).

1287 **Sulfactin,** $C_{38}H_{55}O_7N_{11}S_4$ or $C_{27}H_{40}O_5N_8S_3$ (proposed), hygro-
scopic white needles, m.p. 245–275° (dec.).
Positive Fehling. Reduces $KMnO_4$. Negative biuret,
$FeCl_3$, Molisch, Sakaguchi.
Streptomyces roseus
Renate Junowicz-Kocholaty, Walter Kocholaty and Albert
Kelner, *J. Biol. Chem.* 168 765 (1947).

1288 **Sulfocidin,** yellow-brown crystals, m.p. 166–178°, $[\alpha]_D^{25}$ −58.5°
(c 0.51 in chloroform).
Neutral antibiotic, analysis C 64.88, H 8.38, N 4.25, S
1.80. Negative nitroprusside and azide iodine, ninhydrin,
$FeCl_3$, Sakaguchi, maltol, biuret, Fehling, 2,4-DNPH. De-
colorizes permanganate.
Streptomyces sp.
Morris Zief, Robert Woodside and George E. Ham, "Anti-
biotics Annual 1957–1958," Medical Encyclopedia, Inc., New
York, p. 886.

1289   **Taitomycin,** yellow-brown powder, U.V. at 330, 420 mμ.
C 53.57, H 4.87, N 9.50 ash 2.8.
Positive Fehling and ninhydrin (acid hydrolysate).
Streptomyces afghanensis
Mitsuo Shimo, Tatsuji Shiga, Takashi Tomosugi and Ikuzo Kamoi, *J. Antibiotics* (Japan) 12A 1 (1959).
Takashi Tomosugi, Ikuzo Kamoi, Tatsuji Shiga and Mitsuo Shimo, *ibid.* 12A 7 (1959).

1290   **Tardin,** $C_{11}H_{15}O_3$ (proposed), pale yellow oil, $[\alpha]_D^{20}$ −11.4° (in alcohol).
Positive $FeCl_3$. Negative 2,4-DNPH. Hydrolyzes to an acidic and a neutral fraction.
Penicillium tardum
N. Borodin, F. J. Philpot and H. W. Florey, *Brit. J. Exp. Path.* 28 31 (1947).

1291   **Terrecin,** light yellow prisms, m.p. 219°.
Analysis: C 51.89, H 3.51, N 3.8, Cl 19.1. Alkali soluble. Positive $FeCl_3$.
Aspergillus terreus
Kazuo Iwata and Itiro Yosioka, *J. Antibiotics* (Japan) 3 192 (1950).

1292   **Thiactin,** acid and alkali metal salts (previously identified as bryamycin). M.p. 220–234°, $[\alpha]_D^{27}$ −68.5 −69.5° (c 1 in chloroform).
Streptomyces hawaiiensis
Bernard Heinemann, Irving R. Hooper and Martin J. Cron, British Patent 790,521 (1958).

1293   **Thioaurin** (Orosomycin, Antibiotic HA-9), $C_7H_6O_2N_2S_2$ or $C_{14}H_{12}O_4N_4S_4$ (proposed), yellow crystals, m.p. 178–180°, optically inactive.
Strong U.V. at 232, 370 mμ. Negative $FeCl_3$.
Streptomyces sp. resembling *S. lipmanii*
William A. Bolhofer, Roy A. Machlowitz and Jesse Charney, *Antibiotics and Chemotherapy* 3 382 (1953).
William Eisenman, P. Paul Minieri, Anthony Abbey, John Charlebois, Mary Moncrieff-Yates and Neil E. Rigler, *ibid.* 3 385 (1953).

1294   **Thiomycin,** golden yellow needles, m.p. 176–178° (dec.).
Resembles thioaurin somewhat. May be identical. Analysis: C 49.61, H 5.50, N 8.88, S 16.26. Negative $FeCl_3$, ninhydrin, Fehling.

Streptomyces sp. resembling *S. phaeochromogenes* var. *chloromyceticus*
Yorio Hinuma, Susumu Hamada, Takaaki Yashima and Kyoko Ishikara, *J. Antibiotics* (Japan) 8A 118 (1955).

1295 **Totomycin,** $C_{21}H_{29}O_{11}N$, amorphous.
Streptomyces crystallinus
Jacques Loewe Research Foundation, Inc., British Patent 758,276 (1956).

1296 **Toyocamycin,** $C_{12}H_{14}O_4N_5$, colorless needles, prisms (monohydrate), m.p. 243°.
Analysis: Negative $FeCl_3$, Fehling, Molisch, Millon, Sakaguchi, Ehrlich. Mol. Wt. 286, 266.
Streptomyces toyocaensis
Ko Kikuchi, *J. Antibiotics* (Japan) 8A 145 (1955).
Haruo Nishimura, Ken Katagiri, Kozaburo Sato, Mikao Mayama and Noburo Shimaoka, *ibid.* 9A 60 (1956).

1297 **Tubercidin,** $C_{11}H_{14}O_4N_4$, crystals, m.p. 247° (dec.).
Forms a picrate, reineckate, helianthate, and pentachlorophenolate. A basic substance stable to acid and alkali.
A streptomycete
Kentaro Anzai, Goto Nakamura and Saburo Suzuki, *J. Antibiotics* (Japan) 10A 201 (1957).

1298 **Unclassified Compound,** $C_{17}H_{12}O_2N_2$, m.p. 220° (dec.).
Contains two enolic groups. U.V. bands at 243 and 374 mμ. Photosensitive.
Penicillium puberulum (mycelium)
A. H. Campbell, M. E. Foss, E. L. Hirst and J. K. N. Jones, *Nature* 155 141 (1945).

1299 **Unnamed antibiotic,** $C_{11}H_{17}O_3N$, hygroscopic light yellow crystals, m.p. 195° (dec.).
U.V. absorption at 365, 410 mμ.
Proteus immunitatis anticarcinomatosa n. sp. (on a special blood plasma-bouillon medium)
Atsuo Ushiyama and Takaaki Miyasaka, Japanese Patent Application 3998 (1957).

1300 **Vancomycin** (Hydrochloride), amphoteric white solid, Mol. Wt. 3200–3500 ±200 (titr.).
Streptomyces orientalis n. sp.

M. H. McCormick, W. M. Stark, G. E. Pittenger, R. C. Pittenger and J. M. McGuire, "Antibiotics Annual 1955–1956," Medical Encyclopedia, Inc., New York, p. 606.
H. Nishimura, *Ann. Rept. Shionogi Res. Lab.* 1 479 (1957).

1301 **Variotin,** $C_{18}H_{27}O_4N$, colorless oil, $[\alpha]_D^{25}$ −5.68° (c 1.0 in methanol).
A neutral oil with an ester-like odor. C 67.35, H 8.58, N 4.16, contains no halogen, sulfur or phosphorus. Positive diazo, nitroalkyl and hydroxamic acid reactions; negative ferric chloride, Millon, Ehrlich, Sakaguchi, Molisch, biuret, xanthoprotein and ninhydrin tests.
Paecilomyces variotis Bainier var. *antibioticus*
Hiroshi Yonehara, Setsuo Takeuchi, Hakao Umezawa and Yusuke Sumiki, *J. Antibiotics* (Japan) 12A 109, 195 (1959).

1302 **Vengicide,** $C_{24}H_{29}O_9N_{10}$, white, amorphous, m.p. 241.5–243°, $[\alpha]_D^{20}$ −51.6° (in 0.1 N hydrochloric acid solution).
Mol. Wt. ~600. U.V. λmax. 233.5 and 273.5 mμ in 0.05 N hydrochloric acid. C 47.05, H 4.85, O 24.85, N 23.85.
Streptomyces vendargensis
Oxytetracycline is produced also in this fermentation.
N. V. Koninklijke Nederlandsche Gist—en Spiritus—fabriek, British Patent 764,198 (1956). (*Chem. Abstr.* 51 10009a)
A. P. Struyck, Canadian Patent 514,164 (1955).

1303 **Vertimycin C,** crystalline, m.p. 152–155°. C 62.4, H 6.84, O 21.9, N 8.0.
Streptomyces verticillatus
Canadian Patent 575,235 (1959).

1304 **Violacetin,** fine yellow needles, m.p. (hydrochloride) >210°.
Basic compound. Positive ninhydrin, diazo tests. Precipitated from aqueous solution by picric acid, phosphotungstic acid, forms reineckate. Analysis: C 38.26, H 6.74, N 24.71, Cl 9.33. Negative biuret, Fehling, ninhydrin, glucosamine, maltol, Sakaguchi, Millon, xanthoprotein.
Streptomyces sp. resembling *S. purpurochromogenes*
Kazuyoshi Aiso, Tadashi Arai, Ichiro Shidara, Hiroo Kurihara and Yoshiro Morita, *J. Antibiotics* (Japan) 8A 33 (1955).

1305 **Violarin,** $C_{22\text{-}24}H_{32\text{-}34}O_{8\text{-}9}$, dark violet color or amorphous red powder, dec. 130°, somewhat similar to litmocidin, rubidin and rhodomycetin.

Streptomyces violaceus

N. A. Krasilnikov, G. K. Skryabin and O. I. Artamonova, *Antibiotiki* (U.S.S.R.) 3 (1958).

Idem., *J. Antibiotics* (Japan) 13A 1 (1960).

D. M. Trakhtenberg, L. V. Čerenkova and A. S. Chochlov, Symposium on Antibiotics, Prague (1959).

Viridins, $C_{19}H_{16}O_6$ (isomers).

1306 α-**Viridin,** fine colorless needles, m.p. 208–217° (dec.), $[\alpha]_D^{20}$ −213.4° (in chloroform).

1307 β-**Viridin,** Fine colorless needles, m.p. 140° (dec.), $[\alpha]_D^{20}$ −50.7° (in chloroform).

Both compounds show: negative Schiff, $FeCl_3$, iodoform. Red-violet color with phloroglucinol-hydrochloric acid. Positive ketone derivative tests, Fehling, Tollens.

Trichoderma viride

P. W. Brian and J. C. McGowan, *Nature* 156 144 (1945).

P. W. Brian, P. J. Curtis, H. G. Hemming and J. C. McGowan, *Ann. Appl. Biol.* 33 190 (1946).

E. B. Vischer, S. R. Howland and H. Raudnitz, *Nature* 165 528 (1950).

1308 **Virtosin,** $C_{27}H_{40}O_9N_2$, colorless needles, m.p. 142.5–143°, $[\alpha]_D^{18}$ +80° ± 0.5° (c 1 in acetone).

Positive Fehling and Sakaguchi reactions; negative ninhydrin and maltol tests.

Streptomyces olivochromogenes

Akira Miyake, Shozo Wada, Motoo Shibata, Koichi Nakasawa, Jujo Kaneko and Yasuharu Mamiya (to Takeda Pharmaceutical Industries Ltd.), Japanese Patent Appl. 6149 (1957).

1309 **Wortmannin,** colorless needles, m.p. 240° (yellowing in sunlight).

A neutral antifungal antibiotic, containing only C, H, O. Yields were about 100 mg. per liter.

Penicillium wortmanni Klocker

P. W. Brian, P. J. Curtis, H. G. Hemming and G. L. F. Norris, *Brit. Mycol. Soc. Trans.* 40 365 (1957).

1310 **Xanthicin,** $C_{13}H_{15}O_5N$, yellowish silky crystals, m.p. 211–213° (dec.), $[\alpha]_D^{15}$ +319° (c 0.25 in acetone).

U.V. maxima at 270 mμ (CH_3OH), 260 mμ, 325 mμ (0.1 MKOH). Positive aldehyde, indole, $FeCl_3$ tests. Negative amino, nitro, Fehling's, phosphomolybdic acid tests. Alkaline $KMnO_4$ oxidation gives succinic acid.

Streptomyces xanthochromogenes
Yasuji Sekizawa and Keiko Miwa, *Nippon Nôgei-kagaku Kaishi* 30 471 (1956).

1311 **Xanthomycin-like Antibiotic,** $C_{29}H_{42}O_7N_9S_4Cr$ (Reineckate), yellow-orange glass, U.V. 264.5, 335 mμ in water, pH 2.

Positive Benedict, bromine, silver nitrate, potassium iodide, sodium hydrosulfite and periodic acid.

Streptomyces sp.

James D. Mold and Quentin R. Bartz, *J. Am. Chem. Soc.* 72 1847 (1950).

1312 **Xanthomycins** (Protomycins), $C_{23}H_{29\text{-}31}O_7N_3$, free base: deep orange-red amorphous solid. Dihydrochloride: bright orange-yellow plates, $[\alpha]_D^{25}$ +115° (c 0.4 in water). Reineckate: long, orange needles, m.p. 165–170° (dec.).

Contains components A and B. Acid hydrolysis yields ethanolamine, methylamine and ammonia. Red-purple color with alkali. Positive Br_2 uptake, Benedict, silver nitrate, sodium hydrosulfite, ketone derivatives. Negative ninhydrin, Molisch, Sakaguchi, $FeCl_3$.

Streptomyces sp.

C. B. Thorne and W. H. Peterson, *J. Biol. Chem.* 176 413 (1948).

K. V. Rao and W. H. Peterson, *J. Am. Chem. Soc.* 76 1335 (1954).

1313 **Xanthothricin,** yellow needles, m.p. 165° (s. 161–162°).

Analysis: C 43.64, H 3.82, N 35.21, O 17.34.

Streptomyces sp. similar to *S. albus*

Roy A. Machlowitz, W. P. Fisher, Betsey S. McKay, Alfred A. Tytell and Jesse Charney, *Antibiotics and Chemotherapy* 4 259 (1954).

BIBLIOGRAPHY, REVIEWS AND
GENERAL REFERENCES

A book closely related to this one in intent and format is Walter Karrer's "Konstitution und Vorkommen der organischen Pflanzenstoffe (exclusive Alkaloide)." This lists over 2600 compounds with simple physical properties and thorough referencing. The emphasis is on metabolites of higher plants, although many fungal products are listed.

Another related book is "Type Reactions in Fermentation Chemistry," by Lowell L. Wallen, Frank H. Stodola and Richard W. Jackson. Here the emphasis is on non-sugar substrates, and classification is by type of reaction (oxidation, reduction, etc.) accomplished. Many microbial transformations of steroids are included, for example. Structural formulas, names of microorganisms and references are listed.

The revised edition of W. W. Umbreit's "Metabolic Maps" should be mentioned. This is essentially a list of equations, outlining various metabolic pathways, with no discussion and little referencing, but including catabolic routes and those in higher organisms.

"Naturally Occurring Quinones," by R. Thomson, is similar in method to our handbook, but is confined to the single class of compounds with more thorough discussion of each entry. "The Comparative Biochemistry of the Carotenoids" by T. W. Goodwin is somewhat similar in its restriction to a single class of chemicals. Both books are broader in scope as far as producing organism is concerned, and are not limited to microorganism products.

"The Chemistry of Microorganisms," by Arthur Bracken, is descriptive in style, showing some of the degradations and syntheses leading to establishment of chemical structures and offering essays on related topics. There is, perhaps, some emphasis on substances isolated and characterized by the Raistrick group.

We have not designated antibiotics as such nor have we attempted to separate the commercial from the non-commercial or to give the trade names or the biological properties. Data on biological properties are difficult to evaluate and, on the newer antibiotics, may conflict. Trade names tend to change due, for example, to improvements in dosage forms.

Many antibiotic spectra as well as physical properties and references are given in the "Handbook of Toxicology, Vol. II, Antibiotics" edited by W. S. Spector.

The "Physicians' Desk Reference" is an annual publication listing antibiotics and other medicines by brand name, by manufacturer and by type of medicine. There is also a therapeutic indications index, listing medicines available for the treatment of a given condition, and an index listing professional information (composition, dosage, etc.) on each product.

The "Antibiotics Annual" series also is a useful reference work on antibiotics.

Various other monographs, reviews and general references are in the list below.

1 "Konstitution und Vorkommen der organischen Pflanzenstoffe (exclusive Alkaloide)," Walter Karrer, Birkhäuser Verlag, Basel, 1958, 1207 pp. An index similar in intent to this book, but with its scope the entire plant kingdom. Thoroughly referenced.

2 "Type Reactions in Fermentation Chemistry," L. Wallen, F. Stodola and R. Jackson, Agricultural Research Service, United States Department of Agriculture (ARS–71–13), Peoria, 1959. A compilation of the types of chemical conversions by microorganisms which have been reported in the literature with emphasis on non-sugar substrates.

3 "Metabolic Maps," W. W. Umbreit, Burgess Publishing Co., Minneapolis, 1960.

4 "The Chemistry of Microorganisms," Arthur Bracken, Pitman and Sons, London, 1955, 343 pp.

5 "Antibiotics and Mold Metabolites," a symposium at the March 26, 1956 meeting of the English Chemical Society. Reprinted as Special Publication No. 5.

6 "Chemical Compounds Formed from Sugars by Molds," B. Gould, Scientific Report Series No. 7 of the Sugar Research Foundation, New York, 1947.

7 "The Microbes Contribution to Biology," Albert J. Kluyver and C. van Niel, Harvard University Press, Cambridge, 1956, 182 pp.

8 "Industrial Fermentations," Leland A. Underkofler and Richard J. Hickey, Chemical Publishing Co., Inc., New York, 1954, Vol. I, 565 pp., Vol. II, 578 pp.

9 Industrial and Engineering Chemistry Annual Unit Process Review of Fermentation, Samuel C. Beesch and G. M. Shull, Ind. and Eng. Chem. 48 1585 (1956). These reviews list, among other things, new antibiotics and new microbiological transformations of steroids.

10 Industrial and Engineering Chemistry Annual Unit Processes Review of Fermentation, Samuel C. Beesch and G. M. Shull, Ind. and Eng. Chem. 49 1491 (1957).

11 *Industrial and Engineering Chemistry Annual Unit Process Review of Fermentation,* Samuel C. Beesch and Fred W. Tanner, Jr., *Ind. and Eng. Chem.* 50 1341–1354 (1958).

12 *Biochemistry of microorganisms,* C. B. van Niel, *Ann. Rev. Biochem.* 12 551–586 (1943). A review with 371 references.

13 "Handbook of Toxicology, Vol. II, Antibiotics," W. S. Spector (Ed.), W. B. Saunders and Co., Philadelphia, 1957. This is a compilation of data on physical and biological properties of 340 antibiotics or substances which have been tested as antibiotics. Most of these are microorganism metabolites. Thoroughly referenced. This compilation was prepared under the direction of the Committee on the Handbook of Biological Data, Division of Biology and Agriculture, the National Academy of Sciences, The National Research Council.

14 *Chemistry and biochemistry of antibiotics,* E. B. Chain, *Ann. Rev. Biochem.* 27 167–212 (1958). A review with 297 references.

15 *Structural chemistry of actinomycetes antibiotics,* Eugene van Tamelen, *Fortschr. Chem. org. Naturstoffe* 16 90–138 (1958). A review with 113 references.

16 *Biochemistry of antibiotics,* S. B. Binkley, *Ann. Rev. Biochem.* 24 597–626 (1955). A literature survey complete to October 1954 with 284 references.

17 *Biochemistry of antibiotics,* B. Duggar and V. Singleton, *Ann. Rev. Biochem.* 22 459–496 (1953). A review of the literature to November 1952 with 288 references.

18 "Biochemistry of Some Polypeptide and Steroid Antibiotics," CIBA Lectures in Microbial Biochemistry, E. Abraham, John Wiley and Sons, Inc., New York, 1957.

19 "Topics in Microbial Chemistry," *Antimycin, Coenzyme A, Kinetin and Kinins,* E. R. Squibb Lectures on Chemistry of Microbial Products, F. M. Strong, John Wiley and Sons, Inc., New York, 1957.

20 *Antibiotics produced by fungi,* P. Brian, *Botan. Rev.* 17 357–431 (1951). A review with 276 references.

21 *Antibiotics produced by actinomycetes,* R. Benedict, *Botan. Rev.* 19 229–320 (1953). A review with 251 references.

22 "The Physicians' Desk Reference (to Pharmaceutical Specialties and Biologicals)," 14th Ed., Medical Economics, Inc., Oradell, N. J., 1960.

23 "Lectures in Antibiotics," G. F. Gause, Medgiz, Moscow, 1959, 356 pp. (In Russian)

24 "Antibiotics," Miloš Herold, Czechoslovakian Academy of Science, Prague, 1957, 363 pp. (In Czechoslovakian)

25 "New Antibiotic Binan (Usnic Acid)," Symposium on usnic acid and its use as an antibiotic. (In Russian) Academy of Science. U.S.S.R., 1957, 224 pp.

26 "Streptomycin and Dihydrostreptomycin," Louis Weinstein and N. Joel Ehrenkranz, Antibiotic Monographs No. 10, Medical Encyclopedia Inc., New York, 1958, 111 pp.

27 "Streptomycin, Nature and Practical Applications," Selman A. Waksman (Ed.), The Williams and Wilkins Co., Baltimore, 1949, 612 pp.

28 "Polymyxin, Neomycin, Bacitracin," Ernest Jawetz, Antibiotic Monographs No. 5, Medical Encyclopedia Inc., New York, 1956, 85 pp.

29 "Antibiotics Derived from *Bacillus Polymyxa*," (a symposium) Roy Waldo Miner (Ed.), *Annals of the New York Academy of Sciences,* 51, 853–1000 (1949).

30 "Terramycin, Review of the Literature," Chas. Pfizer and Co., Inc., 1953, 76 pp.

31 "Terramycin, Oxytetracycline," Merle M. Musselman, Medical Encyclopedia Inc., New York, 1956, 141 pp.

32 "Terramycin" (a symposium) Roy Waldo Miner (Ed.), *Annals of the New York Academy of Sciences,* 53, 223–459 (1950).

33 "Tetracycline," Harry F. Dowling, Antibiotics Monographs No. 3, Medical Encyclopedia Inc., New York, 1955, 57 pp.

34 "A Review of the Clinical Uses of Aureomycin," Lederle Laboratories Div., American Cyanamid Co., 1951, 241 pp.

35 "Aureomycin, Chlortetracycline," Mark H. Lepper, Medical Encyclopedia Inc., New York, 1956, 149 pp.

36 "Chloromycetin, Chloramphenicol," Theodore E. Woodward and Charles L. Wisseman, Jr., Antibiotics Monographs No. 8, Medical Encyclopedia Inc., New York, 1958, 152 pp.

37 "Erythromycin," Wallace E. Herrell, Antibiotics Monographs No. 1, Medical Encyclopedia Inc., New York, 1955, 56 pp.

38 "Penicillin," Harold L. Hirsh and Lawrence E. Putnam, Antibiotics Monographs No. 9, Medical Encyclopedia Inc., New York, 1958, 144 pp.

39 "Antibiotics, A Survey of Penicillin, Streptomycin, and Other Antimicrobial Substances from Fungi, Actinomyces, Bacteria, and Plants," H. W. Florey, E. Chain, N. G. Heatley, M. A. Jennings, A. G. Sanders, E. P. Abraham and M. E Florey, Oxford University Press, London, 1949, Vol. I, 628 pp., Vol. II, 1662 pp.

40 "Neomycin, Its Nature and Practical Application," Selman A. Waksman (Ed.), The Williams and Wilkins Co., Baltimore, 1958, 396 pp.

41 "The Fifth Year of Aureomycin," Lederle Laboratories Div., American Cyanamid Co., 1952, 374 pp.

42 "Antibiotics," Robertson Pratt and Jean Dufrenoy, J. P. Lippincott Co., Philadelphia, 2nd. ed., 1953, 369 pp.

43   "Antibiotics and Antibiotic Therapy," Allen E. Hussar and Howard L. Holley, Macmillan Co., New York, 1954, 463 pp.

44   "Chemistry of Proteins," Shiro Akabori (Ed.), Chap. 9, *Antibiotic Polypeptides*, Kyoritsu Shuppan, Tokyo, 1957. (In Japanese)

45   "Physiology of Fungi," Vincent W. Cochrane, John Wiley and Sons, Inc., New York, 1958, 524 pp. Particularly pertinent is Chapter 2 (pp. 35–55), *The Composition of Fungus Cells*.

46   "Chemical Activities of Fungi," Jackson W. Foster, Academic Press, New York, 1949, 648 pp.

47   *Chemistry of the Fungi*, C. Stickings and H. Raistrick, *Ann. Rev. Biochem.* 25 225–256 (1956). A review with 182 references.

48   *Chemistry of the Fungi*, J. Birkinshaw, *Ann. Rev. Biochem.* 22 371–399 (1953). A review with 152 references.

49   *Biochemistry of Fungi*, Edward L. Tatum, *Ann. Rev. Biochem.* 13 667–704 (1944). A review with 333 references.

50   *Biochemistry of the Lower Fungi*, Harold Raistrick, *Ann. Rev. Biochem.* 9 571–592 (1940). A review with 95 references.

51   *Oxygen Heterocyclic Fungal Metabolites*, W. Whalley, *Prog. in Org. Chem.* 4 72–113 (1958).

52   "Essays in Biochemistry," Samuel Graff (Ed.), *Some metabolic products of basidiomycetes*, M. Anchel, John Wiley and Sons, Inc., New York, 1957, pp. 1–13. A review with 40 references.

53   "Organic Acid Production by some Wood-Rotting Basidiomycetes," G. Walter, Univ. Microfilms Publ. No. 10,417, 99 pp. *Dissertation Abstracts* 15 321 (1955).

54   "Chemistry of Lichen Substances," Y. Asahina and S. Shibata, Japan Society for the Promotion of Science, Tokyo, 1954, 240 pp.

55   *Chemistry of Lichens*, Carl Axel Wachtmeister, *Svensk Kem. Tidskr.* 70 117–133 (1958). A review in English with 74 references.

56   *Chemical Constitution and Antibiotic Action of Lichen Substances*, Josef Klosa, *Pharmazie* 8 435–442 (1953). A review with 59 references.

57   *Algal Chemistry*, B. Wickberg, *Svensk Kem. Tidskr.* 71 87–106 (1959). A review in English with 73 references.

58   "The Chemistry and Chemotherapy of Tuberculosis," E. Long, The Williams and Wilkins Co., Baltimore, 3rd ed., 1958.

59   *The Chemistry of the Lipids of the Tubercle Bacillus and Certain Other Microorganisms*, R. J. Anderson, *Fortschr. Chem. org. Naturstoffe* 3 145–302 (1939).

60   *Chemistry of Bacterial Lipids*, J. Asselineau and E. Lederer, *Fortschr. Chem. org. Naturstoffe* 10 170–256 (1953). A review with 362 references; E. Lederer, *Angew. Chem.* 72 372 (1960). (A review)

61 "Bacterial Fermentations," H. Barker, John Wiley and Sons, Inc., New York, 1956, 90 pp.

62 "Bacterial Anatomy," Sixth Symposium of the Society for General Microbiology, E. Spooner and B. Stocker (Eds.), Cambridge University Press, Cambridge, 1956, 360 pp.

63 *The (phenazine) bacterial pigments,* in "Phenazines," George A. Swan and Desmond G. I. Felton, Interscience Publishers, New York, 1957, pp. 174–209.

64 *Structure and Synthesis of Naturally Occurring Polypeptides,* F. Robinson, *J. Pharm. and Pharmacol.* 8 297–308 (1956). A review with 89 references.

65 "Biochemistry of the Amino Acids," Alton Meister, Academic Press, New York, 1957.

66 *Paper Chromatographic Investigation of the Amino Acid Content of a Variety of Bacterial Hydrolysates,* I. Kandler and C. Zehender, *Arch. für Mikrobiol.* 24 41–48 (1956). (Semiquantitative)

67 *Bacterial and fungal products containing amino sugars,* P. W. Kent and M. W. Whitehouse, in "Biochemistry of the Amino Sugars," Butterworths, London, 1955, pp. 133–161.

68 *Branched Chain Sugars of Natural Occurrence,* F. Shafizadeh, *Advances in Carbohydrate Chemistry* 11 263–283 (1956).

69 *Bacterial Dextrans,* M. Stacey and C. Ricketts, *Fortschr. Chem. org. Naturstoffe* 8 28–43 (1951).

70 *Die natürlich vorkommenden Polyacetylen-Verbindungen,* F. Bohlmann, *Angew. Chem.* 67 389 (1955).

71 *Natural Alkynes,* J. Beer, *Wiadomosci Chem.* 9 460–481 (1955). A review with 74 references.

72 *Acetylenverbindungen im Pflanzenreich,* F. Bohlmann and H. Mannhardt, *Fortschr. Chem. org. Naturstoffe* 14 45–53 (1957).

73 *Occurrence of Acetylenic Compounds in Nature,* P. Wailes, *Revs. Pure and Appl. Chem.* (Australia) 6 61–98 (1956). A review with tabulation of ultraviolet absorption data and 89 references.

74 *Acetylenic Compounds as Natural Products,* J. Bu'Lock, *Quart. Rev.* 10 371–394. A review with 102 references.

75 *Carotenoids,* T. W. Goodwin, *Ann. Rev. Biochem.* 24 497–522 (1955).

76 *Carotenoids in fungi, bacteria and algae,* in "The Comparative Biochemistry of the Carotenoids," T. W. Goodwin, The Chemical Publishing Co., New York, 1954, pp. 99–155.

77 *Some Biochemical Aspects of Fungal Carotenoids,* F. Haxo, *Fortschr. Chem. org. Naturstoffe* 12 169–197 (1955). A review with 116 references.

78 *The Biosynthesis and Function of the Carotenoid Pigments,* T. W. Goodwin, *Advances in Enzymology* 21 295–361 (1959).

79 "Naturally Occurring Quinones," R. Thomson, Butterworths, London, 1958. Literature covered through 1956.

80 *Occurrence and Biochemical Behavior of Quinones,* O. Hofmann-Ostenhof, *Fortschr. Chem. org. Naturstoffe* 6 159–224 (1950).

81 *Anthraquinone Pigments Produced by Molds,* Shoji Shibata, *Kagaku* (Science) 26 391–396 (1956). A review with 41 references.

82 *Tetracyclic Triterpenes,* E. Jones and C. Halsall, *Fortschr. Chem. org. Naturstoffe* 12 68–96 (1955).

83 *Chlorine Containing Metabolic Products,* I. Yoshida, *Kagaku no Ryoiki* (*J. Japan. Chem.*) 5 406–409, 419 (1951). A review with 19 references.

84 *Vitamins in Microorganisms,* J. Van Lanen and F. W. Tanner, Jr., *Vitamins and Hormones* 6 163–224 (1948). A review with 361 references.

85 "Special Publication No. 12 of the English Chemical Society," 1958, especially *The Biosynthesis of Aromatic Compounds from C_1 and C_2 Units,* A. J. Birch and Herchel Smith, pp. 1–13, and *Biosynthesis of Aromatic Ring Systems from C_3 and C_4 fragments,* Gösta Ehrensvärd, pp. 17–31.

86 "The Structural Relations of Natural Products," R. Robinson, Oxford University Press, London, 1955, 150 pp.

87 *Biosynthetic Relations of Phenolic and Enolic Compounds,* A. J. Birch, *Fortschr. Chem. org. Naturstoffe* 14 186–216 (1957).

88 "Perspectives in Organic Chemistry," Alexander Todd (Ed.), Interscience Publishers, New York, 1956, especially *Biosynthetic Theories in Organic Chemistry,* A. J. Birch, pp. 134–155, and *Microorganisms in Organic Chemistry,* Karl Folkers, pp. 392–430.

89 *A Region of Biosynthesis,* H. Raistrick, *Proc. Roy. Soc.* A 199 141–168 (1949). A review of fungal metabolites with 157 references.

90 *Microbiological Conversions of Steroids,* Drurey H. Peterson, *Record Chem. Prog.* 17 211–240 (1956).

91 *Transformations of Steroids by Molds,* Gilbert Shull, *Trans. N. Y. Acad. Sci.* 19 147–72 (1956). A review with 63 references.

92 *Microbiological Alterations of Steroids,* P. Enthoven, *Chem. Weekblad* 52 166–172 (1956). A review with 40 references.

93 *Microbiological Conversions of Steroids for Technical Purposes,* E. Vischer and A. Wettstein, *Angew. Chem.* 69 456–463 (1957). A review with 70 references.

94 *Enzymic Transformations of Steroids by Microorganisms,* E. Vischer and A. Wettstein, *Adv. Enzymol.* 20 237–282 (1958). A review.

95 "Chemical Transformations by Microorganisms," F. Stodola, John Wiley and Sons, Inc., New York, 1958, 134 pp.

96 *The oxidation of aromatic rings by microorganisms in metabolism,* F. Happold in Biochemical Symposium No. 5, "Biological Oxidation of Aromatic Rings," R. T. Williams (Ed.), 1950. A review with 46 references.

97 *The use of biochemical oxidations and reductions for preparative purposes,* F. Fisher, "Newer Methods of Preparative Organic Chemistry," Interscience Publishers, Inc., New York, 1948, pp. 159–196.

98 *Allgemeine Methoden zur Ausführung biochemischer Reaktionen,* B. Helferich, H. Stetter and J. Krebs, "Methoden der organishen Chemie," Georg Thieme Verlag, Stuttgart, 1955, Band IV, pp. 822–902.

The Chemical Composition of the Tissues and Large Molecules of Bacteria and Fungi

The composition of the cell wall, the capsule and the protoplast membrane in bacteria and of the mycelial wall in molds is generally more specific to the organism than that of the lower molecular weight metabolites. For that reason these substances are more interesting in taxonomy and immunochemistry. The toxins, pyrogens and lipoproteins are also interesting from these standpoints.

The advent of paper chromatography has so facilitated the identification of amino acids, sugars and other fragments of the hydrolysis of the higher molecular weight components of microorganisms that the literature on this topic has blossomed during recent years.

Some of the results have been unexpected. For example, the actinomycetes, which resemble the molds superficially, have been found closer chemically to the bacteria.

This appendix is a list of references on the subject. While the paper titles may not always so indicate, they are all concerned in some way with the composition or structure of the tissues and macromolecules of bacteria and fungi.

Pasteurella septica (*P. multocida*). I. The occurrence of type-specific polysaccharides containing aldoheptose sugars.
A. P. MacLennan and C. J. M. Rondle, *Nature* 180 1045 (1957).

Specific polysaccharide of *Pasteurella pestis*.
D. A. L. Davies, *Biochem. J.* 63 105 (1956).

Natural occurrence of a new aldoheptose sugar.
D. A. L. Davies, *Nature* 180 1129 (1957).

Elemental and amino acid composition of purified plague toxin.
D. F. Bent, H. Rosen, S. M. Levenson, R. B. Lindberg and Samuel J. Ajl, *Proc. Soc. Exptl. Biol. Med.* 95 178 (1957).

Role of α,ϵ-diaminopimelic acid in the cellular integrity of *Escherichia coli*.
Lionel E. Rhuland, *J. Bacteriol.* 73 778 (1957).

A colicin from *Escherichia coli* SG710.
Rainer Nüske, Gottfried Hösel, Harry Venner and Helmut Zinner, *Biochem. Z.* 329 346 (1957).

An agent from *Escherichia coli* causing hemorrhage and regression of an experimental mouse tumor. IV. Some nitrogenous components of the phospholipid moiety.
Miyoshi Ikawa, J. B. Koepfli, S. G. Mudd and Carl Niemann, *J. Am. Chem. Soc.* **75** 3439 (1953).

Colominic acid, a polymer of N-acetylneuraminic acid.
Guy T. Barry, *J. Exp. Med.* **107** 507 (1958).

Capsular polysaccharides of *Escherichia coli* types K28A and K34A.
Bill B. Wiley and Henry W. Scherp, *Can. J. Microbiol.* **4** 505 (1958).

The chemical and serological relationships of certain polysaccharides containing sialic acid.
Guy T. Barry, Tien-Hu Tsai and Francis P. Chen, *Nature* **185** 597 (1960).

Structure of the capsular polysaccharide of *Aerobacter aerogenes* (NCTC 418).
S. A. Barker, A. B. Foster, I. R. Siddiqui and M. Stacey, *J. Chem. Soc.*, 2358 (1958).

The extracellular polysaccharide of *Aerobacter aerogenes* A_3 (S_1).
J. F. Wilkinson, W. F. Dudman and G. O. Aspinall, *Biochem. J.* **59** 446 (1955).

Chromatographic analysis of hydrolysates of *Salmonella typhosa*.
F. Savoia, *Boll. soc. ital. biol. sper.* **32** 226 (1956).

Chemical composition of *Salmonella antigen* II. Chemical composition of antigen O of *Salmonella kirkei* and *Salmonella hvittingfoss*.
G. Bo, A. Defranceschi and G. C. Nava, *Giorn. microbiol.* **1** 247 (1955).

Contributions to the study of the antityphi-paratyphi vaccines II. A comparative chemical study of the somatic antigens of *Salmonella typhi* (*S. typhosa*) extracts.
E. Soru, C. Barber, S. Toma, V. Gritaenco and B. Bogokowski, *Acad. rep. populare Romine, Studii cercetari chim.* **4** 243 (1956).

The biological action of highly purified pyrogens (lipopolysaccharides) from *Salmonella abortivoequina*.
E. Eichenberger, M. Schmidhauser-Kopp, H. Hurni, M. Fricsay and O. Westphal, *Schweiz. med. Wochschr.* **85** 1190, 1213 (1955).

The hexose constituents of some shigella polysaccharide hydrolyzates.
D. A. R. Simmons, *J. Gen. Microbiol.* **17** 650 (1957).

Epidemiology of *Shigella sonnei*. I. Biochemical characteristics.
Szymona Szturm-Rubensten and Danielle Piéchaud, *Ann. inst. Pasteur* **92** 335 (1957).

The chemical constitution of brucella.
E. M. Gubarev, E. K. Alimova and G. D. Bolgova, *Biokhimiya* **21** 647 (1956).

The specific polysaccharides of some gram-negative bacteria.
D. A. Davies, *Biochem. J.* **59** 696 (1955).

The chemistry and biochemistry of typhoid antigens.
A. De Barbieri, *Atti Congr. intern. standard Immunomicrobiol.*
(Rome) 2 257 (1956).

Toxic end-products from *Pasteurella pestis.* II. Toxin yields as
influenced by conditions of growth.
K. Goodner, *J. Infectious Diseases* 97 246 (1955).

Studies on plague. I. Purification and properties of the toxin of
Pasteurella pestis.
Samuel J. Ajl, Jeanette S. Reedal, E. L. Durram and Joel Warren,
J. Bacteriol. 70 158 (1955).

Isolation of a polysaccharide from *Vibrio fetus.*
S. M. Dennis, *Nature* 183 186 (1959).

Chemical investigation of the endotoxin of *Pseudomonas aerugi-
nosa.*
Fugio Egami, Michio Shimomura, Hiroshi Ishihara, J. Y. Homma,
K. Sagehashi and Seigo Hosoya, *Bull. soc. chim. biol.* 36 779 (1954).

Rhamnose and rhamnolipide biosynthesis by *Pseudomonas aeruginosa.*
George Hauser and Manfred L. Karnovsky, *J. Biol. Chem.* 224 91
(1957).

Chemical studies on endotoxins I. Chemical composition of the
endotoxin of *Shigella flexneri* 2B.
Chiaki Nishimura, Masao Nakamura, Reiko Ofuchi, Shigeo Iwahara
and Yasuhiko Nozaki, *Japan. J. Microbiol.* 2 179 (1958).

Toxins of *Pseudomonas pseudomallei.* II. Characterization.
Robert J. Heckly and Clara Nigg, *J. Bacteriol.* 76 427 (1958).

Occurrence of poly-β-hydroxybutyric acid in aerobic gram-negative
bacteria.
W. G. C. Forsyth, A. C. Hayward and J. B. Roberts, *Nature* 182 800
(1958).

Sulla composizione chimica degli antigeni delle salmonelle. Nota
III. Composizione chim. degli antigeni O delle *Salmonelle tel aviv
cholerae suis e montevideo.*
G. C. Nava, G. Bo and A. Defranceschi, *Giorn. microbiol.* 4 95
(1957).

Characterization of intracellular glucosidic polysaccharide produced by *Brucella suis.*
N. D. Gary, L. L. Kupferberg and L. H. Graf, *J. Bacteriol.* 76 359
(1958).

A group of pseudomonads able to synthesize poly-β-hydroxybutyric
acid.
M. B. Morris and J. B. Roberts, *Nature* 183 1538 (1959).

Production of a mannose polysaccharide by *Pseudomonas fluorescens* from low molecular weight sources.
Robert Garfield Eagen, *Dissertation Abstr.* 20 477 (1959).

Composition of cell walls of variants of *Salmonella typhimurium.*
M. Herzberg, J. H. Green and J. C. Boring, *Bacteriol. Proc.,* 169
(1960).

Enterotoxin.
Kikuo Fujiwara and Tetsujiro Sugiyama, *Nippon Saikingaku Zasshi* 10 189 (1955).

Polyribophosphate, the type-specific substance of *Hemophilus influenzae,* type B.
Stephen Zamenkof, Grace Leidy, Patricia L. Fitzgerald, Hattie E. Alexander and Erwin Chargaff, *J. Biol. Chem.* 203 695 (1953).

The polysaccharide produced by *Azotobacter indicum.*
Clara M. Quinnell, S. G. Knight and P. W. Wilson, *Can. J. Microbiol.* 3 277 (1957).

Extracellular polysaccharides of rhizobium.
Beverly A. Humphrey and J. M. Vincent, *J. Gen Microbiol.* 21 477 (1959).

The isolation of D-fucosamine from the specific polysaccharide of *Chromobacterium violaceum* (NCTC 7917).
M. J. Crumpton and D. A. L. Davies, *Biochem. J.* 70 729 (1958).

A galactan from *Mycoplasma mycoides.*
P. Plackett and S. H. Buttery, *Nature* 182 1236 (1958).

Circular paper chromatography of long-chain fatty acids in the analysis of (gram-negative) bacterial lipopolysaccharides.
A. Nowotny, A. Lüderitz and O. Westphal, *Biochem. Z.* 330 47 (1958).

The extracellular polysaccharide of *Xanthomonas phaseoli.*
S. Lesley and R. Hochster, *Can. J. Biochem. and Physiol.* 37 513 (1959).

A function for the extracellular polysaccharide of *Azotobacter vinelandii.*
Michael H. Proctor, *Nature* 184 1934 (1959).

Lipides of the cell envelope of *Azotobacter vinelandii.*
Allen G. Marr and Tsuneo Kaneshiro, *Bacteriol. Proc.,* 63 (1960).

Chemical composition of cell walls of drug resistant neisseriae.
R. P. Pradhan and W. A. Konetzka, *ibid.,* 170 (1960).

Amino acids of red sulfur bacteria.
H. Mukherjee, *Nature* 184 1742 (1959).

A new amino sugar present in the specific polysaccharides of some strains of *Chromobacterium violaceum.*
M. J. Crumpton and D. A. L. Davies, *Biochem. J.* 64 22p (1956).

Immunopolysaccharides. XI. Structure of an *Acetobacter capsulatum* dextran.
S. A. Barker, E. J. Bourne, G. T. Bruce and M. Stacey, *J. Chem. Soc.,* 4414 (1958).

Oligosaccharide formation during synthesis of cellulose by *Acetobacter acetigenum.*
T. K. Walker and H. B. Wright, *Arch. Biochem. and Biophys.* 69 362 (1957).

Bacterial levans of intermediate molecular weight.
James R. Mattoon, Chester E. Holmlund, Saul A. Schepartz, James J. Vavra and Marvin J. Johnson, *Appl. Microbiol.* 3 321 (1955).

The nature of the polysaccharides of the dextran-producing organisms *Leuconostoc mesenteroides, Leuconostoc dextranicum* and *Streptococcus bovis.*
R. W. Bailey and A. E. Oxford, *J. Gen. Microbiol.* 20 258 (1959).

Characterization of dextrans from four types of *Leuconostoc mesenteroides.*
Allene Jeanes, W. C. Haynes and C. A. Wilham, *J. Bacteriol.* 71 167 (1956).

Characterization and classification of dextrans from ninety-six strains of bacteria.
Allene Jeanes, W. C. Haynes, C. A. Wilham, J. C. Rankin, E. H. Melvin, Marjorie J. Austin, J. E. Cluskey, B. E. Fisher, H. M. Tsuchiya and C. E. Rist, *J. Am. Chem. Soc.* 76 5041 (1954).

Cell wall composition of leptotrichia species.
G. H. G. Davis and A. C. Baird-Parker, *Nature* 183 1206 (1959).

Composition of the cell wall of *Staphylococcus aureus.* Its relation to the mechanism of action of penicillin.
Jack L. Strominger, James T. Park and Richard E. Thompson, *J. Biol. Chem.* 234 3263 (1959).

The amino acid composition of the protein and cell wall of *Staphylococcus aureus.*
R. Hancock, *Biochim. et Biophys. Acta* 37 42 (1960).

Composition of the cell wall of *Staphylococcus aureus* 209P.
Nobutoshi Ishimoto, Masahiro Saito and Eiji Ito, *Nature* 182 959 (1958).

Staphylococcal toxins. III. Partial purification and some properties of δ-lysin.
A. W. Jackson and R. M. Little, *Can. J. Microbiol.* 4 453 (1958).

The intracellular amino acids of *Staphylococcus aureus:* release and analysis.
R. Hancock, *Biochim. et Biophys. Acta* 28 402 (1958).

Constitution of a muco-complex of *Micrococcus lysodeikticus* I. Isolation and purification.
Shichiro Akiya and Otomatsu Hoshino, *Yakugaku Zasshi* 77 777 (1957).

Development of lysozyme resistance in *Micrococcus lysodeikticus* and its association with increased O-acetyl content of the cell wall.
W. Brumfitt, A. C. Wardlaw and J. T. Park, *Nature* 181 1783 (1958).

Partial acid hydrolysis of the cell wall of *Micrococcus lysodeikticus.*
H. R. Perkins and H. J. Rogers, *Biochem. J.* 69 15p (1958).

The chemical composition of the protoplast membrane of *Micrococcus lysodeikticus.*
A. R. Gilby, A. V. Few and Kenneth McQuillen, *Biochim. et. Biophys. Acta* 29 21 (1958).

Products of partial acid hydrolysis of mucopeptide from cell walls of *Micrococcus lysodeikticus.*
H. R. Perkins and H. J. Rogers, *Biochem. J.* 72 647 (1959).

The structure of a disaccharide liberated by lysozyme from the cell walls of *Micrococcus lysodeikticus.*

H. R. Perkins, *ibid.* **74** 182 (1960).

Synthesis of carbohydrates by *Micrococcus ureae* from acetic acid.
V. I. Lyubimov, *Doklady Akad. Nauk S.S.S.R.* **111** 881 (1953).

The biosynthesis of a streptococcal capsular polysaccharide.
Yale J. Topper and Murray M. Lipton, *J. Biol. Chem.* **203** 135 (1953).

The production of capsules, hyaluronic acid, and hyaluronidase by twenty-five strains of group C streptococci.
A. P. MacLennan, *J. Gen. Microbiol.* **15** 485 (1956).

Variation in the group-specific carbohydrate of group A streptococci II. The chemical basis for serological specificity of the carbohydrate.
Maclyn McCarty, *J. Exp. Med.* **104** 629 (1956).

Production of hyaluronic acid in the resting cells of group A *Streptococcus hemolyticus.*
Seiki Hayano and Haruo Iwasawa, *Nippon Saikingaku Zasshi* **10** 269 (1955).

Examination of the L-forms of group A streptococci for the group-specific polysaccharide and M protein.
John T. Sharp, W. Hijmans and L. Dienes, *J. Exp. Med.* **105** 153 (1957).

Studies of streptococcal cell walls. IV. The conversion of D-glucose to cell wall L-rhamnose.
W. H. Southard, J. A. Hayashi and S. S. Barkulis, *J. Bacteriol.* **78** 79 (1959).

Studies of streptococcal cell walls. V. Amino acid composition of cell walls of virulent and avirulent group A hemolytic streptococci.
B. S. Tepper, J. A. Hayashi and S. S. Barkulis, *ibid.* **79** 33 (1960).

Studies of streptococcal cell walls. III. The amino acids of the trypsin-treated cell wall.
James A. Hayashi and S. S. Barkulis, *ibid.* **77** 177 (1959).

Precipitation of the specific polysaccharide of *Cryptococcus neoformans* A by types II and XIV *antipneumococcal sera.*
P. A. Rebers, S. A. Barker, M. Heidelberger, Z. Dische and E. E. Evans, *J. Am. Chem. Soc.* **80** 1135 (1958).

The genus cryptococcus.
Rhoda W. Benham, *Bacteriol. Revs.* **20** 189 (1956).

Immunopolysaccharides. VIII. Enzymic synthesis of 6-O-α-D-glucopyranosyl-3-O-methyl-D-glucose by *Betacoccus arabinosaceous.*
S. A. Barker, E. J. Bourne, P. M. Grant and M. Stacey, *J. Chem. Soc.,* 601 (1958).

The cell wall of *Myxococcus xanthus.*
D. J. Mason and Dorothy Powelson, *Biochim. et Biophys. Acta* **29** 1 (1958).

The cell wall of myxobacteria.
Donald Joseph Mason, *Dissertation Abstr.* **18** 1949 (1958).

A rapid and specific method for the isolation of pneumococci polysaccharide.

A. S. Markowitz and Jack R. Henderson, *Nature* 181 771 (1958).

α,ε-Diaminopimelic acid metabolism and sporulation in *Bacillus sphaericus*.
Joan F. Powell and R. E. Strange, *Biochem. J.* 65 700 (1957).

α,ε-Diaminopimelic acid in the peptide moiety of the cell wall polysaccharide of *Bacillus anthracis*.
H. Smith, R. E. Strange and H. T. Zwartouw, *Nature* 178 865 (1956).

The structure of the immunospecific polysaccharide of *Bacillus anthracis*.
L. Mester and G. Ivanovics, *Chem. and Ind.*, 493 (1957).

Polyglutamic acid from the capsule of *Bacillus anthracis* grown *in vivo;* structure and aggressin activity.
H. T. Zwartouw and H. Smith, *Congr. intern. biochim., Résumés Communs., 3e Congr.* (Brussels), 93 (1955).

Chemical structure of capsular glutamyl polypeptide of *Bacillus megaterium* and *Bacillus anthracis*.
T. Amano, M. Torii, M. Tokuba, O. Kurimura, T. Morishima and S. Utsumi, *Med. J. Osaka Univ.* 8 601 (1958).

The polysaccharide from *Bacillus anthracis* grown *in vivo*.
H. Smith and H. T. Zwartouw, *Biochem. J.* 63 447 (1956).

Polysaccharide containing amino sugar from *Bacillus subtilis*.
Nathan Sharon, *Nature* 179 919 (1957).

Isolation of D- and L-glutamyl polypeptides from culture filtrates of *Bacillus subtilis*.
Curtis B. Thorne and C. Gomez Leonard, *J. Biol. Chem.* 233 1109 (1958).

Physicochemical studies of poly-D-glutamic acid from *Bacillus anthracis* grown *in vitro*.
L. H. Kent, B. R. Record and R. G. Wallis, *Phil. Trans. Roy. Soc. London* 250 1 (1957).

The composition of the spore wall and the wall of the vegetative cell of *Bacillus subtilis*.
M. R. J. Salton and Betty Marshall, *J. Gen. Microbiol.* 21 415 (1959).

The diaminohexose component of a polysaccharide isolated from *Bacillus subtilis*.
Nathan Sharon and Roger W. Jeanloz, *J. Biol. Chem.* 235 1 (1960).

Structure of teichoic acid from the walls of *Bacillus subtilis*.
J. J. Armstrong, J. Baddiley and J. G. Buchanan, *Nature* 184 248 (1959).

Composition of teichoic acids from a number of bacterial walls.
J. J. Armstrong, J. Baddiley, J. G. Buchanan, A. L. Davison, M. V. Kelemen and F. C. Neuhaus, *Nature* 184 247 (1959).

Polysaccharide capsule of *Bacillus megaterium*.
J. Tomcsik and Joyce B. Baumann-Grace, *Proc. Soc. Exp. Biol. Med.* 101 570 (1959).

Biochemical study of the products (polysaccharides) from a growing aerobic bacterium: *Bacillus megatherium*.
J. P. Aubert, *Ann. Inst. Pasteur* 80 644 (1951).

The chemical nature of the cytoplasmic membrane and cell wall of *Bacillus megaterium*, strain M.
C. Weibull and L. Bergstrom, *Biochim. et Biophys. Acta* 30 340 (1958).

The polysaccharide produced by *Bacillus polymyxa* X. Component sugars.
Akira Misaki, Toshihiko Higashi and Shiro Teramoto, *Hakko Kogaku Zasshi* 36 181 (1958).

Studies on the bacterial polysaccharide, rhamnogalactan, produced by *Bacillus polymyxa* var. XI.
Akira Misaki, Yoshiaki Yagi and Shiro Teramoto, *J. Fermentation Technol.* 36 25 (1958).

A mannan produced by *Bacillus polymyxa*.
D. H. Ball and G. A. Adams, *Can. J. Chem.* 37 1012 (1959).

Polysaccharide produced by a strain of *Bacillus polymyxa*.
Akira Misaki and Shiro Teramoto, *J. Fermentation Technol.* 36 266 (1958).

Isolation and chemical nature of capsular and cell wall haptens in a bacillus species.
S. Guex-Holzer and J. Tomcsik, *J. Gen. Microbiol.* 14 14 (1956).

Bacterial cell wall. XIII. Chemical composition of bacterial cell wall and spore membranes.
Nagayuki Yoshida, Yoshifumi Izumi, Isamu Tani, Saburo Tanaka, Kenji Takaishi, Tadayo Hashimoto, Komei Fukui and Chiaki Furukawa, *Tokushima J. Exptl. Med.* 3 8 (1956). (*Chem. Abstr.* 51 13054f)

Isolation and structure of ribitol phosphate derivatives (teichoic acids) from bacterial cell walls.
J. J. Armstrong, J. Baddiley, J. G. Buchanan, B. Carss and G. R. Greenberg, *J. Chem. Soc.*, 4344 (1958).

Paper chromatographic investigation of the amino acid composition of different bacteria hydrolysates.
O. Kandler and C. Zehender, *Arch. Mikrobiol.* 24 41 (1956).

Nucleotides and the bacterial cell wall.
J. J. Armstrong, J. Baddiley, J. G. Buchanan and B. Carss, *Nature* 181 1692 (1958).

The action of fluorodinitrobenzene on bacterial cell walls.
V. M. Ingram and M. R. J. Salton, *Biochim. et Biophys. Acta* 24 9 (1957).

Chemical analysis elucidating the structure of bacterial L-forms.
Claes Weibull, *Acta Pathol. Microbiol. Scand.* 42 324 (1958).

The interpretation and use of bacterial infrared spectra.
Eric K. Rideal and D. M. Adams, *Chem. and Ind.*, 762 (1957).

Bacterial pyrogens.
Ivan L. Bennett, Jr. and Leighton E. Chiff, *Pharmacol. Rev.* 9 427 (1957).

The preparation of bacterial pyrogenic substance and its clinical application. III. The effects of bacterial pyrogenic substance and of

the antitumor substances upon Yoshida sarcoma and ascites carcinoma 130.
Kosaku Aoyama, Fumio Miyazawa, Hiromitsu Kurisu, Sadayosi Hatta, Hideo Arai, Yoiti Fujita, Mikio Urabe, Yugaku Sakai and Takayoshi Aoki, *Eisei Shikenjo Hôkoku* No. 74 361 (1956).

Determination by paper chromatography of compounds constituting bacterial pyrogens.
K. Macek and Jaroslava Hacaperkova, *Českoslov. farm.* 7 300 (1958). (*Chem. Abstr.* 52 18646i)

The chemical composition of the bacterial cell wall.
C. S. Cummins, *Intern. Rev. Cytology* 5 25 (1956).

Bacterial capsules and their relation to the cell wall.
J. Tomcsik, edited by E. T. C. Spooner and B. A. D. Stocker, "Bacterial Anatomy," Cambridge University Press, Cambridge, 1956, pp. 41–67.

Bacterial cell walls.
M. R. J. Salton, *ibid.,* pp. 81–110.

Bacterial protoplasts; their formation and characteristics.
C. Weibull, *ibid.,* pp. 111–126.

Studies of the bacterial cell wall. II. Methods of preparation and some properties of cell walls.
M. R. J. Salton and R. W. Horne, *Biochim. et Biophys. Acta* 7 177 (1951).

The molecular basis of antibody formation.
Leo Szilard, *Proc. Nat. Acad. Sci. U. S.* 46 293 (1960).

Nucleotides and bacterial cell wall components.
J. Baddiley, *Proc. Chem. Soc.,* 177 (1959).

Chemistry of bacterial cell walls.
Friedrich Zilliken, *Federation Proc.* 18 966 (1959).

Bacterial fructosans and fructosanases.
Jakob R. Loewenberg and Elwyn T. Reese, *Can. J. Microbiol.* 3 643 (1957).

Cell wall amino acids and amino sugars.
M. R. J. Salton, *Nature* 180 338 (1957).

Composition of the cell wall of *Lactobacillus bifidus*.
C. S. Cummins, Olivia M. Glendenning and H. Harris, *Nature* 180 337 (1957).

The nature of D-alanine in lactic acid bacteria.
Esmond E. Snell, Norman S. Radin and Miyoshi Ikawa, *J. Biol. Chem.* 217 803 (1955).

Structure of the carbohydrates of the diphtheria bacteria.
O. K. Orlova and E. P. Efimtseva, *Biokhimiya* (U.S.S.R.) 21 505 (1956).

Carbohydrate composition of the envelope of *Corynebacterium equi*.
Tadeusz Mierzejewski, *Ann. Univ. Mariae Curie-Sklodowska, Lublin-Polonia* 10 93 (1955).

Fixed lipids of diphtheria microbes.
E. Alymova, *Biokhimiya* (U.S.S.R.) 22 933 (1958).

Chemical composition of antigens of corynebacterium.
J. Kwapinski, *Acta Microbiol. Polon.* 6 133 (1957).

"Bacterial toxins," W. van Heyningen, Blackwell Scientific Publications, Oxford, 1950, 128 pp.

The mutation of *Corynebacterium pyogenes* to *Corynebacterium hemolyticum.*
W. L. Barksdale, K. Li, C. S. Cummins and H. Harris, *J. Gen. Microbiol.* 16 749 (1957).

Fructosides formed from sucrose by a corynebacterium.
Gad Avigad and David S. Feingold, *Arch. Biochem. and Biophys.* 70 178 (1957).

Structure of the mannan of diphtheria bacteria.
O. K. Orlova, *Biokhimiya* (U.S.S.R.) 23 467 (1958).

Amino acid composition of pure diphtheria toxin and toxoid.
Tokiya Ito, Hisao Uetake and Teuchi Sasaki, *Igaku to Seibutsugaku* 26 49 (1953).

The chemical constituents of *Mycobacterium paratuberculosis.*
A. Larsen and R. Merkal, *Am. Rev. Tuberc. Pulmonary Diseases* 77 712 (1958).

Nature of the specific polysaccharides of tubercle bacilli.
J. Foldes, *Acta Microbiol. Acad. Sci. Hung.* 4 43 (1957).

Polysaccharide components of the tubercle bacillus.
M. Stacey, *CIBA Foundation Symposium on Exptl. Tuberc. Bacillus and Host,* 55 (1955).

Lipides of human avirulent strain H37Ra of *Mycobacterium tuberculosis.*
Jean Asselineau, *Bull. soc. chim. biol.* 38 1397 (1956).

Constituents of a toxic lipide obtained from *Mycobacterium tuberculosis.*
H. Bloch, J. Defaye, E. Lederer and H. Noll, *Biochim. et Biophys. Acta* 23 312 (1957).

Proteins of various mycobacteria. I. Chemical properties of several peptides isolated from tuberculin protein obtained from the human strain Aoyama-β.
Isaku Kasuya, Jinsaku Goto, Sadako Hirai, Taichi Someya and Akira Hagitani, *Japan. J. Med. Sci. and Biol.* 9 93 (1956).

Proteins of various mycobacteria. II. Chemical properties of several peptides isolated from the tuberculin protein of the bacterial cells of human strain Aoyama-β and Frankfurt.
Sadako Hirai, *ibid.* 9 179 (1956).

Immunologic significance of the cell wall of mycobacteria.
Edgar Ribi, Carl L. Larson, Robert List and William Wicht, *Proc. Soc. Exp. Biol. Med.* 98 263 (1958).

The constitution of a lipoid-bound polysaccharide from *Mycobacterium tuberculosis* (Human strain).
Norman Haworth, P. W. Kent and M. Stacey, *J. Chem. Soc.,* 1220 (1948).

Constitution of mycobacteria. II. Amino acid composition of bacterial cells belonging to various species of mycobacteria.
A. Hirsch, C. Cattaneo and M. Morellini, *Giorn. biochim.* **6** 296 (1957).

The composition of the waxes of *Mycobacterium marianum.*
Georges Mickel, *Compt. rend.* 244 2429 (1957).

Chemistry of some native constituents of the purified wax of *Mycobacterium tuberculosis.*
Hans Noll, *J. Biol. Chem.* 224 149 (1957).

Amino acid composition of mycobacteria.
Ben Ginsberg, Sarah L. Lovett and Max S. Dunn, *Arch. Biochem. and Biophys.* **60** 164 (1956).

Amino acid composition of extracellular protein from six mycobacteria.
Sarah L. Lovett and Max S. Dunn, *Proc. Soc. Exp. Biol. Med.* **97** 240 (1958).

Electrophoretic and chromatographic studies on extracts of tubercle bacilli.
G. Dragoni and E. Bozzetti, *Boll. soc. ital. biol. sper.* **32** 894 (1956).

The characterization of mycobacterial strains by the composition of their lipide extract.
D. W. Smith, H. M. Randall, M. M. Gastambide-Odier and A. L. Koevoet, *Ann. N. Y. Acad. Sci.* **69** 145 (1957).

Lipide of bacillus Calmette-Guerin (BCG). I. Glyceryl monomycolate in wax C fraction of the lipide of BCG.
Toru Tsumita, *Japan. J. Med. Sci. and Biol.* **9** 205 (1956).

Formation of ϵ-aminosuccinyllysine from ϵ-aspartyllysine from bacitracin A and from the cell walls of lactobacilli.
D. L. Swallow and E. P. Abraham, *Biochem. J.* **70** 364 (1958).

A comparison of cell wall composition in nocardia, actinomyces, mycobacterium and propionibacterium.
C. S. Cummins and H. Harris, *J. Gen. Microbiol.* **15** ix (1956).

The occurrence of O-methyl ethers of rhamnose and fucose in specific glycolipides of certain mycobacteria.
A. MacLennan, D. Smith and H. Randall, *Proc. Soc. Biochem.* **74** 3 p. (England) (1959).

Isolation of two different cell wall polysaccharides from tubercle bacteria.
J. Foldes, *Naturwissenschaften* 46 432 (1959).

The biochemistry of the actinomycetales. Studies on the cell wall of *Streptomyces fradiae.*
Antonio H. Romano and Walter J. Nickerson, *J. Bacteriol.* **72** 478 (1956).

Comparative biochemical studies of the cell walls of actinomycetales.
Arthur Sohler, *Dissertation Abstr.* **17** 2410 (1957).

Polysaccharide fractions of *Actinomyces globisporus streptomycini.*

A. N. Belozerskii and I. B. Naumova, *Doklady Akad. Nauk S.S.S.R.* 115 957 (1957).

The chemical composition of the actinomycetales: Isolation of a polysaccharide containing D-arabinose and D-galactose from *Nocardia asteroides*.
C. T. Bishop and F. Blank, *Can. J. Microbiol.* 4 35 (1958).

A lipopeptide from *Nocardia asteroides*.
Micheline Guinand, Georges Michel and Edgar Lederer, *Compt. rend.* 246 848 (1958).

Polysaccharide fractions of *Actinomyces rimosus* and *Actinomyces aureofaciens*.
A. N. Belozerskii and I. B. Naumova, *Doklady Akad. Nauk S.S.S.R.* 122 441 (1958).

Studies on the cell wall composition and taxonomy of actinomycetales and related groups.
C. S. Cummins and H. Harris, *J. Gen. Microbiol.* 18 173 (1958).

Biochemistry of the actinomycetales. III. Cell wall composition and the action of lysozyme upon cells and cell walls of the actinomycetales.
Arthur Sohler, Antonio H. Romano and Walter J. Nickerson, *J. Bacteriol.* 75 283 (1958).

Fluorescence of the toxin of *Clostridium botulinum* and its relation to toxicity.
Daniel A. Boroff and John E. Fitzgerald, *Nature* 181 751 (1958).

Botulinus toxin A and hemaglutinin-receptors of erythrocytes.
E. R. Gold and I. Ilian, *Zentr. Bakteriol. Parasitenk., Abt.* I, Orig. 167 386 (1957). (*Chem. Abstr.* 51 10655c)

Polysaccharides isolated from *Clostridium perfringens* Type C.
F. Meisel-Mikolajczyk, *Bull. acad. polon. sci.* 7 213 (1959). (*Chem. Abstr.* 54 1650g)

Toxin production of *Clostridium botulinum* (type E). III. Characterization of toxin precursor.
Genji Sakaguchi and Sumiko Sakaguchi, *J. Bacteriol.* 78 1 (1959).

Isolation of a lipopolysaccharide from *Vibrio fetus*.
S. M. Davis, *Nature* 183 186 (1959).

Amino acids and N-terminal groups of scarlatinic toxin (Erythrogenic toxin).
Eugenia Soru, M. Sternberg and M. Istrati, *Acad. rep. populare Romine, Studii cercetari chim.* 5 213 (1957).

Purification of flagella and flagellin by ammonium sulfate.
Henry Koffler and Toshio Kobayashi, *Arch. Biochem. and Biophys.* 67 246 (1957).

Structure of bacterial flagella.
W. T. Astbury, E. Beighton and C. Weibull, *Symposia Soc. Exptl. Biol.* No. 9, *Fibrous Proteins and Their Biological Significance,* 282 (1954).

The cell wall of yeasts—electron miscroscope and X-ray diffraction study.

A. L. Houwink and D. R. Kreger, *Antonie van Leeuwenhoek J. Microbiol. Serol.* **19** 1 (1953).

Observations on cell walls of yeasts and some other fungi by X-ray diffraction and solubility tests.
D. R. Kreger, *Biochim. et Biophys. Acta* **13** 1 (1954).

Cell wall mannan protein of bakers' yeast.
G. Falcone and Walter J. Nickerson, *Science* **124** 272 (1956).

On the composition of zymosan.
Frederick J. DiCarlo and Joseph V. Fiore, *Science* **127** 756 (1958).

Chemical structure and serologic properties of the polysaccharide of *Candida albicans.*
Ludwik Rzucidlo, Danuta Weyman, Aleksandra Stáchow and Genowefa Rzesa, *Med. Doswiadczalna i Mikrobiol.* **7** 315 (1955).

Mucous substance around the cell wall of yeasts. VIII. Polysaccharide isolated from filtrate of yeast.
Tomojiro Kaibara, *J. Agr. Chem. Soc. Japan* **28** 259 (1954).

Yeast mannan, a cell wall constituent of bakers' yeast.
P. A. Rollofsen, *Biochim. et Biophys. Acta* **10** 477 (1953).

Composition and structure of yeast cell walls.
A. L. Houwink, D. R. Kreger and P. A. Rollofsen, *Nature* **168** 694 (1951).

The composition of fungus cells.
Vincent W. Cochrane, "Physiology of Fungi," John Wiley and Sons, Inc., New York, 1958, pp. 35–55.

Glucomannan-protein complexes from cell walls of yeasts.
Gian Kessler and Walter J. Nickerson, *J. Biol. Chem.* **234** 2281 (1959).

Isolation and chemical composition of zymosan.
E. N. Voluiskaya, N. V. Cheburkina, V. I. Tovarnitskii and I. N. Nikolskaia, *Voprosy Med. Khim.* **5** 143 (1959).

Quantitative estimation of chitin in fungi.
Harold J. Blumenthal and Saul Roseman, *J. Bacteriol.* **74** 222 (1957).

Chitin
M. V. Tracey, *Rev. Pure Appl. Chem.* (Australia) **7** 1 (1957).

Chemical composition of the cell wall of *Haplosporangium parvum.*
F. Blank, *J. Histochem. and Cytochem.* **5** 500 (1957).

The amino acid composition of fusarium mycelium.
C. S. Venkata Ram, *Proc. Natl. Inst. Sci. India* Pt. B., **22** 227 (1956).

A qualitative comparison of the amino acid and sugar content of acid hydrolysates from the mycelium of several anthracnose fungi.
D. F. Crossan and D. L. Lynch, *Phytopathology* **48** 55 (1958).

The chemical composition of the cell walls of dermatophytes.
F. Blank, *Biochim. et Biophys. Acta* **10** 110 (1953).

The protein nature of trichophytins and their amino acid composition.
Jacques Meyer, René Sartory, Jacques Malgras and Jacques Touillier, *Compt. rend.* **234** 2224 (1952).

The cell walls of dimorphic fungi causing systemic infections.
F. Blank, *Can. J. Microbiol.* 1 1 (1954).

Extracellular metabolic products (polysaccharides) of a hirsutella species.
T. C. Loughheed and D. M. MacLeod, *Nature* 182 114 (1958).

An extracellular polysaccharide from *Mucor racemosus*.
L. Hough and M. B. Perry, *Biochem. J.* 61 viii (1955).

The chemical composition of the mycelium of *Penicillium chrysogenum*.
J. Janicki and J. Skupin, *Acta Microbiol. Polon.* 7 139 (1958).

The amino acid composition of the mold bodies of *Aspergillus oryzae* and *Penicillium chrysogenum*.
J. Datta, K. Bhatacharya and D. Roy, *Ann. Biochem. and Exp. Med.* (India) 17 35 (1957).

A new oligosaccharide (fungitetraose) formed from sucrose.
Humio Kurasawa, Yukimasa Yamoto, Ikuo Igaue and Yasuchi Nakamura, *J. Agr. Chem. Soc. Japan* 30 696 (1956).

The structure of a trisaccharide synthesized by action of *Penicillium chrysogenum* on sucrose.
Alessandro Ballio and Serena Russi, *Gazz. chim. ital.* 86 476 (1956).

A chemical and physical investigation of the cell walls of some marine algae.
J. Cronshaw, A. Myers and R. D. Preston, *Biochim. et Biophys. Acta* 27 89 (1958).

Algal (polysaccharide) chemistry.
B. Wickberg, *Svensk Kem. Tidskr.* 71 87 (1959).

Structure of lichenin.
Stanley Peat, W. J. Whelan and J. G. Roberts, *J. Chem. Soc.*, 3916 (1957).

Pathways for biosynthesis of a bacterial capsular polysaccharide.
Walter H. Taylor, Jr., *Dissertation Abstr.* 20 3025 (1960).

On two new antigens in *Staphylococcus aureus*.
Gunnar Haukenes and Per Oeding, *Acta Pathol. Microbiol. Scand.* 49 237 (1960).

Acetylhexosamine compounds released enzymically from *Micrococcus lysodeikticus* cell walls. I. Isolation and composition of acetylhexosamine-peptide complexes.
J. M. Ghuysen and M. R. J. Salton, *Biochim. et Biophys. Acta* 40 462 (1960).

Chemical analysis of the wall of myxobacterial microcysts formed in liquid culture.
Jimmy Clarence Adye, *Dissertation Abstr.* 21 (1960).

New polysaccharide gums produced by microbial synthesis.
Manufacturing Chemist 31 206 (1960).

Physical and chemical analysis of the endotoxin of *Salmonella enteritidis*.
Edgar Ribi, Bill H. Hoyer, Kelsey C. Milner, Theodore D. Perrine, Carl L. Larson, and Granville Goode, *J. Immunol.* 84 32 (1960).

Cell wall composition of lactic acid bacteria.

Miyoshi Ikawa and Esmond E. Snell, *J. Biol. Chem.* 235 1376 (1960).

The cell wall polysaccharides of *Candida albicans:* glucan, mannan and chitin.
C. T. Bishop, F. Blank and P. E. Gardner, *Can. J. Chem.* 38 869 (1960).

Nonulosaminic acid (sialic acid) in protists.
S. Aaronson and T. Lessie, *Nature* 186 719 (1960).

Isolation and chemical composition of the cell walls of BCG.
Shozo Kotani, Toshiyuki Kitaura, Teji Hirano and Akira Tanaka, *Biken's J.* 2 129 (1959). (*Chem. Abstr.* 54 13252c)

Studies on the muco-complex of *Micrococcus lysodeikticus.*
S. Akiya and O. Hoshino, *Chem. and Pharm. Bull.* 8 395 (1960).

Polysaccharides produced by some wood-rotting fungi.
Francis H. Millazzo, *Dissertation Abstr.* 21 (1960).

Cell wall mucopeptides of *Staphylococcus aureus* and *Micrococcus lysodeikticus.*
H. Rogers and H. Perkins, *Nature* 184 520 (1959).

Purification and chemical properties of flagellin.
T. Kobayashi, J. Rinker and H. Koffler, *Arch. Biochem. and Biophys.* 84 342 (1959).

Constitution of a glucomannan from wheat stem rust (*Puccinia graminis tritici*) uredospores.
N. Prentice, L. S. Cuendet, W. F. Geddes and F. Smith, *J. Am. Chem. Soc.* 81 684 (1959).

Structure of a reserve polysaccharide (leucosin) from *Ochromonas malhamensis.*
A. Archibald, D. Manners and J. Ryley, *Chem. and Ind.*, 1516 (1958).

Polysaccharides of bakers' yeast. II. Yeast glucan.
S. Peat, W. J. Whelan and T. E. Edwards, *J. Chem. Soc.*, 3862 (1958).

Mannan structure of diphtheria bacteria.
O. Orlova, *Biokhimiya* 23 502 (1958).

Uridine diphosphate N-acetylamino sugar compounds from *Staphylococcus aureus* strain 209 p. I. Amino acid constituents.
E. Ito, N. Ishimoto and M. Saito, *Arch. Biochem. and Biophys.* 80 431 (1959).

Amino acid composition of Brazilian *Mycobacterium tuberculosis* BCG strain.
I. Krzeczkowski and J. Iskierko, *Med. Doswiadczalna i Mikrobiol.* 9 185 (1957). (*Chem. Abstr.* 52 17 392a)

Studies of streptococcal cell walls. III. The amino acids of the trypsin-treated cell wall.
A. Hayashi and S. Barkulis, *J. Bacteriol.* 77 777 (1959).

Pigmentation and cell wall material of a *Daldinia concentrica* specimen.
D. Allport and J. Bu'lock, *J. Chem. Soc.*, 4090 (1958).

Bacterial endotoxins.
Otto Westphal, *Abstracts 138th Meeting, American Chemical Society,* New York, September 1960, p. 33-O.

Bacterial and Fungal Carotenes

The subject of bacterial and fungal carotenoids is confusing because of the large number of closely related structures and, in some cases, duplications in nomenclature. The following tables were prepared by an authority, Professor T. W. Goodwin of the University of Liverpool. They appeared in his excellent book "The Comparative Biochemistry of the Carotenoids" and are reproduced here with his permission and with the consent of the Chemical Publishing Co., 212 Fifth Ave., New York City.

TABLE I

The Qualitative Distribution of Carotenoids in Fungi

Pigment	α-carotene	β-carotene	γ-carotene	δ-carotene	ζ-carotene	lycopene	neurosporene	phytofluene	phytoene	torulene	rubixanthin	rhodoviolascin	lycoxanthin (or rhodopin)	rhodopurpurene	torularhodin	References
Aleuria aurantia	+	+	+++++													1
Allomyces arbuscula		+	+++	+												2
Allomyces javanicus																2
Allomyces macrogyna																2
Allomyces moniliformis																2
Cantharellus cibarius	+	++				+		+								3
Cantharellus cinnabarinus*						++	?									12
Cantharellus infundibiliformis										++						3
Cantharellus lutescens	+									+						3
Coleosporium senecionis									+	+						1
Dacromyces stillatus			++					+			+		+	+		13
Gymnosporangium juniperivirginianae																14
Lycogala epidendron	++	++	+++		+	++	++	++	++			++	+			1
Neurospora crassa	++	+++	+													4
Phycomyces blakesleeanus					?			+								5,6,7,8,9
Pilobolus kleinii	++		+			+	?									15
Polystigma rubrum																1
Puccinia coronifera																1
Rhodotorula rubra																1,10,11
Rhodotorula sanniei																10
Sporobolomyces roseus															+++	1
Sporobolomyces salmonicolor		++++++								++++						1
Tremella mesenterica						+										1

* Also canthaxanthin.

References to Table I

[1] E. Lederer, *Bull. soc. chim. biol.* **20** 611 (1938).
[2] R. Emerson and D. L. Fox, *Proc. Roy. Soc.* (London) **128B** 275 (1940).
[3] H. Willstaedt, *Svensk. Kem. Tidskr.* **49** 318 (1937).
[4] F. Haxo, *Arch. Biochem.* **20** 400 (1949).
[5] W. H. Schopfer, *Compt. rend. Soc. biol.* **118** 3 (1935).
[6] P. Karrer and E. Krause-Voith, *Helv. chim. Acta* **31** 802 (1947).
[7] K. Bernhard and H. Albrecht, *Helv. chim. Acta* **31** 2214 (1948).
[8] G. A. Garton, T. W. Goodwin and W. Lijinsky, *Biochem. J.* **48** 154 (1951).
[9] T. W. Goodwin, *Biochem. J.* **50** 550 (1952).
[10] H. Fink and E. Zenger, *Wochschr. Brau.* **51** 89 (1934).
[11] J. Bonner, A. Sandoval, Y. W. Tang and L. Zechmeister, *Arch. Biochem.* **10** 113 (1946).
[12] F. Haxo, *Botan. Gaz.* **112** 228 (1950).
[13] T. W. Goodwin, unpublished work (1951).
[14] B. L. Smits, and W. J. Peterson, *Science* **96** 210 (1942).
[15] E. Bunning, *Planta* **26** 719 (1937).

TABLE II
Characteristic Fungal Carotenoids*

Pigment	Melting point	Absorption spectra maxima (mμ)		
		Carbon disulphide	Light petroleum	Chloroform
Torulene[1, 2]	185°	563–5, 520–5, 488–91		539,501,469
Torularhodin[2]	201–203° (decomp.)	582,541,502	537,501,467	554,515,483
Neurosporene[3] (See also Tetra-hydrolycopene)	124°	502.5, 470.5, 439.5	470,441.5	
Acid carotenoid[3] from *Neurospora crassa*	—	512–514	516, 482	
Pigment III ⎱ from *Cortinarius*	—	—	520, 470	462, 405
Pigment VI ⎰ *cinnabarinus*[4]	—	494	—	455
Canthaxanthin	218°	500	—	462

* Pigments first reported in other organisms but also present in fungi are not recorded here.

References to Table II

[1] E. Lederer, *Bull. soc. chim. biol.* 20 611 (1938).
[2] P. Karrer and J. Rutschmann, *Helv. Chim. Acta* 29 355 (1946).
[3] F. Haxo, *Arch. Biochem.* 20 400 (1949).
[4] *Idem., Botan. Gaz.* 112 228 (1950).

TABLE III

Fungi in Which Early Workers[1,2] Have Reported the Presence of Carotenoids,
but Which Have Not Recently Been Investigated

Ascobolus spp. (not A. furfuraceus[3])	Peziza (Lachnea) scutellata
Calocerca cornea	Phragmidium violaceum
Calocerca palmata	Pilobolus crystallimus
Calocerca viscosa	Pilobolus kleinii
Chytridium spp.	Pilobolus oedipus
Coleosporium pulsatilla	Polystigma ochraceum (fulvum)
Ditiola radicata	Puccinia coronata
Leotia lubrica	Saccharomyces (spp.)
Lycogola flavofuscum	Sphaerostilbe coccaphila
Melampsora aecidioides	Spathularia flavida
Melampsora salicis capreae	Stemonitis spp.
Nectria cinnabarina	Triphragmium ulmariae
Peziza aurantia	Uredo (Coleosporium) euphrasie
Peziza (Lachnum) bicolor	Uromyces alchemille

References to Table III

[1] W. Zopf, "Die Pilze," Trewendt, Breslau, 1890.

[2] F. G. Kohl, Untersuchungen über das Carotin und seine physiologische Bedeutung in der Pflanze, Bornträger, Leipzig, 1902.

[3] T. W. Goodwin, *Biochem. J.* 50 550 (1952).

TABLE IV
Fungi from Which Carotenoids Have Been Shown to Be Absent

Agaricus (Telamoria) armillatus[1]	Nephoroma lusitanica[1]
Agaricus laceatus[1]	Oidium violaceum[1]
Alternaria solani[2,*]	Paxillus atrotomentosus[1]
Amanita muscaria[1]	Penicilliopsis clavariaeformis[1]
Amanita pantherina[1]	Peziza aeruginosa[1]
Arthonia spp.[1]	Peziza echinospora[1]
Ascobolus furfuraceus[3]	Peziza sanguinea[1]
Bachospora dryma[1]	Phragmidium violaceum[1]
Bacidia muscorum[1]	Pichia spp.[4]
Biatora fungidula[1]	Polyporus grammocephalus[5]
Bilimbia melaena[1]	Polyporus luzonenis[5]
Boletus luridus[1]	Polyporus rubidus[5]
Boletus scaber[1]	Polyporus zonalis[5]
Buellia spp.[1]	Polystictus hirsutus[5]
Cladonia coccifera[1]	Polystictus sanguineus[5]
Clavaria ternica[1]	Polystictus versicolor[5]
Claviceps spp.[1]	Polystictus xanthopus[5]
Cortinarius bulliardi[1]	Pullularia spp.[4]
Cortinarius violaceus[1]	Rhizoctonia sollani[2,*]
Daedalea flavida[5]	Rhizopogon rubescens[1]
Fusarium lycopersici[2,*]	Russula alutacea[1]
Fusarium moniforme[2,*]	Russula aurata[1]
Fusarium oxysporium[2,*]	Russula emetica[1]
Ganoderma (Fomes) lucidus[5]	Russula integra[1]
Gomphidius glutinosus[1]	Saccobolus violaceus[1]
Gomphidius viscidus[1]	Sarcogyme pruinosa[1]
Helminthosporium sativum[2,*]	Taphrina deformans[2]
Helvella esculenta	Thalloidima candidum[1]
Hydnum ferrugineum[1]	Thelephorus spp.[1]
Hydnum repandum[1]	Thielavia terricola[2,*]
Hygrophorus coccineus[1]	Torulopsis lipofera[4]
Hygrophorus conicus[1]	Torulopsis luteola[4]
Hygrophorus punicens[1]	Torulopsis pulcherrima[4,6]
Lactarius deliciosus[1]	Trametes persooni[5]
Lecidea spp.[1]	Trametes versatilis[5]
Lenzites subferruginea[5]	Zygosaccharomyces spp.[4]

* Only vitamin A-active carotenoids are absent from these species. Inactive carotenoids may possibly be present.

References to Table IV
[1] W. Zopf, "Die Pilze," Trewendt, Breslau, 1890.
[2] D. Gottlieb and G. M. Gilligan, Arch. Biochem. 10 163 (1946).
[3] T. W. Goodwin, Biochem. J. 50 550 (1952).
[4] E. M. Mrak, H. J. Phaff and G. Mackinney, J. Bacteriol. 57 407 (1949).
[5] S. R. Bose, Trans. Nat. Inst. Sci. India 2 69 (1941).
[6] M. F. Champeau and P. J. Luteraan, Ann. Parasit. 21 344 (1946).

TABLE V

Properties of Bacterial Carotenoids

Name	Melting point	Absorption maxima in mμ		
		Light petroleum	Carbon disulphide	Chloroform
Sarcinene[1],*	—	415,440,469		
Sarcinaxanthin[2],†	149–150°	415,440,469	464,494	423,451,480
Xanthophyll[3],† (Lutein) from				
Sarcina lutea	— — —		466,499	451,480
Flavorhodene[4,5],‡	111–113°	442,470	472,503	453,482
(Rhodoviolacein)				
Rhodopurpurene[4,5],§	162°	472,502	479,511,550	458,487,527
Rhodopin[4,5]	171°	440,470,501	478,508,547	453,486,521
Rhodovibrin[4,5]	168°		517,556	
Rhodoviolascin[4,5]	218°		496,530,573.5	476,507,544
(= Spirilloxanthin)				
α-Bacteriopurpurin[6], ‖	—	460,495,528 (in methanol)	498,532,571	
β-Bacteriopurpurin[7],#	—	452,482,502 (in methanol)		
Leprotene[8]	198–200°	425,452,484	477,499,517	428,460,495
Xanthophyll from				
Flavobact. esteroaroma-				
ticum, F. suaveoleus and				
F. faecale[3]	—		453,482,513	460,513
Carotene from F.				
sulphureum[3],*	—		437,466,487	451,481
Xanthophyll from Erwinia				
laythri[2]	—		478,513	458,485
Xanthophyll from E. ananas[2]	—		474,508	460,493
Chrysophlein[9,10]	—	452	487	—

* The probable identity of these with neurosporene cannot be ignored.
† These may be identical.
‡ May be identical with ε-carotene.
§ May be identical with lycopene.
‖ α-Bacteriopurpurin is probably one of Karrer's rhodocarotenoids.
β-Bacteriopurpurin is probably identical with rhodoviolascin.

References to Table V

[1] E. Chargaff and J. Dieryck *Naturwissenchaften* 20 872 (1932).
[2] Y. Takeda and T. Ohta, *Hoppe-Seyl. Z.* 268 1 (1941).
[3] B. Sobin and G. L. Stahly, *J. Bacteriol.* 44 265 (1942).
[4] P. Karrer and U. Solmssen, *Helv. Chim. Acta* 18 25 1306 (1935).
[5] P. Karrer, U. Solmssen and H. Koenig, *Helv. Chim. Acta* 21 545 (1938).
[6] H. F. M. Petter, *Amsterdam Akad. Wiss.* 34 No. 10 (1931).
[7] E. Lederer, *Bull. soc. chim. biol.* 20 611 (1938).
[8] Y. Takeda and T. Ohta, *Hoppe-Seyl. Z.* 262 168 (1939).
[9] G. Turian, *Arch. Sci. Soc. Phys. Hist. Nat. Geneve* 3 79 (1950).
[10] *Idem.*, *Helv. Chim. Acta* 33 1303 (1950).

The Chemical Constituents of Mycobacteria

A great many metabolites of mycobacteria have been characterized, many of them incidental to the study of tuberculosis. The following referenced list was prepared by Dr. Esmond R. Long and appeared in his recent book, *The Chemistry and Chemotherapy of Tuberculosis.* It is reproduced here by permission of the author and of the Williams and Wilkins Publishing Co. of Baltimore. While many of the compounds in this list appeared earlier in the Handbook, it may be useful to see them in aggregate as well.

CONSTITUENTS OF MYCOBACTERIA

(The numbers refer to articles in the reference list that follows)

Substance identified	Source of material						
	Culture medium	Bacillary bodies					
		Human	Bovine	Avian	Leprosy	Timothy	Others
ALCOHOLS							
d-Eicosanol-2 and d-octadecanol-2							
Glycerol..........		6,7,15,17,61,225	42,44	9,170	87	162	
Glycol (phyto-glycol)........		202			14	163	
Leprosol..........					62		
Phthiocerol........		1,61,65,66,89, 170,203,225	44,65		62		
CARBOHYDRATES							
Arabinose........	73,94,147, 171	1,15,52,74,85,94, 103,148,172	55	9,74	8		
2-Desoxyribose....							
Galactose........	94	1,15,52,85,94, 172	39	54 9	8	118	
Glucosamine......		100,172		9			
Glucose..........		6,26,42		17			
Glycogen........		133		53			
Inositol..........	168	6,11,13,17,18, 52,69,68,74, 204,261	17,44	9,17,18,74	8,219	161	

	Col 1	Col 2	Col 3	Col 4	Col 5	Col 6	Col 7
Mannose	73, 94, 147	1, 11, 13, 15, 16, 17, 18, 52, 68, 74, 94, 103, 148, 172, 225	17, 39, 44, 55	9, 17, 18, 74	8, 219	162	
Polysaccharides	73, 94, 128, 146, 147, 157, 171, 180, 187, 190, 201, 224	74, 86, 94, 100, 102, 103, 116, 133, 148, 192, 200	39, 55	17, 74, 122, 171	219		
Polysaccharide I	181, 216						
Polysaccharide II	126, 189						
Ribose							
Trehalose	85		159	54		58	
Uronic acid	12, 63, 76, 159		39	170	14	162	
ENZYMES	34, 71, 92, 155, 175, 176	30, 34, 84, 175	110, 131, 132, 175, 179, 227, 228, 229			71, 77, 78, 175, 176, 233	34, 71, 77, 84, 101, 107, 141, 176, 223, 238
Amidase, Protease						178	
Asparaginase	129	129		125			129
Catalase	60, 83, 154	66, 83, 154		83		83	83
Decarboxylase						99, 206	
Esterase	59	59	59	105, 160, 230		59, 152, 160	59
Lipase				106		152	49
Penicillinase	108						
Peptidase	177	36, 177				177	177
Transaminase						121	
Urease	193	193	193			193, 233	193, 233
Glycerophosphoric acid	6, 13, 68, 191	17, 144	17		219	162, 191	

Substance identified	Culture medium	Source of material — Bacillary bodies					
		Human	Bovine	Avian	Leprosy	Timothy	Others
LIPIDES..........		21, 26, 35, 50, 56, 61, 63, 145, 166, 169, 197, 215	21, 35, 51, 144	17, 171, 229	219	162	214
Acetone soluble wax..........		7, 12, 35, 76	17, 35, 42	17	14, 219	163	
Crotonaldehyde...	3	4, 45, 50					
Fatty acids..........		1, 12, 63, 76					
Anisic..........					14		
Caproic..........			42				
Cerotic..........		7					
Citric..........	138				10, 82, 87		
Leprosinic..........							
Linoleic and Linolenic..........		7					
Malic and succinic..........	209	1, 2, 22, 24, 25, 26, 50, 56, 61, 82, 139, 159, 164, 204, 225, 167	44, 67, 82, 90, 159	8, 9, 82		29, 54, 82, 164	29
Mycolic..........							
Myoceranic..........		89					
Mycocerosic..........							
Myristic..........		48			10, 14		
Octadecanoic..........		6, 15, 89, 164	17	17			
Oleic..........							
Oxalic..........	208						

Palmitic............	6,7,15,48,89,164, 225	17,42,51	17	10,14, 219	162,163	
Pentacosanoic.....	1		8			
Phthalic...........						
Phthioic (hexacosanoic)......	1,6,7,46,47,47, 61,63,76,89, 139,164,199,225	44				
Stearic............	6,15,48,89,139, 164,225	42	17	10,14, 219	163	
Tetracosanoic.....		44	8,9	10,14, 87	164	
Tuberculenone and hydroxy-acid C$_{60}$......	22					
Tuberculostearic...	7,15,48,61,63, 68,76,89,164, 198,220,225	42		219	163	
Glycolipide (lipopolysaccharide)........	23,24,56,158	23,158				
Mycobactin........	6,11,13,16,17, 18,61,63,68, 164,221	17	17,18	219	195 / 29,162	174
Phosphatides......		232				153
Pyridine...........	19					
Sterols............						
Waxes A and B.......	169					
C and D........	35,158,169	35,158				
Purified.........	61,35,172	35,44	170			
Soft wax........	6					
Leprosin.........						
Unsaponifiable..	6,202			10	162	

APPENDIX C—Continued

Substance identified	Culture medium	Source of material					
			Bacillary bodies				
		Human	Bovine	Avian	Leprosy	Timothy	Others
NUCLEIC ACIDS......		44, 114, 140	114			58	
Adenine..........		41, 114, 127, 142, 194	127, 194	222		58	127
Cytosine.........		41, 114, 127, 194	127, 194	222		58	127
Desoxyribonucleic acid..........		75, 102, 114, 117, 134, 165, 194	194	51, 54, 222, 229		75, 117, 118, 134, 165	165
Guanine..........		127, 142, 194	127, 194	222		58	127
5-Methyl-cytosine..		115, 194	194	222			127
Ribonucleic acid ...		75, 117, 127	127	54, 229		75, 117 118	127
Thymidine........							
Thymine.........		41, 114, 194	194	222		58	
Uracil...........		114, 127	127			58	127
PIGMENTS.........	98, 150	64, 149				109	
Azafrin..........							
Carotene........		213	69			51, 93, 109	218
Coproporphyrin...		64, 69	20	20, 227		69, 70, 217	69, 70, 217
Cytochrome......		20				20, 70, 217	70, 217
Kryptoxanthin....						109	
Leprotin.........					97		
Lutein..........						51, 109	161
Phthiocol........		12, 61, 63, 76					218
Zeaxanthin.......						109	

PROTEINS	31, 33, 38, 39, 40, 95, 104, 112, 113, 119, 120, 128, 135, 146, 180, 181, 182, 184, 185, 186, 187, 188, 196, 201, 211, 214, 215	28, 94, 96, 102, 103, 116, 151, 183, 212, 213	151	151, 171, 217		151	195
AMINO ACIDS	112, 181, 188	1, 24, 27, 79, 91, 123, 124, 215	43, 91	91		29, 91, 107	91, 107, 215
α-ϵ-Diaminopimelic acid	188, 226	88, 226	88, 226	88, 226		88	88
Ornithine		88	88				88
VITAMINS							
B_1 (aneurine)	143						
(thiamine)	168						
B_2 (riboflavine)	32, 37, 168	173, 205	173	205, 231		206	
B_6 (pyridoxine)	168						
B_{10} and B_{11}	156						
B_{12}		130				130	144
Biotin	32, 136, 168						
Folic acid	168						
K (phthiocol)		5, 195				195	
Niacin (nicotinic acid) (PP factor)	32, 168, 209 / 72	80	80				
Pantothenic acid	32, 168						
p-Aminobenzoic acid	32, 81, 137, 168, 209						

REFERENCES

1. A. Aebi, J. Asselineau and E. Lederer, *Bull. soc. chim. biol.* 35 661 (1953).
2. A. Aebi, E. Vilkas and E. Lederer, *Bull. soc. chim. France,* 79 (1954).
3. S. Akabori, Y. Yamamura and T. Sasakawa, *Proc. Japan Acad.* 26 37 (1950).
4. C. F. Allen and J. J. Cason, *J. Biol. Chem.* 220 407 (1956).
5. H. J. Almquist and A. A. Klose, *J. Am. Chem. Soc.* 61 1923 (1939).
6. R. J. Anderson, *J. Biol. Chem.* 74 537 (1927); 83 169, 505 (1929); 85 327, 339, 351 (1929); 97 639 (1932); *idem., J. Am. Chem. Soc.* 52 1607 (1930).
7. R. J. Anderson and E. J. Chargaff, *J. Biol. Chem.* 84 703 (1929); 85 77 (1929).
8. R. J. Anderson and M. M. Creighton, *ibid.* 129 57 (1939); 131 549 (1939).
9. R. J. Anderson, M. M. Creighton and R. L. Peck, *ibid.* 133 675 (1940).
10. R. J. Anderson, J. A. Crowder, M. S. Newman and F. H. Stodola, *ibid.* 113 637 (1936).
11. R. J. Anderson, W. C. Lathrop and M. M. Creighton, *ibid.* 125 299 (1938).
12. R. J. Anderson and M. S. Newman, *ibid.* 101 499, 773 (1933); 103 197 (1933).
13. R. J. Anderson, R. L. Peck and M. M. Creighton, *ibid.* 136 211 (1940).
14. R. J. Anderson, R. E. Reeves and J. A. Crowder, *ibid.* 121 669 (1937).
15. R. J. Anderson, R. E. Reeves and F. H. Stodola, *ibid.* 121 649 (1937).
16. R. J. Anderson and A. G. Renfrew, *J. Am. Chem. Soc.* 52 1252 (1930).
17. R. J. Anderson and E. G. Roberts, *J. Biol. Chem.* 85 509, 519, 529 (1930); 89 599, 611 (1930); *idem., J. Am. Chem. Soc.* 52 5023 (1930).
18. R. J. Anderson, E. G. Roberts and A. G. Renfrew, *Proc. Soc. Exp. Biol. Med.* 27 387 (1930).
19. R. J. Anderson, R. Shoenheimer, J. A. Crowder and F. H. Stodola, *Z. physiol. Chem.* 237 40 (1935).
20. A. Andrejew and A. J. Rosenberg, *Bull. soc. chim. biol.* 34 279 (1952).
21. J. Asselineau, *Ann. inst. Pasteur* 81 306 (1951).
22. *Idem., Bull. soc. chim. France,* 557 (1952); 427 (1953); 108 (1954); *idem., Biochim. et Biophys. Acta* 10 453 (1953).
23. J. Asselineau, H. Block and E. Lederer, *Am. Rev. Tuberc.* 67 853 (1953).
24. J. Asselineau, N. Choucroun and E. Lederer, *Biochim. et Biophys. Acta.* 5 197 (1950).
25. J. Asselineau and T. Gendre, *Bull. soc. chim. France,* 1226 (1954).

26. J. Asselineau and E. Lederer, *Bull soc. chim. biol.* **31** 492 (1949); *idem., Experientia* **7** 281 (1951); *idem., Biochim. et Biophys. Acta.* **7** 126 (1951); **17** 161 (1955); *idem., Bull. soc. chim. France,* 335 (1953).
27. J. L. Auclair and J. C. Benoit, *Rev. can. biol.* **11** 509 (1953).
28. R. W. Baldwin, G. A. Gilbert, C. N. Iland and A. S. Jones, *Biochim. et Biophys. Acta* **10** 402 (1953).
29. M. Barbier and E. Lederer, *ibid.* **8** 590 (1952); **14** 246 (1954).
30. F. Bernheim and W. E. DeTurk, *Enzymologia* **16** 69 (1953).
31. E. B. Bevilaqua and J. R. McCarter, *J. Exp. Med.* **87** 229 (1947).
32. O. D. Bird, *Nature* **159** 33 (1947).
33. K. Birkhaug, M. C. Pangborn and E. H. Cummerow, *Am. Rev. Tuberc.* **66** 335 (1952).
34. H. Block, *ibid.* **61** 270 (1950).
35. H. Block, *J. Exp. Med.* **91** 197 (1950); *idem., Am. Rev. Tuberc.* **67** 629, 828, 853 (1953).
36. H. Block and E. Suter, *Schweiz. Z. Path. u. Bakt.* **9** 597 (1946).
37. C. H. Boissevain, W. F. Drea and H. W. Schultz, *Proc. Soc. Exp. Biol. Med.* **39** 481 (1938).
38. A. Boquet and G. Sandor, *Ann. inst. Pasteur* **57** 622 (1936).
39. J. Bourdillon, *N. Y. State Dept. Health, Ann. Rep. Div. Lab. and Research,* 16 (1951); 10 (1952).
40. S. V. Boyden and E. J. Sorkin, *J. Immunol.* **75** 15 (1955).
41. E. B. Brown and T. B. Johnson, *J. Biol. Chem.* **57** 199 (1923); *idem., J. Am. Chem. Soc.* **45** 1823 (1923).
42. M. L. Burt and R. J. Anderson, *J. Biol. Chem.* **94** 451 (1931).
43. L. K. Campbell, *Am. Rev. Tuberc.* **11** 452 (1925).
44. J. Cason and R. J. Anderson, *J. Biol. Chem.* **119** 549 (1937); **126** 527 (1938).
45. J. Cason and G. J. Fonken, *ibid.* **220** 391 (1956).
46. J. Cason and F. S. Prout, *J. Am. Chem. Soc.* **70** 879 (1948).
47. J. Cason and G. Sumrell, *ibid.* **72** 4837 (1950); *idem., J. Biol. Chem.* **192** 405 (1951).
48. J. Cason, G. Sumrell, G. A. Gillies and S. Elberg, *ibid.* **205** 435 (1953).
49. G. Cattaneo, *Arch. sci. med.* **100** 34 (1955).
50. J. D. Chanley and N. Polgar, *Nature* **166** 693 (1950); *idem., J. Chem. Soc.,* 1003, 1008, 1011 (1954).
51. E. Chargaff, *Compt. rend.* **197** 946 (1933); *idem., Z. physiol. Chem.* **217** 115 (1933); *idem., Congr. intern. biochim. 2e Congr.,* Symposium sur le metabolism microbiel, Paris, 1952, p. 41.
52. E. Chargaff and R. J. Anderson, *Z. physiol. Chem.* **191** 172 (1930).
53. E. Chargaff and D. H. Moore, *J. Biol. Chem.* **155** 493 (1944).
54. E. Chargaff and H. F. Saidel, *ibid.* **177** 417 (1949).
55. E. Chargaff and W. Schaefer, *ibid.* **112** 393 (1935).
56. N. Choucroun, *Am. Rev. Tuberc.* **56** 203 (1947).
57. R. Clermonte and E. Lederer, *Compt. rend.* **242** 2600 (1956).
58. R. D. Coghill, *J. Biol. Chem.* **90** 57 (1931).
59. S. Cohen, J. B. Kushnick and C. V. Purdy, *J. Bacteriol.* **66** 266 (1953).

60. M. T. Cohn, C. Kovitz, U. Oda and G. Middlebrook, *Am. Rev. Tuberc.* **70** 641 (1954).
61. M. M. Creighton, L. H. Chang and R. J. Anderson, *J. Biol. Chem.* **154** 569 (1944).
62. J. A. Crowder, F. H. Stodola and R. J. Anderson, *ibid.*, **114** 431 (1936).
63. J. A. Crowder, F. H. Stodola, M. C. Pangborn and R. J. Anderson, *J. Am. Chem. Soc.* **58** 636 (1936).
64. M. O'L. Crowe and A. Walker, *Science* **110** 166 (1949); *idem.*, *Brit. J. Exp. Path.* **32** 1 (1951); *idem.*, *Phys. Rev.* **86** 817 (1951).
65. H. Demarteau-Ginsburg, *Compt. rend.* **243** 2169 (1956).
66. H. Demarteau-Ginsburg, A. Ginsburg and E. Lederer, *Biochim. et Biophys. Acta* **12** 587 (1953).
67. H. Demarteau and E. Lederer, *Compt. rend.* **232** 2494 (1951); **235** 265 (1952).
68. G. I. DeSütö-Nagy and R. J. Anderson, *J. Biol. Chem.* **171** 749, 761 (1947).
69. C. Dhéré, *Schweiz. med. Wochschr.* **33** 948 (1938).
70. C. Dhéré, S. Glücksmann and V. Rapetti, *Compt. rend. soc. biol.* **114** 1250 (1933).
71. M. DiFonzo, *Am. Rev. Tuberc.* **66** 240 (1952).
72. F. DiRaimondo, *Intern. Z. Vitamin Forsch.* **21** 48 (1949).
73. M. Dorset and R. R. Henley, *J. Am. Vet. Med. Ass.* **76** 696 (1930).
74. H. DuMont and R. J. Anderson, *Z. physiol. Chem.* **211** 97 (1932).
75. S. K. Dutla, A. S. Jones and M. Stacey, *Biochim. et Biophys. Acta* **10** 613 (1953).
76. C. O. Edens, M. M. Creighton and R. J. Anderson, *J. Biol. Chem.* **154** 587 (1944).
77. N. L. Edson and F. B. Cousins, *Nature* **171** 702 (1953).
78. N. L. Edson and G. J. E. Hunter, *Biochem. J.* **37** 563 (1943); **41** 139, 145 (1947).
79. S. Eguchi, *J. Biochem.* (Japan) **38** 85 (1951).
80. A. A. Eissa and S. Nour El Din, *J. Roy. Egypt. Med. Assoc.* **36** 14 (1953).
81. T. Ekstrand and B. Sjögren, *Nature* **156** 476 (1945).
82. N. Fethke and R. J. Anderson, *Am. Rev. Tuberc.* **57** 294 (1948).
83. M. K. Finlayson and N. L. Edson, *Proc. Roy. Soc. New Zealand* **77** 284 (1949).
84. R. J. Fitzgerald, F. Bernheim and D. B. Fitzgerald, *Arch. Biochem.* **20** 83 (1949).
85. J. Foldes, *Acta Microbiol. Acad. Sci. Hung.* **2** 297 (1955).
86. T. Fujiwara, *Tokushima J. Med. Sci.* **1** 161 (1954).
87. W. B. Geiger and R. J. Anderson, *J. Biol. Chem.* **131** 539 (1939).
88. T. Gendre and E. Lederer, *Biochim. et Biophys. Acta* **8** 49 (1959); *idem.*, *Ann. Acad. Sci. Fennicae* Ser. A. II, No. 60 313 (1955).
89. L. G. Ginger and R. J. Anderson, *J. Biol. Chem.* **156** 443 (1944); **157** 203, 213 (1945).

90. A Ginsburg and E. Lederer, *Biochim. et Biophys. Acta* 9 328 (1952).
91. B. Ginsburg, S. L. Lovett and M. S. Dunn, *Arch. Biochem. and Biophys.* 60 164 (1956).
92. D. S. Goldman, *J. Bacteriol.* 71 732 (1956).
93. T. W. Goodwin and M. Jamikorn, *Biochem. J.* 62 269 (1956).
94. G. A. C. Gough, *ibid.*, 26 248 (1932); 27 349 (1933).
95. H. H. Green, *Vet. J.* 102 267 (1946).
96. A. Grönwall, *Uppsala Täkaref. Förh.* 52 227 (1947); *idem.*, "The Svedberg 1884–1944," Almquist and Wiksells, Uppsala, 1944, 540 pp.
97. C. Grundmann and Y. Takeda, *Naturwissenschaften* 25 27 (1937).
98. H. G. Haas and L. D. Bushnell, *J. Bacteriol.* 48 219 (1944).
99. Y. S. Halpern and N. Grossowicz, *Proc. Soc. Exp. Biol. Med.* 91 370 (1956).
100. W. N. Haworth, P. W. Kent and M. J. Stacey, *J. Chem. Soc.*, 1211, 1220 (1948).
101. O. Hayaishi and A. Kornberg, *J. Am. Chem. Soc.* 73 2975 (1951).
102. R. J. Heckly and D. W. Watson, *Am. Rev. Tuberc.* 61 798 (1950); 64 602 (1951).
103. M. Heidelberger and A. E. O. Menzel, *J. Biol. Chem.* 104 655 (1934); 118 79 (1937); 124 89 (1938).
104. H. J. Henderson, *Intern. J. Leprosy* 5 267 (1937).
105. K. Hoshishima, *Tokushima J. Med. Sci.* 2 179 (1955).
106. K. Hoshishima, Y. Tanaka, M. Hoshino and M. Rikimaru, *ibid.* 2 121 (1955).
107. G. J. E. Hunter, *Biochem. J.* 55 320 (1953).
108. C. N. Iland and S. Baines, *J. Pathol. Bacteriol.* 61 329 (1949).
109. M. A. Ingraham and H. Steenbock, *Biochem. J.* 29 2553 (1935).
110. F. Ito, J. Sakai and M. Yuasa, *Kekkaku (Tuberculosis)* 30 569 (1955).
111. F. Ito and T. Sugano, *ibid.* 29 368 (1954).
112. M. Itoh, *Japan Soc. for the Promotion of Sci.* (Tokyo) 33 (1955).
113. K. A. Jensen, G. Bindsler, S. Möller, A. Hansen and P. Lind, *Tubercle* 19 383 (1938).
114. T. B. Johnson and E. B. Brown, *J. Biol. Chem.* 54 721, 731 (1922).
115. T. B. Johnson and R. D. Coghill, *J. Am. Chem. Soc.* 47 2838 (1925).
116. T. B. Johnson and G. Renfrew, *Am. Rev. Tuberc.* 18 505 (1928).
117. A. S. Jones, *Biochim. et Biophys. Acta* 10 607 (1953).
118. A. S. Jones and S. G. Faland, *Acta Chem. Scand.* 8 603 (1954).
119. A. Jones, A. B. Larsen, T. H. Vardaman and L. A. Baisden, *Am. Rev. Tuberc.* 68 425, 444 (1953).
120. P. Kallós and G. Hoffmann, *Biochem. Z.* 266 132 (1933).
121. M. Kanski, O. Sakllawska-Szymonowa and M. Szymonowa, *Acta Biochim. Polon.* 1 277 (1954).

122. S. A. Karjala and M. Heidelberger, *J. Biol. Chem.* 137 189 (1941).
123. I. Kasuya and A. Hagitani, *J. Biochem.* (Japan) 42 805 (1955).
124. I. Kasuya, J. Goto, S. Hirai, T. Someya, and A. Hagitani, *Jap. J. Med. Sci. and Biol.* 9 93 (1956).
125. T. Katayama, S. Tanaka and K. Aoki, *Kekkaku (Tuberculosis)* 29 472 (1954).
126. P. W. Kent, *J. Chem. Soc.*, 364 (1951).
127. Y. Khouvine and L. Wysmann, *Compt. rend.* 239 834 (1954).
128. Y. Kinoshita, *Japan J. Tuberc.* 3 42 (1955).
129. W. F. Kirchheimer and C. K. Whittaker, *Am. Rev. Tuberc.* 70 920 (1954).
130. V. Kocher and E. Sorkin, *Helv. Chim. Acta* 35 1741 (1952).
131. M. Kusunose, S. Nagai, E. Kusunose, Y. Yamamura, J. Tani, T. Terai, T. Nagasuga and Y. Yamamura, *Symposia on Enzyme Chem.* (Japan) 10 114 (1954).
132. M. Kusunose, E. Kusunose and Y. Yamamura, *ibid.*, 7 59 (1952).
133. P. P. Laidlow and H. W. Duldey, *Brit. J. Exptl. Pathol.* 6 197 (1925).
134. S. G. Laland, W. G. Overend and M. Webb, *J. Chem. Soc.*, 3224 (1952).
135. A. Lamensans, P. Grabar and J. Bretey, *Compt. rend.* 232 1967 (1951).
136. M. Landy and D. M. Dicken, *Proc. Soc. Exp. Biol. Med.* 46 449 (1941).
137. M. Landy, N. W. Larkum and E. J. Ostwald, *ibid.* 52 337 (1943).
138. Z. Lassot, *Acta Biochim. Polon.* 1 239 (1954).
139. A. Lesuk and R. J. Anderson, *J. Biol. Chem.* 136 603 (1940).
140. P. A. Levene, *J. Med. Research* 6 135 (1901).
141. M. Lindsay, T. V. O'Donnell and N. L. Edson, *Biochem. J.* 46 248 (1950).
142. E. R. Long, *Am. Rev. Tuberc.* 4 842 (1921).
143. A. Lutz, *Experientia* 3 244 (1947).
144. M. A. Macheboeuf and M. Faure, *Compt. rend.* 209 700 (1939).
145. G. J. Martin, *J. Am. Chem. Soc.* 60 768 (1938).
146. E. Marschmann and E. Küster, *Z. physiol. Chem.* 193 215 (1930).
147. P. Masucci, K. L. McAlpine and J. T. Glenn, *Am. Rev. Tuberc.* 22 669, 678 (1930).
148. M. Maxim, *Z. Biochem.* 223 404 (1930).
149. R. L. Mayer, *J. Bacteriol.* 48 337 (1944).
150. R. L. Mayer and M. Rodbart, *Arch. Biochem.* 11 49 (1946).
151. A. E. O. Menzel and M. Heidelberger, *J. Biol. Chem.* 124 89, 301 (1938).
152. J. Meyer, J. Malgras and R. Schär, *Bull. assoc. diplomés microbiol. faculté pharm.* (Nancy), 10 (1953).
153. G. Michel and E. Lederer, *Compt. rend.* 240 2454 (1955).
154. G. Middlebrook, *Am. Rev. Tuberc.* 69 471 (1954).
155. I. Millman and G. P. Youmans, *J. Bacteriol.* 69 320 (1955); *idem., Proc. Soc. Exp. Biol. Med.* 91 271 (1956).

156. R. C. Mills, G. M. Briggs, T. D. Luckey and C. A. Elvehjem, *Proc. Soc. Exp. Biol. Med.* 56 240 (1944).
157. J. H. Mueller, *J. Exp. Med.* 43 9 (1926).
158. H. Noll and H. Block, *J. Biol. Chem.* 214 251 (1955).
159. H. Noll, H. Block, J. Asselineau and E. Lederer, *Biochim. et Biophys. Acta* 20 299 (1956).
160. K. Ogura, S. Imazu, M. Kato and Y. Yamamura, *Kekkaku (Tuberculosis)* 29 128 (1954).
161. T. Ohta, *J. Pharm. Soc. Japan* 71 462 (1951).
162. M. C. Pangborn and R. J. Anderson, *J. Biol. Chem.* 90 45 (1931); 94 465 (1931); 101 105 (1933); *idem.*, *J. Am. Chem. Soc.* 58 10 (1936).
163. M. C. Pangborn, E. Chargaff and R. J. Anderson, *J. Biol. Chem.* 98 43 (1932).
164. R. L. Peck and R. J. Anderson, *ibid.*, 138 135 (1941); 140 89 (1941).
165. F. G. Petrick, *J. Bacteriol.* 48 347 (1944); 51 539 (1946).
166. F. J. Philpot and A. I. Wells, *Am. Rev. Tuberc.* 66 28 (1952).
167. N. Polgar, *J. Chem. Soc.*, 1008, 1011 (1954).
168. H. Pope and D. T. Smith, *Am. Rev. Tuberc.* 54 559 (1946).
169. S. Raffel, J. Asselineau and E. Lederer, *Ciba Found. Symposium Exp. Tuberc.* (London), 174 (1955).
170. R. E. Reeves and R. J. Anderson, *J. Am. Chem. Soc.* 59 858 (1937); *idem.*, *J. Biol. Chem.* 119 535 (1937).
171. A. G. Renfrew, *J. Biol. Chem.* 83 569, 579 (1929).
172. E. G. Roberts and R. J. Anderson, *ibid.* 90 33 (1931).
173. F. Rohner and F. Roulet, *Biochem. Z.* 300 148 (1939).
174. F. F. Rose and G. A. Snow, *Ciba Found. Symposium Exp. Tuberc.* (London), 41 (1955).
175. A. J. Rosenberg and A. Andrejew, *Compt. rend.* 235 1437 (1952).
176. F. Roulet, H. Wydler and E. A. Zeller, *Helv. Chim. Acta* 29 1973 (1946).
177. F. Roulet and E. A. Zeller, *ibid.* 31 1915 (1948).
178. H. Saito, *J. Biochem.* (Japan) 34 223 (1941).
179. T. Sasakawa, T. Kimura and H. Katayama, *Symposia on Enzyme Chem.* (Japan) 10 103 (1954).
180. W. Schaefer, *Ann. inst. Pasteur* 72 783 (1946); 73 749 (1947).
181. F. B. Seibert, *Am. Rev. Tuberc.* 17 403 (1928); 59 86 (1949); *idem.*, *Faraday Soc. Discussion*, No. 13 251 (1953).
182. F. B. Seibert, C. Crumb and M. V. Seibert, *J. Am. Chem. Soc.* 72 2678 (1950).
183. F. B. Seibert and A. M. Fabrizio, *Am. Rev. Tuberc.* 66 314 (1952).
184. F. B. Seibert and J. T. Glenn, *ibid.* 44 9 (1941).
185. F. B. Seibert and B. Munday, *ibid.* 25 724 (1932); 30 713 (1934).
186. F. B. Seibert and J. W. Nelson, *J. Am. Chem. Soc.* 65 272 (1943).
187. F. B. Seibert, K. O. Pedersen and A. Tiselius, *J. Exp. Med.* 68 413 (1938).

188. F. B. Seibert, E. Soto-Figueroa and E. H. DuFour, *Am. Rev. Tuberc.* 71 704 (1955).
189. F. B. Seibert, M. Stacey and R. W. Kent, *Biochim. et Biophys. Acta* 3 632 (1949).
190. F. B. Seibert and D. W. Watson, *J. Biol. Chem.* 140 55 (1941).
191. B. Siegel, G. A. Candela and R. M. Howard, *J. Am. Chem. Soc.* 76 1311 (1954).
192. J. Singer and E. Chrysner, *Am. Rev. Tuberc.* 65 779 (1952).
193. J. D. Smith and G. R. Wyatt, *Biochem. J.* 49 144 (1951).
194. G. A. Snow, *Congr. intern. biochim. 2ᵉ Congr., Résumés communs.,* Paris, 1952, p. 95; *idem., J. Chem. Soc.,* 2588 (1954).
195. E. Sorkin and S. V. Boyden, *J. Immunol.* 75 22 (1955).
196. E. Sorkin, H. Erlenmeyer and H. Block, *Nature* 170 124 (1952).
197. M. A. Spielman, *J. Biol. Chem.* 106 87 (1934).
198. M. A. Spielman and R. J. Anderson, *ibid.* 112 759 (1936).
199. M. Stacey, P. W. Kent and E. Nassau, *Biochim. et Biophys. Acta* 7 146 (1951).
200. W. Steenken, Jr., *J. Biol. Chem.* 141 91 (1941).
201. N. Stendal, *Compt. rend.* 198 1549 (1934).
202. F. H. Stodola and R. J. Anderson, *J. Biol. Chem.* 114 467 (1936).
203. F. H. Stodola, A. Lesuk and R. J. Anderson, *ibid.* 126 505 (1938).
204. H. R. Street and R. E. Reeves, *Proc. Soc. Exp. Biol. Med.* 44 641 (1940).
205. W. B. Sutton, *J. Biol. Chem.* 210 309 (1954); 216 749 (1955).
206. P. Szafranski, *Acta Biochim. Polon.* 1 116 (1954).
207. L. Szarkowska and P. Szafranski, *Acta Biochim. Polon.* 1 225, 249 (1954).
208. J. W. Szarkowski, *Bull. acad. polon. sci.* class II 2 97 (1954).
209. M. Szymonowa and O. Sakllawska-Szymonowa, *Biokhimiya* 19 295 (1954).
210. T. Tada and K. Takeya, *Japan Soc. for the Promotion of Sci.* (Tokyo), 1 (1955).
211. Y. Takeda and T. Hoshino, *Japan. J. Tuberc.* 2 201 (1954).
212. Y. Takeda, N. Kasai and Y. Aoki, *Japan. J. Exptl. Med.* 22 413 (1952).
213. Y. Takeda and T. Ohta, *J. Pharm. Soc. Japan* 64 67 (1944).
214. K. Takeya and I. Mifuchi, *Enzymologia* 16 366 (1954).
215. S. Tamura, *Z. physiol. Chem.* 87 85 (1913).
216. D. M. Tennent and D. W. Watson, *J. Immunol.* 45 179 (1942).
217. C. M. Todd, *Biochem. J.* 45 386 (1949).
218. G. Turian, *Helv. Chim. Acta* 33 1303 (1950); 34, 1060 (1951).
219. N. Uyei and R. J. Anderson, *J. Biol. Chem.* 94 653 (1932); 97 617 (1932).
220. S. F. Velick, *ibid.* 154 497 (1944).
221. E. Vilkas and E. Lederer, *Compt. rend.* 240 1156 (1955); *idem., Bull. soc. chim. France* 38 111 (1956).
222. E. Vischer, S. Zamenkof and E. Chargaff, *J. Biol. Chem.* 177 429 (1949).
223. W. A. Volk and Q. N. Myrvik, *Am. Rev. Tuberc.* 73 589 (1956).

224. D. W. Watson, Dissertation, University of Wisconsin, 1941.
225. C. W. Wieghard and R. J. Anderson, *J. Biol. Chem.* 126 515 (1938).
226. E. Work, *Biochem. J.* 49 17 (1951).
227. Y. Yamamura, *Symposia on Enzyme Chem.* (Japan) 10 114 (1954).
228. Y. Yamamura, M. Kusunose and E. Kusunose, *Nature* 170 207 (1952); *idem., J. Biochem.* (Tokyo) 42 785 (1955).
229. Y. Yamamura, M. Kusunose, S. Nagai, E. Kusunose, Y. Yamamura, J. Tani, T. Terai and T. Nagasuga, *Med. J. Osaka Univ.* 6 489 (1955).
230. Y. Yamamura, K. Ogura and S. Imazu, *Symposium on Enzyme Chem.* (Japan) 8 96 (1953).
231. Y. Yamamura and S. Watanabe, *Kekkaku (Tuberculosis)* 27 414 (1952).
232. Y. Yamamura, K. Matsui and H. Maeda, *J. Biochem.* (Tokyo) 43 409 (1956).
233. E. A. Zeller, L. S. VanOrden, W. F. Kirchheimer and J. C. Lazanas, *J. Bacteriol.* 67 153 (1954); *idem., J. Biol. Chem.* 209 429 (1954).

REFERENCES TO REVIEW BOOKS AND ARTICLES ON CONSTITUENTS OF MYCOBACTERIA

1. R. J. Anderson, *Fortschr. Chem. org. Naturstoffe* 3 145 (1939); *idem., Sigma Xi Quart.* 27 39 (1939); *idem., Harvey Lectures* 35 271 (1939–1940); *idem., Chem. Rev.* 29 225 (1941); *idem., Yale J. Biol. and Med.* 15 311 (1943).
2. J. Asselineau, *Advances in Tuberc. Research* 5 1 (1952).
3. E. Chargaff and J. N. Davidson, "The Nucleic Acids—Chemistry and Biology," Academic Press, Inc., New York, 1955, Vol. I.
4. W. F. Drea and A. Andrejew, "The Metabolism of the Tubercle Bacillus," Charles C. Thomas, Springfield, Ill., 1953.
5. P. Hauduroy, E. Chain, H. Florey, K. A. Jensen, G. Penso and J. Trefouël, "Bacilles tuberculeux et paratuberculeux," Masson et Cie., Paris, 1950.
6. P. W. Kent and M. W. Whitehouse, "Biochemistry of the Aminosugars," Butterworth and Co., Ltd., London, 1955. (Also published by Academic Press, Inc., New York, 1955.)
7. E. Lederer, *Proc. Colloq. Chemotherapy Tuberc.,* Dublin, 1951; *idem., Congr. intern. biochim., 2ᵉ Congr.,* Symposium sur le metabolism microbien, Paris, 1952; *idem., Angew. Chem.* 72 372 (1960).
8. L. Negre, "Les lipoides dans les bacilles tuberculeux et la tuberculose," Masson et Cie., Paris, 1950.
9. F. Roulet and M. Brenner, *Zentr. ges. Tuberk. Forsch.* 56 193 (1943).
10. F. B. Seibert, *Chem. Rev.* 34 107 (1944); *idem., Schweiz. Z.*

Tuberk., Separatum, Fasc. 3 1 (1950); *idem., Ann. Rev. Microbiology* 4 35 (1950).

11. B. Skowronska-Serafinowa, *Wiadomošci Chem.* 7 216 (1953).
12. M. Stacey, *Schweiz. Z. Tuberk.*, Separatum, Fasc. 9 7 (1955).
13. M. Stacey and R. W. Kent, *Advances in Carbohydrate Chem.* 3 311 (1948).

In order to cover pertinent literature appearing as late as December, 1960 this addendum is attached. Also included is a little material from earlier dates which was overlooked. Arrangement is by chapter title, and new compounds eligible for inclusion often are given appropriate entry numbers, but with a letter added to the number so that it is evident in the indexes that such entries are located in the addendum. Due to time restrictions these entries may be abbreviated, but references are listed. The addendum is not indexed.

2. Alcohols, Glycols and Compounds Related to Sugars

17a **Acetyl Methyl Carbinol** (Acetoin)

This substance, mentioned as a co-product of butanediol, is produced by many microorganisms. It is given off by several streptomycetes, including *Streptomyces erythreus*, an erythromycin producer. It is present in such large quantities in some erythromycin fermentations that it interferes with production of the antibiotic.[1]

A survey has been made of 44 species and strains of acetobacter for ability to convert lactate to acetoin.[1a] *A. rancens* and *A. pasteurianus* were good producers, the former yielding one isomer, the latter the other.

Acetoin metabolism of bacteria in general has been studied.[1b]

Biosynthesis of acetoins has been reviewed.[1c]

47a **Galactosyl Lactose**

This trisaccharide was produced by *Penicillium chrysogenum* Thom on a lactose medium and assigned the structure O-β-D-galactopyranosyl-$(1 \rightarrow 6)$-O-β-D-galactopyranosyl-$(1 \rightarrow 4)$-D-glucopyranose.[2]

Several papers have appeared on the mode of action of

[1] V. Musilek, V. Sevcik, M. Musilkova, J. Rokos and P. Prochazka, *Experientia* 14 323 (1958).

[1a] J. de Ley, *J. Gen. Microbiol.* 21 352–365 (1959).

[1b] Yasuhiro Maeda, *Okayama Igakkai Zasshi* 71 8017 (1959). (*Chem. Abstr.* 55 694i)

[1c] H. Oberman, *Postepy Biochemii* 6 181–195 (1960).

[2] A Ballio and S. Russi, *Tetrahedron* 9 125 (1960).

streptomycin. Its effect on *Escherichia coli* has been studied.[3] The cell permeability barrier was altered, reminiscent of detergents and of polymyxin. Preformed cells were undamaged, but defects were caused in cell membranes formed in its presence by non-resistant cells. When C^{14}-labeled streptomycin was used, initial uptake occurred only outside the cell wall and secondary uptake depended on secondary damage to the membrane. The growing membrane was the primary site of action of the antibiotic.

The effect of streptomycin on the excretion of nucleotides by *E. coli* has been investigated.[4] Streptomycin enhanced excretion of 5′-nucleotides and prevented excretion of 2′- or 3′-nucleotides. It was not clear whether streptomycin blocked RNA synthesis *de novo* or whether degradation of RNA to 5′-nucleotides was enhanced.

The same group has published on chloramphenicol-sensitive and chloramphenicol-insensitive phases of the lethal action of streptomycin.[5] It appeared that the lethal effect of streptomycin on *E. coli* was exerted in two phases (1) a preparatory phase, which is markedly less lethal and can be blocked by chloramphenicol (a protein synthesis inhibitor), followed by (2) a more direct lethal phase which is insensitive to chloramphenicol. The induction process might have been due to formation of a permease without which streptomycin could not accumulate in the cell in lethal concentration.

It has been found that, while penicillin inhibits growth of *Staphylococcus aureus* (strain Duncan), it does not cause rapid lysis as, *e.g.*, in the case of *E. coli*. Penicillin and streptomycin added (each at minimally bactericidal concentrations) to exponentially growing cultures caused rapid lysis. Only antibiotically active forms of streptomycin were effective. Under anaerobic conditions lysis was not rapid. (Streptomycin is not ordinarily effective under such conditions.[6])

[3] Nitya Anand and Bernard D. Davis, *Nature* **185** 22, 23 (1959).
[4] Carmen L. Rosano, Richard A. Peabody and Charles Hurwitz, *Biochim. et Biophys. Acta* **37** 380 (1960).
[5] Charles Hurwitz and Carmen L. Rosano, *ibid.* **41** 162 (1960).
[6] R. Hancock, *Nature* **186** 658 (1960).

It has been reported that streptomycin inhibits dehydrogenases by influencing the apoenzyme.[7] The conclusion was made that further search for enzymatic
reactions susceptible to streptomycin should be aimed at
the study of its influence on intracellular synthetic processes, mainly the synthesis of nucleic acids and proteins.

The mode of action of streptomycin in connection with
its binding by *Mycobacterium avium* has been studied.[8]

The stereochemistry of neobiosamine B is as shown.[9]

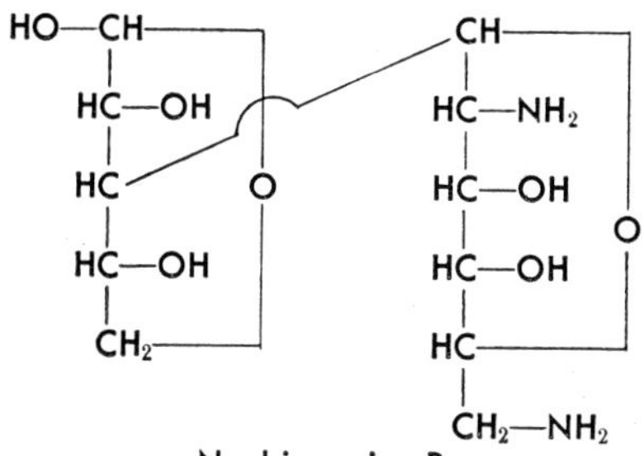

Neobiosamine B

Dextromycin is neomycin B and contains a small
amount of neomycin C.[10]   Framycetin also is identical
with neomycin B.[11]

59a **Aminocidin** (Crestomycin, Antibiotic 1600, Pharmiglucin, F. I.
5853) $C_{23}H_{45}O_{14}N_5$ (Sulfate) $[\alpha]_D^{23} + 51°$ in water.   Produced by *Streptomyces crestomyceticus*, n. sp.[12]   This
antibiotic seems to be similar to or identical with paromomycin.

[7] K. Michalska, Symposium on Antibiotics, Prague, 1959.

[8] Tatsuji Kinoshita, *Nagoya J. Med. Sci.* 21 323 (1958).

[9] Kenneth L. Rinehart, Alexander D. Argoudelis, Townley P. Cul-
bertson, W. Scott Chilton and Klaus Streigler, *J. Am. Chem. Soc.* 82
2970 (1960).

[10] Sueo Tatsuoka, Akira Miyake and Hayao Nawa, *J. Antibiotics*
(Japan) 11A 193 (1958).

[11] Kenneth L. Rinehart, Jr., Alexander D. Argoudelis, William A.
Goss, Arthur Sohler and Carl P. Schaffner, *J. Am. Chem. Soc.* 82
3938 (1960).

[12] F. Arcamone, C. Bertazzoli, M. Ghione and T. Scotti, *Giorn.
Microbiol.* 7 251 (1959).

D-Araboascorbic acid is produced by *Penicillium de-cumbens, P. chrysogenum* mutant *fulvescens, P. notatum, P. meleagrinum* and *P. cyaneofulvum* growing on sucrose, glucose or D-gluconate.[13]

3. Aliphatic Acids and Glycolipides

The name mycoside has been suggested to designate a type-specific glycolipide of mycobacterial origin. To clarify nomenclature it was proposed that C_A from photochromogenic strains be called mycoside A, G_B from bovine strains, mycoside B, and J_{Av} from avian strains mycoside C. Some properties are listed:[14]

Mycoside A:

Nearly colorless solid, m.p. 105°, $[\alpha]_D^{20} - 37°$ (in chloroform). Anal: C 72.2, H 11.3, $-OCH_3$ 8.6, N 0.0, P 0.0. U.V. maxima at 222, 274, 278 mμ (in hexane). Contains 2-O-methylfucose, 2-O-methylrhamnose and 2,4-di-O-methylrhamnose. The lipide part is a mycocerosate of an aromatic alcohol.

Mycoside B:

Colorless wax, m.p. 25°, $[\alpha]_D^{20} - 22°$ (in chloroform). Anal: C 76.6, H 12.0, $-OCH_3$ 4.3, N 0.0, P 0.0. U.V. maxima at 222, 274, 281 mμ. Contains only one sugar, 2-O-methylrhamnose. The lipide moiety is a diester of 2 molecules of a branched-chain acid fraction of mean molecular weight corresponding to $C_{22}H_{44}O_2$ with a phenolic alcohol. It may also sometimes contain mycocerosic acid.

Mycoside C:

A peptide-glycolipide mixture. One component separated on silica gel had the following properties:
m.p. 200°, $[\alpha]_D^{20} - 31°$ (in chloroform). Anal:
Calculated for $C_{73}H_{133}O_{24}N_5$: C 59.8, H 9.1, N 4.8, $-OCH_3$ 6.3
Found: C 60.1, H 8.7, N 5.1, $-OCH_3$ 6.0.
It contains three deoxyhexoses, one being 6-deoxytalose and one 3,4-dimethoxyrhamnose. The peptide moiety is

[13] T. Takahashi, M. Mitsumoto and H. Kayamori, *Nature* **188** 411 (1960).

[14] Donald W. Smith, H. M. Randall, A. P. MacLennan and E. Lederer, *ibid.* **186** 887 (1960).

a pentapeptide containing 1 mole of D-phenylalanine, 2 moles of *allo*-threonine and 2 moles of D-alanine. The lipide moiety was not entirely pure, but may be a hydroxy acid of about $C_{24}H_{48}O_3$. Two O-acetyl groups are present in mycoside C.

The lipoids of mycobacteria, their chemical structures and biological effects have been reviewed.[15]

132a **Mycocerosic Acid,** $C_{32}H_{64}O_2$, isolated by Anderson and collaborators,[16] has been shown to be 2,4,6,8-tetramethyloctacosanoic acid:[17]

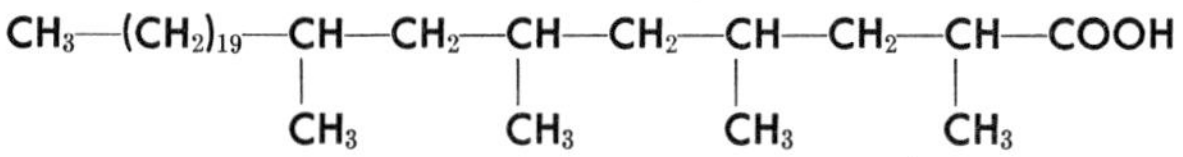

$$CH_3-(CH_2)_{19}-CH-CH_2-CH-CH_2-CH-CH_2-CH-COOH$$

with CH₃ groups:

CH₃ — CH₃ — CH₃ — CH₃

Indications were obtained for the presence in mycobacteria of normal chain acids with 22, 24, 26 and 28 carbon atoms; 2-, 4-, 6-trimethyl-substituted acids with 25, 27 and 29 carbon atoms; and 2-, 4-, 6-, 8-tetramethyl-substituted acids with 30, 32 and 34 carbon atoms.

Succinic, fumaric and acetic acids as well as D,L-5-carboxymethylhydantoin, shown below, have been iso-

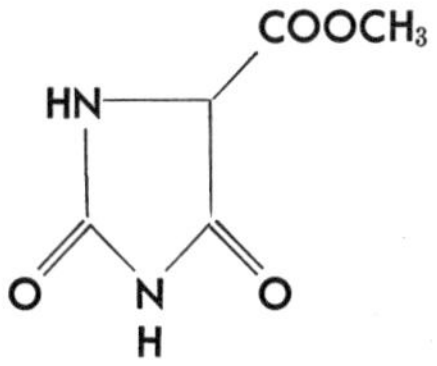

lated as extracellular acids from *Mycobacterium ranae* and from *M. tuberculosis* H37R$_v$.[18]

[15] E. Lederer, *Angew. Chem.* **72** 372 (1960).

[16] L. G. Ginger and R. J. Anderson, *J. Biol. Chem.* **157** 203 (1945) and preceding papers.

[17] Cecile Asselineau, Jean Asselineau, Ragnar Ryhage, Stina Ställberg-Stenhagen and Einar Stenhagen, *Acta Chem. Scand.* **13** 822 (1959).

[18] Andree V. Fowler, Merrill N. Camien and Max S. Dunn, *J. Biol. Chem.* **235** 1386 (1960).

Lipides of *Corynebacterium ovis* have been studied,[19] as have the component fatty acids of *Sporidesmium bakeri* Syd. lipides.[20]

The oil of wheat stem rust uredospores was found to contain a substantial quantity of an acid not previously reported from natural sources, *cis*-9,10-epoxyoctadecanoic acid, $C_{18}H_{34}O_3$, colorless leaflets, m.p. 58.5–59.5°, *cis*-epoxide peak in the infra-red at 845 cm.$^{-1}$.[21]

The chemistry of naturally occurring 1,2-epoxides, including many microbial products, has been reviewed.[21a]

Another new fatty acid, $C_{17}H_{32}O_2$, containing a cyclopropane ring has been reported (in a preliminary communication) as occurring in *Escherichia coli* lipides.[22]

Bongkrekic acid, at a concentration of 10^{-6} molar, is a potent inhibitor of oxidative phosphorylation as carried out by mitochondrial enzymes in heart muscle tissue.[23]

The direct participation of protein-bound biotin in fatty acid biosynthesis has been confirmed.[24]

Both 9- and 10-hydroxystearic acids can replace oleic acid as growth factors for anaerobically grown yeast, which requires unsaturated acid, and these substances may be precursors of oleic acid in yeast.[25]

The role of vitamins in lipide metabolism has been reviewed.[26]

Hydroxypyruvic acid has been isolated as the 2,4-dinitrophenylhydrazone from *Aspergillus niger*. It may arise from 3-phosphoglyceric acid.[27]

[19] A. Diara and J. Pudles, *Bull. soc. chim. biol.* 41 481 (1959).

[20] L. Hartman, J. C. Hawke, Isobel M. Morice and T. B. Shorland, *Biochem. J.* 75 274 (1960).

[21] A. Tulloch, B. Craig and G. Ledingham, *Can. J. Microbiol.* 5 485 (1959).

[21a] A. D. Cross, *Quart. Revs.* 14 317–336 (1960).

[22] Simone Dauchy and Jean Asselineau, *Compt. rend.* 250 2635 (1960).

[23] W. Welling, J. A. Cohen and W. Berends, *Biochem. Pharmacol.* 3 122 (1960).

[24] S. J. Wakil and D. M. Gibson, *Biochim. et Biophys. Acta.* 41 122 (1960).

[25] W. J. Lennarz and Konrad Bloch, *J. Biol. Chem.* 235 PC 26 (1960).

[26] Bacon F. Chow, *Am. J. Clinical Nutrition* 8 321 (1960).

[27] Francis J. Behal, *Arch. Biochem. and Biophys.* 88 110 (1960).

The oxidative degradation of glycolic acid in *E. coli* takes the following course:[28]

$$HOCH_2COOH \xrightarrow{-2H} OHC-COOH \xrightarrow[\text{$-$Acetyl COA}]{\text{$+$Acetyl CoA}} HOOC-CH-CH_2-COOH$$

(with OH group on the CH)

$$\xrightarrow{-2H} HOOC-\underset{\overset{\|}{O}}{C}-CH_2-COOH \xrightarrow{-CO_2} CH_3\underset{\overset{\|}{O}}{C}COOH \xrightarrow[\text{$-$2H, $-$CO}_2]{\text{$+$H}_2O \atop \text{$+$CoA}} Acetyl\ CoA$$

Summation: $OHC-COOH + O_2 \rightarrow 2CO_2 + H_2O$

A study has been made of the synthesis of cell materials from acetate by *Aspergillus niger*,[28a] and by *Escherichia coli*.[28b] Interrelationships of the tricarboxylic acid and glyoxylic acid cycles were discussed.

Lactobacilli produce α-hydroxy acids other than lactic. Two of these have been identified as α-hydroxy-D-isovaleric and D-isocaproic acids:[29]

$$\begin{array}{c} CH_3 \\ \diagdown \\ \hspace{1em} CH-CH-COOH \\ \diagup \hspace{1em} | \\ CH_3 \hspace{1.5em} OH \end{array}$$
D-Isovaleric Acid

$$\begin{array}{c} CH_3 \\ \diagdown \\ \hspace{1em} CH-CH_3-CH-COOH \\ \diagup \hspace{3em} | \\ CH_3 \hspace{3em} OH \end{array}$$
D-Isocaproic Acid

These are growth promoters for certain strains of lactobacilli.

Penicillium atrovenetum, a β-nitropropionic acid producer,[30] was grown on C^{14}-labeled β-alanine, on $NaHC^{14}O_3$ and on 4-C^{14}-D,L-aspartic acid.[31] Since 96 percent of the label was in the 1-position, apparently aspartic acid was incorporated as a unit.

[28] H. L. Kornberg and J. R. Sadler, *Nature* 185 153 (1960).

[28a] J. F. Collin and H. L. Kornberg, *Biochem. J.* 77 430 (1960).

[28b] H. L. Kornberg, P. J. R. Phizackerly and J. R. Sadler, *ibid.* 77 438 (1960).

[29] Merrill N. Camien, Andree V. Fowler and Max S. Dunn, *Arch. Biochem. and Biophys.* 83 408 (1959).

[30] H. Raistrick and A. Stössl, *Biochem. J.* 68 647 (1958).

[31] A. J. Birch, B. J. McLoughlin, Herchel Smith and J. Winter, *Chem. and Ind.*, 840 (1960).

A review of naturally occurring nitro compounds has been published.[32]

The fatty acids of *B. alcaligenes faecalis, S. pullorum, B. fluorescens, S. typhi-murium* and *B. natta* have been analyzed.[33] Palmitic and unsaturated C_{18}-acids were the main components. Unsaturated C_{16}-acids were present to some extent, the unsaturated C_{18}- and C_{16}-acids being largely oleic and palmitoleic. A saturated C_{15}-acid was abundant in the fat of *B. natta*.

Two acids, 13-methyltetradecanoic, m.p. 52.5–53°, and 15-methylhexadecanoic, m.p. 61.0–61.5°, were the main components of the fatty acid fraction of *B. subtilis*.[34]

A new monounsaturated, monohydroxy acid, diphtherocorynic, $C_{53}H_{104}O_3$, has been reported produced by *Corynebacterium diphtheriae*.[35] Its relationship to related compounds has been discussed.[36]

4. Tetronic Acids and Other Lactones and Lactams

Tenuazonic acid (3-acetyl-5-*sec*-butyltetramic acid) has been biosynthesized incorporating 3.9 percent of the tracer from a medium containing $CH_3C^{14}OONa$.[37] Of the total incorporated radioactivity 96 percent was present in the C-2 and C-6 atoms. The remaining 4 percent was shared by C-4 and C-10, and this was explained on the basis of the manner of biosynthesis of isoleucine.

[32] M. Pailer, *Fortschr. Chem. org. Naturstoffe* **18** 55–78 (1960).

[33] Kunihiko Saito, *J. Biochem.* (Tokyo) **47** 699 (1960).

[34] *Idem., ibid.* **47** 710 (1960).

[35] E. M. Gubarev and L. M. Pustovlova, *Ukrain. Biokhim. Zhur.* **30** 569 (1958).

[36] Raoul Toubiana and Jean Asselineau, *Compt. rend.* **251** 884 (1960).

[37] C. E. Stickings and R. J. Townsend, *Proc. Biochem. Soc.,* 36P (1960).

It might be pointed out that, formally, some of the vulpinic acids are tetronic acids although we have not classified them as such.

The chemistry of the tetronic acids has been reviewed.[38]

5. Carotenes and Carotenoids

Another paper has been published on the incorporation of C^{14}-labeled compounds into carotenes by *Neurospora crassa*.[39] Mevalonic acid salts were the best of eight precursors used, but less than 1 percent of the $2\text{-}C^{14}$ activity was incorporated into the carotene fraction. Phytoene, γ-carotene and its isomers (β- and ζ-), phytofluene, neurosporene, spirilloxanthin and its isomers and lycopene were isolated. The presence of much phytoene, whose presence in the theoretical biosynthetic sequence has been questioned, was taken as an argument against formation of the carotenes by stepwise interconversions involving either hydrogenation or dehydrogenation and as an indication, rather, of independent synthesis.

The major carotenoids of some ascomycetes and basidiomycetes have been identified.[40] β-Carotene was predominant in *Epichloë typhina* and *Helotium citrinum*. Cryptoxanthin was second in importance in *Calocera viscosa*. Neurosporene was the major carotenoid in dull yellow *Cantharellus infundibiliformis* with traces of lycopene present. The reverse was true in *Cantharellus lutescens*. No carotenoids, but instead pigments with quinone-like reactions, were detected in the grey *Cantharellus cinereus* and orange-red *Guepinius helvelloides*.

A red pigmented yeast isolated from root nodules of *Lupinus luteus* produced torulene, β-carotene, γ-carotene and torularhodin.[41] Diphenylamine inhibited production of γ-carotene and torularhodin.

Rhodotorula mucilaginosa contained, in decreasing or-

[38] L. J. Haynes and J. R. Plimmer, *Quart. Revs.* 14 292 (1960).

[39] Leo F. Krzeminski and F. W. Quackenbush, *Arch. Biochem. and Biophys.* 88 287 (1960).

[40] Gilbert Turian, *Arch. Mikrobiol.* 36 139 (1960).

[41] Gy. Schneider, B. Matkovics and J. Zsolt, *Acta. Univ. Szegediensis, Acta. Phys. et Chem.* 5 55 (1959).

der of quantity, torularhodin, torulene, γ-carotene and β-carotene, but no phytoene or phytofluene.[42] Ultraviolet irradiation gave stable strains varying greatly from the parent both in quality and quantity of carotenoid content. One of many inhibitors tested, 2-hydroxybiphenyl, inhibited carotenogenesis without affecting culture growth. Doubt was expressed that the different carotenoids are biosynthetically mutually related.

Oil of wheat rust (*Puccinia graminis* var. *tritici*) uredospores contained β- and γ-carotenes with minor amounts of phytoene, lycopene, a *cis*-β-carotene and a *cis*-carotene.[43]

Mycoxanthin is the principal carotenoid of *Mycobacterium battaglini*.[44] Leprotene, a leprotene derivative, β-carotene, α-carotene and an α-carotene monoepoxide probably were present.

A carotenoid pigment in *Spirobacillus cienkowskii* Metchnikoff, a pathogen of cladocera, resembled rhodoviolascin or α-bacteriopurpurin.[45] Astacene and astaxanthin also were thought to be present.

Staphylococcus citreus contains the orange carotenoid, sarcinaxanthin, and the yellow sarcinene.[46] Reference was made to two other uncharacterized carotenoids which have been isolated from natural sources, neoxanthin and corynexanthin.[47]

A new carotenoid has been isolated, which probably has the structure shown below.[48]

175a **Bacterioruberin a,** $C_{40}H_{56}O_2$, mauve-violet needles, m.p. 182° (vac.), U.V. 369, 385, 461, 494, 528 mμ in petroleum ether.

[42] Jean Villoutreix, *Biochim. et Biophys. Acta.* 40 434, 442 (1960).

[43] F. Hougen, B. Craig and G. Ledingham, *Can. J. Microbiol.* 4 521 (1958).

[44] Aldo Gaudiano, *Rend. ist. super. sanita* 22 769 (1959). (*Chem. Abstr.* 54 13253a)

[45] J. Green, *Nature* 183 56 (1959).

[46] Tatsuo Ohta, Toshio Miyazaki and Teruo Ninomiya, *Chem. & Pharm. Bull.* (Tokyo) 7 254 (1959).

[47] W. Hodgkiss, J. Liston, T. W. Goodwin and Malini Jamikorn, *J. Gen. Microbiol.* 11 438 (1954).

[48] Synnöve Liaaen Jensen, *Acta Chem. Scand.* 14 950 (1960).

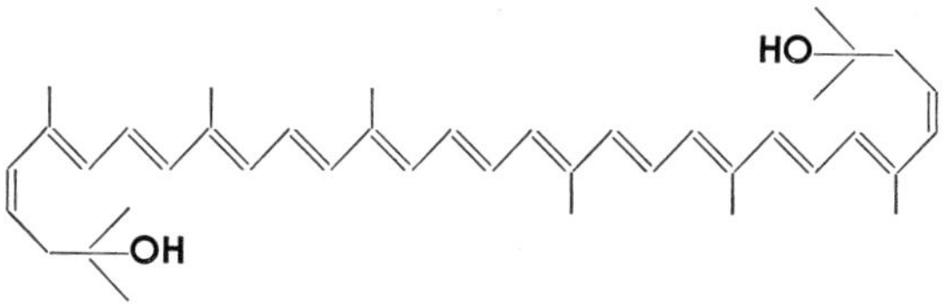

Halobacterium sp.

A mutant of *Staphylococcus aureus* unable to produce bright pigments incorporated the label of 2-c^{14}-mevalonic acid into phytoene, which it accumulated.[48a]

The biosynthesis and function of the carotenoid pigments have been reviewed.[49] Also a review of *cis, trans*-isomeric carotenoid pigments has been published.[50]

6. Polyenes and Polyynes, Excluding Polyene Macrolides

In a review of polyacetylenes[51] a number of substances not included in our list were mentioned without references or physical properties. These are reproduced here:

193a   **Octa-2,6-dien-4-yn-1,8-dioic Acid, $C_8H_6O_4$.**

$$HOOC—CH{=}CH—C{\equiv}C—CH{=}CH—COOH$$

Polyporus anthracophilus

194a   **Non-2-en-4,6,8-triynoic Acid, $C_9H_4O_2$.**

$$HC{\equiv}C—C{\equiv}C—C{\equiv}C—CH{=}CH—COOH$$

Psilocybe sarcocephala

195a   **Non-2-*trans*-oxido-4,6,8-triynol (Biformin?), $C_9H_6O_2$.**

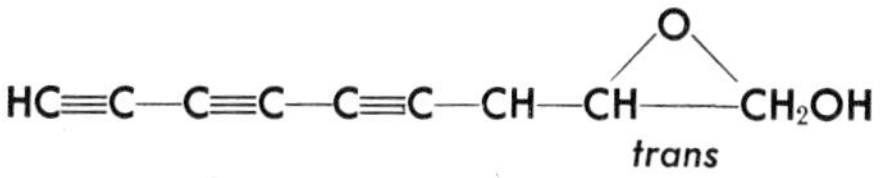

Coprinus quadrifidis (Polyporus biformis?)

[48a] Ginzaburo Suzue, *Biochim. et Biophys. Acta* **45** 616 (1960).
[49] T. W. Goodwin, *Advances in Enzymol.* **21** 295–361 (1959).
[50] L. Zechmeister, *Fortschr. Chem. org. Naturstoffe* **18** (1960).
[51] E. R. H. Jones, *Proc. Chem. Soc.*, 199–211 (1960).

195b   **Non-4-*cis*-en-6,8-diynoic Acid, $C_9H_8O_2$.**

$$HC\equiv C-C\equiv C-CH=CH-CH_2-CH_2-COOH$$
cis

Drosophila subatrata

198a   **Dec-2-*trans*-en-4,6,8-triynoic Acid, $C_{10}H_6O_2$.**

$$CH_3-C\equiv C-C\equiv C-C\equiv C-CH=CH-COOH$$
trans

Pleurotus ulmarius, Tricholoma paneolum

201a   **Dec-2-*trans*-en-4,6,8-triynol, $C_{10}H_8O$.**

trans

$$CH_3-C\equiv C-C\equiv C-C\equiv C-CH=CH-CH_2OH$$

Pleurotus ulmarius

200a   **Deca-4,6,8-triyn-1,10-dioic Acid, $C_{10}H_6O_4$.**

$$HOOC-C\equiv C-C\equiv C-C\equiv C-CH_2-CH_2-COOH$$

Merulius lachrymans

219a   **Tetradec-5-*cis*-en-8,10,12-triyn-1,14-dioic Acid, $C_{14}H_{12}O_4$.**

$$HOOC-C\equiv C-C\equiv C-C\equiv C-CH_2-CH=CH-CH_2-CH_2-CH_2-COOH$$
cis

Poria sinuosa

Four other polyacetylenes have been reported, complete with physical properties:[52]

195c   **Drosophilin E** (*cis*-Non-4-en-6,8-diynoic Acid), $C_9H_8O_2$, light-sensitive prisms, m.p. 35°, U.V. 279.5, 264, 250, 238, 227, 210 mμ.

cis

$$HC\equiv C-C\equiv C-CH=CH-CH_2-CH_2-COOH$$

Drosophila subatrata

209a   **Drosophilin C** (*cis*-Undec-3-en-5,7,10-triynoic Acid), $C_{11}H_8O_2$, colorless needles, slowly yellowing in light at 20°, m.p. 97.5–99°, U.V. 280.5, 264.5, 250.5, 238, 226.5, 210.5 mμ.

$$HC\equiv C-CH_2-C\equiv C-C\equiv C-CH=CH-CH_2-COOH$$

Drosophila subatrata

---

[52] E. R. H. Jones, P. R. Leeming and W. A. Remers, *J. Chem. Soc.*, 2257 (1960).

209b **Drosophilin D** (*cis*-Undeca-3,9,10-trien-5,7-diynoic Acid), $C_{11}H_8O_2$, colorless plates, m.p. 21–28°, U.V. 303.5, 290.5, 274.5, 259, 217 mμ.

$$H_2C\!=\!C\!=\!CH\!-\!C\!\equiv\!C\!-\!C\!\equiv\!C\!-\!CH\!=\!CH\!-\!CH_2\!-\!COOH$$

Drosophila subatrata

219b **Compound 3040** (Dimethyl *trans*-Undeca-2-en-4,6-diyn-1,11-dioate), $C_{13}H_{14}O_4$, colorless crystals, m.p. 15–16°, U.V. 304, 286, 270, 255, 222.5, 215 mμ.

$$CH_3OOC\!-\!CH_2\!-\!CH_2\!-\!CH_2\!-\!C\!\equiv\!C\!-\!C\!\equiv\!C\!-\!CH\!=\!CH\!-\!COOCH_3$$

Drosophila subatrata

An Italian review on the chemical aspects of the basidiomycete antibiotics has been published.[53]

7. Macrocyclic Lactones (Macrolides)

A new tetraene antibiotic has been reported.[54]

233a **Unamycin A,** white needles, m.p. (dec.) 148–150°, $[\alpha]_D^{25}$ −92° (c 1.0 in 80% methanol-water), U.V. 290, 304, 319 mμ in methanol.

An acidic tetraene. Negative $FeCl_3$, Million, Fehling, Tollens tests. Positive Molisch, $KMnO_4$ and Br_2 tests. Pink Schiff test.

A second substance resembling toyocamycin was isolated:

1288a **Unamycin B,** white needles, m.p. 236–238° (dec.), $[\alpha]_D^{15}$ −43° (c 1.0 in acid methanol), N. E. 310.

C 46.4, H 4.46, N 22.25. Gives essentially the same color tests as unamycin A.

The unamycins were produced by *Streptomyces fungicidicus*.

A heptaene which may be new has been reported.[55]

256a **Grubilin** green-yellow, amorphous.

A non-toxic heptaene produced by *Streptomyces* BA-27,

[53] Marcella Magliola, *Annali di Chimica* 50 455–490 (1960).

[54] Masayuke Matsuoka and Hamao Umezawa, *J. Antibiotics* (Japan) 13A 114 (1960).

[55] J. Uri, I. Szilagyi and I. Békési, Symposium on Antibiotics, Prague, 1959.

and differing from amphotericin B, ascosin, aureofacin, AYF, candicidin, candidin, candimycin, PA 150 and trichomycin.

Antimycoin has been separated into A and B components.[56] Mevalonic acid stimulated production of these substances by *Streptomyces aureus*. Of nine other polyene producers tested, *Streptomyces viridoflavus* production of candidin and *Streptomyces* strain 3832 production of a pentaene (antibiotic S-8) of the eurocidin type were stimulated by mevalonic acid addition.

The mechanism of nystatin action on *Candida albicans* has been studied.[57] Respiration was accelerated and glucose uptake diminished, apparently by alteration of cell permeability.

A dissertation has been published (not yet received) entitled *Beitrag zur Kenntnis des Candicidins D*, G. Demuth, Math.-Naturw. Fakultät der Univ. Göttingen, 1959.

Some generalizations can be made now concerning the structures of polyene macrolides.* Tetraenes and heptaenes generally seem to contain nitrogen, while pentaenes and hexaenes do not. Moldicidin and PA-153 are exceptions since they are nitrogen-containing pentaenes. All tetraenes except PA-166 contain mycosamine. PA-166 contains an amino sugar (not a deoxy type) other than mycosamine. Pentaenes are neutral, containing neither amino sugars nor free carboxyl groups.

Heptaenes have been found so far to contain four different nitrogen-containing moieties. Two of these are the amino sugars previously mentioned. The other two are the aromatic amines, *p*-aminoacetophenone and *p*-aminophenylacetone, which are released by alkaline hydrolysis.

---

[56] Robert Samuel Safferman, *Dissertation Abstr.* 20 4264 (1960).

[57] J. W. Harman and J. G. Masterson, *Irish J. Med. Sci.* 378 249 (1957).

* Most of the information below on the polyene macrolides was taken from a seminar given by Dr. Edward Borowsky, Visiting Professor at the Institute for Microbiology at Rutgers University from Gdansk, Poland, in August 1960 and will be published.

$$H_2N-\langle \rangle-\overset{\overset{O}{\|}}{C}-CH_3 \qquad H_2N-\langle \rangle-CH_2-\overset{\overset{O}{\|}}{C}-CH_3$$

p-Aminoacetophenone   p-Aminophenylacetone

Amphotericin B and candidin are examples of heptaenes containing mycosamine. Candicidin, trichomycin and PA-150 contain p-aminoacetophenone.

Hydrocandidin has yielded an oxidation fragment identified as:

$$HOOC-\underset{\underset{CH_3}{|}}{CH}-(CH_2)_{13}-\underset{\underset{CH_3}{|}}{CH}-CO-CH_3$$

Some studies on the biosynthesis of this heptaene show no incorporation of labeled mevalonic acid, propionic acid or methionine. It seems to be derived from acetate.

The pentaene, moldicidin A, $C_{43}H_{22}O_{19}N$ was omitted. Moldicidin B is identical with pentamycin.[57a] Candicidin is identical with ascosin. The main component of the PA-150 complex is identical with one component of the candidin complex. Several substances listed in the unclassified section are actually known to be polyene macrolides. These include: 1072-aliomycin (pentaene), 1067-akitamycin (tetraene), 1095-antibiotic from *Streptomyces fungicidicus* (tetraene), 1096-antibiotic from *S. griseus* (heptaene), 1097-antibiotic 26/1 (heptaene), 1294-substance 1404 (hexaene).

A new heptaene, perimycin (aminomycin), probably $C_{47}H_{75}O_{14}N_2$ and incorporating a p-aminophenyl group, has been reported.[58] Another heptaene, antibiotic 2814H, is produced together with a pentaene, antibiotic 2814P, netropsin and aureothin by *Streptomyces* IA 2814 resembling *S. netropsis*.[59] Analytical and optical data were reported on each.

[57a] Hiroshi Ogawa, Teiichiro Ito, Shigeharu Inoue and Motohiro Nishio, J. *Antibiotics* (Japan) 13A 353 (1960).

[58] Edward Borowsky *et al.*, Abstracts 1960 Conference on Antimicrobial Agents, Washington, D. C., October 26–28, 1960.

[59] Heinz Thrum and I-dschang Dcho, *Naturwissenschaften* 20 474 (1960).

The complete structures of the tetraenes, lagosin and filipin have been reported to be:[60]

C_5H_{11}—CH—OH OH   OH   R=OH=lagosin, $C_{35}H_{58}O_{12}$

O—CO—CH———(CH—$CH_2)_5$—CH—CH—R   R=H=filipin, $C_{35}H_{58}O_{11}$

CH_3—CH—CH—(CH=CH$)_4$—CH=C———CH—OH

     OH CH_3

Humidin $(C_{12}H_{20}O_4)_n$, colorless plates, m.p. 145–146° (dec.), $[\alpha]_D^{34}$ −6° (c 1.0 in ethanol), mol. wt. 550 ± 50, 823 ± 10, is an antifungal antibiotic isolated from the mycelium of *Streptomyces humidus*, which also produces dihydrostreptomycin.[61] It was not clear from the abstract whether or not this substance was of the polyene macrolide type.

Some aspects of the mode of action of polyene antifungal antibiotics have been reviewed.[62]

A nitrogen-containing antifungal polyene antibiotic, capacidin, produced by a streptomycete has been isolated.[63, 64] The substance is levorotatory, has reducing properties, is a primary or secondary alcohol and shows ultraviolet absorption peaks at 318, 332, 350 $m\mu$.

A general review of the polyene antifungal antibiotics has been published.[65]

Two new antibiotics have been reported, one of them, at least, apparently a macrolide.[66]

[60] M. L. Dhar, V. Thaller and M. C. Whiting, *Proc. Chem. Soc.*, 310 (1960).

[61] Koichi Nakazawa, Motoo Shibata, Hiroichi Yamamoto, Toshihiko Kanzaki, Eiji Higashide, Akira Miyake and Satoshi Horii, *Nippon Nôgei Kagaku Kaishi* 32 713 (1958). (*Chem. Abstr.* 54 22843g)

[62] E. Drouhet, L. Hirth and G. Lebeurier, *Annals N. Y. Acad. Sci.* 89 134–155 (1960).

[63] Rachel Brown and Elizabeth Hazen, N. Y. State Dept. Health, Ann. Rept. Div. Labs. and Research 50–52 (1959). (*Chem Abstr.* 54 22824h)

[64] *Idem., Antibiotics and Chemotherapy* 10 702 (1960).

[65] L. C. Vining, *Hindu Antibiotics Bulletin* 3 37–55 (1960).

[66] E. Gäumann, R. Hütter, W. Keller-Schierlein, L. Neipp, V. Prelog and H. Zähner, *Helv. Chim. Acta* 43 601 (1960).

265a Lankamycin, $C_{36}H_{62}O_{14}$, colorless crystals, m.p. 147–150° and at 181–182°, $[\alpha]_D^{20}$ −94° (c 1.23 in ethanol). U.V. 289 mμ.

Typical erythromycin color tests were obtained. It is notable that this macrolide contains no amino sugar.

A second, unclassified antibiotic was isolated from the same culture (*Streptomyces violaceoniger* (Waksman et Curtis) (Waksman et Henrici).

1164a Lankacidin, $C_{46}H_{66}O_{16}N_2$, pale yellow microcrystalline powder, m.p. 165–168°, $[\alpha]_D^{20}$ −161° (c 0.967 in ethanol), U.V. 227 mμ (log 2.95).

Contained no N − CH$_3$ or −OCH$_3$ groups.

It is interesting that spiramycin contains three sugars.[67]

A paper on the mode of action of erythromycin[68] reports that, when the antibiotic was added to growing cells of *E. coli*, synthesis of protein (but not RNA or DNA) was inhibited, as was adaptive formation of β-galactosidase. Lactose was the substrate. Oxygen uptake of resting cells was inhibited in some organisms but not in others, but in no case did cytochrome oxidase appear to be affected.

The wild strain of *Streptomyces kitasatoensis* Hata produces leucomycin, a complex of six macrolide antibiotics, while a mutant produces only two of these, although total macrolide production was the same in each case.[69, 70, 71] Probable empirical formulas of the members of the complex are shown below:

leucomycin	formula	melting point
A$_1$	$C_{46}H_{81}O_{17}N$	
A$_2$	$C_{65}H_{111}O_{22}N$	
B$_1$	$C_{35}H_{59}O_{13}N$	214.5–216.5°
B$_2$	$C_{38}H_{65}O_{16}N$	214–216°
B$_3$	$C_{34}H_{53}O_{13}N$	216–217°
B$_4$	$C_{38}H_{59}O_{16}N$	221–223.8°

[67] Raymond Paul and Serge Tchelitcheff, *Bull. Soc. chim. France,* 150 (1960).

[68] Hiroshi Nakagawa, *Osaka Daigaku Igaku Zasshi* 11 3451 (1959). (*Chem. Abstr.* 54 11154a)

[69] J. Abe, Y. Suzuki, T. Watanabe and K. Satake, *Nippon Kagaku Zasshi* 31 969 (1960).

[70] T. Watanabe *et al., Bull. Chem. Soc. Japan* 33 1100 (1960).

[71] Tetsuo Watanabe, Hisao Nishida, Jinnosuke Abe and Kazuo Satake, *ibid.* 33 1104 (1960).

Methymycin has been found to be biosynthesized principally from propionate, although one mole of acetate may be incorporated.[72]

8. Alicyclic Compounds Other Than Terpenoids and Steroids

An investigation of the biosynthesis of palitantin shows that it is acetate-derived, and that neither shikimic acid nor mevalonic acid are involved.[73]

Several compounds have been isolated which may be related to cycloheximide:

302a **Niromycin B,** $C_{14}H_{21}O_4N$ (suggested), white, hygroscopic crystals, m.p. 47–67°.

A neutral substance produced by *Streptomyces albus*.[74]

302b **Niromycin A,** white hygroscopic, amorphous powder, m.p. 98–105°.

Positive 2,4-dinitrophenylhydrazine and Tollens tests. Negative ninhydrin, $FeCl_3$, Fehlings, Benedicts, Molisch, biuret, $KMnO_4$ tests.

The effect of cycloheximide on the metabolism and growth of *Saccharomyces pastorianus* has been studied.[75]

Some substances related to sarkomycin and produced by the same organism were overlooked.[76] These were:

301a **Sarkomycin E₂,** $C_{10}H_{14}O_4$, m.p. 179°.

301c **Sarkomycin E₁,** $C_{14}H_{18}O_7$, m.p. 169°.

301d **Sarkomycin S₂,** $C_{14}H_{18}O_6S$, m.p. 183°, $[\alpha]_D$ +136°.

---

[72] A. J. Birch, E. Pride, R. W. Rickards, P. J. Thomson, J. D. Dutcher, D. Perlman and C. Djerassi, *Chem. and Ind.,* 1245 (1960).

[73] P. Chaplen and R. Thomas, *Biochem. J.* 77 91 (1960).

[74] Teisuke Osato, Yutaka Morikubo and Hamao Umezawa, *J. Antibiotics* (Japan) 13A 110 (1960).

[75] Bradner Wood Coursen, *Dissertation Abstr.* 21 (1960).

[76] Sueo Tatsuoka *et al., J. Antibiotics* (Japan) 9B 104 (1956).

301e   Sarkomycin S_1, $C_{14}H_{18}O_6S_2$, m.p. 161°, $[\alpha]_D^{22}$ +145°.

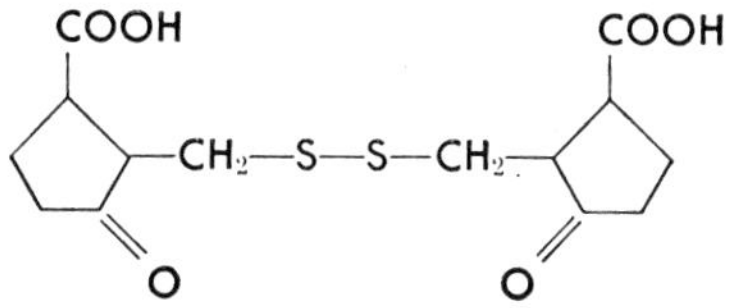

301f   Sarkomycin S_3, m.p. 148°.

C 50.39, H 5.31, S 15.75.

9. Terpenoids and Steroids

A new trichothecin-like antibiotic has been isolated from a basidiomycete.[77]

The oil of wheat stem rust uredospores contains Δ^7-ergostenol (fungisterol).[43]

Another steroidal metabolite of *Poria cocos* has been isolated and characterized. It is:[78]

354a   Pachymic Acid (3β-0-Acetylpolyporenic Acid B), $C_{33}H_{52}O_5$, colorless crystals, m.p. 296–299°, $[\alpha]_D^{22.5}$ 17.7° (c 0.566 in pyridine).

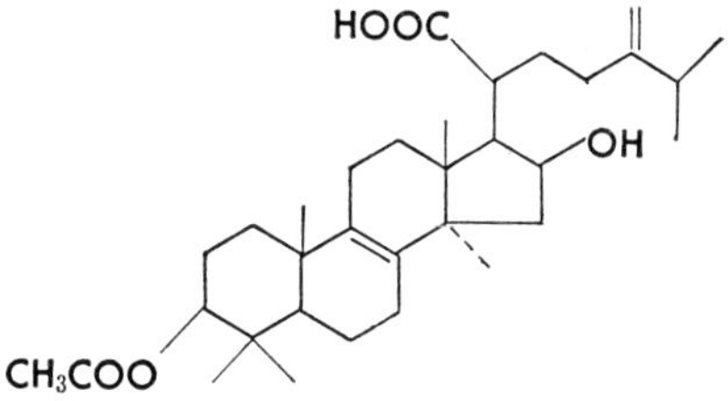

Cholesterol biosynthesis is inhibited by farnesoic acid and its analogues.[79]

The conversion of mevalonate to a mixture of farnesol and nerolidol (probably as their pyrophosphates) by a

[77] Ervin Gláz, Eszter Scheiber, J. Gyimesi, I. Horvath, Katalin Steczek, A. Szentirmai and G. Bohus, *Nature* 184 Suppl. No. 12, 908 (1959).

[78] Shoji Shibata, Shinsaku Natori, Ko Fujita, Isao Kitagawa and Kazue Watanabe, *Chem. & Pharm. Bull.* (Tokyo) 6 608 (1958).

[79] G. Popják, Rita H. Cornforth and K. Clifford, *Lancet*, 1270 (1960).

liver enzyme preparation has suggested that 1 mole of each is involved in the biosynthesis of squalene.[80] The condensation of these two substances would then be analogous to that of isopentenylpyrophosphate with 3,3-dimethylallyl pyrophosphate (or geranyl pyrophosphate).

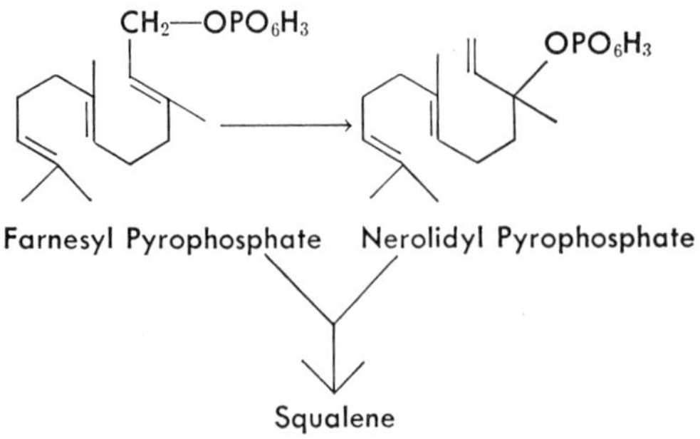

Farnesyl Pyrophosphate   Nerolidyl Pyrophosphate

Squalene

The significant points of the chemical mechanism of squalene biosynthesis were summarized as follows: (a) The process is not a concerted reaction, but proceeds in steps with well-defined stable intermediates. (b) During isomerization of isopentenylpyrophosphate there is an uptake of one proton in the terminal methylene group, and this proton appears finally in one of the terminal methyl groups at each end of squalene, which means the entry into each molecule of squalene of two protons not contained originally in mevalonic acid. (c) There are no reductive steps involved in the synthesis of geranyl or farnesyl pyrophosphates. (d) Farnesyl pyrophosphate and the nerolidyl derivative are the two sesquiterpenoids condensing to the symmetrical dihydroterpene, squalene, a stable intermediate being dihydrosqualene. (e) During stabilization of the condensation product of the farnesyl and nerolidyl derivatives, elimination of two protons, originally attached to C-5 of mevalonate occurs. (f) The final step is a reduction, introducing into squalene two further hydrogen atoms not contained originally in mevalonic acid.

[80] J. W. Cornforth and G. W. Popják, *Tetrahedron Letters* **No. 19** 29 (1959).

10. Tropolone Acids

More data have been published on the structure of heliomycin (entry 1173). It is acidic (pK 5.8), forms a diacetate and may contain a benzotropolone ring system. Empirical formulas $C_{19}H_{14-16}O_5$ or $C_{23}H_{18-20}O_6$ have been suggested.[81]

11. Phenolic Substances

p-Hydroxybenzoic acid, found earlier in *Penicillium patulum* has been isolated also from *Penicillium griseofulvum*.[82] Isolated from the same culture were:

379a **m-Hydroxybenzoic Acid, $C_7H_6O_3$, m.p. 201°**

and

379b **Salicylic Acid (o-Hydroxybenzoic Acid), m.p. 159°.**

The same mold produces homogentisic acid, a metabolite also found in some of the higher fungi.[83]

391a **Homogentisic Acid, $C_8H_8O_4$, m.p. 152–154°.**

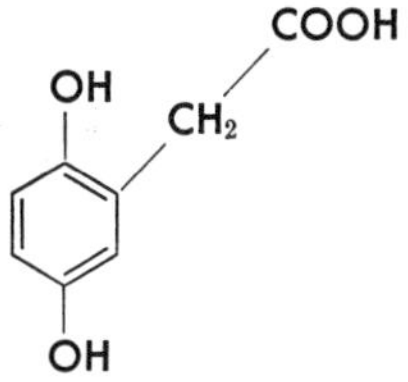

p-Hydroxyphenylpyruvic acid and tyrosine were identified in the culture, and occasionally 1,4-hydroquinone was present.

The production of gallic acid by *Phycomyces blakesleeanus* (sporangiophores) has been confirmed.[84] It was suggested that this substance may be the primary photosensitive pigment involved in the strong negative phototropic response to ultraviolet light which such organs show.

[81] Z. V. Pushkareva, N. M. Voronina, S. I. Omel'chenko, L. B. Radina and Yu. N. Sheinker, *J. Gen. Chem.* (USSR) **29** 3469 (English translation) (1960).

[82] P. Simonart, A. Wiaux and H. Verachtert, *Bull. soc. chim. biol.* **41** 537, 541 (1959).

[83] Paul Simonart, Anselme Wiaux and Hubert Verachtert, *Zentrl. Bakteriol. Parasitenk. Abt. II* **113** 209 (1960).

[84] David S. Dennison, *Nature* **184** 2036 (1960).

C^{14}-Labeled orsellinic acid has been prepared by using *Chaetomium cochliodes* as the producer. Orsellinic acid was known to be a metabolite of *Penicillium barnense,* which also produces penicillic acid. When *Penicillium barnense* was grown in the presence of the labeled orsellinic acid, it could be shown that orsellinic acid was a precursor of penicillic acid in this organism.[85] The sites of labeling and actual modes of cleavage are shown.

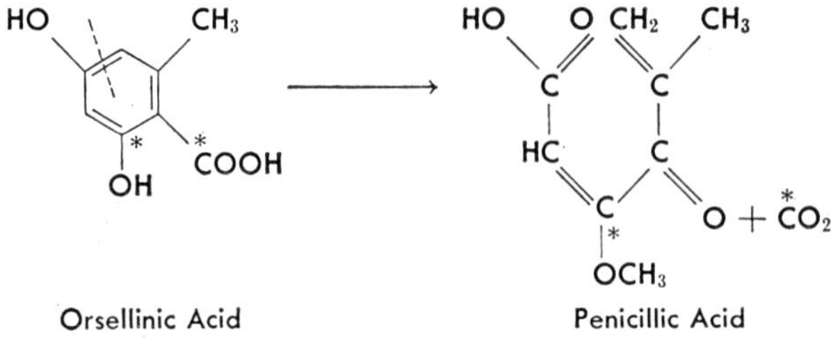

Orsellinic Acid   Penicillic Acid

It appears that orsellinic acid is an intermediate in the biogenesis of the xanthone ravenelin.[86] It has been suggested as an intermediate in the biosynthesis of several other types of compounds, *e.g.*, lichen substances, fungal anthraquinones and alternariol.

An uncharacterized substance has been isolated from *Curvularia lunata.*[87]

417a **Substance from *Curvularia lunata*,** $C_{14}H_{18}O_5$, colorless solid, m.p. 195°.

Apparently phenolic. Mannitol was isolated from the same culture.

Curvularin, also produced by *Curvalaria lunata*, is produced by *Penicillium steckii* as well.[88]

A new depsidone has been isolated from an Australian lichen and characterized as norlobaridone:[89]

[85] Klaus Mosbach, *Acta. Chem. Scand.* 14 457 (1960).

[86] Private communication from Herchel Smith.

[87] T. Krishna Murty and S. Sankara Subramanian, *Indian J. Pharmacy* 20 72 (1958).

[88] D. Fennell, K. B. Raper and F. H. Stodola, *Chem. and Ind.,* 1382 (1959).

[89] G. P. Briner, G. E. Gream and N. V. Riggs, *Australian J. Chem.* 13 275 (1960).

471a Norlobaridone, $C_{23}H_{26}O_6$, colorless crystals, m.p. 188–190°.

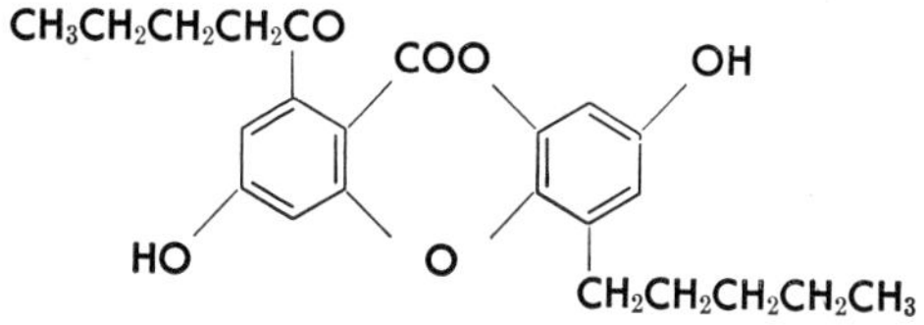

CH₃CH₂CH₂CH₂CO COO OH

HO O
CH₂CH₂CH₂CH₂CH₃

A yield of 2.2% was obtained from *Parmelia conspersa.* The structure of nidulin (and thus of nornidulin) has been completed.[89a] It is:

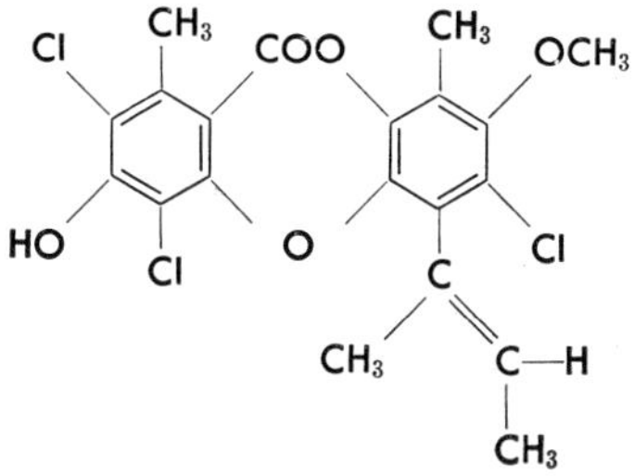

Cl CH₃ COO CH₃ OCH₃

HO Cl O Cl
C
CH₃ C—H
CH₃

The chemistry of the uncommon 1-methylpropenyl substituent is greatly modified by the neighboring chlorine atom.

12. Quinones and Related Compounds

a. BENZOQUINONES

The growth of a mycobacterium was stimulated by coenzyme Q_{10} which suggests a possible role in energy metabolism.[90]

b. NAPHTHOQUINONES

A variety of bacteria (*Bacillus cereus, B. subtilis, Proteus vulgaris, Sarcina flava, Staphylococcus aureus, Mycobacterium phlei, Pseudomonas* spp., *Azotobacter vinelandii, Nocardia* sp.) were examined for vitamin K content.[91] Three types were identified. Vitamin K_2 was

[89a] F. M. Dean, D. S. Deorha, A. D. T. Erni, D. W. Hughes and John C. Roberts, *J. Chem. Soc.,* 4829 (1960).

[90] James O. Norman and Robert P. Williams, *Biochem. and Biophys. Res. Comms.* 2 372 (1960).

[91] Bodil Kruse Jacobsen and Hendrik Dam, *Biochim. et Biophys. Acta* 40 211 (1960).

isolated from *Bacillus cereus* and vitamin K_1 or a related substance from *Mycobacterium phlei*.

A lipide cofactor, perhaps a K vitamin or a tocopherol, has been implicated in the conversion of L-gulonolactone into L-ascorbic acid.[92]

C. ANTHRAQUINONES

In 1955 three substances were isolated from a yellow sterile mold and were called flavomycelin, rhodomycelin and purpurmycelin.[93] Rhodomycelin is identical with islandicin and flavomycelin with luteoskyrin. Acetone solutions of luteoskyrin turn purple on exposure to light, and purpurmycelin was found to be identical with this irradiation product.[94]

The biosynthesis of the pigments of *Penicillium islandicum* has been studied.[95] The acetate origin of islandicin, skyrin, rubroskyrin (luteoskyrin) and iridoskyrin was established. The results of labeling experiments led to the conclusion that, despite the close structural relationship, these pigments are not interconvertible *in vivo*, but seem to be derived from a common pre-aromatic stage. Also mutations fail to block formation of any single pigment. Biogenesis, it was suggested, must not take place by stepwise formations of defined intermediates such as benzene derivatives, but should be dependent throughout on participation of activated acetate.

An acidic substance related to herqueinone has been isolated.[96]

A review of quinones as metabolic products of microorganisms has been published.[97]

There have been two recent publications on the struc-

[92] I. B. Chatterjee, N. C. Kar, N. C. Ghosh and B. C. Guha, *Arch. Biochem. and Biophys.* **86** 154 (1960).

[93] H. Nishikawa, *Tohoku J. Agr. Res.* **5** 285 (1955).

[94] S. Shibata, I. Kitagawa and N. Nishikawa, *Pharm. Bull.* (Tokyo) **5** 383 (1957).

[95] Sten Gatenbeck, *Acta Chem. Scand.* **14** 102, 230, 296 (1960).

[96] K. S. Gopalkrishnan and N. Narasimhachari, "Antibiotics," Council of Scientific and Industrial Research, New Delhi, 1958, pp. 176–179.

[97] J. H. Birkinshaw, *Planta Med.* **7** 367 (1959).

ture of thelephoric acid (entry 493).[98, 99] The second
publication cited reported the synthesis of thelephoric
acid and seems to establish the structure definitely as:

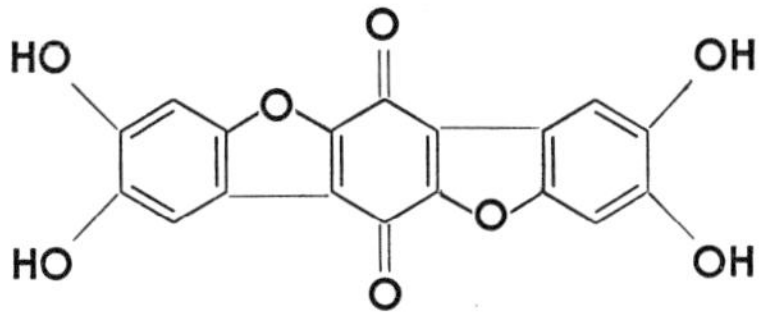

Oösporein (chaetomidin) (entry 487) is reported to be
identical with isooösporein (entry 488).[100]

A reinvestigation of quinones produced by *Phoma terrestris* Hansen identified cynodontin and a small amount
of another anthraquinone, but found no phomazarin (entry 556).[101]

13. Tetracycline, Analogues and Related Substances

The aglycone, aklavinone, of the antibiotic aklavin has
been found to differ from rutilantinone (ϵ-pyrromyci-
none) only by lacking one hydroxyl group.[102]

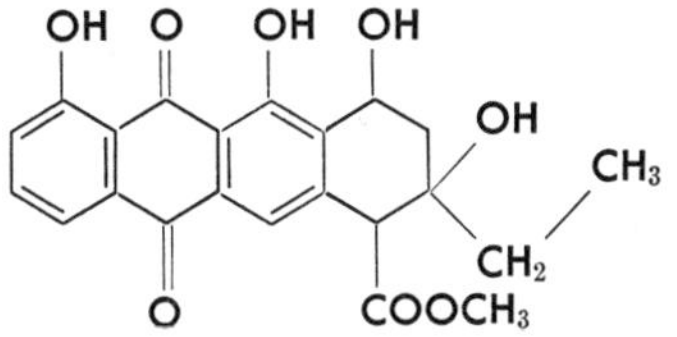

Aklavinone $C_{22}H_{20}O_8$ 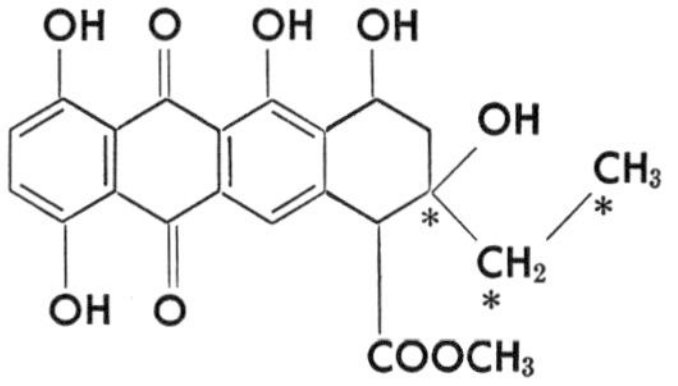   Rutilantinone $C_{22}H_{20}O_9$

A biogenesis was postulated in the following sense:

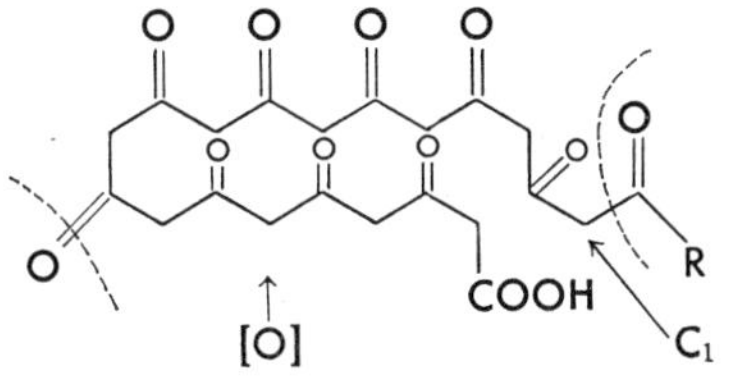

[98] K. Aghoramurthy, K. G. Sarma and T. R. Seshadri, *Tetrahedron
Letters* No. 16 4 (1960).

[99] J. Gripenberg, *Tetrahedron* 10 135 (1960).

[100] J. Smith and R. H. Thomson, *ibid.* 10 148 (1960).

[101] D. E. Wright and K. Schofield, *Nature* 188 233 (1960).

[102] J. J. Gordon, L. M. Jackman, W. D. Ollis and I. O. Sutherland,
Tetrahedron Letters No. 8 28 (1960).

A more recent publication indicates that nine acetate units are incorporated into the rutilanlinone molecule, but that the three starred atoms are from propionate.[103] Methionine would not, then, be involved in the side-chain synthesis.

Two investigations have been made on the chlorination mechanism of *Streptomyces aureofaciens* in the production of aureomycin.[104, 105] The authors of the first reference concluded that incorporation of the chlorine atom does not take place on the finished tetracycline molecule, but at an earlier stage of biosynthesis. Wang's results lead to the same conclusion.

The influence of specific enzyme poisons on the production of oxytetracycline has been studied.[106] Iron-containing oxidases and flavine oxidases participated in the biosynthesis of oxytetracycline. Phenoloxidase inhibitors, on the other hand, stimulated production.

There is little agreement on the mode of action of the tetracycline antibiotics, and it may be that they act in a variety of ways. Inhibition of RNA and DNA synthesis and inhibition of enzymic conversion of uracil to thymine,[107] binding by chelation of metal ions required by coenzymes[108] and blocking of unspecified biosynthetic pathways[109] have been mentioned.

A discussion of the mechanisms of action of antibiotics in general has been published.[110]

[103] W. D. Ollis, I. O. Sutherland, R. C. Codner, J. J. Gordon and G. A. Miller, *Proc. Chem. Soc.*, 347 (1960).

[104] J. Kollar and M. Jarai, Symposium on Antibiotics, Prague, 1959.

[105] E. Lin Wang, *J. Antibiotics* (Japan) 12A 31, 41, 50 (1959).

[106] V. Ševčík, V. Musílek and I. Komersová, Symposium on Antibiotics, Prague, 1959.

[107] T. Balakrishna Rao, D. V. Temhane, D. V. Rege and A. Sreenivasan, "Antibiotics," Council of Scientific and Industrial Research, New Delhi, 1958, p. 212.

[108] E. U. Weinberg, *Bacteriol. Revs.* 21 46 (1957).

[109] J. F. Snell, Florence Z. Thanassi and Dorothy Ann Sypowicz, *Antibiotics and Chemotherapy* 8 57 (1958).

[110] S. G. Bradley and L. A. Jones, *Annals N. Y. Acad. Sci.* 89 123 (1960).

14. Aromatic Compounds Not Classified Elsewhere

The cooccurrence of anisaldehyde and junipal in *Daedalea juniperina* cultures has inspired the suggestion that both substances are derived from a common acetylenic precursor.[111, 112] An earlier report that *Polyporus benzoinus* produces considerable quantities of anisaldehyde was not mentioned in our entry on that substance.[113]

15. Amines

Although the ordinary source of the amine, carnitine, is mammalian muscle, a publication was overlooked in which it was isolated from the mold *Neurospora crassa* grown on a chemically defined medium.[114]

653a   L-**Carnitine,** $C_7H_{15}O_3N$, extremely hygroscopic crystals, m.p. 196–198°, $[\alpha]_D^{20}$ −23.5° (c 0.5 in water).

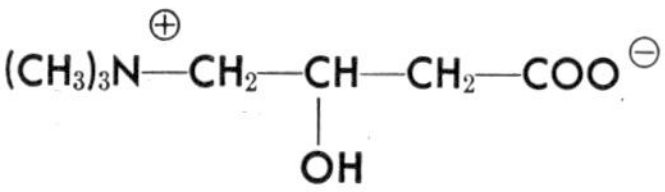

$$(CH_3)_3\overset{\oplus}{N}-CH_2-\underset{\underset{OH}{|}}{CH}-CH_2-COO^{\ominus}$$

This amine would not replace choline in choline-less neurospora mutants. It was not found in *E. coli.* The role of carnitine in lipide metabolism has been reviewed.[115, 116]

An amine related to muscarine has been isolated and characterized by synthesis.[117, 118] It is:

658a   (+)-**Muscaridine,** $C_9H_{22}O_2NCl$ (Chloroaurate), $C_9H_{22}AuCl_4O_2N$, m.p. 129–131°, $[\alpha]_D^{19}$ +20.5° ±0.5° (c 8.3 in water).

[111] J. H. Birkinshaw and P. Chaplen, *Biochem. J.* 60 255 (1955).

[112] K. E. Schulte and N. Jantos, *Arch. Pharm.* 292 536 (1959).

[113] J. H. Birkinshaw, E. N. Morgan and W. P. K. Findlay, *Biochem. J.* 50 509 (1952).

[114] G. Fraenkel, *Biol. Bull.* 104 359 (1953).

[115] G. Fraenkel and S. Freedman, *Vitamins and Hormones* 15 74–115 (1957).

[116] E. P. Adams, P. E. Ballance and A. E. Bender, *Nature* 185 612 (1960).

[117] F. Kögl, C. A. Salemink and P. L. Schuller, *Rec. trav. chim.* 79 278 (1960).

[118] C. A. Salemink and P. L. Schuller, *ibid.* 79 485 (1960).

$$\overset{\oplus}{(CH_3)_3N}\overset{Cl}{\underset{}{}}\overset{\ominus}{}CH_2-CH_2-CH_2-\underset{OH}{CH}-\underset{OH}{CH}-CH_3$$

Amanita muscaria

A survey of 32 fungi and nine bacteria indicated that the production of choline sulfate is limited to the higher fungi.[119] All bacteria were negative as were phycomycetes. Of the ascomycetes, spharioles produced it, but endomycetales did not. Basidiomycetes and all fungi imperfecti examined (except *Torula utilis*) were producers.

List has continued his investigations of the basic constituents of higher fungi. From *Polyporus sulfureus* were isolated the following non-volatile substances: adenine, hypoxanthine, arginine, histidine, lysine, choline, histidine betaine, phenylethylamine, imidazolyl acetate, homarine, trigonelline, γ-butyrobetaine and an uncharacterized hydrochloride, $C_9H_{16}N_2 \cdot 2HCl$.[120]

The mushroom *Coprinus atramentarius* was studied.[121] A prior report that it produced tetraethylthiuram disulfide could not be confirmed. Found, however, were isoamylamine, phenylethylamine, adenine, hypoxanthine, urocanic acid, imidazolyacetic acid, imidazolylpropionic acid, imidazolylethanol, histidine, arginine, choline, lysine, guanidine, ergothioneine, hercynine, glycine, betaine, tyramine, putrescine, cadaverine, δ-aminovaleric acid, α-guanidinobutyric acid, two unidentified bases, glycine, threonine, glutamic acid, aspartic acid, alanine, proline, leucine, valine, isoleucine, citrulline, tyrosine and ornithine.

A dissertation has been published on basic constituents and amino acids of the basidiomycete, *Inocybe patoullardii* Bres.[122]

Found were methylamine, dimethylamine, ethylamine, *n*-propylamine, isoamylamine, β-phenylethylamine, choline, cadaverine, putrescine, hypoxanthine, alanine, pro-

[119] T. Harada and B. Spender, *J. Gen. Microbiol.* 22 520 (1960).

[120] P. List and H. Menssen, *Arch. Pharm.* 292 260–271 (1959).

[121] P. H. List and H. Reith, *Arzneimittel-Forsch.* 10 34–40 (1960).

[122] H. Müller, Dissertation, Naturw. Fakultät Univ. Würzburg, 1959.

line, tyrosine, valine, leucine, cysteine, aspartic acid, glutamic acid, histidine, imidazole-4-acetic acid, arginine, ornithine and the incompletely characterized basic red pigment of the organism, $C_{11}H_{20}O_9N_2$. This was yellow in alkali, red in acid solutions and gave positive Bayer and Pauly diazo tests.

A study of the biogenesis of spermidine (entry 642) in microorganisms has shown that the C_4 moiety is derived from putrescine (or ornithine) while the C_3 chain has its origin in methionine.[123]

Biochemical pathways in legume root nodule nitrogen fixation have been reviewed.[124]

16. Amino Acids and Related Compounds

The lysine, methionine and tryptophan contents of a number of yeasts have been surveyed.[125]

In a study of the interrelationships between folic acid and cobalamin in the synthesis of methionine by extracts of *E. coli,* it was concluded that serine is not on the route of biosynthesis of the methyl group of methionine.[126]

Discussing the two modes of lysine synthesis by lower fungi, Vogel has pointed out that organisms of older evolutionary origin follow the bacterial route.[127] These include eubacteria, pseudomonads and actinomycetes. Ascomycetous and basidiomycetous fungi use the fungal pathway via α-aminoadipic acid.

17. Polypeptides and Related Compounds

The ostreogrycin (E-129) complex was isolated in 1958[128] and reported similar to streptogramin, staphylomycin (A-899), PA-114 and mikamycin.

E-129A probably is identical with staphylomycin M and

[123] H. Tabor, S. M. Rosenthal and C. W. Tabor, *J. Biol. Chem.* **233** 907 (1958).

[124] F. J. Bergersen, *Bacteriol. Revs.* 24 246 (1960).

[125] G. E. N. Nelson, R. F. Anderson, R. A. Rhodes, Margaret C. Shekleton and H. H. Hall, *Appl. Microbiol.* 8 179 (1960).

[126] R. L. Kisliuk and D. D. Woods, *Biochem. J.* 75 467 (1960).

[127] H. J. Vogel, *Biochim. et Biophys. Acta* 41 172 (1960).

[128] S. Ball, B. Boothroyd, K. A. Lees, A. H. Raper and E. Lester Smith, *Biochem, J.* 68 24p (1958).

PA-114A. E-129B may be identical with PA-114B, but different from staphylomycin S:[129]

770a **Ostreogrycin B,** (E-129B) $C_{45}H_{54}O_9N_8$, colorless prisms from methanol with solvation, colorless needles from toluene, m.p. 266–268°, $[\alpha]_D^{20}$ −66.8° (c 0.5 in methanol).

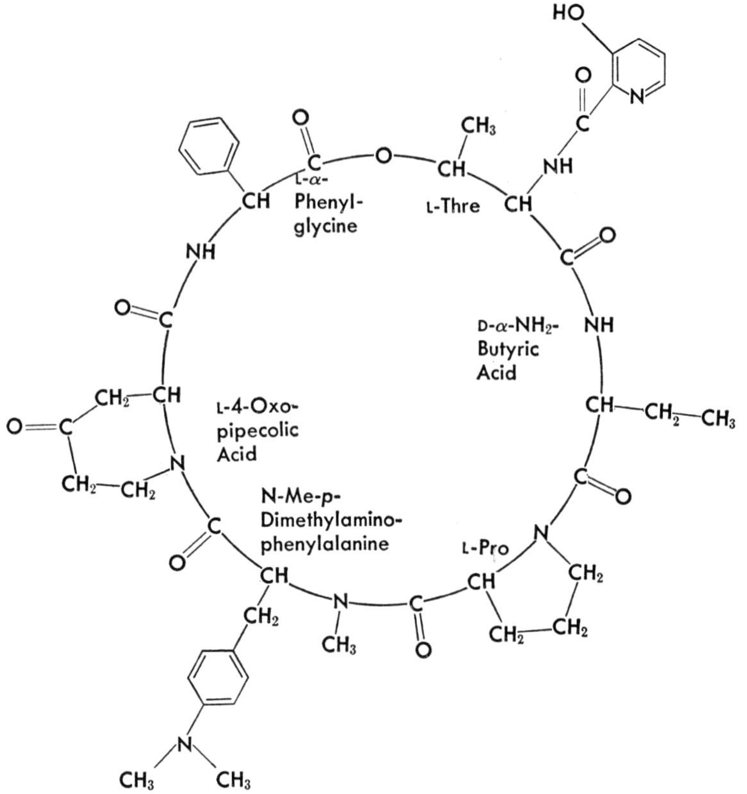

Streptomyces ostreogriseus

This structure differs from staphylomycin only by substitution of *p*-dimethylamino-N-methylphenylalanine for N-methylphenylalanine.

A similar structure has been proposed for mikamycin B, the only difference being a hydroxyl group in the β-posi-

[129] F. W. Eastwood, B. K. Snell and Alexander Todd, *J. Chem. Soc.*, **2286** (1960).

tion of the pyridine moiety adjacent to the carbonyl group in the mikamycin.[129a]

An antiviral polypeptide, cephalomycin, has been reported.[130] It contained leucine, alanine, valine, arginine, glutamic acid, aspartic acid, glycine, threonine, tyrosine, phenylalanine and three unidentified ninhydrin-positive substances.

Some peptide sequences of colimycin have been determined.[131] It resembles polymyxin B, and the sequence L-Dia—L-Dia—D-Leu—L-Leu—L-Dia—L-Dia—L-Dia—L-Dia—L-Thr has been established (L-Dia = α, γ-L-diaminobutyric acid).

An antibiotic named colisan has been isolated from a bacillus.[132, 133]

Sporidesmolide I, a metabolic product of *Sporidesmium bakeri* Syd., colorless needles, m.p. 261–263°, $[\alpha]_D^{17}$ −217° in chloroform (c 1.5) has the empirical formula $C_{33}H_{58}O_8N_4$ and the structure:[133a]

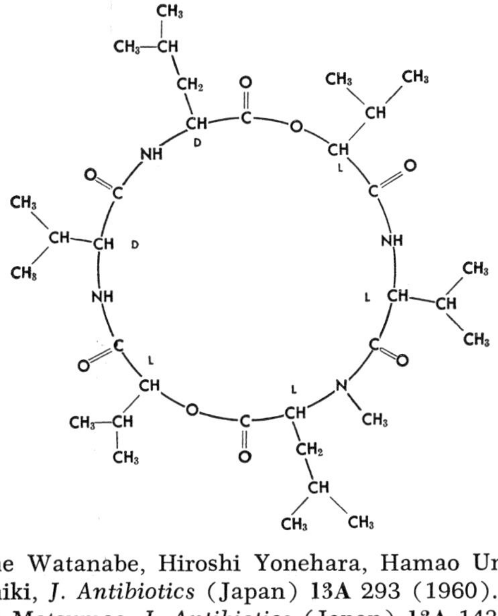

[129a] Kiyoshe Watanabe, Hiroshi Yonehara, Hamao Umezawa and Yusuke Sumiki, *J. Antibiotics* (Japan) 13A 293 (1960).

[130] Akihiro Matsumae, *J. Antibiotics* (Japan) 13A 143 (1960).

[131] Michel Dautrevaux and Gerard Biserte, *Compt. rend. soc. biol.* 153 1346 (1959).

[132] R. Reitler and J. Boxer, *Nature* 158 26 (1946).

[133] R. Reitler and A. Berner, to be published.

[133a] D. W. Russell, *Biochim. et Biophys. Acta* 45 411 (1960).

making it a new member of the depsipeptide or peptolide class. This is the first report of L-α-hydroxyisovaleric acid as a natural product.

A wilt toxin, culmomarasmin, which was 200 times as active as fusaric acid or lycomarasmine, has been isolated from *Fusarium culmorum*.[134] It is a crystalline polypeptide, m.p. 215–218° (dec.), stable below 0°. It is ninhydrin-negative and has the analysis: C 45.31, H 7.08, O 27.56, N 10.36, S 4.76, Cl 4.19, C—CH$_3$ 3.17, —OCH$_3$ 1.08. It also contains iron (1.39% inorganic residue). The amino acids are cystine, leucine, serine, aspartic acid, glutamic acid, alanine, valine, *allo*-isoleucine, proline, glycine, threonine and ammonia.

Two dissertations on wilt toxins have been published.[135, 136]

The antibacterial activities of acyclic decapeptide analogues of gramicidin S have been measured.[137] The mode of action of the acyclic compounds differs from that of the cyclic ones. While gramicidin S causes immediate bacteriostasis, the acyclic analogues are effective only after several cell divisions. The most active analogue was $\frac{1}{10}$ as active as gramicidin S against *E. coli* and $\frac{1}{40}$ as active against *Staphylococcus aureus*.

The mushroom toxin, phalloidin, has been reported to act by inhibition of oxidative phosphorylation.[138] A more recent study claims that it acts, rather, by interference with protein synthesis.[139]

The neuromuscular blocking properties of various polypeptide antibiotics have been investigated.[139a]

A yellow pigment has been isolated from *E. coli*.[140]

[134] J. Kiss, *Chimia* 14 174 (1960).

[135] Hans Gempeler, *Über welkaktive Inhaltsstoffe von Endopathia parasitica (Murr.) und von Fusarium martii*, Dissertation, Eidgenössische Technische Hochschule, 1959.

[136] Fritz Kugler, *Über welkaktive Inhaltsstoffe von Endopathia parasitica (Murr.) und von Fusarium solani (Mart.) v. Martii*, Dissertation, Eidgenössische Technische Hochschule, 1959.

[137] B. F. Erlanger and L. Goode, *Science* 131 669 (1960).

[138] Benno Hess, *Biochem. Z.* 328 325 (1956).

[139] A. von der Decken, H. Low and T. Hultin, *ibid.* 332 503 (1960).

[139a] R. H. Adamson, F. N. Marshall and J. P. Long, *Proc. Soc. Exptl. Biol. and Med.* 105 494 (1960).

[140] K. Ishii and M. Sevag, *Arch. Biochem. and Biophys.* 77 41 (1958).

Acid hydrolysis yielded p-aminobenzoic acid, glutamic acid, alanine, leucine and perhaps another uncharacterized substance (not a pteridine) with an U.V. maximum at 360 mμ.

A total synthesis of gramicidin J_2 has been achieved.[141] The biosynthesis of this substance has been investigated.[142] The antibiotic was concentrated in the RNA-rich protoplast precipitate.

The fact that bacitracin A (especially old samples) stimulates growth of *Phycomyces blakesleanus* may be due to conversion of the thiazoline ring of bacitracin A to a thiazole ring (bacitracin F).[143]

Papers have appeared on metabolism and actinomycin production by streptomycetes[144] and on the citric acid cycle and actinomycin formation.[145]

The cytostatic activity of actinomycins is reversed by high concentrations of purines and pyrimidines.[146] The interpretation of this effect was that actinomycin may react with DNA to form dye-polymer complexes.

Mitomycin C causes bacteria to break down their DNA rapidly, acid-soluble products being formed.[146a]

An actinomycin complex, aurantin, colorless crystals, m.p. 255–257°, $[\alpha]_D{}^{18} - 308°$, has been isolated in Russia.[147] The complex contains threonine, sarcosine, proline, valine, N-methylvaline and isoleucine. It was separated into four biologically active components: A_1 m.p. 205°, A_2 m.p. 225°, A_3 m.p. 226° and A_4 m.p. 152°.

Methionine furnishes the methyl groups attached to the aromatic chromophore of the actinomycins as shown by labeling with C^{14}.[147a]

[141] Y. Noda, *J. Chem. Soc. Japan* **80** 411 (1959).

[142] S. Otani, I. Murakami and S. Chin, Abstr. 118th Meeting, Japanese Antibiotics Association.

[143] Sibor Ebringer, *Naturwissenschaften* **47** 210 (1960).

[144] Paul Präve, *Arch. Mikrobiol.* **32** 278 (1959).

[145] *Idem., ibid.* **32** 286 (1959).

[146] W. Kersten, H. Kersten and H. M. Rauen, *Nature* **187** 60 (1960).

[146a] E. Reich, A. J. Shatkin and E. L. Tatum, *Biochim. et Biophys. Acta* **45** 608 (1960).

[147] A. B. Cilaev, T. I. Orlova, B. C. Kuznetsova and I. B. Mironova, *Antibiotiki* **3** 18 (1960).

[147a] A. J. Birch, D. W. Cameron, P. W. Holloway and R. W. Rickards, *Tetrahedron Letters* No. 25 26 (1960).

A general review of actinomycin structure and synthesis has appeared.[147b]

A colorless, amorphous polypeptide antibiotic, edein, has been isolated from a strain of *Bacillus brevis*.[148] It contained arginine, glycine, glutamic acid, aspartic acid, tyrosine and two unidentified ninhydrin-positive spots.

Two heat stable polypeptides, phytoactin and phytostreptin, have been isolated from an unclassified streptomycete.[149] Both contain valine, α-alanine, proline, leucine or isoleucine, arginine, glycine and serine.

Two peptide antibiotics not mentioned before are coliformin[150] and roseocitrins A and B.[151] Coliformin has the analysis: C 47.6, H 8.22, Cl 3.31, S 0.23, P 0.47 and O 33.15 and contains alanine, glycine, serine, glutamic acid, aspartic acid, lysine, valine and leucine. The roseocitrins appear to resemble streptothricin.

In a review of this class the name depsipeptide has been suggested for substances such as amidomycin and valinomycin, which are composed of α-hydroxy acids and amino acids.[152] Synthetic methods have been devised for both regular and irregular sequences of the two types of acids in these antibiotics.

The biosynthesis of α,γ-diaminobutyric acid in *Bacillus circulans* has been studied.[153]

The structure of amidinomycin, $C_9H_{18}ON_4 \cdot H_2SO_4$, has been shown to be:[153a]

[147b] Hans Brockmann, *Angew. Chem.* **72** 939–948 (1960).

[148] Z. Kurylo-Borowska, Symposium on Antibiotics, Prague, 1959.

[149] Jack Ziffer, S. J. Ishihara, T. J. Cairney and A. W. Chow, *Phytopathology* **47** 539 (1957).

[150] Stig K. L. Freyschuss, Stig O. Pehrson and Borje Steinberg, *Antibiotics and Chemotherapy* **5** 218 (1955).

[151] Hisaya Kato, *J. Antibiotics* (Japan) **6A** 143 (1953).

[152] M. M. Shemyakin, *Angew. Chem.* **72** 342–345 (1960).

[153] Yelahanka Krishnamurthy Murthy, Dissertation, Purdue Univ., 1958.

[153a] Shoshiro Nakamura, Keiko Karasawa, Nobuo Tanaka, Hiroshi Yonehara and Hamao Umezawa, *J. Antibiotics* (Japan) **13A** 362 (1960).

The structure of the antifungal antibiotic, variotin, $C_{18}H_{27}O_4N$, is:[153b]

$$CH_3 \cdot CH_2 - CH_2 - CH = C - CH = C - CH = CH - CH = CH - \overset{\overset{\displaystyle O}{\|}}{C} - NH - CH_2 - CH_2 - CH_2$$

with substituents OH and CH$_3$ on the chain, and

$$- \overset{\overset{\displaystyle O}{\|}}{C} - OCH_3$$

Thus, while it is a tetraene, it is not of the macrolide class.

Siderochromes.

A number of microorganisms have been found to produce iron-containing pigments which absorb in the ultraviolet at 420–440 mμ and have other properties in common. It has been suggested that these be called *siderochromes*.[154]

Some of these substances are antibiotic and are called *sideromycins*. Others are growth factors and may be designated *sideramines*. The antibiotic sideromycins seem to function by inhibiting the growth factor sideramines.

It remains to be seen how broadly the significance of these substances will extend. Some 50 strains of streptomycetes produce sideromycin-like antibiotics.[154] Of 32 common microbial species examined 10 produced coprogen-like substances.[155] The sideramines seem to perform a coenzyme-like function in many microorganisms.

Grisein A and albomycin have broad antibiotic activity. In gram-positive microorganisms, but not in gram-negative ones, their effects are inhibited by sideramines. Ferrimycin is 10 to 50 times as effective as penicillin against gram-positive microorganisms in animal studies.

The following table shows some of the siderochromes which have been best characterized:

[153b] Setsuo Takeuchi, Hiroshi Yonehara, Hamao Umezawa and Yusuke Sumiki, *ibid.* **13A** 289 (1960).

[154] H. Bickel, E. Gäumann, W. Keller-Schierlein, V. Prelog, E. Vischer, A. Wettstein and H. Zähner, *Experientia* **16** 129–133 (1960).

[155] C. W. Hesseltine, A. R. Whitehill, C. Pidacks, M. Ten Hagen, N. Bohonos, B. L. Hutchings and J. H. Williams, *Mycologia* **45** 7 (1953).

Sideromycins	Producing microorganism	Analyses (%)					Mol. wt.	pK	Absorption λ max. $E_1^{1\%}$ cm.	Hydrolysis products	Ref.
		C	H	N	Cl	Fe					
Ferrimycin A (may consist of 2 components)	Streptomyces griseoflavus (Krainsky) Waksman et Henrici, S. galilaeus, S. lavendulae	48.65	7.09	12.95	6.10	4.56	1106	4.18 7.88	228, 282 319, 28 425, 22	Ammonia, Succinic Acid, 1-Amino-5-hydroxyl-aminopentane, δ-aminovaleric Acid, Cadaverine, Cryst. compound (λ max. 227, 323 mμ), Proline and 1 unidentified ninhydrin-positive substance.	156 157 158
Grisein A	Streptomyces griseus Waksman et Henrici	43.95	5.65	12.97		5.14	1034		265, 108 420, 29	Methyluracil, Glutamic Acid, Hydroxylamine	159 160
Albomycin (A complex. The main component has been resolved into two parts.)	Actinomyces subtropicus Kudrina et Kochetkova					4.16	1270–1346			Methyluracil, Serine, Ornithine, Hydroxylamine	161– 166

Sideramines	Producing microorganism	Analyses (%)					Mol. wt.	pK	Absorption λ max. $E_1^{1\%}$ cm.	Hydrolysis products	Ref.
		C	H	N	Cl	Fe					
Ferrichrome	Ustilago sphaerogena Burill ex Ellis et Everh.	44.02	5.90	16.55		7.35	725		425, 39	Ammonia, Glycine, Ornithine, Hydroxylamine, (3 moles), Acetic Acid (3 moles)	167
Ferrichrome A	Ustilago sphaerogena Burill ex Ellis et Everh.	44.75	5.80	11.18		5.3	1100		440, 34	Glycine, Ornithine, Hydroxylamine (3 moles), trans-β-Methylglutaconic Acid (3 moles)	167
Ferrioxamine B	Streptomyces griseoflavus, S. pilosus; S. viridochromogenes, S. olivaceus, S. aureofaciens, S. galilaeus, S. lavendulae, S. polychromogenes, S. griseus	48.04	7.41	11.21	5.25	7.67	704	9.74	430, 39	Ammonia, Succinic Acid, 1-Amino-5-hydroxyl-aminopentane, δ-Aminovaleric Acid, Cadaverine, Acetic Acid	168
Coprogen	Penicillium sp.	50.96	6.83	10.26		6.61			440, 36		169
Terregens factor	Arthrobacter terregens										170

Other less well characterized siderochromes were discussed in reference 156.

In the ferrichromes the iron is bound by coordination with hydroxamic acid derivatives of the aliphatic acid moieties.

[156] H. Bickel, E. Gäumann, W. Keller-Schierlein, V. Prelog, E. Vischer, A. Wettstein and H. Zähner, *Experientia* **16** 128 (1960).

[157] H. Bickel, B. Fechtig, G. E. Hall, W. Keller-Schierlein, V. Prelog and E. Fischer, *Helv. Chim. Acta* **43** 901 (1960).

[158] H. Bickel, *et al.*, to be published.

[159] D. M. Reynolds, A. Schatz and S. A. Waksman, *Proc. Soc. Exp. Biol. Med.* (New York), **64** 50 (1947); D. M. Reynolds and S. A. Waksman, *J. Bacteriol.* **55** 739 (1948).

[160] F. A. Kuehl, M. N. Bishop, L. Chaiet and K. Folkers, *J. Am. Chem. Soc.* **73** 1770 (1951).

[161] M. G. Brazhnikova, N. N. Lomakina and L. I. Murayeva, *Doklady Akad. Nauk. S.S.S.R.* **99** 827 (1954).

[162] E. O. Stapley and R. E. Ormond, *Science* **125** 587 (1957).

[163] G. F. Gause, *Brit. Med. J.* **2** 1177 (1955); G. F. Gause and M. G. Brazhnikova, *Novosti Med.* (Moscow) **23** 3 (1951).

[164] Yu. O. Sazykin, *Mikrobiologiya* **24** 75 (1955).

[165] E. S. Kudrina and G. V. Kochetkova, *Antibiotiki* (Moscow) **3** 63 (1958).

[166] O. Mikes and F. Sorm, Symposium on Antibiotics, Prague, 1959.

[167] J. B. Neilands, *J. Am. Chem. Soc.* **74** 4846 (1952); *idem.*, *J. Biol. Chem.* **205** 643, 647 (1953); *idem.*, *Bacteriol. Revs.* **21** 101 (1957); J. A. Garibaldi and J. B. Neilands, *J. Am. Chem. Soc.* **77** 2429 (1955); Thomas Emery and J. B. Neilands, to be published; T. Emery and J. B. Neilands, *Nature* **184** 1632 (1959).

[168] G. E. Hall, unpublished.

[169] C. W. Hesseltine, C. Pidacks, A. R. Whitehall, N. Bohonos, B. L. Hutchings and J. H. Williams, *J. Am. Chem. Soc.* **74** 1362 (1952); C. W. Hesseltine, A. R. Whitehall, C. Pidacks, M. T. Hagen, N. Bohonos, B. L. Hutchings and J. H. Williams, *Mycologia* **45** 7 (1953); C. Pidacks, A. R. Whitehall, L. Pruess, C. W. Hesseltine, B. L. Hutchings, N. Bohonos and J. H. Williams, *J. Am. Chem. Soc.* **75** 6064 (1953).

[170] A. G. Lochhead, M. O. Burton and R. H. Thexton, *Nature* **170** 282 (1952); A. G. Lochhead and M. O. Burton, *Can. J. Botany* **31** 7 (1953); M. O. Burton, F. J. Sowden and A. G. Lochhead, *Can. J. Biochem. and Physiol.* **32** 400 (1954).

Baccatine A (entry 1114) has been shown to be a mixture of enniatins A and B.[171]

A partial structure has been advanced for PA-114-B-1 (entry 729).[172] It is $C_{48}H_{61}O_{12}N_9$:

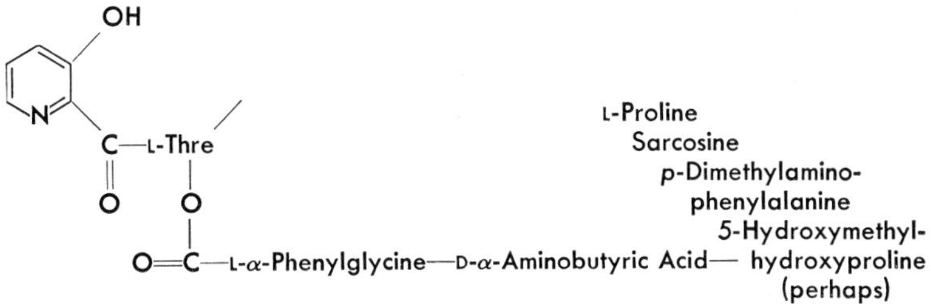

PA-114-B-3, a minor component of this synergistic complex, contains all the same components except sarcosine. It seems to contain another N-methyl amino acid instead. Other synergistic complexes of this sort are streptogramin, staphylomycin, ostreogrycin and mikamycin. These were classified as follows:

Type	Specific compound	Synonyms
A	A_1	PA-114-A-1 Ostreogrycin (E-129) Factor A Mikamycin A Streptogramin main component Staphylomycin M_1
	A_2	Staphylomycin M_2
B	B_1	PA-114-B-1 Ostreogrycin (E-129) Factor B Mikamycin B
	B_2	Staphylomycin S
	B_3	PA-114-B-3
		Streptogramin, minor component

[171] G. E. Hall, *Chem. and Ind.*, 1270 (1960).
[172] D. C. Hobbs and W. D. Celmer, *Nature* **187** 598 (1960).

More data have been published on the purification and physical properties of mycobacillin (entry 795).[173]

Some degradation studies of thiostreptone (entry 809) have been reported.[174] L-Threonine, L-isoleucine, L-alanine and D-cysteine were identified, and several thiazole-containing fragments were isolated. A minimal molecular weight of 1500 is required.

A structure has been proposed for a new antibiotic, racemomycin O.[175] It is produced by *Streptomyces racemochromogenus*, has the empirical formula $C_{25}H_{44}O_{10}N_8$ and is thought to be:

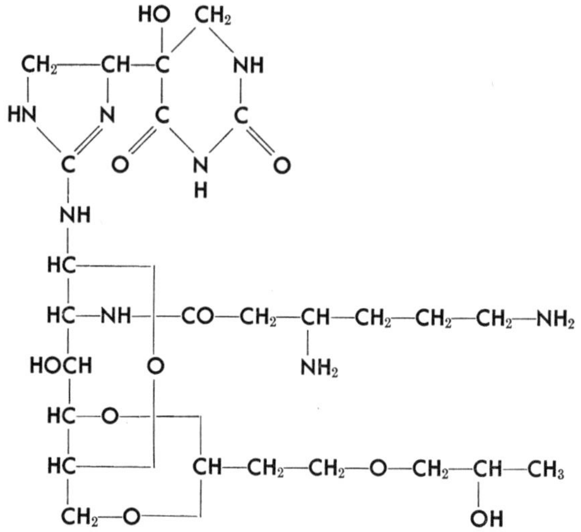

A partial structure has been advanced for roseothricin A (entry 717).[176]

[173] S. K. Majumdar and S. K. Bose, *Arch. Biochem. and Biophys.* **90** 154 (1960).

[174] Miklos Bodanszky, John Timothy Sheehan, Josef Fried, Nina J. Williams and Carolyn A. Birkheimer, *J. Am. Chem. Soc.* **82** 4747 (1960).

[175] S. Takemura, *Chem. & Pharm. Bull.* (Tokyo) **8** 578 (1960).

[176] T. Goto, Y. Hirata, S. Hosoya and N. Komatsu, *Bull. Chem. Soc. Japan* **30** 729 (1957).

```
                    O—
                    ‖
  CH₂——CH——C——CH₂—NH—
      │      │     │
      NH     N    CO—                                    2—CO—
       \    ∥
        \   C                                             —O—
         \ ∕
         NH                                              —NH—
          │                                       }
         HC┐                                             —OH—
          │ │
         HC┘ ├—NH—CO—CH₂—CH—CH₂—CH₂—CH₂—NH₂
          │  │              │
     —O—CH  O              NH₂
          │
     —O—CH
          │
         HC┐
          │ │
         CH₂┘────────────────────────────────O
                                              ‖
                                              2
```

A new polypeptide antibiotic, glumamycin, has been reported.[177] It consists of colorless powder, m.p. 230° (dec.), mol. wt. ~1800 and is composed of 4-isotri-decenoic acid, $C_8H_{17}CH{=}CHC_2H_4{-}COOH$, L-aspartic acid, glycine, L-valine, L-proline, D-pipecolic acid and α,β-diaminobutyric acid.

A number of compounds listed in the unclassified section are known to be or thought to be polypeptides. These include alboverticillin, antibiotic B-456, bacilipins, bacillomycins, bacilysin, datemycin, diplococcin, dista-mycin A, laterosporin, melanosporin, mikamycins, mito-mycins, monilin, mycospocidin, phleomycin, pluramycins, racemomycins, ractinomycins, roseomycin, taitomycin, violacetin and undoubtedly others.

18. Heterocycles

C. PYRANS AND RELATED SUBSTANCES

8-Hydroxy-3,4-dimethylisocoumarin has been isolated from cultures of a wild *Oospora* specimen.[178]

[177] Michitaka Inoue, Hiroshi Hitomi, Komei Mizuno, Masahiko Fujino, Akira Miyake, Koiti Nakazawa, Motoo Shibata and Toshihiko Kanzaki, *ibid.* 33 1014 (1960).

[178] I. Yamamoto and Y. Yamamoto, *Bull. Agr. Chem. Soc.* (Japan) 24 628 (1960).

A survey has shown that α-tocopherol is the only form of vitamin E found in bacteria.[179] It was found in about a dozen chlorophyll-containing organisms, although not in all such bacteria which were studied. Its production is not limited to any particular type of chlorophyll-containing bacterium. Tocopherol production seemed to parallel chlorophyll production, and it was suggested that the same phytol precursor might be used for both.

d. XANTHONES

A labeled precursor investigation of ravenelin by Birch and associates has shown that orsellinic acid is an intermediate in the biosynthesis of xanthones.[180]

e. COMPOUNDS RELATED TO THIOPHENE, IMIDAZOLE, THIAZOLE AND ISOXAZOLE

A comparison of the effects of D-cycloserine and of D-alanine on the incorporation of D,L-alanine-1-C^{14} into bacterial proteins showed that D-cycloserine acts as a D-alanine antagonist.[181, 182]

A paper has been published on the lability of 2-acetyl-thiazolium salts and in support of the proposed mode of action of thiamine.[183]

A paper on the enzymatic formation of thiamine and phosphate esters of the pyrimidine moiety seems to be the first of a series on the biosynthesis of thiamine.[184] A dissertation on the biosynthesis of the thiazole moiety has been published.[185]

[179] J. Green, S. Price and L. Gare, *Nature* 184 1339 (1959).

[180] Private communication from Herchel Smith.

[181] P. Barbieri, A. diMarco, L. Fuoco and A. Rusconi, *Biochem. Pharmacol.* 3 101 (1960).

[182] P. Barbieri, A. diMarco, L. Fuoco, P. Julita, A. Migliacci and A. Rusconi, *ibid.* 3 264 (1960).

[183] Ronald Breslow and Edward McNelis, *J. Am. Chem. Soc.* 82 2394 (1960).

[184] Gerald W. Camiener and Gene M. Brown, *J. Biol. Chem.* 235 2411 (1960).

[185] J. Vogel, Dissertation, University of Bonn, 1960.

f. PYRROLES, PORPHYRINS AND RELATED COMPOUNDS

A dissertation has been published on a prodigiosin-like pigment.[186]

A partial synthesis of vitamin B_{12} has been reported.[187, 188]

Guanosine diphosphate factor B and B diphosphate ester have been indentified as intermediates in the biosynthesis of vitamin B_{12}.[189]

A dissertation has been published on the biosynthesis of members of the vitamin B_{12} group.[190, 191]

A report has been made on the preparation and properties of purified intrinsic factor. The purified material is a better B_{12} binder than the crude, and it is not a mucoprotein as previously believed.[192]

A publication on the biosynthesis of uroporphyrin III from porphobilinogen reported that uroporphyrinogen I is not an intermediate in the biosynthesis of uroporphyrinogen III.[193]

A pink pigment identified as coproporphyrin III was isolated from *Mycobacterium tuberculosis avium*[194] as it had been earlier from *Mycobacterium karlinski*.[195]

At least two kinds of chlorophylls have been shown to be present in green bacteria.[196]

---

[186] Roswitha Zimmer-Galler, Dissertation, Technische Hochschule, München, 1960.

[187] K. Bernhauer, F. Wagner, Hw. Dellweg and P. Zeller, *Helv. Chim. Acta* 43 700 (1960).

[188] W. Friedrich, G. Gross, K. Bernhauer and P. Zeller, *ibid.* 43 704 (1960).

[189] G. Boretti, A. diMarco, L. Fuoco, M. Marnati, A. Migliacci and C. Spalla, *Biochim. et Biophys. Acta* 37 379 (1960).

[190] Fred Sanders, *Dissertation Abstr.* 18 2189 (1959).

[191] F. Sanders and Gerald R. Seaman, *J. Bacteriol.* 79 619 (1960).

[192] Leon Ellenbogen and William L. Williams, *Biochem. and Biophys. Res. Comms.* 2 340 (1960).

[193] Lawrence Bogorad and Gerald S. Marks, *Biochim. et Biophys. Acta* 41 358 (1960).

[194] D. S. P. Patterson, *Biochem. J.* 76 189 (1960).

[195] C. M. Todd, *ibid.* 45 386 (1949).

[196] R. Y. Stanier and J. H. C. Smith, *Biochim. et Biophys. Acta* 41 478 (1960).

A b-type cytochrome has been isolated from the fungus *Sclerotiana libertiana* and identified.[197]

Protoporphyrin IX has been isolated from bacterial catalase and characterized.[198]

Addition of δ-aminolevulinic acid to cultures of propionibacteria caused large increases in the production of porphyrins, but no rise in vitamin B_{12} production, indicating divergent biosynthetic routes.[199]

The structure of the antifungal pigment prodigiosin has been proved by synthesis.[200] It is

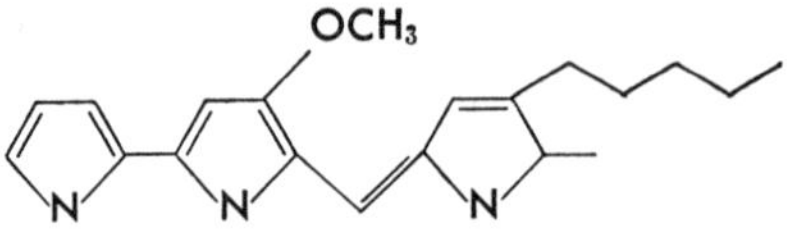

and is thus the second natural product containing a 2,2'-dipyrrole skeleton, vitamin B_{12} being the other.

A streptomycete has been found which produces isobutyropyrrothine, orange-red antibiotic crystals, m.p. 228°:[200a]

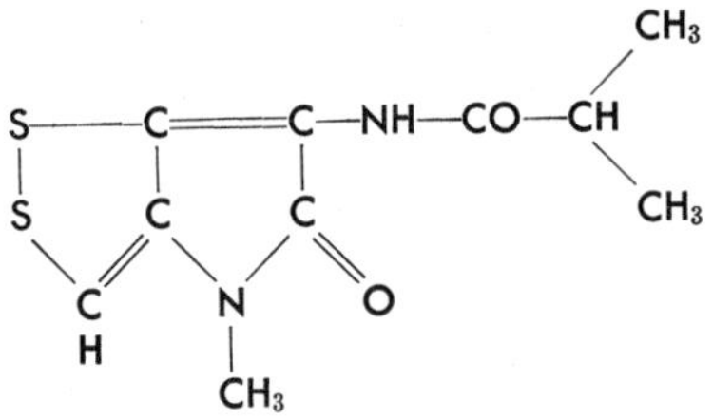

Aureothricin, thiolutin, a colorless base, and a heptaene, hamycin, also were produced.

[197] Tateo Yamanaka, Takehazu Horio and Kazuo Okunuki, *Biochim. et Biophys. Acta* **40** 349 (1960).

[198] Steve Miller, Davis Hawkins and Robert P. Williams, *J. Biol. Chem.* **235** 3280 (1960).

[199] G. V. Pronyakova, *Biokhimiya* (English translation) **25** 223 (1960).

[200] Henry Rapoport and Kenneth G. Holden, *J. Am. Chem. Soc.* **82** 5510 (1960).

[200a] D. S. Bhata, R. K. Hulyakar and S. K. Menon, *Experientia* **16** 504 (1960).

g. INDOLES

The structure previously proposed for echinulin has been confirmed, the only reservation being possible exchange of the groups in the 5 and the 7 positions of the indole nucleus.[201]

926a **Lysergic Acid Amide** (Ergine), $C_{16}H_{17}ON_3$ (Monomethanolate), m.p. 130–135° (efferv.), resolidifies 140°, m.p. 190° with previous dec.

926b **Isolysergic Acid Amide** (Isoergine), $C_{16}H_{17}ON_3$.

937a **Lysergic Acid Methylcarbinolamide,** $C_{18}H_{21}O_2N_3$, colorless prisms, m.p. 135° (dec.), $[\alpha]_D^{20}$ +29° ±2° (~1.0 in dimethylformamide).

937b **Isolysergic Acid Methylcarbinolamide,** $C_{18}H_{21}O_2N_3$, not crystalline.

A yield of about 2 g. per liter of the above alkaloids was produced by *Claviceps paspali* Stevens T. Hall growing in submerged culture.[202] A partial structure is shown for the carbinolamide isomer corresponding to lysergic acid:

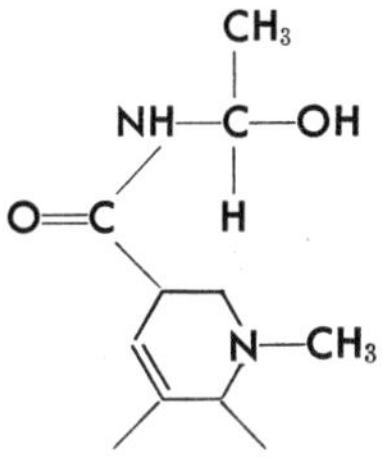

Another new ergot alkaloid, molliclavine, has been reported:[203, 204]

[201] Franco Piozzi, Giuseppe Casnati, Adolfo Quilico and Cesare Cardani, *Gazz. chim. ital.* **90** 451, 476 (1960).

[202] F. Arcamone, C. Bonino, E. B. Chain, A. Ferretti, P. Pennella, A. Tonola and Lidia Vero, *Nature* **187** 238 (1960).

[203] M. Abe, S. Yamatodani, T. Yamano and M. Kusumoto, *J. Agr. Chem. Soc. Japan* **34** 249 (1960).

[204] M. Abe and S. Yamatodani, *Bull. Agr. Chem. Soc.* (Japan) **19** 161 (1955).

930a Molliclavine, $C_{16}H_{18}O_2N_2$, colorless crystals, m.p. 253° (dec.), $[\alpha]_D^{17}$ +30° (c 1.0 in pyridine).

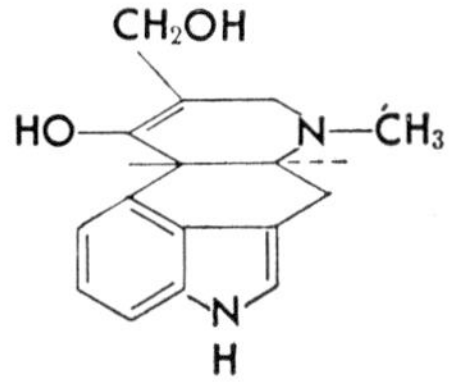

Claviceps purpurea
An antibiotic of novel structure incorporating an indole nucleus is:

301b **PA-155A,** $C_{14}H_{15}O_2N_3$, colorless crystals, m.p. 209°, $[\alpha]_D^{25}$ −214° (c 2.0 in methanol), U.V. 218, 273, 281, 288 mμ.
No reaction with dinitrophenylhydrazine. Negative ninhydrin, $FeCl_3$ tests. Blue Ehrlich's test. Decolorizes Br_2, $KMnO_4$. *Streptomyces albus*[73, 73a]

i. PYRIDINES

The plant toxin, fusaric acid, was produced when *Fusarium oxysporum* var. *lini* was grown on artificial medium or on non-resistant flax tissues, but not when the fungus was grown on resistant strain tissues.[205]

A dissertation has been published on dipicolinic acid formation and other chemical aspects of bacterial sporulation.[206]

The mononucleotide of nicotinic acid has been isolated from a fusarium specimen[207] and from a yeast.[208]

k. PYRAZINES, DIKETOPIPERAZINES

Several diketopiperazines have been isolated from the fungus *Rosellinia necatrix* Berlese.[209] They are L-prolyl-

[73] Koppaka V. Rao, *Antibiotics and Chemotherapy* 10 312 (1960).
[73a] Manfred von Schach, private communication.
[205] E. J. Trione, *Phytopathology* 50 480 (1960).
[206] Herbert M. Nakata, *Dissertation Abstr.* 20 3020 (1960).
[207] A. Ballio and S. Russi, *Arch. Biochem. and Biophys.* 85 567 (1959).
[208] R. W. Wheat, *ibid.* 85 567 (1957).
[209] Yu-Shih Chen, *Bull. Agr. Chem. Soc.* (Japan) 24 372 (1960).

L-leucine anhydride, L-prolyl-L-valine anhydride and an apparently new diketopiperazine, L-prolyl-L-phenylalanine anhydride (compound E) $C_{14}H_{16}O_2N_2$, m.p. 127–128°, $[\alpha]_D^{20}$ −99.8° (c 1.0 in ethanol). A crystalline wax, m.p. 52°, was isolated from the same culture and assumed to be *n*-pentacosane, $C_{25}H_{52}$. Also an uncharacterized substance, white needles, m.p. 206–208°, called rosellinic acid was isolated.

L-Prolyl-L-valine anhydride had been isolated previously from a streptomycete culture.[210] L-Prolyl-L-leucine anhydride had been isolated both from a streptomycete and from *Aspergillus fumigatus*.[211]

Muta-aspergillic acid, $C_{11}H_{18}O_3N_2$, pale yellow needles, m.p. 173° (dec.) (subl.) with alternative structures:

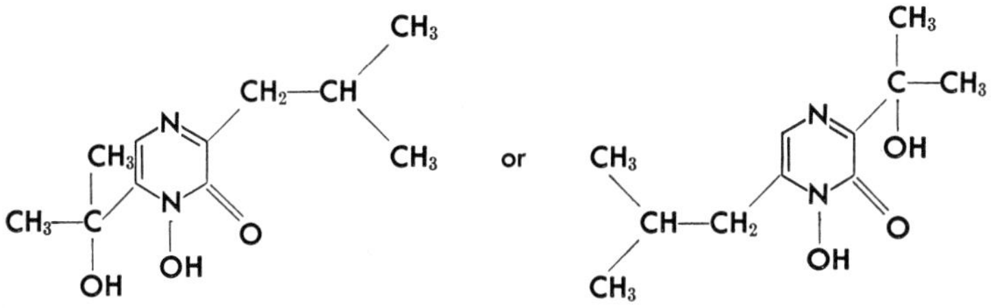

has been reported.[211a]

l. PHENAZINES AND PHENOXAZONES

Three new natural phenazines have been reported.[212]

984b **1-Hydroxymethyl-6-carboxyphenazine,** $C_{15}H_{12}O_3N_2$, light yellow crystals, m.p. 197–201°.

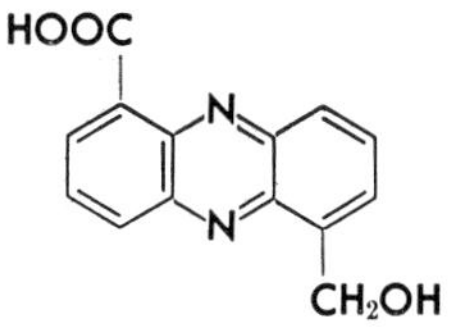

[210] Y. Koaze, *ibid.* 22 98 (1958).

[211] J. L. Johnson, W. G. Jackson and T. E. Elbe, *J. Am. Chem. Soc.* 73 2947 (1951).

[211a] Seiji Nakamura, *Bull. Agr. Chem. Soc.* (Japan) 24 629 (1960).

[212] Koki Yagishita, *J. Antibiotics* (Japan) 13A 83 (1960).

985a 1-Methoxy-4-methyl-9-carboxyphenazine, $C_{16}H_{14}O_3N_2$, yellow needles, m.p. 124–126°.

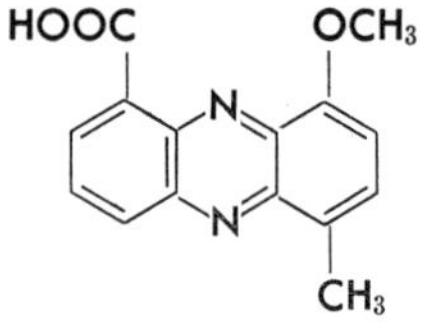

HOOC   OCH₃

CH₃

984a 1-Methoxy-4-hydroxymethyl-9-carboxyphenazine (Griseolutic Acid) $C_{15}H_{12}O_3N$.

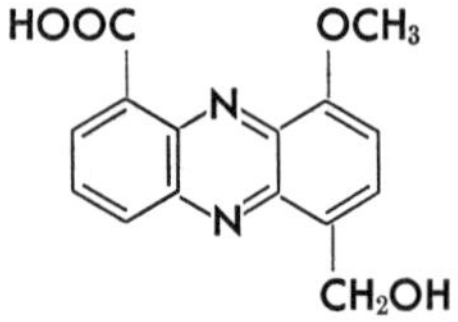

HOOC   OCH₃

CH₂OH

All of these compounds were isolated from a culture of *Streptomyces griseoluteus.*

An unclassified streptomycete produced two substances which were named questiomycins A and B.[213] These have been identified as:

977a 6-Aminophenoxazone (Questiomycin A) $C_{12}H_8O_2N_2$, red crystals, m.p. 241–244° (dec.) subl. from 150°.

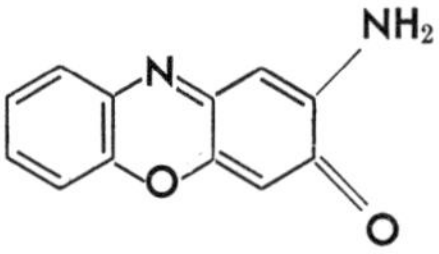

NH₂

O

377a 2-Aminophenol (Questiomycin B), colorless crystals, m.p. 170–175° (subl. 120°).

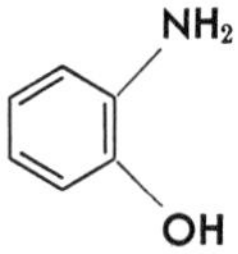

NH₂

OH

The suggestion was made that the aminophenol might be the precursor of the aminophenoxazone.

A purple and a yellow pigment isolated from *Brevibac-*

[213] Kentaro Anzai, Kiyoshi Isono, Kazuhiko Okuma and Saburo Suzuki, *ibid.* 13A 125 (1960).

terium crystalloiodinum Sasaki, Yoshida et Sasaki have been identified as iodinin and 1,6-dihydroxyphenazine, respectively.[214]

m. PYRIMIDINES

Two dissertations have been published on the biosynthesis of pyrimidines, one with rat liver enzymes,[215] the other with *Neurospora crassa.*[216]

Thymidine diphosphate mannose (as well as the previously reported thymidine diphosphate rhamnose) has been isolated from cultures of *Streptomyces griseus.*[217]

It is possible that this substance is an intermediate in the biosynthesis of streptomycin B (α-D-*mannopyranosyl-streptomycin*) which is produced by this organism along with streptomycin.

Tritium labeling experiments indicated that in the case cited, at least, the epimerization of N-acetylglucosamine to N-acetylmannosamine, probably by way of uridine diphosphate N-acetylglucosamine, does not involve oxidation to a ketosugar, followed by stereospecific reduction.[218]

The structure of tubercidin, $C_{11}H_{14}O_4N_4$, m.p. 247° (dec.), $[\alpha]_D^{17}$ −62°, produced by *Streptomyces tubercidicus* and active against *Mycobacterium tuberculosis* and *Candida albicans,* has been reported to be:[218a]

4-amino-7-[D-ribofuranosyl]-pyrrolo-[2,3-d]-pyrimidine

Toyocamycin has a similar structure.[218b]

[214] Tosi Irie, Etsuro Kurosawa and Iwao Nagaoka, *Bull. Chem. Soc. Japan* 33 1057 (1960).

[215] Richard L. Stambaugh, *Dissertation Abstr.* 20 64 (1959).

[216] Kamala P. Chakraborty, *ibid.* 20 3044 (1960).

[217] J. Baddiley and N. L. Blumson, *Biochim et Biophys. Acta* 39 376 (1960).

[218] Luis Glaser, *ibid.* 41 534 (1960).

[218a] Saburo Suzuki and Shingo Marumo, *J. Antibiotics* (Japan) 13A 360 (1960).

[218b] Kazuhiko Ohkuma, *ibid.* 13A 361 (1960).

n. PURINES

Guanosine diphosphate glucose and guanosine diphosphate fructose are produced by *Eremothecium ashbyii.*[219] A dissertation reports the isolation of a new guanine derivative from a riboflavin producer.[220]

A new purine riboside has been isolated from fusarium species.[221] It has been assigned the provisional structure:

2-(1-Carboxyethylamino)-6-hydroxy-9-D-ribofuranosylpurine

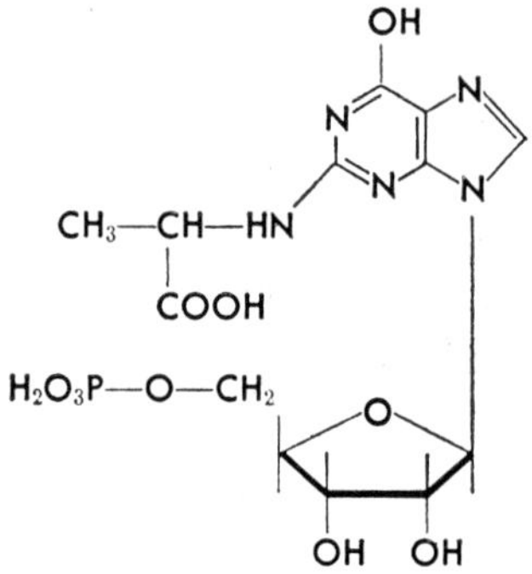

Nebularine (9-β-D-ribofuranosylpurine), produced by *Agaricus nebularis,* has been isolated from a streptomycete.[221a]

The nucleotides of *Aspergillus oryzae* have been characterized.[222]

The mechanism of action of the antibiotic, psicofuranine, against *Staphylococcus aureus* has been studied.[223] A possible effect may be interference with the biosynthesis of guanylic acid from xanthylic acid.

[219] H. G. Pontis, A. L. James and J. Baddiley, *Biochem. J.* **75** 428 (1960).

[220] Usama A. S. Al-Khalidi, *Dissertation Abstr.* **21** (1960).

[221] Alessandro Ballio, Carlo Delfini and Serena Russi, *Nature* **186** 968 (1960).

[221a] Kiyoshi Osono and Saburo Suzuki, *J. Antibiotics* (Japan) **13A** 270 (1960).

[222] Kazuo Okunuki, Kozo Iwasa, Fumio Imamoto and Tadayoshi Higashiyama, *J. Biochem.* (Tokyo) **45** 795 (1958).

[223] Ladislav J. Hanka, *J. Bacteriol.* **80** 30 (1960).

The antibiotic, mitomycin C, blocks DNA synthesis completely in *Escherichia coli,* but does not interfere with RNA synthesis or protein synthesis.[224]   Phage-infected bacteria continued DNA synthesis, but no infective particles were produced when high concentrations of mitomycin were present.

A new incompletely characterized electron transport component has been isolated from *Mycobacterium phlei.*[225]

The mode of inhibition of electron transport by antimycin A has been studied.[226]

Evidence has been published for participation of a *vic*-dithiol in oxidative phosphorylation.[227]

A review of ion transport and respiration has been published.[228]

ATP can replace light in bacterial photosynthesis. This discovery was made with the use of the obligate phototroph chromatium. An acetate medium is adequate, and carbon dioxide is not required.[229]

The biosynthesis of nucleic acids has been reviewed.[230]

The biosynthesis and interconversions of purines and their derivatives have been reviewed.[231]

O. PTERIDINES AND FLAVINES

The prosthetic group of a chromoprotein from mycobacteria may be a pteridine.[232]

In the fly, *Drosophila melanogaster,* labeling studies indicate that glucose carbon atoms are specifically in-

[224] M. Sakiguchi and Y. Takagi, *Biochim. et Biophys. Acta* 41 434 (1960).

[225] W. B. Sutton, *Federation Proc.* 19 31 (1960).

[226] A. L. Tappel, *Biochem. Pharmacol.* 3 289 (1960).

[227] Arvan Fluharty and D. R. Sanadi, *Proc. Nat. Acad. Sci. U.S.A.* 46 608 (1960).

[228] R. N. Robertson, *Biol. Revs.* 35 231–265 (1960).

[229] M. Losada, A. V. Trebst, S. Ogata and Daniel I. Arnon, *Nature* 186 753 (1960).

[230] Arthur Kornberg, *Reviews of Modern Physics* 31 200–209 (1959).

[231] Albert G. Moat and Herman Friedman, *Bacteriol. Revs.* 24 309 (1960).

[232] F. B. Cousins, *Biochim. et Biophys. Acta* 40 532 (1960).

corporated into pteridines, but not into purines produced by the organism.[233]

The structure of "active formaldehyde" (N^5,N^{10}-methylenetetrahydrofolic acid) has been proved by synthesis.[234]

19. Unclassified Metabolites

Streptolydigin probably contains 4 carbon-carbon double bonds conjugated with a β-diketone system.[235] It also contains at least four hydroxyl groups, at least four C-methyl groups and at least one amide group. Methylamine was a base hydrolysis product of tetradecahydrostreptolydigin.

Griseoviridin, empirical formula $C_{22}H_{29\pm2}O_7N_3S$, probably consists of three moieties.[236] A 6 carbon atom fragment has been identified as:

$$CH_3-CH-CH_2-CH=C-CO-N\big<$$
$$\quad\quad\ \ | \quad\quad\quad\quad |$$
$$\quad\quad\ \ O \quad\quad\quad\quad X$$

and the sulfur atom may be attached at the X-position.

The probable structure of a methanolysis product of carzinophilin has been published.[237] It is:

Methyl 1-methyl-7-methoxynaphthalene-6-carboxylate

Mikamycin should be classified as a polypeptide of the etamycin type. L-Proline and glycine have been characterized in a hydrolysate. A monoacetate, a di-2,4-dinitrophenylhydrazone derivative, and a decahydro de-

[233] O. Brenner-Holzbach and F. Leuthardt, *Helv. Chim. Acta* 42 2254 (1959).

[234] M. J. Osborn, P. T. Talbot and F. M. Huennekens, *J. Am. Chem. Soc.* 82 4921 (1960).

[235] Jerome Allen Gourse, Dissertation, Univ. of Illinois, 1959.

[236] P. de Mayo and A. Stoessl, *Can. J. Chem.* 38 950 (1960).

[237] Masao Tanaka, Tcruo Kishi and Yoshiki Maruta, *J. Antibiotics* (Japan) 12B 361 (1959).

rivative have been prepared. The melting point of the yellow crystals is given as 178° (dec.).[238]

Russian antibiotic 6613 may be identical with etamycin.[239]

Monamycin, $C_{22}H_{36-38}O_5N$, needles, m.p. 126°. Monohydrochloride: m.p. 187°, $[\alpha]_D^{18}$ −62 ±5° (c 0.9 in ethanol), containing 1 N—CH_3, 3 C—CH_3 groups, no U.V., I.R. suggestive of amide links, has been isolated from *Streptomyces jamaicensis* n. sp.[240]

Teruchiomycin, $C_{28}H_{43}O_{10}N$, needles, m.p. 202–204° (dec.), a new antibiotic from *Streptomyces antibioticus* has been reported.[241]

A new acidic antibiotic, C-159, U.V. max. 345, 260, 280 mμ, C 58.7, H 7.4, D 24.0, N 9.9% has been patented.[242]

The blue intracellular pigment of *Pseudomonas lemonnieri* has been isolated, purified and characterized.[243]

A preliminary investigation has been made of the pigments of *Trichophyton rubrum*.[244]

Rubidin, a quinoid dark red powder with acid base indicator properties, U.V. 320, 415, 490 mμ in butanol, C 51.9, H 5.56, O 42.54, positive $FeCl_3$ and zinc dust tests, is a substance isolated from an unclassified streptomycete.[245]

A new antibacterial antibiotic has been reported.[246] It had the following properties: yellow needles, m.p. 134°, mol. wt. 397, U.V. maxima at 328.5, 314.5, 298.7 mμ. Positive Millon, Liebermann, Schiff, $FeCl_3$ and NH_3-$AgNO_3$ tests. Probably $C_{22}H_{22}O_7$ with hydroxyl, methyl and 2 ketone groups present.

[238] Koichi Okabe, *ibid.* 12A 86 (1959).

[239] M. Brazhnikova *et al., Antibiotics* (USSR) 4 414 (English translation) (1959).

[240] C. H. Hassall and K. E. Magnus, *Nature,* Suppl. 184 1223 (1959).

[241] H. Umezawa *et al.,* Japanese Patent 850 (1958).

[242] British Patent 814,794 (1959).

[243] Werner Blau, Gladys Cosens and Mortimer P. Starr, *Bacteriol. Proc.,* 153 (1960).

[244] Malati Bacchwal and G. C. Walker, *Can. J. Microbiol.* 6 383 (1960).

[245] A. K. Banerjee, G. P. Sen and P. Nandi, "Antibiotics Annual 1955–1956," Medical Encyclopedia, Inc., New York, p. 640.

[246] Thadée Staron and Albert Faivre–Amiot, *Compt. rend.* 250 1580 (1960).

Bold-faced numbers indicate primary microbial metabolite entries, while Arabic numbers signify incidental mention under such entries. Italic numbers are page numbers, and generally indicate occurrence in a chapter or section introduction. The appendixes and addendum are not indexed.

EMPIRICAL FORMULA INDEX

This index lists the known empirical formulas of microbial metabolites as an aid to future characterizations. Boldfaced numbers are entry numbers, while italic numbers are page numbers reflecting occurrence in a chapter or section introduction. The appendixes and addendum are not indexed.

$C_8H_{12}O_3N_2S$, 897
$C_8H_{13}O_5N$, 1237
$C_8H_{14}O$, 10, 46
$C_8H_{14}O_2S_2$, 99
$C_8H_{14}O_7$, 37
$C_8H_{15}ON_5$, 915
$C_8H_{16}O_2N_2$, 713
C_9H_4O, 193
$C_9H_4O_6$, 374
$C_9H_4O_7$, 375
C_9H_6O, 194
$C_9H_8O_2$, 620
$C_9H_8O_3$, 195
$C_9H_8O_4$, 145
$C_9H_8O_5$, 393, 394, 412
$C_9H_8O_7$, 395
C_9H_9ON, 621
$C_9H_9O_4N$, 971
$C_9H_9O_5N$, 396
$C_9H_9O_5N_5$, 1050
$C_9H_{10}O_2N_2S_2$, 916
$C_9H_{10}O_3$, 622, 853
$C_9H_{10}O_4$, 146
$C_9H_{10}O_6$, 147
$C_9H_{11}O_2N$, 705
$C_9H_{11}O_3N$, 706
$C_9H_{11}O_3N_5$, 1051
$(C_9H_{12}O_3N_2)_n$, 1066
$C_9H_{12}O_6N_2$, 1009
$C_9H_{12}O_7N_2$, 715
$C_9H_{13}O_5N_3$, 1010
$C_9H_{13}O_7N$, 714
$C_9H_{13}O_9N_2P$, 1011
$C_9H_{14}O_5N_4$, 898
$C_9H_{14}O_8N_3P$, 1012, 1013
$C_9H_{15}O_2N_3$, 707
$C_9H_{15}O_2N_3S$, 708
$C_9H_{15}O_3NS$, 899
$C_9H_{15}O_7N_3$, 715
$C_9H_{17}O_5N$, 716
$C_9H_{19}O_2N$, 658
$C_9H_{20}O_2$, 1117
$C_9H_{22}O_2NCl$, 659
$C_9H_{22}O_4N_5$, 737
$C_{10}H_6O$, 197
$C_{10}H_6O_3$, 198
$C_{10}H_6O_4$, 199

$C_{10}H_6O_5$, 516
$C_{10}H_8O$, 200
$C_{10}H_8O_2$, 201, 202
$C_{10}H_8O_3$, 397, 868
$C_{10}H_8O_6$, *185*, 398
$C_{10}H_8O_4 - C_{10}H_{10}O_4$, 376
$C_{10}H_9ON_5$, 1030
$C_{10}H_9O_2N$, 934
$C_{10}H_{10}O$, 203, 204
$C_{10}H_{10}O_2$, 623
$C_{10}H_{10}O_2N_2$, 920
$C_{10}H_{10}O_3$, 205, 399, 400, 624, 869
$C_{10}H_{10}O_4$, 206, 401
$C_{10}H_{10}O_5$, *186*, 402
$C_{10}H_{10}O_6$, 148, *185*, 301, 403
$C_{10}H_{10}O_7$, *186*
$C_{10}H_{11}O_2N$, 972
$C_{10}H_{11}O_6N$, 417
$C_{10}H_{12}ON_2$, 935
$C_{10}H_{12}O_3$, 404, 405
$C_{10}H_{12}O_4$, 406, 498, 854
$C_{10}H_{12}O_4N_2$, 1054
$C_{10}H_{12}O_4N_4$, 1031
$C_{10}H_{12}O_6$, 149
$C_{10}H_{12}O_8N_2$, 1014
$C_{10}H_{13}O_2N$, 407, 973
$C_{10}H_{13}O_3N_5$, 1032
$C_{10}H_{13}O_4N_5$, 1033
$C_{10}H_{13}O_5N_5$, 1034
$C_{10}H_{13}O_8N_4P$, 1035
$C_{10}H_{14}O_4$, 499
$C_{10}H_{14}O_5$, 150
$C_{10}H_{14}O_7N_5P$, 1036, 1037, 1038
$C_{10}H_{14}O_8N_5P$, 1039
$C_{10}H_{15}O_3N$, 151
$C_{10}H_{16}O_3N_2S$, 900
$C_{10}H_{16}O_3$, 417
$C_{10}H_{16}O_4$, 100
$C_{10}H_{16}O_4N_2S$, 901
$C_{10}H_{16}O_6N_2$, 717
$C_{10}H_{16}O_{13}N_5P_3$, 1040
$C_{10}H_{17}O_6N_3S$, 718
$C_{10}H_{18}O_3N_2$, 902
$C_{10}H_{20}O_9$, 38
$C_{10}H_{26}N_4$, 660
$C_{11}H_7O_3NCl_2$, 917
$C_{11}H_8O_2$, 207, 208, 517

$C_{20}H_{28}O_3$, 328
$C_{20}H_{28}O_{19}N_{10}P$, 1045
$C_{20}H_{29}O_2N$, 985
$C_{20}H_{29}O_7N \cdot HCl$, 596
$C_{20}H_{29}O_8N$, 1180
$C_{20}H_{29}O_8N \cdot HCl$, 597
$C_{20}H_{30}O_2$, 329
$C_{20}H_{30}O_3$, 330
$C_{20}H_{30}O_7N_4$, 1167
$C_{20}H_{32}O_8$, 1236
$(C_{20}H_{32}O_9N_2)_n$, 1222
$C_{20}H_{36}O_9N_8$, 731
$C_{20}H_{44}N_2$, 662
$C_{21}H_{18}O_4$, 222
$C_{21}H_{20}O_3$, 223
$C_{21}H_{20}O_7$, 574
$C_{21}H_{21}O_8N_2Cl$, 602
$C_{21}H_{22}O_5$, 880
$C_{21}H_{22}O_5Cl$, 881
$C_{21}H_{22}O_7$, 1176
$C_{21}H_{22}O_8$, 600
$C_{21}H_{22}O_8N_2Cl$, 603
$C_{21}H_{24}O_7$, 469
$C_{21}H_{26}O_5$, 882
$C_{21}H_{27}O_{14}N_7P_2$, 975
$C_{21}H_{28}O_{17}N_7P_3$, 976
$C_{21}H_{29}O_{11}N$, 1297
$C_{21}H_{30}O_8$, 116
$C_{21}H_{31}O_8N$, 1180
$C_{21}H_{36}O_7N$, 1276
$C_{21}H_{36}O_{16}N_7SP_3$, 1046
$C_{21}H_{38}O_6$, 117
$C_{21}H_{38}O_7$, 118
$C_{21}H_{39}O_{12}N_7$, 54
$C_{21}H_{39}O_{13}N_7$, 55
$C_{21}H_{41}O_{12}N_7$, 56
$C_{22}H_{16}O_6$, 575
$C_{22}H_{16}O_7$, 604
$C_{22}H_{16}O_{12}$, 470
$C_{22}H_{18}O_6$, 1140
$C_{22}H_{20}O_7$, 1134
$C_{22}H_{20}O_8$, 605
$C_{22}H_{20}O_9$, 606
$C_{22}H_{20}O_{10}$, 576
$C_{22}H_{21}O_8N_2Cl$, 607
$C_{22}H_{23}O_6N$, 870
$C_{22}H_{23}O_8N_2Br$, 609
$C_{22}H_{23}O_8N_2Cl$, 608

$C_{22}H_{24}O_6N$, 634
$C_{22}H_{24}O_8N_2$, 613
$C_{22}H_{24}O_9N_2$, 610
$C_{22}H_{26}O_5$, 861
$C_{22}H_{26}O_8$, 471
$C_{22}H_{28}O_5N_2$, *186*, 993
$C_{22}H_{29}O_5N_7$, 1047
$C_{22}H_{29}O_7N_3S$, 1169
$C_{22-24}H_{32-34}O_{8-9}$, 1307
$C_{22-23}H_{32-34}O_{11}$, 1132
$C_{22}H_{34}O_5$, 1247
$C_{22}H_{36}O_6$, 1233
$C_{22}H_{38}O_6$, 119
$C_{22}H_{38}O_6N_2$, 738
$C_{22}H_{39}O_4N_5$, 1129
$C_{22}H_{40}O_7$, 120
$C_{22}H_{42}O_8N_4S_2$, 719
$C_{22}H_{44}O_6$, 121
$C_{23}H_{20}O_6$, 611
$C_{23}H_{24}O_5$, 883
$C_{23}H_{25}O_9N \cdot HCl$, 612
$C_{23}H_{26}O_5$, 884
$C_{23}H_{28}O_7$, 474
$C_{23}H_{28}O_7$, 472, 473
$C_{23}H_{29}O_{12}N$, 57
$C_{23}H_{29-31}O_7N_3$, 1314
$C_{23}H_{45}O_{14}N_5$, 59
$C_{23}H_{46}O_{12}N_6$, 60
$C_{24}H_{20}O_{10}$, 475
$C_{24}H_{20}O_{11}$, 476
$C_{24}H_{23}O_5N_5S_4$, 762
$C_{24}H_{28}O_4N_4$, 957
$C_{24}H_{29}O_9N_{10}$, 1304
$C_{24}H_{30}O_7$, 477
$C_{24}H_{30}O_8$, 478
$C_{24}H_{31}O_7N_5Cl_2$, 739
$C_{24}H_{33}O_2N_7$, 922
$C_{24}H_{36}O_9N_2S$, 923
$C_{24}H_{36-40}O_9N_2S$, 258
$C_{24}H_{38}O_{10}$, 1193
$C_{24}H_{40}O_6$, 1232
$C_{24}H_{41}O_6N$, 268
$C_{24}H_{42}O_6N_2$, 740, 741
$C_{24}H_{42}O_7N_2$, 750
$C_{24}H_{48}O_2$, 122
$C_{24}H_{52}O_2N_8$, 742
$C_{24}H_{42}O_7N_2$, 750

Boldfaced numbers are entry numbers of metabolites produced by a microorganism. Italic numbers are page numbers and indicate mention in a chapter or section introduction. The appendixes and addendum are not indexed.